INVERTEBRATE ZOOLOGY

ROBERT D. BARNES, Ph.D.

PROFESSOR OF BIOLOGY
GETTYSBURG COLLEGE

W. B. SAUNDERS COMPANY
PHILADELPHIA / LONDON

Invertebrate Zoology

Reprinted July, 1963, March, 1964, May, 1965 and January, 1966

PREFACE

The following work was undertaken to fulfill the long-standing need for an American textbook of invertebrate zoology. With the exception of the British text by Borradaile, Eastham, Potts, and Saunders, the relatively few volumes in English claiming to be invertebrate texts have actually been more suitable for courses in introductory zoology. Therefore, this text has been designed for upperclass and graduate courses in invertebrate zoology and presumes that the student has had at least one introductory course in zoology or biology.

A textbook preface is always to some extent an apology. This is especially true for a text in invertebrate zoology, where the subject is so vast and the number of specialists for the various invertebrate groups so great and where the instructor's particular field of interest frequently prejudices his requirements. The conventional approach has been to treat the invertebrate groups systematically and to describe in detail a selected biological type for each group. A systematic treatment is certainly the logical approach for an introductory presentation and has been utilized here. Each chapter treats a phylum, a class, or a group of related phyla or classes. Phylogenetic information has been used to provide continuity between the chapters and unity for the book as a whole.

The use of biological types however, has been abandoned. The *type method,* while convenient and of some value, especially for introductory zoology and biology courses, all too frequently produces a distorted and narrow concept of the group concerned. Consider how few undergraduates possess knowledge of invertebrates extending much beyond hydra, planaria, the earthworm, and the crayfish. Moreover, few of the types commonly used are representative of even the majority of species in the group being studied. For example, the crayfish or lobster hardly typifies decapods, much less crustaceans. Furthermore, emphasis on a type often tends to diminish in the mind of the student the importance of the general material that is presented. In the following text, each group has been treated from a general standpoint, similar to the treatment utilized in such research series as Hyman's *The Invertebrates* and Grassé's *Traité de Zoologie.* True, the student is faced with a much greater array of facts and must deal with numerous exceptions, but this approach should help the student to achieve a much more mature and realistic appreciation of the nature and diversity of the invertebrate phyla.

Since laboratory studies must involve the use of selected, easily obtainable forms, reference is made throughout the text to those species commonly utilized as laboratory specimens in order to make the student aware of the particular characteristics that these forms exhibit.

Four groups of invertebrates have been omitted, except for passing reference—the Sporozoa, the Trematoda, the Cestoda, and the Insecta. These classes are covered in the numerous parasitology and entomology texts presently available and they are not usually studied in invertebrate zoology courses. Moreover, their omission in the text permits the inclusion of additional material on other invertebrate groups.

In the general treatment of each group, considerable effort has been made to produce a balanced presentation of taxonomic, anatomical, physiological, embryological, and ecological material. If it appears to the instructor that the text is overly concerned with morphology, he should remember that the average student cannot adequately explore physiological processes of an animal until he knows something of its structure.

A considerable part of the physiological material has been tied in with anatomical description in order to present a functional morphology. Special physiological topics have been treated separately. Students and instructors whose interests are primarily in areas of physiology should keep in mind that not all physiological studies utilizing invertebrate animals represent studies in invertebrate physiology in a strict sense. Perhaps the majority of such physiological studies deal with basic physiological and biochemical problems. Good examples include the many valuable studies on cellular phenomena in sea urchin eggs and on nerve impulse transmission in the giant neurons of squids. Such studies, while valuable for increasing our knowledge of cellular physiology, tell us little about the physiological relationship of sea urchins and squids to their environment. For this reason, *physiological studies that are not directly related to the existence of the animal do not properly belong in this text and have not been included.*

Most of the chapters on the larger phyla contain a systematic résumé after the discussion of each class. The résumé briefly characterizes the orders that the class contains and lists the genera referred to in the preceding text. For a few groups, such as the coelenterate and echinoderm classes, in which the orders are separated on the basis of rather technical characteristics, the systematic résumés have been omitted.

Needless to say, the general treatment of the invertebrate phyla is considerably more difficult than the *type approach.* In this regard, the author is greatly indebted to the works of Libbie Hyman, which in many respects made this text possible. The information available in the present five volumes of Dr. Hyman's series on the invertebrates, representing twenty-five years of collecting and synthesis of material from an enormous literature, and of extensive original research, has made the writing of this text immeasurably easier. Had it been necessary to expend as much research time on all of the chapters as was required for those on phyla not covered by Dr. Hyman, the five years necessary to write this text would have been increased severalfold, and it might never have been completed.

The author is deeply grateful for the suggestions and criticisms offered by the specialists who reviewed various chapters. These readers corrected many errors; they are not, however, responsible for errors that may possibly remain. If the reception given this volume warrants a later edition, it is hoped that any such remaining errors can be eliminated. The introductory chapter and the chapter on the protozoans were reviewed by John O. Corliss of the University of Illinois; the sponges by Willard D. Hartman of the Peabody Museum of Natural History at Yale University; the coelenterates and ctenophores by Frederick M. Bayer of the U. S. National Museum; the flatworms and rhynchocoels by E. Ruffin Jones of the University of Florida; spiral cleavage and the embryology of flatworms and rhynchocoels by John M. Anderson of

Cornell University; the pseudocoelomates by W. T. Edmondson of the University of Washington; the mollusks by R. Tucker Abbott of the Philadelphia Academy of Natural Sciences; and the annelids by Olga Hartman of the Allan Hancock Foundation, University of Southern California.

The introduction to the arthropods and the chelicerates was reviewed by Willis J. Gertsch of the American Museum of Natural History, by Herbert W. Levi of the Museum of Comparative Zoology at Harvard University; and by George W. Wharton of Ohio State University; the crustaceans by Thomas E. Bowman of the U. S. National Museum; the myriapodous arthropods by Ralph E. Crabill of the U. S. National Museum; the lophophorates by Mary Dora Rogick of the College of New Rochelle; the echinoderms by John M. Anderson of Cornell University; and the annelidan and arthropodan allies and the lesser deuterostomes by H. Marguerite Webb of Goucher College.

The author is especially grateful for the many suggestions and comments made by Frederick E. Smith of the University of Michigan, who read the entire manuscript, and to Grover Stephens of the University of Minnesota, who read parts of the first draft.

The majority of the illustrations were executed by the author himself. Drawings for the chapters on the sponges, the coelenterates, the annelid and arthropod allies, and part of those for the chapter on the crustaceans were done by Miss Mary Nell Sargent. Miss Carol Lang made the drawings for the chapters on the lophophorates, the lesser deuterostomes, and part of those for the chapter on the echinoderms. Invaluable assistance in the task of illustrating was also given by Mr. Ronald Reaver, Mrs. Harold Closson, Mrs. John Held, and Miss Demaree Deardorff.

Most of the original illustrations, especially those of the polychaete annelids, were completed at the Duke University Marine Laboratory during the summer of 1959. The author would like to express again his appreciation to the Duke University Marine Laboratory for the facilities extended to him at that time and also to Gettysburg College for the summer study grant that made the work at the marine laboratory possible.

The author also wishes to express his appreciation to Wm. Collins Sons & Co. Ltd., London, for the use of photographs appearing in Figures 5-31, *E;* 11-12; and 12-33, *A.*

The help and encouragement given me by my wife and the continual cooperation of the W. B. Saunders Company in all aspects of the writing and illustrating of this book did much to reduce the burden of the work involved.

ROBERT D. BARNES

Gettysburg, Pennsylvania

CONTENTS

Chapter 13

INTRODUCTION TO THE ARTHROPODS; THE TRILOBITES 321

Chapter 14

THE CHELICERATES 334

Chapter 15

THE CRUSTACEANS 380

Chapter 16
THE MYRIAPODOUS ARTHROPODS 475

Chapter 17
ANNELIDAN AND ARTHROPODAN ALLIES 490

Chapter 18
THE LOPHOPHORATE COELOMATES 505

Chapter 19
THE ECHINODERMS 524

Chapter 20

THE LESSER DEUTEROSTOMES

Chapter 1

INTRODUCTION

There are over a million described species of animals. Of this number about 5 per cent possess a backbone and are known as vertebrates. All others, comprising approximately 95 per cent of the Animal Kingdom, are invertebrates. These animals are the subject of this book.

Division of the Animal Kingdom into vertebrates and invertebrates is artificial and reflects human bias in favor of man's own relatives. One characteristic of a single subphylum of animals is used as the basis for separation of the entire Animal Kingdom into two groups. One could just as logically divide animals into mollusks and nonmollusks or arthropods and nonarthropods. The latter classification could be supported at least from the standpoint of numbers, since approximately 75 per cent of all animals are arthropods.

The artificiality of the invertebrate concept is especially apparent when one considers the vast and heterogeneous assemblage of groups that are lumped together in this category. There is not a single positive characteristic that invertebrates hold in common. The range in size, in structural diversity, and in adaptations to different modes of existence is enormous. Some invertebrates have common phylogenetic origins; others are only remotely related. Some are much more closely related to the vertebrates than to other invertebrate groups.

Quite obviously invertebrate zoology cannot be considered a special field of zoology, certainly not in the same sense as protozoology or entomology. A field that embraces all biological aspects—morphology, physiology, embryology, and ecology—of 95 per cent of the Animal Kingdom represents no distinct area of zoology; it is virtually the subject of zoology itself. For the same reason, no zoologist can truly be called an invertebrate zoologist. He is a protozoologist, a malacologist, an acarologist, or is concerned with some aspect of physiology, embryology, or ecology of one or more animal groups. Beyond such limited areas the number and diversity of invertebrates are too great to permit much more than a good general knowledge of the subject.

For the student who is making the first serious attempt to study invertebrates in some depth, the task may seem overwhelming. Each group has certain structural peculiarities, a special anatomical terminology, and a distinct classification. All of these factors tend to magnify the differences between groups. At the same time the very real danger is also created that the student may lose sight of functional and structural similarities that result from similar modes of existence and similar environmental conditions as well as of homologies arising from close evolutionary relationships.

This danger perhaps may be lessened if a few basic biological principles are kept in mind. All animals must meet the same problems of existence—the procurement of food and oxygen, maintenance of water balance, removal of metabolic wastes, and perpetuation of the species. The body structure necessary to meet these problems is, in large part, determined by three factors: the type of environment in which the animal lives, the size of the animal, and the mode of existence of the animal.

The Animal Kingdom is believed generally to have originated in Archeozoic oceans long before the first fossil record. The salt concentration of protoplasm and tissue fluids closely approximates that of sea water (sea water is often slightly saltier). Every major phylum of animals has at least some marine representatives; some groups, such as coelenterates and echinoderms, are largely or entirely marine. From the ancestral marine environment, different groups of animals have migrated into fresh water; some have moved onto land. Of the three major environments—salt water, fresh water, and land—the marine environment offers the least number of obstacles to existence. Wave action, tides, and vertical and horizontal ocean currents produce a continual mixing of sea water and ensure a medium in which the concentration of dissolved gases and salts fluctuates relatively little. The buoyancy of sea water reduces the problem of support. It is therefore not surprising that the largest invertebrates have always been marine. Since sea water is approximately isotonic to protoplasm and tissue fluids, there is little difficulty in maintaining water balance.

The buoyancy and uniformity of sea water provide an ideal medium for animal reproduction. Eggs in sea water can be shed, fertilized, and undergo development as floating embryos with little danger of desiccation and of water imbalance, or of being swept away by rapid currents into less favorable environments. Larvae are particularly characteristic of marine animals. Larval stages provide a means of wide dispersal of the species, and feeding larvae can obtain food material for completion of their development without the necessity for large amounts of yolk material within the egg.

Fresh water is a much less constant medium than sea water. Streams vary greatly in turbidity, velocity, and volume, not only along their course but from time to time also as a result of droughts or heavy rains. Small ponds and lakes also fluctuate in oxygen content, turbidity, and water volume. In large lakes the environment changes radically with increasing depth, as will be described later.

Like salt water, fresh water is buoyant and aids in support. The low salt concentration, however, creates some difficulty in maintaining water balance. Since the body of the animal contains a higher salt concentration than that of the external environment, there is a tendency for water to diffuse inward. The animal thus has the problem of getting rid of excess water. As a consequence, fresh-water animals usually have some

mechanism for pumping water out of the body and are therefore somewhat like a leaky ship in which bilge pumps must be kept in continual operation. In general, the eggs of fresh-water animals are either retained by the parent or attached to the bottom of the stream or lake, rather than being free-floating as is often true of marine animals. Larval stages are usually absent. Floating eggs and free-swimming larvae are too easily swept away by currents. Since development is usually direct, the eggs typically contain considerable amounts of yolk.

Nitrogenous waste of aquatic animals, both marine and fresh-water, is usually excreted as ammonia. Ammonia is very soluble and toxic and requires considerable water for its removal; but since there is no danger of water loss in aquatic animals, the excretion of ammonia presents no difficulty.

Terrestrial animals live in the harshest environment. The supporting buoyancy of water is absent. Most critical, however, is the problem of water loss by evaporation, and it is the solution of this problem that has caused the evolution of most structural and ecological modifications and adaptations. The integument of terrestrial animals presents a better barrier between the inner and the outer environment than that of aquatic animals. Respiratory surfaces, which must be moist, have developed in the interior of the body to prevent drying out. Nitrogenous wastes are excreted as urea or uric acid, which require less water for removal than does ammonia. Fertilization must be internal; the eggs are usually enclosed in a protective envelope or deposited in a moist environment. Except for insects and a few arachnids, development is direct; and the eggs are usually endowed with large amounts of yolk. Terrestrial animals, which are not well adapted to withstand desiccation, are either nocturnal or are restricted to humid or moist habitats.

A second factor that determines the nature of animal structure is the size of the animal. As the body increases in size, the ratio of surface area to volume decreases. In small animals the surface area is sufficiently great in comparison to the body volume that exchange of gases and waste can be carried out efficiently by diffusion through the general body surface. Also, internal circulation can take place by diffusion alone.

However, as the body increases in size, distances become too great for circulation to take place by diffusion alone; and more efficient transportation mechanisms are necessary. In larger animals this has led to the development of coelomic and blood-vascular circulatory systems. Also, through folding and coiling, the surface area of internal organs and portions of the

equal
pressure

external surface may be increased to facilitate secretion, absorption, gas exchange and other processes.

A third factor that determines the nature of animal structure is the mode of existence. Free-swimming animals are generally bilaterally symmetrical. The nervous system and sense organs are usually concentrated at the anterior end of the body, since this is the part that first comes in contact with the environment. Such an animal is said to be cephalized.

Attached, or sessile, animals tend to have radial symmetry, in which the body consists of a central axis around which are symmetrically arranged similar parts. Radial symmetry is an advantage for sessile existence, since it allows the animal to meet the challenges of its environment from all directions. Skeletons, envelopes, or tubes are commonly present as protection against motile predators. For food, sessile animals either must rely on passing prey, or must subsist on organic detritus or microscopic plants and animals suspended in the surrounding water. The latter type of nutrition usually involves ciliary or setal feeding, in which the animal creates a water current and traps or collects suspended organisms or detritus. Motile larvae are particularly important in sessile animals for dissemination of the species.

Despite the relative uniformity of a marine environment, life is not uniformly distributed throughout the depths and breadths of the world's oceans. The margins of the continents gradually slope seaward in the form of underwater shelves to depths of 200 to 600 feet and then plunge steeply to depths of 12,000 feet or more. Widths of the different continental shelves vary considerably. The edge of the western Atlantic shelf is some 75 miles from the shore, but along the Pacific coast of North America the continental shelf is very narrow. The widest shelf occurs off the coast of Siberia and extends as much as 800 miles into the Arctic Ocean.

Waters over the continental shelves comprise the littoral zone of the world's oceans and support a greater population of marine life than waters over the great ocean depths. The abundance of littoral fauna results from the continual supply of nitrates, phosphates, and other essential substances dumped into coastal waters by rivers and streams. This material provides a rich medium for photosynthetic algae ("the grass of the sea"), which form the base of the food chain for animal life. Similar productive areas, such as the Grand Banks off Nova Scotia, are created by upwellings of water from the ocean floor, mixing accumulated bottom detritus with surface water.

In tropical waters, where the nitrate turn-over is extremely rapid, there is a smaller plant and animal population than in temperate oceans. However, tropical and semitropical seas contain a far greater number of species than do temperate waters. One of the world's richest marine faunas in numbers of species occurs in the East Indies region. The islands of this region—Borneo, Sumatra, the Celebes, and others—represent all that remains of the great, sunken land mass that once connected Australia with southern Asia. The surrounding seas, from the Gulf of Siam to the Arafura Sea between New Guinea and Australia, are very shallow and form the center of the rich Indo-Pacific fauna.

Vertical distribution of marine organisms is largely controlled by the depth of light penetration. Light sufficient for photosynthesis can penetrate down as far as 650 feet, depending on the turbidity of the water. Below this upper, lighted zone lies the twilight zone, where there is insufficient light for photosynthesis, but not total darkness. From the twilight zone down to the ocean floor, total darkness prevails. This region constitutes the aphotic zone. The animals that are permanent inhabitants of the aphotic and twilight zones are carnivorous or detritus feeders and depend ultimately on the photosynthetic activity of the microscopic algae in the upper, lighted regions. Curiously, the twilight zone animals are commonly colored various shades of red; in the aphotic zone, purple and black are dominant.

A similar stratification of the fauna occurs in the deeper, fresh-water lakes, but here temperature is a primary controlling factor. Water reaches its greatest density at 4° C.; and thus when large bodies of water are warmed during spring and summer, the warm water stays at the surface while the heavier, colder water remains at the bottom. Little circulation occurs between the upper and lower levels, so that not only is the bottom zone dark, but it is also relatively stagnant and supports only a limited fauna. With the advent of cold weather, water of the upper stratum becomes heavier and sinks, resulting in a general turnover between the surface and the bottom. Conditions are stabilized again in the winter but with a reversed temperature stratification, for now the lighter, colder water in the form of ice floats at the surface, and the warmer (4° C.), heavier water is at the bottom. In the spring, following the melting of the winter ice, there is another turnover as in the fall.

Both oceans and fresh-water lakes contain a large assemblage of microscopic or very small macroscopic organisms that are free-swimming or suspended in the water. These organisms comprise the plankton and include both plants (phytoplankton) and animals (zooplankton). Although many planktonic organisms are capable of locomotion, they are too small to move independently of currents. Phytoplankton is composed of enormous numbers of diatoms, and microscopic algae; in addition, marine plankton includes reproductive stages of the larger red and brown algae.

Marine zooplankton includes representatives from virtually every group of animals, either as adults or as developmental stages. The animal constituents of fresh-water plankton are more limited in number. Plankton, especially marine plankton, is of primary importance in the aquatic food chain. The photosynthetic phytoplankton forms the first link of the chain and serve as food for zooplankton, which in turn serves as food for larger animals. As would be expected, plankton attains its greatest density in the upper, lighted zone; and in productive waters planktonic organisms may occur in such enormous numbers that the water appears turbid.

In the subsequent chapters the invertebrate phyla are taken up in phylogenetic sequence, and the evolutionary relationships between different phyla and classes provide a thread of continuity that binds the discussion of the different groups together. The evolutionary history of the Animal Kingdom has involved many divergent pathways stemming from certain mainstreams of evolutionary development. Thus, a reconstruction of animal phylogeny produces a pattern that is similar to a great, branching tree. Living and extinct groups of animals are equivalent to terminal twigs and branches that stem at various levels from a number of main branches in this reconstruction.

Many theories exist regarding the evolutionary relationships among animal groups. In the following discussion, one scheme is given preference over the others to avoid confusing the beginning student and to provide maximum continuity between discussions of the different groups. The theories presented here are largely those followed and supported by Dr. Libbie Hyman in her monumental series of volumes (1940-1959) on the invertebrates. Although Dr. Hyman has not yet published a complete series, no zoologist in the twentieth century has contributed more toward an understanding of the invertebrate groups nor has had greater influence on the various theories of invertebrate evolution. Although many zoologists disagree with some of her views, all acknowledge the clarity and soundness of her arguments. Figure 1-1 represents a reconstruction of the evolution of the Animal Kingdom as presented in subsequent chapters.

In discussing phylogenetic relationships, it is convenient to use such terms as *primitive, advanced, lower, higher,* and *specialized.* Unfortunately these terms are not always understood by students and tend to create the erroneous impression that evolution has proceeded from one group to another toward some ideal state or goal of perfection. Such terms as *primitive* and *advanced* are relative and are significant primarily in discussing evolution within a particular group of animals. For example, *primitive species* are those that possess many, or the greatest number of, characteristics believed to have been possessed by the ancestral stock from which the living members of the group arose. *Advanced species* are those that have changed considerably compared with the primitive condition, usually as a result of different environmental situations or the assumption of a different mode of existence. *Specialized* usually refers to characteristics of species that are especially adapted to a particular environmental niche. The terms *specialized* and *advanced,* however, should not be thought of as meaning *more perfect* or *better,* because the environmental conditions for which a particular, specialized species is adapted may not prevail in primitive forms. Moreover, while certain species possess some primitive characteristics, these same species frequently are specialized in other respects.

The terms *primitive* and *advanced* can be particularly misleading when comparing different phyla, because usually only one, or a few, characteristics are being referred to. For example, since multicellular animals evolved from single-celled forms, the protozoans are, in respect to this characteristic, primitive as compared to multicellular phyla. However, beyond this characteristic the term *primitive* has little application to protozoans, for they have undergone at the unicellular level a great evolutionary development, leading to an intracellular specialization unequaled by the cells of any metazoan animals.

The terms *higher* and *lower* usually refer to the levels at which species or groups have stemmed from certain main lines of evolution. Thus sponges and coelenterates are often referred to as *lower* phyla, since they are believed to have originated near the base of the Animal Kingdom phylogenetic tree. This does not imply that sponges and coelenterates are primitive in all respects; for they, like all other groups of animals, have followed certain independent lines of specialization. Furthermore, this does not necessarily imply that higher groups have evolved *directly* through sponges and coelenterates.

No treatment of invertebrates is complete,

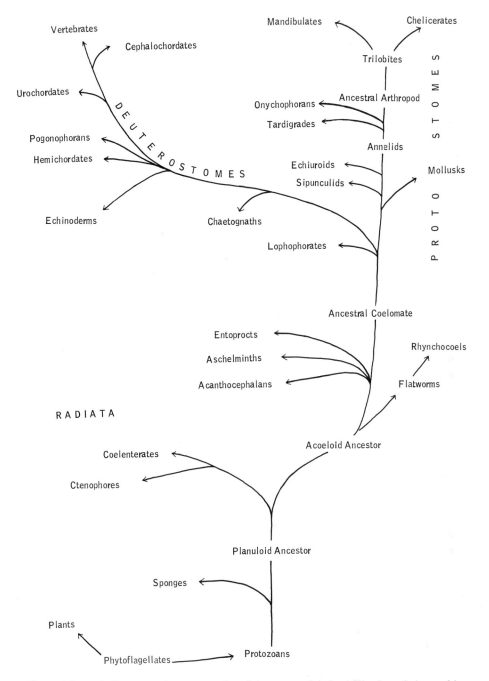

Figure 1-1.   A diagrammatic representation of the suggested Animal Kingdom phylogeny followed in this text. This is but one of several schemes that could be constructed.

nor can there be a proper understanding of invertebrate phylogeny, without some consideration of fossil forms and extinct groups. As much invertebrate paleontology has been included as space permits. From time to time references will be made to different geological eras and periods. For the student who has only a slight background in geology the following geological time table may be of some value for later reference (Fig. 1-2).

The bibliography at the end of each chapter is not intended to be a selection of titles recommended for further reading. The literature on invertebrates is enormous, as one would expect considering the vast area of biology it covers. Most of this literature consists of research papers scattered through hundreds of biological journals published throughout the world over the last 75 years. Obviously, any list of such papers that might be given here would have to be so limited in number and so arbitrary a selection that its value would be highly questionable. The biblio-

ERAS	PERIODS			MOUNTAIN-MAKING EPISODES	LIFE	YEARS AGO
CENOZOIC	QUATERNARY		RECENT	ALPINE-CASCADIAN	AGE OF MAN	15,000
			PLEISTOCENE			1,500,000
	TERTIARY		PLIOCENE		AGE OF MAMMALS AND ANGIOSPERMS	
			MIOCENE			30,000,000
			OLIGOCENE			
			EOCENE	HIMALAYAN		
MESOZOIC	CRETACEOUS			LARAMIDE	AGE OF REPTILES AND GYMNOSPERMS	
	JURASSIC			SIERRA NEVADA		
	TRIASSIC					180,000,000
PALEOZOIC	"CARBONI-FEROUS"		PERMIAN	APPALACHIAN HERCYNIAN		225,000,000
			PENNSYLVANIAN		AGE OF FISHES AND PTERIDOPHYTES	
			MISSISSIPPIAN			
	DEVONIAN					
	SILURIAN			CALEDONIAN-ACADIAN		370,000,000
	ORDOVICIAN					
	CAMBRIAN					
PROTEROZOIC	"PRE-CAMBRIAN"			GRAND CANYON YOUNGER LAURENTIANS	AGE OF INVERTEBRATES AND THALLOPHYTES	500,000,000
ARCHEOZOIC				OLDER LAURENTIANS		2,500,000,000?

Figure 1-2. Subdivisions of geologic time. (Courtesy Darrah, W. C.: Principles of Paleobotany. 2nd Ed. Ronald Press, New York.)

graphies in this text therefore are of a different nature. They consist of two categories. One category comprises the literature cited in the text; the other category, which is of considerably more importance to the student, consists of important reference works on the group of invertebrates with which the chapter deals. Most of these reference citations are followed by a short statement describing the distinctive features of the work. At least some of these works contain the extensive bibliographies that the student should consult for additional information on particular topics.

A listing of journals containing papers on invertebrate zoology would serve little purpose because of the large number involved and because so few are devoted to invertebrates alone. A few hours spent in a good biological library with a bibliography from one of the reference works described above are of much greater value in initiating a student into the nature of biological journals.

There are, however, certain general works with which the student should be familiar. Each is composed of a number of volumes and treats the invertebrate phyla or the entire Animal Kingdom. Two are in English. *The Invertebrates* by L. H. Hyman consists of five volumes at the present time; unfortunately mollusks, annelids, arthropods, and related phyla not yet having

been treated. The other English work is the *Treatise on Invertebrate Paleontology,* which is devoted entirely to fossil invertebrates. Edited by R. C. Moore, the first volumes appeared in 1952; the series is still incomplete.

A notable French work is the Traité de Zoologie, edited by P. Grassé. This series, which was begun in 1948, covers both invertebrates and vertebrates, but it is still incomplete.

Among the German works, the *Handbuch der Zoologie,* edited by W. Kukenthal and T. Krumbach, was published in 1923 and is complete, covering the entire Animal Kingdom. Another work of primary importance is H. G. Bronn's (editor) *Klassen und Ordnungen des Tierreichs,* which was begun in 1873; new sections are still being published today. This is a monumental series covering the entire Animal Kingdom and containing exhaustive treatments of many animal groups.

LITERATURE CITED

Hyman, L. H., 1940: The Invertebrata, Vol. I, Protozoa through Ctenophora. 1951: Vol. II, Platyhelminthes and Rhynchocoela. 1951: Vol. III, Acanthocephala, Aschelminthes, and Entoprocta. 1955: Vol. IV, Echinodermata. 1955: Vol. V, Smaller Coelomate Groups. McGraw-Hill Publishing Co., New York.

Chapter 2

THE PROTOZOANS

The phylum Protozoa is a heterogeneous group *(varied, different)* of microscopic animals united only by their common unicellular structure. This unicellular organization is the only characteristic by which the phylum can be described; in all other respects the phylum displays extreme diversity. Protozoans exhibit all types of symmetry, a great range of structural complexity, and adaptations for all types of environmental conditions. Although the classic approach is followed here and the Protozoa are treated as a phylum, the lack of common structural features above the level of class indicates that these animals actually constitute a subkingdom rather than a phylum. In fact, the protozoans are usually considered to represent both a subkingdom and a phylum.

The protozoan cell possesses all typical cellular structures and carries out all basic cellular processes. Hyman (1940) has pointed out, however, that a protozoan should not be thought of as the equivalent of a single cell within a multicellular animal. Rather, a protozoan, although unicellular, must be recognized as being a complete organism, carrying out all functions found in any multicellular animal. Hyman has therefore proposed the term *acellular*, rather than *unicellular*, to describe protozoans. Unfortunately, the connotations of this adjective are perhaps just as misleading as *unicellular*. Although there are no organs or tissues, parts of the protoplasm are typically specialized to form organelles, which perform various functions. In many cases organelles are analogous to multicellular structures or organs in metazoans. A protozoan cell therefore can attain an extreme

complexity. Sonneborn (1950) makes the statement that *Paramecium*—commonly used as an example of a "simple" animal—is "far more complicated in morphology and physiology than any cell of the body of man."

Protozoans occur wherever moisture is present—in the sea, in all types of fresh water and in soil. There are commensal, symbiotic, and many parasitic species. In fact, the class Sporozoa is entirely parasitic.

Although most protozoans occur as solitary individuals, there are numerous colonial forms. Some colonial forms, such as *Volvox,* attain such a degree of cellular interdependence that they approach a true multicellular level of structure (Fig. 2-2, *C*). Both solitary and colonial species may be either free-moving or sessile.

The great majority of protozoans are microscopic. *Plasmodium,* the malarial parasite, is so small that it occupies only one-quarter or one-fifth of a human red blood cell. At the other extreme, the fresh-water ciliate, *Spirostomum,* may reach a length of 3.0 mm. and be seen with the naked eye. The colonies of some colonial species are even larger.

The protozoan body is usually bounded only by the cell membrane, which may be thin and flexible or relatively rigid. Nonliving external coverings or shells occur in many different groups. Such coverings may be simple gelatinous or cellulose envelopes; or they may be distinct shells, composed of various inorganic and organic materials, or sometimes foreign particles. The cortical cytoplasm, lying beneath the cell membrane, is usually gelatinous and is called

(gelatinous)

ectoplasm, in contrast to the more fluid, internal cytoplasm, called endoplasm. Ectoplasm and endoplasm are merely different colloidal states of protoplasm and are reversible. The nucleus may be vesicular, containing considerable nucleoplasm and one or more large bodies called endosomes; or the nucleus may be compact with densely packed chromatin material.

The locomotor organelles of protozoans may be flagella, cilia, or flowing extensions of the body called pseudopodia. Since the type of locomotor organelle provides the principal basis for division of the phylum into its four classes, discussion of the structure of these organelles is deferred until later.

Characteristic of most protozoans is an organelle called the contractile vacuole (Fig. 2-10, *B*). Contractile vacuoles are water-balancing structures, acting as pumps to remove excess water from the cytoplasm. These usually spherical vacuoles periodically collapse, releasing their fluid contents to the outside. One to several may be present within the animal, and the position and structure vary within the different classes. Contractile vacuoles are most commonly encountered in fresh-water protozoans with cytoplasm hypertonic to the aqueous environment. However, contractile vacuoles are also present in some marine groups.

All types of nutrition occur in protozoans. Some are autotrophic and others are saprozoic; but the majority are holozoic, and digestion occurs intracellularly within food vacuoles. Intracellular digestion has been most studied in amebas and ciliates. The food vacuoles undergo definite changes in pH and in size during the course of digestion. Following ingestion, the vacuole becomes increasingly acid and smaller. After the initial acid phase, enzymes in an alkaline medium pass from the cytoplasm into the vacuole, and the vacuole increases in size and becomes alkaline. The vacuole contents are then digested, the products absorbed, and the undigestible remnants egested to the outside.

Respiration occurs by the diffusion of oxygen across the cell membrane. Protozoans that live in water where there is active decomposition of organic matter, or live as parasites in the digestive tract of other animals, can exist with little or no oxygen present. Some protozoans are facultative anaerobes, utilizing oxygen when present but also capable of anaerobic respiration.

Metabolic wastes are diffused to the outside of the organism. Ammonia is the principal nitrogenous waste, and the amount eliminated varies directly with the amount of protein consumed.

The protozoan reproductive processes and life cycles are varied, and a formidable terminology has been created to describe peculiarities of different groups. Only a few of the more common terms are described here.

Asexual reproduction occurs in all protozoans and is the only known mode of reproduction in some species. Division of the animal into two or more daughter cells is called fission. When this process results in two similar daughter cells, it is termed binary fission; when one daughter cell is much smaller than the other, the process is called budding. In some protozoans multiple fission, or schizogony, is the rule. In schizogony, after a varying number of nuclear divisions, the cell divides into a number of daughter cells. With few exceptions asexual reproduction involves some redifferentiation of missing organelles following fission.

Sexual reproduction may involve fusion (syngamy) of identical gametes (called isogametes), or gametes that differ in size and structure. The latter, called anisogametes or heterogametes, range from types that differ only slightly in size to well differentiated sperm and eggs. Meiosis commonly occurs in the formation of gametes, but in many flagellate protozoans meiosis is postzygotic; that is, occurs following the formation of the zygote as in most algae. In ciliate protozoans there is no formation of distinct gametes; instead two animals adhere together in a process called conjugation, and they exchange nuclei. Each migrating nucleus fuses with a stationary nucleus in the opposite conjugant to form a zygote nucleus (synkaryon). Less common is a process called autogamy, in which two nuclei, each representing a gamete, fuse to form a zygote, all within a single individual.

Encystment is characteristic of the life cycle of many protozoans. In forming a cyst, the protozoan secretes a thickened envelope about itself and becomes inactive. Depending on the species, the protective cyst is resistant to desiccation or low temperatures, and encystment enables the animal to pass through unfavorable environmental conditions. Moreover, cysts can be transported by wind or other agents and are thus important in dispersal. The simplest life cycle includes only two phases: an active phase and a protective, encysted phase. However, the more complex life cycles are often characterized by encysted zygotes or by formation of special reproductive cysts, in which fission, gametogenesis, or other reproductive processes take place.

SUBPHYLUM PLASMODROMA
(FLAGELLA)

The classes Mastigophora, Sarcodina, and Sporozoa are included within the subphylum *producing food by photosynthesis*

Plasmodroma. Animals in this group possess nuclei that are monomorphic (i.e., of only one type) even though more than one nucleus may be present. Sexual reproduction involves syngamy. The locomotor organelles, if present, are typically pseudopodia or flagella.

Class Mastigophora

The class Mastigophora (or Flagellata) includes those protozoans that possess flagella as adult locomotor organelles; it is generally considered to be the most primitive of the four protozoan classes.

Mastigophorans can be conveniently divided into two groups: the phytoflagellates and the zooflagellates. These two groups are commonly given subclass ranking, in which case they are known respectively as the Phytomastigina and the Zoomastigina.

The phytoflagellates typically possess chromoplasts, usually called chromatophores,* which are bodies containing the pigments necessary in photosynthesis (Fig. 2-1, *A* and *B*). These protozoans are thus plant-like and are usually holophytic. The phytoflagellate division contains most of the free-living members of the class and includes such common forms as *Euglena, Chlamydomonas, Volvox,* and *Peranema.*

Botanists treat most species in this division as algae; in fact algologists regard the zoological treatment of the phytoflagellates as a hodgepodge assemblage. There is considerable justification for the inclusion of the phytoflagellates within the Plant Kingdom. They possess chromoplasts; they are holophytic; and the pigments of such forms as *Chlamydomonas* and *Volvox* are identical to those in cells of higher plants. Moreover, motility cannot be considered

*Although *chromatophore* is the more correct term, *chromoplast* has been used here to avoid confusion with the special pigment cells of multicellular animals, which are also called chromatophores.

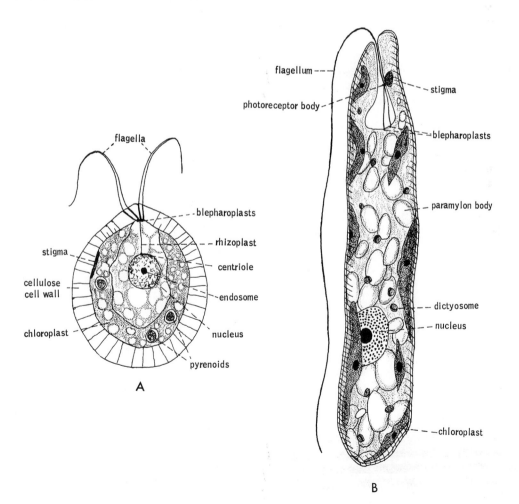

Figure 2-1. *A. Haematococcus,* a phytoflagellate with a single cup-shaped chloroplast. (After Elliot from Hyman.) *B. Euglena gracilis.* (After Hollande.)

a peculiarity of animals; many filamentous algae produce unicellular, flagellated zoospores that are very similar to phytoflagellates. On the other hand, there is no sharp line between the phytoflagellates and the zooflagellates, for there are many phytoflagellates that have lost their chromoplasts and have assumed a saprozoic or holozoic nutrition. Such a loss has occurred independently many times within the phytoflagellates. Some genera, such as *Euglena,* even contain both colored and colorless species.

It is futile to argue the position of the phytoflagellates. That the group grades into the algae on one hand and the protozoans on the other is certainly evidence of their primitive position and of their probably being a common point of origin for both the Plant and Animal Kingdoms.

The zooflagellates lack chromoplasts and are either holozoic or saprozoic. Some are free-living, but the majority of species are commensal, symbiotic, or parasitic in other animals, particularly arthropods and vertebrates. Many groups have become highly specialized. It is unlikely that this division represents a closely related phylogenetic unit. They have probably evolved from a number of different holophytic groups.

Form and Structure. Most flagellates possess distinct anterior and posterior ends, although almost any plan of symmetry occurs. Numerous species of colonial flagellates exist, and in the phytoflagellate family, Volvocidae, colonial organization reaches a remarkably high level. All the volvocids are colonial; and these colonies exist in the form of flattened curved plates or hollow spheres. A gelatinous envelope surrounds the individual cell or surrounds the entire colony as a sheath. *Gonium* consists of 4 to 16 cells in a quadrangular plate (Fig. 2-2, *A*). Colonies of *Pandorina* (Fig. 2-2, *B*) and *Eudorina* have spherical or ovoid shapes with internal cavities of varying sizes and consist of 4 to 64 cells. The largest volvocid colonies, which occur in species of *Volvox* (Fig. 2-2, *C*) and *Pleodorina,* are large, hollow-shaped spheres. Each of these volvocid colonies possesses a synchronized flagellar beat, and swims with a definite anterior pole directed forward. In *Pleodorina* and *Volvox* even a degree of cellular specialization exists. Some of these cells are strictly somatic, while others are reproductive. The reproductive cells are larger and located away from the anterior pole.

The choanoflagellates, a group of zooflagellates that contain a number of interesting colonial forms, are peculiar in having a cylindrical collar around the base of each flagellum (Fig. 2-3, *A*). Most of these colonies are sessile and attached to the substratum directly or by

a stalk. In *Proterospongia,* however, the colony consists of a gelatinous mass into which the flagellated collar cells are imbedded.

The cell membrane may form the only body covering, as in euglenoids, some dinoflagellates, and in most zooflagellates; it may permit some change in shape, such as bulging and bending or even ameboid movement. In Euglenoidida the cell membrane is often modified into a thickened pellicle, which may be striated or ridged (Fig. 2-1, *B*).

Many of the phytoflagellates are provided with nonliving coverings, which take a variety of different forms. The chrysomonads may have a gelatinous covering; or they may be

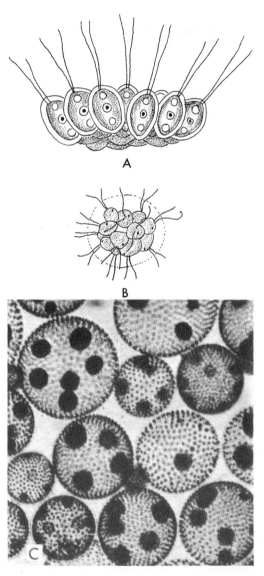

Figure 2-2. Colonial Volvocidae. *A.* Side view of *Gonium pectorale.* (After Stein from Pavillard.) *B. Pandorina morum.* (After Smith from Hall.) *C. Volvox.* Note daughter colonies within parent colonies. (Courtesy of General Biological Supply Co.)

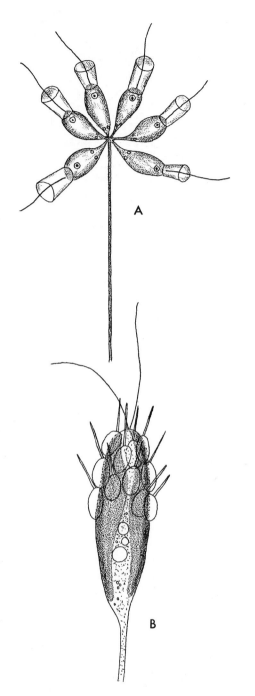

phytoflagellates possessing a nonliving covering is the order Dinoflagellida. The dinoflagellate body is roughly ovoid, but asymmetrical (Fig. 2-4, *A*). Typical dinoflagellates possess two flagella. One is attached a short distance behind the middle of the body; it is directed posteriorly and lies in a longitudinal groove called the sulcus. The other flagellum is transverse and is located in a groove that either rings the body or forms a spiral of several turns. The transverse groove is called the girdle if it is a simple ring, or the annulus, if it is spiralled.

Dinoflagellates can be divided into unarmored and armored types. The unarmored forms are naked or enclosed in a simple, continuous, cellulose envelope. The common fresh-water dinoflagellate, *Gymnodinium,* is an unarmored type (Fig. 2-4, *A*). Armored dinoflagellates, which are primarily marine, have either a cellulose covering consisting of two valves or a covering made of cellulose plates cemented together (Fig. 2-4, *B*). Frequently the armor is sculptured, and often long projections or wing-like extensions protrude from the body, creating very bizarre shapes. For example, *Ceratium,* a common marine and fresh-water genus, possesses an anterior horn and two, long posterior horns, which curve forward, giving the body an anchor-like appearance (Fig. 2-4, *E*). *Histiophysis* is shaped somewhat like a jug (Fig. 2-4, *C*), and *Ornithocercus* has beautiful sail-like wings (Fig. 2-4, *D*).

Dinoflagellates occur in countless numbers in marine plankton, and a number of forms exist abundantly in fresh water. Marine species are responsible for outbreaks of the so-called "red tides" off the coasts of Florida and California, and elsewhere. Under ideal conditions populations of certain species increase to enormous numbers. Riegel and others (1949), describing an outbreak of "red tide" in Monterey Bay, California, reported that the responsible dinoflagellate, *Gonyaulax,* reached a density of 20 to 40 million organisms per cubic centimeter of sea water. As a result, the water was colored red in daylight and was brightly luminescent at night. Moreover, the concentrations of certain metabolic substances reached such a high level that other marine life was killed. The 1948 Florida "red tide", which killed millions of fish, crabs, shrimp, and other animals, was produced by a different species, which gave the water an oily yellow appearance.

Locomotion.   Locomotion of flagellates is typically by means of flagella. The phytoflagellates usually have one or two flagella; the zooflagellates, one to many. When two or more flagella occur, they may be of equal or unequal length, and one may be leading and one trail-

Figure 2-3.   *A.* Colony of the choanoflagellate, *Codosiga botrytis.* (After Stein from Manwell.) *B. Synura splendida* with scales and spines. (After Korschikov from Hollande.)

provided with a siliceous or calcium carbonate skeleton in the form of scales or plates, to which long spines are often attached (Fig. 2-3, *B*). All Phytomonadida, which includes *Volvox, Pandorina, Haematococcus* (Fig. 2-1, *A*), *Polytomella,* and other green, plant-like forms, have a cellulose wall of variable thickness outside the cell membrane.

One of the most interesting groups of

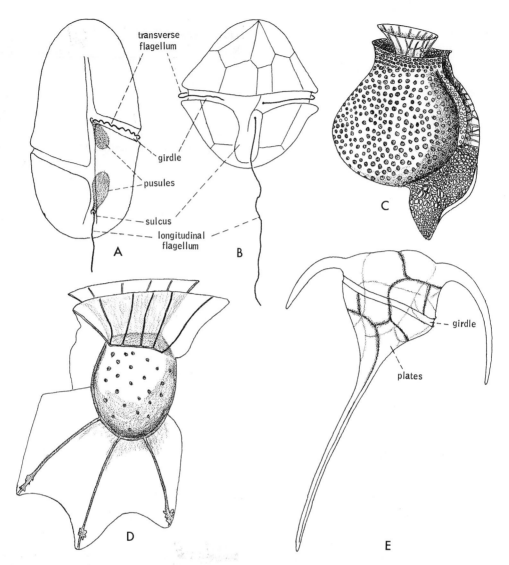

transverse
flagellum

girdle

pusules

sulcus

longitudinal
flagellum

A

B

C

D

E

girdle

plates

Figure 2-4.   Dinoflagellates. *A.* A naked dinoflagellate, *Gymnodinium.* (After Kofoid and Swezy from Hall.) *B.* A fresh-water armored dinoflagellate, *Glenodinium cinctum.* (After Pennak.) *C. Histiophysis rugosa.* Flagella are hidden. *D. Ornithocercus.* (*C* and *D,* after Kofoid and Skogsberg from Chatton.) *E. Ceratium.* (After Jörgenson from Hyman.)

ing, as in *Peranema* (Fig. 2-5, *A*) and the dinoflagellates. Flagella are attached at the anterior end, except in dinoflagellates and some zooflagellates. In the cryptomonads (Fig. 2-5, *B*) and the euglenoids (Figs. 2-1, *B* and 2-5, *A*), the flagella originate from an anterior pit that, when deep and vase-like, is known as a cytopharynx or reservoir. Electron microscopy has revealed that the structures of flagella and cilia are fundamentally similar throughout the Animal and Plant Kingdoms. A single flagellum (or cilium) is constructed very much like a cable. Two central fibers form a core, which is in turn encircled by nine outer fibers. The outer fibers are actually double. The entire bundle is enclosed within a

sheath that is continuous with the cell membrane. The flagella of some species bear one or more rows of delicate, lateral fibrils (or mastigonemes), which cannot be seen with an ordinary light microscope. The flagellum always arises from a basal granule, called a blepharoplast, that lies just beneath the surface. The blepharoplast may act as a centriole; if not, a fibrillar connection called a rhizoplast runs between the blepharoplast and the centriole or nucleus (Figs. 2-1, *A* and 2-5, *B*). Associated with the flagellar apparatus of some symbiotic zooflagellates is an intracellular filament or rod, called the axostyle (Fig. 2-9, *C*). The axostyle usually connects anteriorly with the blepharoplast and runs through the length of the body.

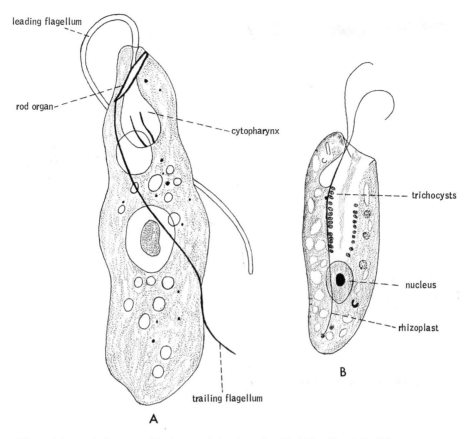

Figure 2-5. *A. Peranema trichophorum,* a holozoic euglenoid. (After Chen.) *B. Chilomonas paramecium,* a cryptomonad. (After Prowazek from Hyman.)

Flagellar propulsion in most mastigophorans essentially follows the same principle as that of the airplane propeller. The flagellum undergoes spiral undulations with the undulatory waves always passing from the base to the tip. A single lash, or beat, describes a helix; the force from the beat drives the animal forward. In addition to forward progression, flagellar action frequently produces spiral rotation of the body. Rotation occurs in such a manner that one surface of the body always faces the central axis of the spiral. Rapidity of the flagellar beat varies, depending not only on the species involved but also on environmental conditions. For example, the flagella of *Polytomella uvella* and *Euglena viridis* beat 29 and 67 times a minute respectively under normal conditions.

Dinoflagellates tend to swim in a generally upright position with the trailing, longitudinal flagellum parallel to the forward axis of movement. The transverse flagellum causes rotation and drives the animal upward or forward. The beating of the longitudinal flagellum produces a larger spiral and thus generally determines the direction of movement. Mastigophorans which have thin, flexible pellicles are often capable of ameboid move-

ment; and some forms, such as chrysomonads, may cast off their flagella and assume an ameboid type of locomotion entirely.

Nutrition. Phytoflagellates are primarily holophytic; but some are saprozoic, holozoic or combine any two of these three modes of nutrition. Colored species possess chromoplasts, which contain chlorophyll and any of a number of xanthophylls. When the chlorophyll is not masked by other pigments, a flagellate appears green in color as in the phytomonads and euglenoids. If the xanthophylls dominate, the color is orange, yellow, or brown as in the dinoflagellates.

Flagellate nutrition has provoked considerable interest in recent years, and the literature on the subject has become enormous. Culturing has been the most frequent method of approach in these studies. A species is grown in a prepared medium, and population growth rate is used as an index of the utilization of particular medium constituents. Such studies indicate that many flagellates cannot be classified as strict holophytes or saprophytes (the term *saprophytic,* used with reference to plant-like forms, is considered here as synonymous to *saprozoic*) and that intermediate conditions between these two types of nutrition exist. Actually, there appear to be relatively few phytoflagellates that are strictly photo-auto-trophic; that is, that can synthesize organic compounds, using an inorganic source of carbon. A large number of these phytoflagellates require an organic carbon source. In experimental cultures, acetates and fatty acids can be used as a carbon source for a great many species. Such species have been called acetate flagellates and include both colored forms (the volvocids) and colorless species [*Chilomonas* (Fig. 2-5, *B*), *Menoidium,* and *Peranema*]. The colorless species have been termed chemo-autotrophic, although *Peranema* is actually holozoic under natural conditions.

Although all colored phytoflagellates are capable of photosynthesis, a number are also facultative saprophytes. For example, *Haematococcus* is holophytic in light and saprophytic in the dark (Fig. 2-1, *A*). *Euglena* also becomes saprophytic in the absence of light and even loses its pigments. A number of chrysomonads and some dinoflagellates are both holozoic and holophytic.

Nitrates or ammonium compounds suffice as nitrogen sources for most holophytic forms. Saprozoic species require ammonium salts, amino acids, or peptones. Green species that can be cultured in the absence of light, such as *Chlamydomonas aglaeformis* and *Haematococcus pluvialis,* require peptones under these conditions. There have also been numerous studies on vitamin and metal requirements in flagellates. The results of these studies, which are beyond the scope of this discussion, have been summarized by Hutner and Provasoli (1951).

Studies on phytoflagellate nutrition have stimulated speculation regarding the original mode of nutrition in living organisms. Were the first organisms autotrophic or saprozoic (heterotrophic)? Horowitz (1945) suggests that the first forms of life were heterotrophs that absorbed and utilized simple organic compounds. It is generally agreed today that such compounds, probably created by solar radiation, were a part of the primeval environment and preceded life itself. As these organic compounds disappeared from the environment, only organisms that evolved enzymes for synthesizing these compounds could survive. Thus, an autotrophic mode of nutrition gradually evolved. Living saprozoic and holozoic species probably are derived secondarily from autotrophic forms, but the necessity for an external organic source of carbon in some colored flagellates may well represent a retention of certain features of the primordial heterotrophs.

Holozoic nutrition occurs in colorless phytoflagellates and in zooflagellates, but some colored phytoflagellates, such as the chrysomonads, and some dinoflagellates also display holozoic tendencies. The mechanics of ingestion and the processes of digestion are still very obscure. The chrysomonads engulf food particles in a food cup, like that in many amebas (page 25). The dinoflagellates also utilize pseudopodia in food capture. *Ceratium* forms a pseudopodial net, which extends through pores in the theca. Some marine dinoflagellates also possess two vacuoles, called pusules, which open to the outside (Fig. 2-4, *A*). These pusules appear to *draw in* fluid and perhaps are used to ingest particulate material.

The mode of ingestion in holozoic euglenoids is still debated. Some authors claim that there is an opening (or cytostome) at the base of the anterior reservoir, from which the flagella extend, and that food particles are driven into the reservoir by the flagella. Others claim that the cytostome is not associated with the anterior reservoir. Chen's (1950) studies on the colorless, fresh-water *Peranema* support the latter view. The anterior of this euglenoid contains two parallel rods, making up a so-called rod organ, located adjacent to the reservoir (Fig. 2-5, *A*). The anterior of the rod organ terminates at the cytostome, which is just below the outer opening of the canal leading from the reservoir. *Peranema* feeds on a wide variety of living organisms, including *Euglena;* and the cytostome can be greatly distended to permit engulfment of large prey. In feeding, the rod organ is protruded and used as an anchor to pull in prey, which is swallowed whole; or the rod organ can cut into the victim, and the contents are then sucked out (Fig. 2-6). Following ingestion, the prey is digested within the food vacuoles.

Among zooflagellates, the choanoflagellates have an interesting mode of ingestion. The beating flagellum drives food particles toward the body, and the collar directs the food particles into an anterior space created by contraction of the body away from its mucous covering. The body then extends forward and forces the collected particles into the cytoplasm.

Phytoflagellates store reserve foods such as oils or fats; or they may store carbohydrates in the form of typical plant starch (as in phytomonads), paramylum (in euglenoids [Fig. 2-1, *B*]), or leucosin. In zooflagellates, glycogen is the usual reserve food product.

Water Balance, Excretion, and Sensory Organelles.   Little information is available on water balance and excretion in flagellates, although contractile vacuoles occur in phytomonads and euglenoids. Phytomonads usually contain two vacuoles located near the base of the flagella; euglenoids have one or two contractile vacuoles, which open into a reservoir (Fig. 2-5, *A*).

Eye spots, or stigmata, composed of granules of a carotin pigment called hematochrome, occur in phytomonads, green euglenoids, and dinoflagellates. In *Euglena* the stigma is composed of a cup of pigment that shades a light-sensitive material, or photoreceptor body, located near the base of the flagellum (Fig. 2-1, *B*). *Euglena* is positively phototactic; and since the pigment shield permits photoreception from one direction only, the animal is able to orient and move in the direction of the light source. In some dinoflagellates the eye spot is even provided with a lens. In addition to acting as a locomotor organelle, the flagellum probably plays an accessory role as a sensory organelle. This appears to be true for *Peranema,* in which flagellar contact with prey illicits a general excitatory response.

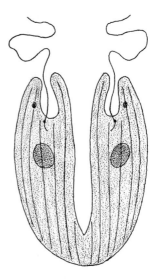

Figure 2-7.   Symmetrogenic, or mirror-image, division. (After Corliss.)

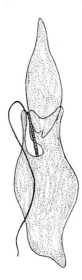

Figure 2-6.   A *Peranema* swallowing a *Euglena*. (After Chen.)

Reproduction and Life Cycles. In the majority of flagellates asexual reproduction occurs by binary fission, and most commonly the animal divides longitudinally. Division is thus said to be symmetrogenic, that is, producing mirror-image daughter cells (Fig. 2-7). In multiflagellate species the flagella are divided between the daughter cells; in those species with few flagella, the one or several flagella may duplicate prior to cell division, equally apportioned to each daughter cell, resorbed and formed anew in each daughter cell, or even unequally apportioned. The same may apply to other organelles. Thus, division in many flagellates is not perfectly symmetrogenic.

In the dinoflagellates division is oblique.

In armored species the two fission products regenerate the missing plates; but in a few species, such as *Glenodinium,* division occurs inside the original parental envelope, which then ruptures to allow two naked daughter cells to escape. Incomplete fission occurs in some dinoflagellates, such as *Ceratium* and *Gymnodinium,* and results in a chain of individuals. Multiple fission is typical of some dinoflagellates and of some parasitic zooflagellates.

Asexual reproduction in the colonial volvocids can be complex. In *Volvox,* for example, any one of a certain few cells at the posterior of the colony may undergo fission to form a daughter colony. As fission proceeds, the daughter cells become arranged in the form of a hollow ball, called a plakea, in which the flagellated ends of the cells are directed toward the interior. The plakea then inverts, or turns inside out, through an opening in one side of the sphere. Following inversion, the hollow spherical form is reassumed, but now the flagellated ends of the cells are directed to the exterior in the normal position. The daughter colonies usually escape by a rupturing of the parent wall.

Sexual reproduction in the flagellates rarely occurs except in the Phytomonadida and the symbiotic Hypermastigida. The phytomonads display all gradations of sexual reproduction from isogamy to highly developed heterogamy. *Chlamydomonas* forms isogametes that are but miniatures of the adults. Other forms related to *Chlamydomonas* show the beginnings of sex differentiation by having gametes that differ just slightly in size. In *Platydorina,* heterogamy is well developed, but the large macrogametes still retain flagella and are free-swimming. Finally, in *Volvox* true eggs and sperm develop from special reproductive cells at the posterior of the colony. The egg is stationary and is fertilized within the parent colony. Volvocid colonies may be either monoecious or dioecious. Meiosis in the phytomonads is postzygotic rather than prezygotic.

The life cycles of phytoflagellates and free-living zooflagellates is usually simple. Non-flagellated ameboid (palmella) stages are characteristic of most phytoflagellates. In the palmella stage the organism loses its flagellum and becomes a ball-like, nonmotil, usually floating, relatively undifferentiated cell, located inside the original parental envelope when such an envelope is present (Fig. 2-8, *A*). Fission often follows so that the palmella consists of a cluster of cells (Fig. 2-8, *B*). Many species, such as some dinoflagellates, may remain in the palmella stage for a long time, making it the dominant stage in the life cycle.

Distinctive cysts are formed in a number of different phytoflagellate groups. Cysts of chryso-monads (Fig. 2-8, *D*) typically have siliceous walls; cysts of dinoflagellates (Fig. 2-8, *A*) are often crescent-shaped. In *Volvox* the zygote secretes a thick, tuberculate, cyst wall. After disintegration of the parent colony, the zygote sinks to the bottom, where it may remain in the encysted stage for many months.

Ecology. Although all of the phytoflagel-late classes have at least some marine and fresh-water representatives, the phytomonads and euglenoids are predominantly fresh-water flagel-lates. Most of the dinoflagellates, on the other hand, are marine. Free-living zooflagellates occur in both fresh and salt water.

The zooflagellates contain most of the parasitic mastigophorans; but there are some dinoflagellates that are ectoparasites on the gills of fish or on marine annelids and crustaceans, or are endoparasites in the digestive tracts of different invertebrates. Parasitic zooflagellates occur largely in arthropods and vertebrates and often have complex life cycles involving two hosts. *Leishmania* and *Trypanosoma* are the most notable parasites in this group.

There are many commensal and symbiotic flagellates. Among the most interesting are the intestinal symbionts of cockroaches, wood roaches, and termites. These flagellates comprise the order Hypermastigida and are extremely complex (Fig. 2-9, *A*). All are multiflagellated with a sac-like or elongated body, usually bear-ing an anterior rostrum and cap. In termites and wood roaches the host is dependent on its flagellate fauna for the digestion of wood. According to Cleveland (1925, 1928, 1934) the wood consumed by the roach or termite is in-gested by the flagellates, and the products of digestion are also utilized by the insect. The host loses its fauna with each molt; but by lick-ing other individuals or by eating cysts passed in feces (in the case of roaches), a new fauna is obtained.

Another commensal group, the order Opalinida, occurs in the gut of frogs and toads. These leaf-like, mouthless flagellates are of in-terest because they are uniformly covered by "longitudinal rows" of cilia rather than flagella (Fig. 2-9, *B*). In fact, until recently, the opalinids were considered primitive ciliates and assigned to the subclass Protociliata. An increasing num-

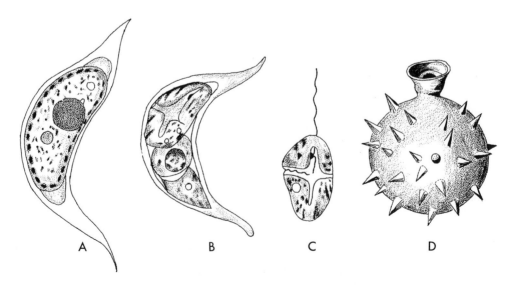

Figure 2-8.   *A* to *C*. Stages in the life cycle of the dinoflagellate, *Cystodinium steinii*. *A*. Palmella stage. *B*. Fission, or spore formation, within cyst. *C*. Dinospore, or flagellate, stage. (After Klebs from Chatton.) *D*. Siliceous cyst of the chrysomonad, *Ochromonas fragilis*. (After Conrad from Hollande.)

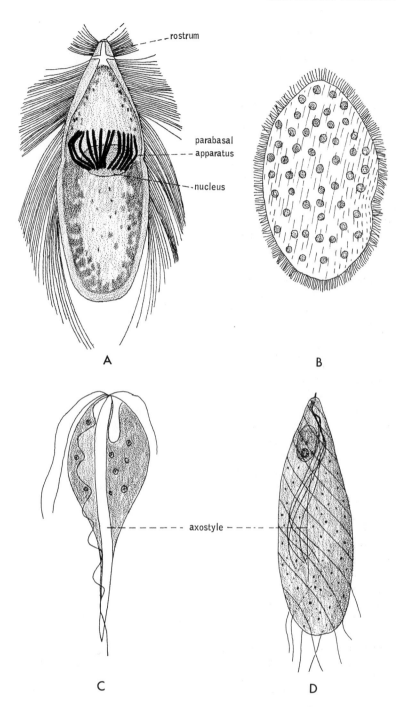

Figure 2-9. *A. Trichonympha agilis,* symbiont in gut of termite. (After Duboscq and Grassé from Grassé.) *B. Opalina,* a commensal flagellate found in the gut of amphibians. (After Corliss.) *C. Trichomonas,* an inhabitant of the gut of vertebrates. (After Hyman.) *D. Pyrsonympha,* a commensal found in gut of termites. (After Powell from Hyman.)

ber of protozoologists, however, now consider them more closely allied with the zooflagellates than with the ciliates. For despite the presence of cilia or cilia-like organelles, the one to several nuclei are of the same type, fission tends to be of the symmetrogenic type, and sexual reproduction involves syngamy.

It recently has been discovered that the symbiotic zooxanthellae, the yellow-brown unicellular "algae" that occur in the tissues of many invertebrates, are actually the palmella stage of certain dinoflagellates. This symbiotic relationship will be referred to again in later chapters.

Systematic Résumé of Class Mastigophora.

Subclass Phytomastigina. Flagellates that are usually colored by the presence of chromoplasts. Most are biflagellate.

Order Chrysomonadida. Small flagellates with yellow or brown chromoplasts and usually two flagella. Siliceous cysts. Marine and fresh-water. *Chromulina, Ochromonas, Synura.*

Order Cryptomonadida. Small, biflagellate, with an anterior depression, or reservoir. Marine and fresh-water. *Chilomonas* is a common colorless genus in polluted water (Fig. 2-5, *B*).

Order Dinoflagellida. Possess transverse and longitudinal flagella, located in grooves. Body either naked or covered by cellulose plates or valves, or by a cellulose membrane. Brown or yellow chromoplasts and stigma usually present. Largely marine; some parasites. Includes the marine genera *Histiophysis, Ornithocercus, Noctiluca, Gonyaulax;* the marine and fresh-water genera *Glenodinium, Gymnodinium, Ceratium.*

Order Euglenoidida. Elongated, green or colorless flagellates with one or two flagella arising from an anterior reservoir. Stigma present in colored forms. Primarily fresh-water. *Euglena, Phacus, Peranema, Menoidium.*

Order Chloromonadida. Small, pale green flagellates with usually two flagella. *Gonyostomum.*

Order Phytomonadida. Body with green chromoplasts, stigma, and two flagella of equal length. Many colonial species. Largely fresh-water forms. *Haematococcus, Chlamydomonas, Polytomella, Gonium, Pandorina, Platydorina, Eudorina, Pleodorina, Volvox.*

Subclass Zoomastigina. Colorless flagellates with one to many flagella.

Order Protomonadida. Mostly small and naked with one or two flagella. Largely parasitic; including *Leishmania, Trypanosoma.* Free-living species in salt or fresh water include the Choanoflagellates.

Order Polymastigida. With three to eight flagella; one, two, sometimes many nuclei. Mostly commensals and parasites of vertebrates and arthropods. *Chilomastix, Pyrsonympha* (Fig. 2-9, *D*).

Order Trichomonadida. Uninucleate or multinucleate species with an axostyle and three to six flagella. Parasites and commensals in vertebrates and insects. *Trichomonas* (Fig. 2-9, *C*).

Order Hypermastigida. Oval or elongated forms with many flagella and one nucleus. Anterior usually provided with a rostrum and cap. All are commensals and symbionts in gut of termites and roaches. *Trichonympha.*

Order Opalinida. Flattened, leaf-like flagellates occurring in the gut of frogs and

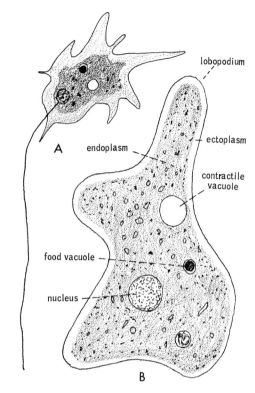

Figure 2-10.   *A. Mastigamoeba.* (After Calkins modified from Hyman.) *B. Amoeba.*

toads. Body uniformly covered with longitudinal rows of cilia. Mouthless. *Opalina.*

Order Rhizomastigida. Ameboid forms with a single flagellum. *Mastigamoeba* (Fig. 2-10, *A*).

Class Sarcodina

The Class Sarcodina contains those protozoans in which adults possess flowing extensions of the body called pseudopodia. Pseudopodia are used for capturing prey in all Sarcodina; and in those groups that move about actively, pseudopodia are also used as locomotor organelles. The class includes the familiar amebas as well as many other marine, fresh-water, and terrestrial forms.

The Sarcodina are either asymmetrical or have a spherical symmetry. They possess relatively few organelles, and in this respect the Sarcodina are perhaps the simplest protozoans. However, skeletal structures, which are found in the majority of species, reach a complexity and beauty that is surpassed by few other animals.

There is considerable evidence that a close phylogenetic relationship between the Sarcodina and the Mastigophora exists. As already mentioned, many mastigophorans undergo ameboid phases, in which the flagellum is lost and progression is effected by pseudopodia. Some Sarcodina have flagellated stages. The close relationship between the two classes is beautifully illustrated by a small number of interesting protozoans, such as *Mastigamoeba* (Fig. 2-10, *A*), which have been placed in the order Rhizomastigida. These animals look like typical amebas, but a long flagellum is also present. The Rhizomastigida have arbitrarily been included as an order of the Mastigophora; but they could just as logically be considered Sarcodina. The presence of flagellated gametes among many Sarcodina would seem to indicate that perhaps the Mastigophora is the ancestral group.

Form and Structure in the Orders of Sarcodina. The Sarcodina contains four groups —the amebas, the foraminiferans, the heliozoans, and the radiolarians—each displaying a relatively distinct and different form and structure.

ORDER AMOEBIDA and ORDER TESTACIDA. The amebas, members of the order Amoebida, which includes the genera *Amoeba* (Fig. 2-10, *B*) and *Pelomyxa,* are naked and asymmetrical and

have a constantly changing body shape. Members of the order Testacida, on the other hand, possess an external shell and are symmetrical. The cytoplasm in amebas is typically divided into an external ectoplasm and an internal endoplasm. The pseudopodia are of one of two types: lobopodia, which are typical of the naked amebas, are rather large with rounded or blunt tips and are composed of both ectoplasm and endoplasm; filopodia, which usually occur in the shelled amebas, tend to have pointed ends and are composed of ectoplasm only. However, environmental conditions can produce considerable variation in pseudopodial structure.

In shelled amebas, the shell is either secreted by the cytoplasm, in which case it contains some siliceous elements, or it is composed of foreign materials imbedded in a cementing matrix. Shelled amebas always have a large opening through which the pseudopodia or body can be protruded. The shape is therefore often similar to that of a vase or a helmet. In *Arcella* (Figs. 2-11, *A* and *B*), one of the most common fresh-water amebas, the brown or

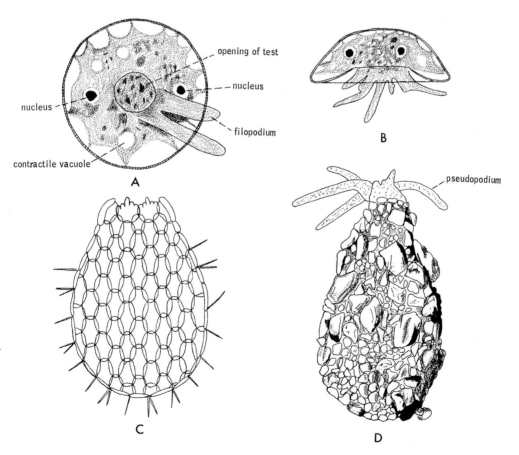

Figure 2-11. Shelled amebas. *A. Arcella vulgaris,* apical view; *B.* Side view. (*A* and *B* after Deflandre.) *C.* Test of *Euglypha strigosa,* composed of siliceous scales and spines. (After Wailes from Deflandre.) *D. Difflugia oblonga* with test of mineral particles. (After Deflandre.)

yellow shell is composed of siliceous prisms imbedded in tectin, a chitinoid substance. Both these elements are secreted by the animal.

The shape of *Arcella* is that of a flattened dome with the aperture in the middle of the underside. When viewed from above, the tips of the filopods can often be seen projecting just beyond the periphery of the shell. In *Euglypha* the secreted shell is constructed of round siliceous scales often beset with spines (Fig. 2-11, *C*). *Difflugia* has a shell composed of mineral particles that are ingested by the animal and imbedded in a secreted matrix (Fig. 2-11, *D*). The shape of the shell is somewhat like that of an egg with an aperture located at one end. The shell of *Difflugia* and related forms is usually colorless but may be tinted red, blue, or violet from iron, manganese, or cobalt in the sand grains.

ORDER FORAMINIFERIDA. The order Foraminiferida is primarily marine; its members occur in tremendous numbers in the sea. The pseudopodia are thread-like, branched, and interconnected and are called reticulopodia (Fig. 2-12, *B*). Although there are a few naked forms, the majority of species possess a shell that is usually composed of calcium carbonate plus small amounts of other inorganic compounds, such as silica and magnesium sulfate. The structure of the foraminiferan shell is quite different from that of the shelled amebas. Some species live within a single-chambered shell and are said to be unilocular; but most forams are multilocular, having many-chambered shells.

Multilocular forms begin life in a single chamber, the proloculum; but as the animal increases in size, the protoplasm overflows through a large opening in the first chamber and secretes another compartment.

This process is continuous throughout the life of the animal and results in the formation of a series of many chambers, each larger than the preceding one. Since the addition of new chambers follows a symmetrical pattern, the shells of multilocular forams have a distinct shape and arrangement of chambers. In some forms the chambers are arranged in a straight line, so that the shell looks like a string of successively larger beads (Fig. 2-12, *A*). In others, each new chamber nearly encloses the previous chamber, resulting in a multichambered shell, somewhat like an onion in structure (Fig. 2-12, *D*). Not infrequently new chambers are added in a spiral manner so that the shell is like that of a snail (Fig. 2-12, *C*). One of the most common forams in marine plankton is *Globigerina* (Fig. 2-12, *B*). The chambers of this multilocular species are spherical but arranged in a somewhat spiral manner.

All the chambers in multilocular species open successively into another chamber; the entire shell is filled with protoplasm that is continuous from one chamber to the next. Unlike the shelled amebas, in which pseudopodia extend through one large opening in the shell, every chamber in a foram shell is pierced by many small openings. It is through these perforations that the reticulopods project.

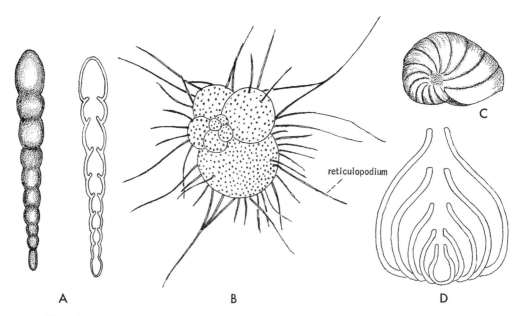

A   B   C   D

Figure 2-12.   Foraminiferans. *A.* Shell of *Rheophax nodulosa* (entire, and in section). (After Brady from Calvez.) *B.* Living *Globigerina.* (After Hyman.) *C.* Shell of *Nonion incisum.* (After Cushman from Calvez.) *D.* Shell of an ellipsoidinid foraminiferan (in section). (After Hyman.)

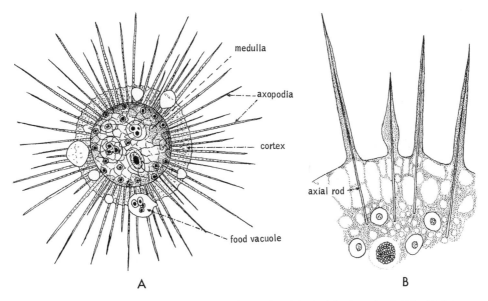

Figure 2-13.   A multinucleate heliozoan, *Actinosphaerium eichorni. A.* Entire animal. (After Doflein from Trégouboff.) *B.* Section of cortex with adjacent axopodia. (After Bütschli from Trégouboff.)

It should be realized that multilocular forams are not colonies but represent single individuals. Some become several millimeters in size.

ORDER HELIOZOIDA.   This group of spherical Sarcodina is commonly known as sun animal-cules. They occur primarily in fresh water and may be either free or sessile, in which case they are usually attached to the substratum by a stalk. The fine, needle-like pseudopodia, called axopodia, radiate from the surface of the body (Fig. 2-13, *B*). Each axopod contains a central axial rod, which is covered with a granular, ad-hesive ectoplasm. Although the axial rod has a supporting function, it is not a permanent skeleton but is composed of protoplasmic fibers or tubes, which can shorten, bend, or even "melt" into typical cytoplasm. Axopods are not used in locomotion but function only for capturing food.

The body of a heliozoan consists of two parts (Figs. 2-13, *A* and 2-14, *C*). There is an outer cytoplasmic sphere, called the cortex, which is often greatly vacuolated. The vacuoles are of two kinds: food vacuoles, and one to many contractile vacuoles. The inner part of the body, or medulla, is composed of dense endo-plasm, containing one to many nuclei and the bases of the axial rods. The axial rods all may be attached to the membrane of a single central nucleus, as in *Actinophrys;* they may be attached to the membranes of numerous nuclei, as in *Camptonema* (Fig. 2-14, *A*); or they may have no connection with the nuclei and originate from the periphery of the medulla, as in the common multinucleate *Actinosphaerium* (Fig. 2-13, *A*).

Skeletons are not uncommon in the helio-zoans and may be composed of foreign particles, such as sand grains or living diatoms, or of separate siliceous pieces secreted by the animal. In either case the skeletal components are im-bedded in an outer gelatinous covering. When the skeleton is secreted, the siliceous pieces assume a great variety of forms, such as plates (Fig. 2-14, *B*), spheres, tubes, or needles. These siliceous pieces may be arranged either tangen-tially to the body in one or more layers or, when the skeleton is composed of long needles (Fig. 2-14, *C*), may radiate like the axopods. In a few cases the skeleton is composed of tectin and is in the form of a beautiful lattice sphere. Regard-less of the nature and arrangement of the skele-ton, openings are present through which the axopods project.

ORDER RADIOLARIDA.   Among the most beautiful of the protozoans are members of the order Radiolarida. The order is entirely marine and primarily planktonic. Radiolarians are relatively large protozoans; some species are several millimeters in diameter and some colonial forms attain a diameter of several centi-meters. Like heliozoans, the bodies of radio-larians are usually spherical and divided into an inner and outer part (Fig. 2-15). The inner region, which contains one to many nuclei, is called the central capsule and is surrounded by a distinct membrane, composed of pseudochitin. The membrane is perforated by openings, which may be evenly distributed (Fig. 2-16, *A*) or may be restricted to one to three regions (called pore fields) of the membrane. The perforations allow the cytoplasm of the central capsule (or intra-

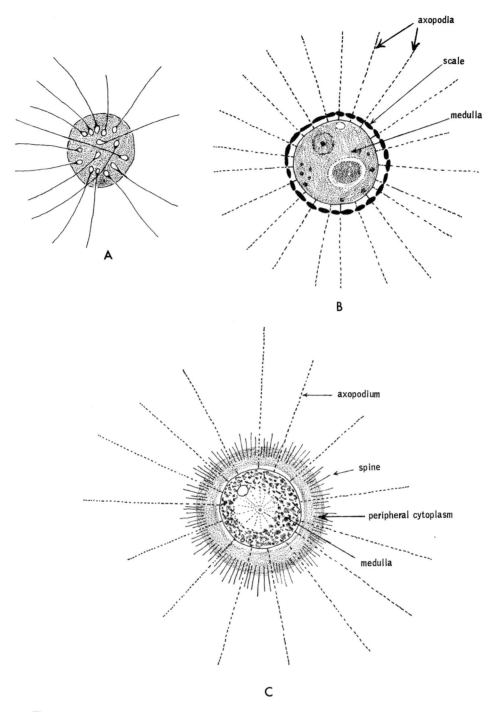

Figure 2-14.   Heliozoans. *A. Camptonema nutans* with axopodia attached to nuclear membranes. (After Schaudinn from Trégouboff.) *B. Pinaciophora fluviatilis* with skeleton of scales. *C. Heterophrys myriopoda* with skeleton in form of spines. (*B* and *C* after Penard from Hall.)

capsular cytoplasm) to be continuous with the cytoplasm of the outer division of the body. This extracapsular cytoplasm forms a broad cortex, called the calymma, which surrounds the central capsule.

The calymma contains large numbers of symbiotic dinoflagellates and chrysomonads in a palmella stage as well as many food vacuoles, which give the cytoplasm a frothy appearance. The pseudopodia are axopods, or sometimes filopods, and radiate from the surface of the body. They originate from the central capsule or just outside of it and extend through the calymma as dense cytoplasm.

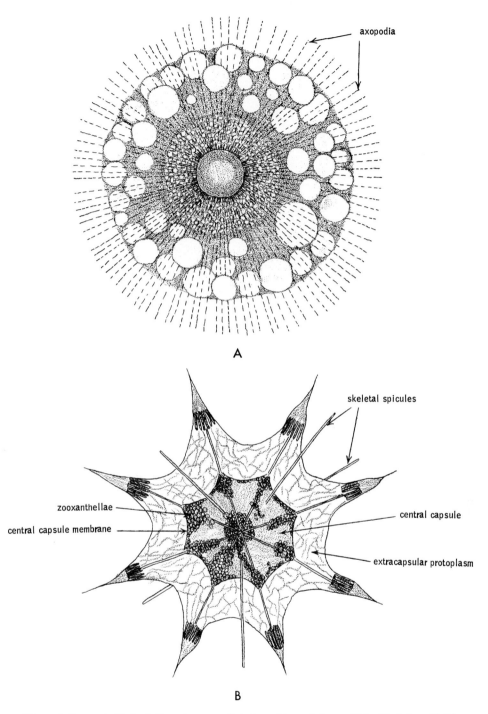

axopodia

skeletal spicules

zooxanthellae

central capsule membrane

central capsule

extracapsular protoplasm

A

B

Figure 2-15.   *A. Thalassicolla nucleata,* a radiolarian with no skeleton. (After Huth from Hall.) *B. Acanthometra,* a radiolarian with skeleton of radiating pieces. (After Moroff and Stiasny from Hyman.)

A skeleton is almost always present in radiolarians and is usually siliceous. Two types of skeletal arrangements occur. One type has a radiating structure, in which the skeleton is composed of long spines or needles that radiate out from the center of the central capsule and extend beyond the outer surface of the body (Fig. 2-15, *B*). The points where the skeletal rods leave the body surface are surrounded by contractile fibrils. The action of these fibrils allows the spines to be moved and can cause the entire calymma to be contracted. The second type of skeleton is constructed in the form of a lattice sphere (Fig. 2-16, *B*). There may be any

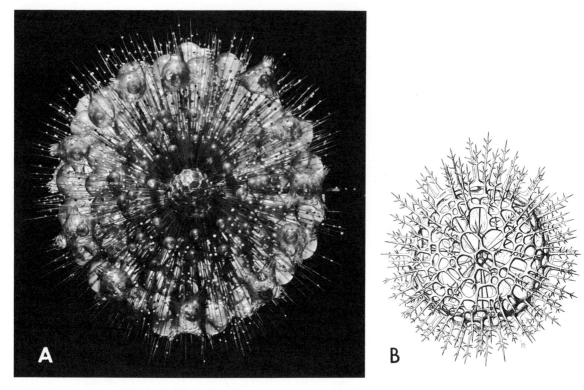

Figure 2-16.   *A.* Glass model of a radiolarian, *Trypanosphaera regina*. (Courtesy of the American Museum of Natural History.) *B.* The internal, siliceous skeleton of a radiolarian. (Courtesy of E. Giltsch, Jena.)

number of such spheres arranged concentrically outside and inside the body. Furthermore, the lattice network is often sculptured and ornamented with barbs and spines of varying size and numbers, and in some species even branched projections are present. Finally, the lattice skeleton may not be spherical, and skeletons of many different bizarre patterns may occur (Fig. 2-17).

In colonial radiolarians there are many central capsules imbedded in a common mass. Each capsule may be surrounded by a skeleton, as for example in *Sphaerozoum,* where the central capsules are enveloped by loose spicules.

Locomotion.   Flowing ameboid movement is limited to those Sarcodina that possess lobopods or filopods and is best developed in the naked amebas. In these animals, locomotion may involve a single large lobopod or several small ones, but in either case only the tips of the pseudopods are in contact with the substratum. The theory of ameboid movement accepted by most zoologists at the present time assumes that cytoplasmic flow results from changes in the colloidal state of the protoplasm. As a result of some initial stimulus, ectoplasm at some point on the body surface undergoes a liquefaction and becomes endoplasm; that is, the colloidal state shifts from a condition of gel

to one of sol. As a result of this change, internal pressure causes the cytoplasm to flow out at this point, forming a pseudopodium.

In the interior of the pseudopodium, the fluid endoplasm flows forward along the line of

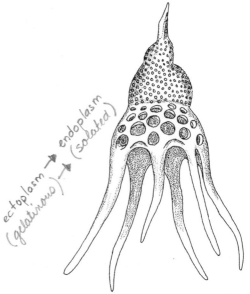

Figure 2-17.   A nonspherical lattice skeleton of a radiolarian of the suborder Nasselaria. (After Haeckel from Hyman.)

progression; around the periphery, endoplasm is converted to ectoplasm thus building up and extending the sides of the pseudopodium. At the posterior of the body, ectoplasm is assumed to be undergoing conversion to endoplasm.

The recent studies of Allen (1962) suggest that on the molecular level ameboid movement is actually a type of slow contraction, similar in many ways to muscle contraction. The endoplasm is thought to contain long protein chains. These protein chains undergo folding—contraction—at the anterior end. Here the endoplasm is converted to ectoplasm, and in ectoplasm (the gel state) the protein chains are in the folded state. The protein chains unfold at the posterior end where the ectoplasm becomes liquefied during its conversion to endoplasm. Thus, according to this front-contraction theory, the body of the animal is literally pulled forward by contraction at the anterior end.

Although there are some pelagic foraminiferans, the majority are bottom-dwellers and creep slowly over the substratum. The body is pulled or dragged along by the reticulopods.

Radiolarians and unattached heliozoans are adapted for a planktonic existence, and their pseudopodia are food-capturing rather than locomotor organelles. However, radiolarians are able to move vertically in the water either by extending or contracting the calymma and axopods or by increasing or decreasing the vacuolated condition of the calymma.

Nutrition. The Sarcodina are entirely holozoic with the exception of some parasitic species. Their food consists of all types of small organisms—algae, diatoms, protozoans, and even small multicellular animals such as rotifers and nematodes. The prey is captured and engulfed by means of the pseudopodia.

In the amebas, pseudopodia extend around the prey in a cup-like fashion eventually enveloping it completely with cytoplasm. The enclosing of the captured organism by cytoplasm results in the formation of a food vacuole within the ameba (Fig. 2-10, B). Commonly, the pseudopodia are not in intimate contact with the prey during engulfment, and a considerable amount of water is enclosed within the food vacuole along with the captured organism. This type of engulfment is known as circumvallation.

Engulfment also may be by a process called circumfluence, in which the enveloping pseudopodia always maintain contact with the surface of the prey. The resulting vacuole is then completely filled by food. Death of the prey takes from three to sixty minutes and results primarily from lack of oxygen. Engulfment in shelled amebas follows essentially the same pattern as in naked forms, although in species with

filopods the food vacuole is formed largely by circumfluence. The vacuole is then moved through the aperture of the shell into the interior of the body.

In foraminiferans, heliozoans, and radiolarians the numerous radiating pseudopodia (chiefly reticulopods or axopods) act primarily as traps in the capture of prey. Any organism that comes in contact with the pseudopodia becomes fastened to the granular, adhesive surface of these organelles. A granular mucoid film is especially evident on the surface of foraminiferan reticulopods and quickly coats the surface of captured prey. This film apparently contains proteolytic secretions, which aid in paralyzing the prey and initiate digestion even during capture. In all three groups the food is eventually enclosed in a food vacuole and drawn toward the interior of the body. The axial rods of heliozoans may contract, drawing the prey into the ectoplasmic cortex; or the axopods may liquefy and surround the food, forming a vacuole at the site of capture. The vacuole will then be moved inward.

Digestion occurs in the cortex of heliozoans and the calymma of radiolarians. Where an enveloping skeletal sphere is present, the food passes through the openings for the pseudopodia. In foraminiferans the vacuole passes to the interior of the body through the large opening in the most recently formed chamber.

Digestion takes place as described on page 8. Protease, amylase, lipase and cellulase have been detected in different species. Egestion can take place at any point on the surface of the body, and in the actively moving amebas, wastes are usually emitted at the posterior, as the animal crawls about.

Water Balance. Contractile vacuoles (Fig. 2-10, B) occur in fresh-water species but are absent in marine Sarcodina. There may be one to many contractile vacuoles, and the expulsion of fluid can occur anywhere on the body surface. In amebas the single or few contractile vacuoles are carried about in the flowing endoplasm. In heliozoans, however, there are numerous contractile vacuoles, all of which are situated in the ectoplasmic cortex (Fig. 2-13, A).

Reproduction and Life Cycles. Asexual reproduction in most amebas, heliozoans, and radiolarians is by binary fission. In amebas with a soft shell, the shell divides into two parts, and each daughter cell forms a new half. When the shell is dense and continuous, such as in *Arcella*, a mass of protoplasm extrudes from the opening prior to division; this extruded mass secretes a new shell. The double-shelled animal now divides, and each daughter cell receives a shell.

In *Difflugia* and other forms in which the

shell is composed of foreign particles, the material used in the construction of the shell is stored up by the parent. In division one daughter cell receives the original shell, and the other receives the necessary particles with which to form a new shell.

Division in the radiolarians is somewhat similar to that in the shelled amebas. Either the skeleton itself divides, and each daughter cell forms the lacking half; or one offspring receives the skeleton, and the other secretes a new one.

Multiple fission is common in multinucleated amebas and heliozoans. In certain shelled amebas the parent animal sporulates a large number of little, naked amebas, each of which produces a new shell in the process of growth.

Sexual reproduction occurs in all six orders of Sarcodina, although it is more frequently encountered and better known in some groups than others. Sexual reproduction is rare among the naked amebas; but hologamy—the fusion of two individuals, each acting as a gamete—is known to occur in some shelled species. For example, in *Difflugia*, two animals attach together in the region of the openings. One member leaves its shell and enters the opposite shell, where it fuses with its partner to form a cyst-like zygote.

Among the heliozoans, sexual reproduction is known in *Actinosphaerium* and *Actinophrys*. In *Actinophrys*, which is naked, the axopods are withdrawn and a cyst is formed. Within the cyst the animal divides into two daughter cells, each of which then undergoes two maturation divisions. Only the nuclei are involved in the maturation divisions, and the chromosome number is reduced from 44 to 22. Following each division, the contents of one nucleus are extruded as a sort of polar body. The two gametic nuclei now fuse to form a single, diploid zygote nucleus. A similar although somewhat more complicated process occurs in the multinucleate *Actinosphaerium*.

Some radiolarians, such as *Collozoum* and *Aulocantha*, form a large number of biflagellated isogametes, following extensive nuclear divisions; but the fate of the gametes is still unknown.

Reproduction in the foraminiferans is complex but relatively uniform throughout the order and involves a definite alternation of asexual and sexual generations (Fig. 2-18). Each species of foraminiferans is dimorphic, and in most multilocular species the two types of individuals differ in the size of the proloculum. One type of individual, known as a schizont, reproduces asexually and has a shell with a small proloculus, called a microspheric shell. The other type, which has a megalospheric shell, is known as a gamont and reproduces sexually.

In a typical life cycle of a multilocular species, the schizont becomes multinucleate and gives rise to a large number of small amebas, each containing a single nucleus. These offspring secrete a megalospheric shell and become gamonts. When mature, the gamonts produce a large number of biflagellated anisogametes, pairs of which fuse to form a zygote. The zygote gives rise to a schizont with a microspheric shell, thus completing the cycle. A similar life cycle occurs in monolocular species, but the shells of the schizonts and the gamonts are not distinguishable.

Ecology. The naked amebas are found in both fresh and salt water and in soil to a depth of several feet. The shelled amebas and the heliozoans are primarily fresh-water groups; the foraminiferans are largely marine; the radiolarians are exclusively marine. With the exception of the radiolarians and some foraminiferans, which are planktonic, the majority of Sarcodina are bottom-dwellers or crawl about over the surfaces of submerged vegetation or other objects. Most sessile forms are heliozoans.

The planktonic radiolarians display a distinct vertical stratification from the ocean surface down to 15,000 foot depths. Some groups occur only at very great depths; others are limited to the upper, lighted zone; some migrate between the surface layer and lower depths, depending on the season. For example, representatives of the suborders Nassellaria and Spumellaria occur in great numbers in the surface waters of the Mediterranean during winter months; but as the temperature of the water rises in the spring, they migrate down to approximately the 1200 foot level.

Although most foraminiferans are benthic, a number of genera, such as *Globigerina* (Fig. 2-12, *B*) and *Orbulina*, are adapted for a planktonic existence and occur in enormous numbers. Their shells are thin and often bear long spines to increase floatation. They are found in marine waters throughout the world.

The great numbers in which planktonic foraminiferans and radiolarians occur is indicated by the fact that their shells, sinking to the bottom at death, form a primary constituent of ocean bottom sediments. From depths of 1800 to 12,000 feet, foraminiferan shells are a prominent part of bottom sediment, which is known as globigerina ooze because of the prevalence of the shells from animals of this genus. At greater depths, where pressures dissolve the calcium carbonate shells of foraminiferans, the bottom sediments are composed of the siliceous skeletons of radiolarians and are known as radiolarian ooze.

Some naked amebas are parasitic. With

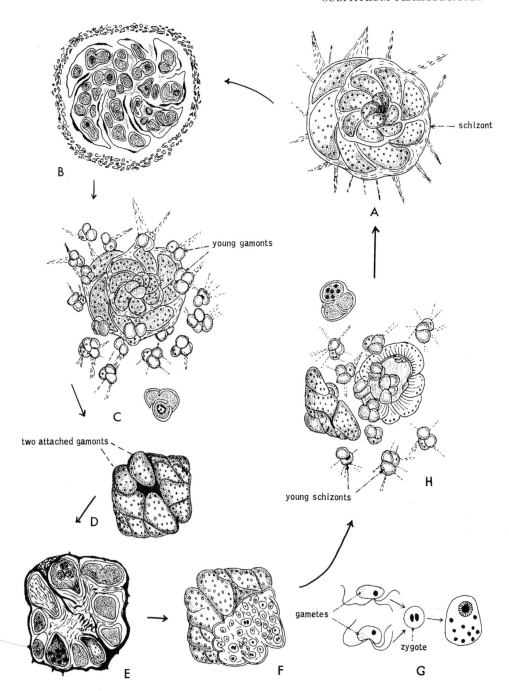

Figure 2-18.   Life cycle of the foraminiferan, *Discorbis patelliformis. A.* Schizont. *B.* Asexual development of gamonts within chambers of schizont. *C.* Liberation of young gamonts from parent schizont. *D, E, F,* and *G.* Formation and fusion of gametes within two attached gamonts. *H.* Separation of attached gamonts accompanied by liberation of young, schizonts. (After Myers from Calvez.)

the exception of *Hydramoeba* and a few species that are parasitic during immature stages in algae, the majority are endoparasites in the digestive tracts of annelids, insects, and vertebrates. Several species occur in the human intestine, but only *Entamoeba histolytica,* which is responsible for the disease known as amebic dysentery, is ordinarily pathogenic. The life

(causing a disease)

cycle of these intestinal amebas is direct, and the parasites are usually transmitted from the digestive tract of one host to that of another by means of cysts that are passed in feces.

Many Sarcodina harbor symbiotic algae or phytoflagellates in a palmella stage. As mentioned earlier, symbiotic dinoflagellates (zooxanthellae) are characteristic of radiolarians.

Zooxanthellae as well as zoochlorellae (unicellular green algae) also occur in many foraminiferans and some radiolarians (Fig. 2-15, *B*). A few amebas, such as *Amoeba stigmata*, contain zoochlorellae. The physiological importance of such symbiotic relationships is still uncertain.

The Sarcodina are the only class of protozoans that have an impressive fossil record. Fossil forms are of course restricted to those with extensive skeletons or shells—the shelled amebas, the foraminiferans, and the radiolarians. The fossil record of the shelled amebas is relatively brief and recent. The group appears as fossils only in the Cenozoic era and consists of forms that are virtually identical with those living today. However, the foraminiferans and radiolarians have a long and abundant fossil record. In fact, the radiolarians are among the oldest known fossils and are said to have been found in Pre-Cambrian rocks. The foraminiferans first appeared in the Cambrian period, and from the late Paleozoic era on, there is an abundant fossil record. Extensive accumulations of foram shells occurred during the Mesozoic and early Cenozoic eras and contributed to the formation of great limestone and chalk deposits, such as the White Cliffs of Dover.

Systematic Résumé of Class Sarcodina

Subclass Actinopoda. Primarily floating or sessile Sarcodina possessing axopodia.

Order Helioflagellata. A small order of marine and fresh-water forms that possess one or more flagella in addition to axopods. *Tetradimorpha*.

Order Heliozoida. Chiefly fresh-water floating species usually having a spherical body with radiating axopods. They possess peripheral cytoplasm forming an outer cortex, which commonly contains skeletal elements. *Actinophrys, Actinosphaerium, Camptonema*.

Order Radiolarida. Marine Sarcodina, in which the body consists of a central capsule of pseudochitin and an outer cortex of vacuolated, extracapsular cytoplasm. From the latter project radiating axopods. A radiating or lattice-like skeleton of strontium sulfate, or more usually silica, is typically present. *Collozoum, Sphaerozoum, Aulocantha*.

Subclass Rhizopoda. Sarcodina with lobopodia or filopodia; axopodia never present. Largely creeping forms.

Order Amoebida. Naked asymmetrical amebas, which move by lobopodia or by the streaming of the entire body. Primarily free-living in sea water, in fresh water, and in soil; a few parasitic. *Pelomyxa, Amoeba, Entamoeba, Hydramoeba*.

Order Testacida. Fresh-water amebas enclosed within a single-chambered shell, or test, which is either secreted or composed of foreign particles imbedded in a secreted matrix. The test has a single aperture for extrusion of lobopodia or filopodia. *Arcella, Difflugia, Centropyxis*.

Order Foraminiferida. Chiefly marine forms with typically multichambered shells of calcium carbonate. Shell bears many perforations for extrusion of cytoplasm. Pseudopodia in form of reticulopods. *Globigerina, Orbulina, Discorbis, Spirillina*.

Class Sporozoa

Closely allied both to the Mastigophora and to the Sarcodina is the class of protozoans known as the Sporozoa. Since sporozoans are entirely parasitic and are studied intensively in courses in parasitology, only major characteristics of the class are outlined here. The name Sporozoa derives from the fact that immature stages of many species become surrounded by resistant walls, and in this state they are called spores and are transmitted from one host to another.

The body shape of sporozoans is variable, although round or oval forms are very common, and the structure is simple with very few organelles. Locomotor organelles are absent in the adults, but immature stages may possess either flagella or pseudopodia.

Nutrition of sporozoans is entirely saprozoic, and with few exceptions food materials are absorbed directly through the general body surface. All are internal parasites. They may infect body spaces, such as the gut, bladder, and coelom; or more commonly they may be intracellular parasites, living in blood cells, muscle tissue, and the epithelial cells lining the digestive tract and other organs. Sporozoans parasitize invertebrates and vertebrates, and most display a relatively great host specificity. The intracellular blood parasite, *Plasmodium*, which causes malaria, is the principal pathogenic form in man; but a number of sporozoans are pathogenic in livestock, producing such diseases as coccidiosis and Texas cattle fever.

The life histories are relatively complex and usually involve an alternation of sexual and asexual generations, as in foraminiferans. Asexually reproducing individuals, or schizonts, undergo multiple fission to produce a large number of individuals called merozoites. A merozoite can become another schizont, re-infecting the host, or can become a sexually reproducing individual, or gamont. By either binary or multiple fission a gamont produces isogametes, which fuse in pairs to form zygotes. The zygotes undergo multiple fission to produce either naked young or spores.

It is either the naked young or spores that commonly are transmitted from one host to another. The spores, upon entering the new host, release several to many sporozoites, and a new cycle is thus begun. The life cycles of most of the species do not require an intermediate host; but in some, particularly the blood parasites, intermediate hosts, such as leeches, mites, ticks, flies, and mosquitoes are the agents of transmission.

Phylogenetically the Sporozoa are a heterogeneous assemblage of parasitic groups, which, judging from the presence of pseudopodia and flagella in the immature stages, have probably arisen independently from different lines of mastigophorans and Sarcodina.

SUBPHYLUM CILIOPHORA; CLASS CILIATA

The subphylum Ciliophora has only one class, the Ciliata. This is the largest and the most homogeneous of the protozoan classes. Some 6,000 species have been described, and many groups are still poorly known.

All possess cilia or compound ciliary structures as locomotor or food-acquiring organelles at some time in the life cycle. Also present is an infraciliary system, composed of basal granules (or kinetosomes) below the cell surface and interconnected by longitudinal fibrils. Such an infraciliary system is present at all stages in the life cycle regardless of the degree of reduction in surface ciliation. Most ciliates possess a cell mouth, or cytostome. In contrast to the other protozoan classes, ciliates are characterized by the presence of two types of nuclei; one vegetative (the macronucleus) and the other reproductive (the micronucleus). Fission is transverse, and sexual reproduction never involves the formation of free gametes.

Form and Structure. The body shape is constant and in general is asymmetrical. Although the majority of ciliates are solitary and free-swimming, there are some sessile and colonial forms. The tintinnids and some heterotrichs have the body housed within a lorica, which is either secreted or composed of foreign material cemented together. In the tintinnids the lorica is attached to the substratum (Fig. 2-19, *B*), but in the heterotrichs the lorica is carried about by the animal.

The ciliate body is typically covered by a complex, living pellicle, usually containing a number of different organelles. The pellicular system has been most studied in *Paramecium*. According to the work of Ehret and Powers (1959), the basic unit of the *Paramecium* pellicle (Fig. 2-20) is the ciliary corpuscle, an apple-shaped organelle surrounding the base of the cilium. The ciliary corpuscles are packed together and comprise the outer stratum of the pellicle. Each corpuscle is composed of an outer and inner peribasal membrane, which encloses a peribasal space. One or two cilia emerge from an elon-

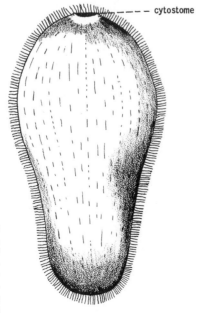

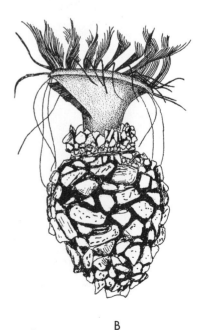

Figure 2-19.   *A. Prorodon,* a primitive ciliate. *B. Tintinnopsis,* a marine ciliate with lorica, or test, composed of foreign particles. Note conspicuous membranelles and tentacle-like organelles interspersed between them. (After Fauré-Fremiet from Corliss.)

- - - - cytostome

A

B

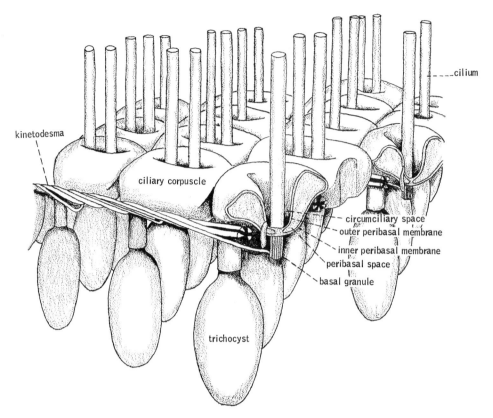

Figure 2-20.   Pellicular system in *Paramecium*. (After Ehret and Powers from Corliss.)

Figure 2-21.   Electron micrograph of discharged trichocysts of *Paramecium*. Note golf-tee-shaped barb and long, striated shaft. (By Jacus and Hall, 1946: Biol. Bull., *91*:141.)

gated pit, the circumciliary space, in the center of the corpuscle. Alternating with the ciliary corpuscles are bottle-shaped organelles, the trichocysts, which form a second, deeper compact layer of the pellicular system.

Trichocysts are peculiar, rod-like or oval organelles characteristic of some ciliates. They are oriented at right angles to the body surface and may have a general distribution or may be limited to certain regions of the body. There are a number of different types of trichocysts. The explosive trichocysts of *Paramecium*, for example, can be discharged to the exterior in only a few milliseconds. The discharged trichocyst consists of a long, striated, thread-like shaft surmounted by a barb, which is shaped somewhat like a golf tee (Fig. 2-21). The shaft is not evident in the undischarged state and is probably formed in the process of discharge.

In *Dileptus anser* the trichocysts are apparently turned inside out at discharge (Fig. 2-22, *A* and *B*). The expelled trichocyst consists of a bulbous base that tapers into a long thread. The positions of these two parts are reversed in the undischarged condition. In some ciliates the discharged trichocysts may perhaps be used in anchoring the animal when feeding. In others, such as *Dileptus*, they are apparently used for defense or for capturing prey. The trichocysts of *D. anser* are reported to paralyze other small protozoans. In *Dileptus gigas* the trichocysts are fluid-filled vesicles, the contents of which can be expelled (Fig. 2-22, *C*). Such trichocysts, called toxicysts, have a definite paralyzing effect on rotifers and other protozoans.

Cilia have the same structure as do flagella; they differ from flagella only in that they are generally more numerous and are considerably shorter. Compound ciliary organelles, evolved from the fusion of varying numbers of individual cilia, are of common occurrence and are described later.

The ciliature can be conveniently divided into the body (or somatic) ciliature, which occurs over the general body surface, and the oral ciliature, which is associated with the mouth region. Distribution of body cilia is quite variable. In the primitive groups, cilia cover the entire animal and are arranged in longitudinal rows (Fig. 2-19, *A*); but in many of the more specialized groups they have become limited to certain regions of the body, as in *Euplotes* (Fig. 2-25, *B*), or have almost disappeared completely, as in *Vorticella* (Fig. 2-25, *A*).

As mentioned earlier, each cilium arises from a basal granule, or kinetosome, located in the alveolar layer (Figs. 2-20 and 2-23). The kinetosomes that form a particular longitudinal row are connected by means of fine fibrils, called

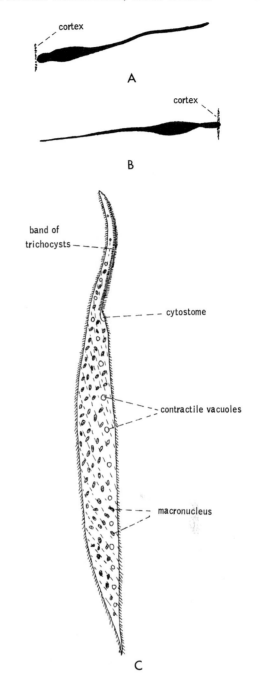

Figure 2-22.   *A* and *B*. Trichocyst of *Dileptus anser*. *A*. Before discharge. *B*. After discharge. (After Hayes from Hall.) *C. Dileptus gigas.* (After Hyman.)

kinetodesmata. The granules plus the fibrils of that row make up a kinety. By means of electron microscopy Metz, Pitelka, and Westfall (1953) have shown that the longitudinal bundle of fibrils runs to the side of the row of kinetosomes and that each kinetosome gives rise to one kinetodesma (fibril), which joins the longitudinal bundle and extends anteriorly. A single kinetodesma is tapered and extends for varying distances as a part of the bundle.

anterior

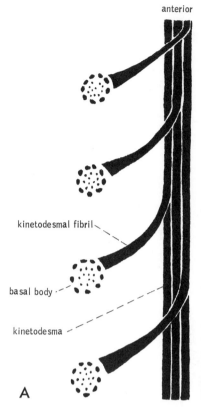

kinetodesmal fibril

basal body

kinetodesma

A

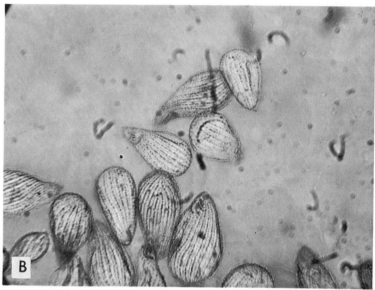

B

Figure 2-23.   *A.* A ciliate kinety. (After Metz *et al* from Grimstone.) *B.* Kinety system of *Tetrahymena;* it appears as dark, longitudinal, parallel lines.

A kinety system is apparently characteristic of all ciliates. Even groups such as the Suctorida, which only possess cilia during developmental stages, retain the kinety system in the adult. Available evidence indicates that the system coordinates ciliary beat.

Locomotion. The ciliates are the fastest moving of the protozoans, some reaching a speed of 2 mm. per second. The action of an individual cilium in locomotion is very much like that of an oar. Each lash consists of an effective stroke and a recovery stroke. In the effective stroke the cilium is outstretched so that water strikes its surface at right angles to its length. In the recovery stroke the cilium is bent, resulting in less water resistance. The recovery stroke is somewhat analogous to feathering oars in rowing.

The beating of the surface cilia is synchronized, and the effective stroke is directed posteriorly and somewhat diagonally to the axis of the longitudinal ciliary rows. The direction of the ciliary beat causes the animal to tend to swim in a spiral course and at the same time rotate on its longitudinal axis. Because the body rotates once for every spiral rotation, the same surface of the body is always directed toward the center of the spiral. The overall movement

is therefore essentially like that in the flagellates.

The ciliary beat can be reversed, and the animal can move backward. This backward movement is associated with the so-called avoiding reaction. In *Paramecium*, for example, when the animal comes in contact with some undesirable substance or object, the ciliary beat

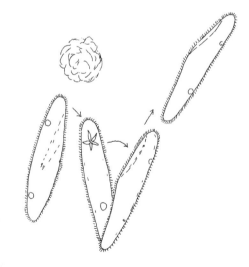

Figure 2-24.   The avoiding reaction of *Paramecium.* (After Hyman.)

is reversed (Fig. 2-24). It moves backward a short distance, turns slightly clockwise or counterclockwise, and moves forward again. If unfavorable conditions are still encountered, the avoiding reaction is repeated. Detection of external stimuli is probably through the cilia; and although perhaps all of the cilia can act as sensory receptors in this respect, there are cer-

tain long, stiff cilia that play no role in movement and are probably entirely sensory.

The highly specialized hypotrichs, such as *Urostyla*, *Stylonychia*, and *Euplotes* (Fig. 2-25, *B*), have their body cilia modified for crawling. The body has become differentiated into distinct dorsal and ventral surfaces, and cilia have largely disappeared except on certain areas of the ven-

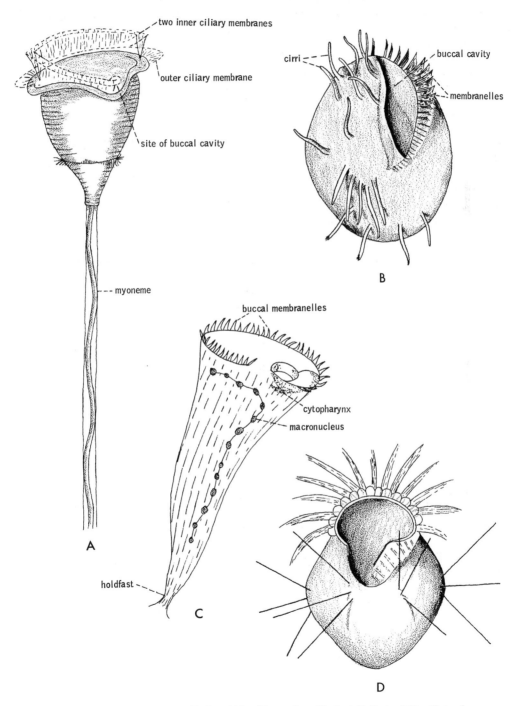

Figure 2-25.   *A. Vorticella. B. Euplotes.* (After Pierson from Corliss.) *C. Stentor.* (After Tartar from Manwell.) *D. Halteria.* Note girdle of long, bristle-like cilia, which produce a popping type of locomotion. (After Corliss.)

tral surface. Here the cilia occur as a number of fused tufts (called cirri), arranged in rows as in *Urostyla,* or in a small number of groups as in *Euplotes.* These compound ciliary organelles act as legs. Even more remarkable is the fact that any single cirrus can be moved in any direction independently of another cirrus.

A peculiar method of locomotion occurs in the little spirotrich, *Halteria* (Fig. 2-25, *D*). A girdle of approximately eleven long bristles, probably representing modified cilia, surrounds the body and replaces other ciliation, except that associated with food acquisition. The animal swims in a popping or bouncing manner as a result of sudden movements of the bristles.

Some ciliates, especially sessile forms, can undergo contractile movements, either shortening the stalk by which the body is attached as in *Vorticella,* or shortening the entire body as in *Stentor.* Contraction is brought about by contractile fibrils, or myonemes, that lie in the alveolar layer of the ectoplasm. These myonemes, which can be very numerous as in *Stentor,* parallel the longitudinal axis of the animal.

In *Vorticella* (Fig. 2-25, *A*) and the colonial *Carchesium,* both of which have bell-shaped bodies attached by a long slender stalk, the myonemes extend into the stalk as a single, large, spiral fiber. The contractions of this spiral myoneme, which functions very much like a coiled spring, produce the familiar popping movements that are so characteristic of *Vorticella* and related genera.

Nutrition. With the exception of parasitic species the ciliates are entirely holozoic. Typically a distinct mouth, or cytostome, is present, although it has been secondarily lost in some groups such as the suctoridans and the parasitic astomatids. In primitive groups the mouth is located anteriorly (Fig. 2-19, *A*), but in most ciliates it has been displaced posteriorly to varying degrees. The mouth opens into a canal or passageway called the cytopharynx, which extends into the endoplasm. The cytopharynx is devoid of cilia, and at its terminal end the food vacuoles are formed. Primitively, as in a great many holotrichs (Figs. 2-19, *A* and 2-26, *A*), the ingestive organelles consist only of the cytostome

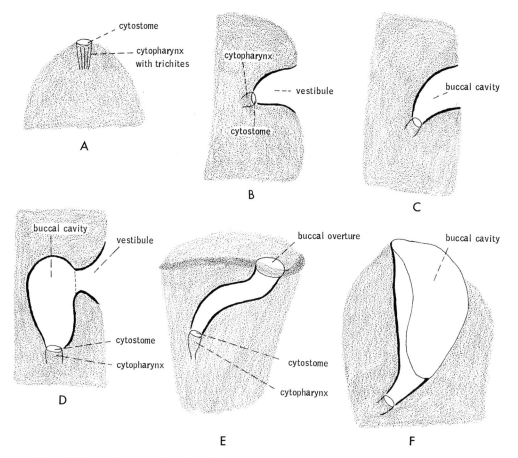

Figure 2-26. Oral areas of various ciliates. *A.* In rhabdophorine gymnostomes; such as, *Coleps, Prorodon,* and *Didinium. B.* In a trichostome with vestibule displaced from anterior end. *C.* In a tetrahymenine hymenostome, such as *Tetrahymena. D.* In a peniculine hymenostome, such as *Paramecium. E.* In a peritrich, such as *Vorticella. F.* In a hypotrich, such as *Euplotes.* (After Corliss.)

and cytopharynx; but in the majority of ciliates the cytostome is preceded by a pre-oral chamber. The pre-oral chamber may take the form of a vestibule, which varies from a slight depression to a deep funnel, with the cytostome at its base (Fig. 2-26, B). The vestibule is clothed with simple cilia derived from the somatic ciliature.

In the higher ciliates the pre-oral chamber is typically a buccal cavity, which differs from a vestibule by containing compound ciliary organelles instead of simple cilia (Fig. 2-26, C to F).

There are two basic types of such ciliary organelles: the undulating membrane and the membranelle. An undulating membrane is a row of fused cilia forming a sheet (Fig. 2-27, A and B). A membranelle is derived from several short rows of cilia, all of which are fused to form a more-or-less rectangular plate and typically occur in a series (Figs. 2-19, B; 2-25, C; and 2-27, B).

The term peristome, which is commonly encountered in the literature, is synonymous

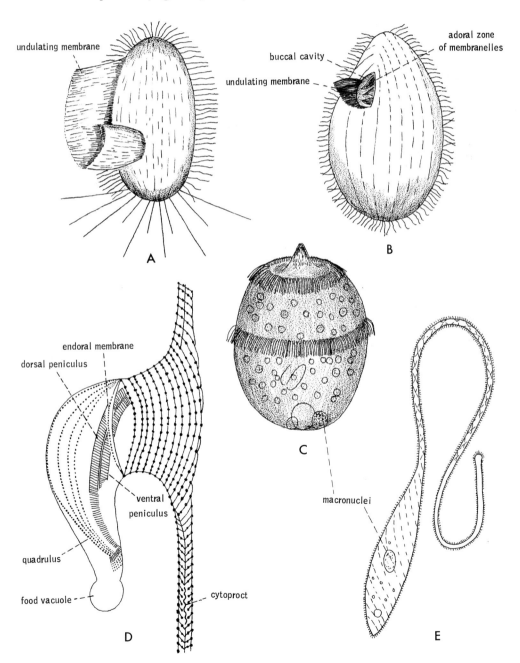

Figure 2-27.   A. Pleuronema. (After Noland from Corliss.) B. Tetrahymena. (After Corliss.) C. Didinium. (After Blochmann from Hyman.) D. Buccal organelles of Paramecium. (After Yusa from Manwell.) E. Lacrymaria. (After Conn from Hyman.)

peristome =

with buccal cavity. In members of a number of orders the buccal organelles project from the buccal cavity; or, as in the Hypotrichida (Fig. 2-25, *B*), the buccal cavity is somewhat shallow so that the organelles occupy a flattened area around the oral region. Such an area is called the peristomial field.

Although primarily ingestive in function, in some ciliates such as *Pleuronema* (Fig. 2-27, *A*) the ciliary organelles are very large and project from the buccal cavity to serve also in locomotion. The buccal cavity may in turn be preceded by a vestibule. This is true of the peniculine hymenostomes, such as *Paramecium* (Figs. 2-26, *D* and 2-27, *D*).

The free-swimming holozoic species display two types of feeding habits. Some are raptorial, in which rotifers, gastrotrichs, and protozoans, including other ciliates are attacked and devoured. Others have become specialized for ciliary feeding. The oral apparatus of raptorial ciliates is typically limited to the cytostome and cytopharynx. The cytopharynx frequently has walls strengthened by a large number of fibers, called trichites, which surround the lumen like the staves of a barrel (Fig. 2-26, *A*).

The mouth in *Coleps* and *Didinium* (Fig. 2-27, *C*) can open to a great diameter, almost as wide as the diameter of the body itself; these forms can consume very large prey. Some species have their anterior extended as a proboscis. The proboscis may be short with the mouth located at the terminal end as in *Didinium*, or the proboscis may be an extremely, long and flexible snout. Although the long proboscis of *Lacrymaria* (Fig. 2-27, *E*) bears the mouth at the terminal end, in many such ciliates (for example *Loxodes* and *Trachelius*) the mouth is a slit or circle located at the base of the proboscis.

Didinium has perhaps been most studied of all the raptorial feeders (Fig. 2-27, *C*). This little barrel-shaped ciliate feeds on other ciliates, particularly *Paramecium*. When *Didinium* attacks a *Paramecium*, the proboscis attaches to the prey through the terminal mouth. The proboscis apparently adheres only to certain types of pellicles; it is this limitation that probably restricts the diet of *Didinium*.

An interesting group of raptorial ciliates is the aberrant order Suctorida, formerly considered a separate class. Suctorians are all sessile and are attached to the substratum directly or by means of a stalk (Fig. 2-28). Cilia are present only in the immature stages. The body is somewhat globular or cone-shaped and differs from that of other ciliates in bearing tentacles (Fig. 2-28). The tentacles may be knobbed at the tip; they are occasionally shaped like long spines (Fig. 2-30, *B*). Each tentacle consists of an inner, somewhat rigid tube. The tube is surrounded by a contractile sheath, which is believed to contain myonemes. The prey adheres

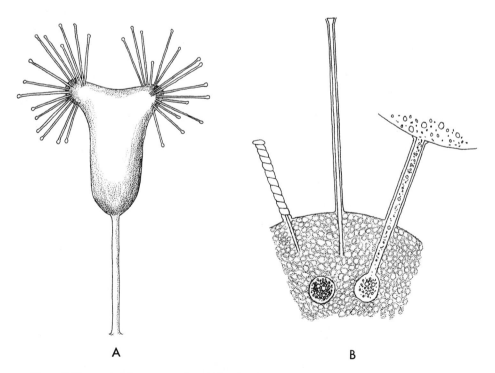

A   B

Figure 2-28.   *A. Acineta,* a suctorian. (After Calkins from Hyman.) *B.* Tentacles of the suctorian, *Tokophrya lemnarum,* retracted, extended, and during feeding. (After Noble from Manwell.)

on contact with the tentacles and is apparently paralyzed by an adhesive secretion. Through a process that is still not understood, the captured protozoan gradually is sucked into the suctorian body through the central tube of the tentacles (Fig. 2-28, *B*).

Typically characteristic of ciliary feeders is the buccal cavity. Food for ciliary feeders consists of any small, dead or living organic particles, particularly bacteria that are suspended in water. Food is brought to the body and into the buccal cavity by the compound ciliary organelles. From the buccal cavity the food particles are driven through the cytostome and into the cytopharynx. When the particles reach the end of the cytopharynx, they collect within a food vacuole.

The holotrich order, Hymenostomatida, contains the most primitive ciliary feeders, at least judging from the nature of the buccal cavity and associated ciliary organelles. According to Corliss (1956), it is probably from this group that the more specialized forms have evolved. *Tetrahymena* is a good example of such a primitive type (Fig. 2-27, *B*). The cytostome is located a little posteriorly and ventrally. Just within the broad opening to the buccal cavity are four ciliary organelles—an undulating membrane on the right side of the chamber and three membranelles on the left. The three membranelles constitute an adoral zone of membranelles, which in many higher groups of ciliates is much more developed and extensive.

The four buccal ciliary organelles are a basic feature of all members of the order Hymenostomatida. However, many hymenostomes possess a considerably more specialized buccal apparatus than does *Tetrahymena*.

In *Paramecium*, perhaps the most familiar genus of the order, an oral groove along the side of the body leads posteriorly to a vestibule, located about midway back from the anterior end. The vestibule, buccal cavity, and cytopharynx together form a large curved funnel (Figs. 2-26, *D* and 2-27, *D*). The undulating membrane, here called the endoral membrane, runs transversely along the right wall and marks the junction of the vestibule and buccal cavity. The three membranelles are also modified. Two, called peniculi, are greatly lengthened and thus tend to be more similar to an undulating membrane in function than to the more typical membranelle.

The peniculi run down the left wall of the buccal cavity. The ventral peniculus stops at the cytostome, but the longer dorsal peniculus crosses over to the right wall at the cytostome and terminates on the right wall of the cytopharynx. The peniculi beat longitudinally in opposite directions. The third membranelle, called the quadrulus, is similar to the peniculi in being greatly elongated but differs in having its four component ciliary rows separated except at each end. The quadrulus originates at the buccal overture near the peniculi, then runs down the dorsal wall of the buccal cavity, crossing over to the right wall near the cytostome to terminate near the end of the dorsal peniculus.

In feeding, the cilia of the oral groove produce a current of water that sweeps in an arc-like manner down the side of the body and over the oral region. The ciliature of the vestibule and buccal cavity pull in food particles and drive them into the forming food vacuole.

In the order Peritrichida, which possess little or no somatic cilia, the buccal ciliary organelles are highly developed and form a large disc-like peristomial field at the apical end of the animal. In the much studied peritrich genus, *Vorticella*, a peripheral shelf-like projection can close over the disc when the animal is retracted (Figs. 2-25, *A* and 2-26, *E*). The ciliary organelles lie in a peristomial groove between the edge of the disc and the peripheral shelf and consist of three ribbon-like membranes. The two inner membranes are three basal granules thick, while the outer membrane is more delicate and projects laterally like a shelf. The bases of all three membranes are close together.

Although peritrich buccal ciliature is probably homologous to the adoral zone of membranelles of other ciliates, it differs in having the cilia fused only at the base and separated distally. The three ciliary bands, or membranes, wind in a counterclockwise direction around the margin of the disc and then turn downward into the funnel-shaped buccal cavity, located to the outer side of the beginning of the spiral. In this region the ciliary membranes separate, the two inner membranes following the inner wall of the buccal cavity, and the outer membrane following the outer wall.

In feeding, food particles are passed along the outer membrane, driven by the undulations of the two inner membranes. Within the buccal cavity water flows downward between the inner membranes and the outer membrane and then flows outward between the inner wall of the cavity and the inner membranes.

Ciliates of the subclass Spirotricha, which includes such familiar forms as *Stentor, Halteria, Spirostomum* and *Euplotes*, are typically ciliary feeders. They usually possess a highly developed adoral zone of many membranelles. In *Stentor* (Fig. 2-25, *C*) the adoral zone winds around the apical pole of the body in a manner superficially similar to the buccal ciliature of *Vorticella*. In *Euplotes* the conspicuous series of membranelles flank the large ventral, triangular buccal overture (Fig. 2-25, *B*). The loricate marine ciliates of the order Tintinnida have a crown of pectinate (or feathery) membranelles with peculiar organelles, called tentaculoids, interspersed among them (Fig. 2-19, *B*).

Many ciliary feeders display considerable selection of food particles. *Stentor* and *Paramecium*, for example, often reject non-nutritive particles; or if such material is ingested, it is eliminated from the vacuole before the digestive cycle is completed.

At the narrow end of the funnel that opens into the endoplasm, the food particles pass into a food vacuole, which forms at the funnel tip like a soap bubble at the end of a pipe. When the food vacuole reaches a certain size, it breaks free from the cytopharynx, and a new vacuole forms in its place. Detached vacuoles then begin a more or less circulatory movement through the endoplasm as a result of cyclosis.

Digestion follows the usual pattern, and a pH as low as 4.0 has been reported during the acid phase in some species. Following digestion, the waste-laden food vacuole moves to a definite anal opening, or cytoproct, at the body surface and expels its contents. The cytoproct varies in position. In *Paramecium* it is located on the side of the animal, near the posterior end (Fig. 2-27, *D*); whereas in the peritrichs it opens into the buccal cavity.

Food reserves in ciliates are stored in the form of glycogen and fat droplets scattered throughout the endoplasm.

Water Balance. Contractile vacuoles are found in both marine and fresh-water species. In the primitive species a single vacuole is located near the posterior, but many species possess more than one vacuole (Fig. 2-22, *C*). In *Paramecium* one vacuole is located at the posterior and one at the anterior of the body (Fig. 2-24). The vacuoles are always associated with the innermost region of the ectoplasm and empty through a distinct canal that penetrates the pellicle. Thus the position of the contractile vacuole is always fixed in ciliates. In most ciliates a system of radiating collecting canals is located around the vacuole and is particularly evident when the vacuole is small and filling (Fig. 2-24).

In *Paramecium* and others, there are many collecting canals completely surrounding the vacuole, but in some genera, such as *Stentor* and *Bursaria,* there is only one large collecting canal. It is doubtful if the vacuole itself is a permanent organelle; rather, it probably re-forms after each expulsion by the fusion of small droplets delivered by the collecting canals. When there is more than one vacuole present, they pulsate at different rates depending on their position. For example, in *Paramecium* the posterior vacuole pulsates faster than the anterior vacuole because of the large amount of water being delivered into the posterior region by the cytopharynx. Although contractile vacuoles are present in marine species, the rate of pulsation is considerably slower than that in fresh-water species; they are probably removing ingested water.

Reproduction. Ciliates differ from all other animals in possessing two distinct types of nuclei—a usually large macronucleus and one or more small micronuclei. The micronuclei are small, rounded bodies and vary in number from one to as many as 80, depending on the species. The micronuclei are the reproductive nuclei and also give rise to the macronuclei. The macronucleus is sometimes called the vegetative nucleus, since it is not critical in reproduction. However, the macronucleus is essential for normal metabolism and is responsible for the genic control of the phenotype.

Usually only one macronucleus is present, but it may assume a variety of shapes (Fig. 2-29). The large macronucleus of *Paramecium* is somewhat oval or bean-shaped and located just anterior to the middle of the body. In *Stentor* and *Spirostomum* the macronucleus is long and shaped like a string of beads. Not infrequently the macronucleus is in the form of a long rod bent in different configurations, such as a C in *Euplotes* or a horseshoe in *Vorticella*. The macronucleus is highly polyploid, the chromosomes having undergone repeated duplication following the micronuclear origin of the macronucleus.

ASEXUAL REPRODUCTION. Asexual reproduction is always by means of binary fission, which is typically transverse. More accurately, fission is described as being homothetogenic, with the division plane cutting across the kineties —the longitudinal rows of cilia or basal granules (Fig. 2-30, *A*). This is in contrast to the symmetrogenic fission of flagellates, in which the plane of division (longitudinal) cuts between the rows of basal granules. Mitotic spindles are typically formed by each of the micronuclei. The behavior of macronuclei is more variable. A spindle does not form, and division is usually accomplished by constriction. When a number of macronuclei are present, they may first combine as a single body before dividing. The same is true of some forms with beaded or elongated macronuclei. In *Stentor,* for example, the macronuclear chain condenses into a single mass and then divides. In still other ciliates the macronucleus degenerates and arises anew from micronuclei.

Modified fission in the form of budding occurs in some ciliate groups, notably the Suctorida. In most members of this order the

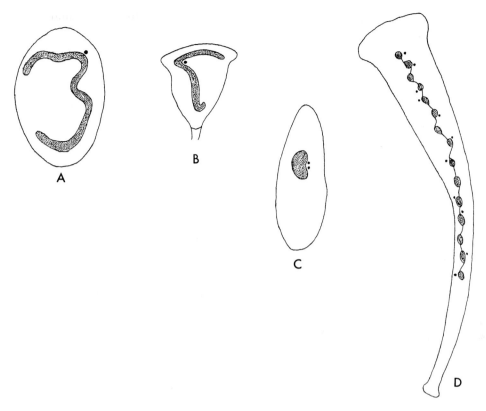

Figure 2-29. Macronuclei (in gray) of various ciliates (micronuclei, in black). *A. Euplotes.* *B. Vorticella. C. Paramecium. D. Stentor.* (After Corliss.)

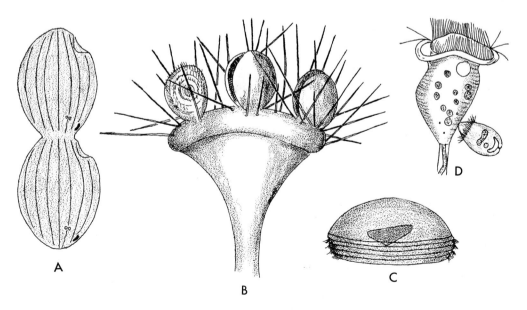

Figure 2-30. *A.* Homothetogenic type of fission, in which the plane of division cuts across the kineties. (After Corliss.) *B.* Suctorian *Ephelota* with external buds. (After Noble from Hyman.) *C.* Detached bud of *Dendrocometes.* (After Pestel from Hyman.) *D.* Conjugation in *Vorticella.* Note the small nonsessile microconjugant. (After Kent from Hyman.)

parent body buds off a varying number of daughter cells from the outer surface (Fig. 2-30, *B*); or there is an internal cavity or brood chamber, and the buds form internally from the chamber wall. In contrast to the sessile adults, which lack cilia, the daughter cells or buds are provided with several circlets of cilia and are free-swimming (Fig. 2-30, *C*). Following a few hours of free existence, the "larva" attaches and assumes the characteristics of the sessile adults.

Like the basal granules of flagellates, the kinetosomes of ciliates are kinetic elements, and at the time of fission all of the kinetosomes divide. Furthermore, the kinetosomes play a primary role in the re-formation of organelles. It has been found that all of the organelles can be re-formed providing the cell contains a piece of macronucleus and some kinetosomes. In the more primitive ciliates, in which the cilia have a general distribution over the body surface, the kinetosomes have equal potentials in the re-formation of organelles. However, in the specialized ciliates there is a corresponding specialization of the kinetosomes; only certain ones are involved in the re-formation of new cellular structures during fission. For example, in hypotrichs such as *Euplotes,* all of the organelles are resorbed at the time of fission; and certain of the kinetosomes on the ventral side of the animal divide to form a special group that is organized in a definite field or pattern. These special "germinal" kinetosomes then migrate to different parts of the body, where they form all of the surface organelles—cirri, peristome, cytopharynx and other structures.

SEXUAL REPRODUCTION. An exchange of nuclear material by conjugation is involved in sexual reproduction. By apparently random contact in the course of swimming, two sexually compatible members of a particular species adhere in the oral or buccal region of the body. Adhesion probably results from the secretion of a sticky substance by the cilia. Following the initial attachment, there is a fusion of protoplasm in the region of contact. Two such fused ciliates are called conjugants; attachment lasts for several hours. During this period a reorganization and exchange of nuclear material occurs (Fig. 2-31, *A* to *F*). Only the micronuclei are involved in conjugation; the macronucleus breaks up and disappears either in the course of, or following, micronuclear exchange.

The steps leading to the exchange of micronuclear material between the two conjugants are relatively constant in all species. All of the micronuclei characteristic of the species undergo three divisions, of which the first two appear to be meiotic divisions. After these three divisions, all of the micronuclei except two degenerate and disappear. Of the two remaining micronuclei, one is stationary and can be considered a female nucleus; the other, called a wandering nucleus, will migrate into the opposite conjugant and can be considered the male nucleus. The wandering nucleus in each conjugant moves through the region of fused protoplasm into the opposite member of the conjugating pair. There the male and female nuclei fuse with one another to form a "zygote" nucleus, or synkaryon.

Shortly after nuclear fusion the two animals separate, and each is now called an exconjugant. After separation, there follows in each exconjugant a varying number of nuclear divisions, leading to the reconstitution of the normal nuclear condition characteristic of the species. This reconstitution usually, but not always, involves a certain number of cytosomal divisions. For example, in some forms where there is but a single macronucleus and a single micronucleus in the adult, the synkaryon divides once. One of the daughter nuclei forms a micronucleus; the other forms the macronucleus. Thus the normal nuclear condition is restored without any cytosomal divisions.

However, in *Paramecium caudatum* (Fig. 2-31, *G* to *N*), which also possesses a single nucleus of each type, the synkaryon divides three times producing eight nuclei. Four become micronuclei and four macronuclei. Three of the micronuclei are then resorbed. The animal now undergoes two cytosomal divisions, during the course of which each of the four resulting daughter cells receives one macronucleus. The single micronucleus in each daughter cell undergoes mitosis at each cytosomal division. Restoration of the normal nuclear state in *Paramecium aurelia,* which possesses one macronucleus and two micronuclei, occurs still differently. Here the synkaryon divides twice to form two micronuclei and two macronuclei. The two micronuclei then each divide again to produce a total of four micronuclei and two macronuclei. The exconjugant then undergoes one cytosomal division with each daughter cell receiving one macronucleus and two micronuclei. In those species that have numerous nuclei of both types, there is no cytosomal division; the synkaryon merely divides a sufficient number of times to produce the requisite number of macronuclei and micronuclei.

In some of the more specialized ciliates, the conjugants are a little smaller than nonconjugating individuals; or the two members of a conjugating pair are of strikingly different sizes. Such macro- and microconjugants occur in *Vorticella* (Fig. 2-30, *D*) and represent an adaptation for conjugation in sessile species. The macro-

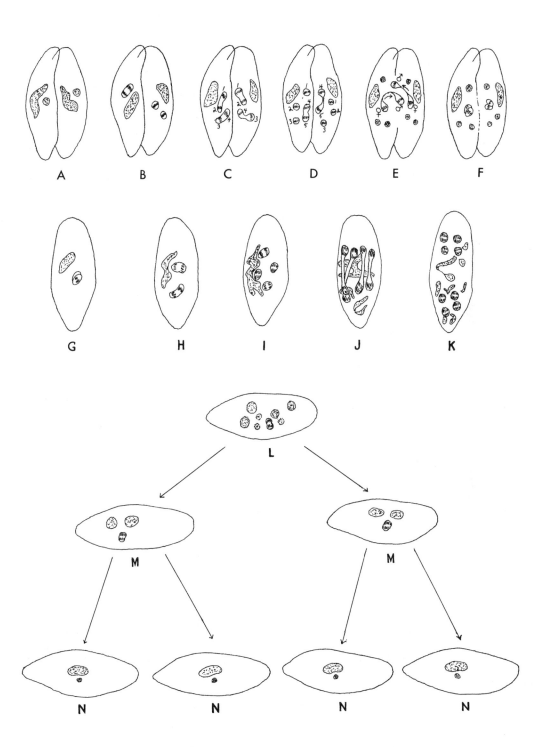

Figure 2-31.   Sexual reproduction in *Paramecium caudatum. A* to *F.* Conjugation. *B* to *D.* Micronuclei undergo three divisions, the first two of which are meiotic. *E.* "Male" micronuclei are exchanged. *F.* They fuse with the stationary micronucleus of the opposite conjugant. *G.* Exconjugant with macronucleus and synkaryon micronucleus; other micronuclei have been resorbed. *H* to *K.* Three divisions of synkaryon, forming eight micronuclei; old macronucleus is resorbed. *L.* Four micronuclei form macronuclei; three are resorbed. *L* and *M.* Remaining micronucleus divides twice in course of two cytosomal divisions. Resulting daughter cells each receive one of the four macronuclei in *L. N.* Normal nuclear condition restored. (Modified after Calkins from Wichterman.)

conjugant, or "female," remains attached; while the small bell of the microconjugant, or "male," breaks free from its stalk and swims about. On contact with an attached macroconjugant the two bells adhere, and nuclear exchange occurs. However, there is no separation after conjugation, and the little "male" conjugant degenerates. In the Suctorida, conjugation takes place between two attached individuals that happen to be located side by side.

The frequency of conjugation is extremely variable. Some species have rarely been observed to undergo the sexual phenomenon of conjugation; others conjugate every few days or weeks. Conjugation brings about a shuffling of hereditary characteristics, just as is true of sexual reproduction in other animals; and in some ciliates this nuclear re-organization has a rejuvenating effect and is necessary for continued asexual fission. For example, it has been shown that some species of Paramecium can pass through only approximately 350 continuous asexual generations. If nuclear re-organization does not occur, the asexual line (or clone) will die out. However, there are many species in which fission can occur indefinitely and conjugation is an unnecessary adjunct for asexual fission. Some early workers cultured so-called "deathless" clones of Paramecium, in which fission supposedly continued indefinitely without any intervening conjugation.

Recent protozoologists have demonstrated that although conjugation may not occur in such "deathless" clones, another type of nuclear reorganization called autogamy takes place and has the same effect on fission as does conjugation. Autogamy involves the same nuclear behavior as does conjugation, but there are no conjugation and exchange of micronuclear material between two individuals. The macronucleus degenerates and the micronucleus divides a number of times to form eight or more nuclei. Two of these nuclei fuse to form a synkaryon; the others degenerate and disappear. The synkaryon then divides to form a new micronucleus and macronuclei as occurs in conjugation. Nuclear re-organization, either in the form of conjugation or in the form of autogamy, is not necessary for continued fission in all ciliates. Some species can reproduce asexually indefinitely.

Definite mating types have been shown to exist in Paramecium, Tetrahymena, Euplotes, Stylonychia, and a few other ciliates. There are a number of varieties, or "syngens," of Paramecium caudatum and P. aurelia, each with two mating types; but in species such as P. bursaria, there are a number of mating types within each variety.

Conjugation is always restricted to a member of the opposite mating type and does not occur between members of the same type, apparently due to a failure of the cytoplasm to adhere. The mating types are hereditary.

Ecology.   Ciliates are widely distributed in both fresh and marine waters. There are relatively few true parasitic forms, although there are many ecto- and entocommensals. One interesting parasite, Foettingeria, is remarkable in having a life cycle that requires two hosts. This little marine ciliate lives inside the gastrovascular cavity of the sea anemone. The motile young leave the anemone and encyst on small crustaceans. When such infected crustaceans are eaten by anemones, the ciliates emerge from their cysts.

Some suctorians are endoparasites. Hosts include mammals, such as the horse, and certain ciliates. Sphaerophrya, for example, lives within the endoplasm of Stentor, and Endosphaera is parasitic within the body of the peritrich, Telotrochidium.

Space limitations permit mention of only a few of the many interesting commensal species. Kerona, a little crawling hypotrich, and Trichodina, a peritrich, are ectocommensals on the surface of hydras. Other free-swimming peritrichs (all of which have a girdle of cilia about the posterior end of the body and move with the posterior end forward) occur on the body surfaces of fresh-water planarians, tadpoles, sponges, and other animals. The holotrich, Balantidium coli, is an entocommensal in the intestine of pigs and is passed by means of cysts in the feces. This ciliate has occasionally been found in man, where it is parasitic and produces a number of pathogenic symptoms.

Perhaps the most interesting entocommensals are the Entodiniomorphida (Fig. 2-32, A), which are among the most specialized of all the ciliates. These spirotrichs live as harmless commensals in the digestive tract of many different hoofed mammals. The ectoplasm of these species is very thick, restricting the endoplasm to a little internal sac-like cavity. The cytopharynx opens into this cavity, and a canal leads away to the cytopyge. Thus, these ciliates possess a "complete digestive tract" on a cytoplasmic level of structure.

A few ciliates display symbiotic relationships with algae. The most notable of these is Paramecium bursaria, in which the endoplasm is filled with green zoochlorellae.

Encystment is typical of most ciliates; however, a few such as Paramecium are believed never to encyst and are passed in an active state from one body of water to another.

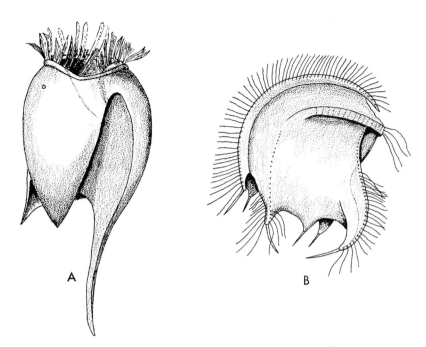

Figure 2-32.   *A. Entodinium caudatum*, commensal ciliate in rumen of cattle and sheep. (After Schuberg from Corliss.) *B. Saprodinium dentatum*, an odontostome ciliate. (After Kahl from Corliss.)

Systematic Résumé of Class Ciliata

The following classification of ciliates follows the system of Corliss (1961).

Subclass Holotricha. With simple and uniform body cilia. Buccal ciliature either absent or, if present, usually inconspicuous.

Order Gymnostomatida. Chiefly large ciliates with no oral ciliature. Cytostome opening directly to outside. *Coleps, Lacrymaria, Prorodon, Dileptus, Didinium, Actinobolina, Nassula.*

Order Trichostomatida. With vestibular but no buccal ciliature. *Colpoda, Tillina, Balantidium.*

Order Chonotrichida. Vase-shaped ciliates lacking body cilia in the adult. A "funnel" at the free end of the body is clothed with vestibular cilia. Chiefly marine and ectocommensal on crustaceans. *Spirochona, Heliochona, Trichochona.*

Order Suctorida. Sessile, stalked ciliates with the distal end bearing few to many tentacles. Adult stage completely devoid of any ciliature. *Acineta, Podophrya, Sphaerophrya.*

Order Apostomatida. Body with spirally arranged ciliation. Cytostome midventral and in the vicinity of a peculiar rosette. Marine parasites or commensals with complex life cycles usually involving two hosts, one of which is commonly a crustacean. *Foettingeria.*

Order Astomatida. Commensals or endoparasites living chiefly in the gut and coelom of oligochaete worms. Cytostome absent; body ciliation uniform. *Anoplophrya, Hoplitophrya.*

Order Hymenostomatida. Small ciliates having a uniform body ciliation but possessing a buccal cavity. Buccal ciliature consists of an undulating membrane and an adoral zone of membranelles. *Colpidium, Tetrahymena, Blepharostoma, Paramecium.*

Order Thigmotrichida. A small group of marine and fresh-water ciliates found in association with bivalve mollusks. Anterior end of body bears a tuft of thigmotactic cilia. *Thigmophrya.*

Order Peritrichida. Adult usually lacks body cilia, but the apical end of the body typically bears a conspicuous buccal ciliature. Mostly attached ciliates and a distinct stalk is often present. *Vorticella, Carchesium, Zoothamnium, Lagenophrys, Trichodina.*

Subclass Spirotricha. With generally reduced body cilia and with well developed and conspicuous buccal ciliature.

Order Heterotrichida. With uniform body cilia or body encased in a lorica and body cilia absent. *Bursaria, Stentor, Metopus, Blepharisma, Spirostomum, Folliculina.*

Order Oligotrichida. Small ciliates with body cilia reduced or absent. Conspicuous buccal membranelles, commonly extending around apical end of body. *Halteria.*

Order Tintinnida. Loricate, free-swimming ciliates with conspicuous oral membranelles when extended. Chiefly marine. *Codonella, Tintinnus, Favella.*

Order Entodiniomorphida. Endocommensal ciliates in the digestive tract of herbivorous mammals. Body cilia reduced or absent. Prominent buccal ciliature often in separate anterior clumps. Posterior end may be drawn out into spines. *Entodinium.*

Order Odontostomatida. A small group of laterally compressed and wedge-shaped ciliates with carapace and reduced body and buccal cilia. *Saprodinium.* (Fig. 2-32, *B*)

Order Hypotrichida. Dorso-ventrally flattened ciliates in which the body cilia are restricted to fused tufts of cilia, or cirri, located on the ventral side of the body. *Euplotes, Uronychia, Kerona, Stylonchia, Urostyla.*

BIBLIOGRAPHY

Allen, R. D., 1962: Amoeboid movement. Sci. Am. *206(2)*: 112–122.

Chen, Y. T., 1950: Investigation of the biology of *Peranema trichophorum.* Quart. J. Micr. Sci., *91*:279–308.

Cleveland, L. R., 1925: Method by which *Trichonympha* ingests solid particles of wood. Biol. Bull., *48* : 282–287.

Cleveland, L. R., 1928: Symbiosis between termites and their intestinal Protozoa. Biol. Bull., *54* : 231–237.

Cleveland, L. R., Hall, S. R., Sanders, E. P., and Collier, J., 1934: The wood-feeding roach *Cryptocercus,* its Protozoa, and the symboisis between Protozoa and the roach. Amer. Acad. Sci., Mem. 17, pp. 185–342.

Corliss, J. O., 1959: An illustrated key to the higher groups of the ciliate Protozoa, with definition of terms. J. Protozool., *6* : 265–281.

Corliss, J. O., 1961: The Ciliated Protozoa: Characterization, Classification, and guide to the Literature. Pergamon Press, New York. A definition of the class Ciliata and its orders and families. This volume contains a very extensive bibliography of the literature on ciliates.

Ehret, C. F., and Powers, E. L., 1959: The cell surface of *Paramecium.* Int. Rev. Cytol., *8* : 97–133.

Grassé, P. (Ed.), 1952: Traité de Zoologie., Vol. 1, pt. 1, Phylogénie; Protozoaires: Généralites, Flagellés. 1953: Vol. 1, pt. 2, Protozoaires: Rhizopodes, Actinopodes, Sporozoaires, Cnidosporidies. Masson et Cié, Paris. A very comprehensive treatment of the Plasmodroma— flagellates, sarcodinans, and sporozoans.

Grimstone, A. V., 1961: Fine structure and morphogenesis in Protozoa. Biol. Rev., *36* : 97–150. A good summary of knowledge regarding the ultrastructure of the protozoan cell.

Hall, R. P., 1953: Protozoology. Prentice-Hall, Englewood Cliffs, N. J. A good general introduction to protozoology.

Horowitz, N. H., 1945: On the evolution of biochemical syntheses. Proc. Nat. Acad. Sci. U.S.A. *31*:153–157.

Hutner, S. H., and Provasoli, L., 1951: The phytoflagellates. *In* Biochemistry and Physiology of Protozoa (A. Lwoff, ed.). Vol. I., Academic Press, Philadelphia, pp. 27–128.

Hyman, L. H., 1940: The Invertebrates: Protozoa through Ctenophora. McGraw-Hill, New York, pp. 44–232. A concise general treatment of the Protozoa, although now out-of-date in many areas. The chapter *Retrospect* in the fifth volume (1959) of this series surveys investigation on protozoans from 1938–1958.

Kudo, R. R., 1954: Protozoology. 4th Ed. Charles C. Thomas, Springfield, Ill. A general account of the protozoans with particular emphasis on the taxonomy of the group.

Lackey, J. B., Deflandre, G., and Noland, L. E., 1959: Zooflagellates; Rhizopoda and Actinopoda; and Ciliophora. *In* Ward and Whipple's Freshwater Biology (W. T. Edmondson, ed.). 2nd Ed. John Wiley, New York, pp. 190–297.

Manwell, R. D., 1961: Introduction to Protozoology. St. Martin's Press, New York. An introduction to the morphology, physiology, and ecology of protozoans. Considerably less emphasis on taxonomy in this text than in those of Hall and Kudo.

Metz, C., Pitelka, D., and Westfall, J., 1953: The fibrillar systems of ciliates as revealed by the electron microscope. Biol. Bull., *104* : 408–425.

Noland, L. E., and Finley, H. E., 1931: Studies on the taxonomy of the genus *Vorticella.* Trans. Amer. Micros. Soc., *50* : 81–123.

Pennak, R. W., 1953: Freshwater Invertebrates of the United States. Ronald Press, New York, pp. 20–76. Figures and keys to the common genera of fresh-water protozoans.

Riegel, B., Stanger, D. W., Wikholm, D. M., Mold, J. D., and Sommer, H., 1949: Paralytic shellfish poison. V. The primary source of the poison, the marine plankton organism, *Gonyaulax caterella.* J. Biol. Chem., *177*:7–11.

Sonneborn, T. M., 1950: *Paramecium* in modern biology. Bios, *21*:31–43.

Sonneborn, T. M., 1957: Breeding systems, reproductive methods, and species problems in Protozoa. *In* The Species Problem (E. May, ed.), AAAS Pub., Washington, pp. 155–324.

Tartar, V., 1961: The Biology of *Stentor.* Pergamon Press, New York. A complete treatment of every aspect of the biology of this genus of ciliates.

Wichterman, R., 1953: The Biology of *Paramecium.* Blakiston Co., New York. An exhaustive treatment of every aspect of the genus *Paramecium.*

Yusa, A., 1957: The morphology and morphogenesis of the buccal organelles in *Paramecium* with particular reference to their systematic significance. J. Protozool. *4*:128–142.

Chapter 3

THE ORIGIN OF THE METAZOA

The only unicellular animals are protozoans; all other members of the Animal Kingdom are built on a multicellular plan of structure and constitute the subkingdom Metazoa. Sometimes the term *Eumetazoa* is used in referring to all multicellular animals with the exception of sponges (subkingdom Parazoa). The reasons for such a separation and the evolution of sponges are discussed in more detail in the next chapter.

Metazoan construction involves more than just a multicellular condition. A specialization of cells for different functions takes place, which in turn produces an interdependency of cells. Cell specialization and interdependency are the characteristics that distinguish true multicellular construction from that of colonial protozoans. Cell specialization has in turn led to the development of tissues, in which similar cells are organized in sheets or layers. In the lower metazoans, development of tissues is relatively primitive; and cells often are arranged in two layers, each containing a number of different cell types. In higher groups not only are true tissues present, but tissues also have become organized to form organs and organ systems.

The origin of metazoans has been a fertile field for zoological theorizing and speculation. Unfortunately, paleontology offers nothing to illuminate this great event in the evolutionary history of the Animal Kingdom. The first metazoans evolved long before the Paleozoic era; and even if an extensive Pre-Cambrian fossil record existed, it is doubtful if the minute, soft-bodied, ancestral metazoans would have left any record as fossils. Thus all theories regarding the origin of multicellular animals must be based on evidence derived from the comparative anatomy and embryology of living forms. As a consequence, little can be proved or disproved.

All zoologists agree that metazoans evolved from unicellular organisms; but as to the particular group of unicellular forms involved and the mode of origin, there is anything but unanimity. The current theories can be grouped around three principal viewpoints: that the ancestral metazoan arose from a multinucleate ① ciliate, which became compartmented or cellularized; that the ancestral metazoan arose by ② way of a colonial flagellate through increasing cellular specialization and interdependence; or ③ that metazoans have had a polyphyletic origin from different unicellular groups.

Hadzi (1953) and Hanson (1958) have been the chief proponents of a ciliate origin for metazoans. Their theory, which may be called the *Syncytial Theory*,* holds that multicellular animals arose from a primitive group of multinucleate ciliates. The ancestral metazoan was at first syncytial in structure, but later became compartmented or cellularized by the acquisition of cell membranes, thus producing a typical multicellular condition. Since many ciliates tend toward bilateral symmetry, proponents of the Syncytial Theory maintain that the ancestral metazoan was bilaterally symmetrical and gave

* *Syncytial* refers to the histological condition in which cell membranes are absent between adjacent nuclei.

rise to the acoel flatworms, which are therefore held to be the most primitive living metazoans. The fact that the acoels are in the same size range as the ciliates, are bilaterally symmetrical, are ciliated, and tend toward a syncytial condition is considered as evidence supporting the primitive position of this group. The ciliate macronucleus, which is absent in acoels, is assumed to have been absent in the multinucleate protociliate stock from which the metazoans arose and is assumed to have developed later in the evolutionary line leading to the higher ciliates.

There are a number of objections to the Syncytial Theory. For this theory to be acceptable, the embryology of the lower metazoans must be considered to have no phylogenetic significance, since nothing comparable to cellularization occurs in the ontogeny of any of these groups.* Actually, the syncytial nature of acoel tissue arises secondarily after typical, cytosomal, embryonic divisions. Furthermore, a ciliate ancestry does not explain the general occurrence of flagellated sperm in metazoans. No comparable cells are produced in ciliates, and it is necessary to assume a *de novo* origin of motile sperm in the metazoan ancestor. The most serious objection to the Syncytial Theory is the necessity for making the acoels the most primitive living metazoans. Bilateral symmetry then becomes the primitive symmetry for metazoans, and the radially symmetrical coelenterates must be derived secondarily from the flatworms. Yet all evidence indicates that the radial symmetry of coelenterates is primary, and not secondarily evolved from a bilateral ancestor.

The *Colonial Theory*, in which the metazoans are derived by way of a colonial flagellate, is the classic and most frequently encountered theory of the origin of multicellular animals. This idea was first conceived by Haeckel (1874), later modified by Metschnikoff (1886), and has more recently been reviewed by Hyman (1940). The Colonial Theory maintains that the flagellates are the ancestors of the metazoans, and in support of such an ancestry the following facts are cited as evidence. Flagellated sperm cells occur throughout the Metazoa. Flagellated body cells commonly occur among lower metazoans, particularly among sponges and coelenterates. True sperm and eggs have evolved in the phytoflagellates. The phytoflagellates display a tendency toward a type of colonial organization that could have led to a multicellular construction; in fact, a differentiation between somatic and reproductive cells has been attained in *Volvox*.

The Colonial Theory holds that the ancestral metazoan probably arose from a spherical,

hollow, colonial flagellate. Like *Volvox*, the cells were flagellated on the outer surface; the colony possessed a distinct anterior-posterior axis and swam with the anterior pole forward; and there was a differentiation of somatic and reproductive cells. This stage was called the blastaea in Haeckel's original theory; and the hollow blastula, or coeloblastula, was considered to be a recapitulation of this stage in the embryology of living metazoans. According to Haeckel, the blastaea invaginated to produce a double-walled, sac-like organism, the gastraea. This gastraea was the hypothetical metazoan ancestor, equivalent to the gastrula stage in the embryological development of living metazoans. In addition to embryological evidence, Haeckel noted the close structural similarity between the gastraea and some lower metazoans such as the hydrozoan coelenterates and certain sponges. Both these latter organisms are double-walled with a single opening leading into a sac-like digestive cavity.

Haeckel's gastraea was later modified by Metschnikoff, who noted that the primitive mode of gastrulation in coelenterates is by ingression, in which cells are proliferated from the blastula wall into the interior blastocoel (Fig. 5-14, *B*). This produces a solid gastrula. Invagination is apparently a secondary embryological short cut. Metschnikoff therefore argued that the gastraea was a solid rather than a hollow organism.

In accordance with Metschnikoff's revision, modern elaborators of the Colonial Theory pick up the evolution of the metazoans with Haeckel's blastaea. Through the migration of cells into the interior, the originally hollow sphere became transformed into an organism having a solid structure (Fig. 3-1). The body of this hypothetical ancestral metazoan is believed to have been ovoid and radially symmetrical. The exterior cells were flagellated and as such assumed a locomotor-perceptive function. The solid mass of interior cells functioned in nutrition and reproduction. There was no mouth, and food could be engulfed anywhere on the exterior surface and passed to the interior. Since this hypothetical organism is very similar to the planula larva of coelenterates (Fig. 5-14, *C*), it has been called the planuloid ancestor.

From such a free-swimming, radially symmetrical, planuloid ancestor the lower metazoans are believed to have arisen. On the basis of this theory the primary radial symmetry of the coelenterates can thus be accounted for as

---

* Cellularization does occur in the superficial cleavage of arthropod eggs, but this is a highly specialized condition associated with abundant yolk material.

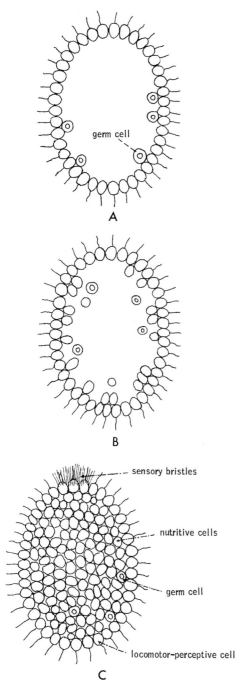

Figure 3-1. *A.* Hypothetical ancestral blastaea. *B.* Multipolar ingression. *C.* Hypothetical planuloid ancestor. (After Hyman.)

plant-like protozoans possess cellulose walls, chlorophyll, and autotrophic nutrition and go through the reduction divisions *following* fertilization. If the phytoflagellates did give rise to the Metazoa, as has indeed been advocated by some recent authors, then it is necessary to postulate that at some time in the course of the evolutionary events previously described, these plant-like characteristics were lost. An alternative hypothesis is that the metazoans arose from some group of now extinct zooflagellates that possessed a colonial organization similar to that in the volvocid phytoflagellates.

A number of authors, most recently Greenberg (1959), have proposed a polyphyletic origin for the metazoans. Greenberg suggests that the sponges, coelenterates, ctenophores, and flatworms each evolved independently from the protozoans. The sponges and coelenterates derived by way of colonial flagellates, and the flatworms and ctenophores by way of the ciliates or perhaps the mesozoans. It is readily apparent that Greenberg's view is a compromise between the Syncytial Theory and the Colonial Theory and is therefore subject to most of the arguments for and against the other two theories.

Despite the difficulties of the Colonial Theory, it is at least the most compatible with the evidence relating to subsequent metazoan evolution; for this reason, the Colonial Theory is followed in subsequent discussions of the phylogeny of the lower metazoan groups. However, it might be well to note here an opinion recently voiced by Dr. Hyman. "The author regards such phylogenetic questions as the origin of the Metazoa from the Protozoa . . . as insoluble on present information. . . . Anything said on these questions lies in the realm of fantasy."

PHYLUM MESOZOA

The phylum Mesozoa is a small group of minute metazoans of very simple structure. The phylogenetic relationships of the group continue to be an interesting but unsolved riddle. Many zoologists maintain that mesozoans are degenerate flatworms; others, especially Hyman (1940, 1959), consider their simple structure to be primary rather than secondary and believe that the mesozoans evolved from some ancestral metazoan form.

The phylum is composed of two orders: the Dicyemida and the Orthonectida. The dicyemids are parasites, probably harmless, which inhabit the nephridia of octopods and squids during the sexual stage of the life cycle. The animal during this stage is called a nematogen and has an elongated, ciliated body not exceed-

being derived directly from the planuloid ancestor. The bilateral symmetry of the flatworms would then represent a later modification in symmetry.

The principal difficulty with the Colonial Theory is that the flagellates that best fulfill the qualifications for metazoan ancestors are the fresh-water volvocid phytoflagellates. These

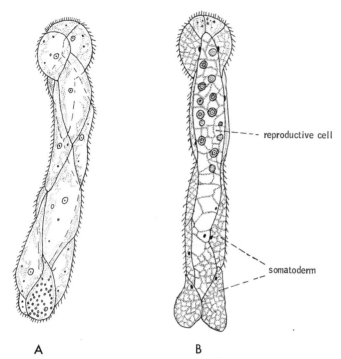

reproductive cell

somatoderm

A   B

Figure 3-2.   *A.* Nematogen of *Pseudicyema truncatum,* a mesozoan in the squid, *Sepia. B.* Longitudinal section of *A.* (After Whitman from Hyman.)

ing 7 mm. in length (Fig. 3-2, *A* and *B*). The body is composed of one internal reproductive cell surrounded by no more than 24 somatic cells, collectively called the somatoderm.

The asexual stage of the rarer Orthonectida exists as a multinucleate ameboid plasmodium, which reportedly has been found in body spaces and tissues of such invertebrates as flatworms, nemerteans, annelids, and a clam.

The life cycles of both the dicyemids and orthonectids are complex and involve alternation of sexual and asexual generations. In the dicyemids, new generations of nematogens are produced internally from the reproductive cell. Eventually a ciliated larva develops from an egg that arises from the internal reproductive cell. The larva escapes and presumably takes up existence in some intermediate host, where the asexual stage of the life cycle occurs and primary nematogens are developed. These nematogens infect young cephalopods.

In the orthonectids the plasmodium reproduces asexually through fragmentation. The sexual forms, which are somewhat similar to the nematogens of dicyemids, develop from certain nuclei of the plasmodium. The sexual forms

escape from the host, and fertilization occurs during a free-swimming existence. Development of the eggs takes place within the female, and eventually a ciliated larva like that of the dicyemids escapes from the parent and infects a new host.

BIBLIOGRAPHY

Greenberg, M. J., 1959: Ancestors, embryos, and symmetry. Systematic Zool., *8(4)*: 212–221.

Hadzi, J., 1953: An attempt to reconstruct the system of animal classification. Systematic Zool., *2*: 145–154.

Haeckel, E., 1874: Die Gasträa Theorie. Jenaische Z. Naturwiss., 8, 9, 10.

Hanson, E. D., 1958: On the origin of the Eumetazoa. Syst. Zool., *7(1)*: 16–47.

Hyman, L. H., 1940: The Invertebrates: Protozoa through Ctenophora. Vol. I. McGraw-Hill, New York, pp. 233–247, 248–253. This volume contains a concise account of the Mesozoa and a discussion of the evolutionary origin of the Metazoa. The chapter *Retrospect* surveys investigations on mesozoans from 1938–1958 in the fifth volume of this series (1959).

Hyman, L. H., 1959: The Invertebrates: Smaller Coelomate Groups. Vol. V. McGraw-Hill, New York, pp. 753–754. Quotation used in this chapter from p. 754.

Metschnikoff, E., 1887: Embryologische Studien an Medusen, mit Atlas. A. Holder, Vienna.

Chapter 4

THE SPONGES

Sponges, which constitute the phylum Porifera, are the most primitive of the multicellular animals. Neither true tissues nor organs are present, and the cells display a considerable degree of independence. All members of the phylum are sessile and exhibit little detectable movement. This combination of characteristics convinced Aristotle, Pliny, and other ancient naturalists that sponges were plants. In fact it was not until 1765, when internal water currents were first observed, that the animal nature of sponges became clearly established.

The Porifera are exclusively marine, except for a single family of fresh-water species. They abound in all seas, wherever there are rocks, shells, submerged timbers, or coral to provide a suitable substratum. A few species live on soft sand or mud bottoms. Most sponges prefer relatively shallow water; but some groups, such as the glass sponges, live at great depths.

Anatomy and Histology. Sponges vary greatly in size. Certain calcareous sponges are approximately the size of a bean, while the large loggerhead sponges would more than fill a large wash tub. Some are radially symmetrical, but the vast majority are irregular and exhibit massive, erect, encrusting, or branching growth patterns (Figs. 4-1 and 4-2). The type of growth pattern displayed is influenced by the nature of the substratum, by the velocity of the water current, and by wave action. Thus a particular species may assume different appearances under different environmental situations; this variation has resulted in

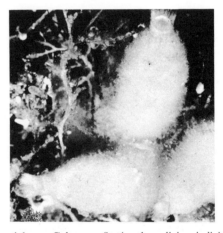

Figure 4-1. Calcarea: *Scypha,* three living individuals. (Courtesy of G. Lower *in* Guthrie and Anderson: General Zoology, Wiley, 1957.)

some taxonomic confusion. Drabness is more the exception than the rule among the Porifera; most of the common species are brightly colored. Green, yellow orange, red, and purple sponges are frequently encountered.

Primitive sponges are radially symmetrical (Fig. 4-3), but most members of the phylum have lost the ancestral symmetry and have become irregular. However, since the radial species display the simplest morphology, the basic structure and histology of sponges can be more easily understood by beginning with these forms.

Porifera that possess the simplest and the most primitive type of structure are called asconoid sponges, a structural term rather than

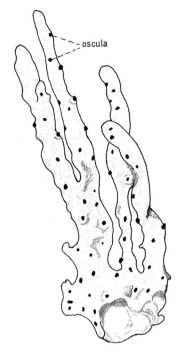

Figure 4-2. *Haliclona,* a Demospongiae. (After Hyman.)

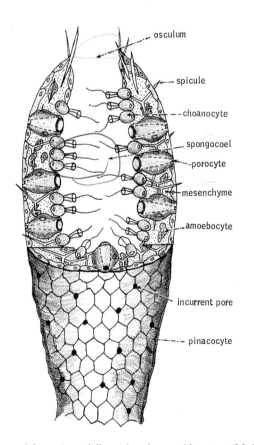

Figure 4-3. A partially sectioned asconoid sponge. (Modified from Buchsbaum.)

a taxonomic one. The asconoid sponge is shaped like a vase and is always small (Fig. 4-3). *Leucosolenia,* which is the most common asconoid sponge along the northern Atlantic coast, rarely exceeds 10 cm. in height. Asconoid sponges of this type are not usually solitary but live in clusters or colonies of vase-like individuals fused together along their long axes or at their bases.

The surface of an asconoid sponge is perforated by many small openings, called ostia or incurrent pores. These pores open into the interior cavity, the spongocoel. The latter in turn opens to the outside through the osculum, a large opening at the top of the vase. A constant stream of water passes through the incurrent pores into the spongocoel and out the osculum.

The body wall is relatively simple. The outer surface is covered by an epidermis of flattened polygonal cells, the pinacocytes. The margins of pinacocytes can be contracted or withdrawn so that the entire animal may increase or decrease slightly in size. The ostia are guarded by a remarkable type of cell, called a porocyte. Each porocyte is shaped like a short tube and extends from the external surface to the spongocoel. The bore, or lumen, of the tube forms the incurrent pore, or ostium; and the outer end of the cell can be closed or opened by contraction.

Beneath the epidermis lies a layer of mesenchyme, which consists of a gelatinous protein matrix, containing skeletal material and wandering amebocytes.

The skeleton is relatively complex and provides a supporting framework for the living cells of the animal. (To avoid repetition the discussion presented here on the sponge skeleton applies to the phylum in general, not just to the asconoid sponges.) The skeleton may be composed of calcareous spicules, siliceous spicules, protein spongin fibers (Fig. 4-4), or a combination of the last two. The spicules exist in a variety of forms and are important in the identification and classification of species. An extensive nomenclature has developed through the use of these structures in sponge taxonomy.

Monaxon spicules are shaped like needles or rods and may be curved or straight (Fig. 4-5, *A* to *D*). The ends are pointed, knobbed, or hooked. Tetraxons are four-pronged spicules (Fig. 4-5, *E* and *F*), but some types are triradiate owing to the absence of one ray (Fig. 4-5, *I*). Tri-axons, or hexactinal spicules, are six-rayed (Fig. 4-5, *J*). Polyaxons are composed of a number of short rods radiating from a common center (Fig. 4-5, *G* and *H*). They may be grouped so they appear like a bur, like a star, or something like a child's jack. Two additional terms are commonly encountered and can apply to any

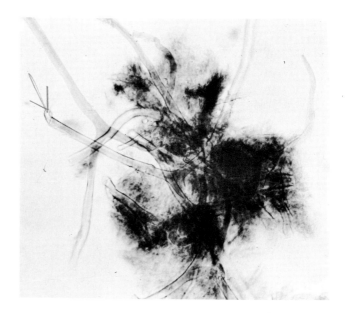

Figure 4-4. Spongin fibers (they appear translucent in photograph).

of the spicule types just described: megascleres, which are larger spicules forming the chief supporting elements in the skeleton, and microscleres, which are considerably smaller.

The skeleton is located primarily in the mesenchyme, but spicules frequently project through the epidermis. The arrangement of spicules within the mesenchyme, although sometimes haphazard, often presents a definite and symmetrical pattern. Some of the spicules may even be fused to form a distinct lattice.

The amebocytes in the mesenchyme are divided into a number of types, depending on their functions; but since it is doubtful that these cells are actually limited to any one function, the names probably do not have much significance. Only two types are mentioned here. Large amebocytes with blunt pseudopodia and large nuclei are called archaeocytes (Fig. 4-5, K). Archaeocytes act as the primordial germ cells, which give rise to the sperm and eggs; and they are also capable of forming any other type of cell that is needed. Such cells, which can transform into any type within an animal, are said to be totipotent. The skeleton, composed of either spicules or spongin fibers, is secreted by amebocytes called scleroblasts or spongioblasts. Several cells are usually involved in the secretion of a single spicule, and the process is relatively complex (Fig. 4-5, I).

Another type of mesenchymal cell requiring mention is the myocyte, which displays some similiarities to the smooth-muscle cell in shape and contractility. The myocytes are located primarily around the osculum, where they are arranged like a band of circular muscle; they control the size of the opening.

On the inner side of the mesenchyme, and lining the spongocoel, is a layer of cells, the choanocytes, which are very similar in structure to choanoflagellate protozoans (Figs. 4-3 and 4-5, L). The choanocyte is ovoid with one end adjacent to the mesenchyme. The opposite end of the choanocyte projects into the spongocoel and bears a flagellum surrounded by a basal contractile collar. The choanocytes are responsible for the movement of water through the sponge and for obtaining food. Both of these processes are described in detail later.

The primitive asconoid structure just described imposes very definite size limitations. The rate of water flow is very slow, because the large spongocoel contains too much water to be pushed out of the osculum rapidly. As the sponge increases in size, the problem of water movement is intensified, because the increase in size does not cause a sufficient increase in surface area of the choanocyte layer to rectify the problem. Thus asconoid sponges are always small.

The problems of water flow and surface area have been overcome during the evolution of sponges by the folding of the body wall and the reducing of the spongocoel. The folding increases the surface area of the choanocyte layer, and the reduction of the spongocoel lessens the volume of water that must be circulated. The net result of these changes is a greatly increased and more efficient water flow through the body. A much greater size now becomes possible, although the original radial symmetry is lost.

Living sponges display various stages in the changes just described. These changes are also recapitulated in the embryology of many species. Sponges that exhibit the first stages of body wall folding are called syconoid sponges. Syconoid sponges include the well known

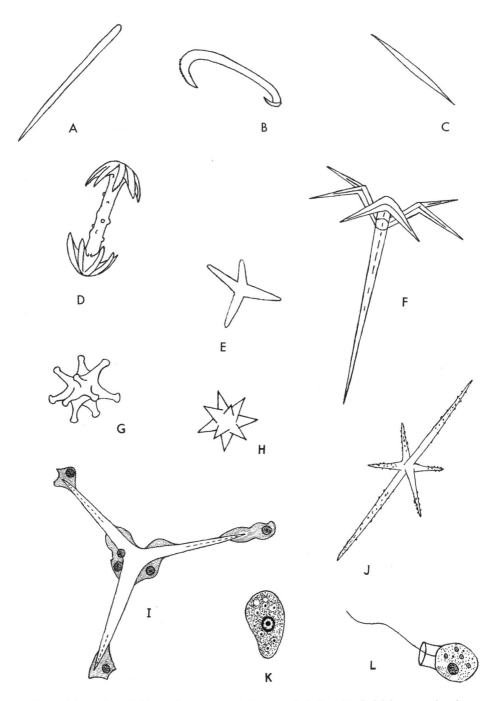

Figure 4-5. *A* to *D*. Types of monaxon spicules. *A* and *C*. Straight. *B*. With recurved ends. *D*. Ends with recurved barbs. *E*. Tetraxon with rays of equal length. *F*. Tetraxon with one long ray and three short, forked rays. *G* and *H*. Polyaxons. *I*. Scleroblasts secreting a type of tetraxon that lacks one ray. *J*. Triaxon or hexaxon. *K*. Archaeocyte. *L*. Collar cell, or choanocyte. (*J* after Villee, Walker, and Smith; others after Hyman.)

genera *Sycon* (the *Grantia* of supply houses) and *Scypha*. In syconoid structure, the body wall has become "folded" horizontally, forming finger-like processes (Fig. 4-6, *B*). This development produces epidermal pockets, extending inward from the outside, and evaginations, extending outward from the spongocoel. The two pockets produced by a fold do not meet, but by-pass each other and are blind. To visualize the syconoid condition, one might imagine pushing the fingers of one hand outward from the spongocoel side and pushing the fingers of the other hand inward from the epidermal side so that they would pass each other rather than meet.

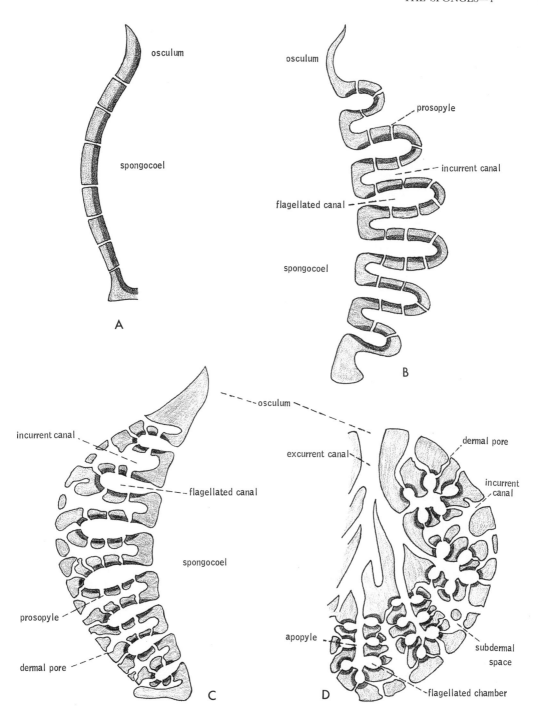

Figure 4-6.   Morphological types of sponges. (Epidermis and mesenchyme in pale gray; choanocyte layer, dark gray.) *A.* Asconoid type. *B.* Syconoid type. *C.* More specialized syconoid type, in which entrance to incurrent canals has been partially filled with epidermis and mesenchyme. *D.* Leuconoid type. (All after Hyman.)

In this more advanced type of sponge, the choanocytes no longer line the spongocoel but are now confined to the evaginations, which are called flagellated or radial canals. The corresponding invaginations from the epidermal side are known as incurrent canals and are lined by the epidermal pinacocytes. The two canals are

connected by openings called prosopyles, which are equivalent to the ostia of asconoid sponges. Porocytes are absent. Water now flows through the incurrent canals, the prosopyles, the flagellated canals, and the spongocoel, and flows out the osculum.

A slightly more specialized stage of the

syconoid structure develops with the plugging of the open ends of the incurrent canals with epidermis and mesenchyme (Fig. 4-6, *C*). Definite pores, called dermal pores, remain to permit entrance of water into incurrent canals. Despite the folding of the body wall, syconoid sponges still retain a radial symmetry.

The highest degree of folding takes place in the leuconoid sponge (Fig. 4-6, *D*). Here radial symmetry has been lost, and the system has become very irregular. The flagellated canals have undergone folding, or evagination, to form small, rounded, flagellated chambers; and the spongocoel has disappeared except for water channels leading to the osculum. Water enters the sponge through the dermal pores and passes into subdermal spaces. The spaces lead into branching incurrent channels, which eventually open into the flagellated chambers through prosopyles. Water leaves the chamber through an apopyle and courses through excurrent channels, which become progressively larger as they are joined by other excurrent channels. A single large channel eventually opens to the outside through the osculum.

Most sponges are built on the leuconoid plan, which is evidence of the efficiency of this type of structure. Leuconoid sponges are always irregular, but may attain considerable size. The body is composed of a mass of flagellated chambers and water channels. Rather than a single osculum, there may be many. Whether a large leuconoid sponge with many oscula represents a colony or a single individual is debatable. A good case can be made for each supposition.

Physiology.   The physiology of a sponge is largely dependent on the current of water flowing through the body. The water brings in oxygen and food and removes waste. Even sperm and eggs are moved in and out by the water currents. The volume of water pumped by a sponge is remarkable. A specimen of *Leuconia* (*Leucandra*), a leuconoid sponge 10 cm. in height and 1 cm. in diameter, has roughly 2,250,000 flagellated chambers and pumps 22.5 liters of water per day through its body. The flow through the osculum is 8.5 cm. per second. Regulating the size of the osculum controls the rate of flow, even stopping it altogether.

The current is produced by the beating of the choanocyte flagella, but there is neither co-ordination nor synchrony of the choanocytes in a particular chamber. The choanocytes are turned toward the apopyle, and each flagellum beats in a spiral manner from its base to its tip (Fig. 4-7). As a result, water is sucked into the flagellated chamber through the small prosopyles located between the bases of the choanocytes. It is then driven to the center of the chamber and out the larger apopyle into an excurrent canal.

Sponges feed on fine detritus particles and small planktonic organisms, such as protozoans, diatoms, and bacteria, brought in by the water currents. The food particles adhere to the surface of the collars of the choanocytes and are then engulfed by the cell body. In sponges with large choanocytes such as *Sycon*, the food is digested intracellularly within the choanocyte. When the choanocytes are small, food is transferred to the amebocytes for digestion or is engulfed directly by the amebocytes located along the course of the canals. Amebocytes also phagocytize large food particles that become lodged in the canals. Whether digestion occurs within choanocytes or within amebocytes, the vacuoles undergo acid and alkaline phases as in

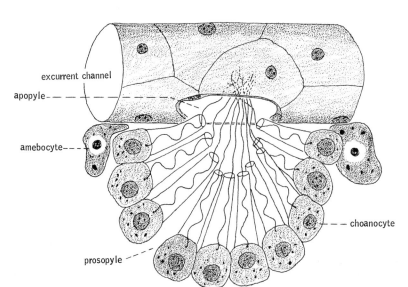

excurrent channel

apopyle

amebocyte

choanocyte

prosopyle

Figure 4-7.   Section through flagellated chamber of fresh-water sponge, *Ephydatia*. (After Kilian from Kaestner.)

protozoans. The amebocytes also act as storage centers for food reserves.

Adult sponges are incapable of any locomotion, although some species can contract or alter the body shape to some degree.

Egested waste and nitrogenous (largely ammonia) waste leave the body in the water currents. Gaseous exchange occurs by simple diffusion between the flowing water and the cells in the sponge along the course of water flow.

There is probably no nervous system in the sponge, and reactions are local and independent. Several French investigators (Pavans de Ceccatty, 1955) claim to have found bipolar nerve cells in the mesenchyme of sponges, but at present there is no physiological evidence that these cells actually have such a function.

Reproduction and Regeneration. Sponges reproduce asexually by budding or by a variety of processes that involve formation and release of an aggregate of essential cells, particularly amebocytes. In many sponges, such an aggregate is called a reduction body. Under adverse conditions the parent sponge falls apart but leaves behind masses of amebocytes covered by epidermal cells. The reduction body forms a new sponge.

Fresh-water sponges, as well as some marine forms, have aggregates called gemmules (Fig. 4-8). In fresh-water sponges a mass of food-filled archaeocytes becomes surrounded by other amebocytes that deposit a hard covering. Spicules are also added, so that a thick resistant shell is formed. Gemmule formation takes place primarily in the fall; a large number of these bodies are formed by each sponge. With the onset of winter, the parent sponge disintegrates. The gemmules are able to withstand freezing and drying and thus are able to carry the species through the winter. In spring the interior cells emerge from the shell through an opening called a micropyle. These cells develop into an adult sponge.

Some marine sponges form gemmules with a spongin coat re-inforced by spicules. Others form gemmules without a spongin coat. The gemmules of still other marine species resemble larvae. The surface cells of the mass develop flagella except at one pole. The flagellated "ball" escapes from the parent and, after a free-swimming existence, attaches at the nonflagellated end and develops into a young sponge.

Considering the relative independence of sponge cells, it is not surprising that these animals should have remarkable powers of regeneration. In fact, regeneration and asexual reproduction are closely related. Some sponges constrict near the ends of branches, causing the

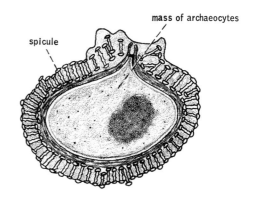

Figure 4-8.   Section through gemmule of fresh-water sponge. (After Evans from Hyman.)

branch ends to fall off and regenerate into new individuals. Any piece of sponge tissue can regenerate into a new sponge. Regeneration is employed in the propogation of commercial sponges in overfished areas off the Florida coast. Pieces of sponge called "cuttings" are attached to cement blocks and dumped into the water. Regeneration and several years growth produce a sponge of marketable size.

The classic experiment demonstrating the regenerative ability of sponges begins with the forcing of living sponge tissue through a silk mesh. The separated cells re-organize after a short period of time and form themselves into a new sponge.

The sexual reproduction and the embryology of sponges display a number of peculiar features. Both hermaphroditic and dioecious sponge species exist. The sperm and eggs arise from choanocytes and archaeocytes, or perhaps from any amebocyte (Fig. 4-9, *A* and *B*). In any case, the germinal cells develop either by engulfing other amebocytes, or by becoming surrounded by amebocytes that act as nurse cells. Sperm leave the sponge by means of water currents and enter other sponges in the same manner. After a sperm has reached a flagellated chamber, it enters a choanocyte. The latter then acts as a carrier and transports the sperm to the egg. After the carrier with its sperm has reached the egg, the carrier fuses with the egg and transfers the sperm to it. Fertilization thus occurs *in situ*.

Embryology. The embryology of the calcareous sponges is the most familiar. The subsequent description is based largely on this group. The fertilized egg begins its development within the mesenchyme of the parent. Cleavage is total and equal; and a flattened, 16-cell embryo, consisting of two tiers of eight cells each, is formed. The tier of eight cells resting against the choanocyte layer of the

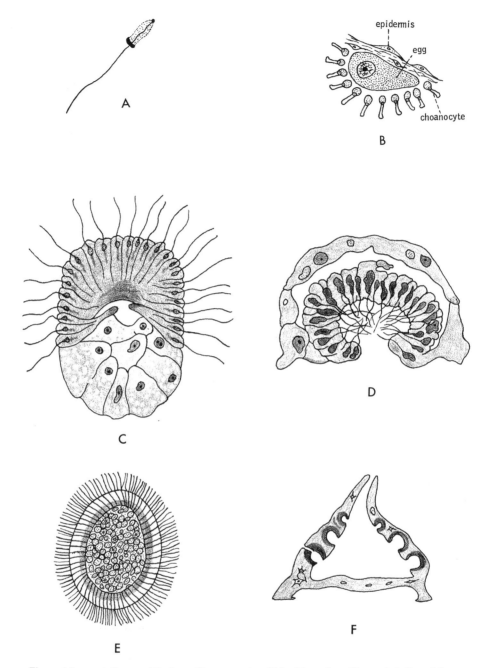

Figure 4-9.   *A.* Sperm of *Reniera,* a Demospongiae. (After Tuzet from Hyman.) *B.* Egg of *Sycon.* (After Hyman.) *C.* Amphiblastula of *Sycon. D.* Embryo of *Sycon,* following attachment and gastrulation. (*C* and *D* after Hammer from Hyman.) *E.* Parenchymula larva of *Leucosolenia.* (After Metschnikoff from Hyman.) *F.* Postlarval rhagon stage. (After Sollas from Hyman.)

parent is destined to form the epidermis, and the other eight-celled tier forms choanocytes. The future choanocyte tier undergoes rapid mitosis, while the pre-epidermal tier remains undivided. Between the two layers a blastocoel develops. The net result of development up to this point is a blastula. One side is composed of many small, elongated micromeres; the other side is composed of the original eight pre-epidermal cells called macromeres. Flagella

develop on the blastocoel ends of the micromeres, and a mouth-like opening extending from the blastocoel to the outside forms between the macromeres. Through this opening the blastula engulfs surrounding amebocytes for nutrition.

A curious process called inversion then occurs. It is strikingly like the process of inversion in the development of volvocid flagellates. The entire embryo turns inside out through the mouth. One hemisphere of the embryo is still composed of eight macromeres, and the other hemisphere of micromeres, but the flagella are now on the exterior. The embryo has now reached a stage called the amphiblastula larva (Fig. 4-9, *C*), characteristic of many calcareous sponges.

The amphiblastula breaks out of the mesenchyme and is carried to the outside by the water currents of the parent sponge. After a short free-swimming existence the amphiblastula attaches, and gastrulation occurs either by epiboly or invagination, or by both. But again the process is peculiar, for in calcareous sponges gastrulation is the reverse of that found in all other animals (Fig. 4-9, *D*). Here the macromeres overgrow the micromeres. The micromeres finally locate inside the gastrula, and the macromeres outside. In all other metazoans it is the macromere that becomes internal.

The larva now settles to the bottom, attaches, and forms a young sponge. The macromeres give rise to the epidermis, the micromeres to the choanocytes, and both layers produce the mesenchymal amebocytes.

The other classes of sponges, and even some calcareous sponges, do not have an amphiblastula larva, but rather another type called a parenchymula larva (Fig. 4-9, *E*). A parenchymula larva is a stereogastrula; that is, it is a gastrula that is solid with no interior cavity. It is similar to the amphiblastula in being flagellated, but the exterior flagellated cells are more extensive and cover all the outer surface except the posterior pole. The interior of the larva is filled with amebocytes that form by a process of gastrulation called ingression—a rapid proliferation of cells into the interior from the blastula wall. Such a parenchymula larva breaks out of the mesenchyme of the parent and has a brief free-swimming existence before settling. Even though gastrulation has already occurred, a reversing of layers still takes place. After settling, the exterior flagellated cells of the parenchymula move inward to take their place in the flagellated chambers. In the fresh-water sponges the choanocytes develop anew within the interior of the larva prior to settling. After attachment, the external flagellated cells are phagocytized by amebocytes and take no part in the formation of the choanocytes.

The reversing of the layers, either in the process of gastrulation or following gastrulation, poses obvious problems with regard to the classic concept of germ-layer formation. In the gastrula of a sponge, what should be called ectoderm and what entoderm? Probably the best solution is to avoid applying the conventional concept of germ layers to sponges and to restrict use of the terms ectoderm, entoderm,

and mesoderm to the embryology of the higher metazoans.

In many of the calcareous sponges that possess a leuconoid structure, the final stages of development after attachment of the larva recapitulates the more primitive asconoid and syconoid structures. For example, a leuconoid sponge undergoes developmental stages resembling the asconoid and syconoid structures before finally reaching the adult leuconoid condition. In other leuconoid sponges, especially the Demospongiae, the leuconoid condition is attained more directly. The first stage is known as a rhagon (Fig. 4-9, *F*). It resembles either the asconoid or the syconoid structure except that the walls are quite thick. The leuconoid plan develops directly from the rhagon stage by means of the formation of channels and flagellated chambers in the thick body wall.

THE CLASSES OF SPONGES

Approximately 5000 species of sponges are described at present, but the systematics of the phylum is far from stable. The phylum is divided into three classes based on the nature of the skeleton.

Class Calcarea. Members of this class, known as calcareous sponges, are distinctive in having spicules composed of calcium carbonate. In the other two classes the spicules are always siliceous. The spicules of calcareous sponges are monaxons or three- or four-pronged types; they are usually separate. All three grades of structure—asconoid, syconoid, and leuconoid—are encountered. Many Calcarea are drab, although brilliant yellow, red, and lavender species are known. They are not as large as species of other classes; all are less than 10 cm. in height. Species of calcareous sponges exist throughout the oceans of the world, but most are restricted to relatively shallow coastal waters. Genera such as *Leucosolenia* and *Sycon* are typical examples used in introductory biology courses.

Class Hexactinellida. Representatives of this class are commonly known as glass sponges. The name Hexactinellida is derived from the fact that the spicules are always of the tri-axon, or six-pointed, type. Furthermore, in several genera some of the spicules are fused to form a lattice-like skeleton, giving the sponges a glass-like appearance when dried. Thus they are called glass sponges. The glass sponges, as a whole, are the most symmetrical and the most individualized of the sponges—that is, there is less tendency to form colonies than in the other classes. The shape is cup-, vase-, or urn-like and they average between 10 and 30 cm. in height. The coloring in most of these sponges is pale. There is a well developed spongocoel, and the osculum is sometimes covered by a sieve plate—a grate-like covering formed from fused spicules. The flagellated canals or chambers are arranged radially and in parallel planes in the sponge wall. In this respect the structure is somewhat syconoid or primitively leuconoid. There is no epidermis of pinacocytes, but instead the surface is covered by a syncytium, through which long spicules project, producing a very delicate effect. Lattice-like skeletons composed of fused spicules in species such as Venus's-flower-basket (*Euplectella*) retain the general body structure and symmetry of the living sponge and are very beautiful; the white, filmy skeleton looks as if it were fashioned from rock wool (Fig. 4-10). The nature of the skeleton has made possible the preservation of these glass sponges as fossils. Members of this class are known to have lived as far back as the Cambrian period.

In contrast to the Calcarea, the Hexactinellida are chiefly deep-water sponges. Most live between depths of 1500 to 3000 feet, but some

Figure 4-10. Venus's-flower-basket, *Euplectella*, a hexactinellid sponge in which the spicules are fused to form a lattice. (Courtesy of the American Museum of Natural History.)

have been dredged from depths as great as 3 miles. The greatest number of species exist in tropical waters. The West Indies and the eastern Pacific from Japan south through the East Indies have particularly rich hexactinellid faunas.

Species of *Euplectella*, Venus's-flower-basket, display an interesting commensal relation with certain species of shrimp. A young male and a young female shrimp enter the spongocoel and, after growth, are unable to escape through the sieve plate covering the osculum. Their entire life is spent in the sponge prison, where they feed on plankton brought in by the sponge's water currents. The sponge with its imprisoned shrimp formerly was used in Japan as a wedding present, symbolizing the idea "till death us do part."

Class Demospongiae. This class contains the greatest number of sponge species and includes most of the common and familiar North American sponges. All Demospongiae are leuconoid and irregular, but all types of growth patterns are displayed. Demospongiae may be shaped like fans, vases, or cushions. Some are encrusting; others have an upright branching growth. The largest sponges are found in this class; some of the tropical loggerhead sponges form cushion-like masses several meters in height and diameter. Except for a single family of fresh-water species, the Demospongiae are all marine and range in habitat from shallow water to great depths. Coloration is frequently brilliant because of pigment granules located in the amebocytes.

The skeleton of this class is variable. It may consist of siliceous spicules or spongin fibers or a combination of both. A few genera lack any sort of skeleton. Those Demospongiae with siliceous skeletons differ from the Hexactinellida in that their larger spicules are never tri-axons but are monaxons or tetraxons. When both spongin fibers and spicules are present, the spicules are usually connected to, or completely imbedded in, the spongin fibers to form a skeletal network.

Several families of Demospongiae deserve mention. The boring sponges, composing the family Clionidae, are able to bore into calcareous structures such as coral and mollusk shells. Channels are formed that the body of the sponge fills. The mechanism of boring, which is begun by the larva, is not understood. *Cliona*, a common boring sponge that lives in shallow water along the Atlantic coast, inhabits old mollusk shells. The bright sulfur yellow of the sponge is visible where the bored channels reach the surface of the shell.

The family Spongillidae contains the only

fresh-water sponges in the Demospongiae. They are world-wide in distribution and live in lakes, streams, and ponds where the water is not turbid. They have an encrusting growth pattern, and some are green in color due to the presence of symbiotic zoochlorellae in the amebocytes. The algae are brought in by water currents and transferred from the choanocytes to the amebocytes.

The family Spongiidae contains the common bath sponges. The skeleton is composed only of spongin fibers. *Spongia* and *Hippospongia*, the two genera of commercial value, are gathered from important sponge fishing grounds in the Gulf of Mexico, the Caribbean, and the Mediterranean. The sponges are gathered by divers, and the living tissue is allowed to decompose in water. The remaining undecomposed skeleton of anastomosing spongin fibers is then washed and bleached. The colored block "sponges" seen on store counters are a synthetic product.

The Phylogenetic Position of Sponges

The evolutionary origin of sponges poses a number of interesting problems. They cannot be derived from the planuloid ancestor described in the preceding chapter, for sponges are considerably more primitive. For example, we do not find in adult sponges a distinct anterior and posterior end, or cellular differentiation, such as interior nutritive and reproductive cells and a definite surface layer or locomotor-perceptive cells. The origin of sponges must therefore antedate the origin of the planuloid ancestor. Some zoologists believe that sponges have evolved from a different and separate group of flagellates than did the other metazoans. The principal evidence supporting this theory is the similarity of sponge choanocytes to the choanoflagellates. The chief objection to this theory is that the larval cells of sponges show little similarity to choanoflagellates. The external cells of the sponge are flagellated, but they are not choanocytes, and only when they become internal do the flagellated cells transform into collar cells.

A second and more attractive theory is that sponges arose from a simple, hollow, free-swimming, colonial flagellate, perhaps the same stock that gave rise to the planuloid ancestor of the other metazoans. The larvae of sponges are quite similar to such flagellate colonies. The mesenchyme perhaps originated from an ingression of cells into the interior, such as occurs in the embryology of some sponges. In conjunction with the assumption of a sessile existence, (it can be hypothesized that) the water canal system developed and the flagellated, exterior cells moved into the interior to become choanocytes. The relegation of flagellated cells to the interior is recapitulated in the embryology of living sponges.

Although the origin of sponges is uncertain, there can be little doubt that sponges have diverged far from the main line of metazoan evolution and have given rise to no other members of the Animal Kingdom. A considerable number of facts would indicate that sponges are a dead-end phylum: No mouth and no digestive cavity exist; the entire body structure is built around a unique water canal system; the epidermal layer is poorly developed; the reversal of layers in the embryology of sponges takes place in some volvocid flagellates but in no other group of metazoans. Because of their isolated phylogenetic position, the sponges are often separated from the other multicellular animals (Eumetazoa) and placed in a separate subkingdom, the Parazoa.

BIBLIOGRAPHY

Hyman, L. H., 1940: The Invertebrates: Protozoa through Ctenophora. Vol. I. McGraw-Hill Co., New York, pp. 284–364. An excellent account of the biology of sponges, including an extensive bibliography. The chapter called *Retrospect* in the fifth volume (1959) of this series summarizes investigations on sponges from 1938 to 1958.

Jewell, M., 1959: Porifera. *In* Ward and Whipple: Freshwater Biology (W. T. Edmondson, ed.) 2nd ed., John Wiley, New York, pp. 298–312. An illustrated key to the common genera and species of fresh-water sponges in the United States.

Kilian, E. F., 1952: Wasserströmung und Nahrungsaufnahme beim Süsswasserschwamm *Ephydatia fluviatilis*. Z. vergl. Physiol., *34* : 407–447.

Pavans de Ceccatty, M., 1955: Le système nerveux des éponges calcaires et silicieuses. Ann. Sci. Natur. Zool., ser. 11, vol. 17.

Pennak, R. W., 1953: Freshwater Invertebrates of the United States. Ronald Press Co., New York, pp. 77–97. Chapter on the fresh-water Spongillidae includes a general account of the biology of the family and a key to the North American species.

Van Weel, P. B., 1948: On the physiology of the tropical fresh-water sponge *Spongilla proliferans:* ingestion, digestion, and excretion. Physiol. Comp. Oecol., *1* : 110–126.

Chapter 5

THE COELENTERATES

The phylum Coelenterata* includes the familiar hydras, jellyfish, sea anemones, and corals. The brilliant coloring of many species, combined with a radial symmetry, often creates a beauty that is surpassed by few other animals.

In accordance with the *Colonial Theory* of metazoan origins, it is hypothesized that the coelenterates arose from the planuloid ancestor and retained the ancestral radial symmetry (Hyman, 1940, 1959; Hand, 1959). Thus the radial symmetry of this phylum like that of the sponges is primary, or primitive. Sponges, coelenterates, and ctenophores are therefore often grouped together in a division of the Animal Kingdom called the Radiata.

Two new structural changes appeared in the development of the original coelenterates. First, the interior mass of nutritive cells of the planuloid ancestor became hollowed out to form a space for digestion called a gastrovascular cavity (Fig. 5-1). This cavity lies along the anterior-posterior (or long) axis of the animal and opens to the outside at one end to form a mouth. The acquisition of a mouth and digestive cavity permits the use of a much greater range of food sizes than was possible in the planuloid ancestor. Second, a circle of tentacles developed as extensions of the body wall around the mouth to aid in the capture and ingestion of food.

The coelenterate body wall consists of three basic layers (Fig. 5-1): an outer layer of epidermis, an inner layer of cells lining the gastrovascular cavity, and between these a layer called

mesoglea. The mesoglea may range from a thin, noncellular membrane to a thick, fibrous, jellylike, mucoid material with or without wandering amebocytes. Histologically, the coelenterates have remained rather primitive, although they anticipate some of the specializations that are found in higher metazoans. A considerable number of different cell types compose the epidermis and gastrodermis, but these cell types are not grouped together to form true tissues. Furthermore, most coelenterate cells lack the functional and structural specializations typical of cells in higher metazoans. Obviously, such a primitive histology prohibits the occurrence of true organs in this phylum.

Although all coelenterates are basically tentaculate and radially symmetrical, two different structural types are encountered within the phylum. One type, which is sessile, is known as a polyp. The other form is free-swimming and is called a medusa. Typically the body of a polyp is a cylindrical stalk in which the oral end, bearing the mouth and tentacles, is directed upward, and the opposite, or aboral, end is attached (Fig. 5-1, *A*).

The medusoid body resembles a bell or an

*Hyman (1940) maintains that the phylum should properly be called *Cnidaria*, since the name Coelenterata, as originally proposed by Leuckart in 1847, included the sponges, the coelenterates, and the ctenophores. However, since the name Coelenterata has become so well established and as now used by the vast majority of modern zoologists does not embrace either ctenophores or sponges, it is questionable if there is anything to be gained by attempting to replace it.

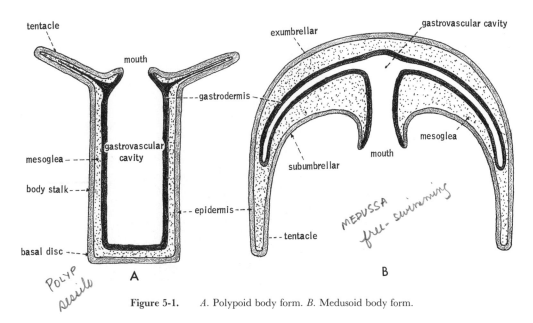

Figure 5-1. *A.* Polypoid body form. *B.* Medusoid body form.

umbrella, with the convex side upward and the mouth located in the center of the concave undersurface (Fig. 5-1, *B*). The tentacles hang down from the margin of the bell. In contrast to the polypoid mesoglea (middle layer), which is more or less thin, the medusoid mesoglea is extremely thick and constitutes the bulk of the animal. Because of this mass of jelly-like mesogleal material, these coelenterate forms are commonly known as jellyfish. Some coelenterates exhibit only the polypoid form, some only the medusoid form, while others pass through both in their life cycle.

Except for the hydras and a few species of fresh-water hydroids, all coelenterates are marine. The majority are littoral; sessile forms abound on rocky coasts or on coral formations in tropical waters. The phylum is composed of approximately 9000 living species, and a rich fossil record dates back as far as the Ordovician period.

Histology and Physiology of Hydra

The introductory description of the histology and physiology of coelenterates is based on the fresh-water hydras, since these animals are familiar to most students from introductory courses. The greater part of this discussion also applies to the other coelenterates; the more important exceptions are mentioned in a survey of the three classes later in the chapter.

Hydras are cylindrical, solitary polyps that range from a few millimeters to a centimeter or more in length (Fig. 5-2). However, the diameter seldom exceeds one millimeter. The aboral end of the cylindrical body stalk forms a basal disc,

by means of which the animal attaches to the substratum. The oral end contains a mound, or cone, called the hypostome, with the mouth at the top. Around the base of the cone is a circle of four to six tentacles.

The Epidermis. The epidermis is composed of five principal types of cells.

EPITHELIO-MUSCLE CELLS. The most important type, in terms of body covering, is the epithelio-muscle cells (Figs. 5-3 and 5-4, *A*). These cells are somewhat columnar in shape with the base resting against the mesoglea and the slightly expanded distal end forming most of the epidermal surface. However, unlike true columnar epithelium, epithelio-muscle cells possess two, three, or more basal extensions each containing a contractile fiber or myoneme. The basal extensions are oriented parallel to the axis of the body stalk and tentacles and thus form a cylindrical layer of contractile fibers. Although this layer corresponds to a layer of longitudinal muscle, it is not composed of true muscle cells.

INTERSTITIAL CELLS. Located beneath the epidermal surface and wedged between the epithelio-muscle cells are small rounded cells with relatively large nuclei. These are known as interstitial cells (Fig. 5-3). The interstitial cells, acting as the germinal or formative cells of the animal, give rise to the sperm and eggs as well as to any other type of cell needed by the animal. Brien (1951) estimates that over a period of 45 days all the cells of hydra are replaced from interstitial cells.

CNIDOBLASTS. A third cell type, the cnidoblast, is located throughout the epidermis but is particularly abundant in the tentacles. These specialized cells contain stinging structures called nematocysts, which are characteristic of

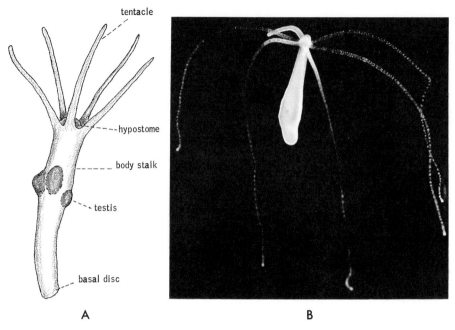

Figure 5-2.   *A.* Hydra with testes. *B.* Photograph of a living hydra. Note extended tentacles and the wart-like batteries of nematocysts that appear along the tentacles. (By Charles Walcott.)

all coelenterates. With few exceptions, nematocysts occur in no other group within the Animal Kingdom. A cnidoblast is a rounded or ovoid cell with a basal nucleus (Figs. 5-3; 5-4, *E* and *G*; and 5-5). One end of the cell contains a short, bristle-like process called a cnidocil, which may be exposed to the surface. The interior of the cell is filled by a capsule containing a coiled tube (Fig. 5-5), and the end of the capsule, directed toward the outside, is covered by a cap or lid.

Nematocysts, which can be discharged from the cnidoblast, are used for anchorage, for defense, and for the capture of prey. The discharge mechanism is still not too well understood, but apparently it involves a change in the permeability of the capsule wall. Under the combined influence of mechanical and chemical stimuli, which are initially received and conducted by the cnidocil, the capsule wall suddenly increases its permeability. This causes an inrushing of water and greatly increased pressure. As a result the lid is forced open, the tube turns inside out, and the entire nematocyst explodes to

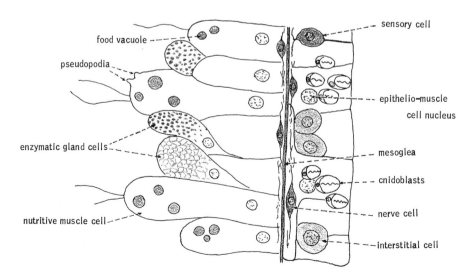

Figure 5-3.   Body wall of hydra (longitudinal section).

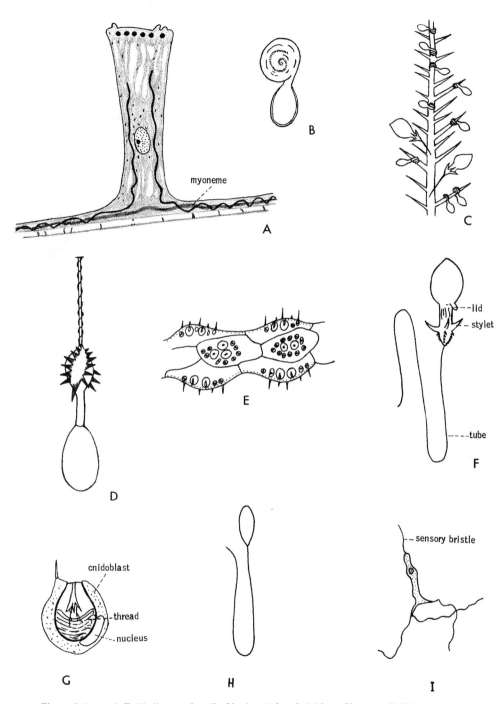

Figure 5-4.   *A.* Epithelio-muscle cell of hydra. (After Gelei from Hyman.) *B.* Volvent nemato-cyst of hydra. *C.* Discharged volvent and penetrant nematocysts on a crustacean bristle. (*B* and *C* after Hyman.) *D.* Open-tubed nematocyst of the hydroid, *Eudendrium.* After Weill from Hyman.) *E.* Nematocyst batteries on tentacle of hydra. *F.* Penetrant nematocyst of hydra. *G.* Undischarged penetrant nematocyst within cnidoblast in hydra. *H.* Spineless nematocyst with open tube of hydra. (*E* to *H* after Hyman.) *I.* Sensory nerve cell of a sea anemone. (After the Hertwigs from Hyman.)

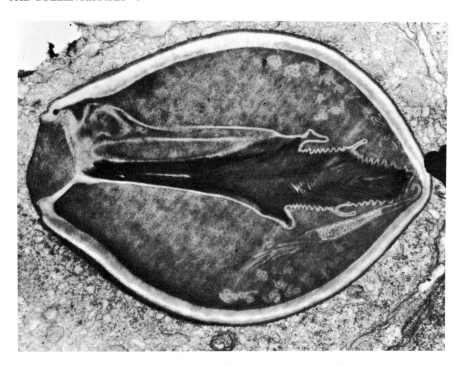

Figure 5-5.   Electron micrograph of an undischarged nematocyst of hydra (sagittal section). (Courtesy of G. B. Chapman, Cornell U. Medical College.)

the outside. Under normal conditions discharge is brought about by mechanical stimuli, such as contact with prey. Usually, however, the mechanical stimulus must be preceded by chemical stimuli that lower the threshold of the cell triggering mechanism. Thus the chemical stimuli emanating from an approaching prey rapidly prepare the nematocyst for discharge when the prey is contacted.

A discharged nematocyst, completely free from the cnidoblast and epidermis, consists of a bulb representing the old capsule and a thread-like tube of varying length (Fig. 5-4, *B, D, F,* and *H*). Frequently the base of the tube is enlarged so that the bulb appears pear-shaped. The tube is also commonly armed with spines, particularly around the base. The arrangement and number of spines give rise to a great variety of nematocyst types, which are constant for the species and of great value to coelenterate taxonomists.

Different species of coelenterates possess variously from one to four structural types of nematocysts. Hydra, for example, possesses four types, which are arranged on the tentacles in groups or batteries (Fig. 5-4, *E*). The batteries appear as bumps or warts when the tentacles are extended.

From a functional standpoint, nematocysts of hydra can be divided into three major types. The first, called a volvent, has a tube that is closed at the end, unarmed, and coiled (Fig. 5-4, *B* and *C*). When discharged, the volvents wrap around and entangle the prey.

The second type is known as a penetrant (Fig. 5-4, *C* and *F*). The tube of a penetrant is open at the tip and frequently armed with barbs and spines. At discharge, the thread penetrates into the tissues of the prey and injects a protein toxin that has a paralyzing action. The toxic effect of the nematocysts of hydra and most other coelenterates is not perceptible to man; but the larger marine forms, such as the Portugese man-of-war and the large jellyfish, can produce a very severe burning sensation and irritation. The last type of nematocyst is a glutinant, in which the tube is open and sticky. This type responds only to mechanical stimuli and is used in anchoring the animal when it walks on its tentacles. The cnidoblast degenerates following discharge of its nematocyst, and new cnidoblasts are formed from nearby interstitial cells.

MUCUS-SECRETING CELLS.   Mucus-secreting gland cells are a fourth type of cell found in the epidermis. They are particularly abundant in the basal disc of hydra and possess contractile extensions similar to the epithelio-muscle cells.

SENSORY AND NERVE CELLS.   The remaining two types of cells are the sensory cells and the nerve cells. Sensory cells double as both sensory neurons and receptors; that is, they both receive and transmit impulses (Figs. 5-3 and 5-4, *I*). They are elongated cells oriented at right angles to the epidermal surface. The base of each cell gives rise to a number of neuron-like processes, and the distal end terminates in a sensory bristle. Sensory cells are particularly abundant on the tentacles.

The nerve cells are located at the base of the epidermis next to the mesoglea and are oriented parallel to it (Fig. 5-3). They are similar to the bipolar or multipolar neurons of higher animals but are more primitive, there being no morphological differentiation of the processes (i.e., the processes are not polarized in the form of axons and dendrites).

The Gastrodermis. The histology of the gastrodermis, or inner layer of the body wall, is somewhat similar to that of the epidermis (Fig. 5-3). However, the cells corresponding to epithelio-muscle cells in the epidermis are called nutritive-muscle cells in the gastrodermis. The two types are similar in shape, but the nutritive-muscle cells are usually flagellated; and the basal contractile extensions, which develop to the highest degree in the hypostome and tentacle bases, are single and much more delicate than those of the epidermis. Furthermore, the contractile fibers of the gastrodermis are oriented at right angles to the long axis of the body stalk and thus form a circular muscle layer.

Interspersed among the nutritive-muscle cells are enzymatic-gland cells. These are wedged-shaped, flagellated cells with their tapered ends directed toward the mesoglea. Enzymatic-gland cells do not exhibit the basal contractile processes.

The remaining cells composing the gastrodermis are identical to those found in the epidermis. Mucus-secreting gland cells are abundant around the mouth. Sensory and nerve cells also exist, but in far fewer numbers. Nematocysts are lacking in the gastrodermis of hydras but are present in many other coelenterates, although restricted in distribution. In some species of hydra the gastrodermal cells contain symbiotic zoochlorellae. This alga, which is apparently *Chlorella,* gives the hydra a bright green color.

Locomotion. The body stalk and tentacles of hydra can extend, contract, or bend to one side or the other. It is usually stated that the epidermal contractile fibers, which are longitudinal, act antagonistically to the circular gastrodermal fibers. However, in hydra the gastrodermal fibers are so poorly developed in most parts of the body that movement is due almost entirely to the contractions of the epidermal fibers. Although hydras are essentially sessile animals, it is possible for them to shift locations. The tentacles and oral end may bend over and touch the substratum while the basal disc is simultaneously released, thus causing a somersaulting movement. Another common method of movement is by floating. The basal disc detaches and secretes a gas bubble that carries the animal to the surface. It may float about upside down for some time.

Nutrition. Hydras, like all coelenterates, are carnivorous and feed mainly on small crustaceans. Contact with the tentacles brings about a discharge of nematocysts, which paralyze and entangle the prey. The tentacles then pull the captured organism toward the mouth, which opens to receive it. Mucus secretions aid in swallowing, and the mouth can be greatly distended. Eventually the prey arrives at the gastrovascular cavity. Enzymatic-gland cells then discharge trypsin-like enzymes that begin the digestion of proteins, and the tissues of the prey are gradually reduced to a soupy broth. The beating of the flagella of the gastrodermal cells aids in mixing. From studies made on other coelenterates, it is probable that during this phase of digestion the proteins are hydrolyzed only as far as polypeptides.

Subsequent to this initial extracellular phase, digestion continues intracellularly. The nutritive-muscle cells produce pseudopodia that engulf small fragments of tissue. Continued digestion of proteins and the digestion of fats occur within food vacuoles in the nutritive-muscle cells. Coelenterates are apparently unable to digest starches. Studies indicate that the food vacuoles in coelenterates undergo the acid and alkaline phases characteristic of protozoans. Products of digestion are circulated by cellular diffusion; fats and glycogen are the chief storage products of excess food. Undigestible materials are ejected from the mouth on contraction of the body.

Respiration and excretion. There are no special organs for respiration and excretion. Gaseous exchange occurs through the general body surface. Nitrogenous wastes are largely in the form of ammonia, which also diffuses through the general body surface.

The Nervous System. The nervous system is quite primitive, as already indicated by the nature of the neurons. The nonpolarized nerve cells are arranged in an irregular nerve net, or plexus, one located on each side of the mesoglea (Fig. 5-6). The two nets are joined by interconnecting fibers. The epidermal plexus, however, is much more strongly developed, and the system is particularly concentrated around the mouth. Since the neurons are not polarized, impulses can travel in any direction. The most recent studies indicate that in hydra the system is not synaptic but a continuous net; that is, the endings of adjacent neurons are in actual contact. Conduction in such a nerve-net system is quite similar to the circular ripples produced when a pebble is dropped into a calm pond.

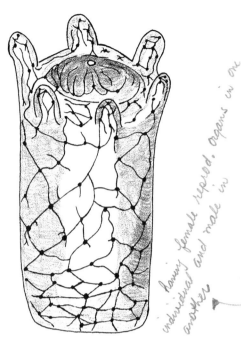

Figure 5-6.   Nerve net of hydra. (After Hadzi from Hyman.)

having female reprod. organs in one individual and male in another

look back

The stimulation of a particular point on the body brings about a radiating transmission that can result in a reaction response from the entire animal.

The association of nerve cells to form conducting chains between receptor and effector shows all degrees of complexity. In its simplest state, a sensory cell directly innervates a contractile fiber. Also there are circuits composed of two neurons in which a sensory cell transmits an impulse directly to a motor cell, innervating a contractile fiber. Finally, the three- or multiple-linked circuit, characteristic of higher metazoans, consists of neurons between sensory and motor cells. The single- and double-linked circuits found in coelenterates are particularly significant, since they undoubtedly represent primitive stages in the evolution of the nervous system.

Reproduction. Hydras reproduce asexually by budding; in fact, this is the usual means of reproduction during the warmer months of the year. A bud develops as a simple evagination of the body wall and contains an extension of the gastrovascular cavity. The mouth and tentacles form at the distal end. Eventually the bud detaches from the parent and becomes an independent hydra.

Considering the facility for asexual reproduction, it is not surprising that hydras, like many coelenterates, have considerable powers of regeneration. A classic experiment is that of Trembley, performed first in 1744. By means of

a knotted thread inserted through the basal disc and drawn out through the mouth, Trembley turned a hydra wrong side out. After a short period the gastrodermal cells re-oriented themselves on the inner side of the mesoglea, and the epidermal cells migrated to the outside. If the body stalk of a hydra is severed into several sections, each will regenerate into a new individual. Furthermore, the original polarity is retained so that the tentacles always form on the end of the section that was closest to the oral end of the intact animal, and a basal disc forms at the other end. A metabolic gradient appears to exist along the body stalk, metabolism being highest at the oral end and decreasing toward the base. Correspondingly, there is a decrease in the rate of regeneration from oral end to basal end.

Sexual reproduction in hydra occurs chiefly in the fall, because the eggs are a means by which the species survives the winter. The majority of hydras are dioecious. As in all coelenterates, the germ cells originate for the most part from interstitial cells, which aggregate to form ovaries or testes. (These are not true gonads.) In general, the testes are located in the epidermis of the upper half of the stalk and the ovaries in the lower half. This difference in location is true particularly of the few hermaphroditic forms.

A single egg is produced in each ovary, while the other interstitial cells of the ovarian aggregate merely serve as food in the egg's formation. As the egg enlarges, a rupture occurs in the overlying epidermis, exposing the egg (Fig. 5-7, *A*). The testis is a conical swelling with a nipple through which the sperm escape (Fig. 5-2). Sperm liberated from the testes into the surrounding water penetrate the exposed surface of the egg, which is thus fertilized *in situ.*

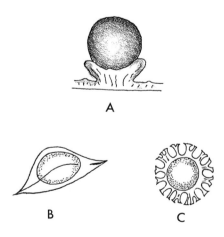

Figure 5-7.   *A.* Extruded egg of a hydra. *B.* Embryonated egg surrounded by chitinous shell of *Pelmatohydra. C.* Chitinous shell and embryonated egg of *Hydra littoralis.*

The egg then undergoes cleavage and simultaneously becomes covered by a chitinous shell (Fig. 5-7, *B* and *C*). When shell formation is complete, the embryonated egg drops off the parent and remains in its protective casing through the winter. With the advent of spring the shell softens, and a young hydra emerges. Since each individual may bear several ovaries or testes, a number of eggs may be produced each season. Sexual reproduction has been included here to complete the description of hydra, but the pattern described for hydra is not typical of coelenterates.

Class Hydrozoa

The class Hydrozoa contains a large number of common coelenterates, but because of their smallness and relative inconspicuousness, the layman is largely unaware of their existence. A considerable part of the marine growth attached to rocks, shells, and wharf pilings, and usually dismissed as "sea weed," is actually composed of hydrozoan coelenterates.

Hydrozoans display either the polypoid or medusoid structure, and some species pass through both forms in their life cycle. Three characteristics unite the members of this class. The mesoglea is never cellular; the gastrodermis lacks nematocysts; and the gonads are epidermal, or if gastrodermal, the eggs and sperm are shed directly to the outside and not into the gastrovascular cavity.

Hydroid Structure. Although some hydrozoans display only the medusoid form, most species possess a polypoid stage in their life cycle. Some forms, such as the hydras, exist as solitary polyps, but the vast majority are colonial. In hydra, buds form on the stalk as simple evaginations of the body wall. The distal end of the bud forms a mouth and a circle of tentacles; then the whole bud drops off to form a new individual. In the development of colonial forms, the buds remain attached; these in turn produce buds so that each polyp is connected to the others. Such a collection of polyps is known as a hydroid colony (Fig. 5-8). The three layers in a hydroid colony—epidermis, mesoglea, and gastrodermis—and the gastrovascular cavities are all continuous; it is impossible to tell where one individual begins and another ends.

A wide variety of growth forms are assumed by hydroid colonies. In most species the colony is anchored to the substratum by a horizontal, root-like structure called a hydrorhiza. In some genera, such as *Tubularia* and *Hydractinia*, (Fig. 5-9), the upright polyps are attached directly to the hydrorhiza, as in bread mold; but in most hydroids, the hydrorhiza gives rise to erect stalks or stems that bear the polyps. These stalks, known as hydrocauli, display a variety of

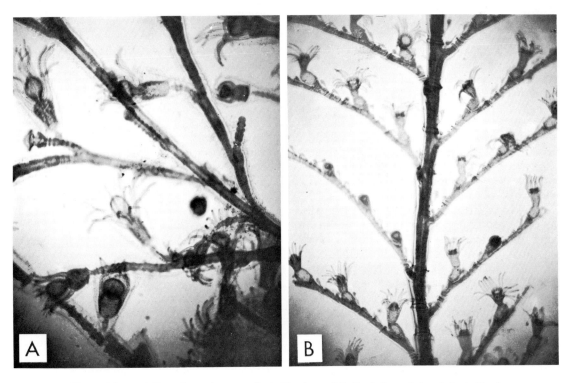

Figure 5-8.   *A.* Part of an arborescent hydroid colony of *Obelia. B.* Part of pinnate hydroid colony of *Plumularia.*

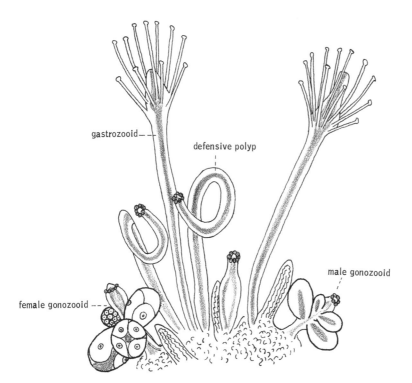

gastrozooid

defensive polyp

male gonozooid

female gonozooid

Figure 5-9.   *Hydractinia.* (After Hyman.)

growth forms. They may be arborescent (tree-like) as in *Obelia* (Fig. 5-8, *A*), or pinnate as in *Plumularia* and others (Fig. 5-8, *B*). The polyps in turn may be scattered over the branches or confined to side branches, as in the pinnate forms. In addition, the polyps may be attached by a little stalk (Fig. 5-10, *A*), or they may be sessile (Fig. 5-10, *B* and *D*).

Most hydroid colonies are only one foot or less in length; individual polyps are approximately the size of the oral end of hydras or smaller. The coloration, which may be pink or orange, is usually not very striking because of the small size.

With the exception of the hydras and a few other groups, at least part of the hydrozoan colony is surrounded by a nonliving chitinous envelope secreted by the epidermis. Such a cylinder is known as the perisarc (Fig. 5-10, *A*), and the living tissue that it surrounds is called the coenosarc. The perisarc may be confined to the hydrocaulus and the stalks of the polyps, but often it continues upward to enclose the polyp itself in a casing known as the hydrotheca, as in *Obelia* and *Campanularia*. The hydrotheca may be bell-like and open (Fig. 5-10, *A*), or its opening may be covered by a lid of from one to several pieces, as in *Abietinaria* (Fig. 5-10, *D*) and *Sertularia*. The lid opens when the polyp is extended and feeding and closes when the polyp contracts. Hydroids with a hydrotheca surrounding the polyp proper are said to be thecate; those without the hydrotheca, athecate.

All hydroid colonies are at least dimorphic; that is, the colony consists of at least two structurally and functionally different types of individuals. In hydroids the most numerous and conspicuous type of individual is the nutritive, or feeding, polyp, called a gastrozooid or trophozooid (Figs. 5-9 and 5-10, *A* and *B*). The feeding polyp looks like a short hydra with a distal mouth, a hypostome and tentacles. There may be a single whorl of tentacles, or there may be two whorls; sometimes the tentacles are not arranged in distinct whorls.

The gastrozooids capture and ingest prey, and thus provide nutrition for the colony. Extracellular digestion takes place in the gastrozooid itself; the partially digested broth then passes into the common gastrovascular cavity of the colony, where intracellular digestion occurs.

In most species the gastrozooids also fulfill the defensive functions of the colony, but in some hydroids there are special defensive polyps. The defensive polyps assume a variety of forms but are frequently club-shaped structures, well supplied with nematocysts and adhesive cells (Figs. 5-9 and 5-10, *B*). Defensive polyps usually are located around the gastrozooid.

All hydroids possess reproductive individuals as part of the colony. The reproductive individuals, called gonophores, are buds that develop into medusae. Gonophores assume a variety of shapes and locations. They may arise from the hydrocaulus, from the hydrorhiza,

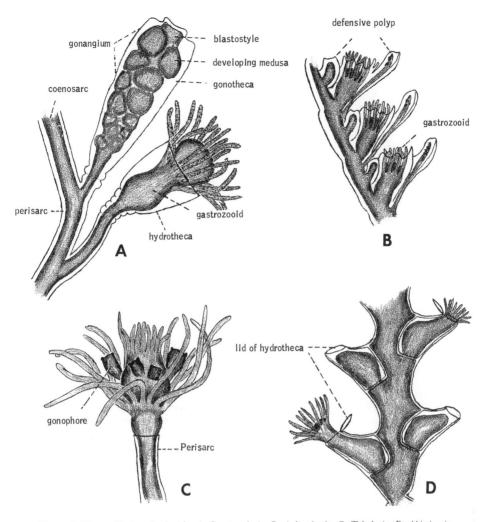

Figure 5-10.   Various hydroids. *A. Campanularia. B. Aglaophenia. C. Tubularia. D. Abietinaria.*

from the gastrozooid stalk, or frequently from the body of the gastrozooid itself. The latter development takes place in such common forms as *Tubularia* (Fig. 5-10, *C*) and *Eudendrium.*

In *Obelia* and *Campanularia,* the gonophores are restricted to special modified polyps called gonangia (Fig. 5-10, *A*). A gonangium consists of a central stalk, called the blastostyle, on which the medusoid buds develop. The perisarc extension around the blastostyle is called the gonotheca. It is usually vase-shaped with a constricted opening at the top. The formation of a medusoid bud is an asexual process. Through growth, each bud may develop into a complete medusa, which swims away as a tiny jellyfish.

Medusoid structure.   Unlike the medusae of the Scyphozoa, hydroid medusae are usually small, ranging from ⅛ inch to several inches in diameter (Figs. 5-11 to 5-13). The upper surface of the bell is called the exumbrella, and the lower surface, the subumbrella. The

epidermal cells of the exumbrella are not elongated but are flattened like squamous epithelium. The margin of the bell projects inward to form a shelf called a velum (characteristic of most hydromedusae). The tentacles that hang down from the margin of the bell vary from four to many and, like the tentacles of polyps, are richly supplied with nematocysts.

The mouth opens at the end of a tube-like extension called the manubrium, which hangs down from the center of the subumbrella. The manubrium also possesses nematocysts and is often lobed or frilled. The gastrovascular cavity is considerably more complex than the simple polypoid sac or tube. The cavity consists of a series of canals, arranged to resemble the hub, spokes, and rim of a wheel. The mouth leads into a central stomach, from which typically extend four radial canals. The radial canals join with a ring canal running around the margin of the umbrella. A bulge known as a tentacular bulb is located at the junction of each radial canal

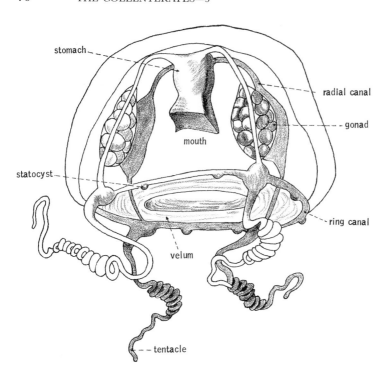

stomach

radial canal

gonad

mouth

statocyst

ring canal

velum

tentacle

Figure 5-11.   Medusa of *Eucopium.*
(After Haeckel from Kaestner.)

with the ring canal. The manubrium, stomach, and canals are all lined by gastrodermis.

As in all medusoid forms, the mesoglea is extremely thick and gelatinous and constitutes the bulk of the animal. The mesoglea of the hydromedusa is devoid of cells but does contain fibers that are probably secreted by the epidermis and gastrodermis. A thin, noncellular membrane separates the mesoglea from the epidermis, and another bounds the gastrodermis.

Medusae are also carnivorous, and the processes of their nutrition are essentially the same as in the polyp. Hyman (1940) has shown that although food particles are distributed throughout the gastrovascular cavity, most intracellular digestion takes place in the manubrium, in the stomach, and in the tentacular bulbs.

The muscular system of the medusa is somewhat more specialized than in the polyp. The gastrodermal cells lack contractile extensions, and the muscular system is thus restricted to the epidermal layer. Furthermore, the muscular system is best developed around the bell margin and subumbrella surface, where the fibers form a radial and circular system. Some of the epithelio-muscle cells of the velum have their contractile extensions oriented to form a powerful, circular band of fibers, which are striated. The contractions of the muscular system, particularly of the circular fibers, produce rhythmic pulsations of the bell. The rather limited swimming movement of the medusa is dependent on these pulsations and is vertical.

The nervous system of the medusa (Fig. 5-13, *A*) is also more highly specialized than that of the polyp. In the margin of the bell, the epidermal nerve cells are usually organized and concentrated into two nerve rings, one above and one below the attachment of the velum. These nerve rings, which can be thought of as a central nervous system, connect with fibers innervating the tentacles, the musculature, and the sense organs. The system is probably not synaptic.

The bell margin is liberally supplied with general sensory cells and also contains two types of true sense organs—light sensitive ocelli and statocysts. The ocelli consist of patches of pigment and photoreceptor cells organized either within a flat disc or a pit. The ocelli are typically located on the outer base of the tentacles. Some medusae are negatively phototropic and descend to deeper water during the day; others are attracted to light. Many, however, show no phototropism.

Statocysts are located at the base of the velum and are usually situated between the tentacles (Fig. 5-13, *B*). They may be either in the form of pits or closed vesicles, but in both cases the walls contain sensory cells with bristles projecting into the lumen. Attached to the bristles are from a few to many calcareous concretions known as statoliths. The statocysts act as organs of equilibrium. When the bell tilts, the statoliths respond to the pull of gravity and stimulate the sensory bristles to which they are attached. The animal may then respond by

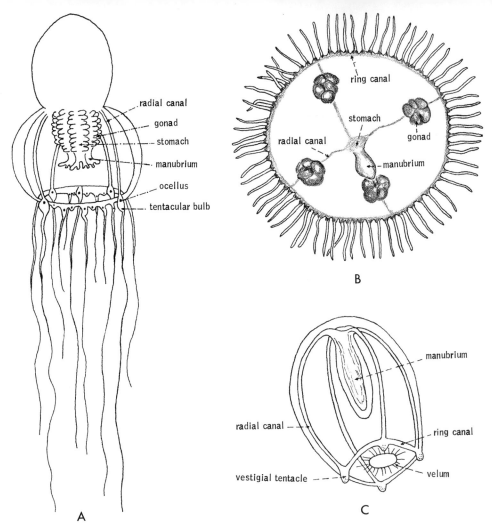

Figure 5-12. *A.* Hydromedusa of *Leuckartiara.* (After Hyman.) *B.* Hydromedusa of *Obelia. C.* Hydromedusa of *Pennaria.* (After Mayer from Hyman.)

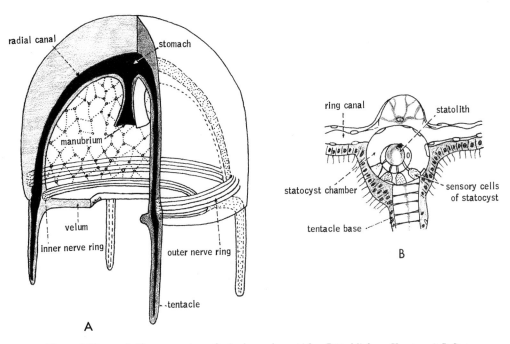

Figure 5-13. *A.* Nervous system of a hydromedusa. (After Bütschli from Kaestner.) *B.* Statocyst of a hydromedusa. (After the Hertwigs from Hyman.)

muscular contractions to bring itself back into a horizontal position.

Reproduction and life cycle. All medusae reproduce sexually. The eggs and sperm arise from epidermal or gastrodermal interstitial cells that have migrated to specific locations in the epidermis. Here these cells cluster to form a gonad. However, as in hydra, the gonads are not true organs but only an aggregation of developing gametes. The gonads are commonly located beneath the radial canals in the epidermis of the subumbrella (Figs. 5-11, 5-12, *B*), but they may also be situated in the epidermis of the manubrium.

Fertilization may be external with the eggs shed into the sea water, or it may be internal with the eggs beginning development in the gonad. Cleavage is complete and a hollow blastula is formed. Gastrulation commonly takes place by a process known as ingression (Fig. 5-14, *B*). In this process, through rapid inward proliferation of the blastula wall, cells move into the blastocoel, so that the blastula is changed into a solid gastrula. Such a gastrula is called a stereogastrula. Ingression may be unipolar, (only from the posterior wall) or multipolar (cells move in from all sides.). In conjunction with the formation of the gastrula, the two germ layers are laid down. The interior mass of cells represents the entoderm, which forms the future gastrodermis; the exterior layer represents the ectoderm, which forms the future epidermis.

The stereogastrula rapidly elongates to become a ciliated, free-swimming planula larva. The planula is elongated and radially symmetrical, but with distinct anterior and posterior ends (Fig. 5-14, *C*). Since the planula retains the stereogastrula structure, there is neither gastrovascular cavity nor mouth. After a free-swimming existence lasting from several hours to several days, the planula larva attaches to an object and develops into a hydroid colony.

Such a life cycle, with a free-swimming medusoid generation as well as a hydroid stage, is displayed by *Obelia, Pennaria, Syncoryne,* and other species of hydrozoans and has been the classic zoological illustration of a phenomenon known as metagenesis—the regular alternation of asexually and sexually reproducing generations. However, Hyman is probably correct in believing that the concept of metagenesis in the Animal Kingdom has no real validity and should be discarded. There are no haploid and diploid generations; the budding off of medusae is but one step in the attainment of sexual reproduction; and, more important, in the case of hydroids, to regard such a life cycle as meta-

genetic is to take the life cycle completely out of its evolutionary context.

The majority of hydroids, such as *Tubularia, Sertularia* and *Plumularia,* do not produce a free-swimming medusa. Instead the medusa remains attached to the parent hydroid (Fig. 5-14, *D*) and displays various degrees of degeneration. Despite the attachment and degeneration of the medusa, it still remains a sexually reproducing individual. In some hydroids the attached medusa has degenerated until only the gonadal tissue remains. Such a degenerate medusa, inappropriately called a sporosac, represents nothing more than a gamete-producing structure. Sporosacs are present in *Tubularia, Hydractinia, Plumularia* and others. Finally, in the hydras no vestige remains of a medusoid generation. Gonads form directly in the epidermis of the polyp stalk.

As is the case in free-swimming medusae, the eggs of attached medusae may be retained, and the early embryonic stages passed through while the eggs remain in the gonad. In some species such as *Orthopyxis* (Fig. 5-14, *G*), the egg may develop through gastrulation within a sporosac; and the embryo escapes as a planula larva. In *Tubularia* even the planula stage is passed in the sporosac, and an actinula larva is eventually released. An actinula looks like a stubby hydra and creeps about on its tentacles (Fig. 5-14, *F*). The fresh-water hydras have no larval stage, which is probably the result of fresh-water existence, in which larval stages are generally absent.

From the discussion thus far it might appear that all hydrozoans are hydroids, but this is by no means true. The medusoid generation is the dominant form in some hydrozoans. In *Liriope* and *Aglaura,* there is no polypoid stage. The planula forms an actinula larva that transforms directly into a medusa. *Gonionemus* and *Craspedacusta* also belong to this group. Although a polypoid stage is present, the polyp is tiny and solitary; and medusae bud off from the sides (Fig. 5-14, *E*). *↶ alternation of generations*

Hydrozoan Evolution. The evolutionary significance of "metagenesis" in hydrozoans is an intriguing problem. Which came first, the polyp or the medusa? In 1886, W. K. Brooks worked out a theory of coelenterate evolution that is still supported by zoologists today. According to Brooks's theory, the ancestral coelenterate form was medusoid. The tendency among hydrozoans has been to suppress the medusoid stage so that, in such forms as hydra, the medusa has completely disappeared. The polyp, on the other hand, represents an evolutionary retention and development of the

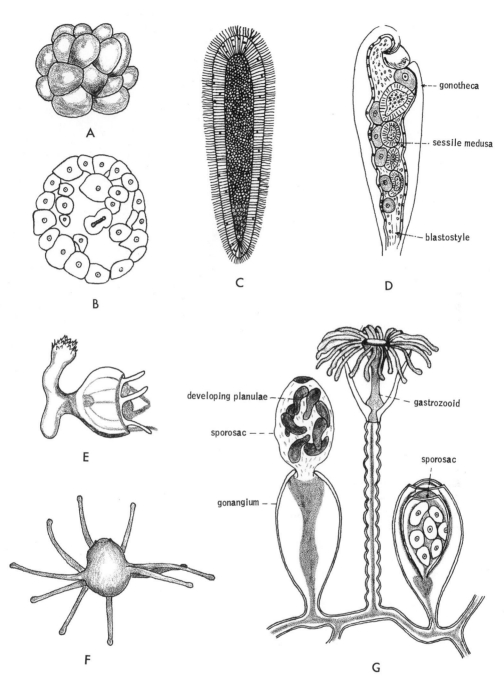

Figure 5-14. *A.* Early cleavage in *Gonothyraea.* (After Wulfert from Hyman.) *B.* Multipolar ingression in *Gonothyraea.* (After Wulfert from Hyman.) *C.* Planula larva. (After Hyman.) *D.* Gonangium of *Campanularia* with sessile medusae. (After Hyman.) *E.* Polyp of *Craspedacusta* with developing medusa. (After Reisinger from Kaestner.) *F.* Actinula larva of *Tubularia.* (After Hyman.) *G.* *Orthopyxis* with uneverted and everted sporosacs. (After Nutting from Hyman.)

larval condition. The sequence of stages in the suppression of the medusa and the origin of the polyp may perhaps be summarized as at the bottom of the page (egg and planula are indicated only in the first and last stages).

The hydroid colony originated from the actinula larva of the ancestral medusa. Budding off of other actinula larvae was followed by a retention of the buds, which resulted in the formation of a colony. The medusa, which primitively was free, gradually became retained and then suppressed until it disappeared completely. Living hydrozoans display life cycles that illustrate different stages in this evolutionary sequence. Hydra illustrates the last stage, in which the medusa has been completely suppressed and the gametes are formed in the epidermis of the polyp. However, hydra has not necessarily evolved from a complex hydroid colony. The hydras are probably derived from a line of hydrozoans in which the polyps were always solitary but originally budded off free-swimming medusae.

Specialized Hydrozoan Orders. Before the conclusion of the discussion on Hydrozoa, a few highly specialized orders must be described briefly.

SIPHONOPHORA.   Members of the order Siphonophora, which includes the familiar *Physalia* (the Portuguese man-of-war) and *Velella* (the purple sail) (Figs. 5-15 and 5-16), exist as large pelagic colonies composed of modified polypoid and medusoid individuals, the majority displaying a remarkable degree of polymorphism. A conspicuous feature of many species is a large gas-filled sac that acts as a float for the colony. The float of the Portuguese man-of-war may attain a length of 30 cm. Some species (but not *Physalia*) can regulate the gas content of the float so that the colony can sink below the surface during stormy weather. Swimming bells are characteristic of many siphonophoran colonies such as *Nectalia* and *Stephalia* (Fig. 5-17). These are modified, pulsating medusae that provide the locomotor power for the colony. Also attached are reproductive medusae.

Feeding is carried on by the polypoid members of the colony. Each nutritive polyp has only one long tentacle, which in *Physalia* may hang down several meters below the float.

Figure 5-15.   *Physalia,* the Portuguese man-of-war, a siphonophoran. (Courtesy of the New York Zoological Society.)

The tentacles of *Physalia* are strewn with nematocysts, and an accidental encounter with a large colony can be a painful and even a dangerous experience for a swimmer. The toxin from the nematocysts can produce such extreme pain that death may result from drowning. In addition to nutritive polyps, defensive and reproductive polyps typically are present. The reproductive polyps are modified, and the reproductive medusae are attached to them.

Siphonophorans are largely tropical and semitropical, but members of *Physalia* are often seen on the north Atlantic coast, following storms that have blown them in from the Gulf Stream.

MILLEPORINA AND STYLASTERINA.   The two small hydrozoan orders Milleporina (Fig. 5-18) and Stylasterina secrete a calcareous skeleton. Both are colonial polypoid hydrozoans with either an encrusting or an upright growth form. Both may attain considerable size and are often brightly colored. Most members of these orders

Medusa → Egg → Planula → Actinula → Medusa.

Medusa → Budding Actinula → Medusa.

Medusa → Hydroid Colony → Medusa.

Attached Medusa → Hydroid Colony → Attached Medusa.

Degenerate Attached Medusa → Hydroid Colony → Degenerate Attached Medusa.

Polyp → Egg → Planula → Polyp.

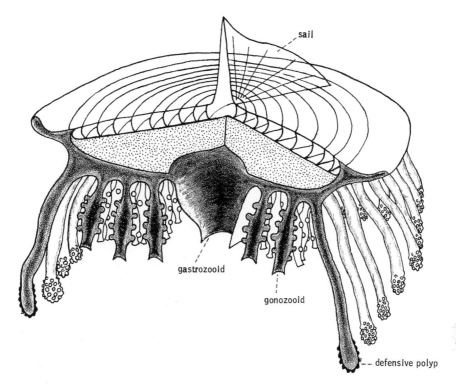

Figure 5-16.   The siphonophoran, *Velella*, with section removed. (After Delage and Herouard redrawn from Buchsbaum.)

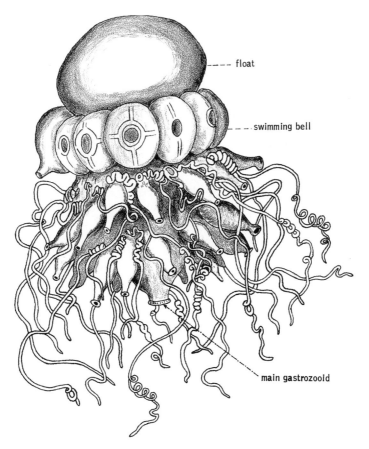

Figure 5-17.   *Stephalia*, a siphonophoran with swimming bells. (After Haeckel from Hyman.)

Figure 5-18. *Millepora,* a hydrozoan coral of the order Milleporina. (Courtesy of the Encyclopaedia Britannica.)

are tropical or semitropical and are common components of coral reefs. The Milleporina are also of some importance in reef formation.

Class Scyphozoa

Scyphozoans are the coelenterates most frequently referred to as jellyfish. In this class the medusa (Fig. 5-19, *A*) is the dominant and conspicuous individual in the life cycle; the polypoid form is restricted to a small larval stage. In addition, scyphozoan medusae are generally larger than hydromedusae. The majority of scyphozoan medusae have a bell diameter ranging from 2 to 40 cm; some species are even larger. The bell of *Cyanea arctica,* which lives in the Arctic Ocean, may reach 7 ft. in diameter. Coloration is often striking; the gonads and other internal structures, which may be deep orange, pink, or other colors, are visible through the colorless or more delicately tinted bell.

Scyphozoans live in all seas from the Arctic to tropical oceans. The majority inhabit coastal waters and are often a nuisance on bathing beaches. Their large size and their nematocysts make them unpleasant and often dangerous swimming companions. The so-called stinging nettles, which inhabit the Atlantic coast in large numbers during the latter part of the summer, are members of this class.

Although these coelenterates are typically free-swimming animals, one order of Arctic and Antarctic scyphozoans (order Stauromedusae) is sessile (Fig. 5-19, *B*). In this group, the bell is inverted and attached by the exumbrellar surface either directly or by means of a stalk, to seaweed, shells, and other objects. Members of this group are thus somewhat polypoid in general structure.

In general, scyphozoan medusae are similar to hydromedusae. The bell varies in shape from a shallow saucer to a deep helmet, and the margin is typically scalloped to form lobes called lappets (Fig. 5-20). A velum is never present. The manubrium is drawn out into four often frilly, oral arms, which aid in the capture and ingestion of prey. The tentacles around the bell margin vary from four to many. In *Aurelia,* the type most often studied in introductory courses, the tentacles are small and form a short fringe around the margin (Fig. 5-21); but in other species the tentacles are much longer (Fig. 5-20). The tentacles, the manubrium, and frequently the umbrella surface possess nematocysts.

The mesoglea of the scyphozoan is similar to that in the hydromedusa, being thick, gelatinous, and fibrous; but unlike that of the hydrozoan, it contains wandering ameboid cells and is a true cellular layer. The cells of the scyphozoan mesoglea appear to originate from the epidermis; therefore, if the term *mesoderm* is used, the layer must be considered ectomeso-

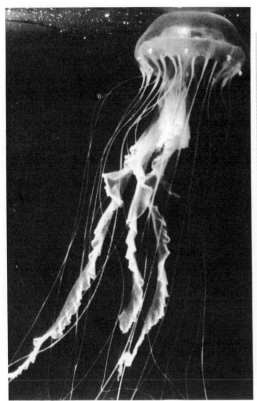

Figure 5-19.   *A*. The sea nettle, *Dactylometra quinquecirrha*, a common scyphozoan along the
Atlantic coast. (Courtesy of William H. Amos.) *B*. Two species of sessile scyphomedusae attached
to an alga. The specimen on the left, *Haliclystus auricula*, has a diameter of less than one inch. The
specimen on the right is *Craterolophus convolvulus*. (Courtesy of D. P. Wilson in Buchsbaum
and Milne: The Lower Animals, Chanticleer Press, 1961.)

dermal in origin and not the true entomesoderm
characteristic of higher metazoans.

The scyphozoan muscular system is like that
of the hydromedusa, and locomotion is brought
about by a band of powerful circular fibers (the
coronal muscle) that surrounds the subumbrella
margin. The pulsations produced by contraction of the coronal fibers tend to move the
animal upward toward the surface. When contractions cease, the animal slowly sinks. The
scyphozoan is moved horizontally mainly by
waves and currents.

The more primitive orders of Scyphozoa
do not display the gastrovascular canal system
seen in the hydromedusa. The mouth opens
through the manubrium into a central stomach,
from which extend four gastric pouches (Fig.
5-22). Between the pouches are septa, which
each contain an opening to aid in water circulation. Thus all four pouches are in direct communication with each other. The margin of the
septum, which faces the central portion of the
stomach, bears a large number of threads, or
filaments, containing nematocysts and gland
cells.

Medusae of the order Semaeostomeae,

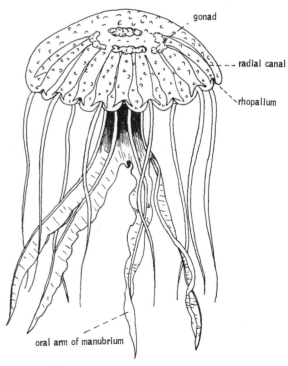

Figure 5-20.   *Pelagia*. (After Hyman.)

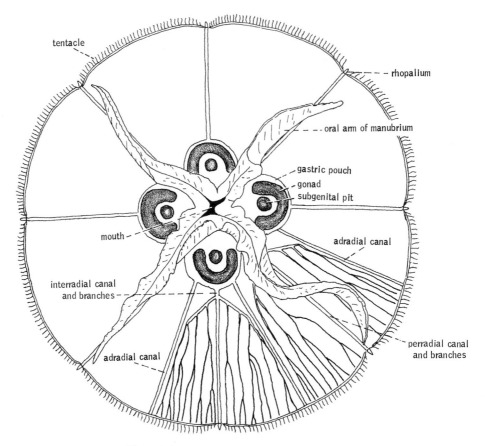

Figure 5-21.   *Aurelia* (oral view). (After Hyman.)

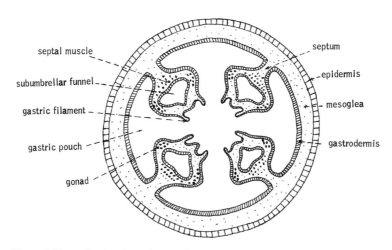

Figure 5-22.   Section through a scyphozoan with gastric pouches. (After Hyman.)

which contains the more familiar North Atlantic jellyfish such as *Aurelia,* have gastric pouches and septa in the larval stage only; as adults they possess a system of radial canals similar to those in the hydromedusa (Fig. 5-21). However, the system of radial canals in the semaeostomes is much more extensive than that in the hydromedusa. Four canals called perradials

extend from the central stomach. These correspond in position to the oral arms of the manubrium and divide the animal into quadrants. Between the perradial canals extend interradial canals, and between the interradials and perradials are the adradial canals. The canals are frequently branched as in *Aurelia,* and a ring canal may be absent. Although septa are absent, filaments are present and are attached interradially to the periphery of the stomach floor.

Adult scyphozoans feed on all types of small animals, from protozoans to small fish. As the medusa sinks slowly downward, prey is captured on contact with the tentacles or oral arms of the manubrium. Many species, *Aurelia* among them, are actually ciliary feeders. As the animal sinks, plankton becomes entrapped in mucus on the subumbrellar surface, which is flagellated in these forms. Flagella then sweep the food to the bell margin, where it is scraped off by the oral arms. Flagellated grooves on the oral arms carry the food to the mouth and stomach.

Digestion is essentially as described in hydra. The gastric filaments are the source of extracellular enzymes, and the gastrodermal nematocysts are probably used to quell prey that is still active.

The nervous system is of the nerve-net type but synaptic, and the sense organs display a greater degree of organization than in the hydromedusa. The specialized sense organs are grouped together in little, club-shaped structures called rhopalia, which are located around the bell margin between lappets and number from 4 to 16. Each rhopalium is flanked by a pair of small specialized lappets called rhopalial lappets and is covered by a hood (Fig. 5-23).

Two sensory pits, a statocyst, and sometimes an ocellus are borne by each rhopalium. The statocyst is located at the tip of the club and the sensory pits at the base. One sensory pit is located on the outer (exumbrellar) side, and one on the inner side. The sensory pits are merely concentrations of the same type of general sensory cells that are distributed over the body surface. When ocelli are present, as in *Aurelia* (Fig. 5-23, *A*), they are simple pits, containing pigment and photoreceptor cells. Many scyphozoans display distinct phototropism. They come to the surface of the water during cloudy weather and at twilight, but move downward in bright sunlight and at night.

With few exceptions, scyphozoans are dioecious, and the gonads are located in the gastrodermis in contrast to the usual epidermal gonad in hydrozoans. In septate groups with gastric pouches, the eight gonads are located on both sides of the four septa (Fig. 5-22). In semaeostome medusae, which lack septa, four horseshoe-shaped gonads lie on the floor of the stomach periphery (Fig. 5-21). When mature, the eggs or sperm break into the gastrovascular cavity and then pass out of the mouth. In most semaeostomes, including *Aurelia*, the eggs become lodged in the frills of the oral arms. This temporary brood chamber is the site of fertilization and early development.

Cleavage produces a hollow blastula that

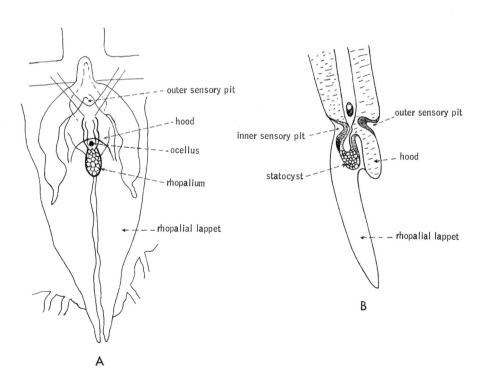

Figure 5-23.   *A*. Rhopalium of *Aurelia* (aboral view). *B*. Rhopalium (side view). (After Hyman.)

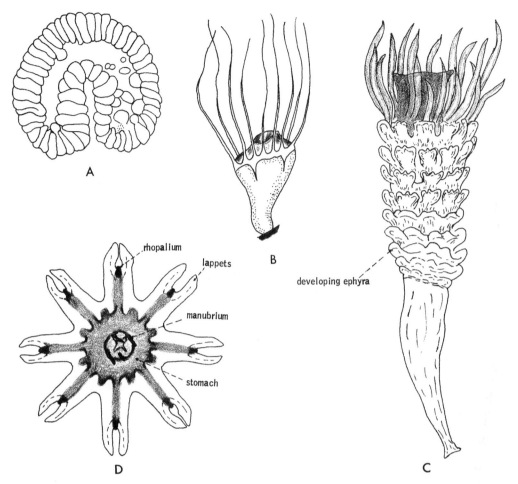

rhopalium

lappets

manubrium

stomach

B

developing ephyra

A

D

C

Figure 5-24.   *A.* Gastrulation in *Cyanea,* showing both invagination and ingression. (After Okado from Hyman.) *B.* Scyphistoma. (After Perez from Hyman.) *C.* Strobila of a semaeostome scyphozoan. (After Hyman.) *D.* Ephyra.

undergoes invagination (Fig. 5-24, *A*) to form a typical planula larva. After a brief free-swimming existence, the planula settles to the bottom and becomes attached by its anterior end. The attached planula then develops into a little polypoid larva called a scyphistoma.

The scyphistoma looks very much like a hydra (Fig. 5-24, *B*). During the summer and fall it feeds and produces new scyphistomae by asexual budding. With the onset of winter and spring, young medusae are formed. Medusa formation, which is accomplished by transverse fission of the oral end of the scyphistoma, is called strobilization (Fig. 5-24, *C*). As a result of this fission, immature medusae called ephyrae are formed and are stacked up like saucers at the oral end of the body stalk. As formation of the ephyrae is completed, they break away from the oral end of the scyphistoma one by one.

After strobilization, the scyphistoma resumes its polypoid existence until the following year, when formation of the ephyrae is repeated. A scyphistoma may live for several years.

The ephyra is almost microscopic, has a deeply incised bell margin, and has incompletely developed adult structures (Fig. 5-24, *D*). Ephyrae feed largely on protozoans, which are caught on the lappets and then wiped across the mouth and manubrium. An ephyra that has formed in the winter will have transformed into a sexually reproducing adult medusa by spring or summer.

Class Anthozoa

Anthozoans are either solitary or colonial polypoid coelenterates in which the medusoid stage is completely absent. Many familiar forms, such as the sea anemones, corals, sea fans, and sea pansies, are members of this class. This is the largest of the coelenterate classes and contains over 6000 species.

Although the anthozoans are polypoid, they differ considerably from hydrozoan polyps. The mouth leads into a tubular pharynx that extends more than half way into the gastrovascular cavity (Figs. 5-26; 5-30; and 5-34). The pharynx is derived from invaginated ectoderm. The gastrovascular cavity is divided by longitudinal septa into radiating compartments, and the edges of the septa bear nematocysts. The gonads, as in the scyphozoans, are gastrodermal, and the mesoglea is cellular.

In order to simplify the survey of this class, which is somewhat heterogeneous, the sea anemones, the stony corals, and the soft corals are dealt with separately.

Sea Anemones.   Sea anemones are solitary polyps and are considerably larger and heavier than the polyps of hydrozoans (Fig. 5-25). Most sea anemones range from half an inch to several inches in length with a diameter varying from the size of a dime to that of a half dollar. Some species attain an even greater size. Specimens of *Stoichactis* on the Great Barrier Reef of Australia may have a diameter of more than one yard at the oral end. Sea anemones are often brightly colored. They may be white, green, blue, orange, or red, or a combination of colors. Some are truly spectacular.

Sea anemones inhabit coastal waters throughout the world but are particularly abundant in tropical oceans. They commonly live attached to rocks, shells, and submerged timbers; a few forms burrow in mud or sand. A number of species are commensal on the shells of hermit crabs. The crab seeks out certain species of the sea anemone, massages its column

until the animal detaches, and then holds the animal against the shell until it adheres. The crab even carries its anemone along when it moves to a new shell. The sea anemone provides some protection and camouflage for the crab, and perhaps in turn obtains some food caught by the crab. Certain crabs attach anemones to their claws, which they then extend toward an intruder as a means of defense.

The major part of the sea anemone body is formed by a heavy column (Fig. 5-26). At the aboral end of the column there is a flattened pedal disc for attachment. At the oral end, the column flares slightly to form the oral disc, which bears a large number of hollow tentacles. In the center of the oral disc is a slit-shaped mouth, bearing at one or both ends a ciliated groove called a siphonoglyph. This groove aids in respiration by providing for the circulation of water into the gastrovascular cavity. The external surface of the sea anemone is not large enough to take care of the respiratory needs caused by the large volume of tissue; the constant flow of water into the gastrovascular cavity provides additional opportunity for the exchange of gases through the gastrodermal surface.

The slit-shaped mouth and siphonoglyphs impose a biradial or bilateral symmetry on sea anemones. They may be considered biradial when there are two siphonoglyphs, and bilateral when there is only one.

When a sea anemone contracts, the upper

A   B

Figure 5-25.   *A.* Cluster of the common Pacific coast sea anemone, *Anthopleura elegantissima.* (Courtesy of Turtox News.) *B.* Two daughter individuals of *Anthopleura elegantissima* just after asexual division. (Courtesy of Woody Williams in Buchsbaum and Milne: The Lower Animals, Chanticleer Press, 1961.)

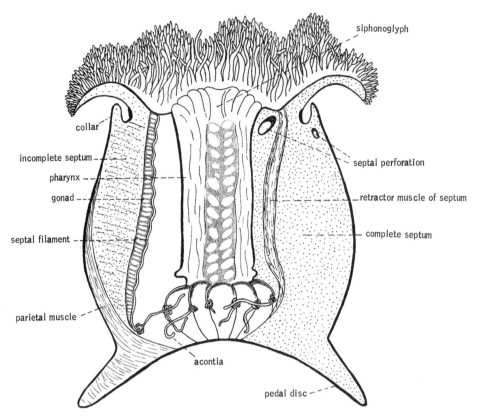

Figure 5-26.   A sea anemone (longitudinal section). (After Hyman.)

surface of the column is pulled over and covers the oral disc. In many sea anemones, including the familiar *Metridium* of the Atlantic coast, the column bears a circular fold at its junction with the oral disc. This fold is known as a collar and covers the oral surface on contraction of the animal (Fig. 5-26).

The mouth leads into the tubular pharynx, which extends approximately two-thirds of the way into the column (Figs. 5-26 and 5-28, *A*). Because the siphonoglyphs extend into the pharynx, the latter tends to be oval, with the long axis of the oval corresponding to the long axis of the mouth opening. The wall of the pharynx, being derived from a true stomodeum, contains the same layers as the body wall. The inner side is covered by a flagellated epidermis, and the outer by gastrodermis. Between the two is a layer of mesoglea.

As in all anthozoans, the gastrovascular cavity of the sea anemone is partitioned by longitudinal, radiating septa. In the sea anemones, there are usually two types of septa, called complete and incomplete. Complete septa are connected to the body wall on one side and to the wall of the pharynx on the other (Figs. 5-26 and 5-28, *A*). Incomplete septa are connected only to the body wall and extend only part way into the gastrovascular

cavity. The septa are located in adjacent pairs, and their position with relation to other pairs is correlated with the bilateral or biradial symmetry of the animal.

There is always a pair of complete septa, called directives, opposite each of the tapered sides of the pharynx. Thus for every pair of septa on one side of the pharynx, there is a corresponding pair on the opposite side. The pairs of septa usually occur in multiples of six. When only six pairs of septa are present, such as in the primitive *Halcampoides,* they are complete and are called the primary cycle. The addition of a cycle of secondary incomplete pairs located between the primary pairs (not between members of a pair), brings the total to 12 pairs. A tertiary cycle of smaller incomplete septa brings the number to 24 pairs, and so on. Many exceptions to the numerical symmetry just described exist. Moreover, asexual reproduction produces considerable irregularity, particularly in *Metridium.*

In the upper part of the pharyngeal region, the septa are pierced by openings that facilitate water circulation (Fig. 5-26). Below the pharynx, the complete septa have free margins and recurve toward the body wall.

Histologically each septum consists of two layers of gastrodermis separated by a layer of mesoglea. Both the gastrodermis and mesoglea are continuous with their corresponding layers in the body wall, and also in the pharynx when the septa are complete.

The free edge of each incomplete septum is trilobed and is called a septal filament (Figs. 5-27 and 5-28, *A*). The lateral lobes, which do not continue below the pharynx, are composed of flagellated cells and aid in water circulation. The middle lobe consists of nematocysts and enzymatic-gland cells. The middle lobe is present on all septa below the pharynx. In some sea anemones, including *Metridium,* the middle lobe continues at the base of the septum as a thread called an acontium, which projects into the gastrovascular cavity.

Sea anemone histology is more or less typical. The epidermis, however, is richly supplied with mucous gland cells and may be flagellated. The mesoglea is much thicker than that of hydrozoan polyps and contains a large number of fibers, as well as wandering amebocytes.

Sea anemones feed on various invertebrates, and large species can capture fish. The prey is paralyzed by nematocysts, caught by the tentacles, and carried to the mouth. In the Red Sea and Indo-Pacific region, a small commensal fish that is immune to the nematocysts lives among the tentacles of *Stoichactis* and other large sea anemones. The fish supposedly lures

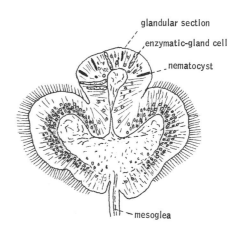

Figure 5-27.   Septal filament of a sea anemone.

larger fish into the tentacles and then shares the captured meal with its host.

Many small sea anemones are actually ciliary feeders. Flagella on the surface of the column beat toward the oral disc, where similar flagellary currents sweep the food to the tips of the tentacles. The tentacles then bend down and deposit the food into the mouth. Planktonic organisms are trapped on the surface of the column and tentacles, where mucus and nematocysts undoubtedly play a role in their capture.

The acontia and the middle lobe of the septal filaments produce the enzymes for extra-

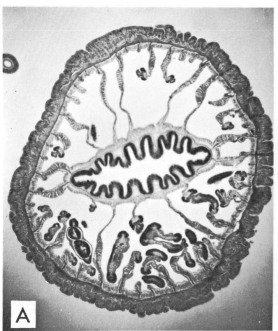

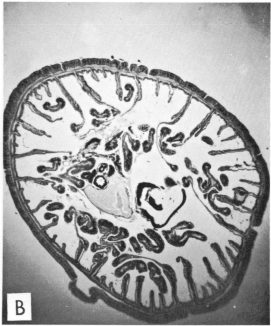

Figure 5-28.   Photomicrographs of transverse sections of the sea anemone, *Epiactis. A.* At the level of the pharynx. *B.* Below the pharynx. In *A,* note the thick layer of mesoglea between the outer thick epidermis and the thin inner gastrodermis. The same layers are present in the pharyngeal wall although reversed in position.

cellular digestion. Not only proteins but also fats are digested extracellularly. Intracellular digestion takes place over the general gastrodermal surface.

The muscular system in sea anemones is much more specialized than that in the other two classes of coelenterates. The longitudinal, epidermal fibers of the column and pharynx have disappeared except in primitive species. They are present, however, in the tentacles. Thus, the muscular system is largely gastrodermal. Bundles of longitudinal fibers imbedded in the septal mesoglea form retractor muscles for shortening the column (Figs. 5-28 and 5-29). Circular muscle fibers in the columnar gastrodermis are well developed and, like the retractor fibers, are located in the mesoglea. At the junction of the column and the oral disc, the circular fibers form a distinct sphincter for covering the oral disc upon retraction of the body.

Although sea anemones are essentially sessile animals, many species are able to change locations. Movement may be accomplished by slow gliding on the pedal disc, by floating, or by walking on the tentacles.

The nervous system presents nothing unusual, although it is synaptic. No specialized sense organs are present.

Asexual reproduction is not uncommon in sea anemones. The most common method is by pedal laceration, in which parts of the pedal disc are left behind as the animal moves. In some instances the disc puts out lobes that pinch off. These detached portions then regenerate into small sea anemones.

Sea anemones may be hermaphroditic or dioecious; the gonads are located in the gastrodermis. The gonads lie on the septa in the form of longitudinal bands behind the septal filament (Figs. 5-26 and 5-29). In hermaphroditic species, eggs and sperm are produced at different times from the same gonads. This is known as protandry and is common among invertebrates.

The eggs may be fertilized in the gastrovascular cavity with development taking place in the septal chambers; or fertilization may occur outside the body in the sea water. Cleavage is either equal or unequal, and a coeloblastula is formed in both cases. The blastula undergoes gastrulation by ingression or invagination to form a typical planula larva. A pharynx forms as a stomodeal invagination at the posterior. Septa then develop from the column wall and grow toward the pharynx. There are still no tentacles, and the young sea anemone lives as a ciliated ball, unattached and free-swimming. In all sea anemones, the young pass through a stage in which there are eight single septa. This is called the Edwardsia stage because of its similarity to the adult condition in the primitive genus *Edwardsia* (Fig. 5-29). This stage is

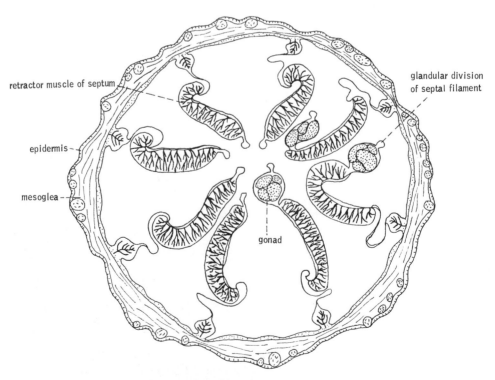

Figure 5-29.   Cross section of *Edwardsia* taken below pharynx. (After Hyman.)

followed by the formation of additional septa to form the adult body plan. During the Edwardsia stage, the larva usually attaches and forms tentacles.

Stony or Madreporarian Corals. Closely related to sea anemones are the stony corals. Unlike the sea anemone, the stony coral produces a calcium carbonate skeleton. Some corals are solitary with polyps reaching 25 cm. in diameter, but the majority are colonial with very small polyps averaging 1 to 3 mm. in diameter. However, the entire colony can become very large. Coral polyps are very similar in structure to sea anemones but do not possess siphonoglyphs (Figs. 5-30 and 5-31, *A*). The septal filaments contain only one glandular lobe with nematocysts. These filaments project as numerous threads into the central portion of the gastrovascular cavity and may even project from the mouth during feeding.

Feeding occurs at night, and corals employ the same methods of obtaining food as sea anemones—both raptorial and ciliary feeding. Debris is removed by special downward flagellated currents on the column.

The skeleton is composed of calcium carbonate crystals and is secreted by the epidermis of the lower half of the column as well as by the basal disc. This secreting process produces a skeletal cup called a theca, within which the polyp is immovably fixed. The bottom of the cup contains thin radiating septa that fit into folds of the basal disc. These folds project upward into the septal chambers of the gastrovascular cavity.

The polyps of colonial corals are all interconnected, but the attachment is lateral rather than aboral as in hydroids. The column wall folds outward above the skeletal cup and connects with similar folds of adjacent polyps. Thus, all the members of the colony are connected by a horizontal sheet of tissue (Fig. 5-30). Since this sheet represents a fold of the body wall, it contains an extension of the gastrovascular cavity as well as an upper and lower layer of gastrodermis and epidermis. The lower epidermal layer secretes the part of the skeleton that is located between the cups in which the polyps lie. The living coral colony, therefore, lies entirely above the skeleton and completely covers it.

The skeletal configurations of various species of corals are due in part to the growth pattern of the colony and in part to the arrangement of polyps in the colony (Figs. 5-31 and 5-32). Some species form flat or rounded skeletal masses, while others have an upright and branching growth form. When the polyps are well separated from each other, the coral skeleton has a pitted appearance as in the eyed coral, *Oculina.* In *Astrangia,* one of the corals living along the North Atlantic coast, the polyps are relatively close together so that just enough intervening skeletal material is present to make the thecae distinct. The polyps of brain coral are arranged in rows (Fig. 5-31, *B*). The rows are well separated, but the polyps comprising a row are so close together that their thecae are confluent. As a result, the skeleton of the colony has the appearance of a human brain, containing troughs or valleys separated by skeletal ridges.

The coral colony increases in size by the budding of new polyps, particularly along the

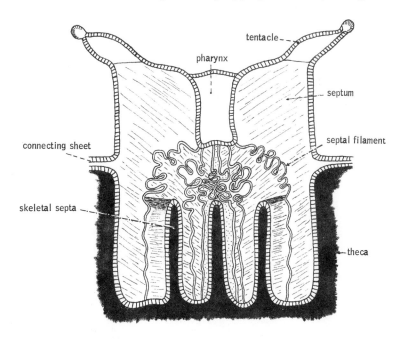

Figure 5-30. A coral polyp in its theca (longitudinal section). (After Hyman.)

Figure 5-31.   Madreporarian, or stony, corals. *A.* Star coral, showing living extended polyps. (Courtesy of the American Museum of Natural History.) *B.* Brain coral on the Great Barrier Reef. (Courtesy of Fritz Goro.) *C.* Staghorn coral from the Great Barrier Reef. (By Allen Keast, courtesy of Buchsbaum and Milne: The Lower Animals, Chanticleer Press, 1961.) *D.* Knobbed and lettuce coral on a Bahamian reef. (By John Storr.) *E.* Cup corals. (By D. P. Wilson.)

margin of the colony. Depending on the species, budding may take place on the horizontal inter-connecting sheet or on the polyps themselves.

Sexual reproduction is similar to that in the sea anemones. The single polyp, which is produced by sexual reproduction, attaches and by sexual budding becomes the parent of all other members of the colony.

Coral species live in temperate, arctic, and antarctic waters, but the richest faunas inhabit the tropical seas. It is in warm oceans that the reef-forming corals are found. In the West Indies there are approximately 35 reef-building species; there are over 200 species contributing to the Great Barrier Reef of Australia. The fact that more coral species inhabit warmer waters is perhaps correlated with the lower solubility of carbon dioxide in warm water. Thus, less energy is required from coral in the secretion of its skeleton in the warm oceans than would be required in cooler waters.

Many species of corals need relatively shallow water and do not live at depths below the light penetration level. This is particularly true of the reef-building species, which have a vertical distribution of 300 feet or less below the water surface. This vertical restriction is probably imposed by the symbiotic zooxanthellae that live in the tissues of most reef corals, as well as in many other coral species. These algae require sunlight for photosynthesis, and the corals in turn utilize the oxygen and perhaps the carbohydrates of the algae. Studies at the Haskins Laboratories have shown that this "alga" is actually a dinoflagellate. When the dinoflagellate is separated from the coral tissue, it acquires flagella and resumes the structure of typical free-living dinoflagellates.

Corals provide a substratum for many other species of animals. A tropical reef is actually an association of several thousand species of different kinds of animals that occupy various ecological niches (Fig. 5-32). Of the many intimate associations between corals and other animals, perhaps the most remarkable are those of the commensal gall-forming crabs and shrimp. These crustaceans inhabit certain types of corals that have branching growth forms. In the case of the crab, the little immature female, after her larval stages, comes to rest in a fork of the coral. The water currents created by this crab over its gills affect the growth pattern of the coral. The coral in the vicinity of the fork then tends to grow around and over the crab and creates a chamber from which the occupant can never escape. Small openings in the coral colony allow the entrance of the tiny male as well as of the plankton on which the crab feeds.

Alcyonarian Corals. Sea anemones and corals, because of their structural similarities, are grouped in the subclass Zoantharia. The remaining anthozoans, including many common marine forms such as sea pens, sea pansies, sea fans, whip corals, and pipe corals, form the subclass Alcyonaria. The Alcyonaria are similar to the Zoantharia in general structure but possess a number of different and distinctive features. Alcyonarians always possess eight tentacles, and these are pinnate—that is, they possess side branches as does a feather (Fig. 5-33, *A*). Cor-

Figure 5-32.   Exposed coral on the Great Barrier Reef off the coast of northeast Australia. Note different growth forms of various species present. (Courtesy of the Australian News and Information Bureau.)

related with the position of the tentacles, there are always eight complete septa. Only one siphonoglyph is present.

The alcyonarians are colonial coelenterates, and the polyps are rather small, similar to those of stony corals. The polyps (Fig. 5-34) of an alcyonarian colony are connected by a mass of tissue called coenenchyme. This consists of a thick mass of mesoglea that is perforated by gastrodermal tubes that are continuous with the gastrovascular cavities of the polyps. The surface of the entire fleshy mass is covered by a layer of epidermis, which joins the epidermis of the polyp column. Only the upper portion of the polyp projects above the coenenchyme.

The amebocytes of the coenenchyme secrete skeletal material that supports the colony. Thus, the skeleton of the Alcyonaria is internal and is an integral part of the tissue. This arrangement is in sharp contrast to that of the stony corals, in which the skeleton is entirely external. The alcyonarian skeleton may be composed of separate or fused calcareous spicules, or of a horny material.

The common names given to the different groups of alcyonarian corals originate from the

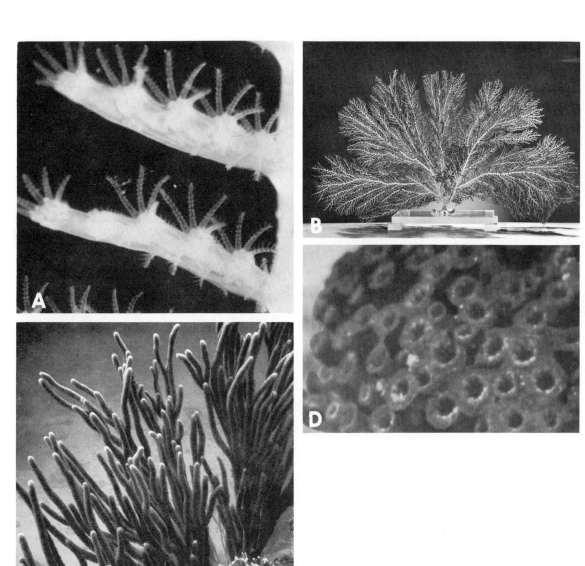

Figure 5-33.   Alcyonarians. A. Polyps of a sea pen. (Courtesy of Turtox News.) B. Sea fan. (Courtesy of the American Museum of Natural History.) C. Sea whips. (Courtesy of T. Parkinson.) D. Organpipe coral, looking into apertures of skeletal tubes. (Courtesy of Jerome M. and Dorothy H. Schweitzer in Buchsbaum and Milne: The Lower Animals, Chanticleer Press, 1961.)

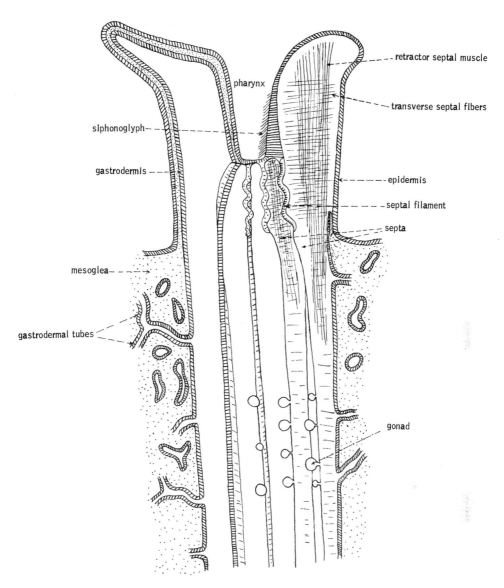

Figure 5-34. A soft coral polyp (longitudinal section). (After Hyman.)

different growth patterns exhibited by them. In whip corals (Fig. 5-33, *C*) an axial rod is covered by coenenchyme and polyps. The related sea fans (Fig. 5-33, *B*) grow in one plane in a lattice-like pattern. Both whip corals and sea fans may grow to be several feet in length; they are colored bright red, orange or yellow. In sea pansies the colony is leaf-shaped with the polyps on the upper side; in sea pens the shape is similar to that of a fern frond (Fig. 5-33, *A*). In both, the colony is attached to the substratum by a stalk or peduncle. Both sea pens and sea pansies possess rather fleshy coenenchyme, although spicules of calcium carbonate are present. The tropical organ-pipe coral, *Tubipora,* has a skeleton of fused spicules that form parallel

tubes in which the long polyps are located (Fig. 5-33, *D*).

BIBLIOGRAPHY

Brien, P., 1951: Contribution a l'étude des hydres d'eau douce. Bull. Soc. Zool. France, *76*:277-296.

Carlgren, O., 1949: A survey of the Ptychodactiaria, Corallimorpharia and Actiniaria. Kungl. Svenska Vetensk. Handl., ser. 4, vol. 1, no. 1. A monograph on the sea anemones of the world; includes a list of all known species and keys to genera.

Fraser, C., 1944: Hydroids of the Atlantic Coast of North America. Univ. of Toronto Press. A monograph on the American North Atlantic hydroids. Keys, figures, and extensive bibliography included.

Hand, C., 1959: On the origin and phylogeny of the coelenterates. Syst. Zool., *8*(4) : 191–202.

Hyman, L. H., 1940: The Invertebrates: Protozoa through Ctenophora Vol. I. McGraw-Hill, New York, pp. 365–661. An excellent general account of the coelenterates; includes an extensive bibliography. The chapter *Retrospect* in the fifth volume (1959) of this series summarizes investigations on coelenterates from 1938–1958 and also discusses current ideas regarding invertebrate phylogeny.

Hyman, L. H., 1959: Coelenterata. *In* Ward and Whipple's Freshwater Biology (W. T. Edmondson, ed.) 2nd Ed., Wiley, New York, pp. 313–322. Illustrated key to the North American fresh-water coelenterates.

Newell, N. D.: Questions of the coral reefs and West Indian reefs. Natural History, *68*(*3*):118, and *68*(*4*):226. A popular account of reef corals and reef formation.

Pennak, R. W., 1953: Freshwater Invertebrates of the United States. Ronald Press, New York, pp. 98–113. A brief treatment of the fresh-water hydrozoans with a key to the North American species.

Yonge, C. M., 1958: Ecology and physiology of reef building corals. *In* Perspectives in Marine Biology (A. A. Buzzati-Traverso, ed.). Univ. of California Press, Berkeley, pp. 117–135.

Chapter 6

THE CTENOPHORES

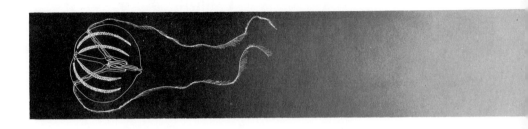

The Ctenophora is a small phylum of marine animals that are commonly known as sea walnuts or comb jellies. The phylum contains approximately 80 species, some of which are abundant in coastal waters. *Pleurobrachia* and *Mnemiopsis* are common genera along the north Atlantic coast.

Ctenophores are believed to be an offshoot from the ancestral medusoid coelenterate. This relationship to the coelenterates is exemplified in a number of ctenophore characteristics. Ctenophores are radially symmetrical, and the general body plan is somewhat similar to that of a medusa. The gastrovascular cavity is in the form of a canal system, and the thick body layer is comparable to the coelenterate mesoglea. On the other hand, ctenophores have undergone considerable specialization and display a number of innovations that indicate a sharp divergence from the coelenterate line. These differences are made clear in the subsequent description of the phylum.

The more primitive or generalized ctenophores, such as *Pleurobrachia* (Fig. 6-1) and *Mertensia*, are spherical or ovoid in shape and range in size from that of a pea to that of a golf ball. They are usually transparent, but various structures such as the tentacles and comb rows may be tinged with white, orange, or purple.

The body wall is composed of an outer epidermis of syncytial, cuboidal, or columnar epithelium. Sensory cells and often mucous gland cells are present, but there are no nematocysts except in a single species. Beneath the epidermis lies a thick layer homologous to the mesoglea of coelenterates. Like the coelenterate mesoglea, this layer is composed of a jelly-like material strewn with fibers and amebocytes and can be considered a type of loose mesenchyme. However, the mesenchyme of ctenophores also contains true muscle cells, which are completely lacking in coelenterates. The muscle cells are smooth and arranged as an anastomosing network.

The spherical body can be divided into two hemispheres (Figs. 6-1 and 6-2). The mouth, on the lower side, forms the oral pole; the diammetrically opposite point on the body bears a statocyst and marks the aboral pole.

The body is further divided into equal sections by eight ciliated bands. These bands, called comb rows, are characteristic of ctenophores and are the structures from which the name of the phylum is derived. Each band extends about four-fifths of the distance from the aboral pole to the oral end of the body and is made up of short transverse plates of long, fused cilia called combs. The combs are arranged in succession one behind the other, to form a comb row.

The combs provide the locomotor power in ctenophores. The ciliary beat functions in waves beginning at the aboral end of the row. The effective sweep of each comb is toward the aboral pole so that the animal is driven with the mouth, or oral end, forward. The beat can be temporarily reversed when some object is encountered. The nervous system and statocyst

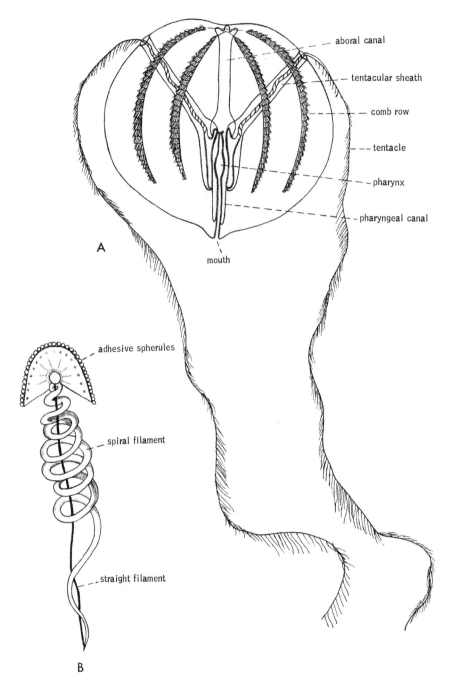

aboral canal

tentacular sheath

comb row

tentacle

pharynx

pharyngeal canal

A

mouth

adhesive spherules

spiral filament

straight filament

B

Figure 6-1.   *A. Pleurobrachia.* (After Hyman.) *B.* Colloblast. (After Koma from Hyman.)

control the synchrony and coordination of the ciliary waves.

From each side of the aboral hemisphere is suspended a long, branched tentacle. Unlike the tentacles of coelenterates, those of ctenophores are not attached to the surface of the sphere, but emerge from the bottom of a deep, ciliated canal called the tentacular sheath. There are two sheath openings, which are located between comb rows on opposite sides of the body,

each approximately at a 45 degree angle from the aboral pole. Although the comb rows are radially arranged, the two tentacles actually impose a biradial rather than a true radial symmetry on ctenophores.

Each tentacle consists of a mesenchymal core covered by epidermis. The muscle cells of the mesenchyme are frequently arranged in bundles so that the tentacles are very contractile. The tentacular epidermis, although

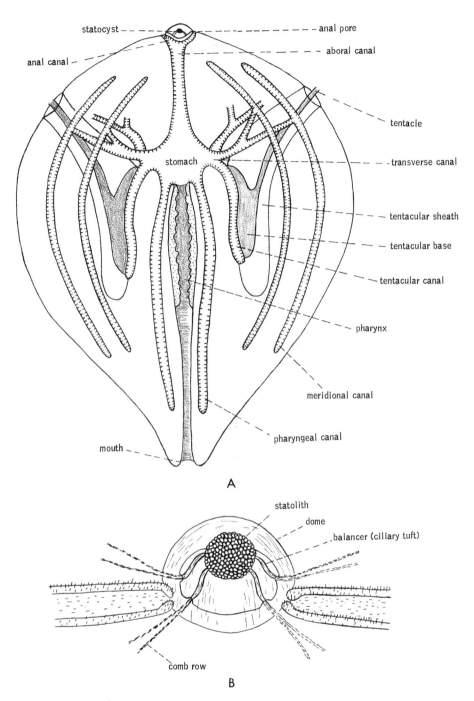

Figure 6-2.   *A.* Digestive system of a cydippid ctenophore. (After Hyman.) *B.* Statocyst of a cydippid ctenophore. (After Chun from Hyman.)

lacking nematocysts, possesses peculiar adhesive cells called colloblasts. A colloblast cell is composed of a hemispherical head located on the surface of the epidermis (Fig. 6-1, *B*). The hemispherical head is connected to the mesenchymal core of the tentacle by means of a straight filament, around which is coiled a contractile spiral filament. The surface head of the colloblast secretes a sticky material used in catching prey.

One ctenophore, *Euchlora rubra,* is known to possess nematocysts. This rare species lacks colloblasts, and the nematocysts are arranged in longitudinal tracts on the unbranched tentacles. The existence of nematocysts on this ctenophore is additional evidence of the coelenterate origin of the Ctenophora.

The digestive system is composed of an elaborate series of canals (Fig. 6-2, *A*). The mouth leads into a long tubular pharynx, which extends along the polar axis toward the aboral pole. The pharyngeal walls are considerably folded and are composed of long, ciliated epithelial cells and gland cells. The pharynx is derived from a stomodeal invagination, as in the Anthozoa.

At a point about two-thirds of the distance toward the aboral pole, the pharynx opens into the small stomach. From the stomach arise five canals: a pair of pharyngeal canals, which extend toward the mouth from the stomach floor; a pair of transverse canals, arising from opposite sides of the stomach; and an aboral canal, leading from the stomach roof. Both the pharyngeal and the transverse canals are oriented parallel to the tentacular plane. The two pharyngeal canals course along both sides of the pharynx and end blindly just before reaching the mouth. The transverse canals are relatively short and terminate in three branches. The first branch, called the tentacular canal, ends in the sides of the tentacular sheath. The other two branches of the transverse canal are known as interradial canals. These slope a short distance aborally and then divide again so that there are four interradials on each side of the body. Each interradial joins a long meridional canal that runs beneath each comb row.

The fifth canal leaving the stomach, the aboral canal, is single and proceeds aborally from the stomach roof along the polar axis. On nearing the aboral pole it branches into four short canals. Two of these terminal branches are called anal canals and open through an anal pore onto the aboral surface near the statocyst. The anal canals are also oriented parallel to the tentacular plane. The remaining two branches are blind. It should be noted also that the canal system is constructed on a biradial plan.

The digestive system, not including the pharynx, is lined by epithelium. In the canals the lining is always thicker on the side toward the polar axis (i.e., the inner side) and is thin and ciliated on the outer side.

The ctenophores are carnivorous, feeding on small planktonic animals. The food is caught on the colloblasts of the extended tentacles and then wiped into the mouth. Digestion begins extracellularly in the pharynx, and the resulting broth then passes into the stomach and canal system, where digestion is completed intracellularly. The cells on the outer, ciliated side of the canals are probably limited to providing circulation of fluid within the system. Indigestible wastes are passed out through the anal pores.

Ctenophores are noted for their luminescence. Light-production takes place in the walls of the meridional canals, so that externally the light appears to emanate from the comb rows. Enlarged motion pictures of luminescent ctenophores are very spectacular.

Also located in the digestive canals are peculiar clusters of cells called cell rosettes, which are believed to play a part in excretion or osmoregulation. The cell rosettes are a circle of ciliated cells that guard an opening between the lumen of the canal and the mesenchyme. Waste or excess fluid possibly may leave the mesenchyme through these openings and pass into the canals.

There are no special organs for respiration.

An epidermal nerve network is particularly well developed beneath the comb rows. The aboral statocyst is the only sense organ. The statocyst (Fig. 6-2, B) is covered by a transparent cap, and the statolith is supported by four ciliary tufts. The supporting tufts emerge from the statocyst as ciliary tracts, divide, and then connect with each comb row. This connection of the statocyst to the locomotor organs provides additional evidence that the statocyst is an organ of equilibrium.

All members of the phylum are hermaphroditic. The gonads are in the form of two bands located in the thickened wall of each meridional canal. One band is an ovary and the other a testis. The eggs are probably fertilized in situ by sperm that have entered the mouth and canal system. The fertilized eggs are then shed directly to the outside through the epidermis that lies over the meridional canals. Whether the sperm are shed in a similar manner or leave by way of the canals and mouth is not certain.

Ctenophore embryology anticipates the embryology of the protostomes in many respects (see Chapter 9). Only a very brief description is given here. Cleavage is total and determinate (see page 125). Eventually a solid blastula is formed that is composed of a large number of micromeres overlying a smaller number of macromeres. Gastrulation takes place by means of epiboly and invagination—that is, the micromeres, which will form the ectoderm, grow downward and enclose the macromeres, which are simultaneously invaginating into the interior to become the entoderm. The mesenchyme appears to derive from the ectoderm like the mesenchyme of coelenterates and therefore must be considered an ectomesoderm.

The gastrula soon develops into a free-swimming larva. This larva, called a cydippid larva, very closely resembles the adult of ctenophores that have the more ovoid or spherical body structure described previously. The flattened species of ctenophores also possess a spherical cydippid larva that undergoes a

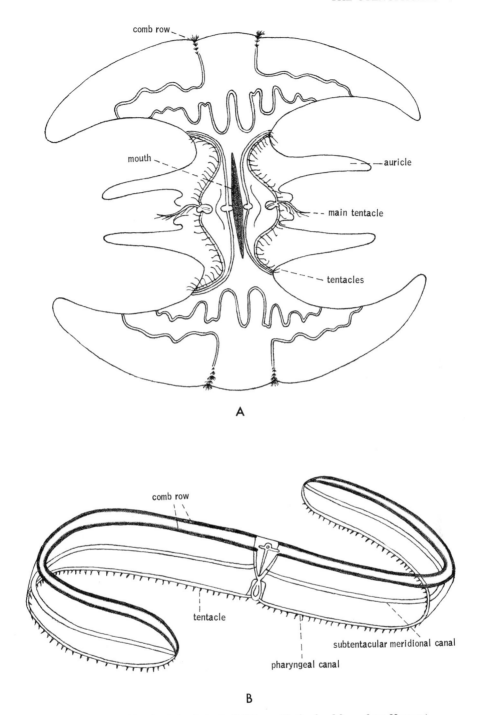

Figure 6-3.   *A. Mnemiopsis* (oral view). *B. Velamen.* (Both after Mayer from Hyman.)

more extensive transformation to attain the adult structure. This general existence of a spherical larva in ctenophores seems to substantiate the belief that the primitive shape was spherical or ovoid.

A tendency in the evolution of ctenophores has been for the body to become expanded or lengthened along the tentacular meridian and flattened or compressed along the opposite meridian. Living ctenophores illustrate various degrees of this modification. Such genera as *Pleurobrachia* and *Mertensia* have retained the primitive or ovoid structure and are not markedly flattened.

Mnemiopsis, a common genus along the north Atlantic coast, is moderately flattened (Fig. 6-3, *A*). Moreover, as further specialization has developed, the middle of the body has be-

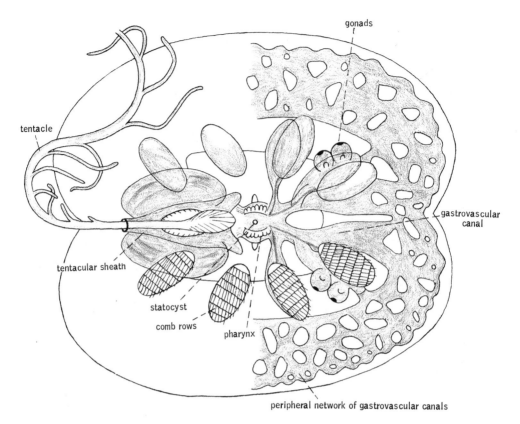

Figure 6-4.   *Ctenoplana.* (After Komai from Hyman.)

come constricted along the tentacular plane, leaving the expanded outer portions in the form of large lobes. The resulting shape is somewhat similar to that of a clam. In the lobate ctenophores, tentacles are short, lack sheaths, and have moved to a position near the mouth. As a result of this change in the position and size of the tentacles, feeding is somewhat modified from that described previously, although plankton are still utilized as food.

Velamen (Fig. 6-3, *B*) and *Cestum,* a genus known as Venus's girdle, have become so expanded and flattened that they look like transparent celluloid belts. One species of *Cestum* reaches a length of over one meter. They swim not only by means of the comb rows but also by muscular undulations.

Before concluding this discussion on the ctenophores, some mention should be made of the peculiar and highly aberrant genera, such as *Ctenoplana* (Fig. 6-4) and *Coeloplana,* that compose the order Platyctenea. All members of this order are greatly flattened dorso-ventrally (i. e., aborally–orally), and most have taken up a creeping or even a sessile mode of existence.

Because of the resemblance of these ctenophores to polyclad flatworms, some zoologists have advocated the theory that the flat-

worm-annelid-arthropod line of invertebrates arose from the ctenophores. The many objections to this theory will be better understood after reading the discussion of the turbellarian flatworms. For the moment, it must suffice to say that, despite the flattening of the body of the Platyctenea and the resulting superficial resemblance to polyclad flatworms, which moreover, is probably not a primitive order, these ctenophores possess in most cases all of the typical structures displayed by other members of the phylum.

The view adopted here, which is in accordance with that of Hyman, is that both the coelenterates and ctenophores are dead-end phyla and have not given rise directly to any higher groups of animals.

1ST TEST COVERS TO HERE

BIBLIOGRAPHY

Hyman, L. H., 1940: The Invertebrates: Protozoa through Ctenophora. Vol. I, McGraw-Hill, New York, pp. 662–696. The most recent and authoritative general account of the Ctenophora; excellent figures and extensive bibliography. The chapter *Retrospect* in the fifth volume (1959) of this series surveys investigations on ctenophores from 1938–1958.

Chapter 7

THE FLATWORMS AND THE ORIGIN OF THE BILATERIA

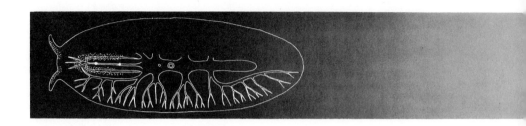

The story of the planuloid organism does not end with the coelenterates and ctenophores, for this hypothetical animal was perhaps the ancestor for the remainder of the Animal Kingdom. These remaining phyla are bilaterally symmetrical and are collectively called the Bilateria. Radial symmetry may exist, as in the echinoderms, but is always of secondary origin. Thus the first problem in the evolution of the bilateral phyla from the planuloid ancestor is that of shifting from a radial to a bilateral symmetry. This change is not as difficult as it might appear. If certain of the ancestral planuloid stock had taken up a life on the ocean bottom and as a result developed a creeping mode of movement over rocks and other objects, this could have led, as is suggested by Hyman (1951), to a differentiation between dorsal and ventral surfaces. Such a differentiation would, of course, result in a bilateral symmetry.

Of all the bilateral phyla, it is generally agreed by most zoologists that the free-living flatworms, of the phylum Platyhelminthes, are the most primitive. These animals beautifully display in many ways the transition from a bilateral planuloid ancestor to the more complex forms of the Bilateria.

Introduction to the Turbellaria

The phylum Platyhelminthes embraces three classes of worms. Two of these are entirely parasitic. The Trematoda comprise flukes and the Cestoda, tapeworms. The third class, the Turbellaria, are free-living; it is with this group that this chapter is primarily concerned.

The Turbellaria, like the other flatworm classes, are usually dorso-ventrally flattened, and the body shape varies from ovoid to elongate. Head projections are not uncommon. These may be in the form of tentacles (Fig. 7-10, A), which vary in number and position, or in the form of lateral projections of the head called auricles (Fig. 7-1, A). The auricles are frequently found in fresh-water planarians. Coloration is largely in shades of black, brown, and gray, although some groups display brightly colored patterns. A few species are green, owing to the presence of symbiotic algae. Turbellarians range in size from microscopic species to species that are more than 60 cm. long, although most are less than 10 mm. in length. Turbellarians are primarily aquatic, and the great majority are marine. Although there are a few pelagic species, most of them are bottom dwellers that live in sand or mud, under stones and shells, or on sea weed. Fresh-water forms, such as the laboratory planarian, *Dugesia* (Fig. 7-1, A), live in lakes, ponds, streams, and springs, where they occupy bottom habitats. Some species have become terrestrial (Fig. 7-1, B), but these are confined to very humid areas and hide beneath logs and leaf mold during the day, emerging only at night to feed. The land planarians are the giants of the Turbellaria, some reaching 60 cm. or more in length. They are largely tropical,

97

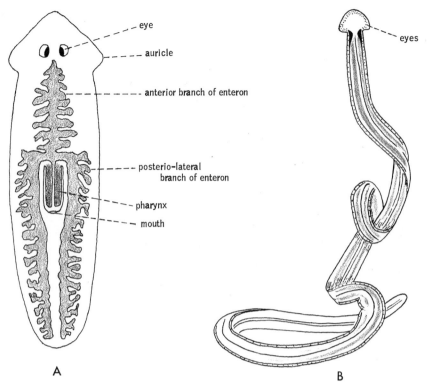

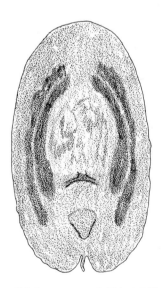

Figure 7-1.   *A.* A fresh-water planarian, a triclad. *B.* The land planarian, *Bipalium kewense.* It is cosmopolitan, found in Florida, Louisiana, California, and in greenhouses throughout the United States. (After Hyman.)

but a few, such as the North American *Bipalium adventitium,* live in temperate regions.

The Acoela

The order Acoela is considered by many zoologists to be the most primitive of the Turbellarian orders.* These little marine worms are particularly interesting because they display many of the characteristics of the planuloid ancestor as well as various stages in the development of structures and organ systems found in higher bilateral animals.

Most acoels are less than 2 mm. in length. The body has an oval or elliptical outline and is covered by a single, ciliated layer of epidermis (Fig. 7-2). In the most primitive condition, the bases of the epidermal cells contain contractile extensions that form an epidermal muscle layer, an arrangement characteristic of the coelenterates. In most acoels, however, a distinct muscle layer has developed that is composed of contractile cells and is no longer associated with the epidermal layer but lies just beneath it. The muscle layer is composed usually of several layers—an outer circular and an inner longitudinal layer with diagonal fibers lying in between. In addition, dorso-ventral muscle strands extend through the interior of the body.

Nervous System. Primitive acoels have a nerve-net type of nervous system similar to that

Figure 7-2.   *Polychoerus,* an acoel. Note tail-like caudal filament. Pale central region is digestive area; it is flanked by longitudinal tracts of developing gametes. Egg masses are median to sperm. The posterior conical body is the penis.

* A considerable number of zoologists hold that the acoels are secondarily reduced and that the Polycladida is the most primitive order of turbellarians.

in coelenterates and lying in the base of the epidermal layer. A particularly well developed network in the anterior end lies over a statocyst; this network may be, as Hyman (1951) has suggested, the forerunner of the brain.

In other acoels, the nervous system, during its evolutionary development, has sunk inward to lie beneath the muscle layers of the body wall; also the network has become organized into strands or cords. Primitively, these nerve cords consist of five pairs—dorsal, dorso-lateral, lateral or marginal, ventro-lateral and ventral (Fig. 7-3, B). They thus have a radiating arrangement and in addition are interconnected by cross strands or commissures. The marginal

pair of nerve cords has disappeared in some forms to reduce the total number to eight. Although the main portion of the nervous system has moved inward, a delicate subepidermal network has remained in many species. In most acoels, the brain has become a much more distinct mass of nervous tissue but still surrounds the statocyst (Fig. 7-3, A).

The cellular composition of the nervous system presents nothing unusual. The connections are synaptic, and the cells, while not having any morphological differentiation of the processes, are of the three typical types—unipolar, bipolar and multipolar.

Sense Organs.   In acoels the most prim-

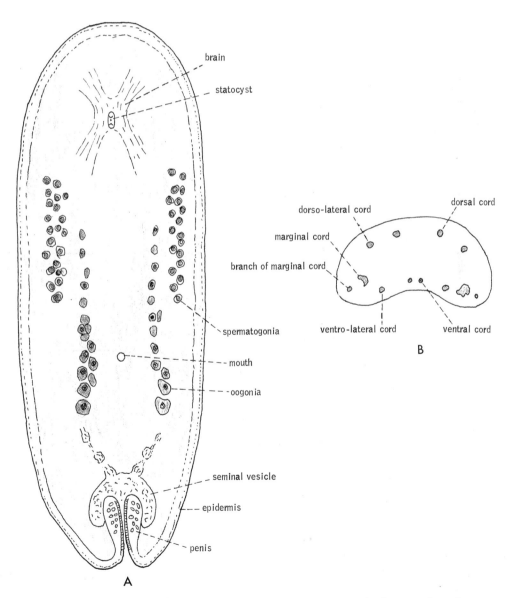

Figure 7-3.   A. Frontal section through acoel, *Afronta*, which possesses simplest type of reproductive system among Turbellaria. (After Hyman.) B. Transverse section of acoel, *Convoluta*, showing nerve cords. (After Graff from Hyman.)

itive sense organs are tactile cells and statocysts. Tactile cells are sensory cells in which bristle-like processes penetrate the epidermal cells. The statocyst lies within the brain. It consists of a vesicle in which one or two concretions are each covered by a special cell called a lithocyte (Fig. 7-15, *C*).

Two or four eyes are characteristic in some acoels. Most acoel eyes resemble a cup of pigment cells with the open part directed outward (Fig. 7-4, *B*). Into this cup, photo-receptor, or retinal, cells project. Such an eye is known as an inverse pigment-cup ocellus. This type of eye is probably not the most primitive photoreceptor organ in the acoels. The original organ was probably a pigment-spot ocellus—a flat disc of surface pigment cells with retinal cells between them (Fig. 7-4, *A*). Only the genus *Otocelis* displays this type of eye. Theoretically, the pigment-cup eye arose from the sinkage of a pigment disc.

Digestive System. The name Acoela was chosen because members of this order lack any sort of digestive cavity. A simple mouth is located on the midventral side of the body (Fig. 7-3, *A*), and in many acoels a simple pharynx that leads from the mouth to the interior has developed. This simple pharynx is a ciliated tube

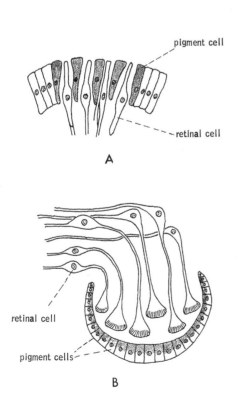

A

B

Figure 7-4. *A*. Pigment-spot ocellus. (After Hyman.) *B*. Inverse pigment-cup ocellus. (After Hesse from Hyman.)

derived from an invagination of the epidermis. Even when a pharynx is present, however, it leads into an internal syncytial mass of nutritive cells (Fig. 7-2). Acoels are carnivorous and feed on small animals such as protozoans, copepods and other crustaceans. In studies on *Convoluta paradoxa*, Jennings (1957) found that small prey is captured and is engulfed by the internal mass of digestive cells partially everted through the mouth. Larger prey is pressed into the mouth and swallowed. After ingestion, the prey passes into the internal mass of nutritive cells. These cells are phagocytic, and digestion takes place intracellularly for the most part. In those species that ingest large organisms, the initial stages of digestion must be extracellular. In some cases a temporary digestive cavity may form around the food.

Gland Cells. Located near the brain of acoels is a cluster of gland cells collectively called the frontal gland (Fig. 7-5). The gland cells have long necks that open at the anterior tip of the worm. The frontal gland is believed to aid in some way the capture of prey. Another group of gland cells called caudal glands is often present at the posterior tip and is perhaps used by the animal in adhering to the substrate.

Mesenchyme. Between the body wall and the internal nutritive cells of the acoel, the body is filled with a syncytial network of cells known as mesenchyme. The spaces within the network are filled with fluid and contain wandering ameboid cells. These fluid-filled spaces act as a primitive circulatory system for the transportation of food, gases, and waste. Respiration is carried on entirely by integumental diffusion, as in all Turbellaria. The acoels lack excretory organs.

Reproductive System. Acoels are hermaphroditic but lack gonads. The germ cells are derived from the wandering ameboid cells and come to lie in two bands in the mesenchyme on each side of the body (Fig. 7-2 and 7-3, *A*). In the most primitive condition, even female ducts are completely absent. The eggs merely rupture through the body wall or pass out through the mouth. A system of male ducts is present, consisting in its simplest state of a pair of sperm ducts that join to form a short tube that opens to the outside through a posterior gonopore (Fig. 7-3, *A*). The terminal portion of this common duct is called the penis and in many acoels is muscular and more specialized. When there is a complete absence of female parts for the reception of the penis, copulation is probably by hypodermic impregnation. In this situation, the penis of the male is armed with stylets that puncture the body wall

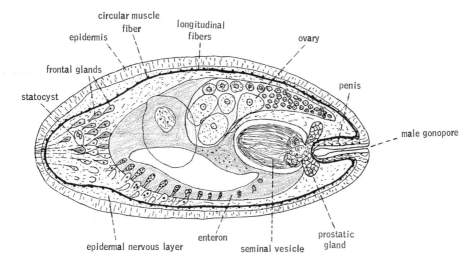

Figure 7-5.   Sagittal section of the acoel, *Nemertoderma*. This acoel is unusual in having a digestive cavity. (After Westblad from Hyman.)

of the female to deposit sperm directly into the mesenchyme.

The reproductive system of all acoels is by no means as simple as this description indicates. However, the increasing complexity of the system can best be understood in a treatment of the class as a whole, and therefore it is discussed later.

Evolution of the Acoels.   At this point it would be well to pause briefly and return again to the origin of the flatworms. If the various primitive features displayed by different acoels are combined, it is possible to reconstruct a picture of a hypothetical ancestral flatworm (Fig. 7-6). This ancestral worm was a marine animal not more than several millimeters long; it crept over the ocean floor and as a result was dorso-ventrally flattened. The body was covered by a single layer of ciliated epidermal cells, which provided for movement. The bases of these cells contained contractile extensions that formed a muscle layer.

A network of nerve cells was located just beneath the epidermis of the ancestral flatworm with the bristles of sensory cells projecting through it. Anteriorly beneath the epidermis was located a statocyst covered by a delicate nerve network. One or two light-sensitive pigment-spot ocelli may also have been present at the anterior end. A mouth, derived from the blastopore and located on the midventral side, opened into a mass of mesenchyme and nutritive cells that filled the interior of the body. This internal mass of cells formed a syncytial network with fluid-filled intercellular spaces containing wandering ameboid cells. Nutrition was probably essentially the same as in modern acoels. The wandering amebocytes were probably totipotent, but they gave rise, in any case, to the gametogonia. Although at least a rudimentary male reproductive system is present in all modern acoels, both female and male reproductive systems were probably lacking in the ancestral form. The ripe gametes either ruptured through the body wall or passed out through the mouth.

Certainly the gap between such an ancestral acoel turbellarian and the planuloid organism is not a very great one, nor does it present great difficulties in bridging. The only fundamental changes necessary are dorso-ventral flattening coupled with the acquisition of a ventral mouth; both of these modifications could have resulted from a bottom-dwelling and creeping mode of life.

In the subsequent evolution of the acoels, a number of fundamental changes appear that foreshadow the structure exhibited by most higher bilateral animals: (1) the separation of the contractile function from the epidermis to form a distinct muscle layer lying beneath the epidermis; (2) the reorganization of an epidermal nerve net into a series of subepidermal longitudinal nerve cords radially arranged; (3) the concentration of nervous tissue around the statocyst to form a brain; (4) the development of a pigment-cup eye from flattened pigment spots; (5) the rudimentary formation of a digestive system with inturning of the epidermis around the mouth to form a short pharynx;

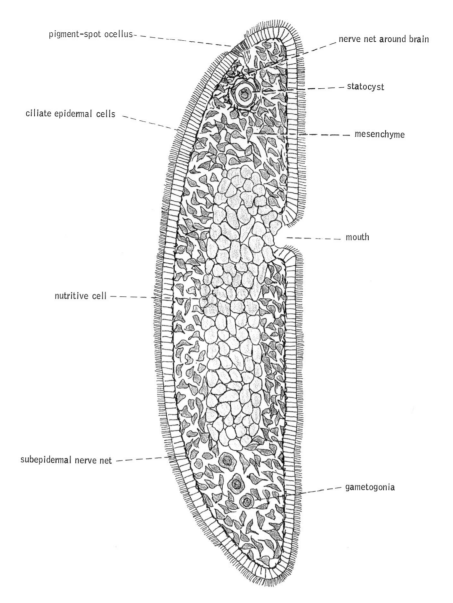

pigment-spot ocellus-

nerve net around brain

statocyst

ciliate epidermal cells

mesenchyme

mouth

nutritive cell

subepidermal nerve net

gametogonia

Figure 7-6.   Hypothetical acoeloid ancestor (sagittal section).

and (6) the rudimentary formation of a reproductive system with structures for conducting, transmitting, and receiving sperm.

The Higher Turbellaria

The remainder of the Turbellaria are grouped into four orders:* Rhabdocoela, Alloeocoela, Tricladida and Polycladida. The last of the four orders named is strictly marine; the others all have some fresh-water representatives. The terrestrial planarians belong to the order Tricladida.

The general body structure of the acoels has been retained in all other Turbellaria. An outer epidermis, a muscle layer (although this is usually more strongly developed than in the acoels), and mesenchyme tissue between the nutritive cells and the muscle layer are all evident. The body of turbellarians is therefore of a solid, or acoelomate, construction. The major changes in these orders are the continued development of systems initiated in the acoels

* Authorities on the Turbellaria have divided the rhabdocoels into three orders and the alloeocoels into four orders, so that the class now consists of eleven orders including the acoela. In order to simplify this general discussion of the class and to avoid taxing the student's patience beyond endurance, the older groupings have been used. The more modern classification is given in the discussion on systematics at the close of this chapter.

and the appearance of water-balancing or excretory organs.

Glands and Rhabdoids. A characteristic feature of turbellarians is the presence of numerous gland cells (Figs. 7-7 and 7-8, *A*). These gland cells may be located entirely within the epidermis but are more commonly situated in the mesenchyme with only the neck of the gland penetrating the epidermis. The glands provide a mucus coating around the animal as well as laying down a slime trail for movement.

In turbellarians, gland cells are frequently grouped together to perform some special function. The caudal and frontal glands (Fig. 7-5) found in the acoels, the alloeocoels, and in a few rhabdocoels operate in this manner. Adhesive glands are another type of aggregation. These glands form a ventral marginal ring of special mesenchymal gland cells around the body. The sticky secretion produced by the adhesive glands plus the fact that the necks of the gland cells can be projected as little papillae enable the animal to adhere very tightly to objects. In *Bdelloura*, which lives as a commensal on the

book gills of the Atlantic horseshoe crab, the caudal part of this adhesive zone is greatly increased to form an adhesive plate.

Still other adhesive organs involve muscle tissue. These adhesive organs, which Hyman (1951) groups as glandulo-muscular organs, are pits or swellings variously located on the ventral surface or the head. They are provided with gland cells as well as with muscle fibers for retraction of the organ. This type of adhesive organ is best developed in the triclads (Fig. 7-8, *B*), where the secretions aid in gripping the surface during locomotion and during the capture of prey.

Although absent in acoels and primitive members of the other orders, a final characteristic of the turbellarian epidermis is the presence of numerous rod-shaped bodies known as rhabdoids (Figs. 7-7 and 7-8, *A*). Arranged at right angles to the surface, the rhabdoids are secreted by epidermal or mesenchymal gland cells. The function remains uncertain, although one still unconfirmed theory suggests that rhabdoids are discharged and then disinte-

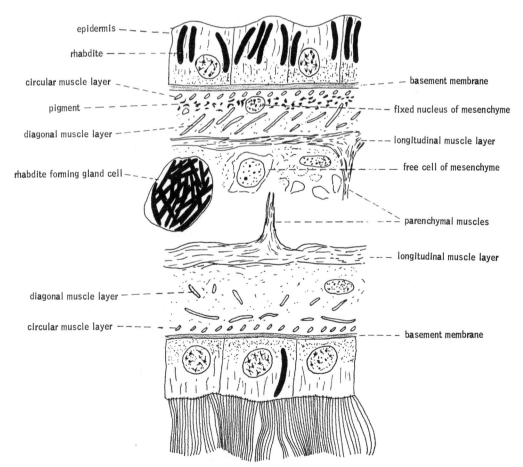

Figure 7-7.   Dorsal and ventral body walls of fresh-water planarian (longitudinal section). (After Hyman.)

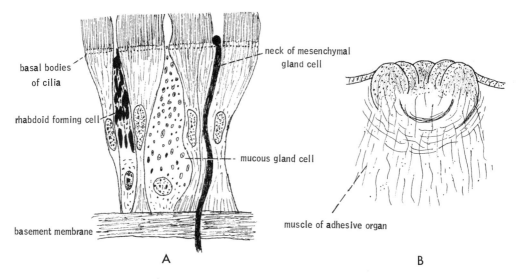

basal bodies
of cilia

rhabdoid forming cell

basement membrane

A

neck of mesenchymal
gland cell

mucous gland cell

muscle of adhesive organ

B

Figure 7-8.   *A.* Section through epidermis of polyclad. (After Bock from Hyman.) *B.* Glandulo-muscular adhesive organ of fresh-water planarian, *Procotyla.* (After Hyman.)

grate to help form a slimy covering around the animal.

Nutrition and the Digestive System.   In the turbellarian orders more advanced than the acoels, the phagocytic nutritive cells have become organized so as to enclose a permanent digestive cavity. This cavity, called the intestine or enteron, is a blind sac with the mouth serving both for ingestion and for egestion. The wall of the enteron is one-layered and composed of large columnar phagocytic cells along with smaller gland cells (Fig. 7-10, *B*).

The form of the enteron is a useful characteristic in recognizing the orders. In the rhabdocoels and alloeocoels the enteron is a simple sac (Figs. 7-9; 7-11, *A*; and 7-14), although in some alloeocoels lateral diverticula are present. Both the triclads and polyclads have a highly branched system, and from its shape the names of the orders are derived. The triclad enteron consists of three principal branches—one anterior and two posteriolateral (Figs. 7-1, *A*; 7-11, *C*; and 7-19). Each of these principal branches in turn has many lateral diverticula. The three branches join in the middle of the body, anterior to the mouth and pharynx. In polyclads the enteron consists of a central tube, from which a great many lateral branches arise (Figs. 7-10, *A* and 7-12, *A*). These in turn are subdivided and may anastomose with other branches.

In the more advanced turbellarian orders, the mouth is primitively located on the midventral surface, as in the acoels, but may be situated anywhere along the midventral line. The connection between the mouth and the enteron shows increasing complexity compared

with the simple pharynx found in many acoels, although the simple form (Fig. 7-10, *C*) has been retained in some alloeocoels and rhabdocoels. A more complex pharynx is the bulbous type (Figs. 7-9; 7-11, *A* and *B*; and 7-14). In this type, the inner half of the simple pharyngeal tube has become highly muscular and forms a bulb that is delimited by a membrane from the underlying mesenchyme. The tip of the bulb projects into the outer half of the pharyngeal tube which has remained nonmuscular and is now called the pharyngeal cavity. The pharyngeal cavity often can be everted to allow the bulbous pharynx to protrude out of the mouth (Fig. 7-11, *B*). Special muscle fibers attaching the pharynx to the body wall provide for protrusion and retraction. The bulbous pharynx is found in both alloeocoels and rhabdocoels.

The final stage in the development of the turbellarian pharynx occurs in the triclads and polyclads and is known as a plicate, or folded, pharynx. In the plicate pharynx the muscular portion has become elongated and projects as a free tube into the pharyngeal cavity. Mesenchyme extends into the tube from the base, and no delimiting membrane is present as in the bulbous pharynx. The location of the attached end of the pharynx varies. The pharynx may project backward (Figs. 7-1, *A*; 7-11, *C*; and 7-19), as in the common fresh-water planarians; or the pharynx may be attached posteriorly and extend forward (Fig. 7-10, *A*). In many polyclads, it hangs down from the roof of the pharyngeal cavity (Fig. 7-12, *A*). The pharynx is frequently connected to the enteron by a short esophagus.

Like the acoels, the other turbellarians

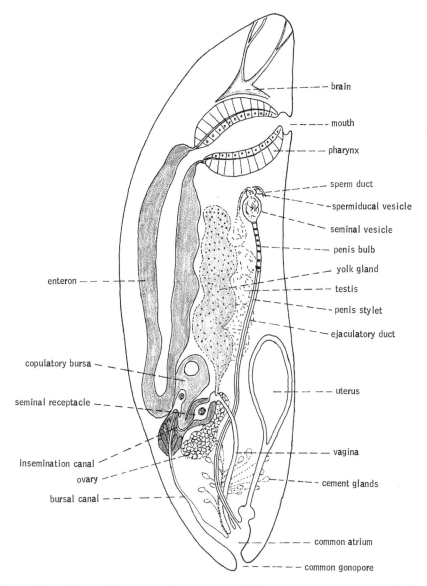

brain

mouth

pharynx

sperm duct

spermiducal vesicle

seminal vesicle

penis bulb

yolk gland

enteron

testis

penis stylet

ejaculatory duct

copulatory bursa

uterus

seminal receptacle

insemination canal

vagina

ovary

cement glands

bursal canal

common atrium

common gonopore

Figure 7-9.   The rhabdocoel, *Anoplodiera voluta,* which lives in gut of sea cucumbers (sagittal section). (After Westblad from Hyman.)

are entirely carnivorous and prey on the various invertebrates that are small enough to be captured, as well as on the dead bodies of animals that sink to the bottom. Some turbellarians have rather restricted diets; *Stylochus frontalis,* for instance, feeds on living oysters, eating bits at a time.

Many turbellarians capture living prey by wrapping themselves around it, entangling it in slime, and pinning it to the substratum by means of the adhesive organs. They then ingest the prey by swallowing it whole or by a sucking or pumping action. Prey is swallowed whole by those turbellarians with a simple pharynx, those with a protrusable bulbous pharynx, and even by the polyclads that have a plicate pharynx.

In the triclads, the pharyngeal tube is extended from the mouth and inserted either into the body of the prey or into carrion. The penetration of the pharynx is aided by proteolytic enzymes produced by glands in the pharynx (Jennings, 1962). The contents are then pumped into the enteron by peristaltic action (Figs. 7-11, *D* and 7-13). Ingestion by a sucking or pumping action is also employed by forms that have a nonprotrusible bulbous pharynx. According to recent work done by Jennings on triclads (1962), digestion is initially extracellular. The gland cells of the enteron secrete proteolytic enzymes that disintegrate the ingested food. The resulting food fragments are then engulfed by the phagocytic cells, in which

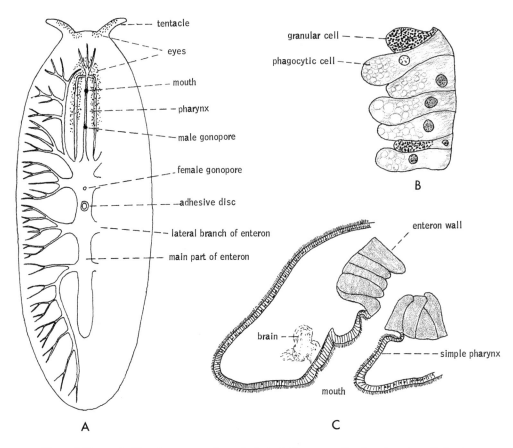

Figure 7-10.   *A.* Digestive system of a polyclad. *B.* Enteron cells of a planarian. *C.* Section through anterior end of *Macrostomum,* a rhabdocoel with simple pharynx. (All after Hyman.)

digestion is completed intracellularly. At least in the triclads, proteins, fats, and starches can be digested. Fat is the principal storage product; in some triclads, both fat and proteins are important storage products.

Fresh-water planarians are able to withstand prolonged experimental starvation. In extreme cases, they utilize part of the enteron and all of the tissue of the mesenchyme and reproductive system. In fact, the body volume may be reduced to as little as 1/300 of the original.

Nervous System.   The re-organization of a simple epidermal nerve net into a system of five pairs of radially arranged longitudinal nerve cords has already been described in the acoels. This plan has been retained in most other turbellarians but with a tendency toward reduction in the number of pairs of cords and toward increased prominence of the ventral pair. This latter feature is of particular evolutionary significance, because it represents the beginning of the ventral nerve cord (embryologically paired) so characteristic of the annelid-arthropod line. The reduction to a single pair of ventral cords has been more or less attained in

fresh-water triclads and most rhabdocoels (Fig. 7-14). Marine triclads and alloeocoels (Fig. 7-15, *B*) are intermediate, possessing three or four pairs of cords—the dorsal, ventral, lateral, and ventro-lateral.

The polyclads are an exception to this sequence of nervous system development. Although the polyclad nervous system lies beneath the muscle layers and is more strongly developed on the ventral side than on the dorsal, it has retained the nerve net plan of the primitive acoels (Fig. 7-15, *A*). This is one of the reasons for the belief that the polyclads arose directly from the acoels rather than through one of the other orders.

The advanced turbellarian brain is either a bilobed mass connected to the cords (Figs. 7-14 and 7-15, *A*) or, as in many triclads, is represented by the swollen anterior ends of the ventral cords. The statocyst of the acoels has disappeared in all but the most primitive members of the other turbellarians orders.

Sensory Cells and Organs.   Eyes in most turbellarians are common and are of the pigment-cup type. Two is the usual number (Figs. 7-1 and 7-14), but two or three pairs are not un-

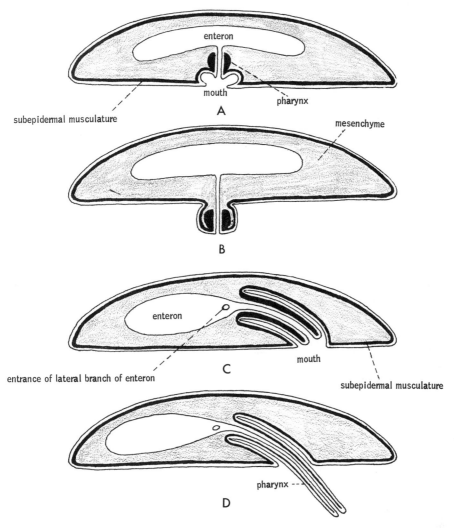

Figure 7-11. *A* and *B*. The rhabdocoel, *Mesostoma,* showing retracted and everted bulbous pharynx (longitudinal section). *C* and *D*. The fresh-water triclad, *Polycelis,* showing retracted and protruded tubular plicate pharynx (longitudinal section). (All after Jennings.)

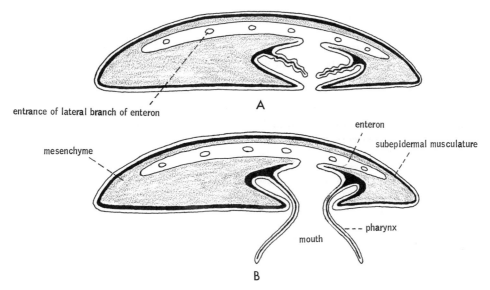

Figure 7-12. The polyclad, *Leptoplana,* showing retracted and protruded ruffled, plicate pharynx (longitudinal section). (After Jennings.)

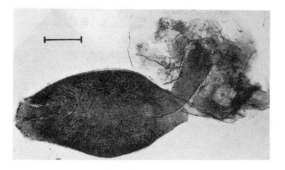

Figure 7-13.   Triclad, *Polycelis,* feeding on large *Daphnia.* (Courtesy of Jennings.)

common; and in the polyclads and the land planarians, there may be a great many eyes (Figs. 7-1, *B* and 7-10, *A*). In *Geoplana mexicana,* a land planarian, eyes are distributed not only along the anterior margin, but also down the sides of the body. The eyes function only in detecting light, and most turbellarians are negatively phototropic.

Tactile and chemoreceptor cells serve as general sense organs. Both are sensory cells with terminal bristles that pierce the epidermis. The tactile sensory cells generally are distributed over the entire body but are particularly concentrated on the tentacles, the auricles, and the body margins.

The chemoreceptors may also have a general distribution but more frequently are confined to special ciliated patches in the head region. These ciliated patches are either sunken pits or grooves in which chemoreceptor cells are concentrated (Fig. 7-15, *D*). The sense organs play an important role in locating food. The cilia maintain a continual current of water over the sensory bristles.

Special rheoreceptor cells—sensory cells that orient the animal to water currents—are found in *Mesostoma* and *Bothromesostoma* (Fig. 7-15, *D*); Hyman believes that they are probably possessed by most turbellarians.

Excretory System. In the orders more advanced than the acoels, a new group of organs appears for the first time. These are the nephridial tubules, excretory organs encountered in a variety of forms and in many phyla. Unlike the excretory tubules of vertebrates, which are concentrated within a single pair of organs, those of invertebrates are usually distributed throughout the body.

Invertebrate nephridia are of several types. They may be blind tubules called protonephridia, leading in from an external opening called the nephridiopore; or they may be open at both ends, in which case they are known as metanephridia. The former is the more primitive and is the type possessed by the flatworms.

The protonephridium of Turbellaria consists of a branched tubule terminating in a number of blind capillaries, which bear at the inner end a tuft of cilia known as a flame bulb. Usually a flame bulb and its capillary consist of a single cell (Fig. 7-16, *B*), which is then called a flame cell; but the term is not always applicable, since in some forms a single cell gives rise to a large number of capillaries and flame bulbs (Fig. 7-16, *A*). The conducting tubule is composed of cuboidal cells or is syncytial and is generally unciliated, although in some rhabdocoels there are tufts of cilia along the walls.

The number of protonephridia and the position of the nephridiopores are variable. The protonephridium may be single with a median dorsal nephridiopore (Fig. 7-14), or there may be one or more pairs. As many as four pairs

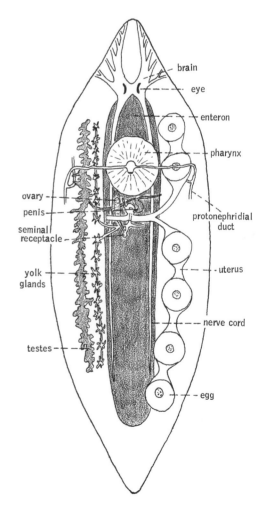

Figure 7-14.   The rhabdocoel, *Mesostoma ehrenbergii* (ventral view).

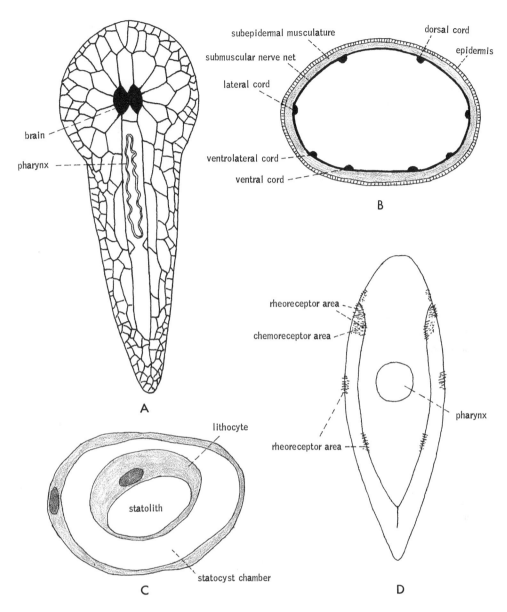

Figure 7-15.   *A.* Ventral, submuscular nerve net of polyclad, *Gnesioceros. B.* An alloeocoel, showing nervous system (transverse section). (*A* and *B* after Hyman.) *C.* Statocyst of the alloeocoel, *Hofstenia.* (After Bock from Hyman.) *D.* Rheoreceptor and chemoreceptor areas of the rhabdocoel, *Bothromesostoma.* (After Müller from Hyman.)

occur in the triclads and often form an anastomosing network with many nephridiopores (Fig. 7-16, *C*).

A considerable diversity of opinion exists concerning the extent to which the protonephridia of turbellarians actually function in excretion, and the results of different workers is conflicting. Because the passing of waste through the tubule has never been observed, Hyman (1951) believes that the protonephridia act as water-balancing organs. Protonephridia are best developed in fresh-water species, whereas the protonephridial system is reduced or absent in marine turbellarians, which have no problem in ridding the body of excess water. It is probable that the capillary walls are responsible for the passage of excess water into the lumen.

Reproductive System. Almost without exception, the Turbellaria are hermaphroditic. Primitively, gonads are absent, and this condition still exists in all of the acoels. In all other turbellarian orders, however, gonads are present, although the gametogonia apparently

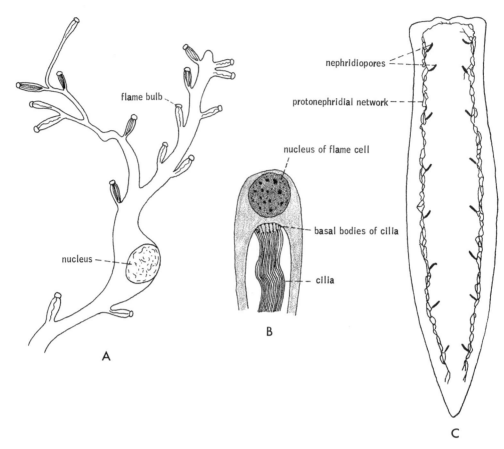

Figure 7-16.   *A*. Part of *Mesostoma* protonephridium. (After Reisinger from Hyman.) *B*. Flame cell of a fresh-water triclad. (After Willey and Kirschner from Hyman.) *C*. Excretory system of triclad, *Dendrocoelum lacteum*. (After Wilhelmi from Hyman.)

still originate in the mesenchyme and migrate into the gonads.

The male and female systems are so complicated and variable that it is extremely difficult to give a generalized picture. Only an outline of the basic structure is possible here.

The male system may consist of one testis or any number of pairs. When the testes are paired, each testis connects by a small ductule to a single pair of sperm ducts (Figs. 7-9 and 7-17, *C*). The sperm ducts carry the sperm toward the copulatory apparatus and often unite before joining it. Prior to entering the apparatus, the sperm may be stored in the dilated base of each sperm duct or the common duct, which is called a spermiducal vesicle (Fig. 7-9).

The lumen of the copulatory apparatus into which the sperm ducts enter is known as the ejaculatory duct and opens at the tip of a penis (Fig. 7-17, *C*). The penis is generally muscular and projects into a male antrum, which opens to the outside through the gonopore. The penis is often armed with a stylet (Fig. 7-9) or occasionally with spines. When the spermiducal

vesicles are absent, part of the ejaculatory duct may be modified to form a seminal vesicle for sperm storage (Fig. 7-5). A few species have both (Fig. 7-9). A final structure often present in the copulatory apparatus is the prostatic apparatus, which consists of a group of gland cells emptying directly, or by way of a prostatic vesicle, into the ejaculatory duct (Fig. 7-5).

All of the basic structures composing the male system are subject to a wide degree of elaboration and modification. A considerable number of species, particularly among the polyclads, display the peculiar characteristic of having multiple male parts, such as prostatic glands, seminal vesicles and penises.

In the most primitive acoels the female system is completely lacking, and the eggs merely rupture to the outside. Other acoels exhibit various stages leading to the well developed female system found in most members of the other orders. In their evolution, the female ducts have developed from the outside inward— that is, in the most primitive condition a gonopore opens into a short, blind vagina for the reception of the male penis. In those acoels that

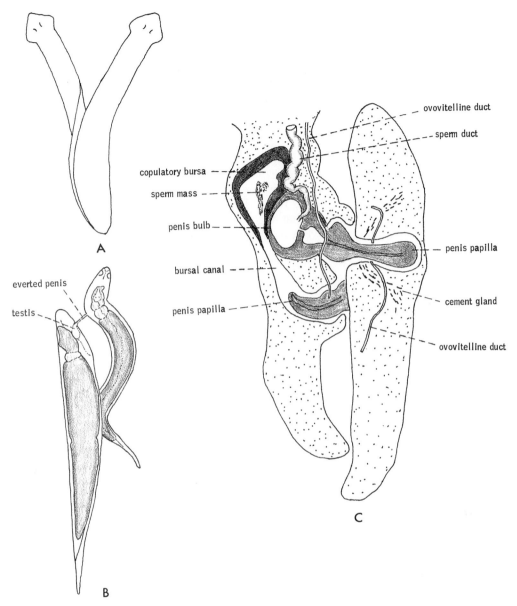

Figure 7-17.   *A.* Copulating planarians. *B.* Hypodermic impregnation in the rhabdocoel, *Stenostomum.* (*A* and *B* after Hyman.) *C.* Section through a pair of copulating *Dugesia.* (After Burr from Hyman.)

possess only a vagina, the sperm apparently migrate to the egg through the mesenchyme. The final step—the development of oviducts connecting the copulatory structure with the ovaries—is missing in acoels but is attained in all the higher orders.

In the female system, as in the case of the male system, there may be a single ovary or one to numerous pairs but with only one pair of oviducts (Fig. 7-17, *C*). With the exception of the polyclads, most turbellarians possess yolk glands along the course of the oviduct (Figs. 7-9 and 7-14). The yolk glands may open into the oviduct directly or by way of special ducts. Thus,

as the egg leaves the ovary and passes down the oviduct, yolk cells are added to it, and the whole mass is eventually enclosed by a single shell. This peculiar condition is found in no other group of animals. Elsewhere in the Animal Kingdom, yolk material is an integral part of the egg cytoplasm. Students interested in the evolutionary origin of the yolk glands should refer to Hyman (1951).

Before opening to the external gonopore, the oviducts enter the female copulatory apparatus. The copulatory apparatus consists of an antrum for the reception of the male penis and regions that receive and store sperm. One such storage center is in the form of a sac, called a copulatory bursa (Figs. 7-9 and 7-17, *C*), which leads off of the antrum. This sac receives the sperm after copulation and stores them for a short time. The sperm then leave the bursa and migrate up the oviduct toward the ovary prior to fertilization. Frequently, the oviducts dilate to provide still another storage center, a seminal receptacle (Figs. 7-9 and 7-14). The sperm are permanently stored in the seminal receptacle until fertilization. The seminal receptacle may receive sperm from the copulatory bursa or, if a bursa is absent, directly after copulation.

In some species, such as in *Bdelloura,* the bursa is not connected to the antrum but has a separate opening and vagina for receiving the male penis. Special canals for transferring the sperm connect the bursa with the oviducts. Such a condition—where two female openings are present, one for the reception of the male penis and sperm, and one for the passage of eggs to the exterior—is not restricted to the flatworms but is encountered among other invertebrates.

A final modification sometimes present in the female system is a temporary storage center, or uterus, for ripe eggs. The uterus may be a blind sac (Fig. 7-14), as in some rhabdocoels; or it may be merely a dilated part of the oviduct, as in the polyclads. However, most Turbellaria lack uteri, because only a few eggs are laid at a time.

The gonopore and antrum of the female system may be separate from the male system (Fig. 7-10, *A*), or a common antrum and a common gonopore may be present (Fig. 7-9). Some alloeocoels display an odd condition in which the male system with its penis opens into the pharyngeal or buccal region.

Reproduction and Regeneration. The usual type of copulation among the turbellarians is mutual; that is, the two worms come together, and the penis of each is inserted into the female gonopore or common gonopore of the other (Fig. 7-17, *C*). During copulation the worms normally face away from each other with the ventral surfaces around the genital region appressed together and elevated (Fig. 7-17, *A*). Hypodermic impregnation (Fig. 7-17, *B*) occurs in some rhabdocoels and polyclads as well as in the acoels.

Self-fertilization apparently takes place only in rare instances. Hyman believes that although almost all Turbellaria are hermaphroditic, self-fertilization is probably precluded, because movement of the sperm mass out of the male system and production of seminal fluid are dependent on ejaculation, which occurs only during copulation.

The acoels and polyclads, both of which are marine and lack yolk glands, lay their eggs in gelatinous masses (Fig. 7-18, *A*), the adhesive jelly being produced by glands in the antrum. In the polyclads, a string of eggs is discharged; and on reaching the exterior, the surface of each egg or of several eggs throws off a shell or capsule, which becomes hardened (Fig. 7-18, *B*). The eggs require up to one week to hatch, and an individual may lay a number of egg masses.

Most rhabdocoels and alloeocoels and all triclads possess yolk glands, and, as a result, egg production is somewhat modified. As the fertilized eggs pass through the oviduct, they are accompanied by yolk cells produced by the yolk glands. On reaching the antrum, one to a number of eggs, along with many yolk cells, are enclosed by a hard capsule produced by the yolk cells themselves. The glands of the antrum produce a cementing secretion that helps the capsules adhere to the substratum. In many forms, including some fresh-water triclads such as the common *Dugesia,* the attachment of the capsules is by means of a stalk (Fig. 7-18, *C*), so that the brownish capsules resemble little balloons stuck to rocks and other debris. One worm can produce a number of capsules.

Fresh-water turbellarians often produce two types of eggs—summer eggs, which are enclosed in a thin capsule and hatch in a relatively short period, and winter eggs, which have a thicker and more resistant capsule. Winter eggs remain dormant during the winter, resisting freezing and drying, and hatch in the spring with the rise in water temperature. In some rhabdocoels, such as *Mesostoma,* the summer eggs develop within the body of the parent (Fig. 7-14). These rhabdocoels are thus ovoviviparous in part—that is, the young are born alive, but nutrition during development comes from yolk material.

Discussion of turbellarian embryology is deferred until the chapter on spiral cleavage.

Many turbellarians are not restricted to sexual reproduction. Some rhabdocoels and the fresh-water and land planarians commonly reproduce asexually by means of fission. In the rhabdocoel genera *Catenula, Stenostomum,* and *Microstomum,* fission is transverse; but the individuals remain attached, so that chains are formed (Fig. 7-18, *D*). The individuals comprising such chains are known as zooids. When a zooid attains a fairly complete degree of development, it detaches from the chain as an independent individual.

Some fresh-water planarians, such as *Dugesia,* also reproduce by transverse fission, but no chains of zooids are formed and regeneration occurs after separation. The fission plane usually forms behind the pharynx, and separation

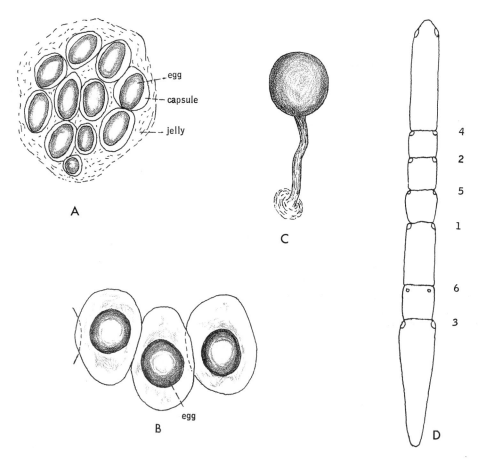

Figure 7-18. *A.* Egg mass of the acoel, *Amphiscolops.* (After Hyman.) *B.* Section of egg ribbon of the polyclad, *Stylochus.* (After Kato from Hyman.) *C.* Stalked cocoon of a fresh-water planarian. (Modified from Pennak.) *D.* Chain of zooids in *Stenostomum.* Numbers indicate order of fission planes. (After Child from Hyman.)

appears to be dependent on locomotion. The posterior of the worm adheres to the substratum, while the anterior half continues to move forward until the worm snaps in two. Each half then regenerates the missing parts to form two new small worms.

A few species of fresh-water planarians, such as members of the genus *Phagocata,* and some land planarians fragment rather than undergo transverse fission. In *Phagocata* each piece forms a cyst in which regeneration takes place and from which a small worm emerges.

It is not surprising that those flatworms that reproduce asexually also have considerable powers of regeneration. This is in sharp contrast to the many forms that lack asexual reproduction and have considerably limited powers of regeneration. The regenerative ability of turbellarians has been investigated by numerous workers; Hyman (1951) gives an excellent résumé of the more important studies. Only a few aspects can be mentioned here. A distinct physiological gradient exists in flatworms, so

that the body is polarized, the anterior representing one pole and the posterior, the other. Regeneration is correlated with this polarity. For example, an excised piece retains its polarity with the cut surface toward the anterior producing a new head and the posterior surface, a new tail. Furthermore, the rapidity of the process and the size of pieces necessary for regeneration are related to the original gradient. The process is fastest anteriorly; for normal regeneration larger pieces cut more posteriorly are required. Mesenchyme cells are apparently the chief source for the regeneration of new tissue.

The Parasitic Flatworms

Two classes of flatworms are entirely parasitic. These are the Trematoda, comprising the flukes and the Cestoda, which include the tapeworms. Because of a parasitic existence, both groups have lost the ciliated epidermis of the free-living Turbellaria and have acquired a cuticle and various types of holdfast organs, such as suckers and hooklets. The trematodes have retained the general body form of the Turbellaria as well as a digestive cavity. The tapeworms, however, have become much more modified, having the body divided into a head, or scolex, followed by a chain of segments, or proglottids. A mouth and digestive cavity are completely lacking in the tapeworms.

It is Hyman's belief that the rhabdocoels are the ancestors of both the trematodes and the cestodes and that these two parasitic classes arose independently. The rhabdocoel origin is based, in part at least, on the commensal relationship exhibited by a number of species within the order. It is assumed that commensalism would precede a parasitic existence.

Systematic Résumé of the Phylum Platyhelminthes

Free-living or parasitic animals that are bilaterally symmetrical and are more or less dorsoventrally flattened. A digestive cavity is present or absent; but when present, the mouth is the only opening to the exterior. Interior of body between body wall and digestive cavity filled with mesenchyme. Nervous system in most cases more or less cephalized with a varying number of longitudinal nerve cords. Protonephridia present in most members; reproductive system hermaphroditic.

Class Turbellaria. Mostly free-living flatworms. Epidermis soft, ciliated at least on the ventral surface, and characterized by the presence of rhabdoids.

Order Acoela. Small marine flatworms, usually measuring less than 2 mm. in length. Mouth and sometimes a simple pharynx present, but no digestive cavity. Protonephridia absent. No distinct gonads, the gametes originating directly from the mesenchyme. Oviducts and yolk glands absent. The acoels are most abundant in the littoral zone under shells, in algae, and in bottom silt. A few species are commensal within the intestine of various echinoderms. Acoel genera include *Afronta, Polychoerus,* and *Convoluta.*

Rhabdocoels. Marine and fresh-water flatworms, usually less than 3 mm. in length. Enteron in the form of a simple elongated sac without lateral diverticula and with a simple or bulbous pharynx. Usually with only two ventral nerve cords. Eyes usually present. Either one or two gonads. Yolk glands present or absent.

Rhabdocoels are common in sand and mud of fresh-water and marine littoral zones. *Stenostomum, Macrostomum, Microstomum* and *Mesostoma*

are common genera. A number of rhabdocoels are commensal with crustaceans, mollusks, echinoderms and sipunculids.

The rhabdocoels were formerly considered a single order, but modern authorities have now raised the suborders to ordinal rank. The group at present consists of the orders Catenulida, Macrostomida, and Neorhabdocoela.

Alloeocoels. Flatworms of moderate size, averaging between 1 and 10 mm. Structure variable and intermediate between the acoels and the triclads. Enteron may be a simple sac or branched; with either a simple, bulbous, or plicate pharynx. Nervous system with three to four pairs of longitudinal nerve cords. The majority of alloeocoels are marine and are common in littoral sand and mud. There are some fresh-water representatives, of which *Prorhynchus, Plagiostomum,* and *Otomesostoma* are common. A few species are terrestrial.

Like the rhabdocoels, the suborders of the former order Alloeocoela are now given the rank of orders. They are Gnathostomulida, Archoophora, Lecithoepitheliata, Holocoela, and Seriata.

Order Tricladida. Relatively large flatworms, known as planarians, ranging from 2 to more than 60 cm. in length in the terrestrial forms. Digestive cavity characteristically three-branched, each with many diverticula, opens to the outside through a plicate pharynx directed backward. Both mouth and pharynx located in the middle of the body. Eyes present in most species. Protonephridia in the form of lateral networks with many nephridiopores.

The order consists of marine, fresh-water, and terrestrial groups, each forming a separate suborder. The marine forms are littoral and live beneath shells and stones. *Bdelloura* (Fig. 7-19) is a common commensal on book gills of horseshoe crabs. The fresh-water species are found in all types of aquatic situations. *Dugesia* and *Phagocata* are common genera. Terrestrial triclads reach the greatest size of any of the turbellarians; many are brightly colored. Most are confined to moist tropical and subtropical situations.

Order Polycladida. Marine flatworms of moderate size, averaging from 2 to 20 mm. in length with a greatly flattened and more or less oval shape. Many are brightly colored. Enteron elongate and centrally located with many highly branched diverticula. Pharynx plicate and frequently pendant from roof of pharyngeal cavity. Eyes numerous. Yolk glands absent.

Most species are bottom dwellers of the littoral zone. Some species live in *Sargassum* and a few are commensal with hermit crabs, on chitons, or in serpent stars. *Stylochus frontalis,* the

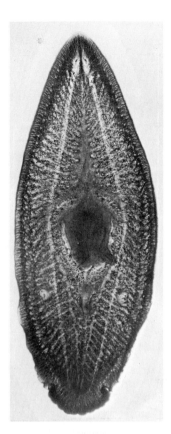

Figure 7-19.   *Bdelloura,* a marine triclad commensal that lives on gills of king crabs. (Courtesy of Ward's Natural Science Establishment.)

oyster leech, is a pest in oyster beds. Common genera include *Leptoplana, Notoplana* and *Stylochoplana.*

Of the five orders of Turbellaria the acoels are considered by many zoologists to be the most primitive and may have given rise to the other orders. The rhabdocoels, alloeocoels, and polyclads probably all stem directly from the acoels. The alloeocoels, however, appear to have been the ancestors of the triclads.

Class Trematoda. Flukes. Ectoparasitic and entoparasitic flatworms lacking an epidermis and covered instead with a cuticle. Digestive system present. Most species possess suckers.

Class Cestoda. Tapeworms. Parasitic flatworms possessing a cuticle and lacking an epidermis as in trematodes. Body usually elongated and composed of linearly arranged sections called proglottids. Anterior end with a head, or scolex, for attachment to host. Digestive system absent.

BIBLIOGRAPHY

Hyman, L. H., Platyhelminthes: *Polychoerus, Stenostomum, Bdelloura, Dugesia, Procotyla,* and *Holoplana. In* Brown, F. A., 1950: Selected Invertebrate Types. John Wiley, New York, pp. 141–158. Directions for laboratory study of representative turbellarians.

Hyman, L. H., 1951: The Invertebrates: Platyhelminthes and Rhynchocoela. Vol. II. McGraw-Hill, New York, pp. 52–219. The most recent and authoritative general account of the flatworms. All aspects of the phylum are covered. Excellent illustrations and an extensive bibliography. The chapter *Retrospect* in the fifth volume (1959) in this series summarizes research on Turbellaria from 1950–1958.

Hyman, L. H., and Jones, E. R., 1959: Turbellaria. *In* Ward and Whipple's Freshwater Biology (W. T. Edmondson, ed.). 2nd Ed., Wiley, New York, pp. 323–365. Key to and figures of the common fresh-water turbellarians.

Jennings, J. B., 1957: Studies on feeding, digestion, and food storage in free-living flatworms. Biol. Bull., *112*(1) : 63–80.

Jennings, J. B., 1962: Further studies on feeding and digestion in triclad Turbellaria. Biol. Bull., *123*(3):571–581.

Pennak, R. W., 1953: Freshwater Invertebrates of the United States. Ronald Press, New York, pp. 114–141. An introductory work on the taxonomy of fresh-water turbellarian genera. Key, figures, and bibliography included, as well as an introductory section on the biology of the group.

Chapter 8

THE NEMERTEANS

The phylum Rhynchocoela, or Nemertina, comprises a group of about 550 species of elongated and often flattened worms. They are commonly known as proboscis worms because of the presence of a remarkable proboscis apparatus used in capturing food. Most of the nemerteans are marine and are bottom dwellers. They live in shallow water, beneath shells and stones, in algae, or burrow in mud and sand. Nemerteans are more abundant in temperate seas than in the tropics, and many species inhabit the Atlantic and Pacific littoral waters of the United States. There is a single genus of fresh-water species; and one genus containing terrestrial forms is confined to the tropics and subtropics. A few commensals live with sea squirts, sea anemones, and mollusks, but no parasitic forms are known.

Evolution. Phylogenetically, nemerteans appear to be an offshoot from the free-living flatworms. An acoelomate plan of construction, in which a solid mass of mesenchyme fills the space between the body wall and the intestine, strongly suggests a flatworm origin. Moreover, both flatworms and nemerteans possess protonephridia, a ciliated epidermis, and similar nervous systems and sense organs.

However, despite their ancestry, nemerteans are more highly organized than flatworms; and although they are probably not on the direct line of protostome evolution leading to the coelomates, they display a number of changes that anticipate conditions found in higher invertebrate groups. The nervous system displays two large lateral nerve cords and a mid-dorsal nerve cord, and the protonephridial system has assumed an excretory function. In addition, for the first time there appear a simple circulatory system, a separate exit (or anus) for the digestive tract, and a coelomic cavity, although the latter is confined to the proboscis apparatus and is not homologous to the coelom of higher invertebrates.

External Structure. In external appearance, nemerteans resemble flatworms but tend to be somewhat larger and more elongated. Many genera, such as the common *Cerebratulus* and *Lineus* (Fig. 8-1, *A*) of the Atlantic coast, are ribbon-shaped and reach a length of 2 meters. No distinct head is evident, but the anterior is often provided with side lobes that make it resemble a spatula or a flattened heart (Fig. 8-1, *B*). In some species the head is lanceolate. Most nemerteans are pale, but some are brightly colored in hues or patterns of yellow, orange, red, and green.

Body Wall and Locomotion. The body wall is like that of flatworms but is more highly organized (Figs. 8-2 and 8-4, *A*). An outer layer of ciliated columnar epithelium rests upon a dermis of connective tissue. Unicellular mucus-secreting glands are scattered throughout the epidermis or are present as clusters of cells with each cluster having a common duct to the outside. The compound glands may be located either in the outer epithelium or sunk below the outer epithelium into the dermis. Beneath the dermis is a well developed body-wall muscu-

116

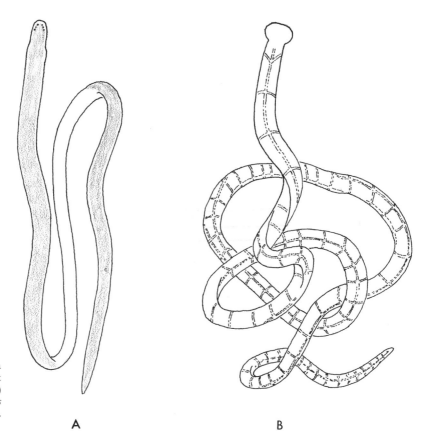

Figure 8-1. *A. Lineus ruber,* a heteronemertean found throughout northern latitudes. (After Hyman.) *B.* The paleonemertean, *Tubulanus capistratus,* from the Pacific coast. (After Coe from Hyman.)

A

B

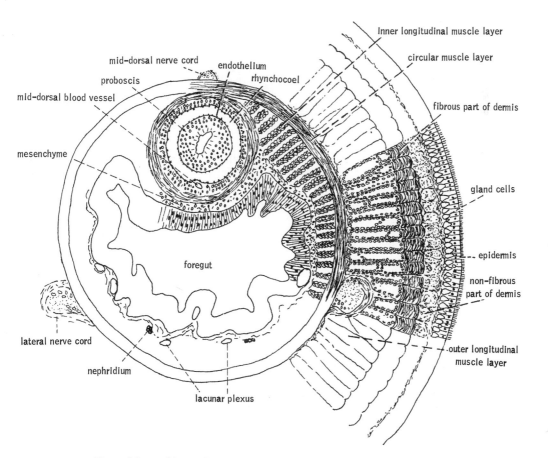

inner longitudinal muscle layer

circular muscle layer

fibrous part of dermis

mid-dorsal nerve cord

endothelium

rhynchocoel

proboscis

mid-dorsal blood vessel

gland cells

mesenchyme

epidermis

non-fibrous part of dermis

foregut

lateral nerve cord

outer longitudinal muscle layer

nephridium

lacunar plexus

Figure 8-2. *Lineus,* a heteronemertean (transverse section). (After Hyman.)

lature, composed of circular and longitudinal smooth muscle in two or three layers. When two-layered, the outer band is circular and the inner band longitudinal. Many rhynchocoels possess three layers of muscle conforming to one of two possible configurations; either the inner and outer layers are circular with a longitudinal layer between, or the outer and inner layers are longitudinal with a circular layer between. Mesenchymal tissue occupies the space between the digestive tract and the muscle layers; bands of muscle extend through the mesenchyme, connecting the dorsal and ventral body walls.

Most nemerteans move, like flatworms, by gliding over the substratum on a trail of slime.

Ciliary action appears to be the primary means of movement, but in larger species muscular undulations become increasingly important. Some species, particularly certain pelagic forms, are able to swim, using muscular undulations exclusively.

Nutrition and Digestive System. The most characteristic feature of the phylum is the proboscis apparatus. Although a proboscis, when present, is usually associated with the digestive tract in invertebrates, the proboscis of nemerteans is not connected to the digestive tract except in a few species. Moreover, the embryological origin of the proboscis is entirely independent from that of the gut. The opening of

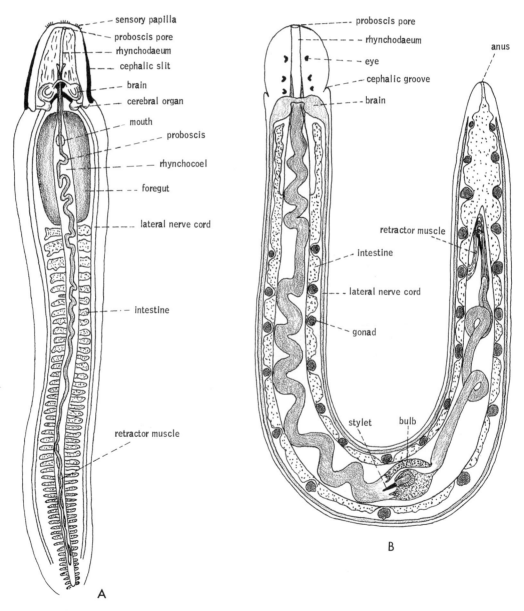

Figure 8-3.   *A. Cerebratulus,* a heteronemertean (dorsal view). (After Bürger from Hyman.) *B. Prostoma rubrum,* a fresh-water hoplonemertean. (After Pennak.)

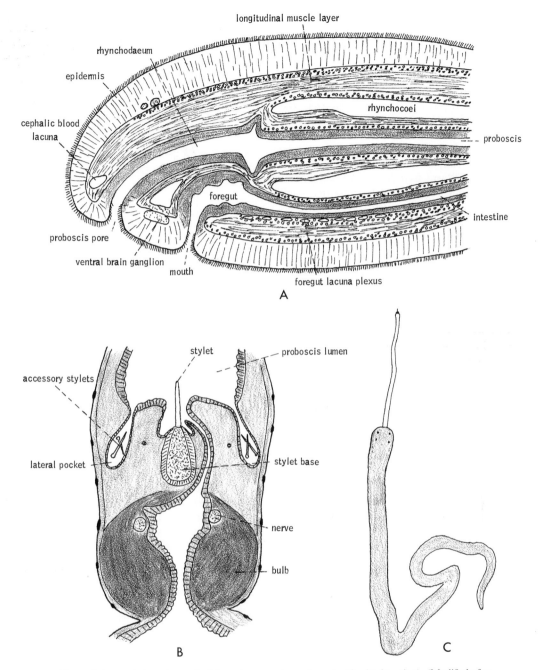

longitudinal muscle layer

rhynchodaeum

epidermis

rhynchocoel

cephalic blood
lacuna

proboscis

foregut

intestine

proboscis pore

ventral brain ganglion

mouth

foregut lacuna plexus

A

accessory stylets

stylet

proboscis lumen

lateral pocket

stylet base

nerve

bulb

B

C

Figure 8-4.   *A.* Anterior end of the paleonemertean, *Procarina* (Sagittal section). (Modified after Nawitzki from Hyman.) *B.* Stylet apparatus of the fresh-water nemertean, *Prostoma.* (Modified after Böhmig from Hyman.) *C.* Armed nemertean with protruded proboscis.

the proboscis apparatus is through a pore at the anterior tip of the worm (Figs. 8-3 and 8-4, *A*). This pore leads into a short canal known as the rhynchodaeum, which extends back to the level of the brain. The histology of the rhynchodaeum wall, as well as the remainder of the proboscis apparatus, is similar to that of the body wall, because the entire structure develops as an ectodermal invagination. Rhabdites are present in the proboscis wall of some species, providing

further evidence of a flatworm origin for the phylum.

The lumen of the rhynchodaeum is continuous with that of the proboscis proper (Fig. 8-4, *A*). The latter consists of a long tube, often coiled, lying free in a fluid-filled cavity called the rhynchocoel. The posterior of the proboscis is blind and is attached to the back of the rhynchocoel by a retractor muscle. A single layer of mesothelium covers the outer surface of the proboscis; mesothelium also forms the lining of the rhynchocoel. Because the rhynchocoel is of mesodermal origin and is lined by mesothelium, it must be considered a true coelom, even though it is limited in extent.

In two of the nemertean orders, the paleonemerteans and heteronemerteans, the proboscis is a simple tube (Fig. 8-3, *A*), but in the hoplonemerteans the proboscis has become more specialized and is armed with a heavy barb called a stylet, which is set in the proboscis wall (Figs. 8-3, *B* and 8-4, *B*). Where the stylet is attached, about two-thirds the distance back from the anterior of the animal, the proboscis wall is greatly swollen, particularly on one side, virtually occluding the lumen of the tube. This swelling, known as the diaphragm, bears the bulbous base of the stylet in a socket on its anterior face. In addition to the main stylet, accessory or reserve stylets are present for replacing the main stylet when necessary.

The proboscis is used for defense and for the capture of prey. It is literally shot out of the body, everting in the process. Because the posterior of the proboscis is attached to the back of the rhynchocoel by the retractor muscle, the proboscis can never be completely everted. In the armed nemerteans the proboscis is only projected as far as the stylet, which then occupies its tip (Fig. 8-4, *C*). The force for eversion is provided by muscular pressure on the fluid in the rhynchocoel, and retraction is effected by the posterior retractor muscle. The proboscis coils around the prey and glandular secretions from the proboscis wall aid in holding it. The stylet of armed nemerteans stabs the prey repeatedly and also probably delivers toxic secretions.

Hyman (1951) believes that the proboscis of nemerteans is evidence of a link with certain rhabdocoel flatworms that possess a short, glandular, anterior proboscis.

The development of an anus in the nemertean digestive system marks a significant change from the digestive system of flatworms. Ingestion and egestion can thus take place simultaneously, a much more efficient arrangement and one that is present in almost all higher invertebrates. The mouth is ventral and located anteriorly at the level of the brain (Figs. 8-3, *A*; 8-4, *A*; and 8-5). It opens into a foregut consisting of a buccal cavity, an esophagus and a glandular stomach (Figs. 8-3, *A* and 8-5). The prominence of these three regions varies. The foregut opens into a long intestine, extending the length of the body posteriorly to the anus. The intestine is provided with lateral diverticula (Fig. 8-5), and in some species it extends anteriorly beyond the junction with the

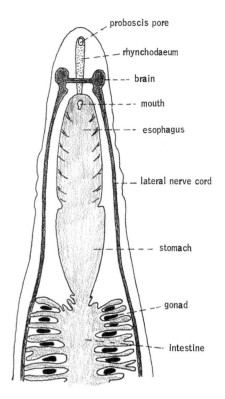

Figure 8-5.   Digestive tract of *Carinoma,* a paleonemertean. (After Coe.)

foregut as a cecum. The intestinal wall is composed of elongated ciliated cells and is richly provided with gland cells.

In many hoplonemerteans, the mouth has disappeared and the esophagus opens into the rhynchodaeum. In all other rhynchocoels, the digestive system is completely separate from the proboscis apparatus.

Nemerteans are entirely carnivorous and feed primarily on annelids, although they also eat other small living or dead invertebrates, such as mollusks and crustaceans. The prey, after capture by the proboscis, is swallowed whole by rapidly being sucked into the mouth.

Jennings (1960) found that in *Lineus,* an unarmed nemertean, the prey is probably killed in the foregut by acid secretions and digestion takes place in the intestine. Digestion is initially extracellular but is concluded intracellularly in phagocytic cells. Proteins, fats, and carbohydrates are all utilized; fats, which are stored in the mesenchyme and in the intestine, serve as the chief food reserve. Food and digestive waste are moved through the gut by cilia.

Like flatworms, nemerteans can withstand prolonged starvation. Experimental studies on *Lineus* have shown that starvation produces extreme reduction in size, along with structural regression to a condition similar to that of the larva.

Nervous System and Sense Organs. The nervous system is similar to that of higher flatworms but with a greater concentration of nervous tissue in the brain and ventral cords (Figs. 8-3, *A*; 8-5; and 8-6, *A*). The brain is four-lobed, consisting of a dorsal and a lateral ganglion on each side of the rhynchodaeum. Each ganglion is connected to the ganglion on the opposite side of the rhynchodaeum by a dorsal or ventral commissure, so that the brain forms a ring around the rhynchodaeum. A pair of large lateral nerves extends posteriorly, either in the body wall or in the mesenchyme. Lateral branches set at frequent intervals extend from the lateral nerves to innervate the body wall and to connect with the opposite nerve cord.

A number of other longitudinal nerves are frequently present and represent vestiges of the primitive radial arrangement of cords found in flatworms. The most common of these minor cords are a mid-dorsal nerve (Fig. 8-2) that extends from the dorsal commissure posteriorly the length of the body, and a pair of esophageal nerves that arise from the ventral ganglia and extend posteriorly to innervate the foregut. Lateral nerves from the lateral cord frequently connect with this mid-dorsal nerve.

The sense organs of nemerteans are also similar to those of flatworms. Tactile sensory cells are located in the epidermis, particularly at the anterior of the animal. Two to six eyes (Fig. 8-3, *B*) are frequently present, located on the dorsal surface anterior to the brain; but there may be as many as several hundred eyes, arranged in rows or groups on each side of the anterior end (Fig. 8-6, *B*). The eyes are inverse pigment cups like those of flatworms. Nemerteans avoid light and are active only at night.

Also located at the anterior of many nemerteans are two types of sense organs, believed to be chemoreceptors. The first type of sense organ consists of ciliated cephalic grooves or slits (Fig. 8-6, *B*), which are glandless epidermal areas richly supplied with ganglion cells. These organs probably have both a tactile and chemoreceptive function.

The second type of sense organ, characteristic of nemerteans and found in most members of the phylum, are the cerebral organs (Fig. 8-6, *A*). These consist of a pair of dorsal ciliated tubes or canals arising as invaginations of the epidermis. The inner ends of the canals contain gland and nerve cells associated with the brain. Water currents in the canals appear to be activated in the presence of food, indicating a chemoreceptive function. *Prostoma*, on which observations of the cerebral organs have been made, is able to locate very small fragments of food in still water up to 17 cm. away. Some investigators have postulated an endocrine function for the cerebral organs because of their association with the brain and because of the abundance of gland cells present.

Circulation and Excretion. Nemerteans are the only acoelomates to possess a true circulatory system. The system is closed— that is, the blood never bathes the tissues

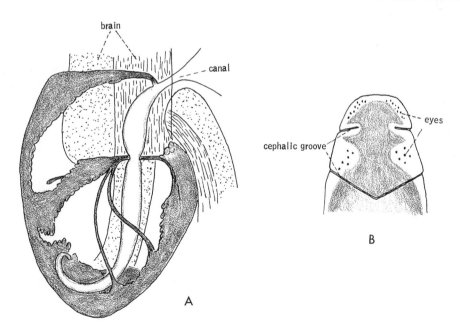

Figure 8-6. *A.* Cerebral organ of *Cerebratulus*. Shaded areas represent gland cells; white areas are filled with ganglion cells. *B.* Head of the hoplonemertean, *Amphiporus angulatus*. (*A* and *B* after Hyman.)

directly but is confined to vessels or spaces with distinct walls. In the simplest form (Fig. 8-7, *A*), there are only two vessels, which are located one on each side of the gut. These are connected anteriorly by a cephalic lacuna and posteriorly by an anal lacuna. The lacunae are mesenchymal spaces but are lined by a thin membrane. In many nemerteans considerable elaboration on this basic plan has taken place. One of the commonest additions to the basic plan is a mid-dorsal vessel (Fig. 8-7, *B*). This vessel arises from a transverse connection between the proboscis apparatus and the gut and eventually connects to the anal lacuna. In the region of the intestine, transverse vessels serve as connections between the lateral and mid-dorsal vessels.

The walls of the smaller vessels are composed of only two layers of squamous epithelium separated by a membrane. The large vessels contain connective tissue and a circular layer of muscle cells in addition to an endothelial lining. The large vessels are contractile, but blood flow is very irregular and does not follow a definite circuit. The blood may flow forward and backward in the longitudinal vessels at the same time, and the flow may even be reversed.

Nemertean blood is usually colorless, but in many species it contains respiratory pigments that are yellow, red, orange, or green. Furthermore, the pigments are always contained in corpuscles, a condition that is duplicated in few other phyla. These corpuscles are nucleated, oval or rounded discs. In addition to the corpuscles, the blood also contains amebocytes.

The excretory system consists primitively of one pair of protonephridia. A nephridiopore is located on each side of the foregut, and a tubule extends anteriorly from the opening of each nephridiopore. The flame bulbs in most nemerteans project into the wall of the lateral blood vessel (Fig. 8-7, *C*), which in some cases has even disappeared, so that the bulbs are directly bathed in blood. This close association between the excretory system and the circulatory system would seem to indicate a true excretory function, in contrast to the purely osmoregulatory function of the flatworm protonephridia. In nemerteans, waste is picked up from the blood, then passed into the capillaries and out the nephridiopores. The excretory system has become considerably modified in many species. Some paleonemerteans possess a so-called nephridial gland. This gland is actually

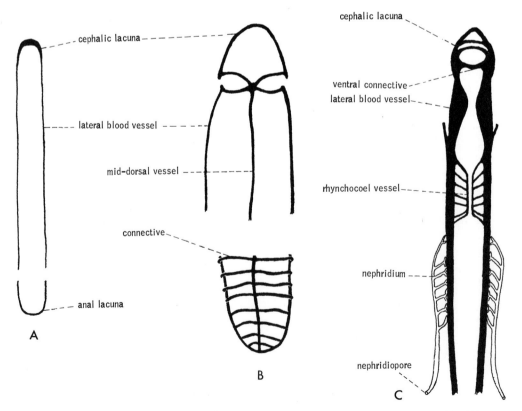

Figure 8-7.   Circulatory systems of various nemerteans. *A. Cephalothrix. B. Amphiporus.* (*A* and *B* after Oudemans from Hyman.) *C. Tubulanus.* (After Bürger from Hyman.)

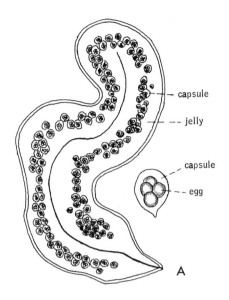

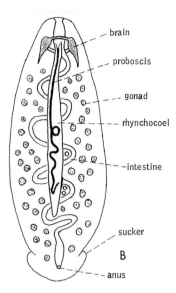

Figure 8-8.   *A.* Egg string of *Lineus ruber.* (After Schmidt from Hyman.) *B. Malacobdella grossa,* a commensal in the mantle cavity of marine clams. Proboscis and esophagus open into common chamber. (After Coe.)

just a ridge projecting into the lumen of a lateral blood vessel. The gland is composed of many protonephridial capillaries that have lost their bulbs.

Another modification of the excretory system parallels the modification in triclad flatworms in which the original protonephridia have become split up to form a large number of separate tubules, each with its own pore. In extreme cases, as many as 35,000 nephridiopores may exist on each side of the foregut.

Reproduction. The majority of nemerteans are dioecious, hermaphroditism existing chiefly among the fresh-water and terrestrial hoplonemerteans. The reproductive system is very simple, and with a few exceptions no copulatory organs are present. The gametes develop from mesenchymal cells that aggregate and become surrounded by a thin-walled sac to form a gonad. A considerable number of such gonads usually form a regular row on each side of the body in the mesenchyme. When intestinal diverticula are present, the gonads are spaced between them (Fig. 8-5).

After maturation of the gametes, a short duct grows from the gonad to the outside allowing the gametes to escape. The eggs are apparently squeezed out of the body by muscular contractions of the body wall. Each gonad produces between one and 50 eggs, depending on the species. The shedding of eggs or sperm does not necessarily require contact between two worms; in some species the males crawl over the females during spawning, or a pair of worms may occupy a common burrow for this purpose. When the eggs reach the outside, they are enclosed in gelatinous strings produced by the epidermal glands (Fig. 8-8, *A*). A few species are ovoviviparous.

Systematic Résumé of the Phylum Rhynchocoela

The phylum Rhynchocoela is considered to have only one class, which is divided into two subclasses and four orders.

Subclass Anopla. Contains the two principal orders of unarmed nemerteans.

Order Paleonemertini. The most primitive members of the phylum belong to this order. All are littoral forms. The musculature of the body wall is either two-layered or three-layered with the longitudinal layer located between two circular layers. The circulatory system is usually limited to two lateral vessels without mid-dorsal or transverse vessels. Eyes and cerebral organs are often absent. *Tubulanus, Carinina, Carinoma,* and *Cephalothrix.*

Order Heteronemertini. The body-wall musculature is three-layered with circular layer between two longitudinal layers. Cerebral organs, mid-dorsal blood vessel, and lateral intestinal diverticula are present. *Cerebratulus* and *Lineus.*

Subclass Enopla. Contains two orders including the armed nemerteans.

Order Hoplonemertini. All of the armed nemerteans belong to this order. The intestine contains lateral diverticula and a cecum; a dorsal blood vessel is present. This order contains several interesting ecological groups, such as the floating or swimming pelagic nemerteans, which live in the open ocean; the fresh-water nemerteans (*Prostoma*); the tropical and subtropical terrestrial nemerteans (*Geonemertes*); and many marine littoral forms (*Amphiporus*).

Order Bdellonemertini. This small order contains but one genus, *Malacobdella* (Fig. 8-8, *B*), with four species, three of which are commensal in the mantle cavity of marine clams and one of which is commensal in the mantle cavity of a fresh-water snail. Although the proboscis is unarmed, it has probably been derived from the armed type. The proboscis and esophagus open into a common chamber. The commensal existence is reflected in the absence of eyes and other special sense organs.

BIBLIOGRAPHY

Coe, W. R., 1943: Biology of the nemerteans of the Atlantic coast of North America. Trans. Connecticut Acad. Arts and Sci., *35* : 129–328.

Hyman, L. H., 1951: The Invertebrates: Platyhelminthes and Rhynchocoela. Vol. II. McGraw-Hill, New York, pp. 459–531. A very complete general treatment of the nemerteans. Excellent figures and extensive bibliography.

Jennings, J. B., 1960: Observations on the nutrition of the Rhynchocoelan *Lineus ruber*. Biol. Bull., *119*(2) : 189-196.

Chapter 9

SPIRAL CLEAVAGE AND THE EMBRYOLOGY OF TURBELLARIANS AND NEMERTEANS

Embryonic development in flatworms, rhynchocoels, annelids, mollusks, and primitive arthropods is strikingly similar. Furthermore, many of the common features are peculiar to these phyla and do not appear in the development of echinoderms and chordates. These embryological differences serve as the principal evidence in support of the division of the bilateral animals into two main evolutionary lines. One line embraces flatworms, annelids, mollusks, and arthropods, as well as a number of smaller allied groups; these groups constitute the division, or branch, called the Protostomia. From the other line have evolved the echinoderms, the chordates, and several smaller phyla; the members of this line are known as the Deuterostomia. Although the deuterostomes appear to have diverged from the protostome line at a point considerably after the flatworms, both divisions must be considered in introducing certain basic features of invertebrate embryology.

The protostomes and deuterostomes each display a basic plan of development that is characteristic and distinct from that of the other. This is not to say that all members of each group have identical patterns of development. There are many examples of modification and deviation in every phylum, largely through changes in the distribution and the amount of yolk material. But each line does display certain characteristic features.

Types of Cleavage and Embryonic Development

Determinate and Indeterminate Cleavage. In a frog embryo, ectodermal cells above the notochord undergo invagination and differentiation to form the spinal cord and brain. If ectodermal cells from the sides of an early gastrula are transplanted to a site above the notochord, the transplant will also form nervous tissue. Obviously, the ultimate fate of ectodermal cells in an early gastrula in the frog is not yet fully fixed or determined, since these cells may follow various lines of development if moved to other positions in the embryo. Also, areas of undifferentiated cells, such as the primitive streak of birds and mammals and the lips of the blastopore in amphibians, persist for some time after gastrulation. This late establishment of the embryonic fate of cells allows the phenomenon of twinning to occur. For example, if a starfish egg is allowed to cleave to the four-cell stage and the cells (blastomeres) are then separated, each cell is capable of forming a complete gastrula and then a larva. This formation of blastomeres in the embryo with unfixed fates is known as *indeterminate cleavage* and is characteristic of deuterostomes.

The flatworm–annelid–arthropod line (the protostomes) displays just the opposite type of embryonic development. In these groups the fate of cells is fixed very early in development. If a marine annelid egg is allowed to undergo two cleavage divisions and the resulting four blastomeres are separated, each blastomere will develop into only a fixed quarter of the gastrula and larva. Thus, each cell has a predetermined and fixed fate which cannot be altered, even if the cell is moved from its original position in the embryo. The formation of blastomeres with fixed embryonic contributions is known as *determinate cleavage* and is characteristic of development in protostomes.

Spiral Cleavage.   Determinate versus indeterminate cleavage is not the only difference between development in protostomes and deuterostomes. The two groups also differ strikingly in the pattern of cleavage. In echinoderms and chordates cleavage is said to be radial. The axes of early cleavage spindles are either parallel or at right angles to the polar axis (the axis between animal and vegetal poles). The resulting blastomeres are thus always situated directly above or below one another (Fig. 9-1).

This arrangement is rare in protostomes. Cleavage is total, but the axes of the cleavage spindles are oblique to the polar axis, rather than at right angles or parallel. This position results in the blastomeres having a spiral arrangement, any one cell being located between the two blastomeres above or below it (Fig. 9-2). Thus one tier or set of cells alternates in position with the next tier. This cleavage pattern is characteristic of protostomes and is known as spiral cleavage.

Since spiral cleavage is determinate and since the fate of the various blastomeres is quite similar throughout the different protostome phyla, it has been found profitable to designate each blastomere in order to trace the lineage of the cells. Such a system of designation was improvised by the American embryologist E. B. Wilson (1892) and has now become the standard system for describing cleavage of the spiral type. An explanation of this system is incorporated in the subsequent discussion on spiral cleavage.

Invertebrates with spiral cleavage usually have moderately telolecithal eggs (having the yolk concentrated toward one pole), so that cleavage is total but not equal. The first two cleavage planes are vertical and divide the egg into four equal blastomeres, designated as macromeres *A, B, C,* and *D.* The third cleavage plane is horizontal but is shifted toward the animal pole so that the upper set of four blastomeres or micromeres is considerably smaller than those below (Fig. 9-2, *A* and *B*). Since the spindle axes are oriented obliquely to the polar axis, the four micromeres sit in the angles formed by the contiguity of the four macromeres. This first set of four micromeres is known as the first quartet and are labeled *1a, 1b, 1c,* and *1d,* depending on which of the four macromeres they were derived from. The four macromeres continue to be designated with capital letters plus the numerical prefix 1. They thus are designated *1A, 1B, 1C,* and *1D.*

The four macromeres now give off a second set of four micromeres (Fig. 9-2, *C* and *D*). If the cleavage of the first quartet was clockwise, then the second quartet issue forth in a counterclockwise direction, again to lie in the angles formed by the first quartet above and the macromeres below. The second quartet is designated *2a, 2b, 2c,* and *2d,* and the macromeres become *2A, 2B, 2C,* and *2D.*

The macromeres form still a third quartet (*3a, 3b, 3c,* and *3d*) (Fig. 9-2, *E* and *F*) and a fourth quartet (*4a, 4b, 4c,* and *4d*) (Fig. 9-3, *B*). The four macromeres, which may now actually be smaller than the cells of the fourth quartet, are designated *4A, 4B, 4C,* and *4D.* All five tiers alternate in position with one another.

Before the fourth quartet is formed, the cells of the first and second quartets have already undergone subsequent divisions (Fig. 9-2, *E* and *F*). These cells are named with an exponent. For example, when blastomere *1a* of the first quartet divides, its daughter cells are called $1a^1$ and $1a^2$. The cell closest to the animal pole takes the exponent *1*. When micromere $1a^2$ divides, another exponent is added in the same manner, so that the daughter cells become $1a^{21}$

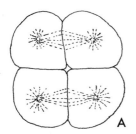
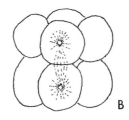
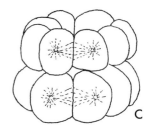

Figure 9-1.   Radial cleavage in the sea cucumber, *Synapta. A.* Polar view. *B* and *C.* Lateral views. (After Selenka from Balinski.)

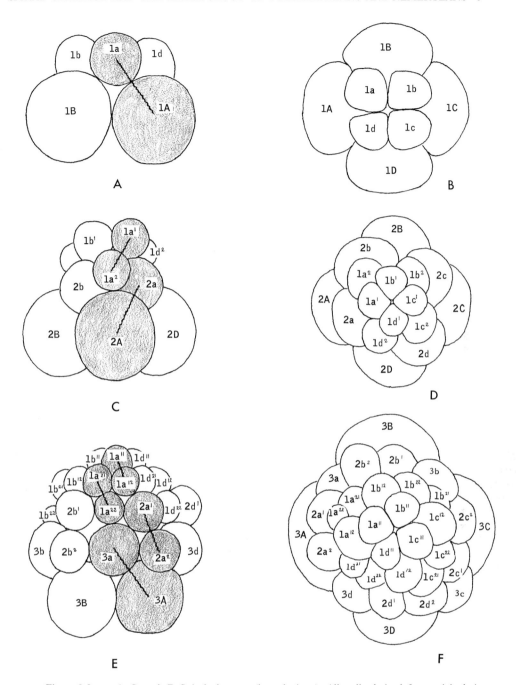

Figure 9-2.   *A, C,* and *E.* Spiral cleavage (lateral views). All cells derived from original *A* blastomere are shaded. Wavy black lines indicate orientation of spindles at each cleavage. (After Villee, Walker, and Smith.) *B, D,* and *F.* Same stages viewed from animal pole. (After Hyman.)

and $1a^{22}$; another division produces cells $1a^{221}$ and $1a^{222}$.

By means of Wilson's system it is possible to reconstruct the origin or lineage of any particular cell. Lower case letters indicate micromeres; capital letters indicate macromeres. The number preceding the letter indicates the quartet from which the cell is derived, and the exponent tells the number of subsequent divisions that have

taken place after the initial formation of the quartet. Not only the lineage of a cell can be derived from this system but also the position of the cell in the embryo. The lower the numbers, the closer the cell is to the animal pole, and the letters indicate the quadrant of the embryo in which the cell is situated. The four macromeres are always located at the vegetal pole.

With the formation of the fourth quartet

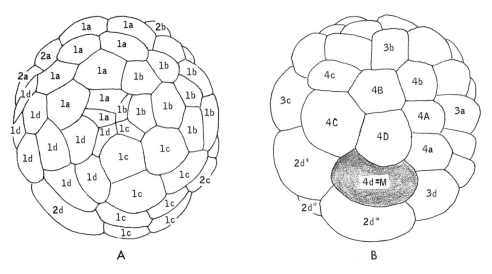

Figure 9-3.   Early blastula of the annelid, *Arenicola*. *A*. View from animal pole. *B*. View from vegetal pole. (Both after Child from Hyman.)

the embryo has become a blastula (Fig. 9-3), which may be either hollow or solid, depending on the amount of yolk present. Also, the germ layers have become fixed. The first three quartets of micromeres form all of the ectoderm as well as the ectomesoderm. The four macromeres, *4A*, *4B*, *4C*, and *4D*, and three cells of the fourth quartet, *4a*, *4b*, and *4c*, form the entoderm. The remaining fourth quartet cell, the *4d* cell, is known as the *M* or mesentoblast cell (Fig. 9-3, *B*). It gives rise to a few cells that contribute to the entoderm and to two teloblast cells, which form all of the entomesoderm.

Gastrulation takes place through epiboly or invagination, or both; and the fourth quartet and four macromeres become located within the gastrula. (Note that the laying down of germ layers is not a result of gastrulation, as so many students assume from a study of vertebrate embryology, but has actually preceded it.) The blastopore closes, and a new opening, the mouth, arises from an ectodermal invagination near the site of the closed blastopore. This invagination is the stomodeum, which meets and become continuous with the entodermal gut.

Mesoderm Origin.   In addition to determinate versus indeterminate cleavage and spiral versus radial cleavage, two further differences between the embryology of protostomes and deuterostomes are evident. In protostomes all of the entomesoderm arises from a single cell, the *4d* blastomere. In deuterostomes on the other hand, the mesoderm primitively arises by a process called enterocoelic pouching, in which the wall of the archenteron evaginates to form coelomic pouches and thus to form the mesoderm. Finally, in protostomes, the mouth forms from the blastopore or near the site of the closed blastopore; in deuterostomes the mouth arises a considerable distance from the site of the blastopore.

Embryology of the Turbellaria

Acoels and Polyclads.   In the acoel and polyclad turbellarians, the yolk is an integral part of the cytoplasm of the egg. This is not the case in the other orders of Turbellaria. In the alloeocoels, the rhabdocoels, and the triclads, yolk formation has become highly specialized. Certain of the original ovaries have evolved into glands that produce yolk cells. These yolk cells pass down the oviduct with the eggs to become enclosed within a common shell. Thus the egg in these groups is ectolecithal—that is, the yolk lies outside the egg—in contrast to the entolecithal condition found in acoels and polyclads and, as a matter of fact, in all other animals. This change in the location of yolk material has also greatly altered the developmental pattern; for this reason the two types must be considered separately.

In the relatively few acoels that have been studied, cleavage is spiral but somewhat different from the cleavage described earlier. The egg undergoes a single vertical cleavage rather than two. As a result, there are only two cells, *A* and *B*, to form the micromeres. The micromeres are produced in duets rather than in quartets, although the typical four sets are formed (Fig. 9-4). After gastrulation, which takes place by epiboly of cells derived from the first three duets, cells *4A*, *4B*, *4a*, and *4b* become internal and form the interior mass. But since there is no intestine in the acoels, entoderm and mesoderm never become distinct. At least part of the interior mass is mesectodermal in origin and comes from cells derived from the second duet and perhaps from the third. The gastrula is thus solid (stereogastrula), and this level of development is retained by the adult.

The blastopore closes, and the mouth forms as a new opening near the same site by means of a stomodeal invagination. The adult digestive tract never progresses beyond this point. The nervous system is derived from the first duet, and the remaining external micromeres form the epidermis. There is no free-swimming larval stage.

Development in the polyclads conforms much more closely to the typical pattern of spiral cleavage described at the beginning of this chapter. The chief difference is in the origin of the entoderm. The four macromeres, $4A$, $4B$, $4C$, and $4D$, and the three cells from the fourth quartet, $4a$, $4b$, and $4c$, are utilized as food material and are not used to form entoderm. The $4d$ cell forms all of the entoderm ($4d^1$) and entomesoderm ($4d^2$). The entomesoderm forms most of the mesodermal structures—mesenchyme, gonads, muscles and mesenchymal glands. The first quartet micromeres form the nervous system, the eyes, the dorsal anterior epidermis, and an apical frontal gland bearing a tuft of long cilia. The second and third quartets contribute to surface ectoderm as well as to ectomesoderm, from which the pharynx musculature is derived.

Gastrulation is by epiboly and produces a stereogastrula. The mouth and the pharynx form from a stomodeal invagination near the original site of the blastopore. This in-vagination connects with the enteron, which has formed from an entodermal mass and become hollow (Fig. 9-5, A).

Prior to emergence as a young worm, the embryo flattens, the frontal gland shifts forward to mark the anterior of the animal, and the mouth shifts posteriorly.

In most polyclads there is no larva, but in some there is a free-swimming stage called a Müller's larva (Fig. 9-5, B). Eight arms or lobes, which are directed posteriorly and bear long cilia, form as extensions of the body. The ciliary tuft of the frontal gland projects forward. The larva swims about for a few days and then settles to the bottom as a young worm. Feeding probably does not commence until after the larval stage has been passed.

Some species of *Stylochus* pass through a similar larval stage called Götte's larva. It differs from a Müller's larva in having only four ciliated lobes.

Alloeocoels, Rhabdocoels, and Triclads. Alloeocoels, rhabdocoels, and triclads have undoubtedly evolved from forms that had spiral cleavage, but the presence of external yolk cells has so altered the pattern of development that it no longer bears any resemblance to the ancestral type. (A few alloeocoels and the catenulid and macrostomid rhabdocoels lack yolk glands and possess the more typical entolecithal eggs.)

The initial blastomeres divide and separate to form an embryonic mass of cells intermingled with yolk cells. In the alloeocoels and rhabdocoels, this is followed by a migration of the yolk cells to one side of the embryonic mass, while the blastomeres assemble at the other. The yolk cells form a syncytium and indicate the future

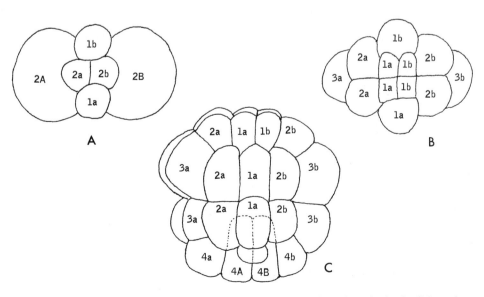

Figure 9-4.   Cleavage in the acoel, *Polychoerus. A* and *B*. Views from the animal pole. *C*. Lateral view. (After Gardiner from Hyman.)

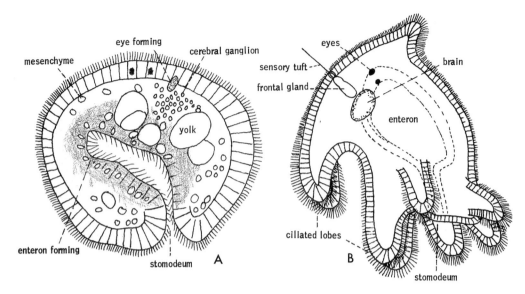

Figure 9-5.   *A*. Late gastrula of the polyclad, *Hoploplana*. (After Surface from Hyman.) *B*. A Müller's larva (lateral view). (After Kato from Hyman.)

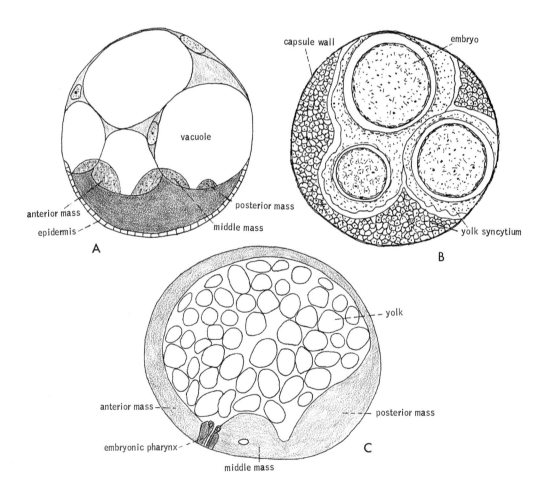

Figure 9-6.   *A*. Embryo of a rhabdocoel, showing formation of three embryonic masses. (After Bresslau from Hyman.) *B*. Section through a triclad capsule, showing three embryos imbedded in yolk syncytium. (After Metschnikoff from Hyman.) C. Triclad embryo after ingestion of yolk and formation of three embryonic masses. (After Fulinski from Hyman.)

dorsal side of the embryo. The blastomeres become oriented into three transverse ventral masses, thus marking the anterior-posterior axis of the embryo (Fig. 9-6, *A*). Peripheral cells from the three masses migrate around the yolk to enclose it and form the epidermis. Cells adjacent to the yolk form the intestine and mesenchyme. The anterior mass of blastomeres gives rise to the nervous system, the middle mass of blastomeres to the pharynx apparatus, and the posterior mass of blastomeres to the reproductive system and to the posterior of the worm.

Triclad development differs from polyclad development chiefly during the stage just prior to the formation of the three ventral masses of blastomeres. After the initial cleavage and separation of blastomeres, some of the cells flatten and form a membrane enclosing the remaining blastomeres and part of the yolk. The blastomeres and yolk surrounded by this membrane are called the embryonic mass. The remainder of the yolk forms a syncytium surrounding the membrane and the embryonic mass. Several such masses are enclosed within a single capsule (Fig. 9-6, *B*). Some of the blastomeres in such an embryonic mass now collect at one point within the membrane and form a temporary pharynx and intestine, which ingest the surrounding yolk syncytium into the interior of the embryo (Fig. 9-6, *C*). The ingested yolk so distends the temporary intestine that the blastomeres that formerly made up the embryonic mass are pushed to the periphery. These now peripherally-located blastomeres form the body wall of the worm, which on the ventral side proliferates the three anterior-posterior masses described earlier.

There is no free-swimming larval stage in these orders of Turbellaria that have ectolecithal development; the young worms emerge from the capsule in a few weeks.

Embryology of the Nemerteans

Cleavage in nemerteans is of the typical spiral type, and a hollow ciliated blastula is formed. Gastrulation takes place by invagination and forms, in most cases, a solid stereogastrula. The gastrula is radially symmetrical with a tuft of cilia at the animal pole, as in polyclad flatworms.

The armed nemerteans have no free-swimming larval stage. After enclosure of the blastopore the embryo flattens, and the apical ciliary tuft shifts forward to indicate the location of the anterior dorsal surface. Near the site of the closed blastopore, a stomodeal invagination forms the foregut, which connects with the interior entoderm. The anus develops from a proctodeal invagination. An ectodermal invagination at the anterior of the embryo forms the internal lining of the proboscis apparatus. The interior mesenchyme surrounding the invagination then splits to form the rhynchocoel; the outer layer of mesenchyme forms the lining of the rhynchocoel, and the inner layer contributes to the wall of the proboscis and its external mesothelial covering. The protonephridia probably arise as ectodermal invaginations, and the blood vessels arise *in situ* within the mesenchyme.

Many heteronemerteans, including *Cerebratulus*, pass through a free-swimming and feeding larval stage. The larva develops directly from the gastrula and is called a pilidium larva (Fig. 9-7). In those species possessing a larval stage, an archenteron is formed as a result of the initial invagination, and the gastrula is not solid. The archenteron forms the larval gut and opens through the persistent blastopore, which forms the larval mouth.

It is postulated that a more extensive invagination takes place after the formation of the archenteron, so that the opening to the exterior is actually a stomodeum. If this is the case, the original blastopore would then move to the interior and would indicate the junction between the stomodeum and the archenteron. The lateral walls of the gastrula now put forth two ciliated lobes that extend to flank the

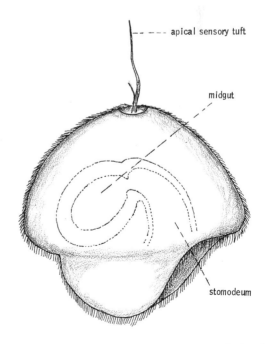

Figure 9-7.   Pilidium larva of the nemertean, *Cerebratulus marginatus.* (After Coe.)

mouth on each side. The aboral side of the larva bears a tuft of long cilia that is imbedded in an invaginated cup of ectodermal cells. These ectodermal cells are known as the sensory plate, which is probably homologous to the embryonic frontal organ of polyclad flatworms. After a free-swimming existence, the pilidium undergoes a rather complicated metamorphosis into a young worm.

The heteronemertean, *Lineus*, forms a spherical ciliated larva called a Desor's larva. However, the Desor's larva remains within the egg envelope and should really be considered only a modification of the pilidium, which contains no oral lobes and sensory plate.

BIBLIOGRAPHY

Hyman, L. H., 1951: The Invertebrates: Platyhelminthes and Rhynchocoela. Vol. II. McGraw-Hill, New York, pp. 10–14, 171–179, and 506–516.

Wilson, E. B., 1892: Cell Lineage of Nereis. J. Morph., *6*:361–480.

Chapter 10

up to here

THE PSEUDOCOELOMATES

Among the bilateral animals, only flatworms and nemerteans have a primitively solid (or acoelomate) type of body construction, in which the space between the digestive tract and the muscle layers of the body wall is filled with mesenchyme. All other bilateral animals have a fluid-filled space called a body cavity located between the body wall and the internal organs; or if a body cavity is absent, such groups have at least derived from forms with a body cavity. The development of a body cavity in the higher invertebrates was probably associated, at least in part, with an increase in animal size. As the volume of the body increases, a solid structure becomes less efficient physiologically. The translocation of gases, food materials, and waste is less easily accomplished in a solid body structure, and the coiling or folding of different organs to increase the surface area is somewhat restricted. With a body cavity, there is more space for the accommodation of coiled or looped internal organs, and the fluid of the cavity may aid in waste removal and in the circulation of food materials and oxygen.

Two types of body cavities exist in the Animal Kingdom—the coelom and the pseudocoel. The majority of animals, including echinoderms, vertebrates, mollusks, annelids, and arthropods, possess a coelom (Fig. 11-1). The coelomic type of cavity develops within the embryonic mesoderm and has a definite lining of epithelial cells that is called the peritoneum. The peritoneum not only lines the inner surface of the body wall but also surrounds the internal

organs and forms the mesenteries. This envelopment of the internal organs by the peritoneum takes place because all organs located within the coelom are actually retroperitoneal—that is, the organ lies behind peritoneum and merely bulges into the cavity, pushing the peritoneum in front of it.

The ancestral coelomates probably evolved from turbellarian stock and, in the course of their evolution, developed not only a coelom but also an egestive opening for the alimentary tract; for an anus is characteristic of all animals above flatworms, except where it has been secondarily lost. As in their flatworm ancestors, the body surface of the ancestral coelomate was probably ciliated and the body wall composed of layers of circular and longitudinal muscle.

How the coelom originated is unknown. There are a number of divergent theories, which, in turn, form the principal bases for the various general schemes of invertebrate phylogeny. One view, originally propounded by Sedgewick (1884) and supported today in a modified form by Remane (1950), Jagersten (1955), and Marcus (1958), maintains that the coelom originally evolved as outpocketings of the gut—that is, it was enterocoelic in origin, and the gastric pouches of anthozoans were the precursors of the first coelom.

As we have already seen, an enterocoelic mode of coelom formation takes place in the embryological development of deuterostomes, but to say that this mode was the original mode of coelom formation necessitates numerous corol-

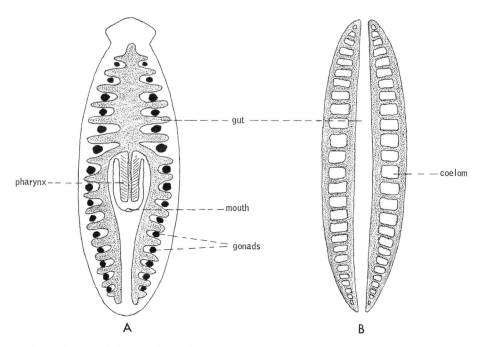

Figure 10-1.   *A.* Gonads alternating with branches of enteron in a triclad flatworm. *B.* Coelomic compartments in an annelid worm resulting from fused adjacent expanded gonads. (Both after Hyman.)

laries that are difficult to support. The problems of the *Enterocoel Theory* have been well summarized by Hyman (1959). If the coelom originated from the gastric pouches of anthozoans, then this group of coelenterates must be considered ancestral to all of the Bilateria. Indeed, the Enterocoel Theory would even make anthozoans ancestral to hydrozoans and scyphozoans, even though they appear to be the most specialized members of the phylum. Furthermore, all Bilateria would then need to be of a coelomate construction, and the flatworms would be considered degenerate animals that had lost the coelom, even though there is no evidence that flatworms ever possessed a coelom. Moreover, the acoels, rather than constituting the primitive members of the Turbellaria would need to be considered the most degenerate, having lost not only the coelom but also the digestive tract.

Hatschek (1878) proposed another theory, which has been supported by many more recent zoologists and has been called the *Gonocoel Theory*. According to this view, the coelom arose from a linear series of gonads located on either side of the gut (Fig 10-1). With the shedding of the gametes, a cavity was left behind, and this cavity was the forerunner of the coelom. The Gonocoel Theory postulates that the coelomates are derived from acoelomate turbellarians; but this theory runs into difficulty, because it links coelom formation with segmentation, or metamerism, and most coelomate phyla are not metameric.

Perhaps, as suggested by Hyman (1951), the coelom merely developed as clefts or spaces in the mesenchyme, for in most of the protostomes this is the embryological method of formation—that is, the coelom appears as cavities within the bands of embryonic mesoderm. Although it is uncertain how the original coelom formed, at least two assumptions appear to be justified. First, the coelomates arose from the acoelomate turbellarians; second, enterocoelous coelom formation, characteristic of deuterostomes, appears to be a secondary development, with the deuterostomes perhaps being an offshoot from some stock of coelomate protostomes.

The second type of body cavity is called a pseudocoel, or false coelom (Fig. 10-16). A pseudocoel differs from a coelom in that the internal organs are actually free within the cavity, since no mesenteries suspend the organs nor is the cavity lined with peritoneum. The nature of the pseudocoel and its relation to internal organs is explained by the embryonic origin of the cavity. After the formation of the archenteron, the blastocoel, rather than being obliterated, remains as an internal body cavity surrounding the digestive tract and other organs. Thus the pseudocoel is a derivative in the adult of the embryonic blastocoel, arising *between* mesoderm and entoderm.

Three phyla of invertebrates possess a pseudocoel—the Aschelminthes, the Acanthocephala, and the Entoprocta. Although these pseudocoelomate groups are structurally diverse and their phylogenetic interrelationships are obscure, they probably represent a monophyletic unit. It is usually assumed that the pseudocoelomate groups comprise a side branch stemming from the main line of evolution between the acoelomates and the ancestral coelomates. Thus from an evolutionary standpoint, the pseudocoelomates represent a terminal group of phyla that is not on the main line of invertebrate evolution. It should be emphasized therefore that a pseudocoel is not a stage in the evolution of the true coelom, but is rather an independent evolutionary acquisition.

PHYLUM ASCHELMINTHES

The phylum Aschelminthes contains the largest number of pseudocoelomate animals and includes such familiar groups as the rotifers, the gastrotrichs, and the nematodes. Most aschelminths are rather elongated and often somewhat cylindrical, especially the worm-like nematodes. Although the anterior of the body is cephalized to a varying degree and bears the mouth and certain sense organs, there is no well-formed head. The body is typically covered with a distinct scleroprotein cuticle, which in some groups is developed into a skeletal encasement. Very likely, the ancestral aschelminths were uniformly ciliated, but surface ciliation is either reduced or absent in living forms. Adhesive glands in varying numbers are characteristic of many species and often open to the outside of the body by projecting cuticular tubes. The digestive tract is usually a complete tube with a mouth and anus, and a specialized pharyngeal region is almost always present. Since most species are aquatic and very small, no respiratory or circulatory system is present. However, protonephridia often exist. A peculiar feature of most members of this phylum is the numerical constancy of the cells, or the nuclei, that compose the various organs. The numbers are characteristic for each species but vary from one species to another. The condition is probably associated with the extremely small size, characteristic of many members of the phylum. Most aschelminths are dioecious, and cleavage is strongly determinate.

Class Rotifera

The class Rotifera contains the very common and abundant fresh-water animals commonly known as rotifers, or wheel animalcules. The name is derived from the presence of a ciliated crown, or corona, which when beating, gives the appearance of a rotating wheel in many species (Fig. 10-2, *A*). Although some marine species exist and some species live in mosses, the majority inhabit fresh-water. Some species may reach two millimeters in length, but most rotifers are approximately the size of ciliate protozoans and are among the smallest metazoan animals. Most rotifers are solitary free-moving animals, but there are some sessile species (Fig. 10-5), as well as some colonial forms (Fig. 10-9, *A*). The body is usually transparent, although some rotifers appear green, orange, red, or brown, owing to coloration of the digestive tract.

External Structure. The elongated or saccular body, which is relatively cylindrical, can be divided into three regions (Figs. 10-2 and 10-7, *B*). The body is composed of a short anterior region, a large trunk composing the major part of the body, and a terminal foot. The body is always covered by a distinct cuticle, which may be ringed, sculptured, or ornamented in various ways.

The broad or narrowed anterior forms the head region and bears a ciliated organ called the corona, which is characteristic of all members of the class. Primitively, the corona is believed to have consisted of a large, ventral, ciliated area called the buccal field (Fig. 10-3, *A*), which surrounded the mouth. If rotifers evolved from a small, ciliated, creeping ancestor as is generally believed, then perhaps the buccal field represented a vestige of the ancestral ventral ciliation. From the buccal field, cilia extended around the anterior margins of the head to form a crown-like ring called the circumapical band. The area in the interior of the ring, which is devoid of cilia, is called the apical field.

The different types of coronas characteristic of different groups of rotifers are believed to have evolved from this basic structural plan. During the derivation of these different types, various parts of the buccal field and the circumapical band have been either lost or have become more highly developed. Not infrequently certain cilia have become modified to form cirri, membranelles, or bristles. A few of the more common types of coronal ciliation are described here.

In *Euchlanis*, the original buccal field and circumapical band have been retained except for a portion posterior to the mouth (Fig. 10-4). In this area only a vestige remains. The cilia along the margin of the buccal field have become modified into stiff cirri, and the cilia of the circumapical band on the lateral sides of the head form large tufts. When the ciliary tuft

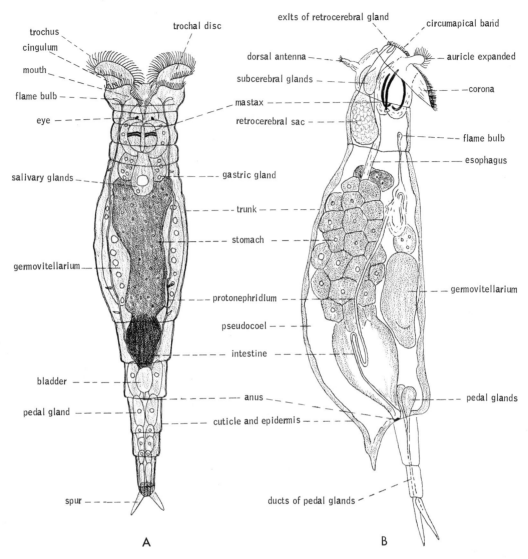

Figure 10-2. *A. Philodina roseola* (ventral view). (After Hickernell from Hyman.) *B. Notommata copeus* (lateral view). (After Hyman.)

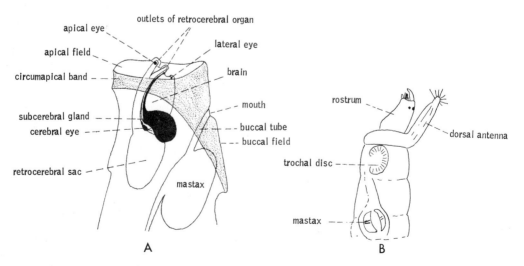

Figure 10-3. *A.* Primitive corona (lateral view). (After Beauchamp from Hyman.) *B.* Anterior end of bdelloid rotifer with trochal disc retracted (lateral view). (After Hyman.)

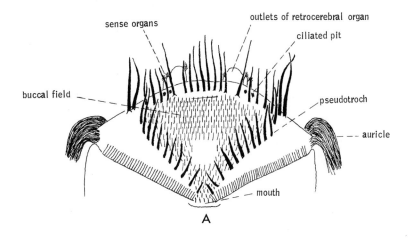

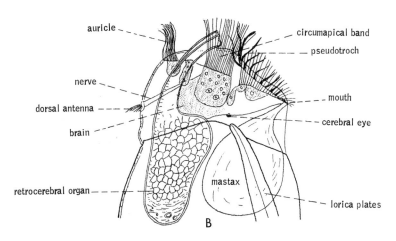

Figure 10-4. Corona of *Euchlanis. A.* Ventral view. (After Stoszberg from Hyman.) *B.* Lateral view. (After Beauchamp from Hyman.)

is located on a projection of the body wall, the projection and tuft collectively are called the auricle. The buccal field in *Collotheca* and related forms is modified into a funnel, and ciliation is reduced (Fig. 10-5). The edges of the buccal field have become expanded forming a varying number of lobes bearing spine-like bristles, or setae, which may be arranged in bundles or tufts. The setae are perhaps derived from cilia. As a result of this expansion of the buccal field, the mouth lies at the apex of the funnel.

In *Hexarthra* and *Testudinella* the buccal field has become reduced and relatively insignificant, and the corona is derived entirely from the circumapical band (Fig. 10-6, *B*). The cilia in the interior of the band are greatly reduced; thus, the circumapical band has been transformed into two circlets of modified cilia—an anterior band called the trochus and a posterior band called the cingulum. Since the trochus

passes above the mouth and the cingulum below the mouth, these rotifers superficially resemble the trochophore larva of annelids and mollusks. On the basis of this similarity, some zoologists have claimed a phylogenetic relationship between the rotifers on one hand and the mollusks and the annelids on the other. But if the two ciliated girdles of these rotifers are actually derived from a single circumapical band, then resemblance to the trochophore larva is entirely superficial; and these rotifers are specialized rather than primitive members of the class.

The corona of bdelloid rotifers, which include many common fresh-water species, represents a still further modification of these two ciliated bands (Fig. 10-2, *A*). The anterior circlet of cilia (the trochus) is raised up on a pedestal and divided into two discs called trochal discs. The posterior circlet passes around the base of the pedestals and runs

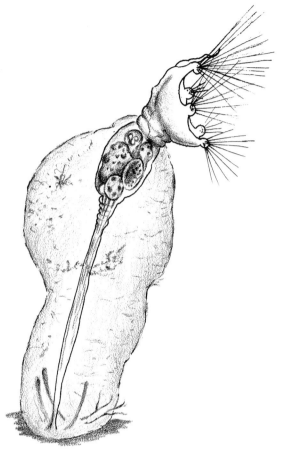

Figure 10-5. *Floscularia cornuta*, a sessile rotifer with funnel-shaped buccal field. Trunk and stalk surrounded by gelatinous mass. Female. (After Hudson.)

beneath the mouth. In living species, the beating membranelles of the trochal discs resemble two rotating wheels at the anterior of the body, and it is from this type of corona that the names rotifer and wheel animalcule are derived. The trochal discs are used both in swimming and in feeding, and the pedestals can be retracted when the discs are not functioning.

The head in bdelloid and notommatid rotifers carries a mid-dorsal projection called the rostrum (Fig. 10-3, *B*). This little projection bears cilia and sensory bristles at its tip. Other head structures in rotifers include the eye, which varies in number and location, and the retrocerebral organ. A typical retrocerebral organ consists of a pair of lateral subcerebral glands, located above and behind the brain (Figs. 10-3, *A* and 10-4, *B*) and a median retrocerebral sac, which is drained by a single duct. Prior to reaching the exterior, the duct forks to open through two pores on the apical field. The ducts of the glands accompany the ducts of the retrocerebral sac. Hyman (1951) believes that the retrocerebral organ is perhaps homologous to the frontal organ of flatworms. The function of this organ in rotifers is unknown.

The straight or saccular trunk composes the major part of the body. The cuticle is frequently much thickened to form a conspicuous encasement, called a lorica (Fig. 10-7). The lorica may be divided into distinct plates or ring-like sections and is usually ornamented with ridges or spines. The spines may be quite long and in some rotifers are movable. In

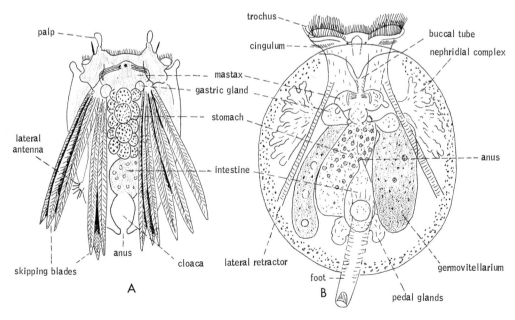

Figure 10-6. *A. Polyarthra trigla*, a pelagic rotifer with skipping blades. *B. Testudinella*, a turtle-shaped swimming rotifer. (Both after Hyman.)

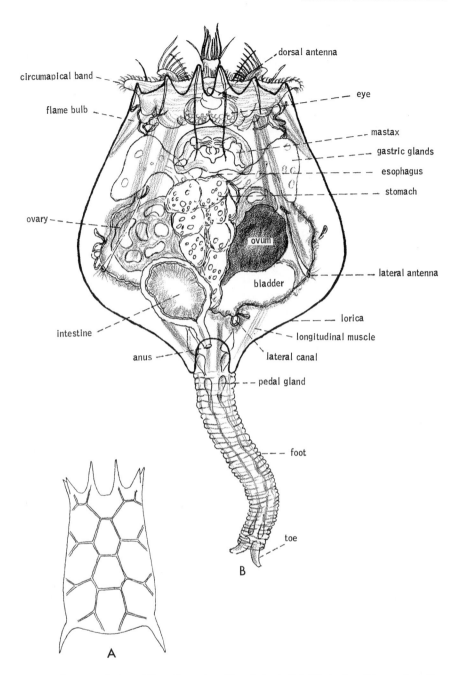

circumapical band

dorsal antenna

flame bulb

eye

mastax

gastric glands

esophagus

stomach

ovary

ovum

lateral antenna

bladder

intestine

lorica

longitudinal muscle

anus

lateral canal

pedal gland

foot

toe

B

A

Figure 10-7.   *A.* Lorica of *Keratella quadrata* (dorsal view). (Modified after Ahlstrom from Pennak.) *B.* A brachionid rotifer. (After Hudson.)

Polyarthra, the spines are flattened to form long skipping blades, which are located in two clusters of six each on either side of the body (Fig. 10-6, *A*).

Typically, the trunk bears three small projections called antennae. Two of the antennae are lateral and are located on each side of the trunk toward the posterior of the body; the other, which is sometimes paired, is located more anteriorly on the dorsal surface.

The antennae frequently bear sensory bristles at their tips.

The terminal portion of the body, or foot, is considerably narrower than the trunk region (Figs. 10-2 and 10-7, *B*). The cuticle is frequently ringed; and in many bdelloids (Fig. 10-2, *A*), the resulting segments, or joints, are able to telescope, enabling the foot to be extended or retracted. The end of the foot usually bears one to four projections called toes.

In both the crawling and sessile rotifers, the foot is used as an attachment organ; in these groups the foot contains 2 to 30 glandular syncytial masses called pedal glands (Fig. 10-8, *A*). These pedal glands produce an adhesive substance that is carried to the exterior by means of ducts opening onto the toes or other parts of the foot.

In a number of common bdelloids, such as *Philodina* (Fig. 10-2, *A*) and *Rotaria,* the pedal glands open onto the ends of two long and diverging conical spurs located near the end of the foot. Functionally the spurs replace the toes, which are very small in these genera. In some sessile rotifers, the secretion from the pedal glands is used in the construction of vase-like cases in which such rotifers live (Fig. 10-9, *B*). In planktonic rotifers, the foot is usually reduced or has disappeared altogether. Often it is turned ventrally.

Body Wall and Pseudocoel. The cuticle is secreted by the underlying epidermis, which is thin and syncytial and always possesses a constant number of nuclei. Beneath the epidermis are the body muscles (Fig. 10-8, *B*). Although some of the muscle fibers are circular (ring muscles) and some are longitudinal (retractor muscles), the body-wall musculature is not organized into distinct circular and longitudinal

sheaths as in flatworms. In addition to the circular and longitudinal muscles, muscular fibers extend from the body wall to the gut. The pseudocoel lies beneath the body wall and surrounds the gut and other internal organs. The pseudocoel is filled with fluid and a syncytial network of branching ameboid cells.

Locomotion. Rotifers move either by creeping leech-like over the bottom or submerged objects, or by swimming. Propulsion for swimming is always created by the beating cilia of the corona, and crawling movements are aided by the foot. The common bdelloids utilize both methods of locomotion. When the animal creeps, the corona is retracted, and the foot adheres to the substratum by using the adhesive secretion produced by the pedal glands. The animal then extends the body, attaches the rostrum, and detaches the foot to move forward and again grip the substratum. During swimming, which is only for short distances, the corona is extended, and the foot is retracted.

Pelagic rotifers swim continuously and never crawl; many benthic species very rarely swim. Among the many strictly pelagic species are a few colonial forms, such as *Conochilus* (Fig. 10-9, *A*). In *Conochilus,* the members of the colony are arranged to resemble a large number of trumpets radiating from a common center.

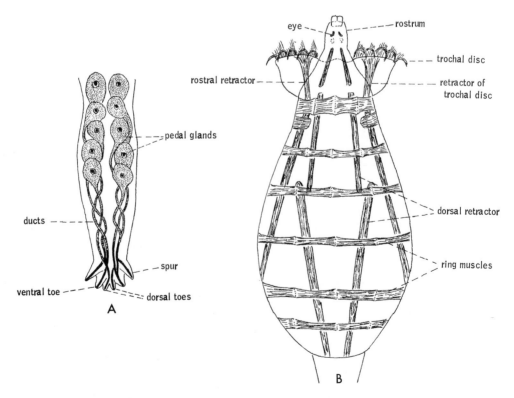

Figure 10-8.   *A.* Foot of *Embata parasitica,* showing pedal glands (dorsal view). *B. Rotaria* musculature (dorsal view). (Both after Brakenhoff from Hyman.)

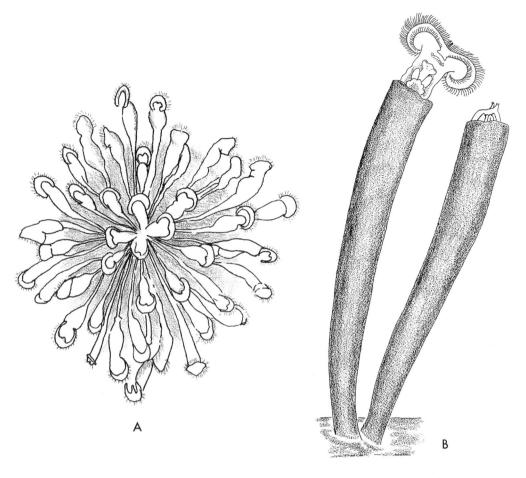

Figure 10-9. *A. Conochilus volvox,* a colonial pelagic rotifer. *B. Limnias ceratophylli,* a tubiculous rotifer in which the tube is secreted. (Both after Hudson.)

The combined ciliary action of the coronae propels the colony through the water.

Nutrition. The mouth of the rotifer is typically ventral and is usually surrounded by some part of the corona. Various modifications of the buccal field may provide the mouth region with lips or other projections, or the mouth may be located at the bottom of a funnel, as in the case of *Collotheca.* The mouth may open directly into the pharynx, or a ciliated buccal tube may be situated between the mouth and the pharynx, as in ciliary feeders. The pharynx, or mastax, (Figs. 10-2 and 10-7, *B*), is characteristic to all rotifers, and its structure is a distinguishing feature of the class. The mastax is usually oval or elongated in shape and highly muscular. The inner walls carry seven large projecting pieces, or trophi, composed of the same material that forms the cuticle. Six of the mastax pieces are paired; the remaining piece is unpaired. The mastax is used both in capturing and in macerating food, and its structure therefore varies considerably, depending upon the type of feeding behavior involved.

Rotifers are either ciliary or raptorial feeders. The ciliary feeders, of which the bdelloids are the most notable examples, feed on minute organic particles that are brought to the mouth in the water current produced by the coronal cilia. In the bdelloids, the membranelles of each trochal disc create a circular current. These two currents move in opposing directions and sweep food particles to the midline of the head. The particles then pass into the mouth through a groove between the anterior and posterior circlets of membranelles. The mastax of ciliary feeders (Fig. 10-10, *A*) is adapted to grinding; two of the pieces are extremely large, plate-like, and ridged. The two plates oppose each other, and the ridges form a surface for grinding. The mastax of ciliary feeders probably also acts as a pump, sucking in particles that have collected at the mouth.

The carnivorous species, which feed on protozoans, rotifers, and other small metazoan

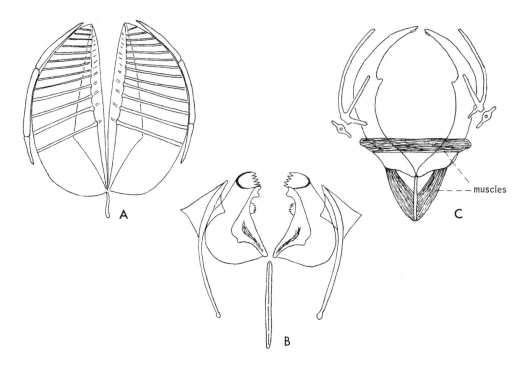

Figure 10-10.   Three types of mastax trophi. *A.* Mastax with trophi adapted for grinding. Note the two large ridged plates that provide grinding surfaces. (After Beauchamp from Hyman.) *B.* Mastax with trophi adapted for grasping. *C.* Mastax of *Synchaeta* with grasping, forceps-like trophi. (*B* and *C* after Hyman.)

animals, capture their prey either by grasping or by trapping. In the grasping species, the pieces of the mastax are constructed like a pair of forceps, the end of which can be projected from the mouth to seize the prey (Figs. 10-10, *B* and *C*). These forms have no buccal tube, and the mouth opens directly into the pharynx. After the prey is seized, it may be brought back into the pharynx and mascerated; more commonly the contents are sucked out, and the remainder of the body is discarded. The feeding behavior of the carnivorous *Chromogaster* has been described in detail by Kolisko (1938). These rotifers feed exclusively on dinoflagellates. After seizing the prey, the protruded end of the forceps-like mastax drills a little hole through the armor of the dinoflagellate and then quickly sucks out the body contents.

Those rotifers that capture prey by trapping include *Collotheca* and other forms that possess a funnel-like buccal field (Fig. 10-5). When small protozoans accidentally swim into the funnel, the setae-bearing lobes of the funnel fold inward preventing escape. The captured organism then passes into the mouth and pharynx. The mastax of trapping rotifers is often very much reduced.

Located in the mastax walls are two to seven glandular masses called salivary glands (Fig. 10-2, *A*). The salivary glands open through ducts just in front of the mastax proper. A

tubular esophagus, which may be either ciliated or lined with cuticle, connects the pharynx with the stomach. At the junction of the esophagus and stomach are a pair of gastric glands (Figs. 10-2 and 10-7, *B*), each of which opens separately by a pore into each side of the digestive tract. The stomach is a large sac or tube composed of distinct granular cells of a constant number except in the bdelloids and some others.

Surrounding the stomach is a network of muscle fibers. The stomach passes into a short intestine, the wall of which is syncytial and may be ciliated. The transition between these two regions may either be gradual or distinct, indicated by a sphincter. The excretory organs and the oviduct open into the terminal end of the intestine, which is sometimes called the cloaca. The anus opens onto the dorsal surface near the posterior of the trunk.

The gastric glands, and perhaps the salivary glands, are believed to produce enzymes; digestion is probably extracellular except in some pelagic forms that have lost the intestine and anus. Absorption takes place in the stomach.

Water Balance.   Typically, two protonephridia are present, one on either side of the body. Each rather long protonephridial tubule bears two to eight flame bulbs (Fig. 10-2, *A*), which are connected to the main tubule by a ciliated capillary. The two protonephridial tubules empty into a bladder (Fig. 10-7, *B*), which opens into the ventral side of the cloaca; in the bdelloids, there is a constriction between the stomach and the intestine, and the somewhat bulbous cloaca acts as a bladder (Fig. 10-2, *A*). The contents of the bladder or cloaca are emptied through the anus by constriction; often the pulsation rate is between one and four times per minute. Such a high rate of discharge is evidence of the osmoregulatory function of the protonephridia; within several minutes a volume of fluid equivalent to the entire weight of the animal is removed.

The Nervous System. The brain consists of a dorsal ganglionic mass lying over the mastax (Figs. 10-4, *B* and 10-11). The brain gives rise to a varying number of paired nerves that extend to the anterior sense organs; it also emits a single pair of pharyngeal nerves, which ramify over the muscles of the mastax as a nerve plexus (Fig. 10-11). The plexus connects to a single mastax ganglion that gives rise in turn to two visceral nerves, which innervate the gut. The largest nerves are two ventro-lateral ganglionated cords that emerge from the side of the brain and run the length of the body. These ventral

cords in turn give rise to other nerves and ganglia innervating the foot and other body structures.

The sense organs consist of sensory bristles, ciliated pits, and eyes. The sensory bristles in the head region are located in various places along the circumapical band or in the apical or buccal fields and probably represent modified cilia (Fig. 10-4, *A*). Such bristles are connected to an underlying sensory cell and are perhaps tactile organs. Similar sensory bristles are found on the dorsal and lateral antennae.

In some rotifers, the apical field contains two ciliated pits that lie above a patch of sensory nerve cells and probably function as chemoreceptors (Fig. 10-4, *A*). The eyes, which are absent in some rotifers, particularly the sessile forms, are simple ocelli and vary from one to five in number (Fig. 10-3, *A*). Usually one or two cerebral eyes composed of one pigmented photoreceptor cell are embedded in the brain. In addition to the cerebral eye, there may be one or two lateral eyes on either side of the corona and a pair of apical eyes in the apical field. The lateral and apical eyes each contain a number of photoreceptor cells that are arranged to resemble a cushion. Various

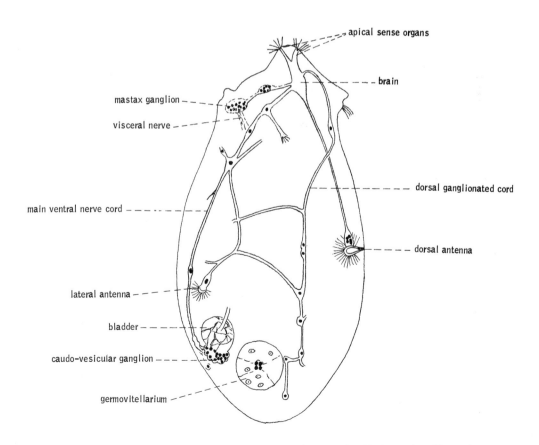

Figure 10-11.   Nervous system of *Asplanchna* (lateral view). (After Nachtwey from Hyman.)

combinations of these eyes appear in rotifers, but apical and lateral eyes are never present in the same species.

Reproduction.   Reproduction is entirely sexual, and like most other aschelminths, rotifers are dioecious. The males (Fig. 10-12) are always smaller than the females, and certain structures in the male, such as the cloaca, are degenerate or absent. The difference in size between sexes varies from species in which the males are only slightly smaller to forms in which the male is only one-tenth the size of the female. Parthenogenesis is common, and in the bdelloids no males have ever been reported.

The female reproductive system in most species consists of a single ovary and a yolk-producing vitellarium, both of which form a single body located anteriorly in the pseudocoel (Figs. 10-2 and 10-7, *B*). The vitellarium supplies yolk to the developing eggs, which then pass through an oviduct into the cloaca.

In the male a single sac-like testis and a ciliated sperm duct (Fig. 10-12) are present. Because a cloaca is usually absent in males, the sperm duct runs directly to a gonopore that is homologous to the anus in females and has the same position. Two or more glandular masses called prostate glands are associated with the sperm duct, and the end of the sperm duct is usually modified to form a copulatory organ. For example, the entire gonopore wall may protrude to act as a penis; or the end of the sperm duct may be modified into a tube with a heavy cuticular lining so that the whole tube can be everted.

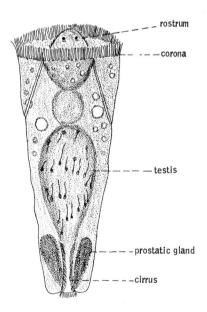

Figure 10-12.   Male of *Chonochilus* (female shown in Fig. 10-9, *A*). (After Wesenberg-Lund from Hyman.)

In most rotifers, copulation is reported to be by hypodermic impregnation. The penis of the male can penetrate any part of the female body wall, and sperm are deposited directly into the pseudocoel. Associated with hypodermic impregnation is a peculiar production of two types of sperm. One type is typical and functions in fertilization; the other type, which consists of a series of little rod-shaped bodies, reportedly only acts to aid the normal sperm in penetrating the female body wall.

Each ovarian nucleus forms one egg, and since only some ten to twenty such nuclei exist in most species, there is a corresponding limit to the number of eggs produced in the lifetime of a particular female. Each egg is surrounded by a shell and a number of egg membranes, all of which are secreted by the egg itself. The eggs are attached to objects on the substratum or may be attached to the body of the female.

Bdelloids, in which there are no known males and development is parthenogenetic, produce eggs that hatch into females only. In other rotifers, however, several different types of eggs are produced. One type, called an amictic egg, is thin-shelled, cannot be fertilized, and develops by parthenogenesis into amictic females. No reduction division takes place in the maturation of these eggs.

A second type of egg, called mictic eggs, are also thin-shelled but are haploid. If these eggs are not fertilized, they produce males parthenogenetically. If they are fertilized, they accumulate a larger amount of yolk material and secrete a heavy resistant shell. Such eggs are now called dormant eggs; in contrast to the thin-shelled unfertilized amictic and mictic eggs, which hatch in several days, these dormant eggs are capable of withstanding desiccation and other adverse environmental conditions and may not hatch for several months. Dormant eggs hatch into females.

The production of thin-shelled eggs that hatch in a short time and of dormant eggs that withstand adverse environmental conditions is particularly characteristic of rotifers that live in temporary ponds and streams. These species usually have a cyclic reproductive pattern. After spring rains with the advent of warmer temperatures, dormant eggs that have passed through the winter hatch into females. These females produce a number of generations of parthenogenetic females, each having a life span of one to two weeks.

In the late spring or early summer when this population reaches a peak and the ponds begin to dry up, males appear, after which dormant eggs carry the species through until the next season. Rotifers inhabiting large permanent bodies of fresh water may display a number of cycles or population peaks during the warmer months or may be present the whole year. A few rotifers such as *Asplanchna* and *Rotaria* are ovoviviparous; the eggs develop within the oviduct.

Embryology. Cleavage in rotifers is spiral and determinate but modified from the pattern described in the previous chapter. Nuclear division is completed early in development and never occurs again. In free-moving species, no larval development takes place. When the females hatch, they have all the adult features and attain sexual maturity after a growth period of a few days. The smaller males do not undergo a growth period but are sexually mature when they leave the egg. The sessile rotifer hatches as a free-swimming "larva" that is structurally very similar to free-swimming species. After a short period they settle down, attach, and assume the characteristics of the sessile adults.

Ecology and Distribution. Rotifers are largely cosmopolitan in distribution, most species living throughout the world, although some are restricted to particular regions. There are only approximately 50 strictly marine forms, most of which are littoral. However, to these must be added a considerable number of littoral species that also inhabit fresh water. The majority of fresh-water rotifers inhabit the substratum or live on submerged vegetation and other objects. In large bodies of fresh water, most of these bottom-dwelling species are limited to shallow water along the shores. Many species of sessile rotifers attach to vegetation and display a remarkable restrictiveness not only to the species of algae or plant to which they attach but also to the site of attachment on the plant. Some species, for example, attach only in the angle formed by the stem and the leaf stalk.

Pelagic or planktonic species swim continuously and display a number of adaptations for such a mode of existence. Usually the body is somewhat saccular in shape with a thin cuticle, and various flotation devices may be present, such as long spines or oil droplets. The foot has disappeared or has turned ventrally.

Many pelagic species undergo seasonal changes in body shape or proportions, a phenomenon known as cyclomorphosis and one that also takes place in small crustaceans. For example, certain individuals during one season of the year have spines that are longer or shorter than those during another season of the year. Formerly it was thought that these differences represented modifications of a flotation device correlated with changes in the density of the water. However, recent investigations

show that cyclomorphosis in rotifers is actually correlated with parthenogenesis. The first generation of females has long spines, but in each subsequent generation of parthenogenic females the spines become shorter. Thus, after a series of many generations, the spines are considerably shorter than those of individuals of the same species earlier in the season.

Most terrestrial rotifers are associated with mosses and lichens and are active only during the short periods when these plants are filled with water. During this time, these terrestrial rotifers swim about in the water films on the leaves and stems of the plants. These species are capable of undergoing desiccation, usually without the formation of a cyst, and can remain in a dormant state for as long as three to four years. Their resistance to both low temperatures and lack of moisture in such a dormant state is remarkable. Some species have been placed in liquid helium ($-272°C$) and in desiccators and vacuums without damaging effects.

There are quite a number of epizoic and parasitic rotifers. Epizoic and ectoparasitic rotifers live primarily on small crustaceans, particularly on the gills. Endoparasitic species inhabit snail eggs, heliozoans, the interior of *Volvox*, the intestine and coelom of earthworms, fresh-water oligochaetes, and slugs. One genus, *Proales,* is parasitic within the filaments of the fresh-water alga *Vaucheria* and produces gall-like swellings. In parasitic rotifers either the foot or the mastax becomes modified as an attachment organ, and the corona is reduced.

Class Gastrotricha

The gastrotrichs are a small class of marine and fresh-water aschelminths. Although not as abundant as the rotifers, many of the fresh-water gastrotrichs are common animals of ponds, streams, and lakes. The class is divided into two orders. The order Macrodasyoidea is entirely composed of marine species and have been reported chiefly from Europe. The order Chaetonotoidea contains all of the fresh-water species, as well as a few marine forms. The chaetonotoids are all bottom dwellers that crawl about over vegetation and other objects.

External Structure. Gastrotrichs are approximately the same size as rotifers and are also ciliated. The body is more or less elongated with a flattened ventral surface and a convex dorsal surface (Figs. 10-13 and 10-14, *A*). There is usually a distinct head, separated from the trunk by a constricted neck region. The trunk is typically straight and often has a forked posterior.

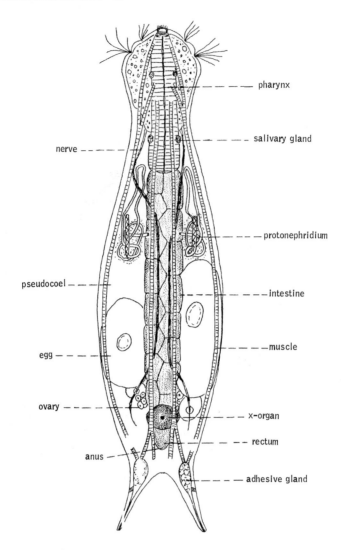

Figure 10-13.   Chaetonotoid gastrotrich (ventral view). (Modified after Zelinka from Pennak.)

The cilia are always restricted to the ventral surface of the trunk and head. The entire ventral surface may be ciliated; or, as in *Chaetonotus* (Fig. 10-14, *B*), the cilia may be arranged in two ventral longitudinal bands that run the length of the body. In other gastrotrichs, the cilia are present in patches arranged in two longitudinal bands or in a number of transverse rows (Fig. 10-14, *C*). In a few species, cilia are present only on the ventral surface of the head. The head ciliation is variable and frequently specialized. Commonly the cilia are arranged in tufts, as in *Chaetonotus* where four ciliated tufts exist, two on either side of the head. Frequently some of the cilia are modified into bristles, which may or may not be motile and are probably sensory in function. The cilia, especially the trunk cilia, are used in locomotion, which takes place by a gliding motion over the substratum, similar to locomotion in flatworms.

The highly specialized cuticle is the distinguishing feature of this class. Often the cuticle is modified in the form of scales, which may abut together or may overlap like shingles (Fig. 10-14, *D*). The scales are commonly ornamented with one or more spines, which may be quite long. In some species, adjacent scales are fused to form plates that cover the ventral surface and are also present on the head.

Adhesive tubes (Fig. 10-14, *A*) are present, as in rotifers. The number and position of the adhesive tubes vary, but they are commonly arranged in longitudinal rows, and as many as 250 may be present. Each tube is movable and supplied by a single gland cell. In

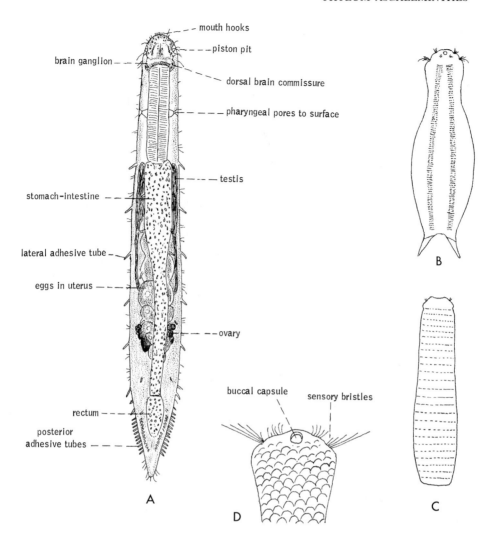

mouth hooks

piston pit

brain ganglion

dorsal brain commissure

pharyngeal pores to surface

testis

stomach-intestine

lateral adhesive tube

eggs in uterus

ovary

rectum

posterior
adhesive tubes

A

B

buccal capsule

sensory bristles

D

C

Figure 10-14.   *A. Macrodasys,* a macrodasyoid gastrotrich. *B.* Ventral ciliation in *Chaetonotus. C.* Ventral ciliation in *Thaumastoderma.* (*A, B,* and *C* after Remane from Hyman.) *D.* Anterior of *Lepidodermella,* showing cuticular scales. (Modified from Hyman.)

some species, however, adhesive tubes are situated in transverse rows or in clusters on the ventral surface of the head and the terminal part of the trunk. In *Chaetonotus* (Fig. 10-13) each of the forked ends at the posterior of the body carries one or two adhesive tubes. Some gastrotrichs move in a leech-like fashion or may be temporarily sessile, and the adhesive tubes play the same role in attachment to the substratum as they do in rotifers.

Internal Structure.   The body wall is essentially like that of rotifers, having a syncytial epidermis and bands of longitudinal and circular muscle fibers. The pseudocoel is much less extensive than in rotifers and in most gastrotrichs consists of only a small, slit-like space between the body wall and the gut. In the macrodasyoids, syncytial strands from the epidermis

have penetrated the pseudocoel to form a partition separating the cavity into two compartments, one enclosing the gut and the other lying just beneath the body wall.

The terminal mouth, which is often surrounded by small hooks, opens directly into the pharynx or, as in some chaetonotoids, opens into a small protrusible buccal capsule (Fig. 10-14, *D*), which is lined with cuticle and may bear ridges or projecting teeth. The pharynx, which is in no way similar to the mastax of rotifers, is an elongated tube, which may contain one to four bulbous swellings (Figs. 10-13 and 10-14, *A*). The pharyngeal wall is composed of columnar epithelium, radial muscle fibers, and some gland cells; the lumen is triangular and lined with cuticle. The pharynx opens into a cylindrical, tapered stomach-intestinal region, the walls of which are composed of a single layer of cuboidal or columnar epithelium. Gland cells are also present. The anus is located at the terminal end of the trunk.

Gastrotrichs feed on small dead or living organic particles, such as bacteria, diatoms, and small protozoans, all of which are sucked into the mouth by the pumping action of the pharynx. Little is known about gastrotrich digestion. It apparently takes place in the stomach-intestinal region and is probably extracellular.

A pair of protonephridia, each with a single flame bulb, is present in the order Chaetonotoidea, which includes all of the fresh-water gastrotrich species. The long, coiled nephridial tubules open through separate nephridiopores on the ventro-lateral surface near the middle of the trunk (Fig. 10-13).

The brain is composed of a ganglionic mass (Fig. 10-14, *A*) on each side of the anterior of the pharynx; the two masses are connected dorsally by a commissure. Each brain mass gives rise to a ganglionated cord that extends the length of the body. The sense organs are represented by the ciliated tufts and bristles on the head, as well as sensory hairs located over the general body surface. The exact function of the sense organs is still unknown, but they are probably tactile receptors. The chaetonotoids possess ciliated pits located on both sides of the head. In a few species, the bottoms of these pits can be projected as tentacles. Eye spots, which are clusters of pigment granules within certain brain cells, are present in a few species.

Reproduction. In contrast to all other aschelminths, gastrotrichs are hermaphroditic, although the male system of chaetonotoids has become so degenerate that functionally all individuals are females. The one or two ovaries, which are simply clusters of germinal cells, are located in the posterior of the trunk. On leaving the ovary, the eggs pass into a rather poorly defined space called a uterus located just in front of the ovaries; or the eggs pass into the central compartment of the pseudocoel, as in the macrodasyoids. The oviduct, which is only present in macrodasyoids, is single and contains an anterior seminal receptacle and a posterior copulatory bursa. The oviduct opens through the anus or through a separate female gonopore in front of the anus.

Although chaetonotoids lack an oviduct, the eggs pass through a sac-like structure called the x-organ, (Fig. 10-13) which opens onto the ventral surface of the body. The male system, which is limited to the macrodasyoids, contains one or two testes (Fig. 10-14, *A*), each with a sperm duct. The sperm ducts open to the outside through either separate pores or a common pore. The male gonopores are located ventrally, either anteriorly in the trunk or near the female gonopore. In a few gastrotrichs, such as *Macrodasys* and *Urodasys,* the terminal end of the sperm duct is modified to serve as a penis. Nothing is known about the transmission of sperm.

Studies on *Lepidodermella* indicate a life span of between 8 and 21 days, during which a female can lay up to five eggs. In fresh-water chaetonotoids, which are entirely parthenogenetic, two types of eggs are produced and attached to the substratum. One type is the dormant egg, like those of rotifers; the other type hatches in one to three days. Young gastrotrichs have all of the adult structures on hatching and reach sexual maturity in about three days. The cleavage is of the spiral type but is considerably modified.

Class Kinorhyncha

The class Kinorhyncha, also known as Echinodera, consists of a small group of marine aschelminths living in the muddy bottoms of coastal waters. The members of this class are somewhat larger than rotifers and gastrotrichs but are always less than one millimeter in length. The general body shape is similar to that of the gastrotrichs, there being a head and trunk separated by a neck region (Fig. 10-15, *A*). However, kinorhynchs differ from both rotifers and gastrotrichs in their complete lack of cilia.

A distinguishing feature of the class is the division of the cuticle into clearly defined segments. The head composes the first segment, the neck makes up the second segment, and the trunk in most species constitutes eleven segments. The cuticle of each segment is subdivided into one dorsal and two ventral plates, and the cuticle between the plates is very thin and flexible, permitting articulation (Fig. 10-16). The dorsal plate of each segment bears large median and lateral, recurved spines, from which the name Echinodera—spiny skin—is derived. The spines are movable and hollow, being filled with epidermal tissue. A single pair of adhesive tubes are located on the ventral surface of the anterior of the trunk.

The anteriorly located mouth is situated at the end of a protrusible cone, which is surrounded at the tip and the base by circlets of spines (Fig. 10-15, *B*), hence the name Kinorhyncha—spiny snout. The entire head can be withdrawn either into the neck or into the first trunk segment. In the former case, the cuticular

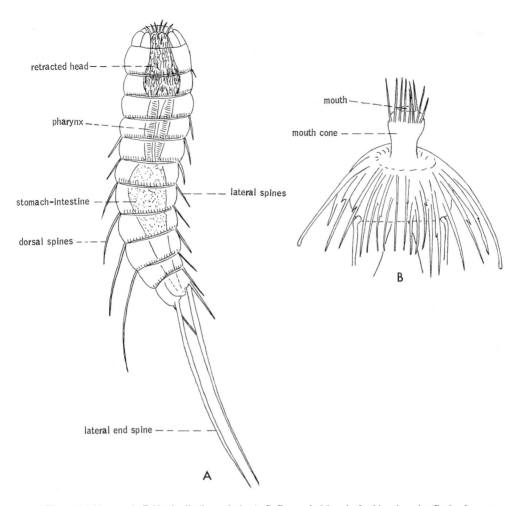

Figure 10-15.   *A. Echinoderella* (lateral view). *B*. Protruded head of a kinorhynch. (Both after Hyman.)

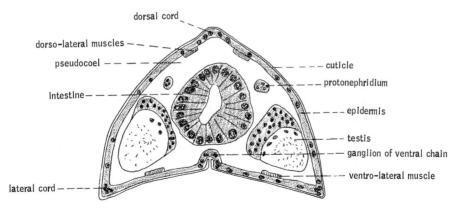

Figure 10-16.   The kinorhynch, *Pycnophyes* (transverse section at level of intestine). (After Zelinka from Hyman.)

plates of the neck are adapted for closing over the retracted head. A similar closing apparatus is present on the first trunk segment in those species in which both head and neck are retracted into the trunk.

The body wall of the kinorhynch is essentially like those of gastrotrichs and rotifers, although the epidermis is thickened along the mid-dorsal line and along each lateral angle to form longitudinal epidermal cords (Fig. 10-16), which bulge slightly into the pseudocoel. The pseudocoel is well developed and contains ameboid cells.

Kinorhynchs move by burrowing, because most of them live in mud and silt. The head extends into the mud and is anchored by the recurved spines. The body is then drawn forward until the head is retracted into the neck or trunk. The head is again pushed forward into the mud, and the process is repeated.

A few kinorhynchs feed on diatoms; the others are all detritus feeders and obtain organic material from the mud through which they burrow. A buccal cavity in the mouth cone leads into a barrel-shaped pharynx lined with cuticle (Fig. 10-15, *A*). Radial muscle fibers are present, as in gastrotrichs, but are located outside the epithelium. The entire pharynx is surrounded by longitudinal protractor muscle bands. The esophagus is also lined with cuticle and anteriorly receives the secretions of two dorsal and two ventral salivary glands. Posteriorly, two or more similar glands, called pancreatic glands, also empty into the esophagus. The esophagus leads into a tapered stomach-intestine, which lacks a cuticular lining. A short hindgut connects the stomach-intestine with the anus, which opens to the outside at the end of the trunk. The details of digestion are unknown.

There are two protonephridia, one on either side of the intestine, and each contains a single flame bulb. The two nephridiopores are located on the dorso-lateral surface of the eleventh segment.

The nervous system is closely associated with the epidermis. The brain consists of a nerve ring around the anterior of the pharynx, and from this ring arises a single, midventral nerve cord containing one cluster of ganglion cells in each segment. Other clusters of ganglion cells are located dorsally and laterally in each segment but are not interconnected to form a distinct cord. The sense organs consist of pigment-cup ocelli at the anterior of the body and sensory bristles located over the general body surface, especially the trunk.

Kinorhynchs are dioecious, but there is little sexual dimorphism. One pair of sac-like ovaries is located in the middle of the body, and a short oviduct leads from each ovary to a distinct female gonopore located on the last segment. One pair of testes and one pair of gonopores are similarly located in the male. The end of the sperm duct usually carries two to three penial spines or spicules. Neither copulation nor eggs have ever been observed. The young, or larvae, are not segmented and do not

Figure 10-17.   Early larva of the kinorhynch, *Echinoderella*. (After Nyholm from Hyman.)

possess spines or a head (Fig. 10-17). The digestive tract is also incompletely developed. When adult characteristics are acquired, periodic molts of the cuticle occur.

Not much is known about kinorhynchs; reported collections are few and scattered. However, most species are probably cosmopolitan. Specimens are obtained by bubbling air through a container of bottom mud and sea water. The kinorhynchs are brought to the surface by the air bubbles and are then removed from the surface film.

Class Priapulida

The class Priapulida consists of only three known species of cucumber-shaped animals that live buried in the bottom sand and mud in the littoral zones of the colder oceans. They range north from Massachusetts and are found in the Baltic Ocean and Siberian waters; some specimens have been taken from Antarctic waters.

The cylindrical body attains a length of several inches and is divided into an anterior proboscis region and a posterior trunk (Fig. 10-18, *A*). The proboscis, which comprises the anterior third of the animal, is somewhat barrel-shaped and ornamented with longitudinal, rib-like rows of papillae. The mouth invaginates into the anterior of the proboscis. The trunk is covered with small spines and tubercles and, like that of the kinorhynchs, is divided superficially into 30 to 100 segments. In the genus *Priapulus*, the terminal end of the

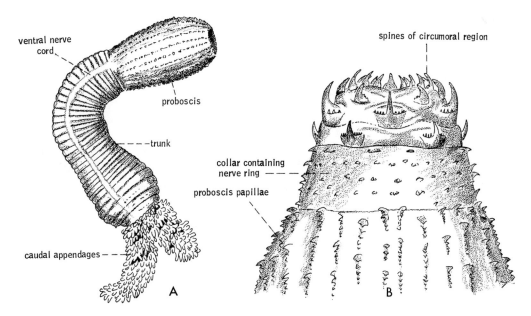

Figure 10-18.   *A. Priapulus bicaudatus* (ventral view). *B. Priapulus;* anterior end with mouth region everted. (Both after Theel from Hyman.)

trunk carries one or two caudal appendages, each consisting of a hollow stalk to which are attached many spherical vesicles. The function of these appendages is unknown.

The body wall is composed of one layer of epithelial cells lying beneath the cuticle and relatively well developed circular and longitudinal muscle layers. The priapulid pseudocoel, which contains amebocytes, differs from that of other aschelminths in being bounded by a noncellular membrane, which also forms mesenteries for the internal organs.

Priapulids are normally oriented vertically in the substratum so that the mouth is located at the surface of the substratum. However, they are capable of burrowing through bottom silt by extension and contraction of the body.

Priapulids are predacious and feed on soft-bodied, slow-moving invertebrates, particularly polychaete worms. The invaginated mouth region (Fig. 10-18, *B*), which is surrounded by several circlets of anteriorly curved spines, is everted in feeding; the spines are used in seizing prey. Food is passed to a muscular pharynx, which is lined with cuticle and is toothed. A straight, tubular intestine connects the pharynx with the short, terminal rectum. The anus is located at the posterior of the trunk. The processes by which digestion takes place are unknown.

Like that in the kinorhynchs, the priapulid nervous system is intimately associated with the epidermis of the body wall and consists of a nerve ring around the anterior of the pharynx and a single midventral ganglionated cord. No eyes are present, but the papillae on the proboscis and trunk probably have a sensory function.

The excretory and genital organs, in contrast to those of other aschelminths, are closely associated. On each side of the intestine, there is an elongated body containing a central protonephridial tubule. Masses of flame cells are connected to one side of the tubule and a single gonad is attached to the opposite side. The gonad is tubular and connects to the protonephridial tubule, which thus functions both as an excretory canal and a genital duct. Each protonephridial tubule opens separately through a nephridiopore at the end of the trunk. The protonephridia seem to be true excretory organs in the priapulids.

The sexes are separate, but knowledge of the reproduction of these animals is almost completely limited to the larvae, which are remarkably similar to rotifers. The priapulid larva possesses a distinct lorica, as well as a foot and toes with adhesive glands, and inhabits bottom mud as do the adults.

Many zoologists seriously question the inclusion of the priapulids within the phylum Aschelminthes, maintaining that the priapulid body cavity is actually a true coelom. When the embryology of these animals becomes better known, it may well be necessary to withdraw them from the Aschelminthes.

Class Nematoda

The Nematoda, commonly called round-worms, is the largest class of aschelminths and contains some of the most widespread and numerous of all multicellular animals. Free-living nematodes are found in the sea, in fresh water, and in the soil. They occur from the polar regions to the tropics in all types of environments, including deserts, hot springs, high mountain elevations, and great ocean depths. They are often present in enormous numbers. One square meter of bottom mud off the Dutch coast has been reported to contain as many as 4,420,000 nematodes. An acre of good farm soil has been estimated to contain from several hundred million to billions of terrestrial nematodes. A single decomposing apple on the ground of an orchard has yielded 90,000 roundworms belonging to a number of different species.

In addition to free-living species, there are many parasitic nematodes. The parasitic forms display all degrees of parasitism and attack virtually all groups of plants and animals. The numerous species that infest food crops, domesticated animals, and man himself make this class one of the most important of the parasitic animal groups. Because the parasitic round-worms (particularly those species of economic and medical significance) are covered extensively in any text on general parasitology, this discussion primarily concerns the free-living species.

External Structure.   Nematodes have a slender, elongated body with both ends gradually tapered in most species (Fig. 10-19). The majority of free-living nematodes, especially fresh-water and terrestrial forms, are less than one millimeter in length and are often microscopic. However, some marine species attain a length of 5 cm.

Two distinctive characteristics of nematodes are the relatively perfect cylindrical shape of the body and the rather striking radial or biradial arrangement of structures around the mouth. Some nematode specialists believe this symmetry is evidence that the ancestral members of the class at first assumed a sessile existence, in which the posterior of the animal was attached to the substratum with the body extended vertically in the water. As the result of such a sessile existence, a radial or biradial symmetry became superimposed upon the original bilateral plan of structure. The nematode body cannot be divided into distinct regions as can be done in other aschelminths. The nematode mouth is located at the tapered anterior of the animal and is surrounded by lips and sensory papillae or bristles.

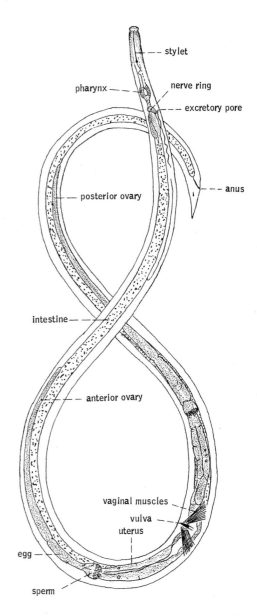

Figure 10-19.   A female *Dolichodorus heterocephalus,* an aquatic nematode. (After Cobb from Chitwood and Allen.)

In many marine nematodes (Fig. 10-20), which are considered the most primitive members of the class, six lip-like lobes border the mouth, three on each side. Each lobe bears an inner and an outer labial papilla, resulting in two circles of labial papillae composed of six papillae each. A third circle of four equidistantly spaced, cephalic papillae is located outside the lips. This primitive pattern is frequently modified in various ways. The number of papillae may be doubled, or the cephalic papillae may be moved inward to join the outer labial circle, resulting in two circles, with the outermost circle containing ten papillae. As a result of

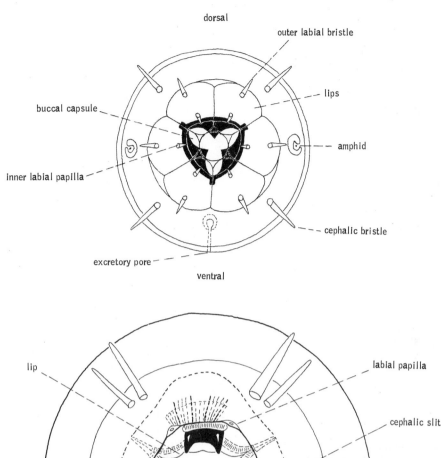

dorsal

outer labial bristle

buccal capsule

lips

amphid

inner labial papilla

cephalic bristle

excretory pore

ventral

lip

labial papilla

cephalic slit

jaw muscles

amphid

cephalic bristle

outer labial bristle

Figure 10-20.   *A.* Anterior of nematode, showing primitive plan of structure. *B.* Anterior of the marine nematode, *Enoplus.* (Both after de Coninck from Hyman.)

fusion, there are often only three lips in terrestrial and parasitic species.

The lips may carry a variety of cuticular projections, ranging from simple rounded eminences to complex branched or even featherlike projections (Fig. 10-21). In some species the cuticle at the base of the lips has developed into large overlapping plates called head shields; the lips of many carnivorous nematodes carry

crowns of teeth. As in other aschelminths, the cuticle of the general body surface is usually sculptured or ornamented in different ways. The surface may be pitted, ridged, or striated and may bear bristles, spines, warts, and papillae arranged in a variety of patterns. Scales may also be present, and in some cases the scales overlap like shingles.

A caudal gland is typical of most free-

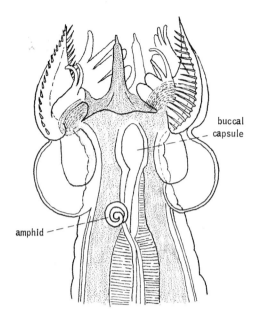

Figure 10-21.   Anterior of *Wilsonema* showing ornate feather-like projections borne by the lips. (After Steiner from Hyman.)

living nematodes. The gland opens at the posterior tip of the body, which is sometimes drawn out to resemble a tube-like tail. The caudal gland in nematodes is homologous to the adhesive tubes of other aschelminths.

Body Wall.   The nematode cuticle is considerably more complex than that of other aschelminths and is composed of several layers having different chemical compositions and different structural arrangements. The epidermis is usually cellular but may be syncytial. A striking feature of the nematode epidermis is the expansion of the cytoplasm into the pseudocoel along the mid-dorsal, midventral,

and midlateral lines of the body (Figs. 10-22, *A* and 10-23, *C*). The bulging epidermis thus forms longitudinal cords that extend the length of the body. All epidermal nuclei are restricted to these cords and are typically arranged in rows. Secondary, or subsidiary cords, are present in some species and are located between the four longitudinal cords.

The muscle layer of the body wall is composed entirely of longitudinal fibers arranged in bands, each strip occupying the space between two longitudinal cords. The nematode pseudocoel is spacious and filled with fluid. No free cells are present, but fixed cells, located either against the inner side of the muscle layers or against the wall of the gut and against the internal organs, are characteristic of many nematodes.

Locomotion.   Considering the class as a whole, locomotion is poorly developed in nematodes; the thrashing movements, involving an alternate bending and straightening of the body so commonly observed in many species, apparently have no locomotor significance. Some species that live in algae are capable of swimming short distances by means of undulatory movements of the body; but since most nematodes are benthic, crawling is the typical mode of locomotion. The ventral cuticle usually bears some type of projection that aids the animal in gripping the surface. Crawling movements in some species are similar to those in earthworms; in others, crawling involves a leech-like or looping movement, in which the adhesive gland, or special elongated ventral bristles called stilt bristles (Fig. 10-22, *B*), provide a means of attachment. In one group of nematodes, stilt bristles are actually used as legs and are lifted and moved forward on the substratum in steps.

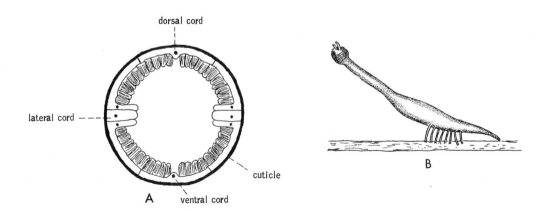

Figure 10-22.   *A*. Transverse section through body wall of a marine nematode. (After Filipjev from Hyman.) *B*. Draconematid nematode with stilt bristles. (After Stauffer from Hyman.)

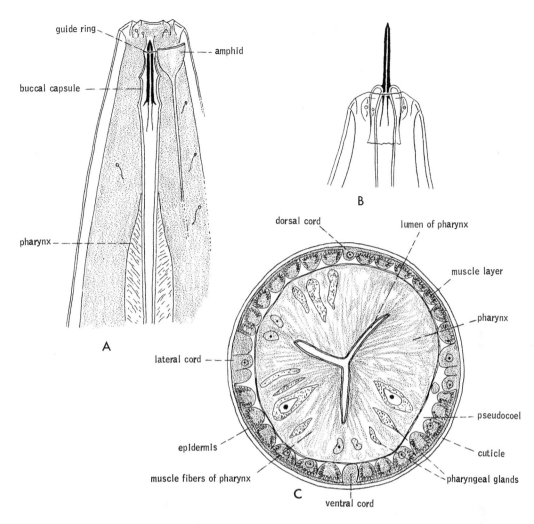

Figure 10-23. *A. Nygolaimus,* a dorylaim nematode; anterior end with spear retracted. *B.* With spear projected. (*A* and *B* after Thorne from Hyman.) *C.* Transverse section of nematode through pharynx. (After Chitwood from Hyman.)

Nutrition. Many free-living nematodes are carnivorous and feed on small metazoan animals, including other nematodes. Others, particularly marine species, are herbivorous and feed on diatoms and algae. A large number of terrestrial species pierce the cells of plant roots and suck out the contents. There are many saprophagous nematodes which live on dead organic matter such as dung or on the decomposing bodies of plants and animals. However, some species that live in dead organic material apparently feed on associated bacteria and fungi and are therefore not truly saprophagous. This is probably true of the common vinegar eel, *Turbatrix aceti,* which lives in the sediment of nonpasteurized vinegar.

The mouth of the nematode opens into a buccal capsule (Figs. 10-20 and 10-23, *A*), which is somewhat tubular and lined with cuticle. The cuticular surface is often strength-ened with ridges, rods, plates; or it may bear a large number of teeth. The teeth are especially typical of carnivorous nematodes; they may be small and numerous or limited to a few large jaw-like processes (Fig. 10-20, *B*). The feeding habits of *Mononchus papillatus,* which is a toothed nematode, have been described by Steiner and Heinly (1922). This terrestrial carnivore, which has one large dorsal tooth and two smaller ventro-lateral teeth, consumes as many as 1000 other nematodes during its life span of approximately 18 weeks. In feeding, the lips of this nematode are attached to the prey and an incision is made in it by the large tooth. The contents of the prey are then pumped out by the pharynx.

In some carnivores, as well as in many species that feed on the contents of plant cells, the buccal capsule carries a long hollow or solid spear (stylet) (Fig. 10-23, *A* and *B*), which can be protruded from the mouth. The stylet is used to puncture the prey; and when the stylet is hollow, it acts as a tube through which the contents of the victim are pumped out. In the stylet-bearing herbivores, it is used to penetrate the plant cell walls.

The buccal capsule leads into a tubular, muscular pharynx (Figs. 10-19 and 10-23, A). The pharyngeal lumen (Fig. 10-23, C) is triangular with one angle always located toward the midventral line (a characteristic feature of nematodes), and the pharyngeal lumen is lined with cuticle. The wall is composed of a syncytial epithelium, gland cells, and radial muscle fibers. The anterior walls of the pharynx usually contain special pharyngeal glands, which open into the anterior lumen of the pharynx or into the buccal cavity.

In the predacious *Aphelenchoides*, which possesses a hollow stylet, secretions from the pharyngeal glands pass into the prey after it is punctured; they apparently have a paralyzing action and initiate digestion. To what extent this is true of other nematodes is unknown.

Frequently the pharynx contains one or more swellings or bulbs (Fig. 10-19 and 10-26, B), which may be separated by valves. From the pharynx, a long tubular intestine of columnar epithelium extends the length of the body. A short cuticle-lined rectum (cloaca in males) connects the intestine with the anus, which is located on the midventral line just in front of the posterior tip of the body (Fig. 10-19).

Digestion is presumably extracellular although the details of the digestive processes in free-living nematodes is virtually unknown.

Excretion.   Protonephridia are absent in all nematodes and apparently disappeared with the ancestral members of the class. However, nematodes do possess a peculiar system of gland cells or tubules that may have an excretory function, although conclusive evidence is still lacking. Primitively, as is true in marine nematodes, the system is glandular in nature and consists of usually one but sometimes two large gland cells. This gland cell (or cells) is called a renette gland (Fig. 10-24, A) and is located ventrally in the pseudocoel near the

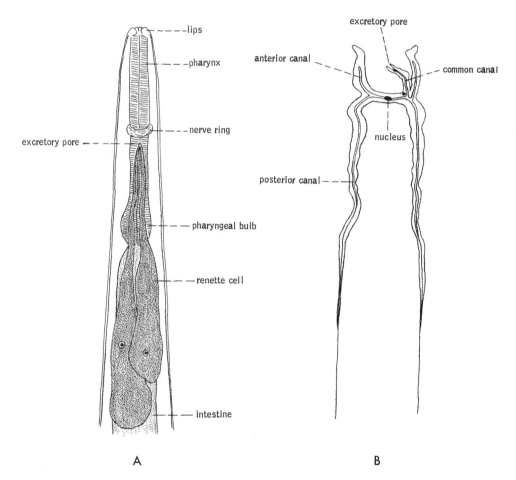

A   B

Figure 10-24.   *A.* Two-celled renette of *Rhabdias.* (After Chitwood from Hyman.) *B.* H-type tubular excretory system. (After Törnquist from Hyman.)

junction of the pharynx and intestine. The gland cell is provided with a neck-like duct that opens ventrally on the midline as an excretory pore.

From such a primitive glandular structure a more specialized tubular system is believed to have evolved. In the tubular system, three long canals are arranged to form an H (Fig. 10-24, *B*). Two are lateral and extend inside the lateral longitudinal cords. The two lateral canals are connected by a single transverse canal, from which a short common excretory canal leads to the excretory pore, located ventrally on the midline. In many nematodes, that part of the two lateral canals anterior to the transverse canals has disappeared, so that the system is shaped like a horseshoe.

Evidence supporting the belief that the tubular system arose from renette glands is evident in a number of nematodes having systems that are transitional between the two types. For example, in *Rhabdias* (Fig. 10-24, *A*) two renette cells exist instead of one, and the necks of the cells join together to form a common excretory canal leading to the outside. In other nematodes that possess two renette cells, each cell possesses a long slender extension representing perhaps the beginnings of a tubular type of system. Some nematodes even possess a transverse tubular connection between the two renette cells. In other nematodes, which possess a tubular system in the adult, the juvenile stages contain renette cells.

Nervous System. The nervous system does not differ greatly from that of other aschelminths (Fig. 10-25, *A*). The brain is represented by a circumenteric nerve ring with a lateral ganglion attached to either side of the ring. From the brain ring extend six anterior papillary nerves, innervating the labial and cephalic papillae or bristles. The papillary nerves are radially arranged—two dorso-lateral, two lateral, and two ventro-lateral. In addition to the six papillary nerves, a pair of nerves runs to the amphids (sense organs that are described later).

A number of nerves extend posteriorly

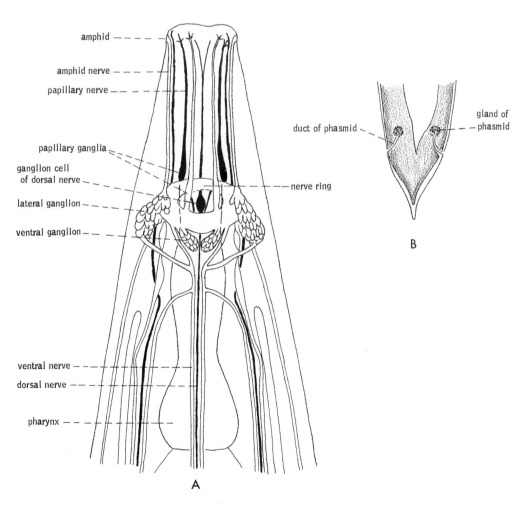

Figure 10-25.   *A.* Anterior part of *Cephalobellus* nervous system. (After the Chitwoods from Hyman.) *B.* Phasmids at posterior of *Rhabditis.* (After Chitwood from Hyman.)

from the brain and run within the longitudinal cords. The largest of these is the ventral nerve, which arises as a double cord from the ventral side of the nerve ring. In the region of the excretory pore, the double cord fuses and continues posteriorly as a ganglionated chain. The ventral nerve terminates in an anal ganglion, from which fibers extend to innervate the tail region. Another posterior nerve is a dorsal nerve that arises from the mid-dorsal side of the nerve ring. This is a motor nerve, and except for a small dorsal ganglion located near its point of origin, no ganglia are present along its length.

A pair of lateral nerves arise from the lateral ganglia of the brain. These lateral nerves are sensory and ganglionated and extend inside the lateral longitudinal cords. The terminal, or lumbar, ganglion of these nerves also innervates the tail. In addition to the lateral and median nerves, ventro-lateral and dorso-lateral nerves exist in some nematodes. A visceral nervous system is present and is composed of a pharyngeal and a rectal division. The pharyngeal division consists of three nerves from the brain to the walls of the pharynx. The rectal division arises from the anal ganglion.

The principal sense organs in nematodes are the papillae or bristles and the amphids. The labial and cephalic papillae are jointed projections of the cuticle (Fig. 10-20), and each contains a nerve fiber from the papillary nerves. Sensory bristles may also be present elsewhere on the body surface; they are sometimes each supplied with a gland cell. The amphids, which reach their highest form of development in the aquatic nematodes, especially marine species, are blind invaginations of the cuticle. One amphid is situated on each side of the head; they are located more or less in the radius of the cephalic bristles (Figs. 10-20 and 10-21). The nature of the invagination varies considerably. It may resemble a simple pouch, opening to the exterior through a slit-like pore; or, more commonly, the amphids are blind tubes, which may be spiraled or looped. The bottom of the pouch or the end of the tube contains a cluster of nerve cells and unicellular gland cells. The amphids are believed to be chemoreceptors.

In the tail region of the nematode are a pair of unicellular glands, called phasmids (Fig. 10-25, B), which open separately on either side of the tail. The phasmids are perhaps glandulo-sensory structures and reach their best development in parasitic nematodes. A pair of eyes are located one on each side of the pharynx of a few marine and fresh-water nematodes. The eyes are of the pigment-cup type with lenses derived from the cuticle. In addition to the specialized sense organs, free nerve endings, which are probably sensory, are abundant over the general body surface.

Reproduction.   Most nematodes are dioecious. Males are typically smaller than females, and the posterior of the male is curled like a hook (Fig. 10-26, A). The gonads are tubular and may be long and coiled. In most nematode orders, the germ cells arise from a large terminal cell located at the distal end of the tube; the germ cells gradually pass through the length of the gonad, during which time growth and maturation take place. In males there is usually one tubular testis, which passes more or less imperceptibly into a long sperm duct (Fig. 10-26, B). The sperm duct eventually widens to form a long seminal vesicle.

A short and muscular ejaculatory duct, containing a varying number of prostatic glands, connects the seminal vesicle with the rectum. The prostatic secretions are adhesive and aid in copulation. The wall of the rectum, or cloaca (since it functions as a part of the reproductive system), is evaginated to form two pouches, which join before they open into the cloacal chamber. Each pouch contains a spicule of cuticle having a cytoplasmic core (Fig. 10-26, A). The spicules vary considerably in length and shape but are usually short and shaped somewhat like a stylet. Special muscles cause the spicules to protrude through the cloaca and out of the anus. In many nematodes the dorsal, and sometimes even the ventral and lateral, walls bear special, cuticular pieces that act as guides in the movement of the spicules through the cloacal chamber.

Usually, two straight or coiled ovaries, which are oriented in opposite directions, are present (Fig. 10-19). The ovary gradually extends into a long, tubular oviduct and then in turn into a much-widened, elongated uterus. Each of the two uteri opens into a short, common, muscular tube called the vagina, which leads to the outside through the gonopore. The female gonopore is located on the midventral line, usually in the midregion of the body. The upper end of the uterus usually functions as a seminal receptacle; in some nematodes the seminal receptacles are separate pouches that open laterally from the upper end of the uterus.

In copulation, the curved posterior of the male nematode is usually coiled at right angles around the body of the female in the region of the genital pores (Fig. 10-26, B). The copulatory spicules of the male are extended through the cloaca and anus and are used to hold open the female gonopore during the transmission of the sperm into the vagina. A nematode sperm is peculiar in that it lacks a flagellum and moves in a more or less ameboid manner. An

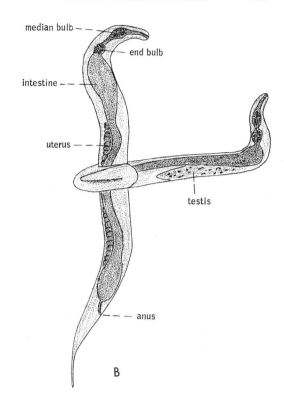

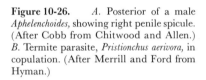

A

B

Figure 10-26.   *A*. Posterior of a male *Aphelenchoides*, showing right penile spicule. (After Cobb from Chitwood and Allen.) *B*. Termite parasite, *Pristionchus aerivora*, in copulation. (After Merrill and Ford from Hyman.)

exception to the usual copulatory mechanism occurs in *Trichosmoides crassicauda*, a nematode parasitic in the urinary tract of rats. The male of this species is minute and lives inside the vagina of the female.

After copulation, the sperm migrate to the upper end of the uterus, where fertilization takes place. The fertilized egg throws off a thick fertilization membrane, which hardens to form the inner part of the shell. To this inner shell is added an outer layer, which is secreted by the uterine wall. The outer surface of nematode eggs is sculptured in various ways and is often important in the detection of parasitic infections from fecal smears. Nematode eggs are stored in the uterus prior to deposition, and not infrequently embryonic development begins while the eggs are still in the female.

Some terrestrial nematodes, particularly the rhabditoids, are hermaphroditic. Sperm develop before the eggs do and are stored. Self-fertilization takes place after the formation of the eggs. Parthenogenesis has also been reported in some terrestrial nematodes. A most remarkable type of parthenogenesis takes place in *Rhabditis monhystera* (Belar, 1924). In this species, males are present, sperm are produced, and copulation occurs. However, the sperm only initiate cleavage and do not fuse with the nucleus of the eggs that are destined to develop into females.

The deposition of the eggs of free-living nematodes is still not well known. Marine species rarely produce more than fifty eggs, which are often deposited in clusters. Terrestrial species may produce up to several hundred eggs, which are deposited in the soil. Many parasitic nematodes and some free-living forms, such as the vinegar eel, are ovoviviparous.

Embryology. Cleavage is determinate, but the spiral pattern has disappeared. A coeloblastula is formed, and gastrulation is by epiboly. The blastocoel persists as the pseudocoel. A remarkable feature of the embryology of nematodes is the very early separation of the future germ cells from the somatic cells. Only in the germ cells is chromosomal integrity maintained. In the somatic cells the chromosomes tend to become somewhat disintegrated through breakage and loss. As in other aschelminths, the various organs of the body contain a fixed number of cells, and these cells have been attained by the time hatching takes place. For example, in *Rhabditis* there are 200 nerve cells, 120 epidermal cells, and the digestive tract is composed of 172 cells.

The young, sometimes called larvae, have all of the adult structures when they hatch except for certain parts of the reproductive system. Growth is accompanied by four molts of the cuticle, the first two of which may occur within the shell before hatching.

Ecology.   Nematodes exist in all types of habitats. With few exceptions, aquatic species are limited to the substratum, and marine forms are found everywhere from the shore to great depths. Marine nematodes occur in enormous numbers wherever the bottom mud is rich in organic matter, regardless of the latitude; they are probably the most abundant metazoan animals of ocean bottoms. Fresh-water nematodes exist in all types of fresh-water habitats. Some species are even adapted for existence in fast flowing mountain streams. Anchorage is maintained in such forms by the adhesive caudal glands at the end of the body.

Other unusual aquatic habitats include hot springs, in which the water temperature may reach 53° C., and the water in tropical, epiphytic pitcher plants. The largest populations of fresh-water nematodes live in the shallow water around lakes. In large lakes, there is often a distinct zonation of the nematode species from the shore line to deeper water. There is almost no overlap of fresh-water and marine faunas, and it is therefore believed that fresh-water nematodes probably evolved from terrestrial species, which came in turn directly from marine forms.

Terrestrial species apparently live in the film of water that surrounds each soil particle, and they are therefore actually aquatic. Although nematodes exist in enormous numbers in the upper few inches of soil, the population decreases rapidly at greater depths. Furthermore, the numbers are greater in the vicinity of plant roots. In addition to the more typical terrestrial habitats, nematodes have also been reported to exist in the accumulations of detritus in leaf axils and in the angles of tree branches. Mosses and lichens maintain a characteristic nematode fauna; and these species, like rotifers and other moss inhabitants, are able to withstand extreme and prolonged desiccation, as well as great extremes of temperature.

A great many fresh-water and terrestrial nematodes have a cosmopolitan distribution. Birds, animals, and floating debris to which small amounts of mud adhere are undoubtedly important agents in the spread of nematodes. Many of the saprophagous nematodes that inhabit dung utilize dung insects as a means of transportation from one habitat to another. *Rhabditis dubia,* for example, during a special stage, wraps itself around the body of the dung-breeding psychodid fly. When the fly alights on new dung, the nematode detaches. Dung beetles are similarly utilized by other species of nematodes.

Parasitism.   The great numbers of parasitic species attack virtually all groups of animals and plants and, except for the absence of ectoparasitic forms on animals, display all degrees and types of parasitism. The types of nematode parasitism and the relation of parasitism to the life cycle have been succinctly outlined by Hyman (1951). A modification of this outline is presented here.

(*a*) Completely free-living. Life cycle is direct, and all stages are free-living.

(*b*) Ectoparasites of plants as juveniles. Juvenile worms feed on the external cells of plants by puncturing the cell wall with stylets and sucking out the cell contents. Adults are free-living in the soil.

(*c*) Endoparasites of plants as juveniles. Worms in juvenile stage enter the plant body and feed on the living cells, producing death of tissue or gall-like structures. Reproduction takes place within the host, and the new generation of juveniles migrates to other plants.

(*d*) Saprophagous type of zooparasitism. Adults and juveniles are free-living in soil, but worm in late juvenile stage enters an invertebrate. The host is not injured, and the worm feeds on the dead tissues when the host dies.

(*e*) Zooparasitic in juvenile stages only. Early stages of development take place within the body of an insect host. Worms in final developmental stages and adults are free-living in the soil.

(*f*) Zooparasitism in adult females only. The young develop in the soil. After copulation the male dies, and the female enters an invertebrate host to produce the next generation.

(*g*) Phytoparasitic juveniles and zooparasitic adults. The female worm produces juveniles within a plant-feeding insect host. Young worms are deposited on plants by insect when laying its eggs. Juveniles enter plant and remain as endoparasites. When mature and after copulation, the female enters the larva of the host, which lives on the same plant. The larva metamorphoses into an adult and deposits a new generation of juvenile worms.

(*h*) Zooparasitic juveniles and phytoparasitic adults. Early stages of development take place within an invertebrate host. Later worms in juvenile stages leave the host and enter the plant on which the host feeds. Worms complete development and reproduce as phytoparasites. The new generation of young then enter the host.

(*i*) Typical zooparasitic life cycle. Worm is entirely parasitic within a single vertebrate or invertebrate host. Transmission from one host to another is by eggs or newly hatched young. In this group belong many common nematode parasites of man, such as hookworms, *Ascaris,* rectal pinworms, and others.

(*j*) Zooparasitic with an intermediate host. Varying degrees of juvenile development take place within an intermediate host, after which there is a re-infection of the primary host, where reproduction takes place. The guinea worms and the filarial worms (elephantiasis) are of this type.

(*k*) Zooparasitic with two intermediate hosts. Such a life cycle is known for only one genus of nematodes, *Gnathostoma*. Early juvenile stages are passed in the water flea, *Cyclops*. Later stages are parasitic in a fish, frog, or a snake. The life cycle is completed in a carnivorous mammal that has fed on an infected second stage host.

Class Nematomorpha

The remaining aschelminths are a small group of extremely long worms, commonly known as hairworms, which comprise the class Nematomorpha. The adults are free-living, but the juveniles are all parasitic in insects and crustaceans. In most hairworms, which comprise the order Gordioidea, the adults live in fresh water and damp soil. The single genus *Nectonema*, which makes up the order Nectonematoidea, is pelagic in marine waters. The body of nematomorphs (Fig. 10-27) is extremely long and thread-like, and lengths of a foot or more are typical. The diameter, however, is usually not much more than one millimeter. The color is usually dark brown to blackish. The hair-like

nature of these worms is so striking, that it was formerly thought that they arose spontaneously from the hairs of a horse's tail.

Like nematodes, the nematomorph body wall is composed of a thick outer cuticle covering the body surface; a cellular epidermis with a ventral, or with a dorsal and a ventral, longitudinal cord; and a muscle layer of longitudinal fibers only. Except in *Nectonema*, the pseudocoel is somewhat reduced by mesenchymal tissue. The digestive tract is vestigial, and the adults do not feed. The nervous system is very similar to that of priapulids and kinorhynchs, in that it is composed of an anterior nerve ring and a ventral cord. The sexes are separate, and in gordioids the two long cylindrical gonads extend the length of the body. As in nematodes, the sperm ducts empty into the rectum, or cloaca, but there are no copulatory spicules present. The ovaries are peculiar in that they transform into uteri because of the development of lateral diverticula after the production of eggs. The oviducts also empty into the cloaca.

Hairworms live in all types of fresh-water habitats in temperate and tropical regions of the world. The females are very inactive, although the males commonly swim or crawl about by whip-like motions of the body. Copulation is similar to that in nematodes, and the eggs are deposited in the water. The young on hatching have a protrusible proboscis armed with spines (Fig. 10-28), somewhat similar to that of priapulids and acanthocephalans.

After hatching, the young enter an arthro-

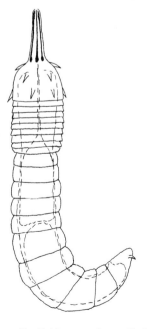

Figure 10-27.   Three female gordioid nematomorphs, or horsehair worms. (Courtesy of R. W. Pennak.)

Figure 10-28.   Gordioid worm larva. Proboscis is protruded. (After Pennak.)

pod host living in the water or along the shore. Hosts are most commonly beetles, cockroaches, crickets, or grasshoppers. The larvae of *Nectonema*, the only marine hairworms, parasitize hermit crabs and true crabs. On penetration of the host, the young enter the hemocoel where development is completed. Their nutrition as parasites is apparently accomplished by direct absorption of food materials through the body wall, and perhaps the production of enzymes that break down the host tissues in the vicinity of the worm follows. After several weeks to months of development, during which a number of molts occur, the worms leave the host as almost completely formed adults. Emergence only occurs when the host is near water. Sexual maturity is shortly attained during the free-living adult phase of the life cycle.

PHYLUM ACANTHOCEPHALA

The acanthocephalans are a phylum of some 500 species of parasitic, worm-like pseudocoelomates. The adults possess a number of structural characteristics that would seem to indicate a close relationship to the aschelminths. However, the embryology, particularly the origin of the pseudocoel, is peculiar and warrants their inclusion in a separate phylum.

All are endoparasites requiring two hosts to complete the life cycle. The juveniles are parasitic within crustaceans and insects, while the adults live in the digestive tract of vertebrates. The body of the adults is elongated and composed of a trunk and a short anterior proboscis and neck region (Fig. 10-29, *A*). Most acanthocephalans are only a few centimeters long, although some species may attain a length of one-half meter. As in priapulids, the proboscis is covered with recurved spines (Fig. 10-29, *B*), hence the name Acanthocephala—spiny head.

The acanthocephalan proboscis and neck can be retracted into the anterior of the trunk. The trunk is typically covered with spines and not infrequently divided into superficial segments. The body wall is peculiar in that it is composed of a syncytial, fibrous epidermis that contains channels or canals. The canals may form either a network or distinct longitudinal

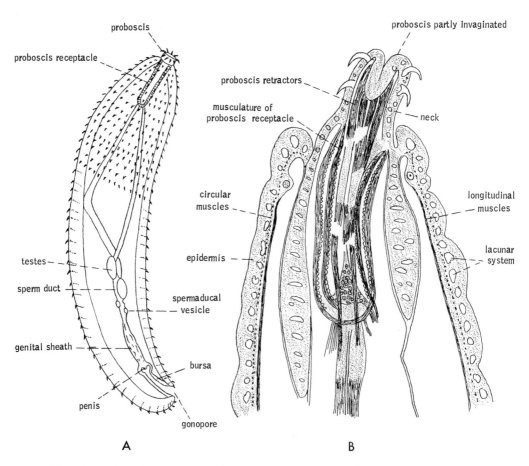

Figure 10-29.   *A. Acanthogyrus.* (After Thapur from Hyman.) *B.* Section through anterior of *Acanthocephalus.* (Modified after Hamann from Hyman.)

channels. The canals are not connected with the exterior or the interior of the animal. They are filled with fluid and are believed to represent a means of circulation of nutritive material absorbed from the host. These worms possess no digestive system, and food is absorbed directly through the body wall from the host. Two protonephridia, which are associated with the reproductive system, are present in one order. The nervous system is composed of a ventral, anterior ganglionic mass, from which arises a varying number of single and paired longitudinal cords.

The sexes are separate, and the gonopore is located at the end of the trunk. The male system includes a protrusible penis, and the eggs are fertilized within the body of the female. Development of the eggs takes place within the female pseudocoel; and when a larval stage having a rostellum with hooks is attained, each larva is enclosed within a shell. The developed eggs (i.e., the encased larvae) then pass out of the vertebrate host with the feces. If the eggs are eaten by an insect, an isopod, or an amphipod, the larvae emerge from the eggs, bore through the gut wall of the host, and become lodged in the hemocoel.

Development in acanthocephalans ceases when the worms have almost reached adulthood. When the intermediate host is eaten by a fish, a bird, or a carnivorous mammal, the worms attach to the intestinal wall of the vertebrate host, using the spiny proboscis. Acanthocephalans often exist in great numbers within the vertebrate host and can do considerable damage to the intestinal wall. As many as 1000 acanthocephalans have been reported present in the intestine of a duck and 1154 in the intestine of a seal.

PHYLUM ENTOPROCTA

The remaining pseudocoelomates comprise a small phylum of some sixty species of mostly sessile animals called the Entoprocta, which were formerly included in the phylum Bryozoa, or moss animals. However, the majority of bryozoans are true coelomate animals and of a higher level of structure than the entoprocts. The phylum Bryozoa is now split into two separate phyla—the coelomate Ectoprocta and the pseudocoelomate Entoprocta. However, the relationship of the entoprocts to the other pseudocoelomate phyla is obscure.

Except for the single fresh-water genus *Urnatella* (Fig. 10-30, *A*), all entoprocts are marine and live attached to rocks, shells, pilings, or are epizoic on crabs, sponges and other marine animals. A few entoprocts are solitary,

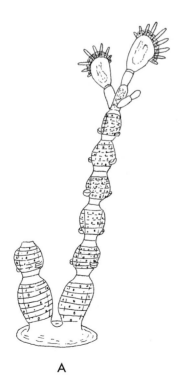

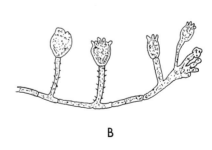

Figure 10-30. *A. Urnatella gracilis,* a fresh-water entoproct. (Modified after Leidy from Pennak.) *B.* Part of a colony of the marine entoproct, *Pedicellina.* (After Ehlers from Hyman.)

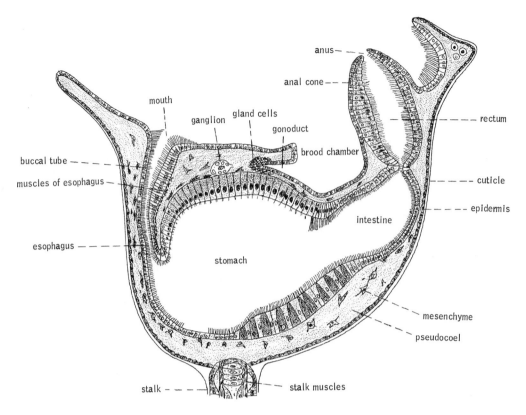

Figure 10-31. *Pedicellina* (median sagittal section). (After Becker from Hyman.)

but the majority are colonial. All are very small and never exceed five millimeters in length. The body (Figs. 10-31 and 10-32) consists of a somewhat ovoid or boat-shaped structure called the calyx, which contains the internal organs, and consists of a stalk by which the calyx is attached to the substratum (Fig. 10-30, *B*). The attached underside of the calyx was originally the dorsal surface, and the upper or free side was originally the ventral surface. The upper margin of the calyx bears an encircling crown of 8 to 30 tentacles, which represent extensions of the body wall.

The area enclosed by the tentacles is known as the vestibule and contains the mouth at one end and the anus at the other. Both mouth and anus, however, are located within the tentacular crown, hence the name Entoprocta—inner anus. The mouth and anus mark the anterior and posterior of the animal and impose a biradial symmetry on the animal. The body is somewhat compressed laterally, and gaps in the tentacular crown appear opposite the mouth and opposite the anus. The bases of the tentacles are connected by a membrane that is pulled over the crown when the tentacles contract and fold inward over the vestibule (Fig. 10-32, *B*).

There may be a single stalk, as in the solitary *Loxosoma* (Fig. 10-32); several stalks

from a common attachment disc; or, as in most entoprocts, numerous stalks arising from a horizontal creeping stolon or upright branching stems (Fig. 10-30). The stalk is separated from the calyx by a septum-like fold of the body wall and is commonly partitioned into short cylinders, or segments. In some species, certain segments are swollen with longitudinal muscle fibers that, on sudden contraction, produce a curious flicking motion in members of the colony.

The body wall consists of a cuticle and an underlying cuboidal epithelium. The muscle layer is limited to longitudinal fibers along the inner wall of the tentacles, in the tentacular membrane, and in certain areas of the calyx. The extensive pseudocoel, which also extends into the tentacles, is filled with a gelatinous material containing both free and fixed cells.

Entoprocts are ciliary feeders, consuming organic particles and small plankton, such as diatoms and small protozoans. The beating of cilia on the sides of the tentacles causes a water current to pass into the vestibule between the tentacles and then to pass upward and out (Fig. 10-33). When suspended food particles pass between the tentacles, they become trapped on frontal cilia located on the inner surface of the tentacles. These frontal cilia beat downward

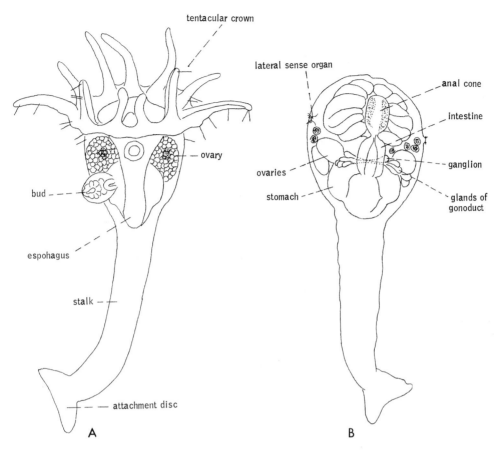

Figure 10-32.   Solitary marine entoproct, *Loxosoma. A.* Expanded. *B.* Retracted. (Both after Atkins from Hyman.)

carrying the food particles to the base of the tentacle. Here the food particles are carried in ciliated vestibular grooves that run along the inner base of the tentacular crown on both sides toward the mouth. If disturbed or if encumbered with excessive detritus, an entoproct ceases feeding and folds its tentacles over the vestibule (Fig. 10-32, *B*).

The digestive tract is U-shaped and completely ciliated (Fig. 10-31). Food particles entering the mouth pass into a short buccal cavity and then into a large bulbous stomach, which composes the major part of the alimentary canal. Certain areas of the stomach wall are glandular and are believed to produce enzymes for extracellular digestion. Absorption is believed to take place in the stomach and in the short ascending intestine located at the posterior of the stomach. The intestine opens into a rectum, and wastes are egested through the anus, located at the posterior of the vestibule. Not infrequently the anus is mounted on a projection called the anal cone.

Two flame bulbs are located between the stomach and the vestibule. The two nephridial ducts from the flame bulbs unite prior to opening through a single median nephridiopore located just behind the mouth. The nervous system contains a single, large, median ganglion situated between the stomach and the vestibule (Fig. 10-31). The ganglion gives rise to three pairs of nerves to the tentacles and three pairs of nerves to the stalk and to certain parts of the calyx. Sensory cells with projecting bristles are located over the body surface, especially on the outer side of the tentacles and along the calyx margin.

Asexual reproduction by budding is common in all entoprocts, and it is by this means that extensive colonies are formed. In most species, the buds arise from segments of the stolon or from the upright branches. In the solitary entoprocts, the buds develop from the calyx (Fig. 10-32, *A*), separate from the parent, and then attach as new individuals. Many entoprocts are capable of shedding the calyx when environmental conditions are unfavorable. New calyces are regenerated when environmental conditions are again suitable.

The phylum includes both dioecious and

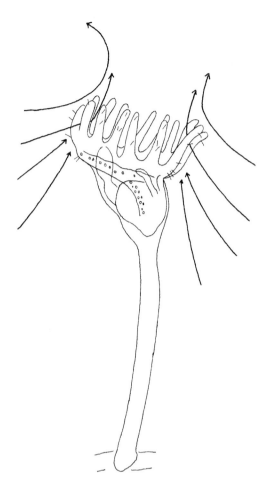

Figure 10-33.   *Loxosoma,* showing water currents during feeding. (After Atkins from Hyman.)

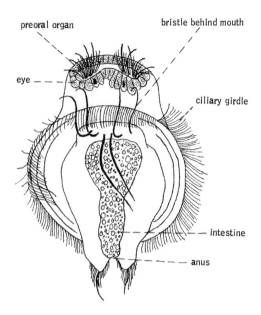

Figure 10-34.   *Loxosoma* larva (ventral view). (After Atkins from Hyman.)

of annelids and mollusks, possesses an apical tuft of cilia at the anterior end and a ciliated girdle around the ventral margin of the body (Fig. 10-34). After a short free-swimming existence, the larva settles to the substratum and undergoes a complex metamorphosis, in which the future calyx rotates 180 degrees to attain the inverted symmetry of the adult.

hermaphroditic species. In dioecious species, two rounded gonads are located between the vestibule and the stomach (Fig. 10-32, *A*). The simple gonoducts become confluent and empty through a single, median gonopore located just posterior to the nephridiopore. In hermaphroditic species, there are two testes and two ovaries, and all four gonoducts become confluent prior to reaching the gonopore.

The eggs are believed to be fertilized in the ovaries, although how sperm reach the ovaries is uncertain. After ovulation, each egg is covered with a membranous envelope secreted by the wall of the gonoduct. When the egg leaves the gonopore, the egg membrane becomes attached to the vestibule wall between the gonopore and the anus. This region of the vestibule acts as a brood chamber (Fig. 10-31); it is here that embryonic development takes place. A ciliated, free-swimming larva hatches from the egg. The larva, which is known as a trochophore because of its superficial resemblance to the trochophore larva

BIBLIOGRAPHY

Belar, L., 1924: Die Cytologie der Merospermie bie Rhabditis-Arten. Ztschr. Zellforsch. Mikro. Anat., 1.

Edmondson, W. T. (ed.), 1959: *In* Ward and Whipple's Freshwater Biology. 2nd Ed., John Wiley, New York. Keys and figures to the fresh-water pseudocoelomates. Nemata (B. G. Chitwood and M. W. Allen), pp. 368–401; Gordiida (B. G. Chitwood), pp. 402–405; Gastrotricha (R. B. Brunson), pp. 406–419; Rotifers (W. T. Edmondson), pp. 420–494.

Goodey, T., 1951: Soil and Freshwater Nematodes. John Wiley, New York.

Hatschek, B., 1878: Studien über Entwicklungsgeschichte der Anneliden. Ein Beitrag zur Morphologie der Bilaterien. Arb. Zool. Inst., Wien, 1.

Hyman, L. H., 1951: The Invertebrates: Platyhelminthes and Rhynchocoela. Vol. II. McGraw-Hill, New York, pp. 18–31.

Hyman, L. H., 1951: The Invertebrates: Acanthocephala, Aschelminthes, and Entoprocta. Vol. III. McGraw-Hill, New York. An extensive, general, authoritative account of the pseudocoelomate phyla. Excellent illustrations and bibliography.

Hyman, L. H., 1959: The Invertebrates: Smaller Coelomate Groups. Vol. V. McGraw-Hill, New York, pp. 750–754.

Jagersten, G., 1955: On the early phylogeny of the Metazoa. Zool. Bidrag, 30.

Koliske, A., 1938: Nahrungsaufnahme bei *Anapus*. Int. Rev. Ges. Hydrobiol., *37*:296–305.

Marcus, E., 1958: On the evolution of the animal phyla. Quart. Rev. Biol., *33*:24–58.

Pennak, R. W., 1953: Freshwater Invertebrates of the United States. Ronald Press, New York. Chapters on the rotifers, gastrotrichs, nematodes, hairworms, and entoprocts, each with a brief introduction to the group and keys and illustrations for the identification of common fresh-water forms.

Remane, A., 1954: Die Geschichte der Tiere. *In* Evolution der Organismen (G. Heberer, ed.), 2nd Ed., Lief. 2.

Sedgewick, A., 1884: On the origin of metameric segmentation and some other morphological questions. Quart J. Micro. Sci., *24*:43–82.

Steiner, G., and Heinly, H., 1922: Possibility of control of *Heterodera* by means of predatory nemas. J. Washington Acad. Sci., *12*:367–386.

Chapter 11

THE ANNELIDS

The phylum Annelida comprises the segmented worms and includes the familiar earthworms and leeches, plus a great number of marine and fresh-water species of which most persons are completely unaware. A shovelful of muddy sand taken from the shore along a coastal sound at low tide usually brings to light a much richer and far more spectacular collection of "worms" than could be found in a backyard garden.

In general, the annelids attain the largest size of any of the worm-like invertebrates and display the greatest structural differentiation. The most distinguishing characteristic of the phylum is the division of the body into similar parts, or segments, which are arranged in a linear series along the antero-posterior axis. This condition is called metamerism, and each segment is termed a metamere. The youngest segments occur at the posterior end of the series; the new segments are formed in front of the terminal segment, or pygidium.

Metamerism is not restricted to external structures but occurs internally as well; in fact, it is probable that metamerism first evolved in relation to internal organs and then proceeded toward the outside. In perfect or "ideal" metamerism, which is more nearly attained in annelids than in other phyla, all the body organs—musculature, blood vessels, nerves, excretory organs, and gonads—are repeated in each segment (Fig. 11-1). Only the digestive system is unaffected, although it too extends through every segment. In annelids, even the coelom is compartmented by intersegmental transverse mesenteries called septa.

Metamerism has arisen independently twice in the Animal Kingdom—in the ancestral annelids and in the chordates. Numerous theories have been proposed to account for the origin of this condition. One of the most popular is the *Fission Theory*. Transverse fission is a common method of asexual reproduction among flatworms, and in some turbellarians new fission planes form before complete detachment takes place at the old fission planes. This results in a chain of partially separated and differentiated individuals, or zooids (Fig. 7-18, *D*). The Fission Theory postulates that metamerism arose through such incomplete separations of chains of zooids. The chief objection to this theory is the lack of gradation of ages in such a chain of zooids as is true of the segments in a metameric animal. As soon as one zooid reaches an advanced state of differentiation, it may undergo transverse fission, so that eventually a random distribution of ages develops in the chain.

Another explanation of the origin of metamerism is gaining favor with many invertebrate zoologists, including Hyman (1951). There is a general tendency for the organs of bilateral animals to distribute themselves more or less evenly along the course of the body. Assuming that such a "premetameric" state existed in the elongated body of the ancestral annelids, true metamerism could have arisen by the imposition of a segmental musculature, resulting from an undulatory mode of locomotion.

Annelids possess a more or less straight digestive tract running from the anterior mouth

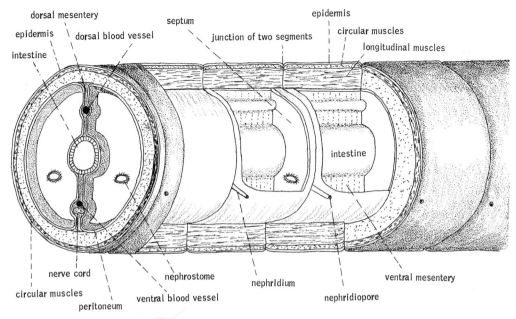

Figure 11-1. Annelid segments. (After Kaestner.)

to the posterior anus. The gut is located in the middle of the coelom and is held in position by longitudinal mesenteries and by the septa, through which the gut penetrates (Fig. 11-1). Digestion is extracellular. Excretion takes place by means of nephridia, primarily metanephridia, and characteristically one pair exists per segment. There is usually a well developed blood-vascular system, in which the blood is usually confined to vessels—that is, the system is closed. The nervous system consists of an anterior, dorsal ganglionic mass, or brain; a pair of anterior connectives surrounding the gut; and a long double or single ventral nerve cord with ganglionic swellings and lateral nerves in each segment.

The phylum is divided into three classes. The class Polychaeta contains the marine annelids and displays the more primitive features of the phylum. The polychaetes probably gave rise to the class Oligochaeta, which includes the fresh-water annelids and the terrestrial earthworms. From some stock of freshwater oligochaetes arose the class Hirudinea, the leeches. In comparison to the other two classes, the oligochaetes display a structure that is somewhat intermediate between that of the ancestral polychaetes and the more specialized leeches.

CLASS POLYCHAETA

Polychaete worms are very common marine animals, but their secretive habits result in their being overlooked by casual observers. The majority of species are five to ten centimeters long with a diameter ranging from two to ten millimeters; but some syllids are no longer than two millimeters, while one species of *Eunice* may attain a length of three meters. Many polychaetes are strikingly beautiful and are colored red, pink, or green or possess a combination of colors; some are iridescent.

The "ideal" polychaete is perfectly metameric with each of the cylindrical body segments being identical and each bearing a pair of lateral, fleshy, paddle-like appendages called parapodia (Fig. 11-4). At the anterior of the worm is a well developed head, called the prostomium, which bears eyes, antennae, and a pair of palps. The mouth is located on the ventral side of the body between the prostomium and the first trunk segment, which is called the peristomium. The terminal segment, the pygidium, carries the anus. Few polychaetes attain such an "ideal" condition. The different modes of existence displayed by the worms of this class have caused varying degrees of modification in this basic plan of structure.

Polychaetes can be divided into two groups—errant (free-moving) forms and sedentary forms. The errant polychaetes, or Errantia, include some species that are strictly pelagic, some that crawl about beneath rocks or shells, some that are active burrowers in sand and mud, and many species that construct and live in tubes. The errant tube-dwellers partially or completely leave their tubes during the search for food or during the breeding season; some carry the tube about with them.

The sedentary polychaetes, or Sedentaria, are largely tubicolous—that is, are tube-dwellers. The tube is fixed to the substratum and usually only the head of the worm ever emerges from the opening. The distinction between errant and sedentary polychaetes is not a sharp one, because some species are intermediate to the two modes of existence; yet the two groups can be taxonomically separated. It is particularly important to note that a tube-dwelling habit does not necessarily imply a completely sedentary existence.

Tube Structure. The tubes vary greatly both in form and composition. The simplest are mucus-lined burrows in sand or mud, such as are excavated by *Nereis;* but in most cases the tube is a very distinct structure that can be removed intact from the surrounding bottom. The most common type of tube is composed of sand grains cemented together with mucus. *Owenia;* the fan-worm, *Sabella;* and the bamboo worms, *Clymenella* (Fig. 11-2, *C*) and *Axiothella* all construct long straight sand-grain tubes that are planted vertically in the bottom. A small part of the tube projects like a chimney above the surface. Frequently, as in *Owenia* and *Sabella,* the tube is made more flexible through the secretion of a membranous lining on the inner surface of the tube.

Even more flexibility is attained in the tubes of *Owenia* by the use of flat sand grains that are attached only at one edge and overlap adjacent grains (Figs. 11-2, *D* and 11-36, *B*). The outer surface of this tube resembles tile roofing with the free edges of the grains projecting upward. Because *Owenia* carries its tube about and uses the chimney end of the tube to burrow through the sand like a screw, a flexible tube is an obvious advantage. *Cistenides* and *Pectinaria* build very delicate sand-grain tubes, which are cone-shaped (Fig. 11-2, *E*). The worm lives head downward in the sand with the pointed end of the tube located just beneath the surface.

Membranous or parchment-like tubes are built by many polychaetes. The parchment tube of some species of *Chaetopterus* is U-shaped, over one foot long, and about three-quarters of an inch in diameter (Fig. 11-21). Each end of the tube is tapered to the size of a large drinking straw. The tube lies buried in the intertidal zone (alternately covered and exposed by the tides) with the two chimneys projecting just above the sand surface.

Some species of *Diopatra* and *Onuphis* build heavy, conspicuous membranous tubes that are fixed vertically in the sand bottom. The projecting chimney of the tube is bent over and flares at the end like a ship's funnel (Fig. 11-3, *B*). This permits these worms, which are raptorial feeders, to emerge from the opening of the tube and seize passing prey. The chimneys are camouflaged with bits of shell, seaweed, and other debris. One species of *Autolytus* constructs a membranous tube of chitin, which is attached to the stems of hydroids. The methods by which the tubes are constructed are described after the discussion of polychaete anatomy.

External Anatomy. Some errant polychaetes nearly attain the generalized or "ideal" polychaete body plan; the sedentary worms, on the other hand, are the most highly modified.

THE HEAD. Such errant worms as *Nereis* (Fig. 11-4), *Autolytus, Diopatra* (Fig. 11-3, *A*), and *Aphrodite* (Fig. 11-5, *B*) possess well developed heads. The dorsal prostomium of the head projects forward like a shelf over the mouth and bears one or two pairs of eyes and from one to five antennae. A pair of anterior lateral palps are usually present and may be short and fleshy, as in *Nereis,* or long, as in *Aphrodite.*

The prostomium is followed by the peristomium, which forms the lateral and ventral margins of the mouth. With some exceptions the peristomium represents in part the first trunk segment or in some instances two or more fused trunk segments; however, these segments are usually modified, and the entire region can be considered part of the polychaete "head". In most errant species the peristomial parapodia are reduced or absent.

The head of burrowing polychaetes is frequently reduced to a pointed or rounded cone. This is true of *Glycera* (Fig. 11-6, *A*), *Orbinia, Scoloplos, Lumbriconereis,* and *Ophelia* (Fig. 11-6, *C*). Appendages and eyes are very much reduced or completely absent. The entire body of *Lumbriconereis* and *Ophelia* is strikingly similar to that of the earthworms.

The head region of sedentary polychaetes is usually highly modified. Since these worms seldom leave the tube, many have become ciliary feeders, and the head has been transformed into a structure for collecting, sifting, and sorting detritus material or plankton. In some instances the head has also become the principal center for respiratory exchange. The prostomium proper is usually quite small and reduced to an upper lip over the mouth, although the structures representing the palps may be enormously developed. Antennae and eyes may be absent.

Among the most beautiful of the sedentary polychaetes are the fanworms, or feather dusters, which comprise the group Sabelliformia. All of the many common members of this group—*Sabella* (Fig. 11-12, *B*), *Potamilla, Hydroides* (Fig. 11-7, *A*), *Serpula,* and *Spirorbis*—have the

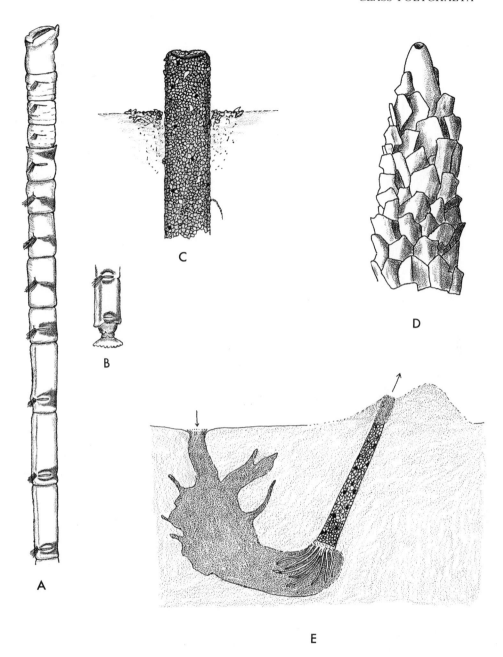

Figure 11-2.   *A.* Anterior half of the bamboo worm, *Clymenella. B.* Posterior. *C.* Sand-grain tube of *Clymenella. D.* Anterior of *Owenia* sand-grain tube with outer layer of overlapping sand grains. The membranous secreted part of the tube projects at the tip. (After Watson.) *E. Pectinaria* and sand-grain tube in normal, buried position. Arrows indicate path of water current. (After Wilcke from Kaestner.)

first segment, or peristomium, developed to form a crown consisting of few to many pinnate processes called radioles. The radioles are rolled up when the worm withdraws its anterior into the free end of the tube. In *Myxicola* the radioles composing each half of the funnel are joined by a thin membrane. The serpulid fanworms, which build calcareous tubes, have the most dorsal radiole on one or both sides modified into a long stalked knob called an operculum (Fig. 11-7). The operculum acts as a protective plug at the end of the tube when the crown is withdrawn, and it may also serve as a brood pouch.

The entire head region of both *Sabellaria* and the cone worm, *Cistenides,* is adapted for blocking the opening of the tube. In *Sabellaria* the head region is formed by three or more anterior setigerous segments to create a broad

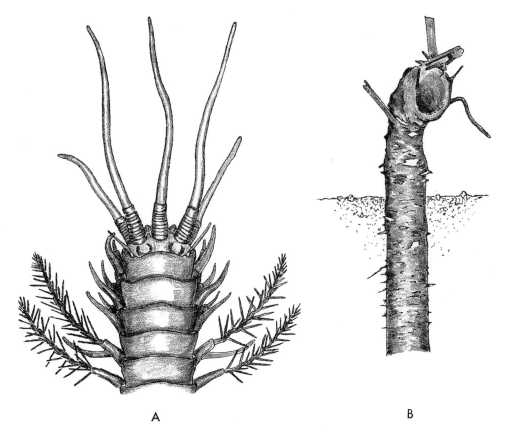

Figure 11-3.   *A.* Head and first two gill-bearing segments of *Diopatra* (dorsal view). *B.* Funnel-shaped parchment tube of *Diopatra.*

truncate operculum (Fig. 11-8); this is equipped with a number of concentric circles of heavy bristles, which are modified setae. The truncate end of the head fits the aperture of the sand tubes in which these worms live.

The terebellid polychaetes, which include the genera *Terebella* and *Amphitrite* (Fig. 11-9), possess a head region composed of the prostomium and the peristomium. Like that of the fanworms, the peristomium is provided with ingestive organs, including a cluster of long, highly mobile and contractile tentacles. In a living worm, the tentacles are a pink coiling mass, which obscures the other head structures.

PARAPODIA. The most distinguishing feature of polychaetes is the presence of parapodia, the pair of lateral appendages extending from each of the body segments. A typical parapodium is a fleshy projection from the body wall and is more or less laterally compressed (Fig. 11-10, *A*). The parapodium is biramous, consisting of an upper division, the notopodium, and a ventral division, the neuropodium. Each division is supported internally by one or more chitinous rods, or acicula; some of the parapodial muscles are attached to the inner ends of

the acicula. The distal end of each of the two parapodial divisions is invaginated to form a pocket or setal sac, in which are located many projecting chitinous bristles, or setae. Each simple seta is secreted by a single cell at the base of the setal sac and usually projects a considerable distance beyond the end of the parapodial division.

Since the parapodia are compressed, the setae attached to each parapodium tend to spread out like a fan. The setae assume a great variety of different shapes, which are of importance in the identification of polychaetes, and the setal bundles of a particular species are usually composed of more than one type of seta. A few of the many forms of setae are illustrated in Figure 11-10, including a jointed type characteristic of many common errant polychaetes. New setae are continually produced by the setal sac as older setae are lost.

A filamentous process projects both from the base of the notopodium on the dorsal side of the worm and from the base of the neuropodium on the ventral side; these processes are known as the dorsal and the ventral cirri. In most polychaetes the cirri are not much longer

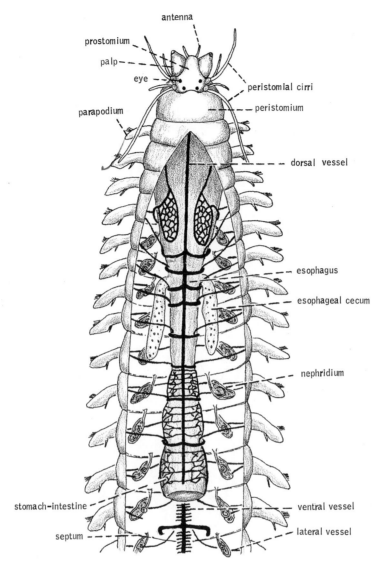

Figure 11-4.   *Nereis* (dorsal view). (After Brown.)

than the notopodia or neuropodia; but members of the burrowing family Cirratulidae, such as *Cirratulus* (Fig. 11-11, *A*) and *Audouinia,* are peculiar in having long, thread-like, dorsal cirri, although the remainder of the parapodium is very much reduced.

The notopodia and neuropodia assume various shapes in different species and may be subdivided into several lobes. Usually the two divisions (the notopodium and the neuropodium) are differently shaped, or one division may be somewhat reduced. In fact, reduction in some polychaetes has resulted in uniramous parapodia. This is true, for example, in most phyllodocids (Fig. 11-23, *C*), where all of the notopodium has disappeared except the dorsal cirrus.

The most highly developed parapodia appear in the errant polychaetes, such as *Nereis, Diopatra, Phyllodoce,* and the scale worms. The scale worms are so named because of the peculiar plate-like scales, or elytra, which are borne on the dorsal surface of the body (Figs. 11-5 and 11-11, *B*). Each scale is a modified dorsal cirrus resembling a plate attached to the dorso-lateral body wall by a little stalk (Fig. 11-22). The scales often exist in pairs and may appear on all or most segments or only on alternating segments. Although there are fewer elytra than segments, the elytra may be large enough to cover the entire dorsal surface of the worm. Each scale overlaps the scale behind it, and the right and left sides overlap alternately.

In *Polynoë* and other genera of scale worms,

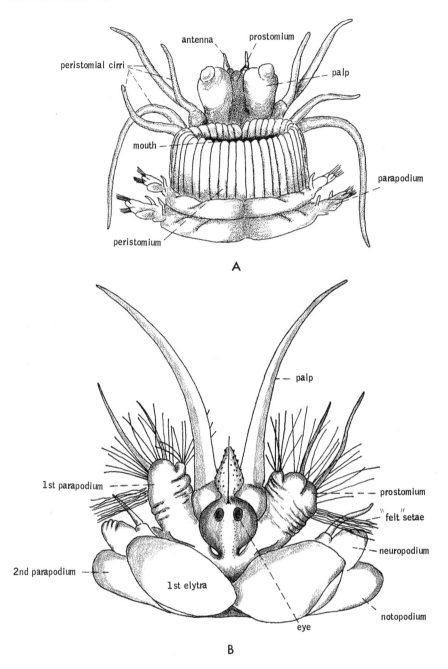

Figure 11-5.   *A.* Anterior of *Nereis* (ventral view). (After Snodgrass.) *B.* Anterior of the sea mouse, *Aphrodite aculeata* (dorsal view). (After Fordham.)

the elytra can be shed when the worm is irritated, and later new elytra can be regenerated. On the other hand, the scales of *Iphionë* are firmly attached and so scleratized that they act as a protective coat of armor over the back of the worm. In the scale worms *Aphrodite* (Fig. 11-12, *A*) and *Laetmonice,* called sea mice, the entire dorsal surface, including the elytra, is covered by hair-like "felt." This "felt" is actually composed of thread-like setae that

arise from the notopodia and trail back over the dorsal surface of the animal (Fig. 11-5, *B*).

The parapodia of burrowing polychaetes are frequently less well developed than those of free-moving species; parapodia of sedentary tube-dwellers are always very much reduced. However, even when the parapodia are rudimentary, setae are still present. For example, in the bamboo worms, *Axiothella* and *Clymenella,* and in *Owenia* and *Thoracophelia*—all sand-grain

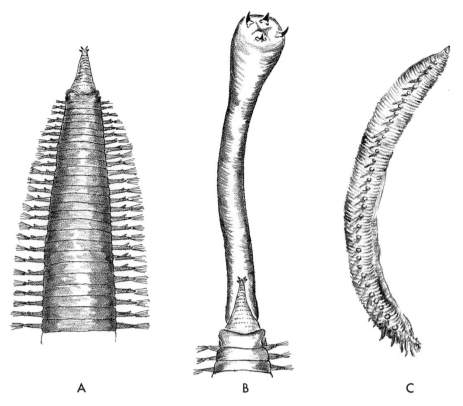

Figure 11-6.   *A.* Anterior of *Glycera* (dorsal view). *B.* Head of *Glycera* with proboscis protruded. *C. Ophelia limacina.* (*A* and *B* from life; *C* after McIntosh from Fauvel.)

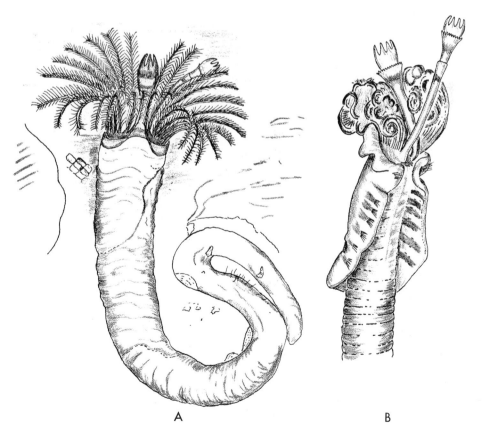

Figure 11-7.   *A.* The serpulid, *Hydroides*, with radioles and opercula extended from end of calcareous tube. *B. Hydroides* removed from tube; radioles retracted.

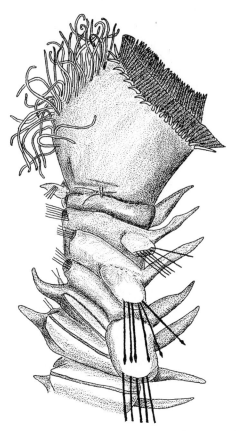

Figure 11-8.   Anterior of *Sabellaria* (lateral view). (After Ebling from Kaestner.)

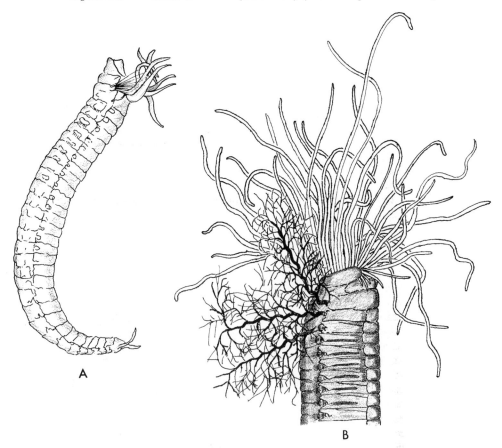

A

B

Figure 11-9.   *A. Amphicteis gunneri.* (After McIntosh from Fauvel.) *B.* Anterior of *Amphitrite* (lateral view). Gills in black.

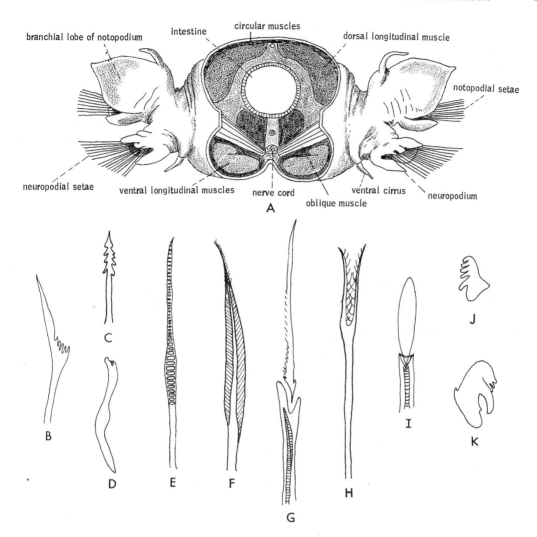

Figure 11-10. *A.* Body segment of *Nereis* (posterior view). (After Snodgrass.) *B.* to *K.* Various types of polychaete setae: *B.* from *Salmacina; C.* from *Hermione,* a scale worm; *D.* uncinal seta from *Arenicola; E.* from *Nephthys; F.* from *Amphitrite; G.* jointed seta from *Nereis; H.* from *Nephthys; I.* swimming seta from a nereid; *J.* uncinal seta from *Serpula; K.* uncinal seta from *Polymnia.* (*B* to *K* after Fauvel.)

tube-dwellers—each parapodium is represented by a slight transverse ridge on both sides of the body, similar to the joint on a bamboo cane (Figs. 11-2, *A* and 11-18, *A*). In the bamboo worms, neither internal skeletal acicula nor dorsal and ventral cirri exist, but setae do project from the crest of the ridge.

In the fanworms and many other sedentary polychaetes, at least some of the setae are modified into hooks called uncini (Fig. 11-10, *J*) One part of the parapodium, either the neuropodium or the notopodium, is represented by a fan of short setae and the opposite division forms a slight ridge bearing from 30 to more than 100 uncini (Fig. 11-13, *B*). The uncini help the worm maintain traction on the inner wall of the tube.

BODY SEGMENTS.   The body segments of errant polychaetes are generally similar; in many sedentary species, however, as well as in some burrowers, there has been a tendency for the trunk to become differentiated into distinct regions. These regional differences may to some extent be due to the differences in the diameter of the segments; but for the most part, the regional differences are caused by variances in the nature of the parapodia, or the presence or absence of gills. For example, the body of the burrowing lugworm, *Arenicola,* contains a "head" composed of the prostomium, the peristomium, and several body segments that have lost their parapodia (Fig. 11-13, *A*). The head region is followed by a "trunk" of 19 segments bearing parapodia and gills, and by a posterior "tail" of

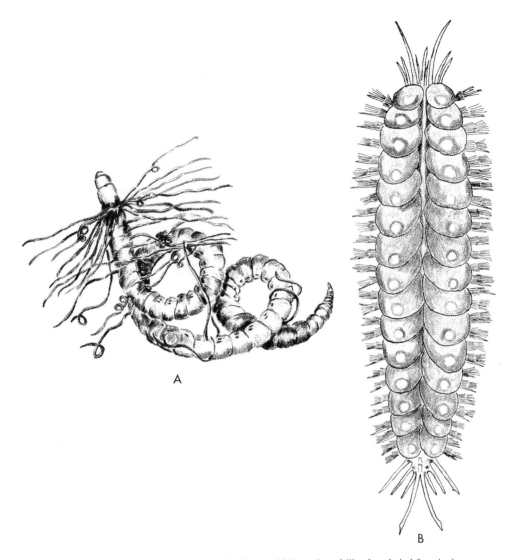

Figure 11-11.   *A. Cirratulus cirratus,* a polychaete with long thread-like dorsal cirri functioning as gills. (After McIntosh from Fauvel.) *B. Lagisca flocculosa,* a scale worm. (After McIntosh.)

smaller segments lacking appendages. A similar condition exists in the terebellids, such as *Amphitrite,* in which the head is followed by the setae-bearing thorax and the posterior abdomen, lacking setae.

Most of the fanworms have a body that is divided into a short thorax with only a few segments, followed by a longer abdomen with more numerous segments. Both thorax and abdomen bear setae, but the arrangement of setae is different on each. In the thorax, the neuropodia bear uncini and the notopodia bear a fan of bristles; on the abdomen, the arrangement is reversed. A few polychaetes, such as *Arenicola* and *Ophelia* (Figs. 11-6, *C* and 11-13, *A*), have the segments subdivided externally into a number of rings, or annuli.

Body Wall and Coelom.   The polychaete integument is composed of a single layer of

columnar epithelium, which is covered by a thin layer of cuticle. Sometimes the cuticle is striated, as in *Diopatra,* producing iridescent purple and green colors. A number of polychaetes, such as syllids, scale worms and some chaetopterids, are luminescent. The luminescent material is present in the mucus secreted by certain of the epithelial gland cells. In the scale worms, the luminescent glands are located on the surface of the elytra. The scales luminesce one after another, giving off blue or green light. The luminescent mucus of *Chaetopterus* often disperses into the water, producing a cloud-like luminescence in the water.

Beneath the epithelium lie in order a thin layer of connective tissue, a layer of circular muscle fibers, and a much thicker layer of longitudinal muscle fibers (Figs. 11-1; 11-10, *A*; and 11-13, *B*). The muscle cells are smooth and anas-

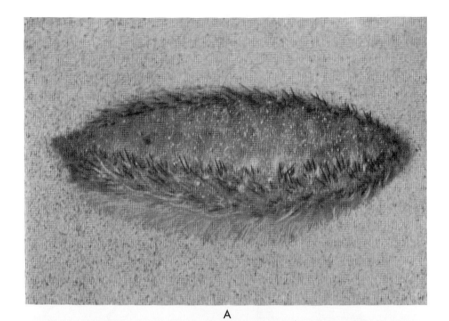

A

Figure 11-12.   *A*. The sea mouse, *Aphrodite aculeata* (dorsal view). The wide uniform dorsal strip is covered by felt setae. *B*. The fan or peacock worm, *Sabella pavonina*, showing the expanded radioles projecting from the aperture of the sand-grain tubes. (Both courtesy of D. P. Wilson.)

B

tomose. Although the muscles of the body wall essentially comprise two sheaths, the longitudinal fibers typically are broken up into four bundles —two dorso-lateral and two ventro-lateral. Oblique muscles are commonly present in polychaetes (Fig. 11-13, *B*). They consist of strands of muscle fibers that extend from the midventral line to the midlateral line on each side of the worm where they join the circular layer. The oblique muscles do not form a continuous sheath through the segment but are concentrated primarily at the level of the parapodia.

A layer of longitudinal muscle borders the coelom and is covered internally by the peritoneum. The spacious coelom of polychaetes is compartmented by transverse septa, each of which is composed of a double layer of peritoneum (Fig. 11-1). The septa are penetrated by the gut, which is also suspended dorsally and ventrally by longitudinal mesenteries. Thus each coelomic compartment is divided into right and left halves. Actually, however, such perfect compartmentation is rarely encountered, for the mesenteries are almost never complete.

Septa have partially or completely disappeared in many polychaetes. In the sea mouse, *Aphrodite*, the septa are weakly developed and

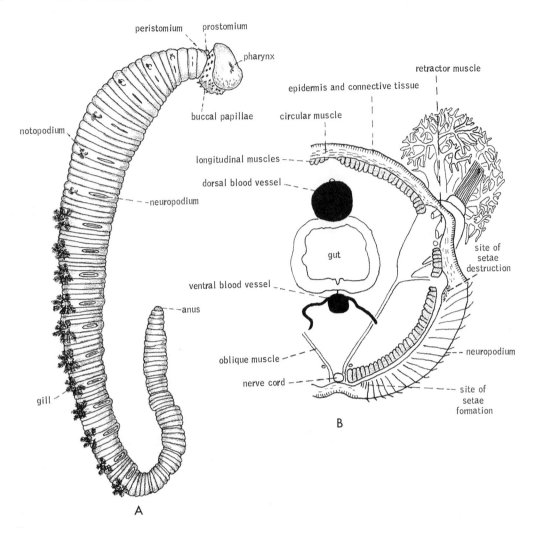

Figure 11-13.   *A. Arenicola* (lateral view). (After Brown.) *B.* A setigerous segment of *Arenicola marina* (transverse section). (Modified from Wells.)

contain many openings. *Glycera,* a burrowing polychaete, has no septa in the anterior of the worm to accommodate a long eversible proboscis. Septa are also absent in the first 40 to 50 segments of the terebellids except between the fourth and fifth segments (Fig. 11-14). This anterior septum is called a diaphragm. Two such diaphragms also are present in the Opheliidae, but all other septa are absent. In *Arenicola,* there are three anterior diaphragms, and typical septa are present in the posterior part of the body (Fig. 11-15).

Locomotion.   Movement in polychaetes is brought about by the combined action of the parapodia, the body-wall musculature, and to some extent the coelomic fluid. The parapodia and setae push against the substratum but rarely act as paddles. Gray (1939) studied the pattern of locomotion in *Nereis,* and his observations may apply to other errant polychaetes. The slow

crawling movement of *Nereis* results entirely from the action of the parapodia. Parapodial movement involves an effective backward stroke in which the parapodia are in contact with the substratum and a forward stroke in which the parapodia are lifted from the ground. Each parapodium describes an ellipse each time it completes one of these two-stroke cycles. Following a pause in the cycle after the backward stroke of the parapodium, the aciculum is retracted, and the parapodium is lifted off the ground and moved forward. When the parapodium reaches an anterior oblique position, the aciculum is extended, and the parapodium is lowered to come in contact with the substratum and then is swept backward.

The combined effective sweeps of the numerous parapodia propel the worm forward. The two parapodia of each segment work alternately rather than simultaneously, and parapodial ac-

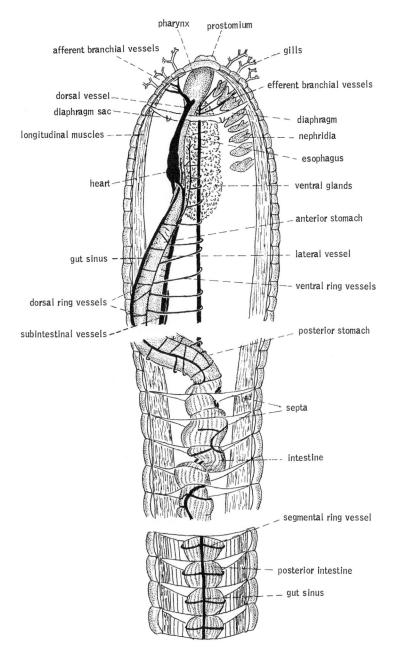

Figure 11-14.   *Amphitrite* (dorsal dissection). (After Brown.)

tion takes place in successive waves along the side of the worm. Gray found that when movement is initiated, a wave of activation sweeps along the worm, affecting every fourth to eighth parapodium.

As soon as one parapodium begins its effective stroke, the next preceding parapodium sweeps forward and starts its effective stroke. The waves of activation thus move forward rather than backward. Activation takes place on both sides of the body, but the waves alternate with each other: when a particular group of parapodia on one side are executing an effective stroke, the parapodia on the opposite side are executing the recovery stroke.

Undulatory body movements in addition to parapodial locomotion give the worm the ability to crawl and swim rapidly. Body undulations are produced by waves of contraction in the longitudinal muscles of the body wall. These waves of contraction coincide with the alternating waves of parapodial activity just described. The longitudinal muscles on one side of each segment contract when the parapodium on that

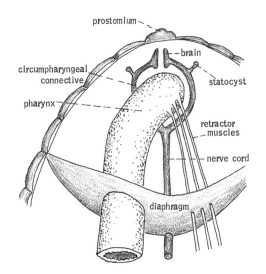

Figure 11-15.   Anterior of *Arenicola* (dorsal dissection). (After Ashworth from Brown.)

side of the segment is moved forward; the muscles then relax as the parapodium sweeps backward in its effective stroke. As Gray points out, the principal force of propulsion in this type of movement comes, not from parapodial movement, but rather from body contractions pulling against points of contact made by the parapodia.

The mechanism of locomotion described for *Nereis* may be typical of other errant polychaetes, including the pelagic groups, which swim by rapid body undulations. In tube-dwellers, the effective sweep of the parapodium occurs against the inner side of the tube.

Movement in the more specialized burrowers, which remain below the surface, and in the sedentary tube-dwellers is similar to movement in earthworms. In both of these groups, the parapodia tend to be reduced or absent. The setae, which remain either as short bristles or as uncini, serve to anchor the body into the mud or serve to grip the inner surface of the tube or burrow. Forward movement results from waves of contraction sweeping along the length of the body affecting the two sides simultaneously rather than alternately. In body regions where the longitudinal muscles are contracted and the circular muscles are relaxed, the body is expanded; and the parapodia, or at least the setae, are extended and anchored against the wall of the burrow or tube. In adjacent regions of the body, the reverse action is taking place; the segments are elongated and are extended forward. In this type of movement, the muscles of the body wall act against the coelomic fluid, which serves as a hydraulic skeleton.

Many burrowing polychaetes have reduced conical heads, which thus can be forced more easily through sand or mud. The sea mouse,

however, uses the large peristomial parapodia like the forelimbs of a mole to sweep the mud and sand to one side (Fig. 11-5, *B*)

Most tubicolous and burrowing species are able to retract the body very rapidly into the sanctuary of the tube or are able to burrow to protect themselves from passing fish and other predators. These escape movements depend upon the longitudinal muscles, which have become greatly developed, especially those on the dorsal side.

Nutrition.   All types of feeding take place among the polychaetes.

RAPTORIAL FEEDERS.   Some errant polychaetes are raptorial feeders. The prey consists of various small invertebrates, including other polychaetes, which are captured by means of an eversible pharynx or proboscis bearing two or more chitinous jaws. The mouth in raptorial feeders, as in all polychaetes, lies beneath the prostomium and is bordered laterally and ventrally by the peristomium (Fig. 11-5, *A*). The mouth opens into the pharynx, which usually occupies approximately the first six body segments. The pharynx is derived embryologically from the stomodeum and is thus lined with a cuticle similar to the integument.

In some raptorial polychaetes, such as *Nephthys* and the nereids, a single pair of large, posteriorly-directed, chitinous jaws is attached to the lateral walls of the pharynx. In *Eunice, Marphysa* (Fig. 11-16), *Diopatra,* and *Onuphis,* there is a more complex pharyngeal armature that consists of a pair of lower jaws and as many as five pairs of upper jaws. Many syllids, on the other hand, have a single tooth or a circlet of teeth (Fig. 11-17, *B*).

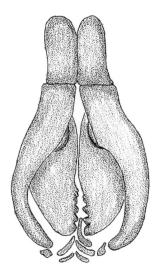

Figure 11-16.   Pharyngeal armature of *Marphysa.* (After Aiyar.)

The polychaete pharynx is rapidly everted; this places the jaws at the anterior of the body and causes them to open. The food is seized by the jaws and the pharynx is retracted. Raptorial tube-dwellers may leave the tube partially or completely when feeding, depending on the species.

Although protractor muscles may be present, an increase in coelomic pressure resulting from the contraction of body-wall muscles is the principal factor in the eversion of the proboscis. When pressure on the coelomic fluid is reduced, the proboscis is withdrawn by the retractor muscles, which extend from the body wall to the back of the pharynx (Fig. 11-17, *A*).

Some raptorial feeders, such as *Glycera* and *Autolytus,* have a long, tubular proboscis. *Glycera* feeds on other invertebrates, particularly worms encountered as it burrows in the sandy mud. The proboscis can be protruded to about one-fifth the length of the body (Fig.

11-6, *B*); when it is retracted, it occupies approximately the first twenty body segments (Fig. 11-17, *A*). Behind the proboscis is located the pharynx, which bears four jaws arranged equidistantly around the body wall. The pharynx is attached to an S-shaped esophagus. No septa are present in these anterior segments, and the proboscis apparatus lies free in the coelom. Wells (1937) reports that just prior to eversion of the proboscis the longitudinal muscles contract violently, sliding the pharynx forward and straightening out the esophagus. The proboscis is then shot out with explosive force, and the four jaws emerge open at the tip.

Autolytus, another polychaete with a tubular proboscis, measures about half an inch in length and lives in membranous tubes attached to the stalks of hydroids (Fig. 11-17, *B*). This little worm leaves its tube and crawls about over the hydroid to feed upon the polyps. The proboscis of *Autolytus,* as well as those of some other syllids,

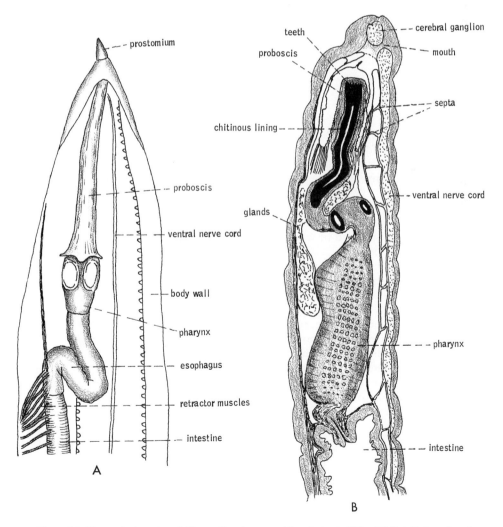

Figure 11-17.   *A.* Anterior of *Glycera* digestive tract (dorsal view). (After Wells.) *B.* Anterior of *Autolytus* (sagittal section). (After Okada.)

is constructed differently from the proboscis of *Glycera*. In *Autolytus* the proboscis is a tube that is free at its anterior and lies within a buccal cavity. The proboscis is lined by a thick layer of chitin, which at the proboscis tip projects to form a circle of teeth. Posteriorly the proboscis opens into a pharynx, the walls of which are composed of radial muscles that produce a sucking action.

The pharynx in turn opens into the intestine. During feeding, the proboscis is extended from the mouth as it is in triclad flatworms, and the projecting crown of teeth are used to cut off tentacles and other parts of the polyps. Food (parts of the polyp) is then sucked in by the pumping action of the pharynx. A closely related genus, *Procerastea*, is reported to insert its proboscis into the gastrovascular cavity of the polyps and suck out the contents.

Some errant polychaetes that bear jaws, particularly some of the nereids, feed on algae and use their jaws to tear off pieces of the plant. A number of burrowing polychaetes, such as *Capitella*, *Ophelia*, *Pectinaria*, and *Arenicola*, obtain their nutrition from organic matter mixed with sand and mud that these worms ingest. They usually possess a short, eversible pharynx, which is unarmed, although it may be provided with papillae. The everted pharynx picks up sand and brings it into the gut on retraction. The septal diaphragms, which are located in the anterior region in *Ophelia* and *Arenicola*, aid in controlling the pressure of the coelomic fluid during eversion of the pharynx.

CILIARY FEEDERS. The ciliary feeders are all sedentary polychaetes. Food for these worms consists of some plankton but primarily of organic debris that is either suspended in water or has accumulated on the substratum. With the exception of the chaetopterids, the palps or other organs derived from the peristomium are used for trapping and transporting the detritus; the process is very similar in all ciliary feeders. Detritus is trapped in mucus on the surface of the palps and is then carried to the mouth in a ciliated groove. In spionids the two long tentacle-like palps are projected from the end of the tube and actively move about. Plankton that adhere to the surface is propelled toward the mouth down the length of the palp in a ciliated channel.

The peristomial ingestive organs of *Amphitrite* and *Terebella* form two large clusters of contractile tentacles, which stretch out over the surface of the substratum (Fig. 11-9, *B*). Surface detritus adheres to the mucus secreted by the tentacular epithelium. The tentacles are nonselective, and all food particles that can be carried are moved down a ciliated groove on the adoral side of the tentacles. Food accumulates at the base of the tentacles which are individually wiped at different times over the upper lip bordering the mouth. Cilia on the lip then drive the food into the mouth. The ampharetids also trap detritus on a cluster of ciliated tentacles, but the tentacles in these worms can be retracted into the mouth.

In *Owenia* and other members of the tubicolous Oweniidae, the peristome bears a short crown of two clusters of flattened, branched, ribbon-like filaments, each of which ends in a bifid lobe (Fig. 11-18). The edges of the filaments are rolled inward toward the longitudinal axis of the filament to form a ciliated gutter. In feeding, the crown of the worm projects from the end of the tube and expands to about twice the diameter of the body. Detritus suspended in the water is swept into the gutters by long cilia located along the edges of the filaments. The food particles are then entangled in mucus and carried by cilia down the gutter to the mouth. Only the oral surface of the filaments are ciliated, although mucous glands are present on both sides. A certain amount of food particle selection takes place. The few large particles that get into the gutter are moved to the edges and then dislodged by periodic muscular contractions of the filaments. Ciliary tracts move the food particles from the base of the crown into the mouth.

The crown of serpulid and sabellid fanworms is composed of two half circles of bipinnate radioles. The two half circles oppose each other and form a funnel when they are expanded outside the end of the tube (Figs. 11-12, *B* and 11-19). Beating of the cilia located on the pinnules produces a current of water that flows through the radioles into the funnel, and then flows upward and out. Particles are trapped on the pinnules and are driven by cilia into a groove running the length of each radiole. The particles are carried along the groove down to the base of the radiole, where a rather complex sorting mechanism functions. The largest particles are rejected, and fine material is carried by ciliated tracts into the mouth. In many sabellids, particles are sorted into three grades with the medium size grade being stored for use in tube construction.

The feeding mechanism of *Chaetopterus* is quite different from that of other ciliary feeders (Figs. 11-20 and 11-21). These worms, which live in U-shaped parchment tubes, have a highly modified body structure. The notopodia on the twelfth segment are extremely long and aliform (i.e., wing-like), and the epithelium is ciliated and richly supplied with mucous glands. The parapodia on the fourteenth, fifteenth, and sixteenth segments are called fans and project

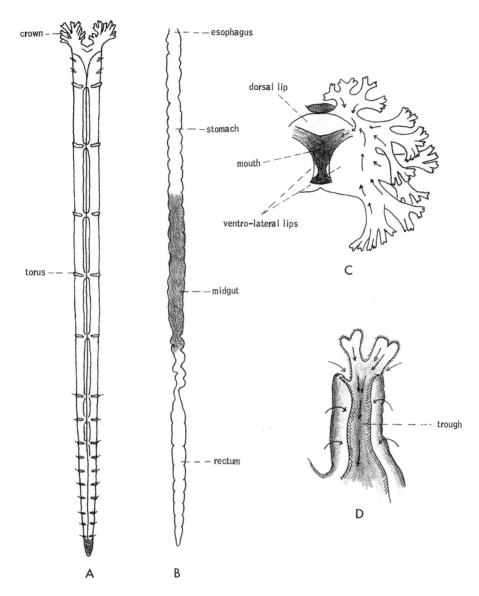

crown

torus

esophagus

stomach

midgut

rectum

dorsal lip

mouth

ventro-lateral lips

C

trough

D

A   B

Figure 11-18. *Owenia. A.* Ventral view. *B.* Digestive tract. *C.* Mouth region and half of crown, showing direction of ciliary currents. *D.* Section of crown, showing trough and direction of ciliary currents. (All after Dales.)

from each side of the body, resembling semicircular "wings." Each pair of these fans forms a sort of piston ring that fits up against the cylindrical wall of the tube.

The beating of the fans produces a current of water that enters the arm of the tube near the anterior of the worm, flows through the tube, and then flows out the opposite chimney. Each fan beats about sixty times a minute to produce the water currents. The aliform notopodia are stretched out in opposite directions toward the walls of the tube, and a sheet of mucus is secreted between them, resembling a net stretched between two poles. The mucus film is continuously secreted from each notopodium

where the film is attached to it. As a result, the sheet assumes the shape of a bag. The end of the bag is grasped by a ciliated, cup-like structure located on the mid-dorsal side of the worm a short distance behind the aliform notopodia. The cupule rolls up the end of the bag as new film is continuously being produced by the notopodia. Almost all of the water going through the tube must pass through the mucus bag, which strains out all suspended detritus and plankton.

Large objects brought into the tube by the water current are detected by peristomial cilia and shunted to either side; the aliform notopodia then are raised to let the large objects pass by. The food-laden mucus bag is continu-

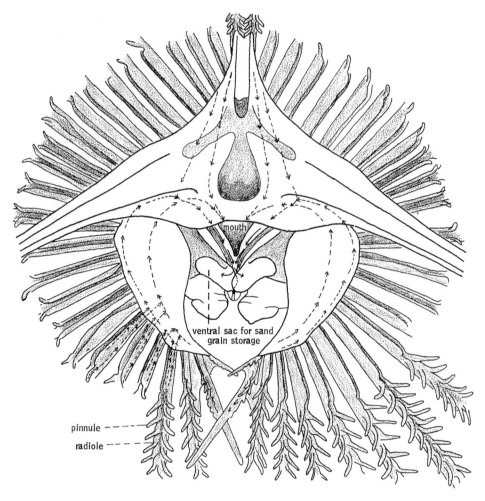

Figure 11-19.   Crown of the fanworm, *Sabella* (anterior view). Only the bases of radioles are shown. (After Nicol.)

ously being rolled up into a ball by the dorsal cupule; when the ball reaches a certain size, the bag is cut loose from the notopodia and rolled up with the ball. The cupule then projects forward and deposits the mucus food ball onto a ciliated mid-dorsal groove, which extends to the anterior of the worm; and the ball is carried to the mouth. MacGinitie (1939) observed that a specimen of *Chaetopterus* between 6 and 8 inches long produced mucus film for the bag at the rate of approximately 1 mm. per second and that the food ball averaged 3 mm. in diameter.

THE ALIMENTARY CANAL. Typically, the alimentary canal of polychaetes is a straight tube extending from the mouth at the anterior of the worm to the anus located in the pygidium. The canal is differentiated into a number of regions. Although some variation exists, the regions most often encountered are the pharynx (or a buccal cavity when the pharynx is absent), a short esophagus, stomach, an intestine, and a rectum.

Often, as in *Nereis,* no stomach is present and the esophagus opens directly into the intestine (Fig. 11-4).

In many species, such as the bamboo worms (*Axiothella*), *Owenia* (Fig. 11-18, *B*) and *Thoracophelia,* these regions can only be detected histologically, and the gross appearance of the digestive tract is that of a simple uniform tube. As a general rule, no specialized digestive glands are present; the epithelial lining of the stomach, or the intestine when the stomach is absent, elaborates enzymes for digestion. Amylases, proteases, and lipases have been reported, and digestion is entirely extracellular. The intestine is the site of absorption; not infrequently the walls are folded to increase the intestinal surface area.

In a few worms, such as *Amphitrite,* increased intestinal surface area for digestion or absorption is attained by intestinal coiling; in other species, the increased area is attained by evaginations of the gut, or ceca. In *Nereis* two large glandular

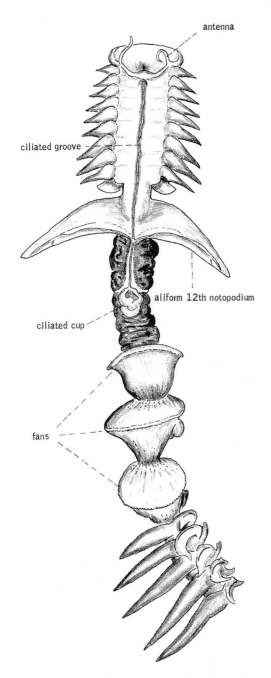

antenna

ciliated groove

alifoum 12th notopodium

ciliated cup

fans

Figure 11-20.   *Chaetopterus variopedatus.* (From life.)

length of the intestine (Fig. 11-22). Digestion begins in the intestine, and digested and partially digested food is forced into the ceca by fluid pressure from the surrounding coelom. The entrance into each cecum is guarded by projecting epithelial cells, which form a sieve and strain out all but the finest particles. Digestion is completed and absorption takes place within the cecum.

Movement of food through the digestive tract is brought about by the contraction of the muscle cells in the gut wall, by the general ciliary action of the gut lining, or by a ventral ciliated groove. A combination of these forces may be involved. For example, in *Amphitrite,* food is moved through the esophagus and stomach by peristalsis; but in the intestine, where the musculature is weakly developed, food is probably moved by a ventral ciliated groove.

The egested wastes from worms living in tubes with double openings are readily removed by water currents. Such flushing, however, is accomplished less efficiently when the tube is closed or, more commonly, when the tube is deeply buried in mud and sand. Some polychaetes, such as the spionids and oweniids, turn around in the tube and thrust the pygidium out of the chimney during defecation. The fanworms have a ciliated midventral groove, which extends from the anus anteriorly. In the thoracic region, the groove curves around the side of the body to the dorsal surface and extends anteriorly to the head. Fecal material is molded with mucus into distinct pellets in the rectum and is then carried out of the tube by the ciliated groove.

Respiration. Gills are common among the polychaetes, but they vary greatly in both structure and location. This lack of consistency would seem to indicate that respiratory organs have arisen independently within the class a number of times. The ancestral polychaetes were probably devoid of gills, and diffusion of gases took place through the general body surface. This mode of respiration is still retained in some polychaetes, such as *Owenia, Castalia,* the scale worms, and the bamboo worms; furthermore, general diffusion of gases through the body surface accounts for some respiration (percentages vary according to species) even when gills are present.

In the scale worms, respiratory diffusion is largely restricted to the dorsal surface, which is roofed over by the elytra (Fig. 11-23, *A*). Cilia on the dorsal surface create a current of water flowing posteriorly beneath the elytra. Some water enters over the head, but the principal inflow is lateral. Cilia on the para-

ceca open into the esophagus (Fig. 11-4). The function of these ceca is still uncertain, but they probably secrete digestive enzymes. A similar pair of esophageal ceca are present in *Arenicola* and are known to produce a protease. *Amphicteis* possesses a single, but very large, ventral cecum, extending anteriorly from the posterior of the stomach.

A more peculiar structure exists in the sea mouse. Here, a pair of lateral ceca empty into the intestine at each segment for the entire

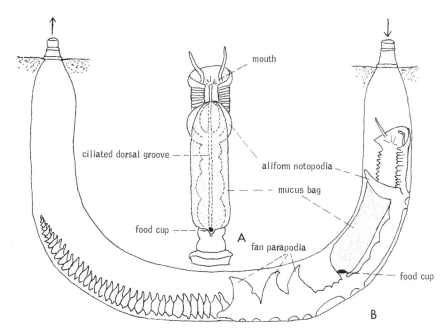

Figure 11-21.   *Chaetopterus* during feeding. *A.* Anterior part of body (dorsal view). *B.* Worm in tube (lateral view). Arrows indicate direction of water current through tube. (After MacGinitie.)

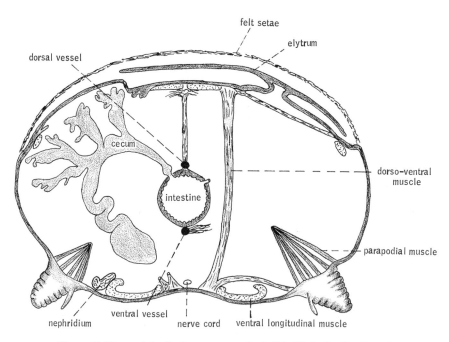

Figure 11-22.   *Aphrodite* (transverse section). (Modified after Fordham.)

podia propel the water upward over the parapodia and then inward between the bases of the elytra, where it becomes confluent with the main stream of water flowing posteriorly.

The felt-covered sea mice lack cilia (Figs. 11-12, *A* and 11-22), but a similar dorsal water current is produced by the animal, which tilts the elytra upward and then rapidly brings them down. The movement begins at the anterior of the body and sweeps posteriorly over successive elytra, thus driving water through the underlying channel.

Most commonly the gills are associated with the parapodia and in most cases are modified parts of the parapodium. The notopodium may possess a flattened branchial lobe, which acts as a gill (Fig. 11-10, *A*). More commonly, the dorsal cirrus of the parapodium is modified as a gill. The cirrus may be formed like a long inverted cone as in *Sabellaria* and *Nerine* (Fig. 11-23, *B*); a large flattened lobe, as in the phyllodocids (Fig. 11-23, *C*); irregularly branched filaments as in *Arenicola* and *Amphitrite* (Figs. 11-9, *B* and 11-13); or a long thread as in *Audouinia* and *Cirratulus* (Fig. 11-11, *A*). In the Eunicidae, the gills arise from the base of

the dorsal cirrus and may be cirriform, as in *Nothria;* pectinate, as in *Marphysa* and *Eunice;* or spirally branched, as in *Diopatra* (Fig. 11-3, *A*).

In polychaetes that are more perfectly metameric, gills are located on most of the segments except at the extreme anterior and posterior of the animal. However, when differentiation of the trunk into distinct regions has taken place,

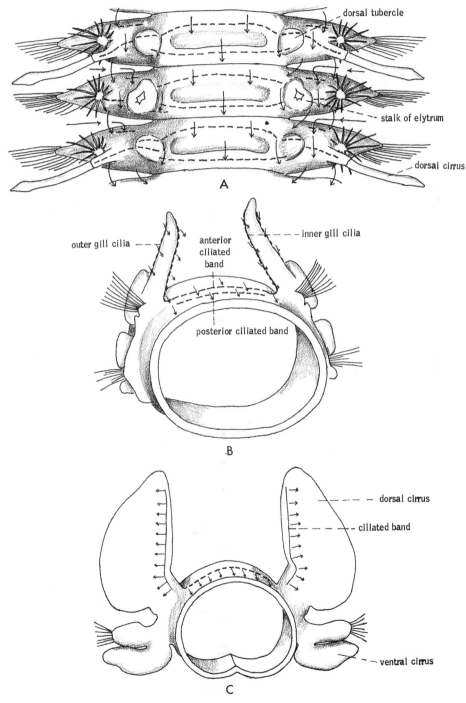

Figure 11-23.   Surface ciliation in three polychaetes. Arrows indicate direction of water currents. *A. Harmothoë imbricata. B. Nerine cirratulus. C. Phyllodoce laminosa.* (After Sheffield.)

there is correlated restriction in the number and location of the gills. For example, in *Amphitrite*, there are only three pairs of gills, which are located on the first three segments (Fig. 11-9, *B*). The gills of *Arenicola* (Fig. 11-13, *A*), while more numerous, are restricted to the seventh through the seventeenth segments.

Fanworms do not have gills associated with the parapodia, but the bipinnate radioles composing the fans, in addition to obtaining food, serve as the principal organs of gaseous exchange.

Ciliary action most commonly produces the respiratory water currents flowing over the gills. Usually, bands of cilia on the dorsal surface of each segment create a water current moving anteriorly or posteriorly. Ciliary tracts on the gills produce lateral currents either entering or leaving the main dorsal current (Figs. 11-23, *B* and *C*).

The Nereidae, the Eunicidae, and the Glyceridae are devoid of any surface ciliation; these worms, which are largely burrowers and tube-dwellers, keep water flowing over the gills and through the tubes or burrows by their undulatory body movements. Some tube-dwellers, such as the sabellid fanworms, pump water through the tube by means of peristaltic contractions of the body wall.

In most tubicolous polychaetes, the circulating water passes through the tube and out through the sand or mud in which the tube is buried (Fig. 11-2, *E*). However, in serpulid fanworms, which live in a blind calcareous tube, inhalant currents enter and exhalant currents leave the opening of the tube. These currents are produced by special ciliary tracts.

Circulation. In the majority of polychaetes there exists a well-developed blood-vascular system, in which the blood is always enclosed within vessels. The basic plan of circulation is relatively simple. Blood flows anteriorly in a dorsal vessel situated over the digestive tract; at the anterior of the body, the dorsal vessel is connected to a ventral vessel by one to several vessels or by a network of vessels passing around the gut. The ventral vessel carries blood posteriorly beneath the alimentary tract.

In each segment, the ventral vessel gives rise to one pair of ventral parapodial vessels, which supply the parapodia, the body wall and the nephridia, and to a single ventral intestinal vessel that supplies the gut. The dorsal vessel, in turn, receives a corresponding pair of dorsal parapodial vessels and a dorsal intestinal vessel. The dorsal and ventral parapodial vessels and the dorsal and ventral intestinal vessels are interconnected by a network of smaller vessels.

According to Karandikar and Thakur (1946), who studied blood flow in the Indian nereid, *Nereis cultrifera*, blood circulates through the parapodial arc from the dorsal vessel to the ventral vessel and from the ventral vessel back to the dorsal vessel through the intestinal arc (Fig. 11-24).

There are many variations of this basic circulatory pattern. The simplest pattern is found in the syllids, the phyllodocids, and

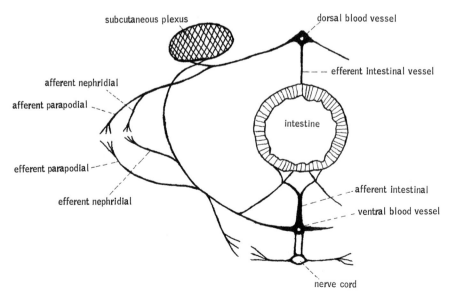

Figure 11-24.   Segmental circulation in the Indian nereid, *Nereis cultrifera*. (After Karandikar and Thakur.)

the sea mice. In the sea mouse the parapodial arc is poorly developed, and there are no vessels in the integument. In worms with differentiated trunk regions and gills that are limited in number and position, the circulatory pathways are considerably modified and more complicated (Fig. 11-25).

Instead of a network of vessels, many species possess a large sinus lying between the epithelium and the muscle layers in the walls of the intestine and stomach. The sinus partially or completely surrounds the gut and replaces the dorsal vessel in this region. The gut sinus is perhaps a primitive feature of the annelid circulatory system; from such a sinus, the dorsal and ventral vessels may have separated.

A typical blood vessel has an internal endothelial lining supported by a connective-tissue membrane. The outer side of this membrane is covered with muscle fibers and peritoneum. In general, the blood vessels are contractile, particularly the dorsal vessel. The contraction of these vessels rather than a distinct pumping center, or heart causes propulsion of the blood. When blood fills a section of a vessel after a peristaltic wave, the contraction is again initiated. Karandikar and Thakur (1946) have reported a flow rate of 15 to 18 mm. per sec. in the dorsal vessel of *Nereis cultrifera*. A peculiar feature of the fanworms and the Opheliidae is the presence of many small, blind, contractile vessels, which project into the coelom. Their significance is still uncertain.

A number of structures called hearts or

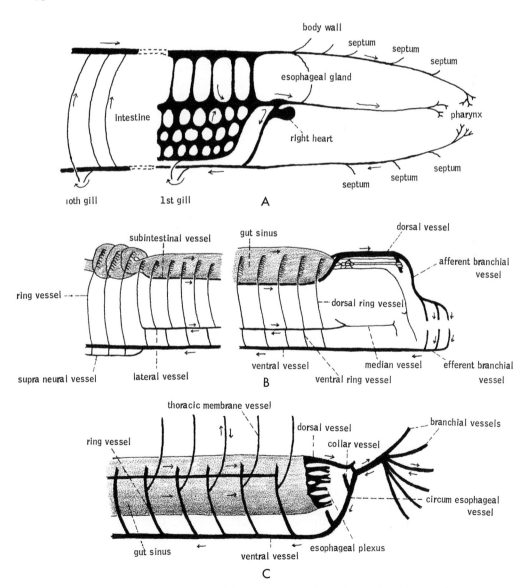

Figure 11-25. Circulatory systems of three polychaetes. *A. Arenicola*. (After Bullough.) *B. Amphitrite. C. Pomatoceros.* (*B* and *C* after Thomas.)

heart bodies appear in polychaetes, but they certainly are not all homologous. The heart in *Chaetopterus* is a bulbous swelling in the dorsal vessel and is reported to be a pumping center. For the most part, however, such hearts are not pumping structures. The heart body in terebellids is a section of the dorsal vessel at the anterior, which is filled with a mass of spongy tissue (Fig. 11-14); hemoglobin destruction has been suggested as a possible function.

Primitively, as in scale worms, phyllodocids, and syllids, the blood is a colorless fluid containing a few amebocytes; but the blood of most polychaetes contains respiratory pigments dissolved in the plasma. Hemoglobin is the most common of these pigments, but chlorocruorin is characteristic of the blood of the serpulid and sabellid fanworms and also of the Flabelligeridae. Chlorocruorin, like hemoglobin, contains iron, but the hematin group is different. Moreover, blood containing chlorocruorin appears bright green.

There are a number of interesting exceptions to the usual disposition of the respiratory pigments just described. The blood of *Serpula* contains both hemoglobin and chlorocruorin. *Glycera* and *Capitella,* although lacking a blood-vascular system, possess corpuscles containing hemoglobin in the coelomic fluid. *Terebella lapidaria* not only possesses such coelomic red corpuscles, but in addition a blood-vascular system with no respiratory pigments. *Magelona* has a blood-vascular system with corpuscles containing a third iron-bearing pigment, which has been called hemerythrin.

Sheffield (1938) has pointed out that with the exception of some sedentary tube-dwellers, there has been a tendency for surface and coelomic ciliation to disappear with the formation of a well developed blood-vascular system containing respiratory pigments. Thus scale worms, which possess a blood-vascular system but lack respiratory pigments, retain surface ciliation; and the coelomic fluid performs some of the functions of circulation, particularly that of oxygen transport.

The Nervous System.   The general plan of the nervous system in polychaetes is relatively simple and more or less uniform throughout the class, as well as in the other classes of annelids. The polychaete nervous system is characterized by a dorsal ganglionic mass, or brain, in the prostomium (or the brain may extend back through the anterior body segments); a pair of connectives surrounding the anterior gut; and a ventral nerve cord extending through the length of the body. The ventral cord typically bears segmental swellings or ganglia, from which extend lateral nerves into each segment.

THE BRAIN.   The brain is usually bilobed lying in the prostomium beneath the dorsal epithelium (Figs. 11-15 and 11-26). The greatest degree of differentiation appears in the errant polychaetes, in contrast to the sedentary polychaetes in which the brain has a relatively simple structure. Some authors have attempted to divide the brain of errant polychaetes into a forebrain, midbrain, and hindbrain. However, it is doubtful if such regional differentiation is of fundamental phylogenetic significance. Rather, such regional differentiation more likely represents independent specializations associated with well developed cephalic sense organs. A concise detailed anatomy of the brain is given by Fauvel (1959). The polychaete brain may give rise to as many as 16 pairs of cerebral nerves (Fig. 11-26), depending on the number of structures—such as, eyes, palps, and antennae —that are innervated.

Typically, a single pair of circumpharyngeal or circumesophageal connectives surround the anterior gut and interconnect the brain and the ventral nerve cord. However, in some species, such as *Sabella,* the connectives are doubled; and in others, such as *Arenicola* (Fig. 11-15) and *Amphitrite,* both of which have very reduced brains very closely associated with the overlying integument, the single pair of connectives are located in the body wall just beneath the epidermis. The connectives are often ganglionated with nerves extending to the tentacular cirri of the peristomium or into the anterior trunk segments.

STOMATOGASTRIC NERVES.   Many polychaetes, particularly those with an eversible proboscis, have a system of stomatogastric nerves, which are involved in the motor control of the proboscis or pharynx. The number and arrangement of these nerves is quite variable. One or two pairs of stomatogastric nerves may arise from the connectives with a single or double dorsal nerve emerging from the back of the brain, or these nerves may arise from both the connectives and the brain.

VENTRAL NERVE CORD.   Primitively, the ventral nerve cord is completely double throughout, with transverse connectives between the separate ganglia; but in most polychaetes the two cords are fused in varying degrees. The primitive, completely doubled condition is still retained by the serpulid and sabellid fanworms (Fig. 11-26, *B*). In the phyllolocids the ganglia are fused, but the cords are still separated. In *Nereis* and *Amphitrite,* the two cords lie side by side bound together by a more or less common connective tissue covering. Complete fusion has developed in the Opheliidae, *Tomopteris,* and *Arenicola* (Fig. 11-13, *B*) with no traces of the

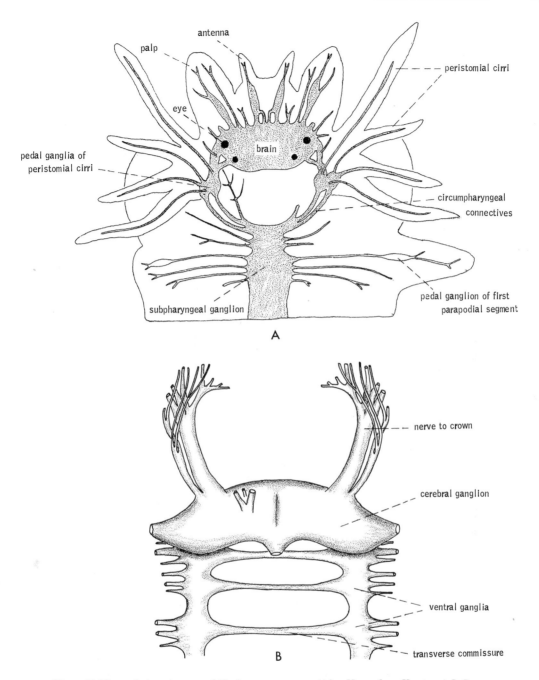

Figure 11-26. *A.* Anterior part of *Nereis* nervous system. (After Henry from Kaestner.) *B. Pomatoceros* nervous system (dorsal view). (After Thomas.)

originally paired condition remaining. In *Arenicola* the ganglia have disappeared, and the cell bodies are distributed along the entire length of both cords. In most polychaetes the ventral nerve cord lies within the muscle layers; but in a few forms, such as *Clymenella*, the ventral nerve cord is associated with the ventral integument.

There is typically one ganglionic swelling per segment, although there are two per seg-

ment in *Sabella.* From each ganglion emerge two to five pairs of lateral nerves, which innervate the body wall of that segment. The lateral nerves probably contain both sensory and motor components—that is, the lateral nerves are mixed. The sensory nerve components form a nerve plexus beneath the surface epithelium; it is here that the sensory cell bodies are located. The motor neurons innervate the parapodial muscles and the muscles of the body wall; the motor cell bodies are located in the ventral half of the segmental ganglia.

PEDAL GANGLIA.   The cell bodies of motor neurons innervating the parapodia are not always located in the ventral ganglia. Some polychaetes have a separate system of pedal ganglia located peripherally near the parapodia. Primitively, the pedal ganglia are interconnected longitudinally by connectives, both of which form a peripheral cord emerging from both sides of the brain and extending the length of the body (Fig. 11-27, A). The pedal ganglia are also joined to the ventral ganglia by transverse connectives. Such a scheme, which appears in Hermodice, is known as tetraneury, because the system contains four longitudinal nerve cords. Tetraneury seems to support the belief that the ventral longitudinal cords of higher protostomes represent a retention of the more ventral longitudinal nerves found in a primitive radial system such as that possessed by certain flatworms.

In a diverse number of polychaetes, such as Nerine and Lepidasthenia (Fig. 11-27, B), pedal ganglia are present, but the longitudinal connectives have disappeared. Only the transverse connectives joining the pedal ganglia to the ventral ganglia are retained.

GIANT AXONS.   The principal defense of most polychaetes against their many predators, is the ability to contract very rapidly. The rapid-contraction reflex is particularly well developed in the tube-dwellers, which emerge from their protective housing to feed. Correlated with this ability to contract rapidly is the presence of giant axons in the ventral nerve cords. The enlarged diameter of the axon increases the rapidity of conduction and therefore increases motor response.

Although giant axons are present in the majority of polychaetes (Nicol, 1948) and reach their greatest development among tube-dwellers, the arrangement and structure is far from uniform; the axons have probably evolved independently within a number of groups. In most cases, there are present three giant axons, as in Nereis, which run the length of the nerve cord. However, fibers may range in number from one, as in Myxicola and Eunice, to many, as in Halla. The fibers may be separate or anastomosed; each axon may have a single cell body or many. A few examples of different giant axon systems are illustrated in Figure 11-27, C-E.

Sense Organs.   The principal specialized sense organs of polychaetes are eyes, nuchal organs, and statocysts.

EYES.   With the exception of the sabellid fanworms, eyes are found only in errant polychaetes, but even here they are sometimes absent. The eyes are located on the surface of the prostomium and number two, three, or four pairs (Figs. 11-4 and 11-5, B). They may be very simple or highly developed, depending on the worm's mode of existence. In general, the polychaete eye is of the retinal-cup variety, the wall of which is composed of rod-like photoreceptors, pigment, and supporting cells (Figs. 11-28, A and C). The photoreceptors are directed toward the lumen of the cup; these eyes are therefore of the direct type. An optic nerve issues from the back of the cup and extends the short distance to the brain. The interior of the eye is filled with a refractive body, which may or may not be connected with the surface cuticle. The surface cuticle acts as a cornea. Such eyes function only in light detection; most polychaetes are negatively phototropic.

The annelid eye reaches its highest development among the pelagic Alciopidae (Fig. 11-28, B). The two large eyes protrude greatly from the surface of the prostomium. Each eye consists of an inner retinal cup, a vitreous body, and an outer bulging lens and cornea. This eye possesses a remarkable mechanism for accommodation which indicates that the eye probably forms an image. Focusing is effected by two methods. An ampulla to the side of the eye forces fluid into the optic vesicle, located between the lens and vitreous body; this pressure forces the lens outward. Also, the lens can be flattened by the action of muscle fibers attached to its side. The lens surface is even striped to control the amount of light entering the eye.

A few species, such as Polyophthalmus have a simple eyespot located on the body wall between each successive parapodium, in addition to the eyes on the prostomium.

The sabellid fanworms, like many other sedentary polychaetes, have lost the prostomial eyes. Members of this family, however, possess eyespots on the branchial filaments. These branchial eyes are located on both sides of the main axis of the filament and in Dasychone, for example, number 10 to 15 pairs per filament. Each branchial eye is composed of a cluster of pigment and photoreceptor cells. Each photoreceptor cell contains an outer large refractive body, so that the eye is essentially compound. The nerve fibrils of the receptors pass into the general epidermal nerve network.

Although the serpulid fanworms lack branchial eyes, the epidermis of the crown contains photoreceptor cells. These worms are very sensitive to sudden light reductions and will immediately withdraw into the tube. This behavior probably represents a protective adaptation against passing predators. The branchial eyes of sabellids probably serve the same purpose.

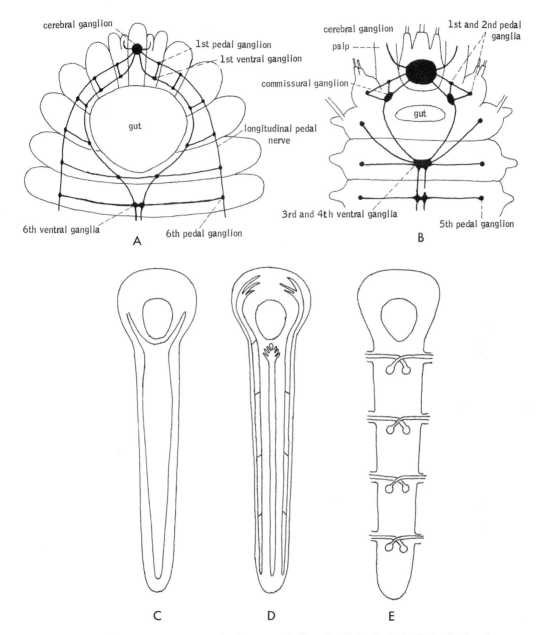

Figure 11-27.   Nervous systems of scale worms: *A. Hermodice; B. Lepidasthenia.* (Both after Storch from Fauvel.) Nervous systems of three polychaetes, showing types of giant axons: *C. Eunice,* with a single giant axon; *D. Nereis,* with medial and lateral giant fibers; *E. Euthalenessa,* with intrasegmental giant axons. (*C* and *D* after Nicol, *E* after Rhodes from Nicol.)

NUCHAL ORGANS.   Nuchal organs consist of a pair of ciliated sensory pits that are located in the head region of most polychaetes. Although of varied structure, all nuchal organs are innervated by the posterior portion of the brain, and all are composed of ciliated columnar cells and sensory cells. Gland cells are sometimes also present. The simplest type of nuchal organ is displayed by the nereids and hesionids; it is merely a ciliated sensory area located behind the eye.

In bamboo worms and ampharetids, the nuchal organs are pits located on either side of the head. A similar type is common in members of the burrowing families, Opheliidae, Orbiniidae and Capitellidae (Fig. 11-28, *D*), but in these families the nuchal organs can be evaginated. The nuchal organs are comprised of chemoreceptors, which are important in the detection of food; for when the organs are destroyed experimentally, the worms no longer feed. Nuchal organs attain their greatest development

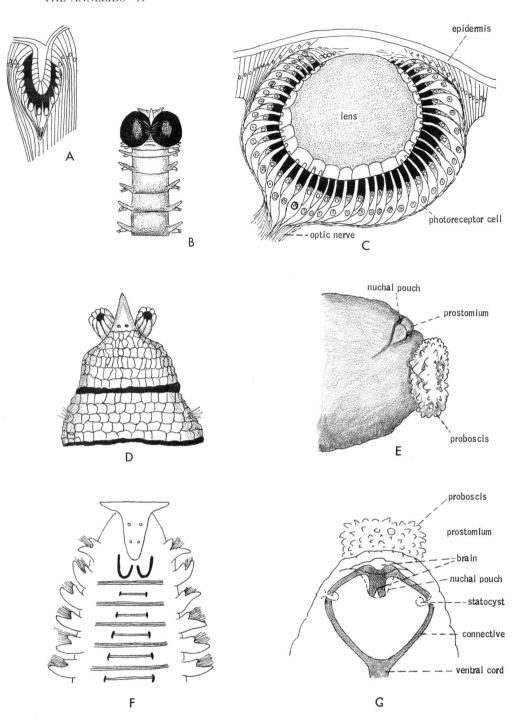

Figure 11-28.   *A.* Simple eye of *Ranzania*. (After Hesse from Fauvel.) *B.* Anterior of the alciopid, *Vanadis grandis,* showing highly developed eyes. (After Izuka from Fauvel.) *C.* Eye of *Nereis.* (After Hesse from Fauvel.) *D.* Anterior of *Notomastus latericeus* with everted nuchal organs. (After Rullier from Fauvel.) *E.* Head of *Arenicola* (side view). (After Wells.) *F.* The spionid, *Colobranchus ciliatus,* showing dorsal sense organs in black. (After Söderström from Fauvel.) *G.* Statocysts and anterior part of nervous system of *Arenicola.* (After Wells.)

in the predatory burrowers; and they are completely absent or rarely appear in the ciliary feeders.

CILIATED SENSE ORGANS.   Specialized ciliated sense organs on the trunk segments are characteristic of some polychaetes. Orbiniids and spionids possess ciliated sensory tubercles, ridges, or bands, called dorsal organs, located on the dorsal surface of the segments (Fig. 11-28, F). Some families, such as the Orbiniidae and the Opheliidae, possess ciliated sensory structures called lateral organs, which are located between the notopodium and neuropodium of each parapodium.

STATOCYSTS.   Statocysts are recognized in some polychaete families, including the Orbiniidae, the Arenicolidae, the Terebellidae, and the Sabellidae. The statocysts of *Arenicola* are located within the body wall of the head and are bulbous with a canal that opens to the outer lateral body surface (Fig. 11-28, G). The statocysts are associated with the circumpharyngeal connectives, which in *Arenicola* run within the body wall. Wells (1950) reports that the statocysts of *Arenicola* contain spicules, diatom shells, and quartz grains, all covered with a chitinoid material. *Arenicola* always burrows head downward, and if an aquarium containing a worm is tilted 90 degrees, the worm makes a compensating 90-degree turn in burrowing. If the statocysts are destroyed, this compensating ability is lost. The sabellid, *Branchiomma*, also has statocysts, but they orient the worm so that it burrows backward, since its crown must be directed upward.

TACTILE CELLS.   In addition to specialized sense organs, the general body surface of polychaetes is supplied with tactile cells, which are particularly concentrated on the parapodial and head appendages. *Nereis*, for example, responds so positively to the sides of an artificial burrow that it can be killed by other environmental factors to which it would normally give a negative response.

Excretion.   Polychaete excretory organs are either protonephridia or metanephridia. There may be one pair of excretory organs per segment or one pair for the entire animal. The distal end of the nephridial tubule is located in the coelom of the segment immediately anterior to that from which the nephridiopore opens (Fig. 11-1). The tubule penetrates the posterior septum of the segment; extends into the next segment, where it may be coiled; and then opens to the exterior in the region of the neuropodium. Both the preseptal portion of the nephridium and the postseptal tubule are covered by a reflected layer of peritoneum from the septum.

Protonephridia, which are more primitive than metanephridia, are found in phyllodocids, tomopterids, glycerids, nephthydids and a few others. The solenocytes are always located at the short preseptal end of the nephridium and are bathed by coelomic fluid. The solenocyte tubules are very slender and delicate and arise from the nephridial wall in bunches. In *Phyllodoce* the preseptal tube is branched, and the solenocyte tubules originate at the tips of the branches (Fig. 11-29). Fluid apparently enters through the walls of the tubules and is then driven by a long, flame flagellum into the lumen of the nephridium. The nephridial tubule is ciliated, and fluid is forced to the exterior through the nephridiopore.

All other polychaetes possess metanephridia, in which the preseptal end of the nephridium possesses an open ciliated funnel, the nephrostome, instead of solenocytes. The metanephridium is thus open at both ends. Goodrich (1946) has divided such open nephridia into several classifications, depending upon their supposed evolutionary origin and their employment as gonoducts. This auxiliary function is discussed in the subsequent section on reproduction. The metanephridium is treated here as a single morphological type.

The typical metanephridium is found in the nereids (Fig. 11-30, C). The nephrostome possesses an outer investment of peritoneum; the edges may be fringed as in *Nereis vexillosa;* the interior of the nephrostome is heavily ciliated. The post-septal canal, which extends into the next successive segment, becomes greatly coiled to form a mass of tubules, which are enclosed in a thin sac-like covering of peritoneal cells. The nephridiopore opens at the base of the neuropodium on the ventral side. The entire lining of the tubules is ciliated.

The metanephridia of most other polychaetes differ only in minor details. The nephrostome may be developed to various degrees. The post-septal tubule may be U-shaped, as in *Nerine* (Fig. 11-30, A), *Odontosyllis* and the scale worms, rather than coiled. The nephridia of spionids and orbiniids are not only U-shaped, but the nephridiopores have shifted to a more dorsal position along with the parapodia.

The absence of septa does not necessarily limit the number of nephridia present in polychaetes; but nephridia, like other segmental organs, may display various degrees of regional restriction in the more specialized families. Such restriction reaches its zenith in the sedentary tubicolous flabelligerids and fanworms, where only one pair of functional anterior nephridia are to be found. In the fanworms the two nephridia join at the midline to form a single

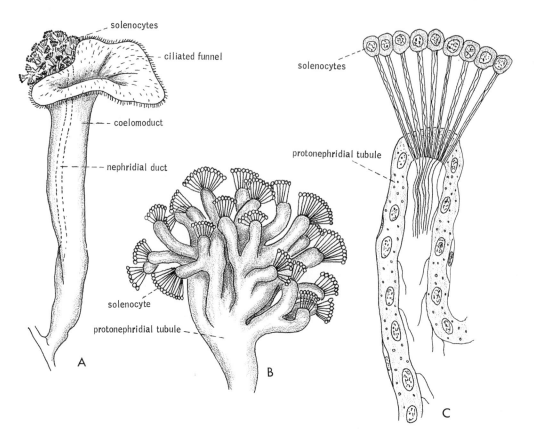

Figure 11-29. Protonephridium and coelomoduct of *Phyllodoce paretti*. *A.* Relation of protonephridium and coelomoduct. *B.* Branched end of protonephridium. *C.* Solenocytes of one protonephridial branch. (All after Goodrich.)

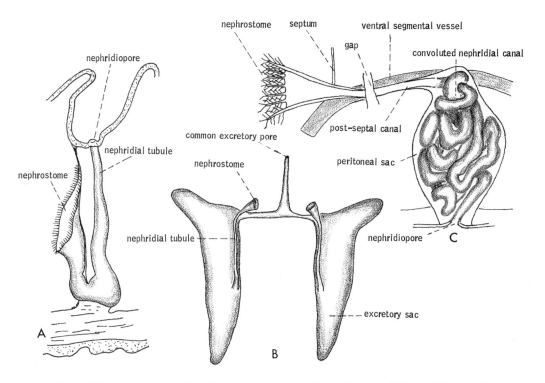

Figure 11-30. Metanephridia of three polychaetes. *A. Nerine.* (After Goodrich.) *B.* The serpulid fanworm, *Pomatoceros.* (After Thomas.) *C. Nereis vexillosa.* (After Jones.)

median canal, which extends forward to open through a single nephridiopore on the head (Fig. 11-30, *B*). Excretory waste is thus deposited directly outside, and fouling of the tube is avoided.

In *Owenia* the problem of tube-fouling has been solved in a different manner. The nephridiopores open into an epidermal canal that extends forward on both sides of the body to the sixth segment from which each canal opens to the outside. The canal represents an epidermal groove that has closed over.

The principal nitrogenous waste in polychaetes is ammonia. Wastes diffuse from the coelomic fluid or from the blood to the nephridial tubule and then are transferred to the lumen for removal to the outside. Particulate waste and waste-laden coelomocytes are probably removed from the coelomic fluid by the ciliated nephrostome. The greatly coiled tubule mass in the nereids appear to be a modification that increases surface area for tubular secretion.

In polychaetes the association of the blood vessels with the nephridia is variable. The fanworms and the arenicolids lack a well developed nephridial blood supply, and the coelomic fluid must be the principal means of waste removal. In other polychaetes, such as *Aphrodite,* the nephridia are surrounded by a network of vessels. In the nereids, the nephridial blood supply varies from one species to the next. For example, in *Nereis vexillosa* there is no distinct association of blood vessels with the nephridium, while in other nereids there is a very close relationship.

Krishnan (1952) has shown that in Indian nereids the degree of vascularization is closely related to the salinity of the habitat. Species living in brackish water display a much closer association between the blood vessels and the nephridia than do species living in a higher saline environment. Thus, in brackish-water species, secretion by the nephridial tubules apparently plays a role in maintaining water and salt balance.

Chloragogen tissue, coelomocytes, and the intestinal wall may play accessory roles in excretion. Chloragogen tissue is composed of brown or greenish cells, located on the wall of the intestine, on various blood vessels, or within the heart body of certain forms. Chloragogen tissue, which has been studied much more extensively in earthworms (see page 216), is an important center of intermediary metabolism and also gives rise to phagocytic coelomocytes. Not infrequently, the intestinal wall is green in color due to the presence of coproporphyrin and pheophorbide pigments. These same green pigments also are present in the epidermis of *Owenia* and other polychaetes. Although the physiological significance of these pigments have not been determined, they may well be excretory products.

Regeneration.   Polychaetes have relatively great powers of regeneration. Tentacles, palps, and other attenuated parts that are lost are soon replaced. Some worms even display self-amputation, or autotomy. For example, the elytra of certain scale worms and the posterior trunk segments of some eunicids, such as *Marphysa* and *Diopatra,* are detached when the worms are disturbed. The lost parts are later regenerated. In general, new trunk segments are more readily regenerated in worms with undifferentiated body regions, and both a new head and a new tail can be re-formed. In worms with a thorax and abdomen or with a tail, caudal regeneration may take place, but the formation of a new head is less common.

Reproduction.   Reproduction in polychaetes is accomplished either asexually or sexually.

ASEXUAL REPRODUCTION.   Asexual reproduction is known in some polychaetes, including syllids, serpulids, fanworms, and spionids; it takes place by budding or division of the body. The chaetopterid, *Phyllochaetopterus,* normally reproduces by division of the body into a number of sections each of which can then form a new individual.

SEXUAL REPRODUCTION.   Most polychaetes are dioecious. Polychaete gonads are not distinct organs but are masses of developing gametes, which develop as projections or swellings of the peritoneum in different parts of some segments. In *Aphrodite,* sex cells arise from the peritoneum of most of the segmental vessels, which thus finally appear like strings of beads. In *Nereis* the ventral septal peritoneum is the site of gamete formation.

Primitively, most of the segments produce gametes; this is true in many scale worms, many nereids, and the eunicids. In general, restriction of segments for gamete formation coincides with specialization of the trunk into different regions. When there is a distinct thoracic and abdominal region, the gonads are usually limited to the abdomen. In the fanworms, all of the abdominal segments form gametes, which arise from the anterior peritoneum of each segment. However, in *Amphitrite* and *Arenicola,* gamete-forming segments are much more limited in number. In *Arenicola* there are only six reproductive segments, which contain relatively distinct gonads, located one pair to a segment on gonadal vessels associated with the nephridia.

The gametes are usually shed into the coelom as gametogonia or primary gametocytes, and maturation takes place largely in the coelomic fluid. When the worm is mature, the coelom is packed with eggs or sperm; in species where the body wall is thin or not heavily pigmented, the gravid condition is easily apparent. For example, the abdomen of a ripe male *Pomatoceros* appears white and the abdomen of a female, bright pink or orange owing to the color of the sperm or the eggs.

Few polychaetes possess separate gonoducts. The gametes most commonly leave the body through the metanephridia or in some cases by the dehiscence, or breakdown, of the body wall. Much of our knowledge of nephridial structure in annelids results from the valuable work of Goodrich (1945), who made extensive studies on the role of nephridia in sperm and egg transport. Goodrich's views on the origin of annelid nephridia are closely associated with the *Gonocoel Theory,* of which he was a strong supporter. Goodrich claimed that primitively each coelomic compartment was drained by one pair of protonephridia and by one pair of coelomoducts. The protonephridia were excretory in function and ectodermal in origin, growing in from the outside; the coelomoducts were genital in function and were derived from the mesoderm, growing outward to the exterior.

Goodrich further claimed that all nephridia —that is, both protonephridia and metanephridia—were homologous and that many metanephridia represent a union of the ciliated funnel of a coelomoduct and the tubule of a protonephridium. Such a structure, functioning both as a genital and excretory outlet, Goodrich called a nephromixium or mixonephridium.

There is no question that this combination has occurred among some polychaetes that possess protonephridia. In *Phyllodoce,* for example, at sexual maturity a coelomoduct arises from the septum near the protonephridium, develops in a posterior direction, and joins the nephridial tubule (Fig. 11-29, *A*). The resulting nephromixium is a branched structure with one branch leading to the solenocytes and the other branch opening through a ciliated funnel, or coelomostome. In a few other forms, this union has developed still further, and the solenocytes have degenerated. This union results in the metanephridium serving both as a genital and an excretory outlet.

The question arises, however, whether or not metanephridia are homologous to protonephridia. Recent embryological investigations indicate that at least some metanephridia develop entirely from mesodermal rather than ectodermal cells. If this is true, then the metanephridia of most polychaetes are probably not homologous to protonephridia and are not the result of union between coelomostomes and ectodermal nephridia. If this is the case, from an evolutionary standpoint most metanephridia must then be newly developed outlets from the coelom and are coelomoducts in their own right.

Regardless of the origin of polychaete metanephridia, they serve as the principal exits for sex cells and, from a functional standpoint, Goodrich's term—nephromixium—is certainly applicable. When production of gametes takes place in most segments, the metanephridia function both as excretory and genital ducts; but when the gonads are restricted to specific segments, the metanephridia serve only in the excretory capacity in the sterile segments and serve in the reproductive capacity only or in both capacities in the fertile segments.

In fanworms, only the large anterior nephridia are excretory, and the nephridia of the fertile abdominal segments function only as exits for the genital products. As the gametes of the fanworm pass through the nephridiopore, they are carried to the ciliated median ventral groove, where they are moved anteriorly and out of the tube.

Gametes probably are moved through the nephridia primarily by cilia, although, in *Arenicola,* body contractions and hydrostatic pressure are important. Also, Scott (1911) has shown that the nephrostomial cilia of *Arenicola* in some way act as a sorting mechanism and prevent the passage of either unripe eggs or coelomocytes.

The escape of gametes through a rupture in the body wall is undoubtedly a specialized condition. Rupturing is found in some nereids, syllids, and eunicids, all of which become pelagic at sexual maturity. After the rupture of the body wall the adults die.

Aside from cases of internal development, fertilization is usually external in the surrounding sea water.

EPITOKY. Epitoky is a reproductive phenomenon characteristic of nereids, syllids, and eunicids. Epitoky is the formation of a reproductive individual, or epitoke, that differs in a varying number of secondary sexual characteristics from a nonsexual form, or atoke. Epitokal modifications include changes in the formation of the head, the structure of the parapodia, the size of the segments, and in other ways.

Often the gamete-bearing segments are the most strikingly modified, so that the body of the worm appears to be divided into two markedly different regions. For example, the epitoke of *Nereis irrorata* has large eyes and reduced prostomial palps and tentacles (Fig. 11-31). The anterior 15 to 20 trunk segments are not greatly modified, but the remaining segments, comprising the epitokal region and packed with gametes, are much enlarged; their parapodia contain fans of long spatulate swimming setae. In *Eunice viridis,* the Samoan palolo worm, the anterior of the worm is unmodified, and the epitokal region consists of a very long chain of narrower but longer posterior segments, each with an eye spot on the ventral side (Fig. 11-32, *A*).

Epitokous individuals arise either by direct transformation from an atokous form, or by budding from an atokous form or from a stolon. Transformation is characteristic of the nereids and the eunicids, while asexual budding of epitokes is common in the syllids. Syllid epitokes usually form at the caudal end, either as a single body or as a chain or cluster of individuals (Fig. 11-32, *C*); but in *Syllis ramosus* numerous epitokes bud from the sides of the body and may in turn form secondary buds (Fig. 11-32, *B*).

SWARMING.   All epitokous polychaetes swim to the surface during the shedding of the eggs and sperm. This behavior is known as swarming. Some swarming nereids and syllids even perform a nuptial dance, in which males and females swim rapidly in small circles. Experimental evidence indicates that the female produces some substance, called fertilizin (not the fertilizin produced by animal eggs), that attracts the male and stimulates shedding of the sperm. The sperm in turn stimulate shedding of the eggs.

To ensure fertilization, swarming in the male and female must coincide and take place over a relatively short period. Thus the swarming phenomenon is usually marked by a very distinct periodicity and often coincides with lunar periods. The most striking examples of such lunar periodicity are displayed by the so-called palolo worms.

The name palolo worm originally referred to a Samoan species of eunicid, *Eunice viridis,* but is now applied to a number of nereid,

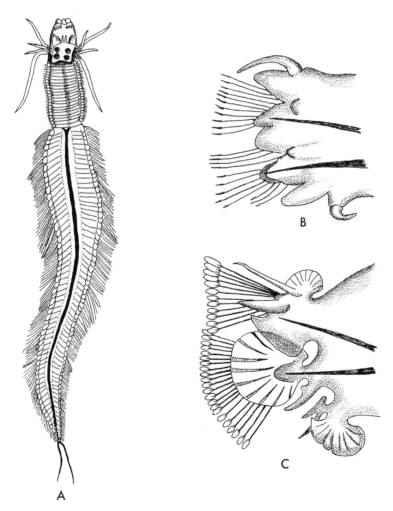

Figure 11-31.   *A*. Epitokous male of *Nereis irrorata.* (After Rullier from Fauvel.) *B* and *C*. Parapodia of atoke (*B*) and epitoke (*C*) of *Nereis irrorata* male. (After Fauvel.)

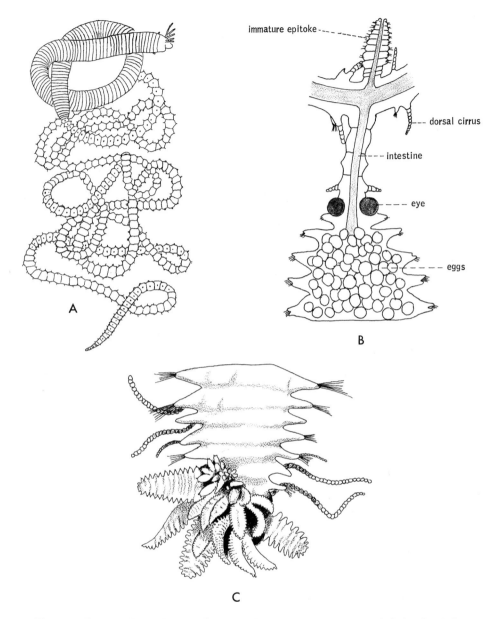

Figure 11-32.   *A. Eunice viridis,* the Samoan palolo worm, with posterior epitokal region. (After Woodworth from Fauvel.) *B. Syllis ramosus,* showing epitokes developing from sides of atoke. (After McIntosh from Potts.) *C.* Posterior of *Trypanosyllis,* showing cluster of budding epitokes. (After Potts from Fauvel.)

eunicid, and syllid polychaetes, all of which exhibit a similar swarming behavior. Clark and Hess (1940) have made a rather complete study of the Atlantic palolo, *Eunice schemacephala.* This West Indian worm lives in rock and coral crevices below the low-tide mark. The worms are negatively phototropic and emerge from the burrows to feed only at night.

Swarming takes place in July during the first or last quarter of a lunar cycle. At three or four in the morning during such a period, the worm backs out of its burrow, and the caudal sexual epitokal region breaks free. The epitoke swims to the surface, where it undergoes spiral swimming movements. By dawn the ocean surface is covered with sexual bodies, and at the rising of the sun the epitokes rupture. Fertilization immediately follows dehiscence, and acres of eggs may cover the sea. A ciliated larval stage is attained by the next day, and in three days the larvae sink to the bottom.

The Samoan palolo worm swarms in October or November at the beginning of the last lunar quarter. The natives, who consider the epitokes a great delicacy, eagerly await the predicted night of swarming in boats when they scoop up great numbers of the worms from the ocean surface. Needless to say, swarming also provides a day of feasting for fish, birds, and other predators.

The physiological causes of swarming and swarming periodicity are still poorly understood. Certainly, a complex of factors is involved. The inherent swarming reflex increases with sexual maturity and is very probably under hormonal control. Studies on nereids and syllids have shown that neurosecretory cells in the brain elaborate some substance that inhibits the formation of gametes and epitokal transformation or budding. For example, if the brain of a young nereid is removed, epitokal characters appear; or if the brain of a young worm is transplanted into the coelom of a mature individual, the epitokal characters in the host are suppressed.

Environmental factors may greatly influence the time of swarming. Clark and Hess (1940) have shown that wave action and turbidity suppress swarming in the Atlantic palolo. Light also suppresses swarming, even moonlight. But the actual role of the moon in swarming is difficult to understand. The relation of lunar phases to swarming periods is different in different species. This variation makes any hypothesis based merely on light intensity difficult to prove.

HERMAPHRODITISM. Relatively few hermaphroditic polychaetes are known, and most of these are fanworms. In most hermaphroditic fanworms, the anterior abdominal segments produce eggs and the posterior segments sperm. However, in *Dasychone*, a sabellid, sperm and eggs are formed in the same segments.

EGG DEPOSITION. In most polychaetes, the eggs are shed freely into the sea water, where they become planktonic and separate. In some polychaetes, however, the eggs are laid in mucus masses that are attached to the tubes or to other objects. *Axiothella* (Fig. 11-33, *A*), a bamboo worm, produces a large ovoid egg mass that is attached to the chimney of the tube.

Arenicola cristata also produces mucus egg masses that are anchored to the surface of the sand bottom. *Scoloplos armiger* displays the same characteristic with each egg mass being approximately one by two centimeters in size and containing six hundred to eighteen hundred eggs. The jelly is believed to be produced by gland cells lining the female nephridia. Some tubicolous worms produce a mucus egg mass that is retained inside the tube; or they attach the eggs directly to the inner surface of the tube wall.

Brooding of eggs is exhibited in a few polychaetes species. Some scale worms use the respiratory water channel beneath the elytra as a brood chamber. Some species of *Spirorbis* brood their eggs in the cavity of the operculum, and *Autolytus* possesses a special brood sac for this purpose on the ventral surface of the body. The parapodia may be used to retain the eggs. In *Pionosyllis*, an egg is attached to the base of each dorsal cirrus. Another syllid, *Grubea*, attaches three or four large eggs directly to the dorsal surface of each segment (Fig. 11-33, *B*), and the phyllodocid polychaete, *Notophyllum*, uses the same site to attach agglutinated bands of eggs.

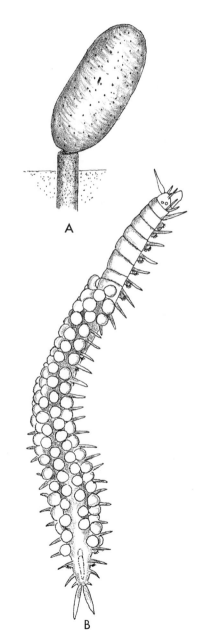

Figure 11-33. *A. Axothella mucosa* egg mass attached to end of tube. *B. Grubea*, with eggs attached to dorsal surface. (After Viguier and Pierantoni from Potts.)

There are a few polychaetes, such as the serpulid, *Salmacina dysteri,* and some nereids, that release developing larvae, but this is relatively rare. *Ctenodrilus* is reported to be truly viviparous, nutrition for the embryo being supplied by maternal blood vessels.

Embryology.   The polychaete egg is telolecithal with a variable amount of yolk. Cleavage is spiral, reflecting the pattern described in Chapter 9. A displaced blastocoel is usually present, but a stereoblastula develops in *Nereis, Capitella,* and others. Gastrulation takes place by means of invagination, epiboly, or both.

THE TROCHOPHORE.   After gastrulation, the embryo rapidly develops into a larval stage known as a trochophore (Fig. 11-34, *B*). The trochophore larva is not only characteristic of polychaetes but also occurs in mollusks and other phyla. In polychaetes, the trochophore structure usually begins to appear on about the second day of development. The embryo assumes a top-shaped form, the cells of the first quartet being located at the apex, or aboral end. A characteristic feature of the trochophore is the presence of a girdle of ciliated cells; this girdle of cells is called the prototroch and rings the larva just above the equator.

The prototroch cells are derived in part from the first quartet—specifically the $1a^2$ to $1d^2$ cells, called the primary trochoblasts. The primary trochoblasts form only the group of ciliated cells in each quadrant. The completion of the girdle comes from the secondary trochoblasts, which fill in between the primary groups. In many polychaetes, cells derived from the first quartet form a conspicuous cross-like pattern. The $1a^{112}$ to $1d^{112}$ cells form the rays of the cross, which extend from the apical sensory plate. Cells of the apical sensory plate usually bear a tuft of cilia as in the larvae of turbellarians and rhynchocoels.

At the oral end of the embryo, the blastopore becomes elongated, extending along the lower side of the embryo. The upper end of the blastopore forms the mouth and stomodeum, which, because of differential growth, develops so that it lies just beneath the prototroch. The remainder of the blastopore closes, and a new opening, the anus, forms at the site of the lower blastoporal slit and connects with the gut.

Two additional girdles of cilia commonly appear after the formation of the prototroch and after further differentiation of the oral end of the embryo. The first girdle of cilia is called the telotroch and rings the embryo just above

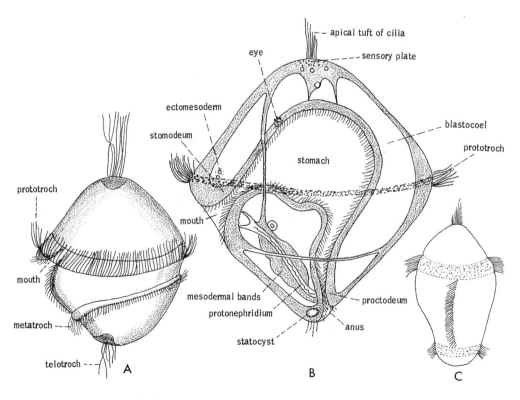

Figure 11-34.   *A.* Trochophore of *Polygordius,* showing prototroch, metatroch, and telotroch. (After Dawydoff.) *B.* Structure of an annelid trochophore. (After Shearer from Hyman.) *C.* Trochophore of *Marphysa.* (After Dawydoff.)

the anus (Fig. 11-34, *A* and *C*); the second girdle of cilia, which appears still later and is called the metatroch, forms just below the mouth (Fig. 11-34, *A*).

Internally the two teloblast cells, derived from the *4d* cell, each give rise to a band of mesoderm, which extends dorsally toward the mouth from both sides of the anus (Fig. 11-34, *B*). The mesodermal bands form all of the entomesoderm. The larval alimentary tract consists of the stomodeum, formed from second and third quartet ectoderm, and the stomach and intestine, derived from the endoderm.

Blastomeres *4A*, *4B*, *4C*, and *4D*, plus a few offspring from the *4d* cells, form all of the entoderm. The old blastocoel remains in the form of a large cavity lying between the gut and the outer ectoderm; into this cavity is proliferated ectomesoderm from the second and third quartets. This ectomesoderm forms larval muscle bands that become attached to the gut and to the ciliary girdles. Third quartet ectoderm also forms two larval protonephridia that lie in the blastocoel cavity on both sides of the intestine. Finally, in a highly developed trochophore, radial nerves emerge from a ganglionic mass lying beneath the apical plate. The radial nerves connect with one to several longitudinal nerves encircling the larva.

The fully developed trochophore larva can be divided into three regions: the prototrochal region, consisting of the apical plate, the prototroch, and the mouth region; the pygidium consisting of the telotroch and the anal region behind it; and the growth zone, which includes all of the larva between the mouth region and the telotroch. The growth region eventually forms all of the trunk segments of the body.

Primitively, the trochophore is a planktonic, free-swimming larva. Planktonic trochophores appear in the development of *Podarke*, *Eupomatus*, certain nereids, *Spirorbis*, *Sabellaria*, and *Haploscoloplos*. The greatest development of larval structures is attained in these trochophores, which are not only free-swimming but are also often feeding larvae as well.

In many polychaetes, however, the trochophore is not free-swimming; the stage is passed in the egg prior to hatching (Fig. 11-35). The larval structures of this form are poorly developed as compared to those in planktonic forms.

METAMORPHOSIS. Additional development takes place as the trochophore metamorphoses into the adult body form. In polychaetes with planktonic feeding trochophores, metamorphosis is somewhat indirect and results in the loss of many of the larval structures, such as nephridia, ectomesodermal muscle bands, and ciliated girdles. In species where the trochophore stage is

passed in the egg, metamorphosis is more direct, since larval structures are never greatly developed to begin with. In some cases, metamorphosis may result in the immediate termination of a planktonic existence, but more often the metamorphosing worm passes through a number of intermediate, free-swimming stages before settling to the bottom.

The most conspicuous feature of metamorphosis is the gradual lengthening of the growth zone—the region between the mouth and the telotroch—due to the formation and development of trunk segments (Fig. 11-35). The segments develop from anterior to posterior, and the germinal region always remains just in front of the terminal pygidium. The mesodermal bands undergo active proliferation and anteriorly lay down a pair of somites for each newly formed segment.

Each somite becomes hollow, forming half the coelomic compartment; the mesodermal cells form the peritoneum, the body wall and gut musculature, the blood vessels, and the nephridia for each segment. Since somite development takes place in the blastocoel, this cavity is gradually obliterated. In almost all polychaetes studied so far, all trunk ectoderm originates from blastomere *2d*. Ectoderm forms not only the integument but also the ganglia of each segment. The formation of body segments is marked externally by the development of setal sacs and setae. Also, each of the early segments is often ringed by a girdle of cilia.

In the prototrochal region, which originally formed the major part of the body of the trochophore, the cells of the apical plate form the prostomium and the brain. The brain gives rise to the circumpharyngeal connectives, which grow ventrally around the gut and connect with the subesophageal ganglion. Mesodermal tissue grows forward and invades the prostomium.

The mouth region may give rise to the peristomium, in which case the peristomium is without setae (achetous) and does not contain the subesophageal ganglion. Commonly, as in *Nereis*, *Capitella*, and the fanworms, the mouth region fuses with the first trunk segments to form the peristomium, in which case the peristomium contains the subesophageal ganglion—the ganglion of the first trunk segment. The peristomium, however, may still be achetous, as in *Nereis*, owing to resorption of the setal sacs. Thus, this difference in peristomial origins indicates that the peristomia of different polychaetes are not necessarily homologous.

The elongated, metamorphosing larvae remain planktonic for varying lengths of time. *Nereis fucata* settles to the bottom 22 days after

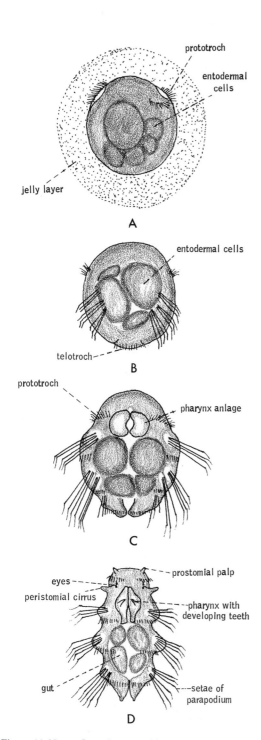

prototroch

entodermal cells

jelly layer

A

entodermal cells

telotroch

B

prototroch

pharynx anlage

C

eyes

peristomial cirrus

prostomial palp

pharynx with developing teeth

gut

setae of parapodium

D

Figure 11-35.   Larval stages of *Nereis diversicolor*. *A*. Young trochophore before hatching. *B*. Early larva with three setigerous segments. *C*. Older larva with three setigerous segments. *D*. Later larva, after three weeks. (All after Dales.)

the trochophore stage has begun; at the time of settling, there are six or seven setae-bearing segments. The larvae of *Ophelia bicornis* are free-swimming until three pairs of setae-bearing segments have developed. In both *Arenicola marina* and *Nereis diversicolor,* the trochophore larvae are not active swimmers and remain on the bottom.

When the trochophore stage is embryonic, hatching occurs at various times during advanced development; and there may yet be a free-swimming, post-trochophoral, larval stage. For example, in *Autolytus* an elongated achetous larva breaks free from the brood sac of the mother. On the other hand, *Axiothella mucosa* and *Scoloplos armiger* have no planktonic stages and assume the adult mode of existence on emerging from the jelly egg case. In any event, the larvae eventually sink to the bottom, where they complete postlarval development and assume the habits of the adult.

Ecology and Distribution.   MECHANICS OF TUBE CONSTRUCTION. In both sabellid fan-worms, which build tubes of sand grains and mucus, and in serpulid fanworms, which construct calcareous tubes, the peristomium is folded back to form a very distinct collar. The collar fits over the margin of the tube at the opening and is the principal structure used to mold additions on the end of the tube. In the serpulids, two large calcium carbonate secreting glands open beneath the collar folds. When additions are made to the tube, the calcium carbonate secretions flow out between the collar and the body wall. This space then acts as a mold in which the secretion hardens and is simultaneously fused as a new ring on the end of the tube.

In the sabellids, the collar folds also act as a mold. Nicol (1930) has given an excellent account of the process in *Sabella*, which constructs a tube of sand grains imbedded in mucus. These worms sort detritus collected by the ciliated fans, and sand grains that are of suitable size for tube construction are stored in a pair of opposing ventral sacs located below the mouth.

The walls of the ventral sacs produce mucus, which is mixed with the sand grains within the sacs. When additions are to be made at the end of the tube (Fig. 11-36, *A*), the ventral sacs deliver a rope-like string of mucus and sand grains to the collar folds below, which is divided midventrally, like the front of a shirt collar. The string of building materials is received at the collar folds. The worm rotates slowly in the tube, and the collar folds act like a pair of hands, molding and attaching the rope to the end of the tube. The operation is quite similar to an Indian method of making pottery.

In both sabellids and serpulids, the ventral surface of each segment bears a pair of large mucus-secreting pads called gland shields. When the worm rotates, these glands lay down a mucus coating on the inner surface of the tube. Ventral gland shields are found in the terebellids (Fig. 11-14) and are used to line the burrow, which is excavated in mud and sand. Gland shields are found in many other tube-building polychaetes, and may be located on the dorsal surface instead of the ventral. In other polychaetes, the mucus used in tube construction comes from glands around the parapodia.

The method of tube construction in the Oweniidae is also known in some detail (Fig. 11-36, B). The tubes of this family are composed of an outer layer of flattened sand grains that are attached only at one edge and are laid down in an overlapping manner like the shingles of a roof. The sand grains are attached to a cementing material that forms the middle layer of the tube. The inner layer is membranous; and at the mouth of the tube, it projects

beyond the sand and cement crust, resembling a cone with a small opening.

In oweniids, the first seven segments of the body each contain a pair of long glands that lie in the lateral portions of the coelom. A duct extends from each gland through the body wall and opens in the vicinity of the setal bundles (parapodia are absent). These glands produce a viscous material that forms the membranous lining of the tube. In producing the lining, the worm revolves in the tube, and the setae of the gland-bearing segments act as brushes for applying the secretion to the wall as it flows from the duct openings.

The addition of material to the sand-grain and cement layers is an entirely separate operation. A ventral pouch, which stores sand grains suitable for tube construction, is located beneath the mouth. During construction of the tube, the pouch projects outward and downward below the membranous, inner-layer cone and fastens a grain to the margin of the tube. The pouch apparently also secretes the cementing material.

COMMENSALISM.   Many polychaetes have

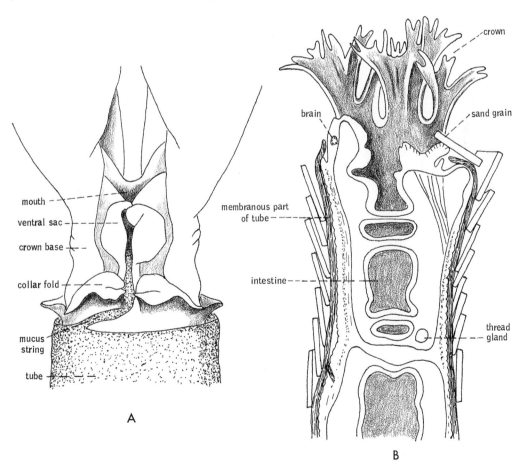

Figure 11-36.   *A.* The fanworm, *Sabella pavonina,* in process of tube construction (ventral view). (After Nicol.) *B. Owenia,* adding a sand grain to tube (longitudinal section). (After Watson.)

commensal relationships with other animals, but, with the exception of the scale worms, most polychaetes are hosts rather than guests. As might be expected, the role of host is played primarily by the tube-dwellers and the burrowing polychaetes. Guests include scale worms and crustaceans, particularly species of little crabs.

Perhaps the most notable example is a species of crab that lives exclusively in *Chaetopterus* tubes and belongs to the genus *Pinnixa*. Other species of *Pinnixa* live in maldanid tubes. The crabs enter the tubes as juveniles and in *Chaetopterus* later become too large to leave the chimney. The crabs feed on food material brought in by the water currents. A male and a female crab are almost always found together; the larval stages are swept out by water circulating through the tube. A few nontube-dwellers also harbor commensals; for example, *Pseudophythina rugifera*, a small clam, lives attached to the ventral surface of the sea mouse.

Polychaetes known to be commensal with other animals are distributed in numerous families throughout the class. They live in tubes and burrows of other polychaetes and crustaceans, on echiuroid worms, in the ambulacral grooves of sea stars, and on sea cucumbers and other animals. Several species of *Arctonoë*, Pacific scale worms, live associated with sea cucumbers, sea stars, and mollusks; they display colors similar to those of the host and have the setae modified for clinging. One species of scale worm found in Europe lives beneath the elytra of another scale worm. All scale worms are not commensals; most are free-living.

PARASITISM.   Parasitism is not common among polychaetes. *Labrorostratus*, a eunicid, lives in the coelom of other polychaetes and may be almost as big as its host. Clark (1956) has noted that endoparasitic polychaetes are not markedly modified, as is usually the case in endoparasitism. The life histories of these parasites are unknown; perhaps they leave the host and assume a free-swimming existence at sexual maturity. Polychaete ectoparasites include the Histriobdellidae (Fig. 11-37, *A*), which are parasites in the gill chambers of crustaceans, and the Ichthyotomidae (Fig. 11-37, *B*) which attach to the fins of marine eels. The Ichthyotomidae suck blood by means of piercing stylets and a pumping pharynx.

A most interesting group of commensal and parasitic polychaetes are the myzostomes, sometimes placed in a separate phylum or class, the Myzostomida. These little worms are rarely more than a few millimeters long and resemble flatworms (Fig. 11-37, *C*). The body is greatly flattened and the five pairs of parapodia are carried on the undersurface. The most peculiar feature of the myzostomes is their constant association with echinoderms. Moreover, except for a relatively small number of species that live on brittle stars and sea stars, the majority of the myzostomes are restricted to crinoids, or sea lilies. Most myzostomes are commensals, living on plankton gathered by the arms of the host; and they are either sedentary or crawl about over the surface of the host's body. Parasitic myzostomes live in the body wall, the coelom, or the digestive tract of the host. Development includes a typical free-swimming polychaete larva.

ENVIRONMENT.   Polychaetes inhabit all oceans. The majority are littoral and many live in the intertidal zone. They occur in tremendous numbers. A mud or sand flat, when exposed at low tide, often appears studded with the tubes of many species. Beneath the surface of the flat there is usually an even greater population.

McConnaughey and Fox (1949) have taken population counts of the little burrowing opheliid, *Thoracophelia mucronata*, which measures about 25 mm. long and not over 2 mm. in diameter. These worms inhabit the intertidal zone on the Pacific coast of the United States and form colonies that occupy extensive stretches of protected beaches. In such colonies, the number of worms averages 2500 to 3000 per square foot. The worms feed on organic matter absorbed from ingested sand grains. McConnaughey and Fox estimate that worms occupying a typical strip of beach one mile long, ten feet wide, and one foot thick would ingest approximately 14,600 tons of sand each year.

Many polychaetes, particularly nereids, can tolerate low salinities, and have become adapted to life in brackish sounds and estuaries. A few species live in fresh water, and some live in moist earth. In his volume on fresh-water invertebrates, Pennak (1953) gives a brief but interesting account of the fresh-water polychaetes. He points out that most of these species have been reported from fresh-water bodies that are close to the sea, perhaps indicating a relatively recent migration.

Systematic Résumé of Class Polychaeta

This résumé has been adapted from that of Fauvel (1959), who, along with most modern authorities, considers the families of polychaetes too heterogeneous to be grouped into orders. This list includes the more common families to which references have been made in the preceding discussion. Lack of space permits

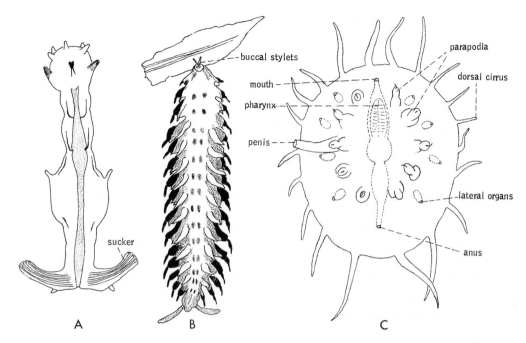

Figure 11-37. *A. Histriobdella,* an ectoparasite in crustacean gill chambers. (After Haswell from Fauvel.) *B. Ichthyotomus,* an ectoparasite on fins of marine eels. (After Eisig from Fauvel.) *C. Myzostomum,* a commensal on crinoids. (After Müller from Prenant.)

mention of only the most striking characteristics of some of these groups.

Subclass Errantia. Polychaetes with numerous and usually similar segments; parapodia with acicula. Usually possess head appendages. Swimming, crawling, burrowing, and tube-dwelling forms.

Family Aphroditidae. Dorsal surface bears elytra. Includes the sea mice—*Aphrodita, Hermione, Laetmonice;* and the scale worms—*Lepidonotus, Harmothoë, Polynoë, Lepidasthenia.*

Family Phyllodocidae. Uniramous parapodia with flattened leaf-like cirri. *Notophyllum, Phyllodoce.*

Family Alciopidae. Pelagic worms; possess transparent bodies and two large eyes. *Alciopa.*

Family Tomopteridae. Tomopteris.
Family Hesionidae. Podarke.
Family Syllidae. Small worms with long delicate bodies and uniramous parapodia. *Syllis, Odontosyllis, Pionosyllis, Autolytus, Procerastea.*

Family Nereidae. Four eyes and four pairs of peristomial cirri. Pharynx contains a pair of jaws. *Nereis.*

Family Glyceridae. Burrowing worms; possess conical prostomium and long proboscis with at least four jaws. *Glycera.*

Family Eunicidae. Elongated worms with proboscis armature of at least two pieces. *Eunice, Marphysa, Lysidice, Onuphis, Diopatra, Arabella, Labrorostratus, Nothria, Halla, Lumbriconereis.*

Family Histriobdellidae. Ectoparasitic. *Histriobdella.*

Family Ichthyotomidae. Ectoparasitic. *Ichthyotomus.*

Family Myzostomidae. Greatly flattened commensals and parasites of echinoderms, particularly crinoids. *Myzostoma.*

Subclass Sedentaria. Body usually displays regional differentiation. Prostomium small. Parapodia reduced and without acicula. Typically tube-dwellers.

Family Orbiniidae. Orbinia, Scoloplos.
Family Spionidae. Prostomium with two long palps. *Spio, Nerine.*
Family Magelonidae. Magelona.
Family Chaetopteridae. Chaetopterus, Phyllochaetopterus.

Family Cirratulidae. Segments bear long thread-like gills. *Audouinia, Cirratulus, Ctenodrilus.*

Family Flabelligeridae. Flabelligera.
Family Opheliidae. Ophelia, Polyophthalmus, Thoracophelia.
Family Capitellidae. Dasybranchus, Capitella.

Family Arenicolidae. The lugworms. *Arenicola.*

Family Maldanidae. The bamboo worms. *Axiothella, Clymenella, Maldane.*

Family Oweniidae. Owenia.
Family Sabellariidae. Sabellaria.
Family Amphictenidae. The cone worms. *Pectenaria, Cistenides.*

Family Ampharetidae. Amphicteis.

Family Terebellidae.   Peristomium bears numerous long filiform tentacles.   *Terebella, Amphitrite.*

Family Sabellidae.   The fanworms or feather duster worms. Noncalcareous tubes. *Branchiomma, Dasychone, Sabella, Myxicola, Potamilla.*

Family Serpulidae.   The fanworms or feather duster worms. Tubes calcareous. *Serpula, Apomatus, Salmacina, Spirorbis, Hydroides, Pomatoceros.*

Class Archiannelida.   Most modern authorities on the annelids agree that members of the old phylum or class Archiannelida characterized by the absence of setae, actually represent a heterogeneous assortment of aberrant polychaetes. The concept *Archiannelida* is therefore artificial, and should be suppressed.

CLASS OLIGOCHAETA

The class Oligochaeta contains the familiar earthworms and many species that live in fresh water. Some fresh-water forms burrow in the bottom mud and silt; others live among submerged vegetation. In general, oligochaetes approximate the polychaetes in size, but reach greater extremes. Some species of the fresh-water genus *Chaetogaster* reach a maximum length of one-half millimeter, while the giant Australian earthworm may exceed three meters in length.

External Anatomy.   Oligochaetes probably evolved from polychaetes, or at least from some common ancestor. Like primitive polychaetes, they display an almost perfect external metamerism. However, oligochaetes differ from polychaetes in that they completely lack parapodia. The oligochaete head is reduced (Figs. 11-38, *A* and 11-39, *A*). The prostomium is usually a small rounded lobe or a small cone. In a few genera, such as *Stylaria* (Fig. 11-38, *C*), the prostomium may be drawn out into a sort of snout or proboscis. The prostomium is usually distinct from the peristomium, but the two regions may be indistinguishably fused.

Although oligochaetes have lost the parapodia of their polychaete ancestors, they have, with few exceptions, retained the setae. Like those of polychaetes, the oligochaete setae display a variety of forms. They may be long or short; heavy or needle-like; straight or curved; and blunt, pointed, forked, pectinate, or even plumose. Commonly the shaft of the oligochaete seta is S-shaped with a swelling, or nodulus, in the middle (Fig. 11-38, *B*).

In general, the longer setae are characteristic of the aquatic swimming species, while the setae of earthworms project only a short distance beyond the integument. The setae are usually located in four groups or bundles in each segment. Two of the groups are ventral and two are ventro-lateral or dorso-lateral. The number of setae per bundle varies from one to as many as twenty-five. In any case, they are less numerous in these worms than in polychaetes, hence the origin of the name Oligochaeta—"few setae."

In most earthworms, such as *Lumbricus,* and in some aquatic families, the setal number is limited to eight, with two setae forming each group (Fig. 11-38, *A*). From this lumbricine arrangement has evolved independently in several groups of earthworms, such as the Megascolecidae, a more specialized condition in which fifty to more than one hundred setae form a ring or girdle around each segment. Attached to the base of each seta are protractor and retractor muscles that allow the seta to be extended or withdrawn (Fig. 11-38, *B*).

As in polychaetes, oligochaete setae are located and produced in setal sacs. In the lumbricids a separate setal sac exists for each seta (Fig. 11-38, *B*). The sac surrounds the shaft of the seta, but in the region of the nodulus, which is just below the surface of the integument, the seta is unattached and lies within a distinct cavity. At the base of each sac is a large cell that secretes the seta and surrounds its basal tip. As old setae are lost, new ones are formed; but in the lumbricids at least, the secretion of a new seta takes place in a new setal sac, which forms adjacent to the old degenerating sac.

In mature oligochaetes, certain adjacent segments are thickened and swollen by glands that secrete mucus for copulation and also secrete the cocoon. The glandular area of these segments, collectively called the clitellum, partially or completely covers the segments and often forms a conspicuous girdle around the body (Fig. 11-38, *A*). The position of the clitellum along the trunk is variable but is always located on the anterior half of the worm. The clitellum is discussed in more detail in the section dealing with reproduction.

Locomotion.   Movement in oligochaetes, which has been most extensively studied in earthworms, is not undulatory, as in many polychaetes, but rather involves extension, anchoring, and contraction of the body. According to the studies of Gray and Lissman (1938), a wave of contraction affecting the circular muscles begins at the anterior and sweeps down the body. After the circular wave has passed over the front half of the worm, a wave of longitudinal muscle contraction sets in. This is then succeeded by another wave of circular contraction, and the process is repeated.

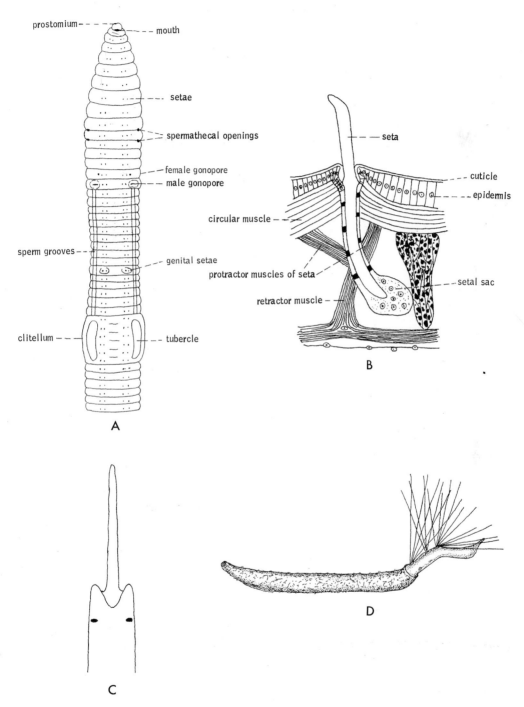

Figure 11-38.   *A.* Antero-ventral surface of the earthworm, *Lumbricus terrestris.* (After Stephenson from Avel.) *B.* Body wall of the earthworm, *Pheretima* (transverse section). (After Bahl from Avel.) *C.* Head of *Stylaria fossularis,* an aquatic olicochaete. (After Pennak.) *D.* The tubicolous fresh-water naidid, *Ripistes parasita.* (After Cori from Avel.)

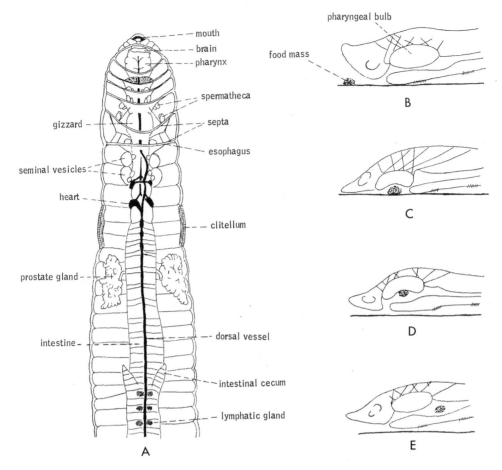

Figure 11-39.   *A.* Anterior of the earthworm, *Pheretima posthuma* (dorsal view). (After Bahl from Avel.) *B* to *E.* Mechanism of ingestion in *Aulophorus carteri.* (After Marcus from Avel.)

Each wave of contraction affects both sides of the body simultaneously in contrast to the alternating pattern in undulatory progression in polychaetes. Segments in a state of longitudinal contraction do not move and are anchored to the ground by the extended setae. This type of grip allows the segments in front to move forward as they lengthen during the circular contraction. Thus each segment tends to move forward in steps of two to three centimeters, at the rate of seven to ten steps per minute. The setae are extended during longitudinal contraction and retracted during circular contraction.

Although fresh-water species move in the same manner as do the earthworms, an undulatory mode of progression is characteristic of the few forms that are able to swim.

Body Wall and Coelom.   The structure and histology of the oligochaete body wall is essentially like that of the polychaetes. The septa partitioning the coelom are relatively complete except at the anterior and posterior extremities, but there is usually a large perforation

in the septum through which the ventral nerve cord extends. In *Lumbricus,* as well as oligochaetes, this perforation is provided with a sphincter to control the flow of coelomic fluid from one segment to another.

As in polychaetes, the coelomic fluid acts as a hydraulic skeleton. Muscle fibers are present between the peritoneal layers of each septum and apparently aid in regulating coelomic fluid pressure during contractions of the body wall muscles. The septa of certain cephalic segments of the larger earthworms extend posteriorly, resembling pockets, and they are very muscular. The contraction of these pouches increases the coelomic pressure and can cause the eversion of the pharynx or, if the mouth is kept closed, can cause elongation of the first segment for burrowing.

In most earthworms each coelomic compartment, except at the extremities, is connected to the outside by a sphinctered mid-dorsal pore, located in the intersegmental furrows. These pores exude coelomic fluid, which aids in keeping the integument moist. Some giant earthworms squirt fluid several centimeters when disturbed.

Nutrition. The majority of oligochaete species, both aquatic and terrestrial, are scavengers and feed on dead organic matter, particularly vegetation. Organic matter is also obtained from mud or soil that is ingested in the course of burrowing.

THE PHARYNX. The digestive tract is straight and relatively simple (Fig. 11-39, *A*). The mouth, located beneath the prostomium, opens into a small buccal cavity, which in turn opens into a more spacious pharynx. The dorsal wall of the pharyngeal chamber is both very muscular and glandular and forms sort of a bulb or pad, which is the principal ingestive organ.

In aquatic forms, to ingest food the pharynx is everted, and the muscular disc is applied to the surface of food particles like a suction cup (Fig. 11-39, *B-E*). The mucus covering of the disc causes particles to adhere to its surface, and the pharynx is then retracted.

In earthworms the pharynx acts as a pump. The anterior of the worm extends from the burrow, and the mouth is pressed against bits of humus lying on the ground. The pharynx then undergoes a series of contractions that pump the food into the mouth. In both aquatic and terrestrial species the action of the pharynx is augmented by the action of strands of muscle fibers extending from the pharynx to the body wall.

The pharyngeal glands produce a salivary secretion containing mucus and, at least in the lumbricids, a protease. The glands are often greatly developed and include more than one type. Those of the aquatic naidids, *Dero* and *Aulophorus*, project through the outer surface of the pharynx. In some species, such as *Eisenia*, certain of the glands, called septal glands, are located entirely outside the pharynx on the surfaces of adjacent septa. A long duct extends from the glandular mass through the dorsal pharyngeal wall and opens into the lumen of the pharynx.

THE ESOPHAGUS. The pharynx opens into a narrow tubular esophagus, which may be modified at different levels to form a stomach, a crop or a gizzard. Both a crop and a gizzard are commonly found in terrestrial oligochaetes, although their positions vary. In *Lumbricus*, as well as in other members of the same family, both a crop and a gizzard are present at the end of the esophagus. On the other hand, the crop and gizzard of earthworms belonging to the family Megascolecidae are located at the anterior of the esophagus shortly behind the pharynx (Fig. 11-39, *A*). In some forms, a series of gizzards, two to ten, each

occupy a separate segment. Where a single gizzard is the rule, as in *Lumbricus*, it occupies several segments.

The crop is thin-walled and acts as a storage chamber. The gizzard, which is used for grinding food particles, is lined with cuticle and is very muscular. That the gizzard represents an adaptation to terrestrial feeding is indicated by the very great size reduction of the gizzard in those earthworms that have returned to an aquatic environment or at least to wet boggy soils.

In the aquatic naidids, the esophagus is dilated posteriorly to form a stomach. However, the function of the stomach is not certain, since histologically it appears to be very similar to the intestine.

CALCIFEROUS GLANDS. A characteristic feature of the oligochaete esophagus is the presence of calciferous glands. The gland cells are located in special evaginations of the esophageal wall at different levels, depending on the family. Calciferous glands attain their greatest development in the lumbricids, in which the posterior esophageal wall has become greatly folded, and the inner tips of the folds have fused to form a new interior wall (Fig. 11-40). Thus, the glandular region becomes completely separated from the esophageal lumen and may appear externally as lateral or dorsal swellings. However, outlets to the lumen of the esophagus are retained to allow passage of the glandular products.

The calciferous glands are excretory rather than digestive organs and function in controlling the level of certain ions in the blood, particularly calcium and carbonate ions. When the level of these ions becomes excessive in the blood, they are removed by the glands and excreted into the esophagus as calcite, which is not absorbed in transit through the intestine.

THE INTESTINE. The intestine forms the remainder of the digestive tract and extends as a straight tube through all but about the anterior quarter of the body. As in polychaetes the oligochaete intestine is the principal site of digestion and absorption. The intestinal epithelium consists of secretory cells and absorptive cells. In *Lumbricus* each gland cell is surrounded by small contractile ciliated cells, which by their contractile ability cause the glandular cell to open or close. The absorbed food materials are passed to blood sinuses that lie between the mucosal epithelium and the intestinal muscles.

A ridge or fold, called a typhlosole, projects internally from the mid-dorsal wall in most terrestrial oligochaetes. The size of the typhlosole is variable; it may consist of a simple fold or of multiple folds. The typhlosole attains its greatest degree of development in the lumbricids. A typhlosole is lacking in fresh-water oligochaetes.

ATYPICAL FEEDERS.   A few species of oligochaetes have evolved somewhat different feeding habits from those of most members of the class. The little tube-dwelling naidid, *Ripistes,* has long setae on the sixth, seventh and eighth segments (Fig. 11-38, *D*). In feeding, the anterior of the body is extended from the tube, and the long setae are moved about in the water. Detritus collected on the setae is then periodically wiped off in the mouth by the worm. Another genus of naidids, *Chaetogaster,* contains the only carnivorous oligochaetes. These worms feed on crustaceans, rotifers, and other small invertebrates.

Respiration.   Respiration in almost all oligochaetes, both aquatic and terrestrial, takes place by the diffusion of gases through the general body integument, which in the larger species contains a capillary network within the outer epidermal layer. In terrestrial species, the film of moisture necessary for the diffusion of gases into the body surface is supplied by nephridial excretions, mucous glands, and coelomic fluid.

True gills rarely occur in oligochaetes. Species of the aquatic genera, *Dero* (Fig. 11-41, *B*) and *Aulophorus,* have a circle of finger-like gills at the posterior of the body. A tropical genus, *Branchiodrilus,* like the cirratulid polychaetes, has a long filament extending from the lateral surfaces of each segment. A tubificid, *Branchiura* (Fig. 11-41 A), also has filamentous gills, but they are located dorsally and ventrally rather than laterally and are limited to segments in the posterior quarter of the body (Fig. 11-41, *A*). A South American earthworm that

lives in mud has tuft-like gills on the lateral surface of each segment.

Most aquatic oligochaetes tolerate relatively low oxygen levels and for a short period of time even a complete lack of oxygen. *Tubifex* (Fig. 11-41, *C*) increases contact with the water by extending its posterior out of the tube and waving it about, but this behavior is exhibited only when the oxygen tension of the water is low.

Circulation.   The circulatory system of oligochaetes is basically like that of polychaetes. Primitively, as in *Aelosoma,* the dorsal vessel begins over the anterior of the intestine and drains an intestinal sinus (Fig. 11-42). Two pairs of commissural vessels surround the anterior of the gut and connect the dorsal and ventral vessels. These commissural vessels provide the only connection between the two longitudinal vessels, aside from the drainage to and from the intestinal sinus.

In the majority of oligochaetes, the dorsal vessel has completely separated from the intestinal sinus and extends back to the posterior of the worm (Fig. 11-39, *A*). Three other longitudinal vessels are commonly present, all associated with the nerve cord. Two are lateroneural vessels located one on each side of the cord; and one, the subneural vessel, is located on the underside of the cord.

Although only a single connection exists between the dorsal and ventral vessels in the primitive system of *Aelosoma,* in most oligochaetes the two vessels are connected by lateral vessels in every segment. Branches from the segmental vessels irrigate the integument and supply the various segmental organs. As in polychaetes, the dorsal vessel carries blood anteriorly; but in oligochaetes the dorsal vessel receives blood from the intestinal sinus and the segmental vessels. The ventral vessel carries blood posteriorly and distributes it to the intestinal sinus and to the segmental vessels.

The dorsal vessel is contractile and is the principal means by which the blood is propelled. The vessels in oligochaetes commonly referred to as hearts are certain anterior commissural vessels that are conspicuously contractile. The number of such hearts varies (Fig. 11-39, *A*). Five are present in *Lumbricus* and surround the esophagus. Only one pair of hearts is present in *Tubifex,* and this pair is circumintestinal. A single pair is also characteristic of the naidids. It is possible that such segmental hearts, at least in the earthworms, act as pressure regulators as well as accessory organs for blood propulsion.

Respiratory pigments are lacking in the blood of the primitive Aelosomatidae and in many Naididae and Enchytraeidae, all of

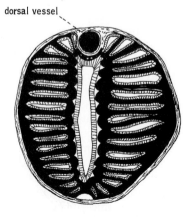

dorsal vessel

Figure 11-40.   Section through the esophagus of the earthworm, *Allolobophora,* showing surrounding calciferous gland. (After Combault from Avel.)

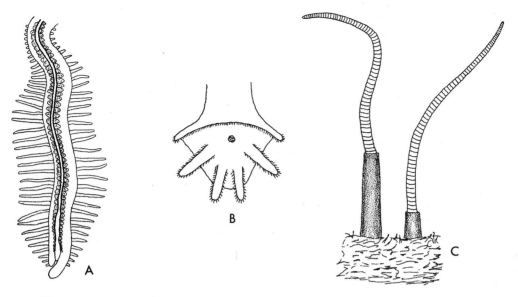

Figure 11-41.   *A.* Posterior of *Branchiura sowerbyi,* showing dorsal and ventral filamentous gills. (After Beddard from Avel.) *B.* Posterior of *Dero,* showing circlet of gills around anus. (After Pennak.) *C. Tubifex,* facilitating respiration. Posterior of body is projected from tube and waved about in water. (After Pennak.)

which are small. Other oligochaetes have hemoglobin dissolved in the plasma. The blood also contains amebocytes.

Excretion.   The oligochaete excretory organs are always metanephridia, although in some cases a secondary loss of the nephrostome has occurred. Typically, there is one pair of metanephridia per segment except at the extreme anterior and posterior ends; the structure of the metanephridia is basically like that of polychaetes. In the segment following the nephrostome, the tubule is greatly coiled, and in some species, such as *Lumbricus,* there are several separate groups of loops or coils (Fig. 11-43). Before the nephridial tubule opens to the outside, it is sometimes dilated to form a bladder. The nephridiopores are located on the ventro-lateral surfaces of each segment.

In contrast to the majority of oligochaetes, which possess in each segment a single typical pair of nephridia called holonephridia, many species of the Megascolecidae and the Glosso-scolecidae are peculiar in possessing several additional types of modified nephridia. One type, called meronephridia, are multiple nephridia and arise from a division of the original embryonic cord of cells that in other annelids forms a single nephridium. Another type of nephridium in these two families is branched, having as many as 100 united divisions. The holonephridia, the meronephridia, and the branched nephridia may open to the outside through nephridiopores; or they may open into various parts of the digestive tract, in which case they are termed enteronephric.

A single worm may posses a number of different types of these nephridia, each being restricted to certain parts of the body. *Pheretima posthuma,* a megascolecid earthworm of India, exemplifies the complexity that can be found in

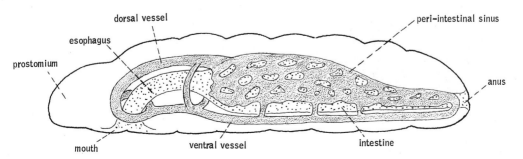

Figure 11-42.   Circulatory system of the primitive fresh-water oligochaete, *Aelosoma.* (After Marcus from Avel.)

some oligochaete excretory systems. The nephridia of the fourth, fifth, and sixth segments are branched. Each nephridium consists of hundreds of branches in which the nephrostomes have degenerated. The common tubule of each nephridial cluster opens into the pharynx; these branched nephridia are thus enteronephric.

The seventh through the fifteenth segments each contain 200 to 250 very small separate meronephridia, which lack nephrostomes and open onto the body surface. Each of the remaining posterior segments contains a single pair of large holonephridia, which are enteronephric and empty into the intestine by way of a pair of longitudinal excretory canals located above the intestine, one on each side of the typhlosole. These canals open into the lumen of the intestine in each segment.

Aquatic oligochaetes excrete ammonia, and terrestrial species excrete urea; but earthworms are less perfectly ureotelic than are other terrestrial animals. Although urea is present in the urine of *Lumbricus* and other earthworms and although the level of urea varies depending upon the condition of the worm and the environmental situation, ammonia remains an important excretory product.

Salt and water balance, which is of particular importance in fresh-water and terrestrial environments, is regulated in large part by the

nephridia. The urine of both terrestrial and fresh-water species contains a far lower concentration of salts than do the coelomic fluid and blood. Thus, considerable re-absorption of salts must take place as fluid passes through the nephridial tubule.

In the terrestrial earthworms, re-absorption of water by the nephridia is important in water conservation, and the enteronephric nephridia represent an even further adaptation for the retention of water. By passing the urine into the digestive tract, most of the remaining water can be re-absorbed as it goes through the intestine. Worms with enteronephric systems can tolerate much drier soils; or they do not have to burrow to deeper levels during dry periods. The nephridia are also employed in removal of the products of hemoglobin destruction. The walls of certain sections of the tubule, where this function is performed, are filled with hematochrome pigments

Considering the number of functions performed by nephridia, it is not surprising that different regions of the tubule are specialized for different processes. The differentiation of the nephridial tubule is particularly striking in *Lumbricus* and other terrestrial oligochaetes and parallels similar tubular specialization in the vertebrate kidney.

Chloragogen Tissue. Surrounding the intestine and investing the dorsal vessel of oligochaetes is a layer of yellowish cells, called chloragogen cells, which play a vital role in intermediary metabolism, similar to the role of the liver in vertebrates. Chloragogen tissue is the chief center of glycogen and fat synthesis and storage. Deamination of proteins, the formation of ammonia and the synthesis of urea also take place in these cells. Furthermore, Semal-Van Gansen (1956) has shown that in terrestrial species the silicates obtained from food material and the soil are removed from the body and deposited in the chloragogen cells as waste concretions.

Histologically the chloragogen tissue is derived from the peritoneum. Its color is due to greenish-yellow lipid inclusions. Chloragogen cells are released into the coelom as free cells called eleocytes, but their significance is uncertain. Liebman (1946) states that eleocytes are laden with food reserves and migrate to different tissues of the body, including developing eggs, where the food materials are then transferred. On the other hand, Semal-Van Gansen considers eleocytes as degenerate chloragogen cells, which are eventually destroyed by phagocytic coelomocytes.

Nervous System. The nervous system of the Aelosomatidae is very similar to that of

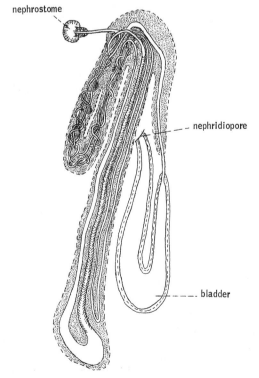

Figure 11-43.   Nephridium of *Lumbricus*. (After Maziarski from Avel.)

primitive polychaetes. The two ventral nerve cords are separate and lie beneath the epidermis; and the brain is located at the posterior limits of the prostomium. However, in most oligochaetes the two ventral cords are fused and located within the muscle layers of the body wall. The oligochaete brain has shifted posteriorly and in lumbricids lies in the third segment, above the anterior margin of the pharynx (Fig. 11-44, A).

Cerebral innervation of the prostomium is retained by the presence of a pair of long prostomial nerves. In the naidids, the first and second trunk segments are innervated by three pairs of cerebral nerves, but in other groups the innervation of these segments is effected by nerves from both the base of each circumpharyngeal commissure and the subpharyngeal ganglion. Most aquatic oligochaetes have four pairs of lateral nerves per segment; usually only three pairs are present in terrestrial families. Studies on the lumbricids indicate that the segmental nerves contain both sensory and motor components. Moreover, the sensory fibers of each nerve innervate epidermal sections of both the adjacent preceding and following segments, in addition to epidermal sections of the segments in which the nerve itself is located (Fig. 11-44, B).

As in polychaetes, giant nerve fibers are present in oligochaetes except for the aelosomatids. The earthworms possess five giant nerve fibers. Three are quite large and are grouped at the mid-dorsal side of the ventral nerve cord. The other two giant nerve fibers are less conspicuous; they are situated midventrally and are rather widely separated.

The relation of the nervous system to locomotion has been studied extensively in earthworms. If the ventral nerve cord is cut or destroyed, the muscles of the body wall posterior to the point of severance do not contract, demonstrating that such contraction is not intrinsic within the muscles themselves. Although the basic peristaltic rhythm appears to arise from the ventral nerve cord, contraction can be initiated indirectly by way of reflex arcs involving sensory neurons in the body wall. A wave of longitudinal muscular contraction exerts a pull on the following segments. This pull apparently stimulates the sensory neurons of those following segments, and a reflex action is initiated that causes the contraction of the circular muscle layer and the elongation of the segments. This traction-stimulated reflex was beautifully illustrated by Friedlander (1888), who severed a worm and loosely connected the two parts by a thread. Although the nerve cord was cut, a peristaltic wave continued from one part of the worm to the other, resulting from the pull of the thread on the severed posterior half and from the initiation of the traction reflex.

The anterior end of the ventral nerve cord exhibits a distinct dominance over the more posterior sections. The subpharyngeal ganglion is the principal center of motor control and vital reflexes, and dominates the succeeding ganglia in the chain. All movement ceases when the subpharyngeal ganglion is destroyed. Motor control continues normally, following removal of the brain, but the worm loses its ability to correlate movement with external environmental conditions. The relation of the subpharyngeal ganglion to the brain is thus somewhat analogous to the relation of the medulla to the higher brain centers in vertebrates.

A superficial nervous system exists in both the muscle layers and the epidermis of the body wall. Nerve cells in the muscle layers, believed to be proprioceptive, make connection with muscle cells and with segmental nerve fibers. Also unusual are the numerous nerve cells that are located between the epidermis and the circular muscle layer of each segment. These neurons are not connected to the central nervous system; rather their processes run directly between the epidermis and the circular muscle fibers. It can only be assumed that they are capable of bringing about direct local responses of these muscles. These epidermal neurons, plus the great number of sensory nerve cells, form a distinct nerve plexus lying beneath the epidermis.

Studies on *Lumbricus* (Millot, 1943) have demonstrated the presence of a well developed enteric nerve system, which in many respects parallels that of vertebrates. A similar system undoubtedly exists in other annelids. Attached to the posterior ends of the circumpharyngeal connectives is a series of pharyngeal ganglia, which form a relay center for motor impulses from the brain and subpharyngeal ganglia to the muscle fibers of the gut wall.

Sensory fibers from the digestive tract also enter the central nervous system by way of these ganglia. Impulses from this relay center appear to effect some control in the total tone of the gut musculature. Within each segment there also exists a dual system of motor fibers arising from the ventral nerve cord and innervating the muscles of the gut wall. One set of fibers, which leaves the ventral nerve cord by way of the two posterior segmental nerves, is excitatory and has been shown to secrete acetylcholine; the other fibers are associated with all three segmental nerves, have an inhibitory effect on nerve impulse transmission, and secrete sympathin.

Sense Organs. Oligochaetes lack eyes, except for a few aquatic forms that have simple pigment-cup ocelli. However, the integument is

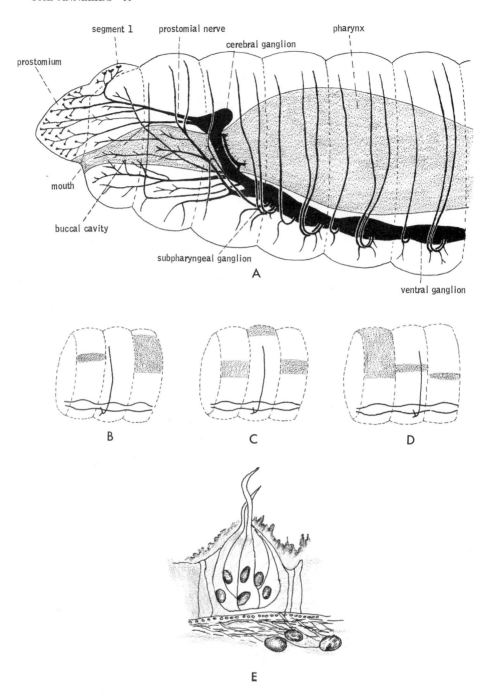

Figure 11-44.   *A. Lumbricus* nervous system (lateral view). (After Hess from Avel.) *B–D.* Sensory innervation of anterior, middle, and posterior lateral nerves of each segment. Shaded areas are *not* innervated by the particular nerve depicted. Each nerve supplies not only its own segment, but also anterior and posterior adjacent segments. (After Prosser from Avel.) *E.* Sensory tubercle on prostomium of *Slavina.* (After Marcus from Avel.)

well supplied with photoreceptor cells. The photoreceptors are largely isolated cells located in the inner part of the epidermis. Each photoreceptor is lens-shaped with a basal process that enters the subepidermal nerve plexus. Although existing in every segment, photoreceptors do not

occur on the ventral surface of the body, and are more abundant at both the anterior (particularly on the prostomium) and the terminal posterior segment of the worm.

In *Lumbricus,* many of the prostomial photoreceptors occur in clusters well beneath the epidermal surface, and are directly connected to branches of the cerebral nerves. Most oligochaetes are negatively phototropic to strong light and positive to weak light. There is some evidence that these two opposing responses are associated with two different types of photoreceptors.

The other sensory structures have a more or less general distribution in the integument. Clusters of sensory cells that form a projecting tubercle with sensory processes extending above the cuticle appear to be chemoreceptors (Fig. 11-44, E). The basal processes from each cell in the cluster unite to form a nerve, which joins a segmental nerve. The tubercles form three rings around each segment and are particularly numerous on the more anterior segments, especially the prostomium, where in *Lumbricus* there may be as many as 700 per square millimeter.

The integument is richly supplied with free nerve endings, which may be tactile in function. Some other epidermal cells are undoubtedly sensory, but their exact function is unknown.

Reproduction. THE REPRODUCTIVE SYSTEM. The reproductive system of oligochaetes differs from that of polychaetes in a number of important respects. Oligochaetes are all hermaphroditic, they possess distinct gonads, and the number of reproductive segments present is very much limited. The only exception to this rule appears in members of the primitive family, Aelosomatidae, which, although hermaphroditic, are similar to polychaetes in lacking distinct gonads and in the large number of segments capable of producing gametes. Moreover, these worms possess no gonoduct, and the sperm, at least, utilize the nephridia to exit from the body.

In aquatic families, usually one ovarian segment and one testicular segment are present; but in the terrestrial groups, two male segments occur. The reproductive segments are located in the anterior half of the worm, and the female segment or segments are always located just preceding the male segments. The exact location of fertile segments along the trunk varies in different families.

The ovaries and testes, both of which are typically paired, are situated in the fertile segments on the lower part of the anterior septum and project into the coelom. Both are small and often pear-shaped, particularly the ovaries; the testes may be lobed or digitate. As in polychaetes, the gametes are released from the gonads as gametogonia, and maturation takes place mostly in the coelom where the gametes are unattached. However, in earthworms the eggs are detached as oocytes.

Although maturation of the gametes is completed in the coelom, it is typically restricted to special coelomic pouches called seminal vesicles and ovisacs. Both arise as outpocketings of the septa of the reproductive segments, but the number, size, and position vary. For example, in the naidids (Fig. 11-45, A), where only one pair of testes is present, there is also a single pair of very large seminal vesicles, which project backward from the posterior septum of the male segment and penetrate the four succeeding segments. The tubificids possess, in addition, a smaller second pair of seminal vesicles that arise from the anterior septum of the male segment and project forward into the preceding segment.

In *Lumbricus,* there are two male segments with three pairs of seminal vesicles (Fig. 11-45, B). One pair projects backward from the posterior septum of each of the two male segments, and one pair projects forward from the anterior septum of the first male segment. The aelosomatids and most species of the Enchytraeidae and the Moniligastridae lack seminal vesicles.

The ovisacs closely resemble the seminal vesicles, but since only one ovarian segment usually is present, there is typically only one pair of ovisacs. The pair of ovisacs projects backward from the posterior septum of the single ovarian segment. Ovisacs are absent in the enchytraeids; are large and project through several segments in the naidids and the tubificids; and are small or sometimes absent in the terrestrial oligochaetes (*Lumbricus*).

The reproductive segments, whether male or female, are each provided with a pair of ducts, either vas deferentia or oviducts, for the exit of sperm or eggs. The male and female ducts are quite similar and in their basic plan are very much like that of a nephridium. The internal opening is through a ciliated funnel located on the posterior septum of the fertile segment. From the funnel a tubule extends backward penetrating the septum and passing through one or more segments before opening on the ventral surface of the body. The tubule is at least partially ciliated.

The sperm duct may be coiled, or it may be straight, as in the earthworm (Fig. 11-45, B). Furthermore, in earthworms the two pairs of sperm ducts on each side of the body become confluent prior to opening to the outside through a single common male genital pore, which has a raised border, or lips. In many aquatic species, the sperm duct opens into an ectodermal atrium that can be evaginated through the male genital pore. In some tubificids and phreodrilids, the atrium contains a chitinous penis.

Glandular tissue, called prostate glands, is commonly associated with the male gonoducts.

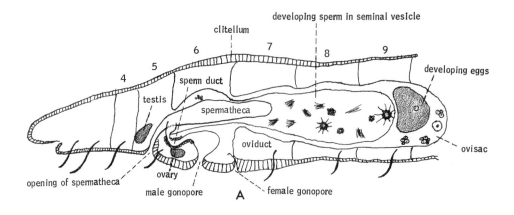

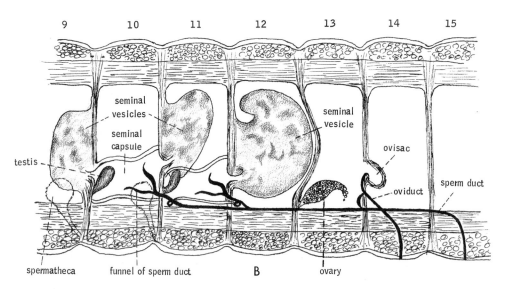

Figure 11-45.   *A.* Reproductive system of a Naididae (lateral view). (After Stephenson from Avel.) *B.* Reproductive segments of the earthworm, *Lumbricus* (lateral view). (After Hesse from Avel.)

In most aquatic groups, the posterior portion of the sperm duct wall is glandular and forms the prostate. Often, however, the prostate is a separate glandular mass that is drained by a duct into the vas deferens at a point near the gonopore (Fig. 11-39, *A*). In some megascolecid earthworms, the prostates are not connected to the vas deferens, and they open separately onto the ventral surface of segments adjacent to those bearing the male gonopore.

Although constructed on the same plan as the sperm ducts, the oviducts are smaller, simpler, and open through two female genital pores located on the segment following the ovarian segment (Fig. 11-45, *B*). Forming a part of the female reproductive system, but completely separated from the female gonoducts,

are the seminal receptacles. These storage chambers are simple pairs of sacs, opening onto the ventral surface of the segment containing them. The number of seminal receptacles ranges from one to five pairs, each pair in a separate segment. Although they are usually located in certain segments anterior to the ovarian segment, the exact position is variable.

In some terrestrial species, including *Lumbricus,* the male segment is partitioned so that the testes, the sperm duct funnel, and the opening to the seminal vesicles are enclosed in a special ventral compartment called a seminal capsule (Fig. 11-45, *B*). The seminal capsule is completely separated from the larger, remaining portion of the coelomic cavity. For this reason, the testes are not visible in the usual dorsal dissection. A somewhat similar seminal capsule and an ovarian chamber as well are present in the Moniligastridae.

The general plan of the oligochaete reproductive system is relatively uniform, but the numbers of various structures, the segments in which they are located and the segments from which the genital pores open are extremely variable. This variation is of considerable importance in the taxonomy of oligochaetes.

THE CLITELLUM.   The clitellum is a reproductive structure characteristic of oligochaetes. It consists of certain adjacent segments in which the epidermis is greatly swollen with unicellular glands that form a girdle partially or almost completely encircling the body from the dorsal side downward (Figs. 11-38, *A* and 11-39, *A*). The clitellum is always poorly developed ventrally. The number of segments composing the clitellum varies considerably; there are two clitellar segments in most aquatic forms, six or seven in *Lumbricus,* and as many as sixty in certain Glossoscolecidae. In aquatic species, the clitellum is often located in the same region as the genital pores; while in the lumbricids, the clitellum is considerably posterior to the gonopores.

The glands of the clitellum produce mucus for copulation, secrete the wall of the cocoon, and secrete albumin in which the eggs are deposited within the cocoon. In the earthworms, the glands performing each of these three different functions form three distinct layers (Fig. 11-46). The large albumin-secreting glands comprise the deepest and thickest layer, while the mucous glands make up the surface layer. In immature individuals, the clitellum may be absent or inconspicuous.

COPULATION.   Copulation is the rule in oligochaetes, and mutual dissemination of sperm occurs. The ventral anterior surfaces of a pair of copulating worms are in contact, with the anterior of one worm directed toward the posterior of the other. In all oligochaetes except the lumbricids, the male genital pores of one worm directly appose the seminal receptacles of the other. The two worms are held in position by a common, enveloping mucus coat secreted by the clitellum; they may also be hooked together by genital setae. The genital setae are modified ventral setae generally located in the region of the male gonopore or the seminal receptacles.

Additional anchorage is obtained when the raised rim or lips of the male pore, or the everted penis or atrium, are inserted into the opening of the seminal receptacle. Transmission of sperm into one pair of seminal receptacles in the earthworm *Pheretima communissima* takes

over an hour and a half, and then is repeated for each of the other two pairs of receptacles (Fig. 11-47, *A*).

In the lumbricids, the male genital pores do not appose the seminal receptacles during copulation, so that the semen must travel a considerable distance from one opening to the other (Fig. 11-47, *B*). During copulation, the posteriorly placed clitellum of one worm attaches to the segments containing the seminal receptacles of the opposite worm. Attachment is accomplished by means of an adhesive slime tube and by the genital setae.

The genital setae on the clitellum pierce the body wall of the apposing worm; those setae near the seminal receptacles act as claspers. The intervening region between the two clitella is less rigidly attached, although each worm is covered by a slime tube. At the emission of the sperm, certain muscles in the body wall of the segments posterior to the male gonopores contract and form a pair of ventral sperm grooves, which extend posteriorly to the clitellum. Because the grooves are roofed over by the enveloping slime tube, the sperm are actually passed through an enclosed channel.

The movement of sperm down the sperm groove is effected by a greater contraction of the muscles producing the groove. A pit is thus formed that extends the length of the groove,

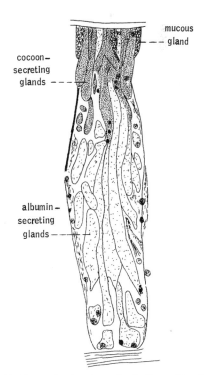

mucous
gland

cocoon-
secreting
glands

albumin-
secreting
glands

Figure 11-46.   Section through clitellum of *Lumbricus terrestris*. (After Grove from Avel.)

carrying small amounts of semen. When the semen reaches the region of the clitellum, the semen then passes over to the other worm and enters the seminal receptacles. The mucus tube obviously must be incomplete in this region. The emission of semen may or may not be accomplished simultaneously in both members of the copulating pair. Copulation in *Lumbricus* continues from two to three hours.

THE COCOON.   A few days after copulation, a cocoon is secreted for the deposition of the eggs. First a mucus tube is secreted around the anterior segments, including the clitellum. Then the clitellum secretes a tough chitin-like material that encircles the clitellum like a cigar band; this material forms the cocoon. The deeper layer of clitellar glands secrete albumin into the space between the wall of the cocoon and the clitellum.

When the cocoon is completely formed, it slips forward over the anterior end of the worm in the same manner as removing the band from a cigar. In *Eisenia,* the eggs are discharged from the female gonopores, and they somehow enter the cocoon before it leaves the clitellum. Sperm are deposited in the cocoon as it passes over the seminal receptacles. As the cocoon slips over the head of the worm and is freed from the body, the mucus tube quickly disintegrates; and the ends of the cocoon constrict and seal themselves. The cocoons of terrestrial species are left in the soil and the cocoons of aquatic species are left in the bottom debris or in mud, or are attached to vegetation.

The cocoons are yellowish in color and ovoid in shape (Fig. 11-47, *C*). Cocoons of *Tubifex* are 1.60 mm. × 0.85 mm., while those of *Lumbricus terrestris* are approximately 7.0 mm. × 5.0 mm. The largest cocoons, 75 mm. × 22 mm., are produced by the giant Australian earthworm, *Megascolides australis*. A cocoon contains anywhere from one to twenty eggs, depending on the species; a succession of cocoons may be produced. *Lumbricus terrestris* mates continually during the spring and fall, and cocoons are formed every three or four days.

Self-fertilization (which takes place inside the cocoon) is known to occur in a few isolated cases. The seminal receptacles of isolated individuals of the tubificid, *Limnodrilus udekemianus,* have been found to contain sperm, and such isolated specimens produce cocoons and young. Parthenogenesis also occurs normally in a few species.

ASEXUAL REPRODUCTION.   Asexual reproduction is very common among many species of aquatic oligochaetes, particularly the aelosomatids and the naidids. In fact, there are many asexually reproducing naidids in which sexual individuals are rare or have never been observed. Asexual reproduction always involves a transverse division of the parent worm into two or more new individuals. When regeneration and formation of new segments take place only after separation, such division is called fragmentation. Fragmentation is not common but is known to occur in a few species. Usually the parent divides into more

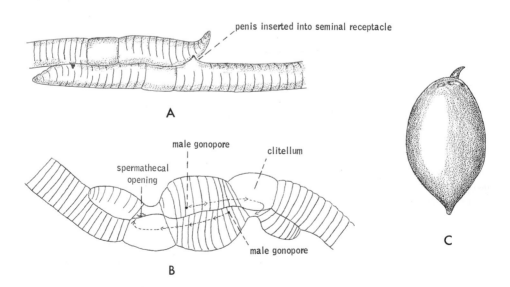

Figure 11-47.   *A.* Copulation by direct sperm transmission in the earthworm, *Pheretima communissima*. (After Oishi from Avel.) *B.* Copulation by indirect sperm transmission in the lumbricid, *Eisenia foetida.* Arrows indicate path of sperm from male gonopores to openings of spermathecae. (After Grove and Cowley from Avel.) *C.* Cocoon of the lumbricid, *Allobophora terrestris.* (After Avel.)

than two pieces. In *Nais paraguayensis*, six to eight fragments are formed, each of which regenerates into a new individual; in two months a single worm can produce 15,000 descendents.

Division by fission zones is much more frequently encountered. In this type of division, regeneration precedes the separation of the daughter individuals to a certain extent. Before fission, a zone of new cells appears at some point along the body of the parent, giving rise to the formation of a new head and a tail for the future daughter individual. Division always takes place through the fission zone, some of the bud cells going to one individual and some to the other.

Not infrequently, as in species of *Nais*, a new fission zone forms before division has occurred in an old one. Such delayed divisions produce chains of individuals or zooids, similar to those in certain turbellarian flatworms. Chains containing as many as eight zooids have been reported in some species. A clone of *Aulophorus furcatus* was traced through 150 generations for a three-year period with no appearance of sexual individuals and with no diminishing of the asexual fission rate.

Needless to say, oligochaetes have considerable capability for regeneration. Lack of space does not permit a review of the voluminous literature on the subject; in general, the results from regeneration experiments are essentially the same as those obtained in experiments with polychaetes.

Embryology.   In general, the eggs of aquatic groups, particularly the primitive families, contain a relatively large amount of yolk. On the other hand, terrestrial species have much smaller eggs with much less yolk; the abundant albumin in the cocoon supplies most of the nutritive needs of the embryo. In both aquatic and terrestrial groups, development is direct with no larval stages, and all development takes place within the cocoon.

The cleavage pattern, while retaining some traces of the spiral character of the cleavage pattern of the polychaetes, is considerably modified in oligochaetes, especially in earthworms. Segmentation is complete and unequal in the oligochaete cleavage pattern but much less regular than in typical spiral cleavage. The mesoderm, however, still arises from special mesoblast cells that form mesodermal cords as in the polychaetes.

The oligochaete young hatch from cocoons after eight days to ten weeks of development, depending not only on the species, but also on environmental conditions. *Lumbricus* hatches in two to three weeks. Usually only some of the original number of eggs deposited in the cocoon

hatch. In *Lumbricus terrestris*, only one egg develops. The young worms emerge from the ends of the cocoon after hatching.

Ecology and Distribution.   Aquatic species live in all types of fresh-water habitats, but are most abundant where the water is shallow. At depths of more than one meter, the oligochaete fauna decreases greatly. *Tubifex* is an exception and inhabits the bottoms of deep lakes in concentrations as great as 8000 per square meter.

Some species crawl about submerged vegetation and other objects, where they feed on surface debris. Most aquatic forms burrow in mud and debris on the substratum. A number of species, such as members of the genus *Tubifex*, construct tubes, that are either attached or carried about by the worm. In the construction of these tubes, mud, mineral particles, and other debris are cemented together with mucus, as in the polychaetes. A tropical naidid, *Aulophorus carteri*, builds its tube with spores from aquatic ferns (Fig. 11-48, *B*).

A few oligochaete species are capable of encystment during unfavorable environmental conditions. The worm secretes a tough mucus covering that forms the cyst wall. Some species form summer cysts for protection against desiccation; others form winter cysts when the water temperature becomes low.

The littoral zone, particularly the intertidal regions of sounds and estuaries, contains a surprisingly large number of oligochaetes. These marine species belong to a number of families, including the tubificids and enchytraeids. Although the majority of these marine species are shallow burrowers or live beneath intertidal rocks or in algal drift, some live below the low-tide mark.

Many species of the Haplotaxidae, and the Enchytraeidae are amphibious or transitional between a strictly aquatic and a strictly terrestrial environment. These worms live in marshy or boggy land and around the margins of ponds and streams.

The terrestrial oligochaetes include the four families of earthworms—Glossoscolecidae, Lumbricidae, Megascolecidae, and Eudrilidae—many enchytraeids, and numerous representatives from other families. All are burrowers and are found everywhere except in deserts. They often abound in tremendous numbers. As many as 8000 enchytraeids and 700 lumbricids have been reported from one square meter of meadow soil.

Soils containing considerable organic matter, or at least a layer of humus on the surface, maintain the largest fauna of worms, but other edaphic factors are important to the distribution of terrestrial species. The amount of moisture,

A

B

Figure 11-48. *A. Stephanodrilus,* a member of the leech-like family of oligochaetes, Branchiobdellidae; they are parasitic, and commensal with fresh-water crayfish. (After Yamaguchi from Avel.) *B. Aulophorus carteri,* a tropical naidid, building its tube with fern spores. (After Carter and Beadle from Avel.)

the degree of acidity, the amount of oxygen (a factor in wet soils), and the soil texture may all impose limitations on distribution. Acid soils are particularly unfavorable habitats owing to the lack of free calcium ions necessary for removing excessive carbon dioxide.

A cross section through soil reveals a distinct vertical stratification of worms. The tunnels of larger species, such as *Lumbricus terrestris,* range from the surface to several meters depth, depending on the nature of the soil. Young worms and small species are restricted to the few inches of upper humus, while others have a wider distribution but are still limited to the upper level of the soil that contains some organic matter.

The terrestrial oligochaete constructs its burrow by forcing its anterior through crevices and by swallowing soil. The egested material plus mucus is plastered against the burrow wall, forming a distinct lining. Some egested material is removed from the burrow as castings. The burrows may be complex with two openings and horizontal and vertical ramifications. During dry seasons or during the winter, earthworms migrate to deeper levels of the soil, down to ten feet in the case of certain Indian species. Since the amount of oxygen in the soil decreases

with depth, the availability of oxygen can limit the extent of such migrations.

After moving to deeper levels, during dry periods an earthworm often undergoes a period of quiescence, losing as much as 70 per cent of its water. Balance is quickly restored and activity resumed as soon as water is again available. Species of the lumbricid genus *Allobophora* undergo a more profound period of inactivity that is essentially a type of diapause. The worm rolls up into a ball inside a deep mucus-lined chamber and remains this way for as long as two months. The starting and terminating of diapause is apparently intrinsic and not a direct result of environmental conditions as is quiescence.

The activities of earthworms have a beneficial effect on the soil. The extensive burrows increase soil drainage and aeration, but more important is the mixing and churning of the soil resulting from burrowing. Deeper soil is brought to the surface as castings and organic material is moved to lower levels. Darwin's *The Formation of Vegetable Mould through the Action of Worms* is a classic treatment of this subject.

In the tropics a number of arboreal species have been reported. The terrestrial forms live in accumulated humus and detritus in leaf axils and branches of trees. Aquatic species inhabit the water reservoirs of bromeliad epiphytes, living on the trunks and branches of tropical trees.

Parasitism is confined to the family Branchiobdellidae, all of which are parasitic or commensal on fresh-water crayfish. Members of this family are the only highly modified oligochaetes and are strikingly similar to leeches, although unrelated (Fig. 11-48, *A*). All are very small and composed of fourteen to fifteen segments. The head is modified into a sucker with a circle of finger-like projections. The buccal cavity contains two teeth. The posterior segments are also modified to form a sucker, and all of the segments lack setae. Some species are ectoparasitic on the gills of crayfish; others live on the outer surface of the exoskeleton and are probably merely commensal. Some enchytraeids and naidids are also commensal. Certain enchytraeids live attached to the anterior of lumbricids.

Members of the major aquatic families occur throughout the world, wherever suitable habitats exist. Many terrestrial species, however, have very limited geographical distribution. Among the four families of earthworms, that have been most studied in this respect, many species are endemic, that is, have very restricted distributions; others are perigrine, that is, are widely distributed throughout the world.

The distribution of endemic species of the family Lumbricidae collectively forms a belt encircling the temperate regions of Europe, Asia, and eastern North America. In Europe, no endemic lumbricids live north of a line running through the Low Countries and middle Germany. This line represents the southernmost extent of glaciation during the Pleistocene epoch. On the other hand, certain perigrine lumbricids, mostly species of European origin, have been reported from many localities throughout the world, particularly in the Southern Hemisphere. Man has certainly been an important agent in the immigrations of these species, and in many instances these species have displaced native endemic forms. For example, the earthworm fauna of the larger Chilian cities is comprised of European species only.

Systematic Résumé of Class Oligochaeta

Strongly metameric annelids with reduced setae and no parapodia. Prostomium small with no appendages and usually lacking eyes. All are hermaphroditic, with a glandular clitellum for cocoon formation. Reproductive segments limited in number, but with distinct gonads. Primarily fresh-water and terrestrial species.

Order Plesiopora. Male gonopores located in the segment immediately following that containing the testes. Seminal receptacles located in the same region as the genital segments. Mostly aquatic.

Family Aelosomatidae. Primitive. *Aelosoma*.

Family Naididae. *Nais, Stylaria, Dero*, the carnivorous *Chaetogaster*.

Family Tubificidae. *Tubifex, Branchiura*.

Family Enchytraeidae. Terrestrial and semiterrestrial. *Enchytraeus*.

Order Prosopora. Male gonopores located on the same segment as that containing the testes or on segment containing the second pair of testes when two pairs of testes are present. Aquatic.

Family Lumbriculidae.

Family Branchiobdellidae. Parasitic.

Order Opisthopora. Male gonopores located behind (usually some distance behind) segments bearing testes.

Family Haplotaxidae. Fresh-water and amphibious.

Family Moniligastridae.

Family Glossoscolecidae. Earthworms. *Pontoscolex, Alma*.

Family Lumbricidae. Earthworms. *Lumbricus, Eisenia, Dendrobaena, Allolobophora*.

Family Megascolecidae. Earthworms. *Megascolides, Pheretima*.

Family Eudrilidae.

CLASS HIRUDINEA

The Class Hirudinea contains over 300 species of marine, fresh-water, and terrestrial worms, commonly known as leeches. Although they are all popularly considered to be bloodsuckers, a large number of leeches are not parasitic.

As a group, the leeches are certainly the most specialized annelids. They undoubtedly evolved from the oligochaetes and display many oligochaete features, but most of the distinguishing characteristics of the class have no counterpart in the other two annelid groups.

Leeches are never as small as many polychaetes and oligochaetes. The smallest leeches are one centimeter in length, and most species are between two and five centimeters long. Some species, including *Hirudo medicinalis*, may attain a length of twenty centimeters. The coloration is often striking. Black, brown, olive-green, and red are common colors, and striped and spotted patterns are not unusual.

External Anatomy.   The body is dorso-ventrally flattened and frequently tapered at the anterior (Fig. 11-49). The segments at both extremities have been modified to form suckers. The anterior sucker is smaller than the posterior sucker and frequently surrounds the mouth. The posterior sucker is disc-shaped and turned ventrally. Metamerism is very much reduced. The number of segments, unlike other annelids, is fixed at 33, but secondary external annulation has obscured the original external segmentation. As in oligochaetes, a clitellum is present and is always formed by segments IX, X, and XI.

The body of a leech can be divided into five regions. A reduced prostomium plus four segments compose the head, or cephalic region.

Dorsally the head bears a number of eyes and ventrally it bears the anterior sucker. The anterior sucker may lie behind the mouth, as in *Glossiphonia* and other rhynchobdellids; more frequently the sucker surrounds the mouth. In *Hirudo,* the medicinal leech, the anterior sucker forms a hood-like covering over the mouth (Fig. 11-53, *A*).

The head is followed by a preclitellar region of four segments and a clitellar region of three segments. Midventrally the clitellar segments bear a single male gonopore and a single female gonopore. The clitellum is rarely conspicuous except during reproductive periods; in the Glossiphoniidae it is never conspicuous.

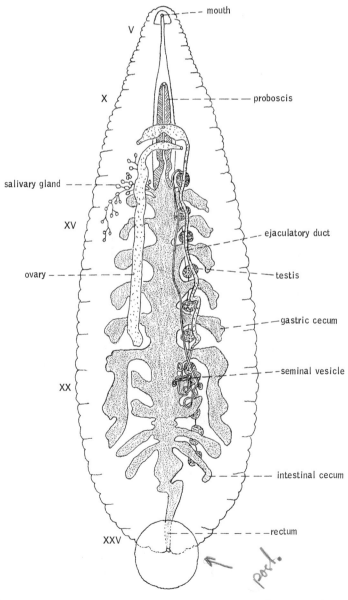

Figure 11-49.   *Glossiphonia complanata,* a rhynchobdellid (ventral view). (After Harding and Moore from Pennak.)

The middle region of the body, containing 15 segments (XII to XXVI), comprises the greater part of the trunk. The terminal, or posterior, region is composed of six fused segments, which are modified to form the large ventral posterior sucker. The anus, representing a new secondary aperture, opens dorsally in front of the sucker, since the pygidium is vestigial and has become incorporated into the sucker.

The number of annuli per segment varies not only in different regions of the body, but also in different species. For example, in *Glossiphonia*, segments I and II are composed of one annulus; segment III of two annuli; and segments IV to XXII of three annuli each. However, the midregion of the body in *Hirudo* contains five annuli per segment. The only means of determining the segmentation of leeches and the relationship of annuli to the primary segments is by a study of the nervous system and the innervation of the annuli by segmental nerves.

Body Wall and Locomotion.   The integument is basically similar to that of other annelids. A more distinct connective-tissue dermis is present, and some of the unicellular gland cells of the integument are very large and sunken into the connective tissue layer. A layer of oblique muscles lies between the longitudinal and circular muscle layers, and all three layers are crossed by dorso-ventral muscle strands extending from one side of the body to the other. The longitudinal muscle layer is powerfully developed, and the fibers converge in the suckers at each end. The circular muscles in the suckers are arranged concentrically.

Movement in leeches involves the same type of contraction pattern exhibited by earthworms, but the points of contact with the substratum are provided entirely by the anterior and posterior suckers. When the posterior sucker is attached, a wave of circular contraction sweeps over the animal, and the body is lengthened and extended forward. The anterior sucker then attaches, and the posterior sucker releases. A wave of longitudinal contractions occurs, shortening the animal and moving the posterior sucker forward. In swimming, the dorso-ventral muscle bands are maintained in a constant state of contraction, flattening the body. Waves of contraction along the longitudinal muscles then produce vertical undulations.

Coelom, Circulation, and Respiration. A striking difference between leeches and other annelids is loss of the distinct coelom by the leeches. Only in a single, primitive species is there any indication of the septa and coelomic compartments so typical of most annelids. In all other leeches septa have disappeared, and the coelomic cavity has been invaded by connective tissue, sometimes called botryoidal tissue. This connective-tissue invasion has reduced the coelom to a system of interconnecting coelomic sinuses.

As in other annelids, the coelomic sinuses contain unattached, floating coelomocytes, but within the connective tissue are located two cell types that are peculiar to leeches. The first, called fat cells, contain large fat droplets and some glycogen. The disposition and concentration of these fat cells vary. The second type, called yellow cells, are filled with yellow, brown, or green granules and are found throughout the connective tissue. The yellow cells appear to be excretory in function, similar in this respect to chloragogen tissue.

The coelomic sinuses act as an auxiliary circulatory system in the rhynchobdellids, which have retained the blood-vascular system of oligochaetes; but in the other leech orders the ancestral circulatory system has disappeared, and the coelomic sinuses and fluid have been modified to form a true blood-vascular system.

In all leech orders, the coelomic sinuses form a regular system of channels. In the rhynchobdellids, a median dorsal and a ventral longitudinal channel run the length of the body (Fig. 11-50). The two channels are separated by the digestive tract. A smaller longitudinal channel, called the lateral channel, is located at each of the two extreme lateral margins of the body. The lateral channel on each side joins the two median channels in the region of the anterior and posterior suckers. A less well defined and less regular intermediate channel exists between the lateral and median channel on each side.

Finally, a subepidermal network of sinuses is located between the epidermis and the muscles of the body wall and communicates with the lateral and intermediate channels. All of the longitudinal sinuses are interconnected. With the exception of the Piscicolidae, which possess contractile vesicles associated with the lateral sinuses, coelomic fluid circulates irregularly as a result of body movements (Fig. 11-51, *A*).

The rhynchobdellid circulatory system is built essentially on the same plan as that of oligochaetes (Fig. 11-51, *B*). The dorsal vessel lies above the alimentary canal and is enclosed within the dorsal coelomic sinus. In the region of each sucker, the dorsal vessel connects through a number of loops with a ventral vessel located beneath the gut and within the ventral sinus. The anterior half of the dorsal vessel is folded like an accordion, and at each bend an internal cluster of cells, serving as a valve, projects into the lumen. One posterior median pouch and

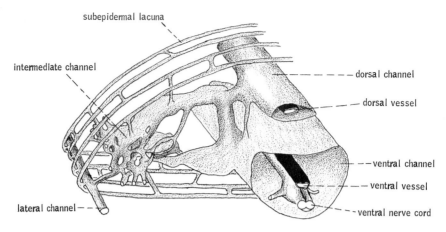

subepidermal lacuna

intermediate channel

dorsal channel

dorsal vessel

ventral channel

ventral vessel

lateral channel

ventral nerve cord

Figure 11-50.   Section of coelomic sinus system of the rhynchobdellid, *Placobdella costata.* (After Oka from Harant and Grassé.)

four pairs of lateral blind pouches extend from the posterior half of the dorsal vessel. The vascular pouches, which lie over the intestine and cecae, probably provide increased surface area for absorption into the blood. The walls of the vessels are contractile, and blood flows in the typical annelidan pattern. The blood usually lacks respiratory pigments and is therefore colorless.

In the other orders of leeches, the original circulatory system has disappeared, and the coelomic sinuses have become modified to form a true blood-vascular system. The sinus channels described for the rhynchobdellids become the principal blood vessels and are provided with more distinct walls. However, a dorsal vessel is not always present. In *Hirudo,* that which is the equivalent of the subepidermal sinus of the rhynchobdellids has become a remarkably developed system of subepidermal capillaries. The ventral vessel is the largest vessel; it surrounds the ventral nerve cord and is swollen in the region of each ganglion. Transverse vessels connect the lateral vessel on each side of the body with the ventral vessel.

In eleven of the more posterior segments, the transverse vessels are dilated to form contractile vesicles (Fig. 11-55). There are four vesicles per segment; two are located on each side, one in front of the other. Although contractile, the vesicles are apparently not responsible for pumping the blood, but rather they appear to secrete pigment granules that become impregnated in the walls of the vessels. The blood (actually the equivalent of coelomic fluid) contains hemoglobin dissolved in the plasma and is propelled by contractions of the lateral longitudinal vessels.

Nutrition.   The mouth opens into an extensive foregut region, derived from ectoderm and containing the ingestive organs. Two types of ingestive organs exist in the leeches. A proboscis is characteristic of both the single primitive acanthobdellid and the rhynchobdellids (hence the name) (Figs. 11-49 and 11-52). The gnathobdellids and the pharyngobdellids lack a proboscis but possess instead a muscular, sucking pharynx, which is provided with toothed jaws in the gnathobdellids (Fig. 11-53, *A*).

In proboscidate leeches, the proboscis is an unattached tube lying within a proboscis cavity, which is connected to the ventral mouth by a short narrow canal. The proboscis is highly muscular, has a triangular lumen, and is lined internally and externally with cuticle. Cuticle also lines the proboscis cavity. Ducts from unicellular salivary glands open into the proboscis. When feeding, the animal extends the proboscis anteriorly out of the mouth.

In the gnathobdellids, which lack a proboscis, the mouth is located in the anterior sucker and is flanked by an upper and lower lip (Fig. 11-53, *A*). Just within the mouth cavity, three large oval blade-like jaws each bear along the edge a large number of small teeth. The three jaws are arranged in a triangle, one dorsally and two laterally. When the animal feeds, the anterior sucker is attached to the surface of the prey or host, and the edge of the jaws slice through the integument like a razor (Fig. 11-53, *B* and *C*). The jaws swing toward and away from each other, activated by muscles attached to their bases.

Immediately behind the teeth, the buccal cavity opens into a muscular, pumping pharynx. Imbedded in the pharyngeal walls are masses of unicellular salivary glands, which open between the teeth on the jaws. The salivary glands

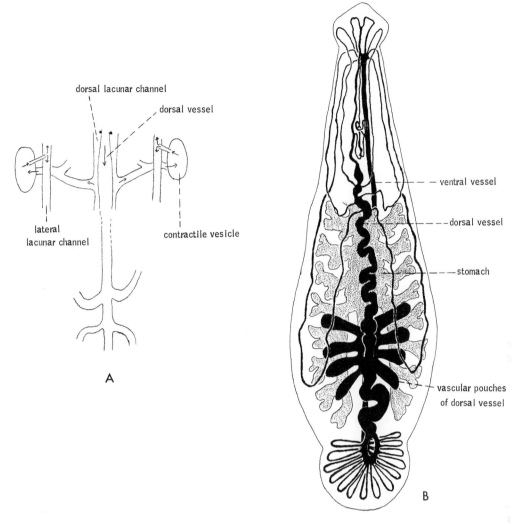

Figure 11-51.   *A*. Coelomic circulation in the fish leech, *Piscicola*. (After Autrum from Harant and Grassé.) *B*. Circulatory system of the rhynchobdellid, *Hemiclepsis*. (After Oka from Harant and Grassé.)

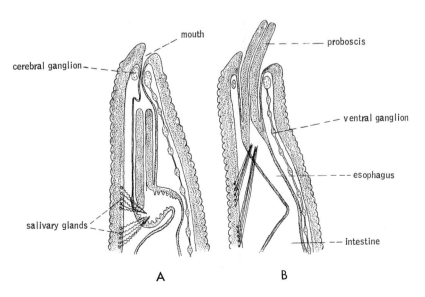

Figure 11-52.   Anterior of *Glossiphonia complanata*, showing proboscis. *A*. Retracted. *B*. Protruded. (After Scribin from Harant and Grassé.)

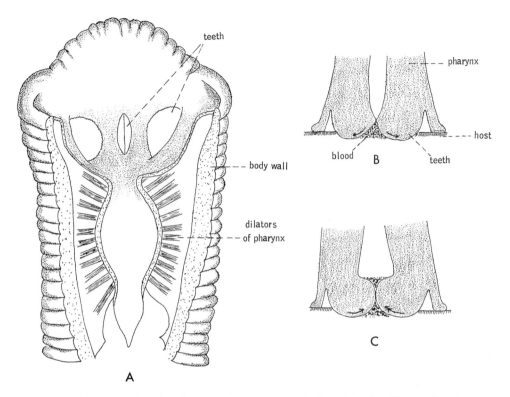

Figure 11-53.   *A.* Anterior of *Hirudo* (ventral dissection). (Modified after Pfurtscheller from Pennak.) *B.* and *C.* Ingestion by *Hirudo.* Outward movement of teeth (*B*), followed by medial movement of teeth and dilation of pharynx (*C*). (After Herter from Harant and Grassé.)

secrete an anticoagulant called hirudin. The pharyngobdellids also have a pharynx, but the teeth are replaced by muscular folds.

The remainder of the digestive tract is relatively uniform throughout the class. A short esophagus opens into a relatively long stomach. The stomach may be a straight tube, as in the erpobdellids, but more commonly it is provided with one to eleven pairs of lateral cecae (Fig. 11-49). The more posterior cecae are usually larger, and in some Piscicolidae the last two pairs have fused together.

The posterior third of the alimentary canal is composed of the intestine, which is often separated from the stomach by a pyloric sphincter. The intestine may be a simple tube or, as in the rhynchobdellids, may be provided with four pairs of slender lateral cecae. The intestine opens into a short rectum, which empties to the outside through the dorsal anus, located in front of the posterior sucker.

Many leeches are predacious and feed on worms, snails, insect larvae, and other invertebrates. It is true that the jaw-bearing gnathobdellids include the most notable bloodsuckers, and that a great many of the rhynchobdellids are predacious; but both types of feeding habits are found in all three of the principal orders.

Furthermore, some species that are exclusively bloodsuckers as adults are predacious during juvenile stages.

Predatory leeches always feed on invertebrates, although some are scavengers. Terrestrial species live on earthworms, slugs, and insect larvae. Feeding is relatively frequent, and the prey is usually swallowed whole. The European leech, *Haemopis sanguisuga,* will seize an earthworm by the middle of its body, fold back its two ends, and then slowly swallow it.

Bloodsucking leeches attack a variety of hosts. Some feed only on invertebrates, such as mollusks, crustaceans and insects. Species of *Helobdella* are always associated with snails and are known as snail leeches. Others suck blood from vertebrates. Fish, amphibians, and turtles are common hosts, and some of these leeches attack warm-blooded vertebrates. *Haemopis marmorata,* the horse leech, lives in drinking troughs and ponds; it feeds on the blood of horses and other livestock. The tropical, terrestrial Haemadipsidae are mostly limited to warm-blooded hosts, including birds.

The gnathobdellid leeches select a thin area of the host's integument, attach the anterior sucker very tightly to this area, and then painlessly slit the skin. The pharynx provides continual suction, and the secretion of hirudin prevents coagulation of the blood. Penetration of the host's skin is not well understood in the many species that are bloodsuckers but jawless. It is possible that an opening is formed by enzymatic action.

Bloodsuckers feed infrequently, but when they do, they can consume an enormous quantity of blood. These leeches can tolerate long periods of fasting. Medicinal leeches are reported to have gone without food for one and a half years without fatal results.

The physiology of digestion is still poorly understood. Ingested food is stored in the stomach, where it may remain for a long time, filling the cecae. Digestion supposedly takes place in the intestine, and lipases and proteases have been reported from *Haemopis*. However in *Hirudo*, evidence indicates that the hemoglobin of ingested blood is directly absorbed either by the cells of the stomach or by the intestine or perhaps by both.

The digestive tract in both *Placobdella* and *Piscicola* contains a symbiotic bacterial flora. The role of the bacteria is uncertain, but they may be involved in the hemolysis of ingested blood.

Excretion. Leeches contain from ten to seventeen pairs of nephridia located in the middle third of the body, one pair per segment. The leech nephridium differs from that of the oligochaetes in a number of respects (Fig. 11-54). As a result of the coelom reduction and the loss of septa in the leech body, the nephridial tubules are imbedded in connective tissue, and the nephrostomes project into the coelomic channels. Each nephrostome opens into a nonciliated capsule that forms a phagocytic organ.

The nephridial tubule in leeches is especially peculiar. It is composed of a cord of cells, through the interior of which runs a nonciliated, intracellular canal. The canal may or may not be connected with the nephrostome and capsule. The nephridial canal drains many finer branching canals, which are also intracellular. A short terminal ciliated section, which is derived from ectoderm, opens to the outside through the nephridiopore. The nephridiopores are ventro-laterally located.

In the piscicolids, the nephridial tubules are interconnected, but no reduction in the number of nephridiopores or other parts has taken place. The nephridia of the hirudids (Fig. 11-55) are further specialized because of the conversion of the coelomic channels into a blood-vascular system. Phagocytic capsules are absent as well as nephrostomes. The blind end of the nephridium rests against, or is very near, the wall of one of the contractile sinus vesicles. The interior of the vesicle contains a peculiar projecting ciliated organ. It is quite possible that this ciliated organ represents a nephrostome, since the vesicle is actually a part of the coelom. In hirudids, the terminal part of the tubule is enlarged, forming a distinct bladder.

Ammonia is the principal waste and is apparently removed by cells of the nephridial tubule. The nephrostome appears to be primarily involved in the removal of particulate matter from the coelomic fluid. After removal, the particles are phagocytized by amebocytes in the capsule wall. These amebocytes, as well as those in the coelomic sinuses, eventually migrate to the epidermis or the epithelium of the digestive tract, where they disintegrate and pass to the outside. Connective-tissue cells lining the coelomic channels are also able to absorb waste materials, and like the amebocytes they migrate to the epidermis.

Nervous System. The nervous system of leeches is considerably more specialized than those of the other annelid classes. The cell bodies of the ganglia are grouped into distinct masses, or follicles (Fig. 11-56). Each ganglion is composed of six such follicles, arranged in two ventral transverse triads. In the fifth and sixth segments, a large ganglionic nerve ring surrounds the pharynx or proboscis. This collar represents the brain, the circumpharyngeal connectives, and the subpharyngeal ganglion of other annelids, plus the ganglia of the first three or four segments, which have migrated posteriorly.

The number of ganglia that have been added to the subpharyngeal ganglion can be determined by the number of follicles present. For example, in *Pontobdella* there are thirty follicles in the subpharyngeal mass, indicating an association of five ganglia. The cerebral ganglia consist of six pairs of follicles that have

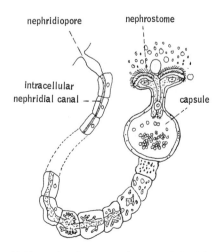

Figure 11-54.   Nephridium of a glossiphoniid. (After Graf from Harant and Grassé.)

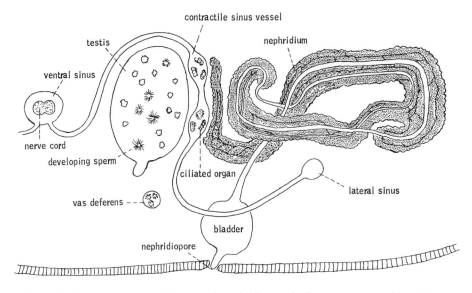

Figure 11-55.   Transverse section through nephridium and adjacent structures of *Hirudo*. (After Grassé from Harant and Grassé.)

migrated laterally and ventrally to varying degrees. From the peripharyngeal nerve mass extend a varying number of nerves innervating the anterior segments and the prostomium.

Although the ganglia are fused, there are two ventral nerve cords (Fig. 11-56). Two pairs of mixed nerves arise from each trunk ganglion. The anterior pair innervates the dorsal side, and the posterior pair innervates the ventral side of the annuli of particular segments. The seven last ganglia of the chain are grouped in a single posterior mass, but their follicles and lateral nerves follow the same plan as those of the trunk ganglia.

The visceral nervous system is composed of three pairs of nerves that leave the brain and form a network of nerve fibers around the pharynx or proboscis.

The functions of the various parts of the hirudinean nervous system are essentially the same as described for the oligochaetes.

Sense Organs.   As in oligochaetes, the general epidermis in leeches contains isolated sensory cells of a number of types—free nerve endings, sensory cells with terminal bristles, and photoreceptor cells. The specialized sense organs in leeches are eyes and sensory papillae. The eyes consist of a cluster of photoreceptor cells essentially like the isolated cells and surrounded by a pigment cup (Fig. 11-57). The eyes are located on the dorsal surfaces of the anterior segments and vary in number from two to ten.

The sensory papillae are small projecting discs arranged in a dorsal row or in a complete ring around one annulus of each segment. Each papilla consists of a cluster of many sensory cells and supporting epithelium. The sensory cells each bear a terminal bristle, which projects above the cuticle surface. The function of the papillae is still uncertain. The number and arrangement of both eyes and sensory papillae have considerable taxonomic value.

Reproduction.   Leeches do not reproduce asexually. Like oligochaetes, all leeches are hermaphroditic, with distinct gonads and ducts having a relatively fixed position. Although the ovaries lie in front of the testes, the position of the gonopores is reversed. The single median male gonopore is located on the ventral side of segment X just in front of the single female gonopore on segment XI. The cavity of each ovary and of each testis represents a specialized part of the coelom and is thus a true gonocoel.

Four to ten pairs of spherical testes are arranged segmentally, beginning in either segment XII or XIII (Fig. 11-58). A short vas efferens connects each testis to a vas deferens, which runs anteriorly on each side of the body. Anterior to the first pair of testes, each vas deferens enlarges or becomes greatly coiled to form a seminal vesicle (Fig. 11-58, *B*). An ejaculatory duct issues from each vesicle to empty into a single median atrium, which opens to the outside through the male gonopore.

The atrium is highly muscular and surrounded by gland cells that open through the atrium walls into the lumen. The atrium of both the rhynchobdellids and the pharyngobdellids is not eversible and does not act as a penis. Instead it is a chamber for the formation and expulsion of a spermatophore. The sperma-

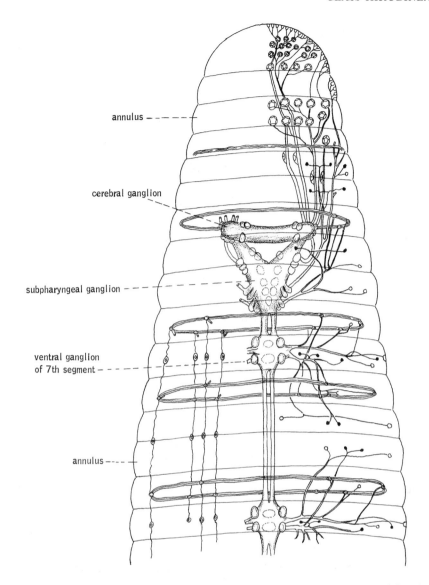

annulus

cerebral ganglion

subpharyngeal ganglion

ventral ganglion
of 7th segment

annulus

Figure 11-56.   Nervous system of *Erpobdella lateralis*. (After Bristol from Harant and Grassé.)

Figure 11-57.   Inverse eye of *Erpobdella*. (After Hesse from Harant and Grassé.)

tophore varies in shape, depending on the shape of the atrium, but it always consists of two bundles of sperm, one bundle from each ejaculatory duct, fused together to varying degrees (Fig. 11-59, *D*).

In the gnathobdellids, the atrium is more complex, and its distal wall can be everted through the gonopore to form a penis (Fig. 11-59, *A*). The proximal enveloping glands are called a prostate. Spermatophores are not formed.

Spermatogenesis in leeches takes place primarily in the lumen of the testis, just as it does in the coelom of other annelids.

The ovaries are always limited to a single pair, located between the most anterior pair of testes and the male atrium. Each ovary is a mass of germinal tissue, or sometimes a number

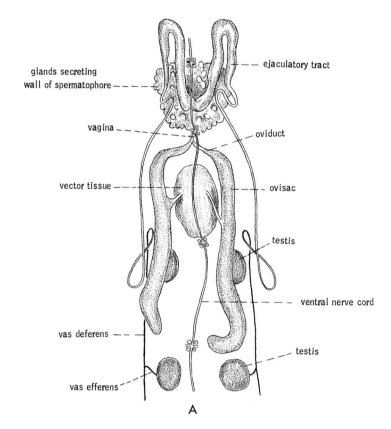

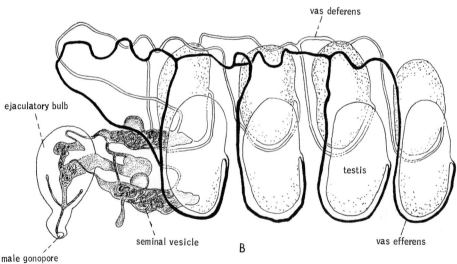

Figure 11-58.   *A.* Reproductive system of *Piscicola geometra*. (After Brumpt from Harant and Grassé.) *B.* Male reproductive system of the fish leech, *Ozobranchus* (lateral view). (After Mac-Callums from Harant and Grassé.)

of masses, enclosed within an ovisac (Fig 11-58, *A*). The cavity of the ovisac is derived from the coelom. Each ovisac is usually elongated and sometimes folded forward on itself.

A short oviduct extends anteriorly from each ovisac and joins its opposite member to form a vagina, which opens through the female gonopore on the ventral surface of segment XI. The vagina is sometimes preceded by a common oviduct, as in *Haemopis*. The eggs leave the ovaries as oocytes and maturation is completed in the fluid of the ovisac.

Copulation in the gnathobdellids, which possess a penis, is similar to direct sperm transmission in earthworms (Fig. 11-59, *C*). The ventral surface of the clitellar regions of a copulating pair are brought together with the anterior of each worm directed toward the posterior of the other. Thus the male gonopore of one worm apposes the female gonopore of the other. The penis is everted into the female gonopore, and sperm are introduced into the vagina, which probably also acts as a storage center.

Copulation in the rhynchobdellids and the pharyngobdellids, which lack a penis, is by hypodermic impregnation. In the rhynchob-

dellids, the two copulating worms grasp each other with the anterior sucker. The ventral clitellar regions are in apposition, and by muscular contraction of the atrium, a spermatophore is expelled from one worm and penetrates the integument of the other.

The site of penetration is usually posterior to the female gonopore, and in many rhynchobdellids the integument here is modified and called a copulatory area. As soon as the head of the spermatophore has penetrated the integument, perhaps by a combination of expulsion pressure and a cytolytic action by the spermatophore itself, the sperm are discharged into the tissues. In the majority of species a special tissue, called vector tissue, lies beneath the copulatory area and connects with the ovisacs (Fig. 11-58, *A*). This vector tissue acts as a pathway for sperm moving to the ovisacs, where fertilization takes place. In the pharyngobdellids the spermatophore head of one worm penetrates the integument of the other and discharges its sperm without ever leaving the atrium.

Eggs are laid from two days to many months after copulation. At this time, the clitellum becomes conspicuous and secretes a

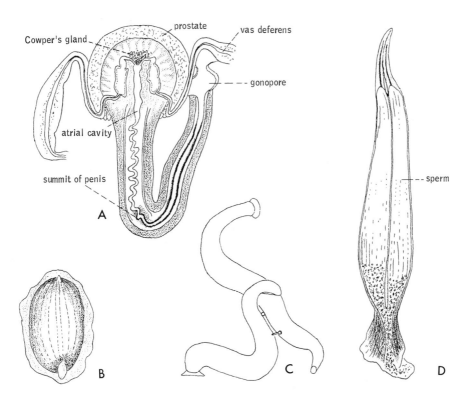

Figure 11-59.   *A.* Male genital atrium of *Hirudo medicinalis*. (After Brandes from Harant and Grassé.) *B.* Cocoon of *Erpobdella octoculata*. (After Pavlovsky from Harant and Grassé.) *C.* Copulation in *Hirudo*. (After Bojanus from Harant and Grassé.) *D.* Spermatophore of the rhynchobdellid, *Haementeria*. (After Pavlovsky from Harant and Grassé.)

cocoon as is done in the oligochaetes. The cocoon is filled with a nutritive albumin produced by certain of the clitellar glands. The cocoon then receives the fertilized eggs as it passes over the female gonopore. A cocoon contains only one egg in the Piscicolidae, but in other leeches the number varies from a few to many. The cocoons may be buried in the mud at the bottom of a pond or stream but more frequently are affixed to submerged objects or vegetation (Fig. 11-59, *B*). Many piscicolids attach their cocoons to their host. Terrestrial species place them in damp soil beneath stones and other objects.

The glossiphoniids brood their eggs. The atypical cocoons are membranous and transparent and are attached to the ventral surface of the parent. Several cocoons are produced during one period, each containing several to many eggs. After hatching, the young attach to the mother with their posterior sucker.

One species of leech is known to be viviparous. This African glossiphoniid, *Marsupiobdella africana*, even has an incubating chamber on the ventral surface of the clitellar region for brooding the young.

Development in leeches follows essentially the same pattern as in oligochaetes.

Ecology and Distribution.   Although some leeches are marine, most aquatic species live in fresh water. Relatively few species tolerate rapid currents; most prefer the shallow water bordering ponds, lakes, and sluggish streams. Since predacious species hide during the day and are active only at night, rocky bottoms or at least water with submerged wood or vegetation support the greatest fauna. In favorable environments, overturned rocks reveal an amazing number of individuals; hundreds of leeches per square meter have been reported from several ponds and streams in the United States. Some species are able to estivate during periods of drought by burrowing into mud at the bottom of a pond or stream.

Many parasitic species attach to their host only to feed; but some, such as many of the fish leeches (Piscicolidae), leave the host only to breed, and some even attach their cocoons to the host.

Although temperate species of *Haemopis* live beneath stones a considerable distance from the water's edge, most truly terrestrial leeches live in the tropics. Most of these terrestrial species belong to the family Haemadipsidae and live in humid environments on the ground or in vegetation. They are primarily bloodsuckers of warm-blooded animals and drop on the host as it passes through the vegetation.

Leeches occur throughout the world except in deserts and on some Pacific islands, and endemic species are relatively rare. In the United States, leeches are more numerous in the North than in the South, undoubtedly because of the greater number of lakes in the northern states.

Systematic Résumé of Class Hirudinea

Annelids composed of 33 segments, which lack parapodia and setae, and subdivided externally as annuli. Anterior and posterior suckers present. Coelom reduced to a network of sinuses, and internal metamerism only evident in nervous and excretory systems. All are hermaphroditic, with one male and one female gonopore. Marine, fresh-water, and terrestrial; many parasitic.

Order Acanthobdellida. A primitive order, contains a single Russian species parasitic on salmon. Setae and a compartmented coelom are present.

Order Rhynchobdellida. Strictly aquatic leeches with a proboscis and a circulatory system that is separate from the coelomic sinuses.

Family Glossiphoniidae. Marsupiobdella, Glossiphonia, Helobdella, Placobdella, Theromyzon.

Family Piscicolidae. The fish leeches. *Piscicola, Pontobdella, Trachelobdella, Branchellion, Ozobranchus.*

Order Gnathobdellida. Aquatic or terrestrial leeches having a noneversible pharynx and three pairs of jaws.

Family Hirudidae. Haemopis, Hirudo, Macrobdella, Philobdella.

Family Haemadipsidae. Terrestrial leeches of tropical Asia, attacking chiefly warm-blooded vertebrates. *Haemadipsa, Phytobdella.*

Order Pharyngobdellida. Contains five families, all having a nonprotrusible pharynx; teeth are lacking, although one or two stylets may be present. Terrestrial and aquatic.

Family Erpobdellidae. Erpobdella, Dina.

BIBLIOGRAPHY

Clark, L. B., and Hess, W. N., 1940: Swarming of the Atlantic palolo worm, *Leodice fucata*. Tortugas Lab. Papers, *33(2)*:21–70.

Clark, R. B., 1956: *Capitella capitata* as a commensal, with a bibliography of parasitism and commensalism in polychaetes. Ann. Mag. Nat. Hist., *9(102)*:433–448.

Dales, R. P., 1957: The feeding mechanism and structure of the gut of *Owenia fusiformis*. J. Mar. Biol. Assoc. U. K., *36(1)*:81–89.

Darwin, C. R., 1881: The Formation of Vegetable Mould Through the Action of Worms, with Observations on Their Habits. London.

Fauvel, P., Avel, M., Harant, H., Grassé, P., and Dawydoff, C., 1959: Embranchement des Annelides. *In* P. Grassé (ed.) Traité de Zoologie, vol. 5, pt. 1, Masson et Cié, pp. 3–686. An excellent general comprehensive treatment of the annelids. Beautiful illustrations and extensive bibliography.

Fordham, M. G. C., 1925: *Aphrodite aculeata.* Liverpool Mar. Biol. Com. Mem., no. 27, pp. 121–216.

Freidlander, B., 1888: Über das Kriechen der Regenwürmer. Biol. Zbl., *8*:363–366.

Goodnight, C. J., Hartman, O., and Moore, J. P., 1959: Oligochaeta, Polychaeta and Hirudinea. *In* Ward and Whipple's Freshwater Biology (W. T. Edmondson, ed.). 2nd Edition, Wiley, New York, pp. 522–557. The most recent introductory guide for the identification of fresh-water annelids. Keys and figures.

Goodrich, E. S., 1945: The study of nephridia and genital ducts since 1895. Quart. J. Micr. Sci., *86* : 113–392.

Gray, J., 1939: Studies in animal locomotion, VIII. The kinetics of locomotion of *Nereis diversicolor.* J. Exp. Biol., *16* : 9–17.

Gray, J., and Lissmann, H. W., 1938: Studies in animal locomotion, VII. Locomotory reflexes in the earthworm. J. Exp. Biol., *15* : 506–517.

Gray, J., Lissmann, H. W., and Pumphrey, R. J., 1938: The mechanism of locomotion in the leech. J. Exp. Biol., *15*:408–430.

Hanson, J., 1949: The histology of the blood system in Oligochaeta and Polychaeta. Biol. Rev., *24* : 127–173.

Hartman, O., 1951: Literature of the Polychaetous Annelids. Vol. I, Bibilography. Privately published. A complete listing of the literature on polychaetes from Linnaeus, 1758 through 1959. A required reference for any serious student of this group. 1959: Vol. II, Catalogue of the polychaetous annelids of the world. Parts I and II. Allan Hancock Found. Publ., Occas. Pap. no. 23.

Hyman, L. H., 1951: The Invertebrates: Platyhelminthes and Rhynchocoela. Vol. II. McGraw-Hill, New York, pp. 21-32. An excellent résumé of the various theories on the origin of the coelom and metamerism.

Karandikar, K. R., and Thakur, S. S., 1946: Circulatory system of *Nereis cultrifera.* Univ. Bombay J., *14*:31–36.

Krishnan, G., 1952: On the nephridia of Nereidae in relation to habitat. Proc. Nat. Inst. Sci. India, *18*:241–255.

Liebmann, E., 1946: On trephocytes and trephocytosis; a study on the role of leucocytes in nutrition and growth. Growth, *10*:291–329.

McConnaughey, B., and Fox, D. L., 1949: The anatomy and biology of the marine polychaete *Thoracophelia mucronata.* Univ. Calif. Publ. Zool., *47(12)*:319–339.

MacGinitie, G. E., 1939: The method of feeding of *Chaetopterus.* Biol. Bull., *77*:115–118.

Mann, K. H., 1962: Leeches (Hirudinea), Their Structure, Physiology, Ecology, and Embryology. Vol. 11, Pergamon Press, New York.

Millott, N., 1943: The visceral nervous system of the earthworm. II. Evidence of chemical transmission. Proc. Roy. Soc. London, ser. B. *131*:362–373.

Nicol, E. A. T., 1930: The feeding mechanism, formation of the tube, and physiology of digestion in *Sabella pavonina.* Trans. Roy. Soc. Edinburgh, *56(3)*:537–598.

Nicol, J. A. C., 1948: The giant axons of annelids. Quart. Rev. Biol., *23(4)*:291–323.

Pennak, R. W., 1953: Freshwater Invertebrates of the United States. Ronald Press, New York, pp. 278–320. A brief general account of the fresh-water annelids with figures and keys to families and genera.

Scott, J. W., 1911: Further experiments on the methods of egg-laying in *Amphitrite.* Biol. Bull., *20*:252–265.

Semal-Van Gansen, P., 1956: Les cellules chloragogenes des Lombriciens. Bull. Biol. France et Belgique, *90*:335–356.

Sheffield, F., 1938: An account of surface ciliation in some polychaete worms. Zool. Soc. London, ser. B, *108*:85–107.

Sutton, Muriel F., 1957: The feeding mechanism, functional morphology, and histology of the alimentary canal of *Terebella lapidaria.* Proc. Zool. Soc. London, *129*:487–523.

Stephenson, J., 1930: The Oligochaeta. Oxford Univ. Press. A classic account of the oligochaetes. Out of date in some areas but still of great value.

Thomas, J. G., 1940: *Pomatoceros, Sabella* and *Amphitrite.* Liverpool Mar. Biol. Com. Mem., no. 33.

Watson, A. T., 1901: On the structure and habits of the Polychaeta of the family Ammocharidae. J. Linn. Soc. London, *28(181)*:230–260.

Wells, G. P., 1937: The movements of the proboscis in *Glycera dibranchiata.* J. Exp. Biol., *14*:290–301.

Chapter 12

THE MOLLUSKS

Members of the phylum Mollusca are among the most conspicuous invertebrate animals and include such familiar forms as clams, oysters, squids, octopods, and snails. This phylum is one of the few invertebrate groups that has attained any popularity with laymen and amateur collectors. During the late eighteenth and nineteenth centuries, when natural history occupied the time of many well-to-do gentlemen, shell collections were as popular as they are today. Courses in how to make a shell collection were even included in the curriculum of some finishing schools for young ladies. Such collections, often containing species gathered from various parts of the world, have contributed considerably to our knowledge of the phylum. As a result, mollusks rank at present next to birds and mammals, as the best known taxonomically of all the larger groups of animals.

In abundance of species, mollusks comprise the largest invertebrate phylum aside from the arthropods. Over 80,000 living species have been described. In addition, some 35,000 fossil species are known, for the phylum has had a long geological history; and the possession of a mineral shell by the animal, which increases the chances of preservation, has resulted in a rich fossil record that dates back to the Cambrian.

A superficial survey of the classes of living mollusks seems to indicate a heterogeneous assemblage. Clams, for instance, appear to have little structural similarity to squids, and snails seem quite different from either group. Yet all

mollusks are built on the same fundamental plan.

Perhaps the best approach to understanding the basic design of molluscan structure is to begin by examining a hypothetical ancestral mollusk. Since mollusks are pre-Cambrian in origin, evidence for the ancestral condition can be drawn only from a comparative study of living forms. This description is therefore entirely hypothetical.*

The ancestral mollusk was an inhabitant of the pre-Cambrian oceans, where it crawled about over rocks and other types of hard bottom in shallow water (Fig. 12-1, A). It was bilaterally symmetrical, probably not much over one inch in length, and was possessed of a somewhat ovoid shape. It exhibited a well-defined head, bearing a pair of tentacles with perhaps a pair of pigment-spot ocelli at their bases. The ventral surface had become flattened and muscular to form a creeping sole, or foot. The dorsal surface was covered and protected by an oval, convex, shield-like shell. At first the shell was probably little more than a tough cuticle composed of a

---

*The description of the ancestral mollusk in this chapter is based on the work of several authors but largely embodies the views of Yonge, particularly in regard to the mantle cavity and gill structure. Numerous theories of molluscan origin and phylogeny exist, but this description not only has a considerable body of evidence to support it, but also facilitates an understanding of the structure of existing mollusks, which is the chief purpose of this chapter.

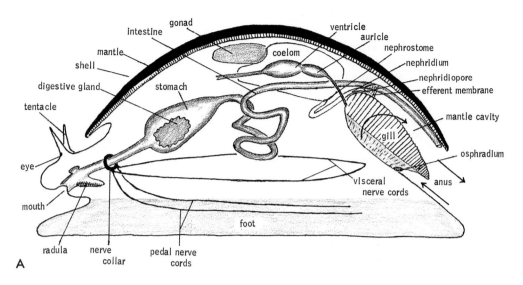

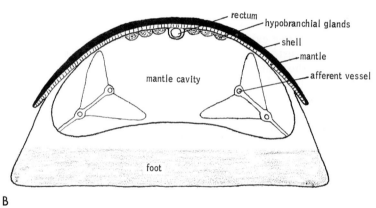

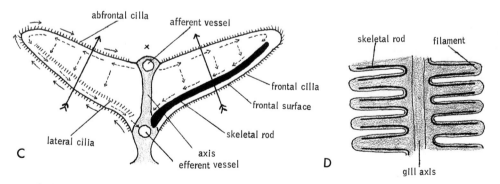

Figure 12-1.   *A.* Hypothetical ancestral mollusk (lateral view). Arrows indicate path of water current through mantle cavity. (Adapted from Yonge and others.) *B.* Transverse section through body of ancestral mollusk at level of mantle cavity. *C.* Transverse section through gill of the primitive gastropod, *Haliotis*. Large arrows indicate direction of water current over gill filaments; small, solid arrows indicate direction of cleansing, ciliary currents; small, broken arrows indicate direction of blood flow within gill filaments. *D.* Frontal section through primitive gill, showing alternating filaments and supporting chitinous rods. (*B* to *D* after Yonge.)

horny organic material called conchiolin; but later the shell became re-inforced with calcium carbonate. The underlying epidermis, called the mantle, secreted the animal's shell. Secretion was most active around the edge of the mantle, although some new material was added to the older portions of the shell. Thus the shell could increase in diameter and thickness at the same time.

A pair of retractor muscles enabled the body, particularly the foot, to be withdrawn into the shell to a limited extent. Each retractor muscle was attached to the inner surface of the shell near the top of the dome, or apex, and was inserted into each side of the foot.

The periphery of the shell, as well as its underlying mantle, overhung the body only slightly, except at the posterior, where the overhang was so great that it created a chamber called the mantle cavity. Within this protective chamber was located a pair of gills, as well as openings from a pair of nephridia.

Assuming that the gills of the ancestral mollusk were similar to those of primitive existing snails and bivalves, each gill consisted of a long flattened axis projecting from the anterior wall of the mantle cavity and contained blood vessels, muscles, and nerves (Fig. 12-1, A). To each side of the broad surface of the axis were attached flattened triangular or wedge-shaped filaments, which alternated in position with those filaments on the opposite side of the axis (Fig. 12-1, C and D). The gills were located on opposite sides of the mantle cavity and held in position by a ventral membrane and a dorsal membrane. The ventral membrane connected the ventral margin of the gill axis with the lateral floor of the mantle cavity. The dorsal, or efferent, membrane suspended the gills from the midline of the roof but was limited to the more anterior part of the gill axis. Functionally, the position of the gills divided the mantle cavity into an upper and lower chamber (Fig. 12-1, A). Water entered the lower, or inhalant, chamber from the posterior, passed upward through the gills into the dorsal, or exhalant, chamber, and then moved posteriorly out of the cavity again.

The margin of the gill filament first encountering the inhalant current is called the frontal surface (roughly equivalent to the ventral margin); the opposite margin is called the abfrontal surface (Fig. 12-1, C). To prevent the filaments from collapsing under the flow of water, the frontal margin of the ancestral mollusk was re-inforced by a tiny chitinous skeletal rod. Propulsion of water through the mantle cavity was partially effected by the cilia of the mantle wall but also largely by the beating of a powerful band of lateral cilia located on the

gills just behind the frontal margin. Sediment brought in by water currents and trapped on the gills was carried upward first by frontal cilia and then by abfrontal cilia toward the axis, where it was swept out by the exhalant current. Some sediment was trapped in mucus secreted by the hypobranchial glands along the roof of the mantle cavity and was carried outward by mantle cilia.

Two blood vessels ran through the gill axis in the ancestral mollusk. The afferent vessel, which brought blood into the gill, ran just within the abfrontal margin. The efferent vessel, which drained the gill, ran along the frontal margin. Blood diffused through the filaments from the afferent to the efferent vessel (Fig. 12-1, C).

Not only the mantle epidermis, but also the epidermis of the remainder of the exposed body parts, including the foot, were covered by cilia and contained mucous gland cells. Mucous glands were particularly prevalent on the foot, from which they lubricated the substratum for locomotion. Like flatworms, the ancestral mollusk moved by means of a gliding motion over the substratum, employing a combination of ciliary action and muscular contractions that took place in anterior-posterior waves along the length of the foot. Considering the size of the animal, muscular contractions, rather than cilia, probably played the principal role in locomotion.

The ancestral mollusk probably was a microphagous herbivore that fed on algae and diatoms growing on rocks in tidal pools and shallow water. The anterior mouth opened into a chitin-lined buccal cavity (Fig. 12-2, A). The posterior wall of the buccal cavity was evaginated to form the pocket-like radula sac, which contained on its floor a remarkable ingestive organ, the radula. The radula apparatus consisted of an elongated cartilaginous base, the odontophore. Over the odontophore and around its anterior was stretched a membranous belt, the radula proper, which bore a number of longitudinal rows of recurved chitinous teeth.

Protractor and retractor muscles were attached to the odontophore, as well as to the radula. Thus, not only could the odontophore be projected out of the mouth, but the radula could move back and forth to some extent over the odontophore. Within the sac the lateral margins of the radula tended to roll up; this action protected the walls of the sac from the teeth. As the radula moved over the end of the odontophore, the belt would flatten and the teeth become erect. The radula functioned as a scraper. The odontophore was extended from the mouth against the substratum and then retracted, similar to the process of licking with the

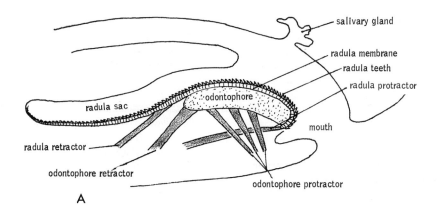

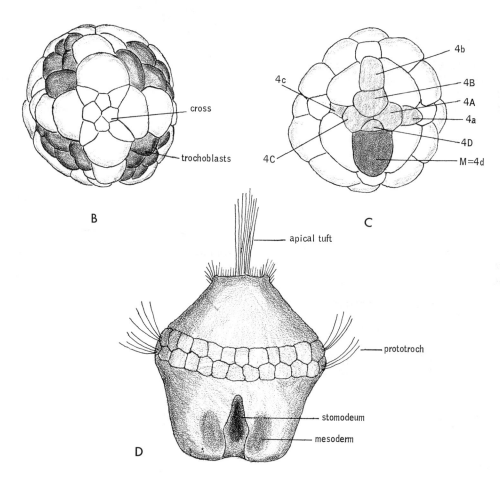

Figure 12-2. *A.* Mollusk buccal cavity, showing radula apparatus (lateral view). *B* to *C.* Blastula of the amphineuran, *Ischnochiton.* *B.* Animal hemisphere. *C.* Vegetal hemisphere. *D.* Trochophore larva of the gastropod, *Patella.* (After Patten.)

tongue. Since the radula teeth recurved posteriorly, the effective scraping stroke was backward when the radula was retracted. In this way, algae and other particles were scraped away from the surface of the rock.

To compensate for the continual wear of the radula at the anterior, new teeth were con-

tinuously secreted posteriorly by the radula sac. A pair of salivary glands opened onto the anterior dorsal wall of the buccal cavity. These glands secreted mucus, which probably lubricated the radula and entangled the ingested food particles.

Food passed from the buccal cavity of the

ancestral mollusk into a tubular esophagus, from which it was moved posteriorly toward the stomach along a ciliated tract (Fig. 12-1, *A*). Additional mucus was secreted by the esophageal walls, particularly in the posterior section of the esophagus where the lateral walls were perhaps even slightly pouched. The stomach was shaped like an ice cream cone with a broad hemispherical anterior, into which the esophagus opened, and a tapered posterior, which led into the intestine. The anterior region of the stomach was lined by chitin except for a ciliated ridged sorting region and the entrance point for two ducts from a pair of lateral digestive glands (liver) (Fig. 12-18, *B*). The posterior conical region of the stomach, called the style sac, was lined by cilia but devoid of chitin. Two folds extended the length of the stomach floor, bounding a median ciliated groove.

Incoming food particles passed over the sorting region, from which the smaller particles were sent into the digestive gland. Other particles were moved along with the mucus into the style sac, in which the whole mass was simultaneously rotated, compacted, and squeezed by muscular contractions of the stomach walls. The chitinous lining of the anterior of the stomach wall protected against sharp fragments. While the mass was being compressed, fluid with additional fine particles was probably squeezed out and passed into the digestive gland. The remaining mass of material was sent into the intestine as waste.

Digestion in the ancestral mollusk was probably completely intracellular and took place in the walls of the small distal tubules that composed the digestive gland. Waste from intracellular digestion was passed back into the stomach and then to the intestine by way of the ventral groove in the stomach floor. This groove probably also served as an exit for some large particles rejected by the sorting region or squeezed out by the action of the style sac.

The long, coiled intestine functioned only in the formation of fecal pellets. The anus opened mid-dorsally at the posterior margin of the mantle cavity, and the wastes were swept away by the exhalant current (Fig. 12-1, *A*). The formation of compact fecal pellets decreased the risk of contaminating the mantle cavity and gills with wastes.

A large coelomic cavity was located in the mid-dorsal region of the body (Fig. 12-1, *A*). The cavity surrounded the heart dorsally and a portion of the intestine ventrally and thus represented both a pericardial and perivisceral coelom. The heart consisted of a pair of posterior auricles and a single anterior ventricle. The auricles drained blood from each gill. Blood

then passed into the muscular ventricle, which pumped it anteriorly through a single aorta. The aorta branched into smaller blood vessels that delivered the blood into sinuses where the tissues were bathed directly. This then was an open circulatory system. Return drainage through the sinuses caused the blood to travel by way of the gills back to the auricles. The blood contained amebocytes as well as a respiratory pigment called hemocyanin. Hemocyanin contains copper as a constituent instead of iron as does hemoglobin. When oxygenated, hemocyanin is pale blue; when reduced, it is colorless.

The excretory organs consisted of a pair of U-shaped metanephridia (Fig. 12-1, *A*). At one end the nephridium connected with the coelom through a nephrostome; and at the other end, the nephridium opened into the posterior of the mantle cavity through a nephridiopore that was located laterally to the intestine. The nephridium, like that of the annelids, received waste from two sources—the coelomic fluid and the blood. The ciliated nephrostome eliminated waste from the pericardial coelom, and the cells of the tubule wall absorbed waste from the surrounding blood and secreted it into the lumen.

The nervous system of the ancestral mollusk consisted of a subepidermal nerve plexus in addition to the central nervous system. The central nervous system was composed of a nerve ring around the esophagus, from the underside of which two pairs of nerve cords extended posteriorly. The ventral pair, called the pedal cords, innervated the muscles of the foot; the dorsal pair, called the visceral cords, innervated the mantle and visceral organs. As in flatworms, there were probably no ganglia; instead, the cell bodies were scattered all along the course of the nerve cords.

The sense organs consisted of the tentacles, eye spots, the pair of statocysts in the foot, and two osphradia. The osphradia were patches of sensory epithelium located on the posterior margin of each of the afferent gill membranes; they functioned in determining the amount of sediment in the inhalant current (Fig. 12-1, *A*).

A pair of anterior dorso-lateral gonads was present on each side of the coelom. When ripe, the eggs or sperm broke into the coelomic cavity and were transported to the outside through the nephridia. Fertilization took place externally in the surrounding sea water.

The embryogeny of the ancestral mollusk must certainly have been very similar to the early embryogeny of most presently existing species. In existing species, the zygote undergoes typical spiral cleavage, as described in Chapter 9, and gastrulation is by epiboly or invagination, or both. The resulting gastrula quickly develops into a free-swimming trochophore larva (Fig. 12-2, *D*). The structure of the trochophore and the fate of the cleavage quartets is virtually identical to that of the annelids. A cross is present but has a different origin from that of the annelid cross. The molluscan cross is derived from the *la*[12] to *ld*[12] cells plus some second quartet cells (Fig. 12-2, *B*). Thus, the rays of the molluscan cross lie between the cells that form the annelid cross. Development after the trochophore stage varies in different molluscan classes and so must be considered later in this chapter.

In the ancestral mollusk, the trochophore probably metamorphosed directly into a juvenile form without passing through any additional larval stages. The half of the larva posterior to the prototroch lengthened; a foot appeared behind the mouth, while a shell gland and subsequently a shell formed on the opposite, or dorsal, side. During the course of this metamorphosis, the prototroch degenerated, and the larva sank to the bottom to assume the benthic habit of the adult.

All classes of existing mollusks can be derived from this ancestral form, and the primitive members of each class display at least some of these ancestral characteristics. Aside from those specializations characteristic of the different classes of mollusks, a number of general evolutionary tendencies are evident within the phylum as a whole. (1) There has been a tendency toward either an herbivorous or carnivorous macrophagous feeding habit, and for digestion to become at least partly extracellular. (2) The nervous system has become ganglionated in most existing mollusks, and a tendency for these ganglia to concentrate at the anterior end has developed. (3) The walls of the nephridia have tended to become evaginated and folded (usually in the more proximal half of the tubule) to effect an increase in the surface area for tubular secretion of waste picked up from the surrounding blood. (4) The gonads have tended to lose their primitive association with the pericardial cavity and have tended to acquire special exits to the outside.

Class Amphineura

The Amphineura are a small class of marine mollusks that have a reduced head and a non-ganglionated bilaterally symmetrical nervous system. The class is divided into two subclasses—the Polyplacophora, containing the familiar chitons; and the Aplacophora, a very small group of worm-like mollusks. The Aplacophora are so aberrant and specialized that they are treated separately after a discussion of the chitons.

The Polyplacophora (Loricata) are commonly considered to be the most primitive of the existing groups of mollusks. This is certainly true in regard to some features of their internal anatomy and embryology; but in most respects they are rather specialized. Chitons have continued to live on the ancestral hard substratum and have become highly adapted for adhering to rocks and shells. They are bilaterally symmetrical with an ovoid body that is very greatly flattened dorso-ventrally (Fig. 12-3, *A*). The distinct head of the ancestral mollusk has virtually disappeared along with cephalic eyes and tentacles. The mantle, usually called the girdle in chitons, is very heavy, and the foot is broad and flat to facilitate adhesion to hard substrata.

Chiton species range in size from half an inch in length in the case of the little Atlantic coast chiton, *Chaetopleura apiculata*, (Fig. 12-3, *A*)

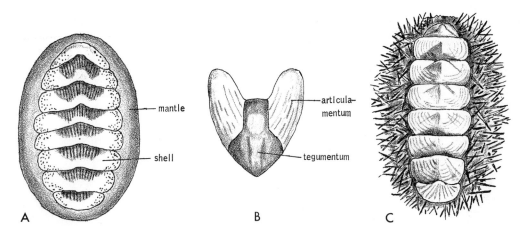

Figure 12-3. *A.* Common Atlantic coast chiton, *Chaetopleura apiculata.* (After Pierce.) *B.* Single shell plate of *Katharina. C. Chiton.* (After Borradaile and others.)

and the Gulf of Mexico chiton, *Ischnochiton papillosus,* to over a foot in the giant Pacific species, *Amicula stelleri* (Fig. 12-4, *C*). However, most species are one to three inches in length. Chitons are usually not brightly colored; drab shades of red, brown, yellow and green are common.

Shell and Mantle. The most distinctive characteristic of chitons is the shell (Fig. 12-3, *C*). The solid dome of the ancestral mollusk has become divided into eight overlapping transverse plates, which are wide and somewhat convex. From the nature of the shell is derived the name of the subclass, Polyplacophora—bearer of many plates. Each plate is identical except for the first and the last, the cephalic and the anal plates. The posterior margin projects backward, and each anterior lateral margin bears a large wing that projects forward. These projections fit beneath the plate in front, and each plate overlaps the one behind. Except for the overlapping posterior edge, the margins of each plate are covered by a reflexed fold of mantle tissue. Thus, the shell of chitons is partially imbedded in the mantle.

The degree of lateral mantle reflexion varies. In *Lepidochitona, Placiphorella,* and *Chaetopleura* (Fig. 12-3, *A*), most of the plate width is exposed. In *Katharina,* only the midsection of each plate is uncovered; thus the visible part of the shell appears as a narrow median strip extending over the dorsal surface of the animal (Fig. 12-4, *A*). In *Symmetrogephyrus,* only the apex of each plate is visible (Fig. 12-4, *B*). Finally, in *Amicula,* the shell is completely covered by the mantle (Fig. 12-4, *C*).

The shell plates are composed of only two layers (Fig. 12-3, *B*). The upper layer, called the tegmentum, consists of an organic conchiolin matrix impregnated with calcium carbonate and is sculptured on its exposed surface. Beneath the tegmentum lies a thicker, denser layer, called the articulamentum, which is composed entirely of calcium carbonate. The anterior articulating projections of each plate are composed only of the second layer.

The girdle is very heavy and extends a considerable distance beyond the lateral margins of the plates. The girdle surface displays a variety of ornamentation. It may be naked and smooth or covered by scales, "hairs," or calcareous spines (Fig. 12-3, *C*). The "hairs" or spines may be so long and dense that the animal has a mossy or shaggy appearance.

Foot and Locomotion. The broad flat foot occupies most of the ventral surface and functions in adhesion as well as in locomotion (Fig. 12-5, *A*). Chitons are very sluggish animals, particularly older individuals; and if an adequate supply of food is present, they may remain in one spot for a long period. A large specimen of *Chiton tuberculatus* that was attached to the vertical face of a concrete wharf in Bermuda was observed by Arey and Crozier (1919) for a period of nine months. During this time, the animal did not leave an area greater than six square feet and would frequently remain immobile for several weeks. A relatively small amount of mucus is secreted by the foot, and propulsion is accomplished entirely by muscular waves.

Adhesion is effected by both the foot and girdle. The foot is responsible for ordinary adhesion, but when a chiton is disturbed, the girdle is also employed. The girdle is clamped down especially tightly against the substratum,

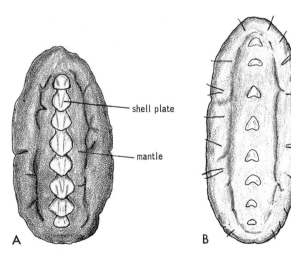
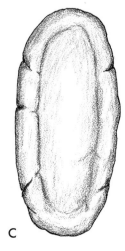

shell plate

mantle

Figure 12-4.   Three chitons (dorsal view), showing varying degrees of mantle reflexion over shell plates. *A. Katharina. B. Symmetrogephyrus. C. Amicula.* (*B* and *C* after Abbott.)

and the inner margin is then raised. This creates a vacuum that enables the animal to grip the substratum with great tenacity. Chitons are usually found only on smooth rocks and shells, since a smooth surface results in better adhesion.

The division of the shell into transverse plates and their articulation with one another enable the chiton to roll up in a ball. This is perhaps a defensive mechanism, but since it takes place only when the animal is dislodged, it probably rarely occurs under normal conditions. Flexion of the body, however, does enable the chiton to move over and adhere to a sharply curved surface.

Water Circulation and Respiration. Adaptation for a life on rocky surfaces has resulted in marked changes in the mantle cavity and gills of chitons compared to those of the ancestral mollusk. Extreme dorso-ventral flattening of the body has virtually obliterated the original spacious posterior chamber, and the mantle cavity has extended forward as a groove on both sides of the body between the foot and mantle edge (Fig. 12-5, *A*).

Instead of a single pair of gills, chitons have a large number of paired gills, which are arranged in a linear series within the two mantle troughs (Fig. 12-5, *A*). The number of pairs varies in different species and even within a single species. For example, the number of gills in *Lepidopleurus asellus* varies from 11 to 13 pairs and in *Tonicella marmorea* from 19 to 26 pairs. Structurally, chiton gill filaments are essentially like those of the ancestral mollusk, although the lateral margins are more rounded (Fig. 12-5, *B*) in chitons. Yonge (1939) considers the large number of gills in chitons to be a multiplication of the original single pair. With depression of the body and extension of the mantle cavity as shallow lateral troughs, adequate space no longer existed for a single pair of large gills. A large number of smaller gills, therefore, evolved.

Obviously, the changes in the mantle cavity and in the number of gills necessitated a change in the path of water circulation. The margins of the chiton mantle are held tightly against the substratum making the pallial groove a closed chamber. Within the groove, the gills, which hang from the roof, curve downward, and their tips touch the lower margin of the foot. The gills thus divide the mantle trough into a ventro-lateral inhalant chamber and a dorso-median exhalant chamber. On each side of the mantle trough toward the anterior end, the mantle margins are raised to form two inhalant openings. Water enters each inhalant chamber through these anterior openings, runs along the course of the groove, and passes up through the gills into each dorsal exhalant chamber. The two exhalant currents converge posteriorly and pass to the outside through one or two exhalant openings created by the locally raised mantle. Arrows in Figure 12-5, *A* indicate the course of water currents in *Lepidochitona*.

Nutrition. Chitons are herbivorous and feed on unicellular and multicellular algae that they scrape from the surface of rocks and shells. The mouth is located on the ventral surface in front of the foot and opens into the chitin-lined buccal cavity (Fig. 12-5, *A*). A long radula sac opens into the back of the buccal cavity, as does a smaller more ventral evagination called the subradula sac (Fig. 12-5, *C*). The latter contains a cushion-shaped sensory structure, the subradula organ, hanging from the roof. A pair of salivary glands open through the anterior dorsal wall of the buccal cavity.

When a chiton feeds, the subradula organ is first protruded and applied against the rock. If food is present, the odontophore and its radula project from the mouth and begin to scrape. When the radula is retracted, the collected food particles are pressed against the roof of the buccal cavity and carried into the esophagus. Periodically during feeding, the subradula organ is protruded and tests the substratum. The salivary secretion contains no enzymes and acts merely as a lubricant for the radula and as a medium for transporting food particles.

From the buccal cavity, mucus-entangled food particles enter the esophagus and are carried along a ciliated food channel toward the stomach (Fig. 12-5, *C* and *D*). During this passage, the food particles are mixed with amylase secretions produced by a pair of large esophageal glands (or sugar glands), the ducts from which open approximately into the midpoint of the esophagus.

The esophagus opens into the anterior of an irregularly-shaped stomach, which contains a large ventral sac. In the stomach, the food is further mixed with proteolytic secretions from the digestive gland, which opens into the stomach through two ducts. Contractions of the stomach aid in mixing the food and enzymes and, in conjunction with some ciliary action, move the food into the anterior portion of the intestine. Digestion is almost entirely extracellular and takes place in the anterior intestine as well as in the stomach. The walls of these two chambers are also the principal sites of absorption.

Some phagocytic cells wander in and out of the intestinal and stomach walls and engulf small food particles, which are then digested intracellularly. However, the contribution of these cells to digestion is apparently very minor.

The anterior intestine loops and then joins

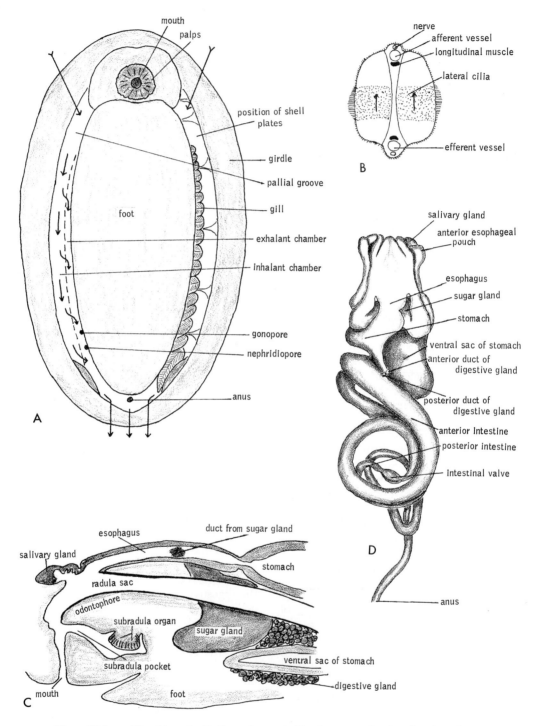

Figure 12-5.   The chiton, *Lepidochitona cinereus. A.* Mantle groove, showing direction of water currents (ventral view). *B.* Transverse section through gill axis. Arrows indicate direction of water current over filament surface. (*A* and *B* after Yonge.) *C.* Buccal region (lateral view). *D.* Digestive tract (dorsal view). (*C* and *D* after Fretter.)

a large coiled posterior intestine (Fig. 12-5, *D*). Between these two intestinal divisions is a sphincter, forming an intestinal valve. Waste leaving the intestine is compacted in mucus that is secreted along the entire length of the digestive tract. As the compacted waste enters the posterior intestine, the intestinal valve divides it into short fecal pellets. The valve also slows down the passage of food through the stomach and anterior intestine to allow adequate time for digestion and absorption.

Ciliary tracts move the fecal pellets through the posterior intestine, where further consolidation of waste takes place. The anus opens at the midline just behind the posterior margin of the foot, and the egested fecal pellets are swept out with the exhalant current.

Circulation and Excretion.   The pericardial cavity is large and located beneath the last two shell plates (Fig. 12-6). A single pair of auricles collects blood from all of the gills, only one aorta is present, and it issues from the ventricle anteriorly.

The two nephridia are large and extend anteriorly on each side of the body as long U-shaped tubes. Their walls are greatly evaginated to form many diverticula that ramify in the hemocoel. The nephridiopore for each kidney opens into the pallial groove located on each side between two of the more posterior pairs of gills (Fig. 12-5, *A*).

Nervous System and Sense Organs.   The nervous system is very primitive and similar to that of the ancestral mollusk (Fig. 12-7, *A*). Ganglia are lacking or at least poorly developed, and the cell bodies of neurons are scattered along the length of the nerve cords, as in the flatworms. A nerve ring surrounds the esophagus and nerves issue from it anteriorly to innervate the buccal cavity and subradula organ. Posteriorly the nerve ring gives rise to a large pair of pedal nerve cords, innervating the muscles of the foot, and a large pair of pallio-visceral nerve cords, innervating the mantle and visceral organs. The pallio-visceral nerve cords are interconnected posteriorly to form a complete nerve ring, and both pairs of nerve cords give off a large number of lateral interconnecting nerves.

Statocysts are not present in chitons, and the cephalic eyes and tentacles have disappeared as the head has become reduced in size. The only specialized sense organs are the subradula organ and in some families the aesthetes. Aesthetes, which are peculiar to chitons, are mantle sensory cells that penetrate the articulamentum of the shell and are lodged within ver-

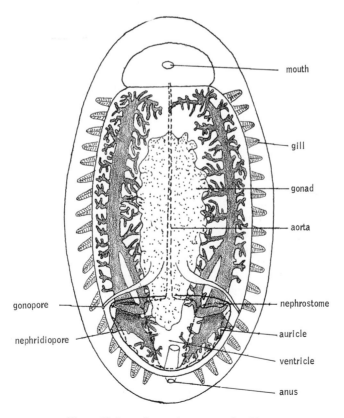

Figure 12-6.   Internal structure of a chiton.

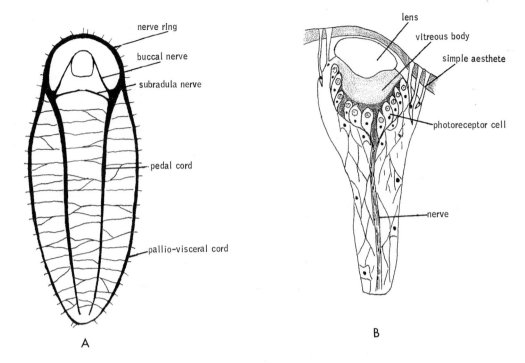

Figure 12-7.   *A.* Nervous system of a chiton. (After Thiele from Parker and Haswell.) *B.* Aesthete eye of *Acanthopleura.* (After Nowikoff from Parker and Haswell.)

tical canals in the upper tegmentum (Fig. 12-7, *B*). The canals and sensory endings open onto the surface of the shell plates.

The complexity of the aesthetes varies considerably. In some groups, such as *Chiton,* the aesthetes are simple tactoreceptors; and, as a result, the general surface of the shell is tactilely sensitive. In other chitons, the aesthetes are much more complex and consist of bundles of sensory cells that form an ocellus. These shell eyes may be composed of merely a cluster of photoreceptor cells and pigment, or they may be modified to contain a cornea, lens, and retina, as in *Acanthopleura.* These chiton ocelli may number in the thousands per individual and are usually located on the anterior shell plates. It has been reported that young chitons are negatively phototropic and that this response may disappear in older animals as the aesthetes become covered by organisms encrusting the shells.

The mantle surface that extends beyond the margins of the shell plates is liberally supplied with tactile and photoreceptor cells even when this surface is ornamented with scales and spines.

Patches of sensory epithelium are located at various places on the walls of the mantle trough in chitons and are considered to be equivalent to the osphradia of other mollusks. The subradula organ is probably the principal site of chemoreception, but chemoreceptors may

also be located on the epithelial fold, sometimes called the palps, which surrounds the mouth.

Reproduction and Embryology.   All chitons are dioecious. The paired gonads of the ancestral mollusk have become fused to form a single median organ that is located in front of the pericardial cavity beneath the middle shell plates (Fig. 12-6). Two gonoducts still remain, but they have lost their primitive connection with the pericardial cavity and open directly to the outside. A gonopore is located in each pallial groove in front of the nephridiopore (Fig. 12-5, *A*).

Copulation does not take place, and fertilization in most cases occurs in the mantle cavity. Sperm leave the male in the exhalant currents and are carried by inhalant currents into the pallial grooves of the female. The usual gregariousness of chitons facilitates fertilization. The eggs are shed into the sea either singly or in strings. The eggs that issue singly are enclosed in a spiny envelope. In some species, the eggs are retained between the gills, and prelarval development or, as in *Hemiarthrum,* the entire course of development takes place in the mantle cavity. *Callistrochiton viviparus* gives birth to its young, which have undergone development in the oviducts.

Development is typical. A coeloblastula is formed and gastrulation is accomplished by invagination. The molluscan cross is very distinct

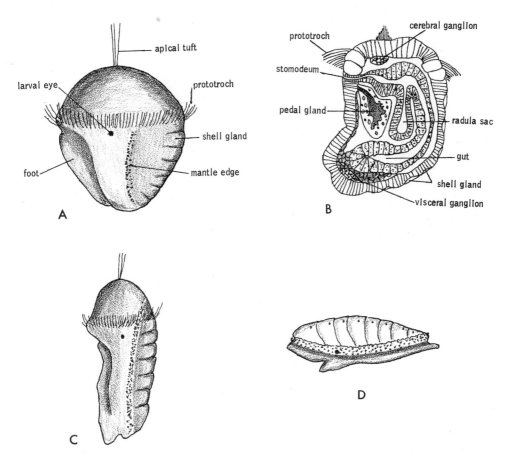

Figure 12-8.   Development of chitons. *A.* Trochophore of *Ischnochiton. B.* Section through trochophore of *Chiton. C.* and *D.* Metamorphosis of *Ischnochiton.* (*A, C,* and *D* after Heath from Dawydoff; *B* after Kowalevsky from Dawydoff.)

and a free-swimming trochophore is always present, except in some of those forms that brood their eggs (Fig. 12-8, *A*). A shell gland develops on the dorsal surface of the post-trochal region and is very soon divided by transverse grooves (Fig. 12-8, *B*). The foot develops on the side opposite the shell gland, and a pair of larval eyes form just behind the prototroch.

A primitive feature of amphineuran embryogeny is the direct metamorphosis of the trochophore into the adult form. In all other classes of mollusks that exhibit indirect development, the trochophore passes into an advanced larval stage called a veliger. In the metamorphosis of the chiton trochophore, the post-trochal region elongates to form the major part of the body (Fig. 12-8, *C* and *D*). The shell gland extends up into the pretrochal region, and the shell plates are formed in the transverse grooves. The prototroch degenerates, and the animal sinks to the bottom as a young chiton. The larval eyes are retained for some time after metamorphosis.

Distribution.   There are approximately 600 existing species of chitons. The fossil record,

which dates back to the upper Cambrian period, is rather sparse. Only approximately 100 fossil chitons are known.

The majority of chitons are littoral and are common throughout the world wherever there is a hard substratum. The rocky Pacific coast of the United States, Canada, and Alaska has a rich fauna of some 50 species, and approximately 40 species inhabit the Atlantic coast. A few species live in deep water; *Lepidochitona bentha* has been dredged from a depth of 13,800 feet.

The Aplacophora

The Aplacophora are a small group of aberrant amphineurans, consisting of approximately 100 species. They are all somewhat worm-like, and about an inch in length (Fig. 12-9). The aplacophoran does not possess a shell, although the mantle surface is imbedded with calcareous spicules. The foot is reduced to a small median ventral ridge lying in a small longitudinal groove, a vestige of the mantle cavity. The in-

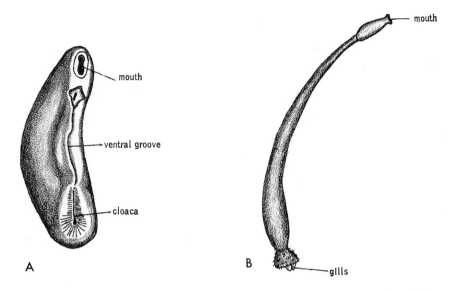

Figure 12-9.   Aplacophorans. *A. Neomenia.* (After Hansen from Parker and Haswell.) *B. Chaeto-derma.* (After Simroth from Parker and Haswell.)

turned mantle edge covers the remainder of the ventral surface on each side of the median groove.

In one group of aplacophorans, the Chaetodermomorpha, the foot and ventral groove are absent, and the margins of the mantle have fused to form a cylindrical body.

The digestive tract is straight and somewhat simplified; usually a radula is present, although it often is modified. The posterior end of the body contains a cavity called the cloaca, into which the anus and a pair of nephridiopores empty. The cloaca perhaps is another remnant of the mantle cavity. Gills are lacking in many species such as *Proneomenia;* but in some, including *Chaetoderma,* secondary gills are present in the cloacal chamber (Fig. 12-9, *B*). The aplacophoran nervous system is similar to that of chitons, but no specialized sense organs are present.

The Aplacophora are either hermaphroditic (*Proneomenia*) or dioecious (*Chaetoderma*). The gametes pass into the pericardial cavity and then through the nephridia to the outside. The egg develops into a typical free-swimming trochophore. Late development differs from that of the chitons in that the three rings of cells comprising the prototroch form an envelope, or test, that surrounds the rest of the post-trochal region of the body. During metamorphosis, the entire test is shed. A similar test is also found in primitive species of clams (Fig. 12-49, *A*). In *Dondersia,* seven dorsal shell plates have been reported present in newly metamorphosed individuals. The presence of such plates is evidence that the aplacophorans are derived from chitons.

The aplacophorans all live in deep water.

One group, the Chaetodermomorpha, are burrowers in bottom sand and mud, where they feed on annelids and other small invertebrates (Fig. 12-9, *B*). The other aplacophorans, the Neomeniomorpha, parasitize hydroids and corals (Fig. 12-9, *A*). *Chaetoderma* and *Neomenia* occur off the Atlantic coast of North America but are not commonly encountered.

Class Gastropoda

The class Gastropoda is the largest class of mollusks. Over 35,000 existing species have been described and to this total should be added some 15,000 fossil forms. The class has had an unbroken fossil record beginning with the early Cambrian period and apparently is now at the peak of its evolutionary development.

The Gastropoda is the only class of mollusks that has undergone an extensive adaptive radiation. Considering the wide variety of habitats the gastropods have invaded, they are certainly the most successful of the molluscan classes. Marine species have become adapted to life on all types of bottoms, as well as to a swimming pelagic existence. They have invaded fresh water, and the pulmonate snails, which compose almost one thousand genera, have conquered land with the elimination of the gills and conversion of the mantle cavity into a lung.

Origin and Evolution. *   In many respects,

---

* Discussion of the origin and evolution of gastropods is based primarily on the work of Yonge (1947).

gastropods exhibit the least change from the ancestral molluscan plan. The most significant modification, and the one to which most of the other changes are related, is the twisting, or torsion, that the body has undergone. Torsion is not merely the coiling of the shell; fossil evidence indicates that coiling of the shell evolved before torsion. The pre-torsion shell was plano-spiral; that is, the shell was not a conical spiral, but rather each spiral was located completely outside of the one preceding it and in the same plane, like a hose that is coiled flat on the ground. Thus the shell, though spiral, was bilaterally symmetrical.

Torsion was a much more drastic change than the spiralling of the shell. Viewing the animal dorsally, most of the body behind the head, including the visceral mass, mantle, and mantle cavity, was twisted 180 degrees counterclockwise (Fig. 12-10, *A* and *B*). The mantle cavity, gills, and anal and renal openings were now located in the anterior part of the body behind the head. Internally the digestive tract and nervous system were twisted into a U-shape. The shell remained a symmetrical spiral.

Torsion is not merely an evolutionary hypothesis, for it appears in the embryological development of living gastropods. The larva is at first bilaterally symmetrical and then quite suddenly undergoes twisting.

Many theories have been advanced to explain the evolutionary significance of torsion. Garstang (1928) maintained that torsion was a larval adaptation that developed essentially as it does in the larvae of living forms. Before torsion takes place, the velum, which is a ciliated larval locomotor organ, could not be retracted into the mantle cavity, because it was blocked by the foot. Twisting of the mantle cavity to the anterior of the body enabled the larva to accomplish this retraction. If attacked by a predator, the beating of the cilia would stop, and the larva could escape by sinking to the bottom. Torsion was of no adaptive value to the adult; rather it was a *fait accompli* that was imposed on the animal during larval development, and for the adult torsion created a considerable number of problems. However, it is difficult to understand how halting locomotion could greatly increase the chances of escape for the larva from some plankton-feeding predator.

A more recently advanced hypothesis maintains that torsion in gastropods was not a larval adaptation but was of advantage to the adult. This hypothesis holds that gastropods, like many other animals, oriented themselves in their environment, so that they faced external water currents. Changing the mantle cavity to

an anterior position made it possible for the inhalant current to move in the same direction as external currents, that is, posteriorly. Thus the external currents helped to flush out the mantle cavity. As attractive as this hypothesis might appear, there are many serious objections. There has been a general tendency among all mollusks to restrict the opening into the mantle cavity and to rely completely upon ciliary or, in some cases, muscular action for propelling water through the chamber. This tendency has been no less true within the gastropods, many species of which have developed incurrent siphons with narrow apertures. If the gastropod were actually benefiting from external currents flowing into the mantle cavity, there would be no reason to nullify this benefit by restricting the mantle opening.

Regardless of the evolutionary purpose of torsion, there is no question that it created a number of functional problems, and many of the modifications exhibited by gastropods represent attempts to adjust to these problems. The chief problem was fouling. After the development of torsion, if the water circuit though the mantle cavity had remained as it had been in the ancestral mollusk, waste from the anus and nephridia would have been dumped on top of the head. This problem was solved in the primitive gastropods by the formation over the mantle cavity of a cleft or split in the shell and mantle (Fig. 12-10, *D*). At the same time, the anus was withdrawn from the edge of the mantle cavity to a position beneath the inner margin of the cleft. The inhalant current continued to come in over the head and pass over the gills, but now instead of making a U-turn and passing out in the same direction, the water current flowed up and out through the cleft in the shell, taking waste from the anus and nephridia with it.

Up to this point we have been considering a gastropod with a symmetrical plano-spiral shell. Such a form is not entirely hypothetical, for there are numerous early fossil species with symmetrical plano-spiral shells bearing a cleft along the mid-dorsal edge. The cleft indicates the anterior median position of the mantle cavity.

Eventually a final change took place that resulted in the typical gastropod structure. This change involved the shell. Although there are fossil species with plano-spiral shells, all existing gastropods possess asymmetrical shells; or if the shells are symmetrical, they have been secondarily derived. The plano-spiral shell had the disadvantage of not being very compact; since each coil lay completely outside of the preceding one, the diameter of the shell could become

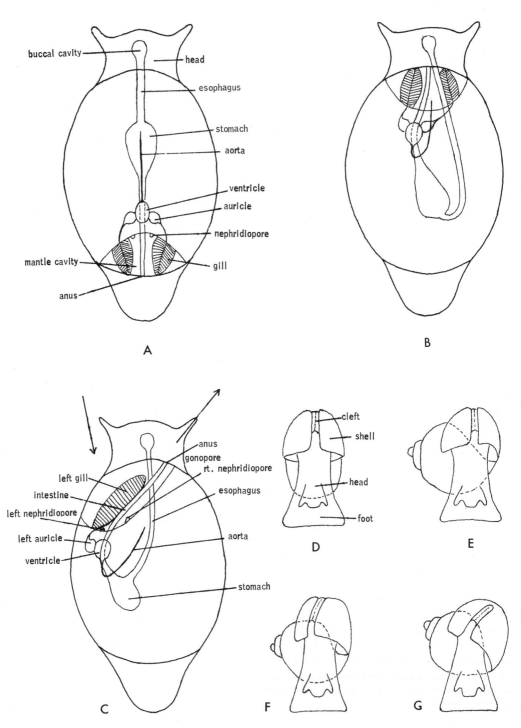

Figure 12-10.   Dorsal view of ancestral gastropod. *A.* Prior to torsion. *B.* After torsion. *C.* Typical prosobranch gastropod, with a single gill and mantle cavity on left side of animal. Arrows indicate path of water current through mantle cavity. *D* to *G.* Evolution of the asymmetrical gastropod shell. Slot in shell for exhalant water current marks location of mantle cavity. *D.* Ancestral post-torsion gastropod with plano-spiral shell. *E.* Apex of spiral is drawn out, producing a more compact shell. *F.* Position of shell over body shifted, providing more equal distribution of weight. *G.* Final position of shell over body, typical of most living gastropods. Axis of shell is oblique to long axis of body, and mantle cavity is located on left side of body. Right side of body is compressed by shell. (*A* to *C* after Graham; *D* to *G* after Yonge.)

relatively great (Fig. 12-10, *D*). The problem was solved with the evolution of asymmetrical coiling, in which the coils were laid down around a central axis called the columella and each coil lay beneath the preceding coil (Fig. 12-10, *E*). Thus, the conical spiral shell of modern gastropods evolved. Such a shell is much more compact and does not require the rapid increase in diameter characteristic of the ancestral plano-spiral shell.

The new spiral cone shell obviously could not be carried as was the old plano-spiral shell, because all the weight would hang on one side of the body (Fig. 12-10, *E*). In order to obtain the proper distribution of weight, the shell position became shifted, so that the axis of the spiral slanted upward and somewhat posteriorly. The net result was that the shell was eventually carried obliquely to the long axis of the body, as in living gastropods.

The new position of the shell restricted the mantle cavity to one side of the body, and the opposite side of the body was pressed against the shell (Fig. 12-10, *G*). This compression has had profound effects; it has resulted in the decrease in size, or the complete loss, of the gill, auricle, and kidney on that side of the body.

After evolution of the modern conical gastropod shell, solution of the problem of sanitation in modern gastropods followed three different courses: retention of the primitive cleft or perforated shell; modification to a single-gill arrangement in the new mantle cavity and development of a water circuit to the side of the head; and detorsion, in which the body underwent a reversal of the twisting process of torsion. Detorsion placed the mantle cavity and anus again at the posterior end, and the body adopted a secondarily derived bilateral symmetry.

With this background of possible gastropod evolution, we can now pause to consider the manner in which existing gastropods are classified before discussing the various organ systems of the class. The gastropods are divided into three subclasses. The first, known as the Prosobranchia, includes all gastropods that respire by gills and in which the mantle cavity, gills and anus are located at the anterior of the body—in other words, those gastropods in which torsion is evident. The majority of gastropods are prosobranchs.

From the Prosobranchia evolved the two remaining subclasses, the Pulmonata and Opisthobranchia. The subclass Pulmonata, which includes the land snails, has retained the post-torsion anterior position of the anus and mantle cavity; but the gills have disappeared, and the mantle cavity has been modified into a lung. The Opisthobranchia display various

stages of detorsion, and many have adopted a secondary bilateral symmetry. The shell is usually either reduced in size or absent, and many members have assumed a pelagic or swimming existence. The sea hares and the sea slugs (nudibranchs) are perhaps the most familiar members of this subclass.

Shell and Mantle.   The typical gastropod shell is a conical spire composed of tubular whorls and containing the visceral mass of the animal (Fig. 12-11, *A*). Starting at the apex, which contains the smallest and oldest whorls, successively larger whorls are coiled about a central axis, called the columella; the largest whorl eventually terminates at the opening, or aperture, from which the head and foot of the living animal protrude. A shell may be spiralled clockwise or counterclockwise, or, as it is more frequently stated, displays a right-handed or left-handed spiral. A shell possesses a right-handed spiral when the aperture opens to the right of the columella (if the shell is held with spire up and aperture facing observer) and left-handed when it opens to the left. Most gastropods are right-handed, a few are left-handed, and some species have both right-handed and left-handed individuals.

The first shell is laid down by the larva and is called the protoconch; it is represented by the smallest whorl at the apex of the shell. The protoconch can usually be differentiated from the newer parts of the shell, because it is smooth and lacks the sculpturing characteristic of the later parts of the shell. Except for the protoconch, the rest of the shell has uniform structure and is laid down by the edges of the mantle. A typical gastropod shell is composed of three layers—an outer periostracum, a middle prismatic layer, and an inner nacreous layer. The periostracum is thin and composed of a horny organic material called conchiolin. The two inner layers consist of calcium carbonate. In the prismatic layer, the mineral is formed into vertical crystals; in the nacreous layer it is layed down as thin lustrous sheets or lamellae. Reserve calcium carbonate for the secretion of these two shell layers is stored as spherules in certain cells of the digestive gland.

Gastropod shells display an infinite variety of colors, patterns, shapes, and sculpturing (Fig. 12-11). An introduction to the extensive terminology that has developed in connection with the description of shells can be found in any good field guide to shells. Only a few of the more radical modifications in shell form are mentioned here. In a considerable number of gastropods, the shell is conspicuously spiralled only in the juvenile stages. The coiled nature disappears with growth, and the adult shell

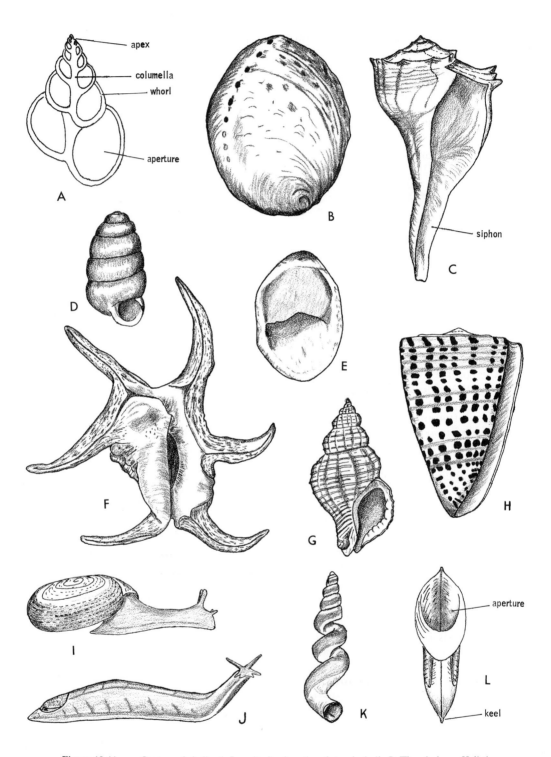

Figure 12-11.   Gastropod shells. *A.* Longitudinal section through shell. *B.* The abalone, *Haliotis*, with shell perforations over mantle cavity. *C. Busycon carica*, the common Atlantic Coast conch. *D.* The land snail, *Pupa*, smallest of the gastropods. (After Baker.) *E. Crepidula*, the slipper shell (ventral view). *F.* Aperture side of *Lambis*, the spider shell. *G.* The oyster drill, *Urosalpinx cinerea*. (After Abbott.) *H. Conus spurius*, a poisonous gastropod from the Florida coast and Gulf of Mexico. *I. Helicodiscus*, a land snail. *J. Testacella*, a land slug with reduced shell. (*I* and *J* after Baker.) *K.* The worm shell, *Vermicularia*. *L.* Shell of the swimming heteropod, *Atlanta peroni*. (After Abbott.)

represents a single large expanded whorl. In the abalone, *Haliotis* (Fig. 12-11, *B*), and in the slipper shell, *Crepidula* (Fig. 12-11, *E*), the shell remains asymmetrical; but in the limpets (Fig. 12-15, *A*), the shell, which looks like a Chinese hat, has become secondarily symmetrical.

An interesting modification in shell form has taken place in the family Vermetidae, the worm shells (Fig. 12-11, *K*). The larval and juvenile shells are typical; but as the animal grows older, the whorls become completely separate, and the adult shell looks like a cork screw.

Size reduction or loss of the shell has evolved among many gastropods. In the proso-branch, *Sinum,* the ear shell, the foot and mantle are very large, and the mantle has become reflexed back over the shell so that the shell is completely covered. The animal, which is unable to withdraw into its shell, looks like a lump of lard or fat. Among the pulmonates, the land slugs show varying degrees of shell reduction and loss. *Testacella,* a European slug that has been introduced into the United States, carries a small flattened shell on the posterior of the body (Fig. 12-11, *J*). In other slugs, such as *Limax* and *Philomycus,* the shell is reduced to a small flattened plate that is covered by the mantle.

Shell reduction is particularly characteristic

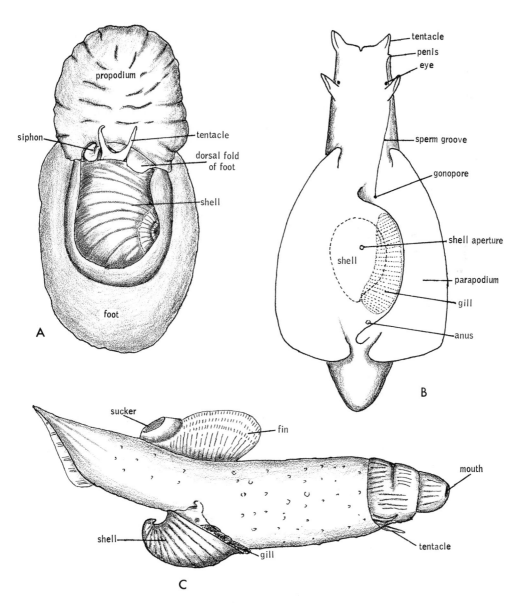

Figure 12-12. *A. Polinices,* a burrowing gastropod (dorsal view). (Drawn from life.) *B.* The sea hare, *Aplysia* (dorsal view). (After Bullough.) *C. Carinaria,* a swimming heteropod. (After Abbott.)

of the opisthobranchs, and the degree of shell reduction is closely related to the degree of detorsion. The bubble shells, the ectoparasitic Pyramidellidae, and many pteropods (sea butterflies) all have relatively well developed shells. In the sea hares the shell is reduced and covered by the mantle (Fig. 12-12, *B*). The nudibranch sea slugs, which have undergone complete detorsion, have lost the shell entirely (Fig. 12-16, *A* and *D*).

In regard to shell size, the smallest species with well-developed shells are the little terrestrial pulmonates belonging to the genus *Pupa* (Fig. 12-11, *D*). The height of the shell (the distance between the apex and the lower margin of the aperture) in these little snails does not exceed one millimeter. The largest shells, which may reach a height of two feet, are found in the marine species of *Megalotractus.*

The gastropod head and foot are withdrawn into the shell by a retractor muscle. This muscle, called the columellar muscle, actually arises in the foot but appears to emerge from the mantle on the right side (Fig. 12-16, *C*). The muscle is inserted into the columella of the shell. Primitively, two retractor muscles are present; this paired arrangement is found in the limpets and in *Haliotis,* although in the latter, the left muscle is very small (Fig. 12-14, *B*). In most gastropods the left muscle has disappeared and only the right muscle remains.

Other features of the shell and mantle are discussed in connection with their association with various functions.

The Foot.   The typical gastropod foot is a flat creeping sole similar to that of the ancestral mollusk, but it has become adapted for locomotion over a variety of substrata. The limpets have remained on the ancestral hard bottom and, like chitons, have become even more adapted for clinging and moving on rocky surfaces (Fig. 12-15, *D*). Many marine gastropods, as well as many fresh-water species, inhabit soft sand or mud bottoms. Others live on seaweed or, in the case of the pulmonates, on terrestrial vegetation, rotten leaves, and logs. Typically, a pedal mucous gland opens onto the dorsal or ventral anterior surface of the foot for the elaboration of a mucus-slime trail. Waves of fine muscular contractions that sweep from the anterior to the posterior of the foot provide the principal power for movement.

A few gastropods employ a different manner of pedal progression. The marsh-dwelling pulmonate, *Melampus,* extends the anterior of the foot and then pulls up the rest of the body behind it. In the marine snail, *Lacuna,* the foot is divided into right and left halves by a groove down the middle, and the snail moves by advancing one side of the foot and then the other.

Some prosobranchs that live on soft sand bottoms have become adapted for burrowing. In *Polinices,* which is a burrower, the front of the foot, called the propodium, acts like a shovel, and a dorsal flap-like fold of the foot covers the head as a protective shield (Fig. 12-12, *A*).

The foot of a great many shelled gastropods bears either a periostracum or calcium carbonate horny disc, called the operculum, on the posterior dorsal surface of the foot (Fig. 12-17). When the foot is withdrawn into the shell, the operculum may neatly fill the aperture of the shell and thus act as a protective door or lid. In *Strombus,* the foot is somewhat reduced in size and the operculum is formed into a large claw that digs into the bottom and pushes or "poles" the animal forward.

A swimming pelagic existence has been adopted by a group of prosobranchs, the Heteropoda, and by the sea butterflies among the opisthobranchs. In both of these groups, the foot has become modified into a powerful fin-like, swimming organ. The Heteropoda are greatly compressed, so that the foot is transformed into a ventral fin even though these animals swim upside down (Fig. 12-12, *C*). In *Carinaria,* the shell is much reduced; but in *Atlanta* it is well developed, symmetrically compressed, and displays keeled whorls (Fig. 12-11, *L*).

The swimming foot of certain opisthobranchs is modified differently. Two fins, called parapodia, arise as lateral projections from the side of the foot. In the sea hare, which is symmetrical with an internal shell, the fins arise from the middle of the body and are very broad (Fig. 12-12, *B*). The Pteropoda, the sea butterflies, have much longer and more anteriorly located parapodia, and the ventral part of the foot has been reduced to three small lobes (Fig. 12-13).

A few gastropods are sessile. The slipper shells, *Crepidula,* attach to shells of other living or dead mollusks (Figs. 12-11, *E* and 12-27, *A*). While not immovably fixed, they travel about very little. The foot has not been lost but rather has become an effective sucker for attachment (Fig. 12-22, *A*). The worm shells are immobile (Fig. 12-11, *K*). They either attach to other shells or are entangled in sponges.

Water Circulation and Respiration.   The most primitive type of gill structure and water circulation occurs in those prosobranchs with cleft or perforated shells—the primitive solution to the sanitation problems caused by torsion. These prosobranchs belong to the primitive

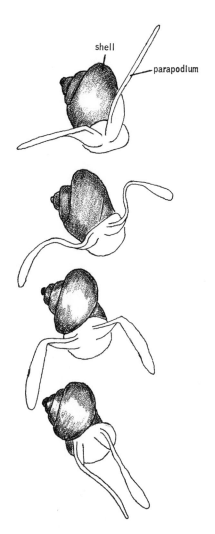

Figure 12-13. The sea butterfly, *Limacina*, an opistho-branch, while swimming. (After Morton.)

suborder Archaeogastropoda and include *Haliotis, Scissurella,* and the keyhole limpets. In all three groups, two gills are present; these gills have the primitive bipectinate condition of the ancestral mollusk. Also, the rectum and anus are removed from the edge of the mantle cavity and open beneath the shell perforation or cleft.

Haliotis tuberculata is asymmetrical with the mantle cavity displaced to the left side of the body; the shell above the cavity contains a line of five holes (Figs. 12-11, *B* and 12-14, *A* and *B*). The mantle is cleft along the line of shell perforations, and the edges of the mantle fit together and project into the shell openings to form a lining for each hole. The anus and the nephridial openings lie beneath the fourth perforation (the first perforation being the most anterior). Water is brought in at the anterior of the body by the action of the lateral cilia of the gills. The outstretched gills divide the mantle cavity into a ventral inhalant chamber and a dorsal exhalant chamber. The inhalant current flows posteriorly into the inhalant chamber and then up through the gills into the exhalant chamber. The exhalant current flows dorsally out through all the five shell perforations. The current flowing through the fourth opening also carries out waste from the anus and kidneys, as well as the genital products.

Scissurella, like *Haliotis,* has a spiral shell and also has a similar respiratory current (Fig. 12-14, *C*). However, instead of having a perforated shell, the anterior margin bears a deep cleft. The exhalant current passes upward through the notch carrying with it waste from the anus, which opens at the posterior margin of the cleft.

The keyhole limpets have a conical, secondarily symmetrical shell, which has either a cleft at the anterior margin or a hole at the apex. The latter arrangement appears in *Diodora* (Fig. 12-15, *A-C*). The opening arises as a notch along the shell margin during early stages of development. The notch then becomes enclosed and through differential growth gradually assumes a position at the apex of the shell. The mantle projects through the opening to form a siphon. Water enters the mantle cavity anteriorly, flows over the gills, and issues as a powerful stream from the opening at the shell apex. The anus and urogenital openings are located just beneath the posterior margin of the shell opening.

The Patellacea, the true marine limpets, are another group of Archaeogastropoda and are similar to the keyhole limpets in that they have a secondarily symmetrical conical shell, but they lack shell openings or clefts. This group displays a tendency toward both reduction and loss of gills. *Acmaea* (Fig. 12-15, *D*), a Patellacea, possesses but one gill, which projects to the right side of the body. As in all the true limpets, the mantle has developed a considerable overhang, so that there is a distinct pallial groove on each side of the foot, as in the chitons. The inhalant respiratory current enters the mantle cavity anteriorly on the left side. Part of the current flows posteriorly in the left lateral mantle groove; the rest of the current flows over the gill and then down the right mantle groove. The two exhalant streams converge posteriorly behind the foot and leave the body.

Patella is a true marine limpet. The original gills have completely disappeared and secondary gills have formed as folds of the mantle and project into the pallial groove along the side of the body. The inhalant current enters the pallial grooves anteriorly, and the exhalant current leaves posteriorly. The marine limpets, like the

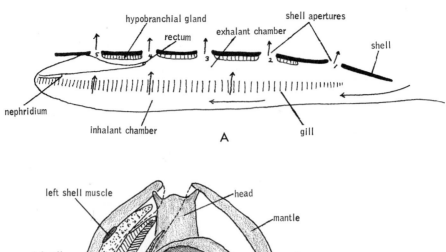

Figure 12-14.   *A. Haliotis,* showing path of water current through mantle cavity (lateral view). *B. Haliotis* with shell removed (dorsal view). *C. Scissurella,* a gastropod with slotted shell for exit of the exhalant current. (All after Yonge.)

chitons, have become adapted to a life on rocky shores, and the two groups have undergone a strikingly parallel evolution.

All of the remaining prosobranchs have undergone radical changes both in gill structure and water circulation. The right gill has disappeared, and except in the fresh-water *Valvata* the remaining left gill has lost its primitive bipectinate condition. Only the filaments along one side of the axis are developed; those on the opposite side have disappeared (Fig. 12-10, *C*).

Furthermore, the entire axis of the gill is attached to the inner, or body side, of the mantle cavity. Water enters the mantle cavity

to the left of the head, and the exhalant current leaves on the right side. To prevent fouling the inhalant current with waste, the rectum has become elongated, and the anus opens near the right mantle edge in the region of the exhalant current. The utilization of this type of gill structure and respiratory current by the vast majority of prosobranchs and its striking uniformity seems to indicate that this has been the most satisfactory solution to problems caused by torsion in the aquatic prosobranchs.

The effectiveness of the respiratory current has been further increased in many gastropod families by a spout-like inhalant siphon, formed by the folding of the mantle edges (Fig. 12-17).

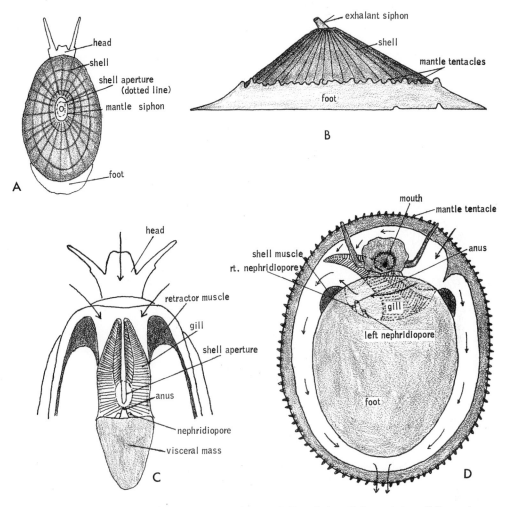

Figure 12-15.   *A–C.* The keyhole limpet, *Diodora. A.* Dorsal view. *B.* Lateral view. *C.* Exposed mantle cavity (dorsal view). *D.* The marine limpet, *Acmaea* (ventral view). Arrows indicate path of water circulation. (All after Yonge.)

In some species, such as the whelks and the conchs—*Buccinum, Colus, Busycon* (Fig. 12-11, *C*), and *Fasciolaria*—the anterior margin of the shell aperture has become elongated and grooved to house the siphon.

The remaining two subclasses of gastropods, the Opisthobranchia and Pulmonata, are probably both derived from prosobranchs that had only the single left gill. In the opisthobranchs there has been a tendency, associated with detorsion, toward loss of the original gill and the formation of secondary gills. The bubble shells and sea hares have retained the original single gill, although it is located on the right side of the body as a result of partial detorsion (Fig. 12-12, *B*).

In the sea slugs, or nudibranchs, which have undergone complete detorsion, both the mantle cavity and gill have disappeared. In these opisthobranchs, respiration takes place through the general body surface or through secondary gills. The dorsal body surface area is greatly increased in many nudibranchs by numerous projections called cerata, which are usually arranged in rows (Fig. 12-16, *A*).

The cerata may be club-shaped, as in *Aeolidia,* or branched, as in *Dendronotus.* Cerata are lacking in some nudibranchs, such as *Doris,* but these sea slugs have secondary gills arranged in a circle around the posterior anus (Fig. 12-16, *D*). The cerata, as well as other parts of the nudibranch body, are usually brilliantly colored and commonly include red, yellow, orange, blue, and green, as well as combinations of colors. The sea slugs certainly rank among the most spectacular and beautiful mollusks. The British species were beautifully illustrated in a monograph for the Ray Society by Alder and Hancock in 1845.

The Pulmonata are one of the few groups

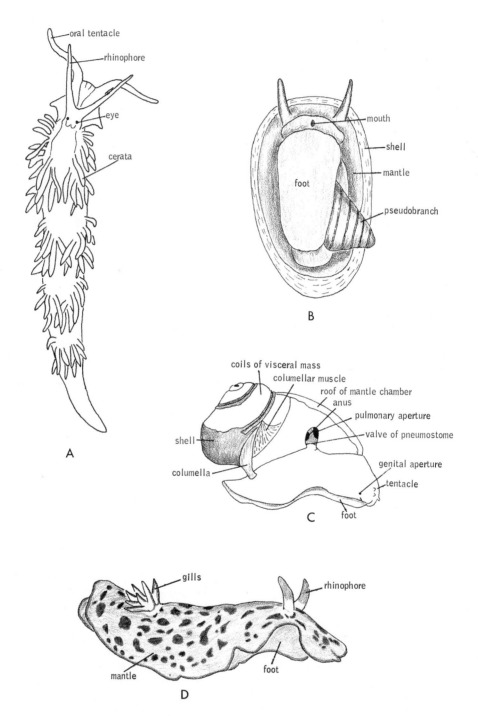

Figure 12-16.   *A. Aeolidia papillosa,* a nudibranch, with cerata (dorsal view). (After Pierce.) *B.* The fresh-water snail, *Ferrissia,* an aquatic pulmonate with secondary gill (ventral view). (After Pennack.) *C.* The land snail, *Helix,* partially dissected to show pneumostome. (After Rowett: Histology and Embryology.) *D. Glossodoris,* a nudibranch with secondary anal gills. Color in life is yellow with red spots. (After photograph by Zahl.)

of invertebrates, aside from the arthropods, that have successfully invaded the terrestrial environment. Land snails probably evolved from fresh-water prosobranchs, but the adopting of a terrestrial existence involved a radical change in the respiratory mechanism. The gill disappeared, and the mantle cavity became highly vascularized and was converted into a lung. The edges of the mantle fit tightly against the foot, except for a small opening on the right side called the pneumostome (Fig. 12-16, C). The floor of the mantle cavity is muscular and acts like a diaphragm. During the relaxation phase of respiration, the floor is arched upward; at contraction, the floor flattens, increasing the volume of the chamber, and air enters through the pneumostome. The pneumostome then closes, and the muscles of the chamber floor relax, so that the volume of the mantle cavity is reduced. This increases the pressure of the gases within the cavity and facilitates the diffusion of oxygen into the blood vessels lining the walls of the chamber.

A few land snails, such as *Janella,* have a mantle cavity in which the surface area has been greatly increased by evagination to form tubular extensions, called tracheae because of their resemblance to the respiratory system of insects and some arachnids.

The pulmonates are not the only gastropods that have become terrestrial. There are approximately 4000 species of terrestrial prosobranchs (as compared to some 15,000 species of land pulmonates). These prosobranchs belong primarily to three operculate families—the Helicinidae, the Cyclophoridae, and the Pomatiasidae. Many of the operculate land snails have evolved a lung from the mantle cavity as in the pulmonates. In contrast to the pulmonates, the operculate land snails are largely restricted to the tropics.

Many fresh-water snails are actually pulmonates that have secondarily returned to an aquatic environment. The respiratory structures of this group have evolved along several lines. Some of these snails, such as members of the families Lymnaeidae and Physidae, have retained the terrestrial mode of respiration; they come to the surface to obtain air. In both the lymnaeids and physids, the edges of the mantle around the pneumostome periodically form a long retractile siphon that can be extended to the water surface to obtain air. Depending on the amount of oxygen in the water, aquatic air-breathing snails can remain submerged from several minutes to several hours.

Some of the species of these two families never come to the surface for air but obtain oxygen from the water circulated through the mantle cavity.

Complete adaptation to aquatic respiration has developed in the pulmonate families, Planorbidae and Ancylidae (the fresh-water limpets) in which the mantle cavity has become reduced, and a conical projection from the left side of the foot called the pseudobranch has evolved as a secondary gill (Fig. 12-16, B). The exposed body surface, particularly that of the mantle, undoubtedly plays a varying role in the respiration of all gastropods.

Excretion and Water Balance. Members of the Archaeogastropoda possess two nephridia (Fig. 12-15, D), but in all other gastropods the right nephridium has disappeared, except for a small section that contributes to the reproductive duct. Also, as a result of torsion, the nephridium is located anteriorly in the visceral mass (Fig. 12-17). The structure of the nephridium is basically like that in other mollusks. It is U-shaped and the walls are greatly folded to increase the surface area for secretion. Wastes are eliminated through a short ureter. Primitively, the distal end of the nephridium connects with the pericardial cavity, but in most gastropods the connection between nephridium and pericardial cavity is a small renopericardial canal (Fig. 12-26, A). This canal opens into the more proximal part of the nephridium, in some cases at the level of the ureter.

The nephridiopore of both prosobranchs and opisthobranchs opens at the back of the mantle cavity, and wastes are removed by the circulating water current (Fig. 12-17). Such an arrangement is not possible in the pulmonates, because the mantle cavity functions as a lung. As a result, the ureter has lengthened along the right wall of the mantle and opens to the outside near the anus and the pneumostome.

Aquatic gastropods, like most other aquatic invertebrates, excrete ammonia or ammonium compounds. Terrestrial pulmonates, in order to conserve water, convert ammonia to the relatively insoluble uric acid. This adaptation to conserve water is particularly striking in the Indian apple snail, which is seasonally amphibious. During its aquatic phase, this snail excretes ammonium compounds; and during its terrestrial phase, it excretes uric acid.

Terrestrial pulmonates have not been very successful in controlling water loss through the body surface, and as a result, the majority require a humid environment. They are either nocturnal or live in damp environments, such as beneath logs or in leaf mold on forest floors. During dry periods in the tropics and during winter in temperate regions, snails burrow into humus or soil and become inactive. The edges of the mantle

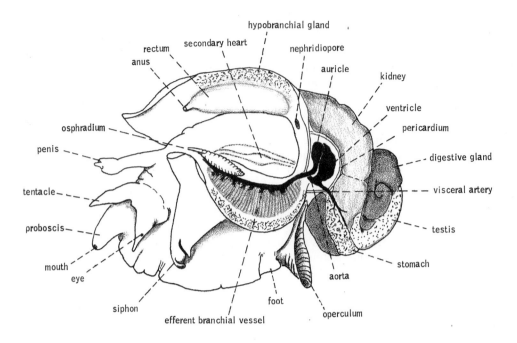

Figure 12-17.   Male of the conch, *Busycon,* with shell removed. (After Pierce.)

are drawn together in front of the shell aperture, and they secrete a thin protective calcareous membrane. Fresh-water snails also estivate when temporary ponds dry up and hibernate when the water is frozen.

In most gastropods, the digestive gland appears to play some role in excretion. A number of histological studies have demonstrated the presence of excretory cells in this organ; waste from this gland would be eliminated from the body by way of the stomach and intestine.

Circulation.   As a result of torsion, the heart of gastropods is located anteriorly in the visceral mass (Fig. 12-10, *B*). Other than this change in the position of the heart, the primitive archaeogastropods have retained the circulatory plan of the ancestral mollusk, and they possess two auricles. However, in all other gastropods, the right auricle either has become vestigial or in most instances has disappeared as a result of the loss of the right gill, which supplied it with blood (Fig. 12-10, *C*). The ventricle gives rise to a short single aorta, which then branches to form both a posterior visceral artery supplying the visceral mass and an anterior cephalic vessel supplying the head and foot. An enlargement of the anterior vessel, or second heart, in the head region may be present, as in *Busycon,* and probably functions in controlling blood pressure (Fig. 12-17). Blood from the kidney usually enters the branchial circulation, but in some cases it returns directly to the heart.

Gastropod blood presents nothing unusual.

In a few forms, such as *Planorbis,* the plasma contains hemoglobin rather than hemocyanin.

Nutrition.   Virtually every type of feeding habit is exhibited by the gastropods. Gastropods include herbivores, carnivores, scavengers, ciliary feeders, and parasites. Furthermore, the different types of feeding habits have arisen independently more than once within the class, so that the associated modifications of the gut are not always identical in the different gastropod groups even though the diets are similar. Despite differences in feeding habits, it is possible to make a few generalizations. (1) A radula is almost always employed in feeding. (2) Digestion is always at least partly extracellular. (3) With few exceptions, the enzymes for extracellular digestion are produced by the salivary glands, esophageal pouches, the digestive gland, or by a combination of these structures. (4) The stomach is the site of extracellular digestion, and the liver is the site of absorption and of intracellular digestion, if such digestion takes place. (5) Food is moved through the gut at least partly by ciliary tracts. (6) As a result of torsion, the stomach has been rotated 180 degrees, so that the esophagus enters the stomach posteriorly and the intestine leaves anteriorly (Fig. 12-10, *B* and 12-18, *B*). In the higher gastropods, there has been a tendency for the esophageal opening to migrate forward again toward the more usual anterior position (Fig. 12-10, *C*).

A radula is absent in very few gastropods; in most gastropods, it has become

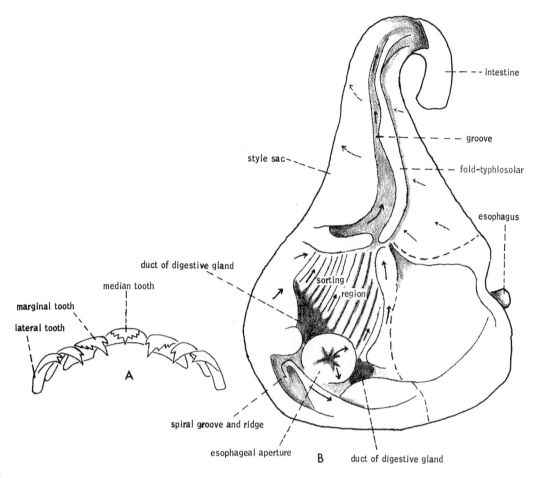

Figure 12-18. *A.* Transverse row of radula teeth of *Lanistes.* (After Turner.) *B.* Stomach of *Diodora apertura,* opened dorsally. Broken lines indicate extent of area lined with chitin. (After Graham.)

a highly-developed feeding organ. The teeth vary in number from 16 to 750,000 and are always arranged in rows. Usually there is a median row of teeth, on each side of which is a varying number of rows of teeth called marginals and laterals (Fig. 12-18, *A*). The median, marginal, and lateral teeth usually differ in shape and structure. The character and form of the radula teeth are relatively constant within taxonomic groups and are of considerable importance in the systematics of gastropods, particularly pulmonates.

The feeding movements of the radula are relatively complex and differ in detail from group to group. The radula may act as a grater, rasp, brush, or comb. Eigenbrodt (1941) and others have shown that, depending on the type of radula action, characteristic feeding trails are left on the substratum.

THE PRIMITIVE DIGESTIVE TRACT. In terms of structure, the most primitive type of digestive tract is found in certain archaeogastropods, such as *Diodora, Neritina,* and *Monodonta.* According to Graham (1939), *Diodora,* a keyhole limpet, feeds

primarily on sponges that are rasped from the substratum by the radula (Fig. 12-15, *A* and *B*). The salivary glands have retained their primitive functions of radula lubrication and secretion of mucus for food transport; however, the esophageal pouches are well developed and probably elaborate enzymes for extracellular digestion. Other enzymes are produced by the digestive gland.

The region of the stomach nearest the esophagus is partially lined by chitin and contains a ridged sorting region (Fig. 12-18, *B*). The end nearest the intestine is conical and forms the style sac. A deep groove runs the length of the style sac and into the stomach. Digestion appears to be primarily extracellular, and the products of digestion pass into the ducts of the digestive gland for absorption. The sorting region directs indigestible particles, such as sponge spicules, toward the style sac. Some of these particles pass through the style sac groove; others are picked up and compacted in the mass of rotating mucus and pass into the intestine.

Most gastropods are macrophagous herbivores, carnivores, or scavengers. Digestion has become entirely extracellular and takes place in the stomach, which has lost most of its primitive features—chitinous lining, sorting area, style sac —and has become a more or less simple sac.

HERBIVORES.   Many families of prosobranchs and opisthobranchs and most pulmonates are herbivores. In general, the radula of herbivores bears a large number of small teeth, and the upper margin of the buccal cavity frequently bears a chitinous jaw. The chitinous jaw is particularly common in pulmonates, in which a lateral pair of jaws may also be present.

In many herbivore species, the esophagus is enlarged to form a crop just before the esophagus opens into the stomach (Fig. 12-19). The crop serves as a temporary storage center and is the area where enzymes from the salivary and digestive glands begin digestion. In *Aplysia,* which feeds on the larger seaweeds, the crop is lined with chitinous plates and actually functions as a gizzard (Fig. 12-20, *A*).

The salivary glands of *Aplysia* are reported to secrete amylase and the liver to secrete protease and lipase. Cellulase has been reported in terrestrial pulmonates, such as *Helix.*

CARNIVORES.   Although a few of the carnivorous gastropods are pulmonates, the majority of carnivorous families are prosobranchs and opisthobranchs. In these families, the radula usually contains much larger but fewer teeth. In most prosobranchs, jaws are absent, and the buccal cavity has become folded to form a highly extensible proboscis (Fig. 12-17). The proboscis is constructed similarly to that in the triclad flatworms and lies free in a proboscis cavity, which opens to the outside through the mouth. The lumen of the proboscis contains the radula and is continuous with the esophagus. During feeding the proboscis can be extended from the mouth to a considerable length (Fig. 12-22, *D*). The radula protrudes from the proboscis tip and, as in the flatworms, food enters the proboscis rather than the mouth. When feeding is terminated, the proboscis is retracted into the proboscis cavity.

Several common prosobranch families, such as the Muricidae (*Urosalpinx, Murex, Eupleura*) and the Naticidae (*Polinices*), feed exclusively on bivalve mollusks. In all of these prosobranch families, the radula is adapted for drilling neat circular holes in the shells of the hosts. The mechanism of drilling has been most extensively studied in the Muricidae, par-

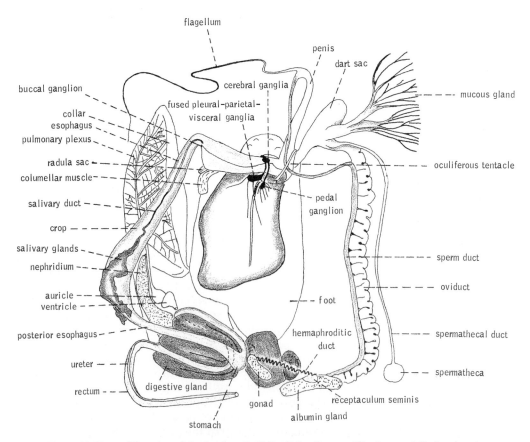

Figure 12-19.   Dissection of the land snail, *Helix*. (After Rowett: Histology and Embryology.)

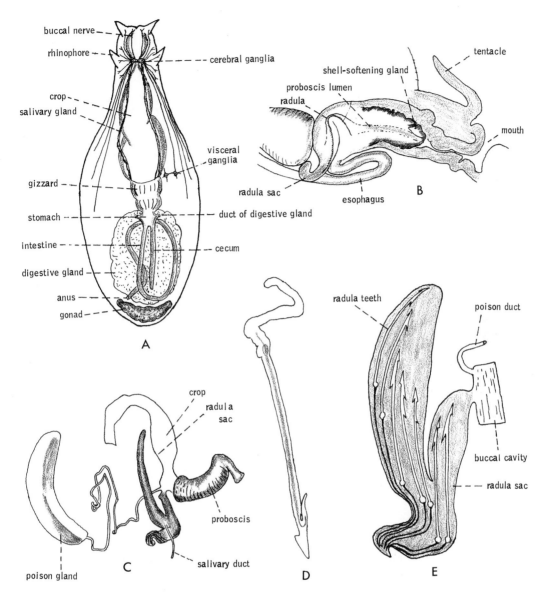

Figure 12-20.   *A.* Digestive and nervous systems of the sea hare, *Aplysia.* (After Bullough.) *B.* Head of the boring gastropod, *Polinices* (longitudinal section). *C.* Buccal structures of the poisonous cone shell, *Conus striatus. D.* Radula tooth of *Conus striatus. E.* Radula sac of *Conus striatus.* (*C* to *E* after Clench.)

ticularly in *Urosalpinx,* which causes tremendous damage to oyster beds. The anterior sole of the foot contains an eversible gland, which is applied to the area to be drilled.

The exact nature of the secretion produced by this gland is still uncertain, but it is not an acid. Carriker (1959) suggests that the secretion contains chelating agents, which combine with the calcium of the prey's shell to form water-soluble substances. The snail alternately drills and soaks the site of operation until the shell has been completely perforated. When drilling is completed, the proboscis is extended through the hole, and the soft tissues of the prey are torn by the radula and ingested. In the naticids, the shell-softening gland is located in the proboscis tip rather than on the foot (Fig. 12-20, *B*). The adaptation for drilling apparently evolved early in geological history, for perforated pelecypod and brachiopod shells have been found from the Devonian period.

The posterior of the esophagus is enlarged in some carnivores. The enlarged region may function as a crop, as in *Busycon,* or as a gizzard, as in *Scaphander,* a shelled opisthobranch that feeds on other small mollusks. In this genus, the prey is swallowed whole and then crushed by the chitinous plates lining the gizzard walls.

One of the most remarkable groups of carnivores are members of the marine prosobranch genus, *Conus*. Cone shells are tropical and subtropical in distribution and are found mainly in the western Atlantic and the Indo-Pacific areas (Fig. 12-11, *H*). The cone shells feed primarily on live fish and marine annelids, which they stab and poison with the radula teeth. In these marine gastropods, the odontophore has disappeared, and the radula is greatly modified (Fig. 12-20, *C* to *E*). The teeth are long, hollow, and barbed at the end, and they are attached to the radula membrane by a slender cord of tissue. The duct from the large poison gland opens into the buccal cavity just above the opening of the radula sac.

The cone shells have a long, highly maneuverable proboscis, which can be shot out with explosive force. When the proboscis is projected, the barbed end of a single radula tooth slips out of the radula sac into the buccal cavity, and as the proboscis strikes, the tooth is rammed into the prey like a harpoon. The victim very quickly becomes immobilized by a poison, but the mechanism of poison injection is still uncertain. The teeth are hollow, but the lumen ends blindly at the tip of the tooth. Furthermore, the poison gland is not directly associated with the radula. Clench (1946) suggests that either the poison flows into the wound made by the tooth, or else the tip of the tooth breaks when it is inserted, allowing the poison to be injected hypodermically.

The effect of the poison is very rapid and it apparently acts like curare, paralyzing the nerve-muscle junction. Kline (1956) reported that a species of *Conus geographus* died in five minutes after being stung by *Conus textilis*. The bite, or sting, of a number of South Pacific species, such as *Conus marmoreus, aulicus, tulipa, textile,* and *geographus,* is highly toxic to humans; a few deaths have been reported, in one case within four hours. American troops during World War II were warned against picking up these colorful shells.

The digestive tract of many carnivorous nudibranchs has several interesting modifications. The Aeolidiidae feed on hydroids and sea anemones. The buccal cavity contains a pair of blade-like jaws, which are used to cut small pieces of tissue from the prey. Neither a proboscis nor esophageal pouches are present; the salivary glands secrete mucus and perhaps enzymes that pass with food into a simple bilaterally symmetrical stomach (Fig. 12-21, *A*). The stomach floor contains cilia that cause currents to move posteriorly toward the three to five ducts of the digestive gland. The digestive gland in these carnivorous nudibranchs is

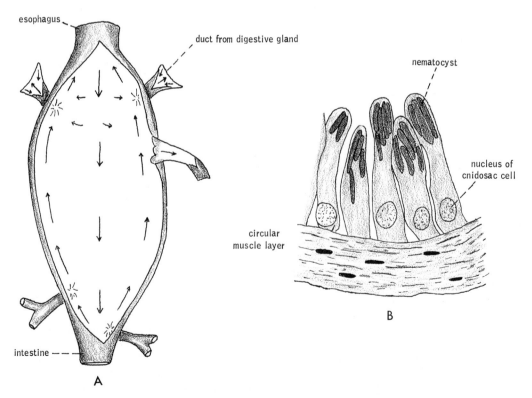

Figure 12-21.   *A.* Stomach of the sea slug, *Aeolidia papillosa,* opened dorsally. *B.* Cnidosac of *Aeolidina* (transverse section). (Both after Graham.)

peculiar in being confined entirely within the numerous club-shaped cerata, which cover the dorsal surface of the body (Fig. 12-16, *A*).

Each ceras contains a tubule of the digestive gland, and the tubules are joined together by a system of branching ducts leaving the stomach (Fig. 12-21, *A*). Thus the digestive gland of these nudibranchs is a diffuse rather than a compact organ, as it is in most mollusks. The secretory cells of the digestive tubules in the cerata produce a protease and diastase, which pass into the stomach and act extracellularly. Absorption takes place in the stomach walls and in the digestive gland. According to Graham (1938), some intracellular digestion of small particles, largely glycogen, takes place within the digestive gland.

The most remarkable feature of these nudibranchs is their utilization of the prey's nematocysts. Ciliary tracts in the stomach and in the ducts from the digestive gland carry the undischarged nematocysts to the cerata, in which they are engulfed but not digested. Instead, these undischarged nematocysts are moved to the distal tips of the cerata, called cnidosacs, which open to the exterior. There the nematocysts are used by the nudibranchs for defense. The discharge mechanism is not thoroughly understood. Graham (1938) suggests that discharge of the nematocyst is caused by pressure exerted either by circular muscle fibers around the cnidosac or else by the enemy.

STYLE-BEARERS AND CILIARY FEEDERS.   Crystalline styles are found in many of the ciliary feeders, such as *Crepidula* and *Vermetus*, which are sessile, and certain radula-feeding herbivorous forms, such as *Strombus*. A crystalline style—which is much more common in bivalve mollusks—is a firm gelatinous protein rod that lies in the intestinal, or anterior, end of the stomach (the style sac), and projects into the rounded posterior end (Fig. 12-45). The rod is formed by the secretion from the epithelium of the style sac and contains carbohydrate-splitting enzymes adsorbed onto the protein molecules forming the rod matrix. The beating of cilia in the style sac causes the style to rotate, and the projecting free end is rubbed against the chitinous plate-like gastric shield on the stomach wall. This abrasive action erodes the end of the style and liberates the enzymes into the stomach. The rotation of the style also aids in mixing the stomach contents. The presence of a crystalline style in gastropods is associated with the more or less continuous feeding of the animal on a diet of phytoplankton or organic detritus.

In *Crepidula,* a ciliary feeder, the gill filaments have been tremendously lengthened to provide an increased surface area for trapping plankton (Fig. 12-22, *A* and *B*). The shell and mantle edges are held tightly against the substratum except for a slight gap on each side of the anterior. Water enters the left side and leaves from the right; and as plankton passes through the mantle cavity, it is trapped in mucus on the surface of the long gill filaments.

Gill cilia carry the plankton particles to the right toward the tips of the filaments, which curl back against the sides of the body. The particles then pass into a longitudinal groove, which lies along the side of the body and which is in contact with gill filaments. Here the particles collect and are compacted into a mucus string. The anterior end of the groove is located close to the mouth, and at intervals the end of the mucus string is seized by the radula and pulled into the buccal cavity. The particles are then carried to the stomach along an esophageal food groove.

The salivary glands in *Crepidula* have retained their primitive radula-lubricating function and produce no enzymes; no esophageal pouches are present. Food enters the stomach near the middle and is carried by a crescent-shaped ciliated fold toward the gastric shield at the extreme posterior end. Here the food is mixed with carbohydrate-splitting enzymes from the end of the style. Products of digestion and other small particles pass into the ducts of the digestive gland, in which digestion is completed intracellularly and absorption occurs. A deep groove parallel to the style sac conveys waste particles into the intestine.

Lambis, the spider shell, and *Strombus,* the conch shell, are both style-bearers but feed on algae rasped with a very delicate radula. In *Strombus,* both the salivary gland and esophageal pouches, in addition to the style, produce amylase and cellulase. Free proteolytic enzymes are never produced in mollusks with crystalline styles, since the protein style itself would be digested.

Limacina, a shell-bearing sea butterfly, is a ciliary feeder and has no crystalline style, although a vestigial style sac is present. *Limacina* feeds primarily on diatoms and Foraminifera that are removed from water circulating through the mantle cavity. This food is trapped in mucus on the walls of the mantle cavity and then compacted to form a mucus string. A ciliated tract carries the string of food out of the mantle cavity to the mouth, where portions of the string are detached by the radula.

The posterior of the esophagus is expanded and acts both as a pump and as a gizzard. The esophageal walls here contain four large opposing teeth that fit closely together and crush the diatom and foraminiferan shells. The action of the teeth also tends to move food along the

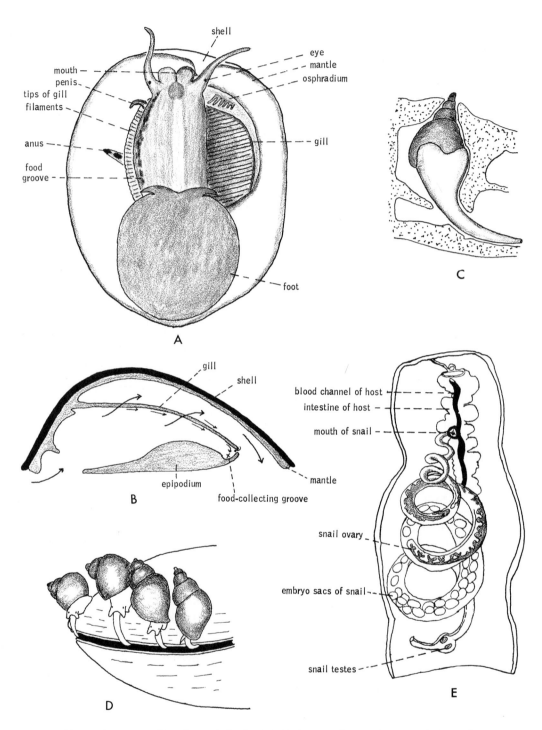

Figure 12-22.   *A.* The slipper shell, *Crepidula fornicata,* a ciliary feeder (ventral view). (Drawn from life.) *B. Crepidula,* showing direction of water current (large arrows) through mantle cavity. Ciliary currents (small arrows) carry food particles. (After Orton.) *C.* The parasite, *Stylifer,* imbedded in body wall of a sea star. *D. Brachystomia,* an ectoparasite, shown feeding on body fluids of a clam. (*C–D* after Abbott.) *E.* The endoparasite, *Entoconcha,* within body cavity of a sea cucumber. (After Baur from Hyman.)

esophagus and into the stomach. Digestion is entirely extracellular and takes place in the stomach by means of enzymes produced by the digestive gland. The products of digestion pass into the large single opening of the digestive gland, where absorption takes place.

PARASITES.   Parasitism has developed in a few gastropods, of which the Pyramidellacea is the most notable example. This group of opisthobranchs contains several families of ectoparasites and endoparasites. The pyram snails are ectoparasites on polychaetes and on marine bivalves (Fig. 12-22, *D*). The long proboscis of these snails is equipped with a sucker and a stylet for gripping and piercing the host. The tissue fluids are then ingested by a pumping action of the buccal cavity.

Stylifer lives imbedded in the body wall of echinoderms, such as starfish, on which it feeds (Fig. 12-22, *C*). The shell is still present in these snails, but only the top of the spire projects above the exterior surface of the host. The most modified of the Pyramidellacea are members of the endoparasitic genus *Entoconcha,* which live in the gonad of *Synapta,* a sea cucumber (Fig. 12-22, *E*). They feed on the blood of the host by attaching the mouth region to one of the host's blood vessels. The body is worm-like, and a shell is present only during larval development.

The Nervous System.   The nervous system in gastropods is distinctly ganglionated and somewhat complex. The basic pattern may be more easily understood if the nervous system is first described as if torsion had not taken place (Fig. 12-23, *A*). A pair of adjacent cerebral ganglia lie over the posterior of the esophagus and give rise to nerves anteriorly that connect to the eyes, tentacles and to a pair of buccal ganglia, located in the back wall of the buccal cavity. The buccal ganglia innervate the muscles of the radula and other structures in this vicinity. A nerve cord issues ventrally from each cerebral ganglion on each side of the esophagus. These are the two pedal nerve cords, which extend anteriorly to a pair of ganglia located in the midline of the foot and which innervate the foot muscles.

A final pair of nerve cords, the visceral nerves, arise from the cerebral ganglia and extend posteriorly, until they terminate in a pair of visceral ganglia located in the visceral mass, or hump. Along the course of the visceral nerves are located two other pairs of ganglia. Located close to the cerebral ganglia are the pleural ganglia; the more distal ganglia are known as the parietal ganglia. The pleural ganglia innervate the columellar muscle and the mantle and are joined by a pair of connectives to the pedal

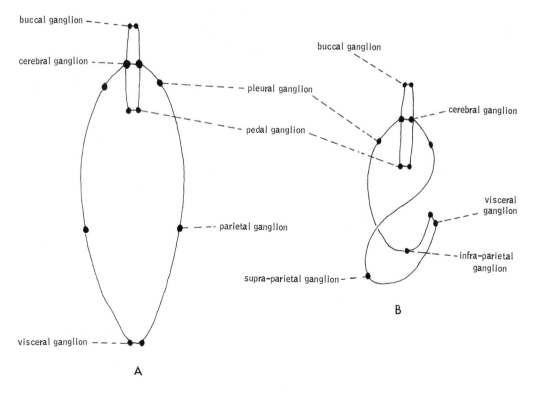

Figure 12-23.   *A.* Hypothetical pre-torsion nervous system. *B.* Post-torsion nervous system.

ganglia; the parietal ganglia innervate the gills, osphradia and the mantle, and the visceral ganglia send nerves to various structures in the visceral mass.

THE EFFECT OF TORSION.   Although the visceral cords are described here as bilateral, they are actually asymmetrical and twisted into a figure eight, as a result of torsion (Fig. 12-23, B). This twisting reverses the original positions, so that the former right parietal ganglion is now on the left and the former left parietal ganglion is now on the right. Furthermore, the present left ganglion (the pre-torsional right ganglion) is located higher in the visceral mass than its opposite member; the two ganglia are therefore sometimes called supra- and infraparietal ganglia. The pleural ganglia are not affected by torsion because of their anterior position.

The twisted condition is a primitive feature of the gastropod nervous system, since torsion has developed during the evolutionary history of all gastropods. Another primitive feature of the gastropod nervous system is the separation of the ganglia by nerve cords, as previously described. Such a primitive nervous system is found, with some modifications, in many prosobranchs, such as Patella and Haliotis (Fig. 12-24, A). However, in most gastropods the original arrangement is obscured because of two evolutionary tendencies. First, there has been a tendency toward both concentration and fusion of ganglia with a consequent shortening of the connectives between ganglia. Second, there has been a tendency for the ganglia and cords to adopt a secondary bilateral symmetry.

Virtually every gastropod displays some degree of ganglial concentration. The pleural ganglia are always located adjacent to the cerebral ganglia. Not infrequently, as in Patella and Busycon, the two visceral ganglia have fused to form a single center (Fig. 12-24, B). In Haliotis, each pedal ganglion has fused with a pleural ganglion, and from each fused pedal-pleural ganglion issues a long pedal nerve to the foot (Fig. 12-24, A). A high degree of concentration is present in Busycon, where all ganglia except the visceral ganglia have migrated forward and are located around the esophagus and below the cerebral ganglia (Fig. 12-24, B). All connectives between ganglia have thus disappeared except those between the parietal and visceral ganglia.

In the pulmonates even the visceral ganglia have migrated forward (Fig. 12-24, C). This shortening of all the connectives has resulted in a secondary bilateral symmetry of the nervous system.

Those opisthobranchs that have undergone complete detorsion also have a symmetrical system due to the untwisting of the visceral cords.

In Aplysia, the left parietal ganglion has disappeared, and the right parietal ganglion now lies beside the single fused visceral ganglion (Fig. 12-24, D).

SENSE ORGANS.   The sense organs of gastropods include eyes, tentacles, osphradia, and statocysts. Eyes are characteristic of most gastropods, and one is located at the base of each cephalic tentacle. Primitively, as in Patella, the eye is a simple pit containing photoreceptor and pigment cells (Fig. 12-25, A), but in most higher gastropods the pit has become closed over and differentiated into a cornea and a lens (Fig. 12-25, B). The tentacular eyes of gastropods are always direct; that is, the photoreceptors are directed toward the source of light. The most highly developed eyes are found among the pelagic sea snails (the Heteropoda) and are supposedly superior to eyes found in many fish. However, the eyes of most gastropods function only in the detection of light.

A single pair of cephalic tentacles are displayed by prosobranchs, and two pair are found in most pulmonates and opisthobranchs. In addition to bearing the eyes, the cephalic tentacles contain tactile and chemoreceptor cells. The second pair of tentacles are knobbed in many pulmonates, and in the nudibranchs the upper half of the tentacle wall displays plate-like folds that increase the surface area for chemoreception. These modified tentacles of nudibranchs are called rhinophores (Fig. 12-16, A and D).

Typically, a pair of closed statocysts are located in the foot near the pedal ganglia of gastropods. In nudibranchs and certain other opisthobranchs, the statocysts have migrated to a position near the cerebral ganglia.

The evolution of the osphradium of gastropods closely parallels that of the gills. In the primitive Archaeogastropoda, an osphradium is present for each gill and is essentially like that described for the ancestral mollusk. In the other prosobranchs, which possess but one gill, there is also only one osphradium, which is located on the mantle cavity wall anterior and superior to the attachment of the gill (Figs. 12-17 and 12-22, A). In most cases, the osphradium has either become filamentous or become folded, thereby increasing the surface area. The osphradium has disappeared in those gastropods that have lost the gill, that possess a reduced mantle cavity, or that have taken up a strictly pelagic existence. This variation in the presence of the osphradium in gastropods tends to support Yonge's (1947) view that the main function of the osphradium is to detect sediment in the water passing over the gills.

Reproductive System.   Many gastropods are dioecious. The single gonad, either ovary or

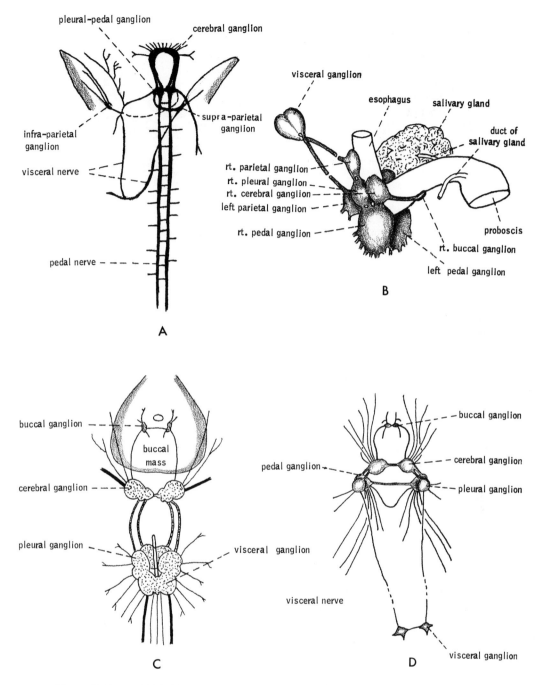

Figure 12-24. *A.* Primitive nervous system in *Haliotis.* (After Lacaze-Duthiers from Parker and Haswell.) *B.* Concentrated nervous system in *Busycon.* (After Pierce.) *C* and *D.* Secondarily symmetrical nervous systems. *C.* In the pulmonate, *Helix. D.* In the opisthobranch, *Aplysia.* (Both after Bullough.)

testis, is located in the spirals of the visceral mass next to the digestive gland (Fig. 12-17). The gonoduct ranges from a very simple to a highly complex structure, but in all cases it has developed in close association with the right nephridium. In the primitive Archaeogastropoda, both nephridia are functional, and the right

nephridium provides outlet for either the sperm or eggs (Fig. 12-26, *A*). The gametes pass through a short duct that extends from the gonad and opens into the kidney at various points; the gametes are then conducted by the kidney into the mantle cavity through the nephridiopore. The genital duct is thus formed

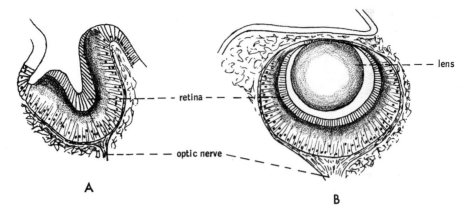

Figure 12-25.   Eyes of two marine prosobranchs. *A. Patella,* a limpet. *B. Murex.* (Both after Helger from Parker and Haswell.)

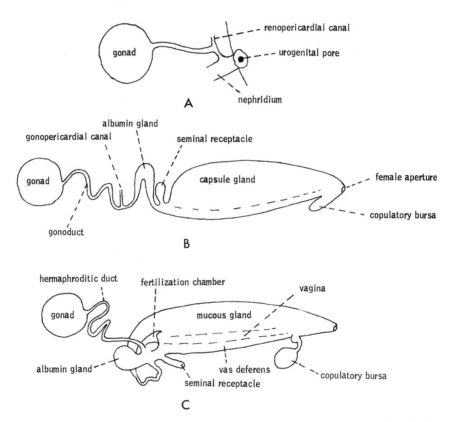

Figure 12-26.   Reproductive tracts of three gastropods. *A.* A trochid, a primitive dioecious prosobranch. *B.* Female system of *Nucella,* a prosobranch. *C.* The sea hare, *Aplysia,* a monoecious opisthobranch. (All after Fretter.)

from two elements—the gonoduct proper and the right kidney. In this type of reproductive system, the eggs are provided, at most, with gelatinous envelopes produced by the ovary, since the gonoduct is not sufficiently elaborate to produce tertiary membranes. There is thus no need for copulatory organs, and fertilization takes place in the sea water after the eggs are swept out of the mantle cavity.

In all the other gastropods, the right nephridium has degenerated except for the portion that functions as part of the genital duct. Furthermore, the genital duct has become considerably lengthened by a third addition, derived from the mantle; as a result, the genital pore is located at the opening of the mantle cavity. According to Fretter (1946), this third section, which might be called the pallial duct, probably first arose as a ciliated groove extending from the nephridiopore, but in all existing gastropods the groove has become closed over to form a distinct tube (Fig. 12-26, *B*). In many species, the pallial duct has even sunk inward into the hemocoel and become separated from the mantle. It is the pallial portion of the genital duct that has undergone elaboration or differentiation to provide for sperm storage, and egg membrane formation.

In reproductive systems where the production of tertiary egg membranes by the pallial section of the oviduct takes place, a penis has evolved in the male so that fertilization may take place before the formation of the egg capsules or cases. This penis is a long cylindrical extension or fold of the body wall arising just behind the right cephalic tentacle. In some gastropods, such as *Busycon,* the vas deferens continues to open at the back of the mantle cavity, and the pallial section appears in part as a glandular ciliated groove, which extends to the tip of the penis (Fig. 12-17). In others, the groove has closed over, and the vas deferens opens at the penial tip. At least a portion of the pallial section forms a prostate for producing seminal secretion. The duct from the testis is usually coiled and provides a storage place for the sperm before copulation. The entire male duct thus consists of: a coiled duct from the testis, representing the original gonoduct; a short renal contribution to the vas deferens; and the pallial vas deferens, containing the prostate.

In the female, the pallial section of the oviduct is modified to form both an albumin gland and a large jelly gland or capsule gland (Fig. 12-26, *B*). Species such as *Cerithium* imbed the eggs in jelly masses produced by the jelly gland; but in most of the higher prosobranchs, the eggs are enclosed in a capsule. At the end of the pallial oviduct proximal to the gonad is a seminal receptacle for the reception and storage of sperm from the penis. Also, the eggs are fertilized at this point before they enter the secretory portion of the oviduct. In a great many genera, such as *Littorina, Urosalpinx, Murex, Nassarius,* and *Busycon,* the sperm are not directly received by the seminal receptacle; instead, during copulation, they enter a copulatory bursa at the distal end of the oviduct (Fig. 12-26, *B*). From the bursa the sperm later pass posteriorly along a ventral channel in the oviduct and enter the seminal receptacle. The outgoing eggs pass through the dorsal portion of the oviduct, where the membranes are applied.

A few prosobranchs, and all opisthobranchs and pulmonates are hermaphroditic. Some, such as *Crepidula,* are protandrous, but most are simultaneously male and female. In either case,

the single gonad produces both eggs and sperm, and the genital duct becomes divided either functionally or morphologically for the passage of both sperm and egg.

In *Aplysia,* the sea hare, the gonadal and renal sections of the genital duct form a common hermaphroditic duct, which becomes separated by means of grooves into two channels at the end most distal from the gonad (Fig. 12-26, *C*). One channel conducts sperm into the vas deferens, which is derived from the lower part of the pallial genital duct. The midsection of the vas deferens is only functionally separated from the female tract above. The vas deferens continues beyond the female aperture to the tip of the penis. The pallial portion of the female tract is divided into a vagina and oviduct. The vagina communicates with a seminal receptacle, which supposedly receives sperm directly from the penis. There is also a copulatory bursa, but its exact function in this case is uncertain.

The hermaphroditic system of the pulmonates is built on the same general plan as that in *Aplysia,* although it differs in detail. In the European land snail, *Helix,* which has been studied extensively, the anterior of the female portion of the reproductive tract contains both an arborescent mucous gland, which apparently has a lubricating function, and an oval dart sac, which secretes a calcareous spicule (Fig. 12-19). Prior to copulation, the pair of snails display a very peculiar courtship behavior. The two animals approach each other each with the genital atrium everted. When the snails are approximate, the calcareous darts from each are driven with such great force into the body wall of the opposite animal that they are buried deep into the internal organs. A new dart is secreted later by the dart sac. After this rather drastic form of stimulation, copulation takes place with the penis of each snail being placed into the vagina of the other. The sperm are bound together as spermatophores and fertilization is reciprocal. The penis in pulmonates lies within the outer end of the male reproductive tract until protruded.

Crepidula, the slipper shells, is a protandric hermaphroditic genus and its life cycle has been extensively studied by Coe (1936). In this more or less sessile prosobranch group, individuals tend to live stacked up on one another (Fig. 12-27, *A*). Young specimens are always males. This initial, male phase is followed by a period of transition in which the male reproductive tract degenerates; the animal now develops into either a female or another male. The sex of these older individuals is influenced at least partly by the presence or absence of other sexes in the association. An older male will remain

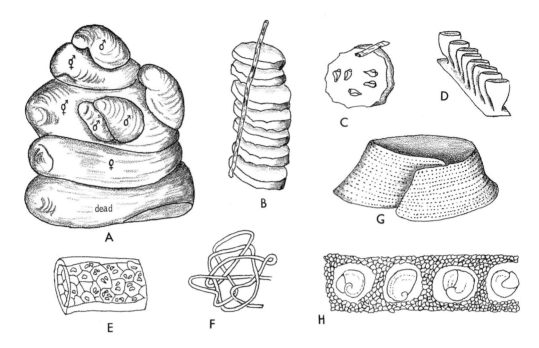

Figure 12-27.   *A.* Cluster of slipper shells, *Crepidula.* Two individuals are in process of changing from male to female sex. Male at top will fertilize individual below when female phase is reached. (After Coe.) *B* to *D.* Parchment egg cases. *B* and *C. Busycon. D. Conus. E* and *F.* Gelatinous egg string of sea hare, *Aplysia. E.* Enlarged section. *F.* Entire string. *G* and *H.* Sand-grain egg case of the moon shell, *Lunatia heros. G.* Entire case. *H.* Section of case. (*B* to *H* after Abbott.)

male as long as it is attached to a female. If such a male is removed or isolated, it will develop into a female. The presence of a large number of males influences certain of the males to become female. When the individual once becomes female, it remains in that state.

Embryology. The eggs of primitive prosobranchs are fertilized externally and are either laid singly or aggregated in gelatinous ribbons or masses. However, the majority of prosobranchs, fresh-water pulmonates, and opisthobranchs display much more highly developed egg membranes. In some species such as *Littorina*, individual eggs are surrounded by albumen and a shell, and then a large number of such shelled eggs are imbedded in a gelatinous mass. In many others, such as *Crepidula, Busycon,* and the fresh-water pulmonates, *Physa* and *Ancylis*, several eggs imbedded in an albumen mass are surrounded by a single capsule or case, which is either planktonic or attached to the substratum. The size and shape of the case and the nature of its wall, which may be leathery or gelatinous, are extremely variable and characteristic of the species. A number of types of gastropod egg cases are illustrated in Figure 12-27.

The capsules of fresh-water pulmonates are usually gelatinous; the eggs of terrestrial pulmonates are usually enclosed in separate shells that are calcified to prevent excessive water loss.

The free-swimming trochophore larva is found only in the primitive Archaeogastropoda; in all the other gastropods, the trochophore stage is reduced and is passed through in the egg.

More characteristic of marine gastropods is a free-swimming larval type called a veliger. The veliger larva is derived from a trochophore but represents a more complex stage of development (Fig. 12-28). The characteristic feature of the veliger is the swimming organ, called a velum, which consists of two large semicircular folds bearing long cilia. The velum forms as an outward extension of the prototroch of the trochophore. Other structures of the veliger larva show a greater degree of development than those in the trochophore larva. The foot, eyes, and tentacles appear; the shell, which first formed in the trochophore, develops spirally in the veliger because of unequal growth; the stomodeum develops into the buccal structures and esophagus, and connects with the stomach; and larval retractor muscles are formed.

During the course of the veliger stage, torsion occurs and the shell and visceral mass twist 180 degrees in relation to the head and foot. It should be noted that spiraling of the shell does not result from torsion but

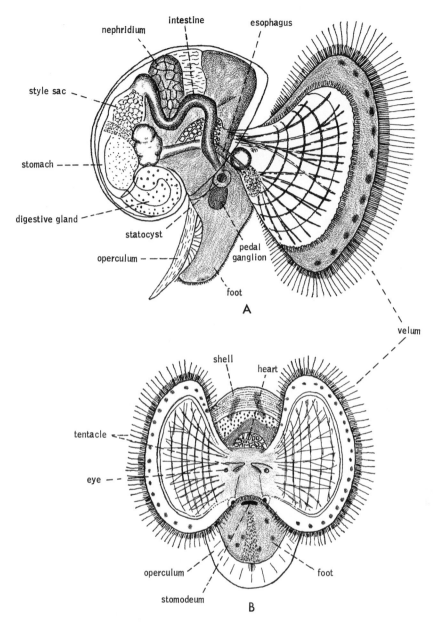

Figure 12-28.   Veliger larva of the slipper shell, *Crepidula. A.* Lateral view. *B.* Frontal view. (Both after Werner from Raven.)

usually has preceded it. Torsion may be very rapid (only about three minutes in the marine limpet, *Acmaea*), or it may be a gradual process (ten days in the terrestrial prosobranch, *Pomatias*). In many archaeogastropods, such as *Haliotis, Patella,* and *Calliostoma,* torsion takes place in two 90-degree phases, in which the first is relatively rapid and the second more gradual.

When torsion is rapid, the development of the larval retractor muscle appears to be the primary cause of the torsion (Fig. 12-29). This muscle is composed of six large spindle-shaped muscle cells, which connect as a bundle to the pre-torsional right side of the shell apex. The

opposite end of the bundle fans out into the foot rudiment, the mantle, and the stomodeal region. Four of these cells are sickle-shaped when they first develop, but they straighten out just before they reach a functional state. Torsion coincides with, and is probably largely caused by, the asymmetrical growth or straightening of these cells, which forces the visceral mass and foot to twist.

As development proceeds, the veliger reaches a point at which not only can it swim by means of the velum, but the foot is also sufficiently formed to allow creeping. Gradually the velum becomes smaller, and the young

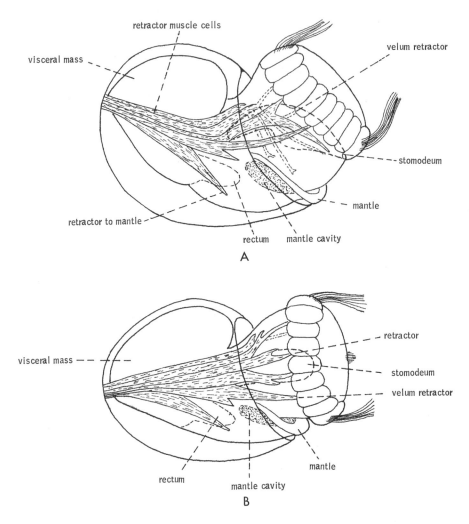

Figure 12-29.   Torsion in veliger larva of *Haliotis. A.* Pre-torsion. *B.* Post-torsion. (After Crofts from Raven.)

gastropod adopts the adult mode of locomotion.

The embryology of opisthobranchs recapitulates several stages in their evolution. Torsion takes place in the veliger, although it is not complete, and is then followed by detorsion. In the nudibranchs, which are shell-less as adults, a shell appears in the veliger, which is cast off during metamorphosis.

A trochophore larva, when it exists, is always succeeded by a veliger; but in most marine gastropods, the trochophore stage is passed in the egg, and the veliger larva is the hatching stage. Some marine prosobranchs, such as *Busycon, Conus* and *Natica,* nearly all fresh-water prosobranchs, and all pulmonates have no free-swimming larvae; but both trochophore and veliger stages can be recognized within the egg. At hatching, a tiny snail emerges from the protective shell or case. A few gastropods, such as some species of *Littorina* and the fresh-water

prosobranch family Viviparidae (*Viviparus* and *Campeloma*), are ovoviviparous.

Economic Importance.   Gastropods serve as food for numerous other animals, but the principal predators of aquatic gastropods are fish, aquatic birds, and mammals, many of which are adapted to a molluscan diet. Land snails serve as food for birds, salamanders, and small mammals.

Various species of gastropods are utilized as food by man in different parts of the world. The west coast abalone, *Haliotis,* is consumed in California, but state law prevents its exportation from the state. Conch is eaten in southern Florida. North Americans, except for patrons of French restaurants, have never acquired a taste for snails, but in southern Europe the large land snail, *Helix pomatia,* is considered a delicacy.

Of greater importance to global economy

are the destructive activities of some gastropods. The predacity of muricids on oysters has already been mentioned. Certain species of land snails and slugs do extensive damage to cultivated plants. Slugs attack both the underground and aerial portions of plants and are a common pest in greenhouses and in truck gardens. Several species of snails such as *Zonitoides* in eastern United States may extensively damage gardens. An attempt to eradicate destructive species in western truck farms has recently been made by introducing certain species of carnivorous snails from the South Pacific. The success of this attempt has not yet been determined.

From a medical standpoint, snails are of considerable importance as secondary hosts for many trematode parasites of man and domesticated animals. Developmental stages of blood flukes, liver flukes, and lung flukes take place in fresh-water snails in various parts of the world where these diseases are epidemic. Marine snails also serve as hosts for trematode parasites of shore birds and fish.

Systematic Résumé of Class Gastropoda

Subclass Prosobranchia. Marine and fresh-water, gill-bearing forms in which the mantle cavity and contained organs are located anteriorly. A shell is present.

Order Archaeogastropoda (Aspidobranchia). Primitive forms in which reduction of the right gill, auricle, and kidney has not taken place—that is, two gills, two auricles, and two kidneys are present. Nervous system is never concentrated. Shell is coiled or secondarily symmetrical in limpets. Largely marine with a few fresh-water species. Includes forms with slit or perforated shells (*Scissurella, Haliotis*), the keyhole limpets (*Emarginula, Puncturella, Diodora*), limpets (*Patella, Acmaea*), and top shells (*Margarites, Calliostoma, Trochus, Monodonta*). Species of the Neritacea (*Neritina, Nerita, Helicina,* and *Proserpina*) have invaded brackish, fresh-water, and terrestrial areas of the world, especially in the tropics.

Order Mesogastropoda (Pectinibranchia). Possess only one gill, one auricle, and one kidney; those of the post-torsional right side have disappeared. Operculum may be present; proboscis typical. Chiefly marine but many fresh-water genera. This is the largest order of gastropods and includes many common species: periwinkles (*Littorina*), the pelagic *Janthina*, slipper shells (*Crepidula*), *Strombus, Lambis, Cerithium Nassarius,* the boring naticids (*Polinices, Sinum, Natica*), the pelagic swimming heteropoda (*Atlanta, Carinaria*), the worm shells (*Vermetus*), and the fresh-water snails (*Viviparus, Campeloma, Hydrobia, Goniobasis*). Members of the operculate families Pomatiasidae and Cyclophoridae are terrestrial but are largely restricted to the tropics.

Order Neogastropoda (Stenoglossa). This order differs from the mesogastropods because members have a bipectinate osphradium, a concentrated nervous system, and a shell usually with a siphonal canal. Carnivorous species have a proboscis with a radula containing two or three large teeth in each row; some possess a poison gland; nearly all have an operculum; all are marine. Includes the boring muricids (*Murex, Urosalpinx, Purpura*), *Busycon, Oliva, Mitra, Voluta, Buccinum, Colus, Fasciolaria,* and genera with a poison gland associated with the radula (*Conus, Terebra*).

Subclass Opisthobranchia. Have one auricle and one kidney, but display various degrees of detorsion and reduction of shell and mantle cavity. Entirely marine.

Order Tectibranchia. Shell present, although it may be reduced and covered by mantle; one true gill still present; secondary bilateral symmetry in some. Includes bubble shells (*Acteon, Bulla, Scaphander, Philine*), swimming sea hares (*Aplysia, Pleurobranchus*), and the parasitic pyrams (Pyramidellacea—*Pyramidella, Entoconcha, Stylifera*).

Order Pteropoda. Sea butterflies; pelagic, shelled and shell-less opisthobranchs. Anterior part of foot expanded to form swimming fins. Suborder Thecosomata has shells; includes *Spiratella, Clio, Cavolina, Limacina,* and *Cuvierina.* Suborder Gymnosomata lacks shells; includes *Pneumoderma, Cliopsis,* and *Notobranchaea.*

Order Nudibranchia. Nudibranchs or sea slugs. Shell absent and body secondarily symmetrical; mantle cavity and true gill absent; respiration through general body surface; cerata or secondary gills around anus. Digestive gland extensively branched and ramified through body; nervous system concentrated. Second pair of tentacles modified as rhinophores. Includes *Doris, Dendronotus, Elysia,* and *Aeolidia.*

Subclass Pulmonata. Have one auricle and one kidney, but gills absent and anterior mantle cavity converted into a vascularized chamber for respiration in air or secondarily for water. Nervous system concentrated and symmetrical. Shell usually present, but never an operculum. Hermaphroditic, development direct. Members are terrestrial and fresh-water, and a few are marine.

Order Stylommatophora. Pulmonates with two pairs of tentacles and with eyes located at tip of posterior pair. Entirely terrestrial; mostly land snails. Includes *Helix, Polygyra, Retinella, Pupa, Janella,* and the land slugs (*Deroceras, Philomycus, Pallifera, Testacella, Limax*).

Order Basommatophora. Pulmonates with one pair of tentacles; eyes located near the tentacle base. Primarily fresh-water forms. Require air for respiration, although some take water into mantle cavity, and a few have developed secondary gills. Some terrestrial species, and a few marine forms in littoral waters. Includes *Lymnaea, Planorbis, Physa,* and the fresh-water limpets (*Ferrissia, Ancylus*).

Class Pelecypoda

The Pelecypoda, or Lamellibranchia, is comprised of mollusks known as bivalves and includes such common forms as clams, oysters, and mussels. Pelecypods are all laterally compressed and possess a shell with two valves hinged dorsally. The foot, like the remainder of the body, is also laterally compressed, hence the origin of the name Pelecypoda—hatchet foot. The head is greatly reduced in size. The mantle cavity is the most capacious of any class of mollusks, and the gills are usually very large, having assumed in most species a food-collecting function in addition to that of respiration.

Most of these characteristics represent modifications that enabled pelecypods to leave the hard substratum to which the ancestral mollusk was confined and take up an existence in the much more numerous soft-bottom habitats. In these new environments, the pelecypod became burrowers, for which the lateral compression of the body is better suited. However, these adaptations for burrowing in mud and sand appear to have taken pelecypods so far down the road of specialization that they have become largely chained to a soft-bottom existence. A few groups have made attempts to migrate to other habitats, but none have been very successful in reaching widely diverse environments.

Pelecypoda consists of four orders: the Protobranchia, the Filibranchia, the Eulamellibranchia, and the Septibranchia. The protobranchs are generally believed to be the most primitive of existing pelecypods. The septibranchs are highly specialized and have lost their gills. The filibranchs and eulamellibranchs contain the majority of the pelecypod species.

Shell and Mantle. A typical pelecypod shell consists of two similar, more or less oval, convex valves, which are attached, and articulate dorsally with each other (Fig. 12-30, *A* and *D*). The pelecypod shell is composed of the same layers—periostracum, prismatic, and nacreous layers—as the gastropod shell. Dorsally and somewhat anteriorly, each valve bears a protuberance called the umbo, which rises above the line of articulation. The umbo is the oldest part of the shell, and the concentric lines around it are lines of shell growth. The umbo is usually directed anteriorly, making it possible to determine the right and left valves of the animal. The two valves are attached by an elastic band called the hinge ligament. The hinge ligament is composed of the same horny organic material (conchiolin) as the periostracum and is continuous with the periostracum.

The hinge ligament varies in structure, but in all cases it is so constructed that when the valves are pulled together, the ligament is either stretched or compressed (Fig. 12-30, *A* to *C*). Thus, when the adductor muscles relax, the ligament causes the valves to open. To prevent lateral slipping, the two valves in most species are locked together by teeth and opposing sockets, located on the hinge line of the shell beneath the ligament (Fig. 12-30, *D*).

In most pelecypods, the two valves are similar and equal in size, but in some sessile families, such as the Anomiidae (jingle shells), Ostreidae (oysters), and the Spondylidae (spiny oysters) (Fig. 12-31, *B*), the upper, or left, valve is always larger than the right valve, by which the animal attaches.

The valves of the shell are pulled together by two large dorsal muscles, called adductors, which act antagonistically to the hinge ligament (Fig. 12-30, *A* and *D*). The adductors extend transversely between the valves anteriorly and posteriorly; there are scars on the inner surface of the valves where these muscles are attached.

Primitively, the two adductor muscles are equal in size, but in many families, such as the Anomiidae and the Mytilidae, there has been a tendency for the anterior adductor to become reduced. In oysters and scallops, the anterior adductor has completely disappeared, and the posterior adductor has shifted to a more central location between the valves (Fig. 12-47). This large single adductor muscle of the scallop serves as food for man. In the scallop, as well as in other pelecypods, the valves can be snapped shut rapidly, here the adductor muscle is divided into one section of striated fibers and one section of smooth fibers, called the quick muscles and the catch muscles, respectively. The striated muscle cells cause rapid closing of the valves, but sustained contraction is effected by the smooth muscle fibers.

The shells of pelecypods exhibit an infinite variety of sizes, shapes, surface sculpturing, and colors. The shells range in size from the tiny

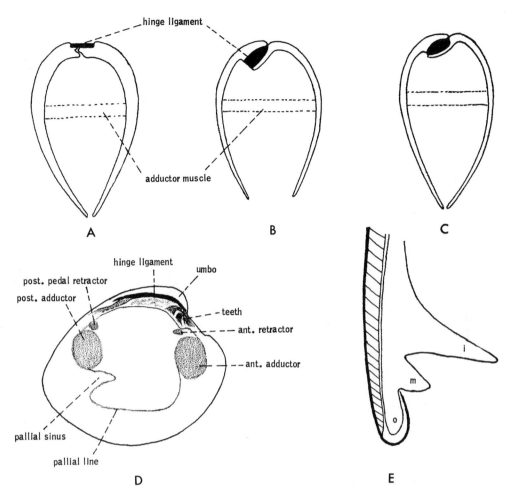

Figure 12-30. *A* to *C.* Transverse sections of pelecypod shells, showing types of hinge ligaments. *A.* Hinge ligament stretched when valves are closed. *B* and *C.* Hinge ligament compressed when valves are closed. (*A* to *C* after Shrock and Twenhofel.) *D.* Inner surface of left valve of the marine clam, *Venus. E.* Transverse section of mantle margin, showing inner (i), middle (m), and outer (o) mantle folds. (*E* after Yonge.)

seed shells of the fresh-water family, Sphaeriidae, which usually do not exceed two millimeters in length, to the giant clam, *Tridacna,* (Fig. 12-31, *A*) of the South Pacific, which attains a length of over four feet and may weigh over 500 pounds. All colors and combinations of colors exist; some of the variations in shape and sculpturing are shown in Figure 12-31. Shell characteristics are of great importance for the identification of pelecypods; and, as in gastropods, specialized terms have developed for describing these characteristics.

Like the shell, the mantle greatly overhangs the body, and it forms a large sheet of tissue lying beneath the valves (Fig. 12-41). The edge of the mantle bears three folds—an inner, middle, and outer fold (Fig. 12-30, *E*). The innermost fold is the largest and contains radial and circular muscles. The middle fold is

sensory in function. The outer fold is related to the secretion of the shell. The inner surface of the outer fold lays down the periostracum, and the outer surface secretes the prismatic and nacreous layers. The nacreous layer is also secreted by the entire outer surface of the mantle.

Foreign particles are prevented from lodging between the mantle and shell, because the mantle is attached to the shell by the muscle of the inner lobe along a semicircular line a short distance from the shell edge. The line of mantle attachment is impressed on the inner surface of the shell as a scar, called the pallial line (Fig. 12-30, *D*).

Despite the attachment of the mantle, occasionally some foreign object, such as a sand grain or a parasite, lodges between the mantle and the shell. The object then becomes a

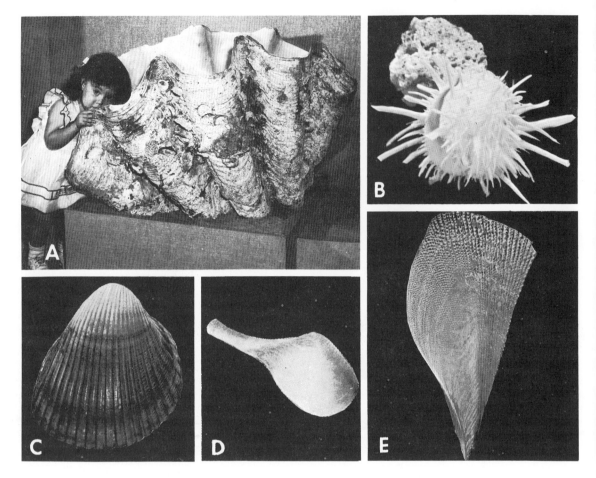

Figure 12-31.   *A.* The giant clam, *Tridacna.* (Courtesy of Cranbrook Institute of Science.) *B.* Atlantic thorny oyster, *Spondylus americanus. C.* Giant Atlantic cockle, *Dinocardium robustum. D.* Rostrate Cuspidaria, *Cuspidaria rostrata. E.* Saw-toothed pen shell, *Atrina serrata.* (*B* to *E* from Abbott's AMERICAN SEASHELLS, copyright 1954, D. Van Nostrand Company, Inc., Princeton, N.J.)

nucleus around which is laid concentric layers of nacreous shell. In this manner a pearl is formed. If the nucleus is moved about during secretion, the pearl becomes spherical or ovoid. Sometimes, however, the developing pearl adheres to or even becomes completely imbedded in the shell.

The finest natural pearls are produced by the pearl oysters, *Pinctada margaritifera* and *Pinctada mertensi,* which inhabit most of the warmer Pacific areas, but pearls are formed in most pelecypods, including fresh-water clams. Bead pearls are produced by purposely introducing a shell bead between the mantle and shell of the pearl oyster. The oyster then lays down a nacreous coating approximately one millimeter thick around the bead. Most cultured pearls are started by placing a microscopic globule of liquid or solid irritant in an oyster. The resulting year-old seed pearl is then transplanted in another oyster. A pearl of marketable size is obtained three years after transplantation.

The Foot.   The pelecypod foot has become compressed, blade-like, and directed anteriorly as adaptations for burrowing. In the primitive Protobranchia, such as *Nucula, Solemya,* and *Yoldia,* the foot still retains to a small extent a flattened sole (Fig. 12-32). However, the two sides of the sole can be folded together producing a blade-like edge; in this condition the foot is thrust into the mud or sand. The sole then opens and serves as an anchor, and the remainder of the body is pulled downward after the sole. *Solemya,* a rapid mud burrower, can completely disappear under the mud surface with two thrusts of the foot. In the other pelecypod orders, the sole has disappeared, but the function of the foot in burrowing is essentially the same. The distal end of the foot dilates after being thrust into the substratum, and the body is then pulled in following the foot.

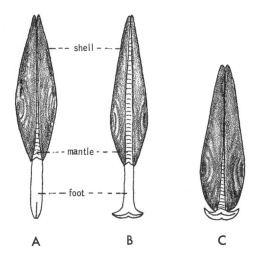

Figure 12-32.   Operation of foot of *Yoldia limatula,* a protobranch. *A.* End of foot folded and extended into substratum. *B.* Foot opened and anchored. *C.* Body drawn down into substratum. (All after Yonge.)

Foot movement is effected by a combination of blood pressure and muscle action. Engorgement of the foot with blood plus the action of a pair of pedal protractor muscles produces extension. The protractors extend from each side of the foot to the opposite valve, where they are attached to the shell just below and behind the anterior adductor muscle (Fig. 12-37, *A*). Withdrawal of the foot is effected by the contraction of a pair of anterior and a pair of posterior retractors also attached to foot and shell and by the contraction of muscle fibers within the foot itself. The scars of the pedal retractors are situated just above those of the adductors (Figs. 12-30, *D* and 12-37, *A*).

Cardium (cockle shells) and some other pelecypods can move along the bottom surface by means of a jumping motion. The foot is extended and then contracted violently, moving backward in the process. The foot thus acts like a spring, kicking the animal forward slightly.

In sessile pelecypod families, such as the oysters and the jingle shells (*Anomia*), the foot is very much reduced in size. The foot is also reduced in the scallops (*Pecten*), which do not burrow but have developed a means of jerky swimming by use of jet propulsion (Fig. 12-47). The valves are slammed shut, and water is shot out dorsally in two streams, one at each end of the hinge line. The best pelecypod swimmer is *Lima,* which uses the same method as *Pecten* but can eject water ventrally as well as dorsally (Fig. 12-33, *A*).

Some clams, notably the Mytilidae, or mussels, live attached to wharf pilings, rocks, and oyster beds. They are held in position not by

fusion of the valve with the substratum, as in oysters, but by means of strong horny threads called byssal threads (Fig. 12-34). The threads are secreted by a gland in the foot that is probably homologous to the pedal mucous gland of gastropods. The gland is located just above and behind the small cylindrical foot.

In the formation of a byssal thread, the foot is pressed against the stone or piling to which

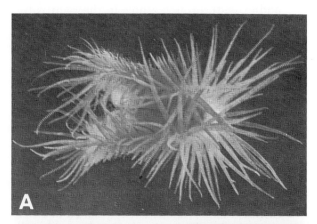

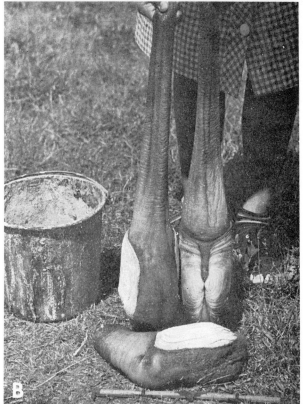

Figure 12-33.   *A.* File shell, *Lima,* a swimming pelecypod. (Courtesy of D. P. Wilson.) *B.* The geoduck, *Panope generosa,* a giant Californian pelecypod in which body and siphon cannot be enclosed within valves. (From Milne & Milne: Animal Life, Prentice-Hall, Inc., 1959.)

the clam is attaching. The glandular secretion then flows down a groove along the back side of the foot and out to the tip of the foot, which is in contact with the substratum. The secretion hardens on exposure to sea water, the foot is withdrawn, and a completely formed thread remains behind. The foot then secretes another thread in a new location, and eventually the clam is tied down by a mass of threads. *Anomia,* too, is actually attached by a byssal thread, but in this group the thread has become calcified and extends through a hole in the right valve, which lies against the substratum.

The Mantle Cavity and Water Circulation.
In the evolution of the pelecypods, the mantle cavity, like that of chitons, became extended anteriorly and to each side of the body. In chitons the mantle cavity was restricted to a shallow trough, because the body remained dorsoventrally flattened; however, in pelecypods the body became so greatly lengthened dorso-ventrally and the overhang of the shell increased so greatly to enclose it that a very extensive mantle cavity was formed on each side of the body.

According to Yonge (1941), this anterior extension of the mantle cavity resulted in a new pathway for water circulation. The inhalant current shifted from posterior to anterior. Water now entered the mantle cavity anteriorly, passed over the gills, and left the cavity posteriorly.

The little primitive protobranchs, *Nucula* and *Solemya,* exhibit such an anterior inhalant current. Both burrow completely under the surface. When *Nucula* is not moving, the mantle edges are appressed together except for a gap at the anterior and posterior ends (Fig. 12-38, *C*). Water enters the anterior opening, passes over the gills, and the exhalant current leaves through the posterior opening. Some sediment enters with the inhalant current even though the water currents are slow. Cleansing cilia on the gill, foot, and mantle surfaces sweep the heavier sediment to the ventral mantle edge, where it accumulates and is periodically expelled by sudden contractions of the valves. *Nucula* has also retained well developed hypobranchial glands for consolidating the finer sediment that passes through the gills.

The principal problem arising from burrowing in soft bottoms is that of the sediment brought in by water currents. Muscles along the edge of the mantle enable the mantle edges to be appressed together, even when the valves gape slightly; but since circulation of water through the mantle cavity is necessary for respiration, at least some part of the mantle must be opened for entrance of water, with which sediment enters.

If the plan of water circulation as displayed by *Nucula* is actually primitive, it was apparently not very efficient, and the majority of pelecypods have not retained this arrangement. Several fundamental changes have taken place.

In most protobranchia and in all other pelecypod orders, the inhalant current has returned to the posterior end. Water again enters posteriorly and ventrally, makes a U-turn through the gills, and passes back out posteriorly and dorsally (Fig. 12-37, *A*). This enables the animal to burrow anterior end first into the

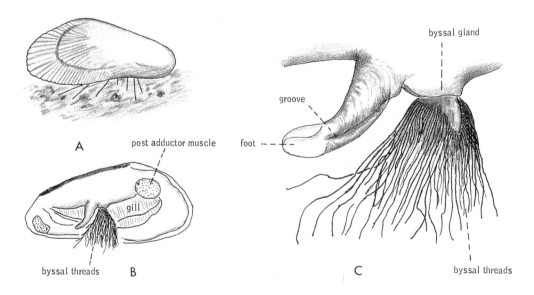

Figure 12-34.   *A.* The sessile marine mussel, *Mytilus. A.* Attached by byssal threads. *B.* With left valve removed (lateral view). *C.* Foot and byssal gland. (All drawn from life.)

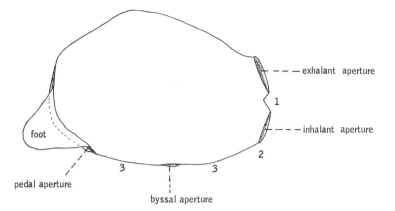

Figure 12-35.   Areas of mantle fusion in pelecypods. *1.* Between inhalant and exhalant apertures or siphons, the most common point of fusion. *2.* Fusion below inhalant aperture or siphon. *3.* Fusion between inhalant aperture and foot, leaving only a pedal aperture for extension of foot. A byssal aperture is present in only a very few pelecypods.

mud or sand, leaving the inhalant posterior end projecting just above the surface of the bottom and thus clear of excessive sediment.

A second modification has been a tendency toward the morphological sealing of the mantle edges where openings are not necessary (Fig. 12-35). This in turn led to the formation of distinct inhalant and exhalant siphons. The most frequent point of fusion of the mantle edges is at the posterior between the inhalant and exhalant openings. This fusion forms a distinct exhalant aperture. A functional inhalant opening is present since the mantle edges are pressed together below the opening, although the mantle edges are not morphologically fused. This type of structure is found in the protobranch, *Nuculana,* and the fresh-water eulamellibranch clams, *Anodonta* and *Unio.* A second point of fusion just below the inhalant opening, forming a distinct inhalant aperture, has evolved in many pelecypods, such as *Cardium, Macoma,* and *Tagelus.*

Frequently, when such inhalant and exhalant apertures have formed, the mantle edges surrounding them have become elongated to form tubular siphons of varying lengths (Figs. 12-33, *B*; 12-36; and 12-43, *A*). The advantages of such siphons are obvious; the animals can be completely buried in the mud and only the siphon tips need project above the bottom. The siphons can be withdrawn by siphon retractor

muscles derived from muscle tissue of the innermost mantle fold.

The existence of siphons in a particular pelecypod species can be determined from the scars on the inner face of the valve. When well developed siphons are present, the pallial line impression is recurved sharply inward just below the posterior adductor and represents the point of attachment of the siphon retractor. This bay in the pallial line is called the pallial sinus (Fig. 12-30, *D*). Considerable variation exists in siphon structure. They may be short and only slightly developed, or when extended, longer than the length of the body, as in the razor clam, *Tagelus.* Also, the siphons may be of equal or unequal length, separate, fused at the base, or fused throughout. The siphons of the Pacific coast geoduck, *Panope generosa,* which burrows in the mud to a depth of three feet, are so large they can no longer be retracted and enclosed within the valves (Fig. 12-33, *B*).

Still further mantle fusion has developed in some species, and most of the ventral margin anterior to the inhalant aperture has become sealed. Thus, three apertures remain—the inhalant and exhalant apertures and an anterior pedal aperture through which the foot protrudes. *Cardium, Solemya, Ensis,* and *Tagelus* are pelecypods having pedal apertures. Finally, a few pelecypods, such as *Lyonsia,* have a fourth aperture that is located just posterior to the pedal

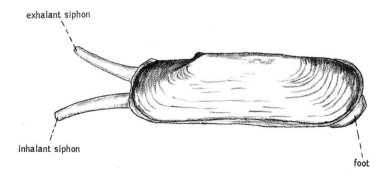

Figure 12-36.   *Tagelus,* a common marine bivalve, occurring in intertidal and coastal sands of the Atlantic Ocean. (Drawn from life.)

opening. A byssal thread passes through this opening.

The Gill and Respiration. Pelecypods have retained the single pair of gills of the ancestral mollusk; the apparent double set of gills on each side of the body in many groups is actually derived by the folding of the single gill.

With the formation of a large lateral mantle cavity during the evolution of the class, the original posterior gills took a more lateral position and became both longer and directed anteriorly toward the mouth. These lengthened gills divide the mantle cavity on each side of the body into a large ventral inhalant chamber and a smaller

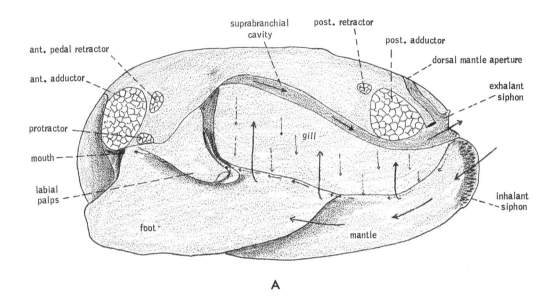

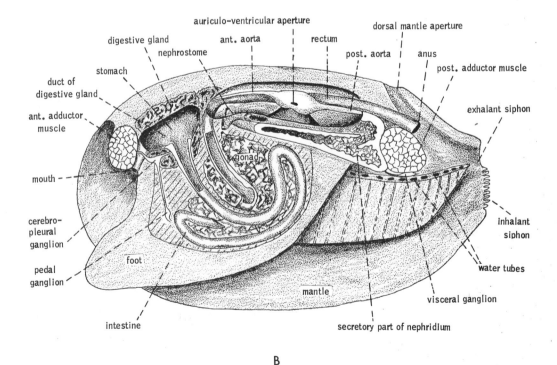

Figure 12-37.   The fresh-water clam, *Anodonta. A.* With left valve and mantle removed (lateral view). *B.* Internal structure (viewed from left side). Gonopore and nephridiopore open into suprabranchial cavity just below nephrostome. (Both after Parker and Haswell.)

dorsal exhalant chamber, or suprabranchial cavity, as it is frequently called in the more specialized orders (Fig. 12-37, *A*).

In the primitive protobranch, *Nucula*, the gills are very similar in structure to those of the ancestral mollusk (Fig. 12-38). They differ primarily in being somewhat longer and in having the adjacent filaments of a single gill loosely interconnected by tufts of intermingled cilia. The interlocking ciliary junctions are located on both sides of the lateral surface of each gill filament. Ciliary junctions also lock together the gills on each side, posterior to the point where the gills are separated by the foot. Finally, there are interlocking ciliary tufts at the ends of the inner and outer filaments of each gill. These ciliary tufts lock the filaments to the sides of the foot and inner surface of the mantle. The net effect of all such junctions is to hold the gills securely in place within the mantle cavity.

As in the case of the ancestral mollusk, the lateral cilia of pelecypods power the movement of water. Heavy sediment trapped on the ventral surface of the gill filaments is carried by frontal cilia to the midline, then moved anteriorly along the gill to the foot, and down to the ventral mantle edge. Finer sediment passing through the gills is trapped by secretions of the hypobranchial glands located over the exhalant chamber.

In the Filibranchia and Eulamellibranchia, the gills have also taken over the function of obtaining food; as a result, the gills have undergone considerable modification. Many filaments have been added to the gills so that they extend even further anteriorly than in *Nucula*. Also, each filament has become greatly lengthened. Perhaps during the evolution of the more typical pelecypod gills, these attenuated filaments at first projected somewhat laterally and then became bent or flexed downward in the middle (Fig. 12-39, *A* to *C*). At the angle of flexure, the frontal surface of each filament developed an indentation, or notch, which when lined up with the notches of adjacent filaments, created a food groove that extended the length of the underside of the gill.

Yonge (1941) suggests that the appearance of the food groove probably preceded folding, since the groove was necessary for nutrition. In any case, each gill filament on each side of the axis became folded, or U-shaped. Such folded filaments are characteristic of the orders Filibranchia and Eulamellibranchia. The arm of the U that is attached to the axis of the gill is called the descending limb and the free arm is called the ascending limb. Since the filaments on both sides of the axis have become folded, the net result has been to transform the original single gill into a pair of gills, or demibranchs,

the original outer filaments forming one member of the pair and the inner filaments forming the other (Fig. 12-39, *C*).

In the Filibranchia the individual filaments are still discrete, and hence, the derivation of the name of the order. Bars of tissue called interlamellar junctions have grown (Fig. 12-39, *D* and *E*) between the two limbs of each U at intervals, but adjacent filaments are still only attached by tufts or discs of cilia. Thus each gill is composed of two lamellae, one formed from the union of adjacent descending limbs and one formed from the union of ascending limbs. The U-shaped filaments on the other side of the original gill axis have also formed two lamellae.

These modifications in gill structure have necessitated a change both in ciliation and circulation. The frontal cilia carry food particles trapped on the gill surface downward to the food groove (Fig. 12-39, *E* and 12-40, *B*). Lateral cilia still produce the water current through the gills. Along the angles of the limbs, between the lateral and frontal cilia, is present a new ciliary tract composed of latero-frontal cilia. These cilia prevent large particles from clogging the gills. The respiratory water current enters the inhalant chamber at the posterior end of the animal, flows between the filaments, and then moves up between the two lamellae. From the interlamellar spaces, water passes into the exhalant, or suprabranchial, chamber and finally flows out through the posterior exhalant opening. Hypobranchial glands have disappeared as a result of the more tightly meshed gill structure, which prevents all but the finest sediment from entering the suprabranchial cavity with the water current.

In the primitive gills of protobranchs, the efferent, or drainage vessel, ran within the axis of the filament beneath the afferent vessel, as in the ancestral molluscan gill. With both elongation and folding of the filaments, the drainage vessel has split and migrated to the ends of the ascending limbs of each filament (Fig. 12-39, *C*). After this migration, the blood diffused from the longitudinal afferent vessel down through the descending limbs of the filament and up into the longitudinal efferent vessel at the tips of the ascending filaments. Thus even in the filibranchs, the tips of adjacent ascending filaments must be fused morphologically to allow passage for the longitudinal efferent vessel.

The filibranch gill just described is found in *Mytilus, Pecten,* and many other members of the order. Nevertheless, many variations and gradations exist. In *Arca,* the ark shells, for example, there are no interlamellar junctions.

In the Eulamellibranchia, the union of filaments has developed further (Fig. 12-39, *F* and

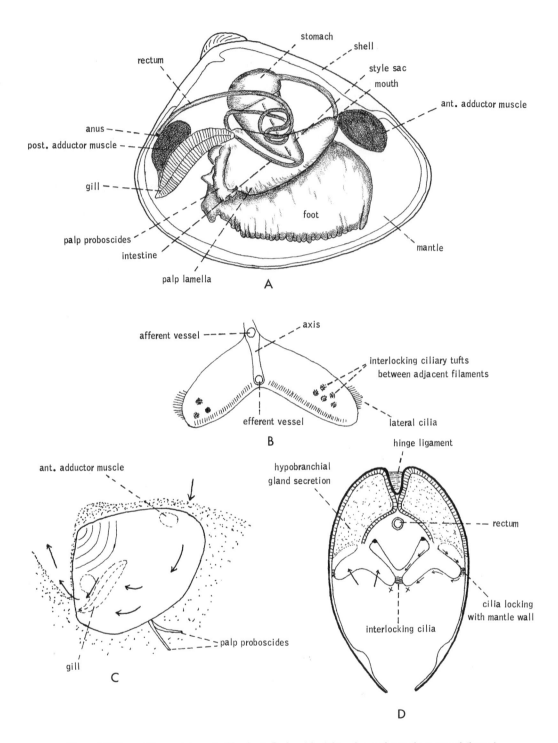

Figure 12-38.   The protobranch, *Nucula. A.* Body with right valve and mantle removed (lateral view). *B.* Gill, showing lateral filaments (transverse section). Note similarity to gill of the primitive gastropod, *Haliotis,* shown in Figure 12-1, *C. C.* Feeding position. Arrows indicate direction of water current through mantle cavity. *D.* Position of gills in mantle cavity (transverse section). (All after Yonge.)

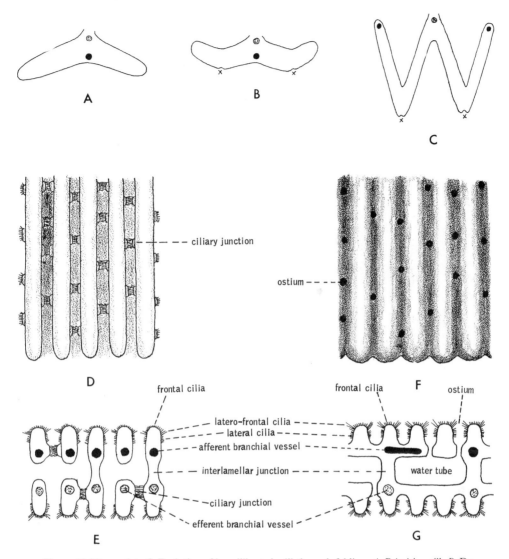

Figure 12-39.   *A* to *C.* Evolution of lamellibranch gill through folding. *A.* Primitive gill. *B.* Development of food groove on midfrontal surface. *C.* Folding at food groove to form an ascending and a descending limb for each filament. *D* and *E.* Fillibranch gill. *D.* Five adjacent filaments (surface view). *E.* Frontal section. *F* and *G.* Eulamellibranch gill. *F.* Five fused, adjacent filaments (surface view). *G.* Frontal section.

G). Ciliary junctions have been replaced by actual tissue fusion, so that the lamellae actually consist of solid sheets of tissue. Furthermore, interlamellar junctions have increased in number and extend the length of the lamellae (dorsoventrally). Thus the interlamellar space is partitioned into vertical water tubes. Instead of diffusing through the lamellae, the blood is carried in vertical vessels that course within the interlamellar junctions. The tips of the ascending limbs have become fused with the upper surface of the mantle on the outside and the foot on the inside, morphologically separating the inhalant chamber from the suprabranchial chamber. Ciliation remains the same, for the

frontal edge of the filaments are not involved in the interfilamentous fusion. Thus, a frontal section of the eulamellibranch gill exhibits a lamella with a ridged outer surface, each ridge representing one of the original filaments (Fig. 12-39, *G*). Water in the inhalant chamber circulates between the ridges and enters the water tubes through numerous pores (ostia) in the lamella. Oxygenation takes place as the water moves dorsally in the water tubes. The water then flows into the suprabranchial cavity and out the exhalant opening.

In many eulamellibranchs such as *Ensis,* the surface area of the lamellae has been increased by folding (Fig. 12-40, *A*). The gill

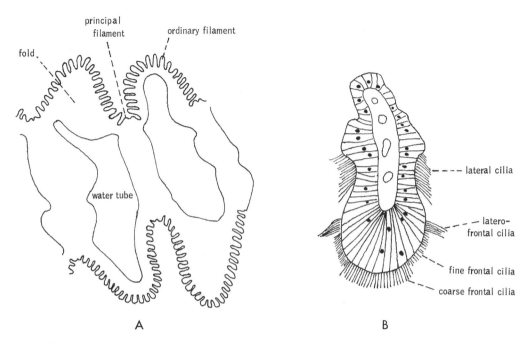

Figure 12-40. *A. Ensis* gill, showing folds (frontal section). *B.* Ordinary filament of *Solen marginatus.* (Both after Atkins.)

surface of these pelecypods presents an undulated appearance.

In all pelecypods, the inner mantle surface contributes to some extent in oxygenation, although most of this function is performed by the gills. However, in the Septibranchia (*Poromya* and *Cuspidaria*), the mantle has completely taken over the function of respiration, and the gills have become degenerate and modified to form a pair of perforated muscular septa, which separate the suprabranchial chambers from the inhalant chambers (Fig. 12-41, *C*). By muscular contractions, the septum moves up and down and forces water into the inhalant chambers and out of the suprabranchial chambers.

Nutrition.   Most pelecypods are ciliary feeders in which the gills have assumed the function of trapping food materials in addition to that of respiration. This is not, however, true of the primitive Protobranchia, nor was it probably true of the ancestral pelecypods. In the ancestral mollusk, the mouth rested against the hard bottom over which the animal crawled. However, according to Yonge (1941), when pelecypods became adapted for burrowing in sand or mud, the mouth was lifted high above the substratum as a result of both the lateral compression of the body and the greatly increased height of the dorso-ventral axis. To re-establish contact with the substratum, the upper margin of the mouth was probably elongated on both sides to form a muscular proboscis and a

pair of flap-like lamellae (palps), which extended back toward the gills.

In the new soft-bottom environment, the proboscis was used to obtain food. Such a method of feeding is possessed by most protobranchs; *Nucula, Nuculana, Yoldia, Yoldiella,* and *Malletia* all feed on bottom detritus. In *Nucula,* the two proboscides are extended anteriorly through the gape of the shell and inserted into the surrounding mud or sand (Fig. 12-42). A heavily ciliated groove is located on the ventral side of each proboscis, and organic debris is carried along the groove to the base of the proboscis. Here the material is transferred to the palps, from which it passes between the two lamellae.

The inner, opposing surfaces of the lamellae are ridged and ciliated and act as a sorting device. Particles for ingestion are conveyed forward to the mouth along a deep oral groove; rejected particles are swept to the edge of the lamellae and moved forward to the tips, which touch the mantle. Here they are transferred to the mantle surface and carried to the bottom of the mantle cavity accompanied by sediment brought in by the water current.

The structure and physiology of the digestive tract of protobranchs has retained many primitive features which are correlated to the habit of detritus-feeding. The subsequent description is based on *Malletia* but applies to most protobranchs (Fig. 12-43).

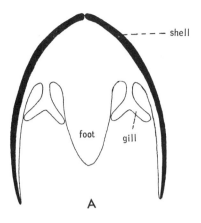

portion of the stomach is lined by chitin except for a large folded and ciliated sorting region, into which the ducts of the digestive gland open. At the apex of the stomach is a tooth-like projection arising from the chitinous girdle and called the gastric shield.

Food enters the dorsal part of the stomach and is conveyed ventrally along a ciliated tract on the edge of the sorting region toward a pocket called the cecum. As the food moves toward the cecum, it passes two duct openings from the digestive gland. Some of the finer particles enter these ducts, but most of the food particles continue along the ciliary tract into and out of the cecum. After the food material leaves the cecum, it becomes enmeshed in a great mass of mucus that fills the conical ventral style sac. This mucus mass, called the style (not a crystalline style), is secreted by the sac and is rotated counterclockwise by cilia lining its walls. Concurrently, the mass is pushed dorsally into the upper region of the stomach, partly by the contractions of circular muscles in the wall of the style sac and partly by the cilia.

The anterior tip of the mucus mass is wound around the tooth-like gastric shield and also pressed tightly against the chitinous girdle. This winding process causes large and coarse particles to be broken against the chitinous walls. The smaller bits are then picked up by the sorting region. Here ciliated folds and grooves send the finest material into the ducts of the digestive gland, while the rejected coarse particles are conveyed ventrally into a deep groove along the anterior wall of the style sac. The style sac groove carries the rejected material directly into the intestine.

Extracellular digestion does not take place. The ducts of the digestive gland are ciliated and divided into an incurrent and excurrent tract. Food particles that enter the ducts are carried

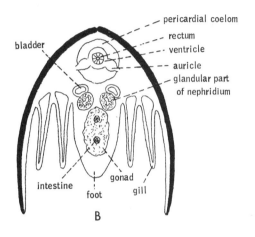

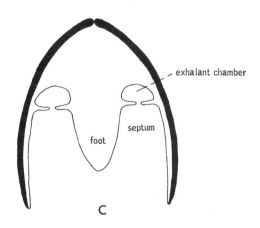

Figure 12-41. *A.* Protobranch pelecypod (transverse section). *B.* Lamellibranch pelecypod (transverse section). *C.* Septibranch pelecypod (transverse section).

Food enters the mouth and is conducted posteriorly to the stomach through a short ciliated tubular esophagus. The stomach, which is surrounded by the large digestive gland, is divided into two regions: a dorsal portion, into which the esophagus and ducts of the digestive gland enter, and a ventral style sac. The dorsal

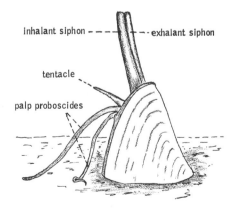

Figure 12-42. The protobranch, *Yoldia limatula,* during feeding. (After Yonge.)

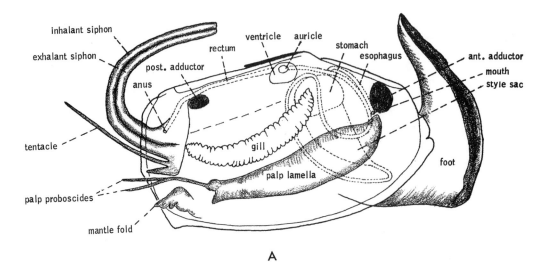

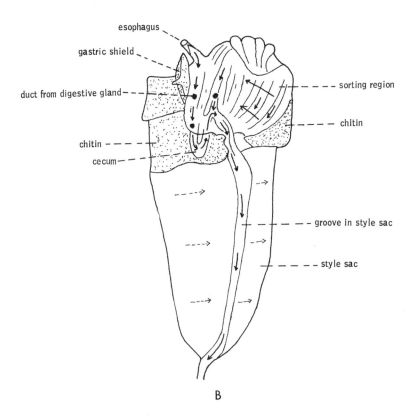

Figure 12-43.   *A.* The protobranch, *Malletia,* with right mantle and valve removed (lateral view). *B.* Stomach of *Malletia,* opened. Solid arrows indicate food tracts; broken arrows indicate direction of beat of style-rotating cilia. (Both after Yonge.)

by the incurrent tract to the lumen of the smaller tubules that compose the gland itself. Here the particles are engulfed by the cells of the tubule wall and are digested intracellularly. Digestion wastes are dumped back into the lumen, returned by the excurrent ciliary tract to the stomach, and then swept into the style sac groove and intestine.

The long intestine loops once or twice in the vicinity of the stomach and then passes dorsally between the anterior adductor muscle and stomach and becomes the rectum. The rectum extends through both the heart and the pericardial cavity, passes over the posterior adductor muscle, and opens through the anus at the posterior of the suprabranchial cavity. The intestine is composed of ciliated epithelium and mucous glands. A conspicuous ridge extends the length of the intestine gradually decreasing in height as it approaches the rectum. This ridge has been called a typhlosole; but this is incorrect, because the intestine plays no role in absorption. Furthermore, the ridge is not actually a fold but merely a region of elongated epithelial cells. The intestinal ridge is continuous with one of the ridges located to the side of the style sac groove.

The intestine functions exclusively to form feces, and the intestinal ridge is probably involved in molding and conveyance of the feces. Feces formation also accounts for the considerable length of the intestine. The rectum is also cili-

ated but lacks the ridge. The feces emerge from the anus as well formed pellets, which in *Malletia* do not flake even when teased with a dissecting needle (Yonge, 1941); the feces then are carried out of the animal by the exhalant current.

In the Filibranchia and the Eulamellibranchia, the gills have assumed the function of food acquisition. The proboscides have disappeared, although the lamellae have been retained. The new mode of obtaining food has also resulted in a diet change; these orders feed on small plankton, largely phytoplankton, and considerably fewer coarse particles ever reach the stomach than in other pelecypods.

In *Mytilus* the plankton is trapped in mucus on the surface of the gills, and carried ven-

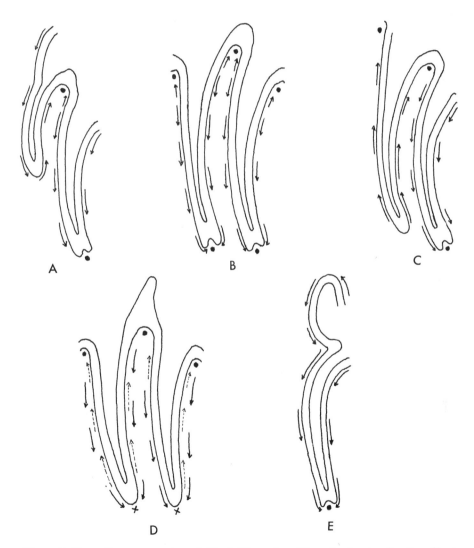

Figure 12-44.   Transverse sections of gills of different lamellibranchs, showing direction of beat of frontal cilia and position of anteriorly moving food tracts (black circles). In *D* broken arrows indicate fine frontal cilia carrying food particles; solid arrows indicate coarse frontal cilia carrying rejected waste particles to ventral, posteriorly moving channels (crosses). Inner demibranch, or gill, is on right in all cases. *A*. Most eulamellibranchs. *B*. Mytilidae and Pinnidae. *C*. Unionidae (freshwater). *D*. Arcidae and Anomiidae. *E*. Most Tellinidae and Semelidae. (All after Atkins.)

trally by frontal cilia to the food groove (Fig. 12-44, *B*). Here the plankton is conveyed anteriorly along the gills and transferred to the lamellae.

More frequently, both dorsal and ventral food grooves are present, as in *Pecten,* and the fresh-water Unionidae, and many others. In *Arca* and *Anomia,* the food grooves are restricted entirely to the dorsal margins of the lamellae, and the ventral margins carry waste (Fig. 12-44, *D*). To function thus, vertical tracts of gill cilia beating in opposite directions are required. Coarse frontal cilia carry heavy rejected particles downward, and finer food material is moved upward to the food grooves by the more delicate frontal tracts. Figure 12-44 illustrates some of the different types of gills and their food currents.

In Filibranchia and Eulamellibranchia, the palpal lamellae have the same sorting and conveying function as in the Protobranchia (Fig.

12-37, *A*). The oral groove between the flaps carries the accepted food particles to the mouth; rejected particles are carried forward to the ventral edge of the mantle and then posteriorly to accumulate behind the inhalant aperture. When the valves are closed periodically, water is forced out the inhalant opening taking these accumulated wastes with it. The utilization of finer particles as food in the Filibranchia and Eulamellibranchia is reflected in a number of stomach modifications. Since a need for macerating food particles no longer exists, the girdle of chitin, present in the protobranchs, has disappeared except for a small plate that represents a true gastric shield (Fig. 12-45).

A style sac is present, but the mucus has become consolidated into a very compact and often long rod, the crystalline style. The structure and function of the crystalline style are very similar to those in the gastropods. In addition to the protein matrix of the style itself, the

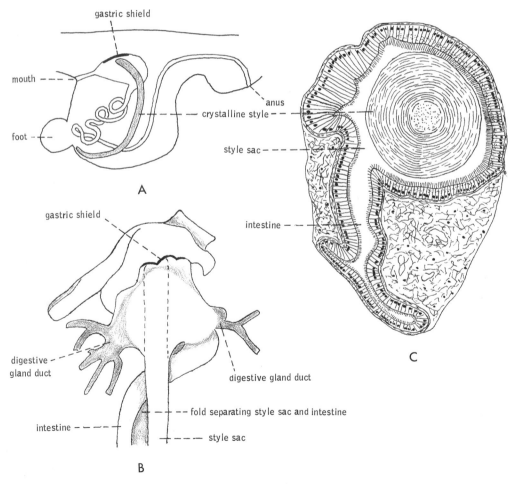

Figure 12-45.   *A.* Digestive tract of *Mya. B.* Stomach of the oyster, *Ostrea edulis. C.* Style sac and intestine of the fresh-water clam, *Lampsilis anodontoides* (transverse section). (*A* and *B* after Yonge; *C* after Nelson from Yonge.)

style sac secretes amylase, which is adsorbed onto the style in its formation. The projecting anterior end of the style is rotated against the plate-like gastric shield by the style sac cilia, and in the process the enzymes are rubbed off. Thus starches are digested at least in part extracellularly. The rotation of the style probably also aids in mixing the enzymes with the stomach contents.

The sorting region of the stomach has been retained, and performs the same function as in protobranchs. Cilia move the finer particles into the digestive gland ducts, which vary in number from two to twenty. The incurrent tract of each duct conveys the partially digested food into the distal tubules of the gland. Here intracellular digestion of proteins, perhaps further digestion of carbohydrates, and absorption take place. Rejected particles from the sorting region and waste from the digestive gland are passed directly into the intestine.

In many forms, such as *Donax, Mya, Ensis, Meretrix,* and the giant clam, *Tridacna,* the style sac has become separated from the stomach and the style is located in a sac that projects from the anterior of the intestine, or is located in the anterior of the intestine itself. In the latter condition, the style and secretory epithelium are separated from the intestinal lumen by a fold. The style itself, however, continues to project into the stomach. In these forms, rejected particles and waste are conveyed to the intestine along the fold on the stomach floor. This fold is continuous with the fold in the intestine.

The presence of a crystalline style precludes any extracellular digestion of proteins, since a protease would digest the style itself. The style sac continually secretes additions to the base of the style as the projecting style anterior is eroded. The type of style located in the intestine or in a sac off the intestine is always present, but those types produced in a stomach style sac may be completely dissolved and re-formed only as feeding takes place. This is true of the intertidal *Crassostrea virginica* and *Lasaea rubra,* which feed only at high tide. The crystalline style in both these pelecypods is re-formed twice every twenty-four hours, coinciding with the occurrence of high tide.

The length of the style varies, but it is remarkably long considering the size of the animal. In most pelecypods, the style is approximately one inch long; but a four-inch *Tagelus* may have a two-inch style, and Yonge (1932) reported a thirteen-inch style in a three-foot *Tridacna.* The style of the fresh-water clam, *Anodonta,* is reported to rotate eleven times a minute, but in very young oyster spat the style may turn as rapidly as seventy times a minute.

However, temperature, pH, and food pressure all influence the rotation rate.

The intestine and rectum are essentially the same as those in the Protobranchia.

The Septibranchia, which have lost the gills, have become either carnivorous or scavengers. The force of the pumping septum is sufficiently great to bring small animals, such as crustaceans and worms, into the mantle cavity. These prey are then seized by the reduced but muscular lamellae of the Septibranchia and carried to the mouth. The stomach is muscular, lined with chitin, and acts as a crushing gizzard. The style is reduced to a small rod, which according to Yonge (1947) probably functions only in coating hard and sharp fragments with mucus to avoid injury to the intestine during their outward passage.

The nutrition of the giant clam, *Tridacna* is quite remarkable. In addition to the usual feeding activities, *Tridacna* literally "farms" unicellular algae as a supplementary source of food. Zooxanthellae live in the mantle tissue. The shell of the clam ordinarily rests on the bottom of shallow water with the hinge down and the ventral margin up. The mantle lobes are protruded through the gape between the valves and are bent back over part of the shell. The zooxanthellae thus receive the necessary sunlight for photosynthesis. Moreover, crystalloid vesicles in the mantle diffuse sunlight deep in the tissue, enabling the algae to live at deeper levels than would normally be possible. Some of the algae are engulfed and digested by phagocytic cells, thus providing an additional source of food for the clam.

Circulation. In the majority of pelecypods, the ventricle of the heart has become folded around the gut (rectum), so that the pericardial cavity encloses not only the heart, but also a short section of the digestive tract (Figs. 12-37, *B*: 12-41, *B*; and 12-47). In a few Protobranchia such as *Nucula* and in *Ostrea,* the rectum and heart are separated, but even here the separation is apparently secondary. Except for the association between the rectum and heart, the circulatory system is similar in most respects to that of the ancestral mollusk. The thin-walled auricles are attached laterally to the muscular ventricle surrounding the rectum. The contractions of the ventricle can be easily observed in large clams from which one of the valves has been carefully removed. Pulsations are slow; in *Anodonta* the pulsations average about twenty per minute.

Primitively, a single anterior aorta issues from the ventricle. This condition is found in all protobranchs and many filibranchs such as *Mytilus* (Fig. 12-46, *A*). In the eulamelli-

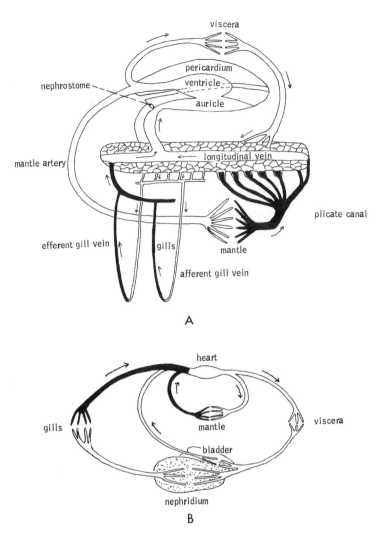

viscera

pericardium

ventricle

nephrostome

auricle

mantle artery

longitudinal vein

plicate canal

efferent gill vein

gills

mantle

afferent gill vein

A

heart

gills

mantle

viscera

bladder

nephridium

B

Figure 12-46.   *A.* Circulatory system of *Mytilus.* (After Field from Borradaile and others.)
B. Circulatory system of the fresh-water clam, *Anodonta.* (After Borradaile and others.)

branchs, a posterior aorta is also present, although it is often smaller than the anterior vessel (Figs. 12-37, *B*; 12-46, *B*; and 12-47). In *Mercenaria,* the posterior aorta is enlarged just before it issues from the pericardial cavity. The function of this swelling, called the bulbus arteriosus, has not been determined. Its contractions may provide additional pumping force for the propulsion of blood, or it may be involved only in regulating blood pressure.

The typical molluscan circulatory route—heart, tissue sinuses, nephridia, gills, heart—is exhibited in the pelecypods, although some modifications of this circuit have taken place in different species. In *Mytilus,* for example, all blood from the body sinuses flows into the kidneys (Fig. 12-46, *A*). Part of the blood then collects in a large longitudinal vein within the kidney and is returned to the auricles; the

remainder circulates through the gills and returns to the kidney, where it enters the longitudinal vein and is then sent to the heart.

In *Anodonta,* only a small amount of blood is sent from the kidney to the heart; the major portion is sent to the gills, and from there it returns directly to the heart (Fig. 12-46, *B*). Nevertheless, in both *Mytilus* and *Anodonta,* the heart receives both oxygenated and unoxygenated blood. In all pelecypods, there is a more or less well developed circulatory pathway through the mantle, which is an additional site of oxygenation. In *Pecten* and *Anodonta,* the mantle pathway forms a separate circuit with blood returning directly to the heart; in *Mytilus,* blood returns to the heart by way of the kidney.

The blood is similar to that of gastropods. In some pelecypods, such as *Arca* and *Lima,* hemoglobin rather than hemocyanin is present,

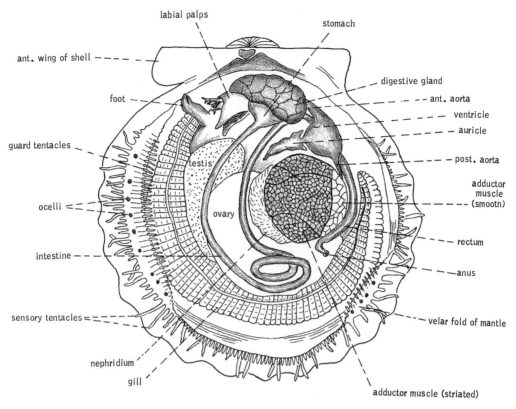

Figure 12-47.   Structure of the scallop, *Pecten* (viewed from the left). (After Pierce.)

giving the mantle and other tissues a bright red color.

Excretion. The two nephridia of pelecypods are located beneath the pericardial cavity or slightly posterior to it, and are folded to form a long U (Figs. 12-37, *B*; 12-41, *B*; and 12-47). One arm of the U is glandular and opens into the anterior of the pericardial cavity; the other arm forms a bladder and opens through a nephridiopore at the anterior of the suprabranchial cavity. In the primitive Protobranchia, the histological differentiation of the nephridium found in the higher members of the class does not exist. There are no distinct bladder and glandular portions; instead the walls of the tube are glandular throughout and have not undergone the evagination and folding characteristic of the glandular sections of most pelecypod nephridia.

Nervous System and Sense Organs. The nervous system is bilateral and relatively simple (Fig. 12-37, *B*). There are three pairs of ganglia and two pairs of long nerve cords. On each side of the esophagus is located a cerebro-pleural ganglion, which is connected to its opposite member by a short commissure across the top of the esophagus. From each cerebro-pleural ganglion arise two more or less poste-

riorly directed nerve cords. The upper pair of nerve cords (one from each ganglion) extend directly back through the viscera and terminate in a pair of closely adjacent visceral ganglia located beneath the posterior adductor muscle. The second pair of cords arising from the cerebro-pleural ganglia extend posteriorly and ventrally into the foot and connect with a pair of pedal ganglia.

The margin of the mantle, particularly the middle fold, is the principal location of most of the pelecypod sense organs. In many species, the mantle edge bears pallial tentacles, which contain tactile and chemoreceptor cells. The entire margin may bear tentacles, as in *Pecten* and *Lima* (Figs. 12-33, *A* and 12-47); more commonly tentacles are restricted to the inhalant or exhalant apertures or siphons, or they may even fringe the pedal aperture. *Malletia* and other Nuculanidae are peculiar in that they possess only one long tentacle attached to the underside of the base of the fused siphons (Fig. 12-43, *A*).

A statocyst is usually found in pelecypods and is located either near or imbedded in the pedal ganglia. In the primitive *Nucula*, the statocyst retains a pit-like form and is connected to the outer surface by means of a canal.

Ocelli may be present along the mantle edge or even on the siphons in some pelecypods; in most cases, they are simple pigment-spot ocelli. However, in *Spondylus* and *Pecten,* the ocelli are remarkably well developed. The eyes of *Pecten* are bright blue and located along the edge of the mantle (Fig. 12-47). Each eye consists of a cornea, a lens, and a retina in which the photoreceptor cells are directed away from the source of light. The eyes of *Pecten* probably cannot form an image, but the degree of development is undoubtedly correlated to their active swimming habit. The eyes can detect sudden changes in light intensity.

Immediately beneath the posterior adductor muscle in the exhalant chamber, there is a patch of sensory epithelium that is usually called an osphradium. The osphradium has been considered an organ of chemoreception for testing the water passing through the mantle cavity; however, its function is by no means certain, and its position in the exhalant chamber makes it doubtful that it is actually homologous with the osphradium of gastropods.

Reproduction. The majority of pelecypods are dioecious. The two gonads encompass the intestinal loops and are usually so closely adjacent to one another that the paired condition is difficult to detect (Figs. 12-37, *B*; 12-41, *B*; and 12-47). The gonoducts are always simple, since there is no copulation. In the Protobranchia and the Filibranchia, the nephridia provide exit for the sperm and eggs, but the gonads do not open into the pericardial cavity; instead they connect to the nephridia directly. In general, the short gonoduct opens into the upper part of the nephridium in the protobranchs and into the lower part nearer the nephridiopore in the filibranchs. In the Eulamellibranchia, the gonoducts are no longer associated with the nephridia and open separately into the mantle cavity but still very close to the nephridiopore (Fig. 12-37, *B*). In *Mercenaria* and many other species, the gonopore and nephridopore are located on a common papilla.

The hermaphroditic pelecypod species include *Cardium, Poromya,* some species of oysters and scallops, the fresh-water Sphaeriidae, and a few Unionidae. In scallops, the gonad is divided into a ventral ovary and a dorsal testis, both of which lie on the anterior side of the adductor muscle (Fig. 12-47).

Embryology. In most pelecypods, fertilization occurs in the surrounding water; the sperm and eggs are shed into the suprabranchial cavity and then swept out with the exhalant current. However, there are some exceptions, largely pertaining to those species that brood their eggs. In the European oyster, *Ostrea edulis,* fertilization occurs in the suprabranchial cavity when sperm are brought in by water currents. The eggs undergo development in the gill filaments. In the hermaphroditic, fresh-water family, Sphaeriidae, self- fertilization is believed to occur in the genital ducts before the eggs are liberated into the suprabranchial cavity. The fertilized eggs then pass into the water tubes of the gills, where development takes place. In the

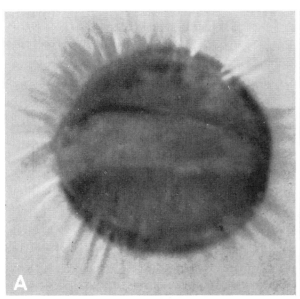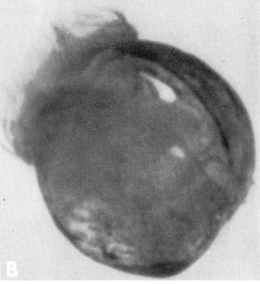

Figure 12-48.   Veliger of *Teredo. A.* View looking down on velum projected from bivalve shell. *B.* Velum being retracted. (By C. E. Lane in Scientific American, February, 1961.)

fresh-water Unionidae, the eggs also pass into the water tubes and are fertilized there by sperm brought in by the respiratory water currents. The zygotes remain in the water tubes through early development.

The development of a free-swimming trochopore, succeeded by a veliger larva, is typical in marine pelecypods. The structure of these larvae is essentially like that in the gastropods, but the veliger is always symmetrical, since torsion does not take place (Fig. 12-48). The shell and shell gland are present at first in the form of a single dorsal plate, which then grows laterally and ventrally. As a result, the dorsal plate becomes folded and forms the two valves characteristic of pelecypods. The loss of the velum during metamorphosis is very sudden in pelecypods. At a certain point during metamorphosis, the entire velum suddenly fragments and is cast off. The apical plate then sinks downward and relocates above the mouth, where it forms part of the labial palps.

Certain peculiarities in the development of Protobranchia are not found in the other orders. The prototroch of the trochophore is composed of four rows of very large cells, which form a girdle-like test (Fig. 12-49, A and B). The shell, shell gland, and the other adult structures are formed inside this test. During metamorphosis, the test suddenly disintegrates, liberating the young clam. This test is similar to the one mentioned as developing in the Aplacophora.

Direct development is characteristic of the fresh-water Sphaeriidae. The fertilized eggs pass into the water tubes between the gill lamellae, which act as temporary incubating chambers. Although direct, embryonic development shows stages similar to those in the larvae of marine pelecypods. Both a nonmotile trochophore and a veliger are present; but the prototroch is very much reduced, and the velum is absent. At the completion of development, the young clams are shed from the gills.

The fresh-water Unionidae display an indirect but very specialized development. As in the sphaeriids, the eggs are brooded between the gill lamellae, where they develop through the veliger stage. However, the veliger, which is called a glochidium in this family, has become

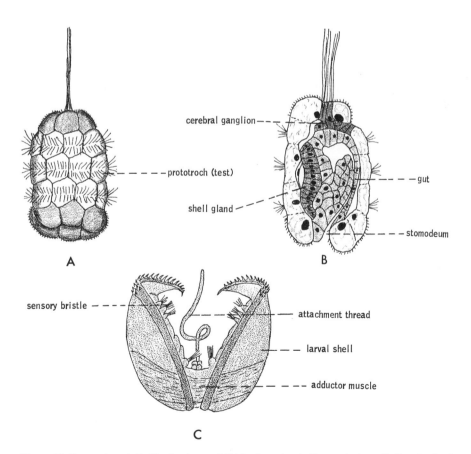

Figure 12-49.   *A* and *B*. Trochophore of *Yoldia limatula*. *A*. External view. *B*. Longitudinal section. (Both after Drew from Dawydoff.) *C*. Glochidium of the fresh-water clam, *Anodonta*. (After Harms from Kaestner.)

highly modified for a parasitic existence. The larva is enclosed by two valves, each edge of which bears a hook in *Anodonta* (Fig. 12-49, *C*). The shell valves cover a larval mantle, which bears four clusters of sensory bristles. A rudimentary foot is present, to which is attached a long adhesive thread. There is neither mouth nor anus, and the digestive tract is rather poorly developed.

When mature, the glochidia range in size from .05 mm. to .5 mm., depending upon the species. In *Unio* and *Anodonta,* the glochidia leave the gills through the suprabranchial cavity and exhalant aperture. In *Lampsilis,* the glochidia emerge directly from gills through temporary openings. In either case, the freed larvae sink to the bottom. Here they remain until they come in contact with a fish swimming over the bottom.

The glochidia of *Anodonta,* which bear hooks, immediately clamp onto the fins and other parts of the body surface of the fish. Hookless glochidia are picked up by the respiratory currents of the fish and attach to the gills. In either case, the tissue of the fish in the vicinity of the attached glochidium is stimulated to grow around the parasite and form a cyst. The larval mantle contains phagocytic cells that feed on the tissues of the host and obtain nutrition for the developing clam. During this parasitic period, which lasts from ten to thirty days, many of the larval structures (sensory bristles on the mantle, the adhesive thread, the larval adductor muscle, the larval mantle) disappear, and the adult organs begin development. Eventually the immature clam breaks out of the cyst, falls to the bottom, and burrows in the mud. Here the remainder of development is completed, and the adult habit is gradually assumed.

Some of the larger fresh-water mussels may produce as many as 3,000,000 glochidia, and a single fish has been reported to contain 3000 glochidia. Adult fish are apparently not harmed by the parasitic glochidia, but young fry may die from secondary infection.

Some pelecypod glochidia require certain species of fish as hosts; others can tolerate a wide range of host species. A genus of Unionidae, *Simpsoniconcha,* parasitizes the mud puppy, *Necturus,* but is reported also to be able to undergo direct development within the parent gills.

Ecology and Distribution. Although pelecypods are strictly aquatic, many genera, such as the mussels, *Modiolus* and *Mytilus,* and the oyster live in the intertidal zone and are exposed to the air at low tide. During this time, they are inactive, and the gills are kept moist by water retained in the mantle cavity.

Most pelecypods are marine, and most of the marine pelecypods are littoral. However, some species live at considerable depths; species of *Abra* and *Callocardia* have been dredged from depths of over 17,000 feet.

Except for random representatives of different marine families such as the oyster, which can tolerate low salinities and have invaded brackish estuaries and marshes, the fresh-water pelecypods are members of five families—the Unionidae, the Sphaeriidae, the Corbiculidae, the Aetheriidae and the Margaritiferidae. The North American fresh-water pelecypods are primarily comprised of Unionidae and Sphaeriidae, although one Japanese *Corbicula* has been introduced throughout the Pacific coast drainage system.

Pelecypods are primarily inhabitants of soft sand and mud bottoms, but some species have invaded harder substrata, such as clay, rock, or wood pilings. In every instance, however, such forms have either become sessile or borers. Adaptations for boring have become well developed in a number of families. In general, the shell is elongated, and the anterior margins of the valves are equipped with abrasive serrations for drilling (Fig. 12-50, *A*). Hinge teeth are either absent or poorly developed, since the valves must rotate against one another during the boring process. In some rock borers the hinge ligament has been replaced by a ball-and-socket joint formed by the two valves. Drilling in some cases is accomplished by upward movements of the anterior end of both valves while the body is held in place by the sucker-like foot (Fig. 12-50, *B*).

The boring activity of many species such as *Petricola* is restricted to clay banks and soft rock; others are capable of drilling into concrete and relatively hard rock (Fig. 12-50, *C*). *Hiatella arctica* is capable of destroying concrete jetties and breakwaters. This species is approximately one inch in length and drills a hole about six inches deep, attaching itself within the burrow by means of byssal threads.

Martesia and the shipworms (Teredinidae) burrow in wood. *Martesia* is no more modified than the clay and rock borers; but the shipworms are highly specialized, and, as their name indicates, they have a worm-like appearance. *Teredo navalis,* the common North Atlantic shipworm, does extensive damage to wooden pilings and ship bottoms (Fig. 12-51). Penetration of the wood takes place immediately after the larva settles. The burrow is enlarged as the animal increases in length, and adults may become one foot in length. The shell is reduced in

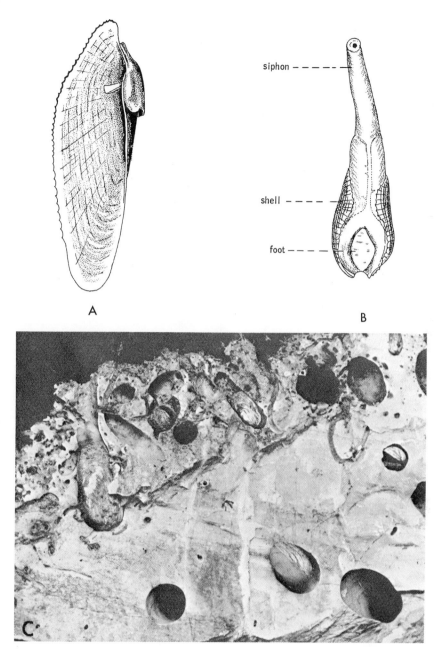

A   B

Figure 12-50.   *A.* Interior of right valve of the boring pelecypod, *Pholas dactylus. B.* The rock borer, *Barnea parva.* (Both after Yonge.) *C.* Burrows of rock-boring bivalves; excavated in limestone. (By E. B. Wilson.)

size to two small anterior valves, which are used for drilling. Thus the major portion of the body is not enclosed in the shell. The body is long and cylindrical and fills the tube-like burrow; the mantle produces a calcareous lining within the tunnel. The long delicate siphons open at the entrance of the burrow, which always remains small so that the animal is confined within it.

A number of pelecypods are commensal with other marine animals. Commensal pelecypods include: *Phylyctaenachlamys,* which lives in the burrows of a shrimp on the Great Barrier Reef; *Lepton,* in the burrows of shrimp and polychaetes; *Modiolaria,* in the test of sea squirts; and *Vulsella,* within sponges. A few parasitic pelecypods exist, such as *Entovalva,* which is parasitic within the gut of the sea cucumber, *Synapta.*

Pelecypods serve as an important source of

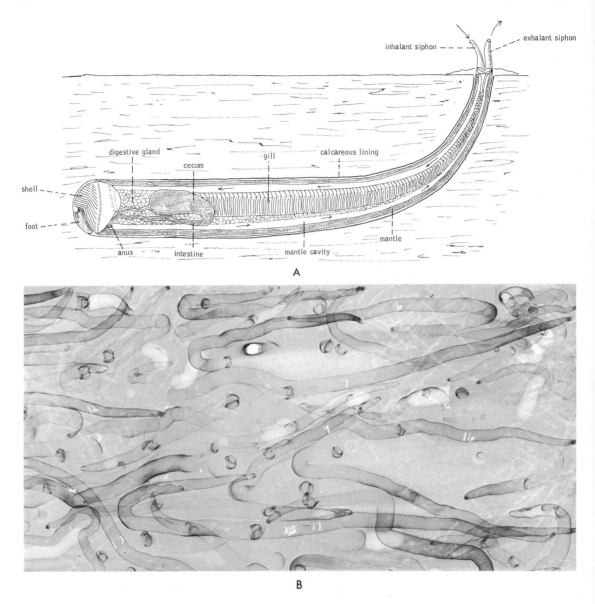

Figure 12-51.   The shipworm, *Teredo*, a wood-boring pelecypod. (After Lane.) *B.* X-ray photograph marine timber section showing shipworms. (By C. E. Lane in Scientific American, February, 1961.)

food for many animals, including man. Gastropods, fish, and shore birds are the worst predators of pelecypods.

Systematic Résumé of Class Pelecypoda

Order Protobranchia. Primitive; gill filaments are not folded; palpal proboscides frequently present. Includes *Nucula, Nuculana, Yoldia, Solemya, Malletia.*

Order Filibranchia. Possess attenuated, reflexed gill filaments. Filaments incompletely fused; interlamellar junctions present, but adjacent filaments joined only by ciliary tufts.

Includes the mussels—*Mytilus* and *Modiolus; Arca;* the oysters—*Ostrea, Crassostrea* and *Spondylus; Anomia; Lima;* the scallops—*Pecten;* and the boring *Lithophaga.*

Order Eulamellibranchia. Reflexed gill filaments are morphologically fused to form true lamellae. Includes *Lasaea; Cardium; Callocardia;* the common edible clam—*Mercenaria;* the boring clams—*Petricola, Hiatella, Martesia* and *Teredo;* the razor clams—*Tagelus* and *Ensis; Donax; Abra; Pholas; Lyonsia; Macoma; Meretrix;* the fresh-water Unionidae—*Unio, Lampsilis, Anodonta,* and *Simpsoniconcha;* and the fresh-water Sphaeriidae and Margaritiferidae.

Order Septibranchia. Gills are absent; inhalant chamber and suprabranchia cavity separated by a pumping septum. Includes *Poromya* and *Cuspidaria.*

Class Scaphopoda

The class Scaphopoda contains about two hundred species of burrowing marine mollusks that are popularly known as tusk or tooth shells. These names are derived from the shape

of the shell, which is an elongated cylindrical tube usually shaped like a trumpet or elephant's tusk. Both ends of the tube are open, and when tusk- or toothed-shaped, as in *Dentalium,* the diameter of the tube increases from one end to the other, and the whole tube is slightly curved (Fig. 12-52, *B*). In the genus *Cadulus,* the shell is somewhat cucumber-shaped (Fig. 12-52, *A*).

The shells of most scaphopods average between one and two inches in length, but *Cadulus mayori* found off the Florida coast, does not ex-

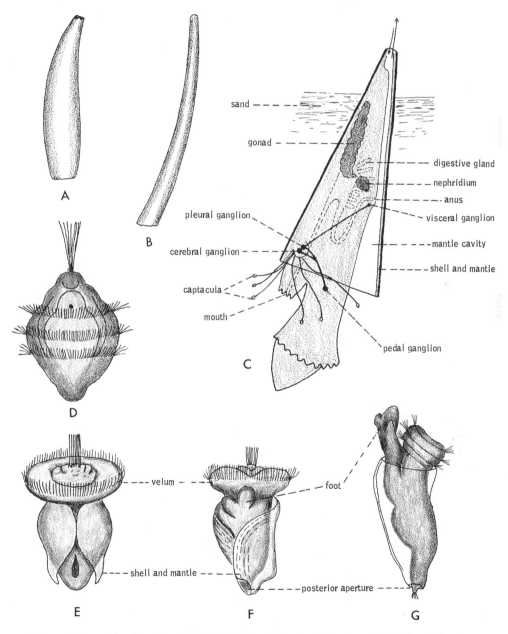

Figure 12-52.   Scaphopoda. *A.* Shell of *Cadulus. B.* Shell of *Dentalium.* (Both after Abbott.) *C.* Structure of *Dentalium.* Arrows indicate water current direction through mantle cavity. (After Naef from Borradaile and others.) *D* to *G.* Development in *Dentalium. D.* Trochophore larva. *E.* Veliger. *F* and *G.* Metamorphosis. (*D* and *G* after Lacaze-Duthiers from Dawydoff.)

ceed 4 mm. in length. *Dentalium vernedei,* found off Japan, is the largest living species, reaching a maximum length of 5¼ in. However, a fossil species of *Dentalium* has a shell 10 in. long with a maximum diameter of well over one inch. The shells of American scaphopods are somewhat white or somewhat yellow, but an East Indian species of *Dentalium* is a brilliant jade green.

The body of the scaphopod is greatly elongated along the anterior-posterior axis (Fig. 12-52, *C*). The head and foot project from the larger and anterior aperture of the shell, and the small shell aperture marks the posterior of the body. When the shell is slightly curved, the concavity lies over the dorsal surface. Scaphopods live buried in sand head downward with the body steeply inclined; only the small posterior aperture projects above the surface.

Adapted to a burrowing habit, the head is reduced to a short conical projection, or proboscis, bearing the mouth. The foot is shaped like a short cone in *Dentalium* and can be projected downward into the sand when the animal burrows. In species of *Cadulus* and allied genera, the foot is more or less elongated, and the tip can be expanded to form a disc that serves as an anchor, a condition somewhat parallel to that found in certain primitive clams.

The scaphopod mantle cavity is large and extends the entire length of the ventral surface. The posterior aperture serves for both inhalant and exhalant water currents. Water circulation occurs in two phases. Water slowly enters the mantle cavity as a result of ciliary action. The cilia are located on vertical ridges of the mantle wall approximately midway between anterior and posterior ends of the mantle cavity. The remaining mantle surface is very weakly ciliated. After 10 to 12 minutes of inhalation, a violent muscular contraction expels the water from the same opening it entered. There are no gills; diffusion of gases takes place through the mantle surface.

Scaphopods feed on microscopic organisms in the surrounding sand and water. Two lobes located on each side of the head, bear a large number of thread-like tentacles called captacula. Each tentacle has an adhesive knob at the tip and extends out in the sand to capture food, which is then brought back to the mouth. Some planktonic particles brought into the mantle cavity during water circulation are driven anteriorly to the captacula by the cilia on the mantle ridges. The digestive tract is typical. The buccal cavity contains a well developed radula with large flattened teeth. The radula functions in the ingesting and shredding of the prey seized by the captacula. The stomach and the digestive gland are located in the middle of the body. The intestine extends anteriorly from the stomach and then bends back posteriorly to open through the anus into the mantle cavity. The details of scaphopod digestion and absorption are still unknown.

The circulatory system is reduced to a system of blood sinuses, and there is no heart. The nervous system is ganglionated and not concentrated. The typical cerebral, pleural, pedal, and visceral ganglia and their corresponding nerve cords are present. However, the usual molluscan sense organs—eyes, tentacles, osphradia—are not present. A pair of nephridia are present, but since the heart has disappeared, there are no reno-pericardial openings. The nephridiopores are located near the anus.

Scaphopods are dioecious. The unpaired gonad fills most of the posterior part of the body, and the sperm or eggs reach the outside by way of the right nephridium. The eggs are shed singly and are planktonic. Fertilization is external.

Scaphopod development very closely parallels that of the marine pelecypods. There is a free-swimming trochophore larva, succeeded by a bilaterally symmetrical veliger (Fig. 12-52, *D* and *E*). As in pelecypods, the larval mantle and shell in scaphopods are at first bilobed, but then the mantle lobes fuse along their ventral margin (Fig. 12-52, *E*). This fusion thus results in a cylindrical mantle and shell that remain open at each end (Fig. 12-52, *F*). Metamorphosis is gradual and is accompanied by elongation of the body (Fig. 12-52, *G*).

Although a few scaphopods inhabit shallow water or burrow in mud, the majority of species burrow in sand under water ranging in depth from 18 to 6000 feet. The living animals are therefore not frequently encountered, but judging from the number of shells washed up on beaches, scaphopods are common benthic animals.

Some fourteen species of scaphopods, including eleven species of *Dentalium,* have been found in the Atlantic coastal waters of North America; the majority occur south of Cape Hatteras. The Pacific coast fauna is much sparser although one species was commonly used as currency by the Indian tribes of the northwest Pacific coast.

Several lines of evidence seem to indicate that scaphopods are an offshoot from the ancestral pelecypod stock. The symmetry of the body and its orientation within the shell, the reduction of the head, the burrowing habit, the symmetrical veliger, and the embryonic bilobed mantle and shell, are strikingly similar to the respective pelecypod characteristics. The captacula may well be homologous to the proboscides of protobranchs.

Class Cephalopoda

The class Cephalopoda contains the nautili, squids, and octopods. Although some cephalopods such as the octopus have secondarily assumed a less active bottom-dwelling habit, the class as a whole has become adapted for a swimming existence and are the most specialized and highly organized of all mollusks. The head projects into a circle, or crown, of large prehensile tentacles, or arms, which are homologous to the anterior of the foot of other mollusks. In the evolution of the cephalopods, the body became greatly lengthened along the dorsoventral axis; and, as a result of a change in the manner of locomotion, this axis became the functional anterior-posterior axis. The circle of tentacles is thus located at the anterior of the body, and the visceral hump is posterior. The original posterior mantle cavity is now ventral.

The cephalopods have attained the largest size of any invertebrates. Although the majority range between a few inches to several feet in length, including the tentacles, some species reach giant proportions. The largest cephalopods are the giant squids, *Architeuthis*, of the North Atlantic, one specimen of which has been reported to have attained a total body length of 55 feet, including the tentacles. The tentacles alone were 35 feet long, and the circumference of the body was 12 feet. Giant octopods are found only in Hollywood. *Octopus punctatus* from the Pacific coast is the largest species of this group, and the body length does not exceed one foot, although the rather slender arms may reach 16 feet in length.

From an evolutionary standpoint, cephalopods appear to be a waning group, for only some 400 species now exist as compared to the more than 10,000 different fossil forms. The class first appeared in the Cambrian period and then, once during the Paleozoic era and once in the Mesozoic era, underwent two great periods of evolutionary development with the formation of many species. The abundance and number of fossil species make the cephalopods an extremely important index group.

Existing cephalopods are divided into two subclasses, the Tetrabranchia and the Dibranchia. The Tetrabranchia possess an external shell and two pairs of gills. Only one group of Tetrabranchia now exists, the genus *Nautilus*, but into this order are also placed most of the fossil forms (Fig. 12-53). The remaining living cephalopods, the squids and octopods belong to the order Dibranchia, in which only a single pair of gills is present and the shell is either internal or absent.

This classification is satisfactory for living cephalopods but not for fossil species. It is impossible to determine the number of gills from the shell, which forms the only fossil remains, and it is by no means certain that all the fossil shelled cephalopods had four gills. Paleontologists use a different system of classification, which is described after discussion of the shell structure.

The Shell. A completely developed shell is found only in the tetrabranchs, being displayed by the existing *Nautilus* and the fossil representatives of the order. In squids the shell is reduced and internal, and in the octopods it is completely lacking. The shell of *Nautilus* is coiled over the head in a bilaterally symmetrical plano-spiral (Fig. 12-53). Only the last two whorls are visible since they cover the inner whorls. Although coiled, the shell of *Nautilus* is radically different from the gastropod shell. The shell of *Nautilus*, like all cephalopod shells, is divided by transverse septa into internal chambers and only the last chamber is occupied by the living animal. As the animal grows, it periodically moves forward, and the posterior part of the mantle secretes a new septum.

Viewed from the anterior, each septum is concave—that is, is bowed backward. Where the septum joins the wall of the shell, there is a scar, or suture. The septa are perforated in the middle, and through the opening a cord of body tissue, called the siphuncle, extends from the visceral mass. The siphuncle secretes gas into the empty chambers, making the shell buoyant and allowing the animal to swim. The gas is similar to air but has a slightly higher nitrogen content. The shell is composed of an outer porcellanous layer, containing prisms of calcium carbonate in an organic matrix, and there is an inner nacreous layer. The outer surface is often tinted with alternating bands of orange and white, or it may be pearly white.

Not all fossil cephalopods have coiled shells, nor are the shells of all coiled species similar to *Nautilus*. The ancestral cephalopods probably had a straight shell shaped like a cone (Fig. 12-54, *A*). The earliest fossil cephalopod shell was of this type or was curved like a tusk. The straight shells of some species from the Ordovician period exceeded 15 feet in length, and the aperture was one foot in diameter. However, a straight or curved shell is not always an indication of primitiveness, for at different periods in the course of cephalopod evolution, the shells of various groups became secondarily uncoiled and straight again.

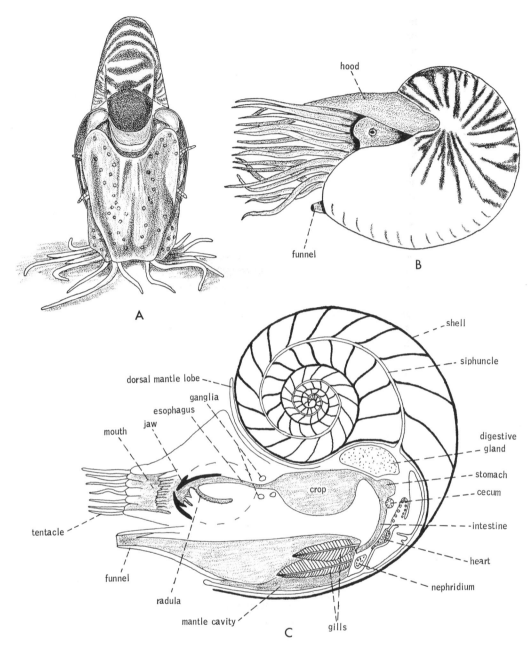

Figure 12-53. *Nautilus,* the only living shelled cephalopod. *A.* Resting on substratum, with head covered by hood. (After Willey from Parker and Haswell.) *B.* Swimming. (After Moore and others.) *C.* Sagittal section. (After Naef from Shrock and Twenhofel.)

Coiling in the fossil cephalopods typically resulted in a plano-spiral (Fig. 12-54, *C*), but the apex in a few groups was drawn out as in the snails (Fig. 12-54, *D*). In some cases the shell was so loosely coiled that the whorls were unconnected (Fig. 12-54, *B*); others displayed fused coils, but these coils were not always impressed into one another, as in *Nautilus,* and each whorl was visible (Fig. 12-54, *C*). Many were similar to *Nautilus.* The coils of some fossil forms were exogastric as in *Nautilus*—that

is, the ventral surface was located along the outer perimeter of the whorl (Fig. 12-54, *G* and *H*). Others were endogastric—the shell was coiled beneath the animal, and the dorsal surface was on the outside of the whorl (Fig. 12-54, *I* and *J*). The largest fossil species with a coiled shell was *Pachydiscus seppenradensis* from the Cretaceous period, which had a shell diameter of 8½ feet. However, many of these fossil cephalopods were tiny species with shells only one inch in diameter.

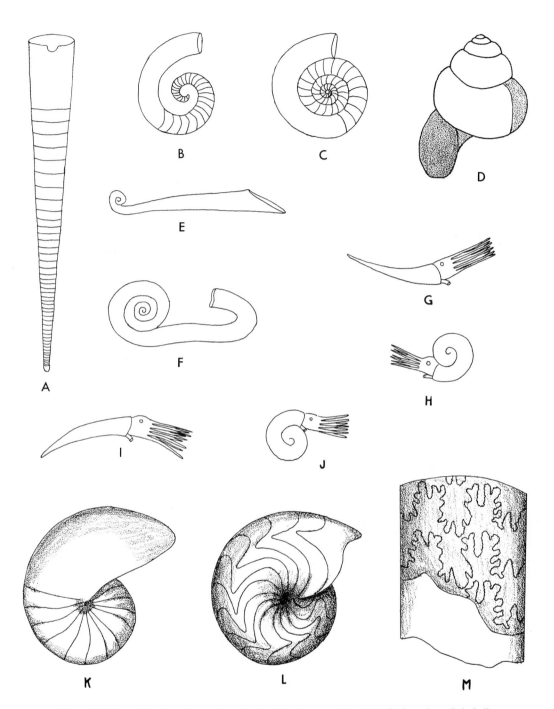

Figure 12-54.   Fossil cephalopod shells. *A.* Primitive straight shell. *B.* Loosely coiled shell. *C.* Plano-spiraled shell. (*A* to *C* after Flower from Shrock and Twenhofel.) *D.* Asymmetrically coiled shell. Shading indicates area occupied by animal. (After Moore and others.) *E* and *F.* Modified coiled shells. *E. Baculites,* from the Cretaceous period. *F. Scaphites* from the Cretaceous period. *G* and *H.* Exogastric coiling, in which ventral surface is located along outer perimeter of shell. *I* and *J.* Endogastric coiling, in which dorsal surface is located along outer perimeter of shell. (*E* to *J* after Shrock and Twenhofel.) *K. Nautilus undulatus,* a Cretaceous cephalopod with simple sutures. (After Sharp from Shrock and Twenhofel.) *L.* The Mississippian *Muensteroceras rotarius,* an ammonoid with angular sutures. (After Shrock and Twenhofel.) *M. Buculites,* a Cretaceous ammonoid with complex sutures. (After Meek from Shrock and Twenhofel.)

One of the most important characteristics for the classification of fossil cephalopods is the nature of the internal sutures—the point of junction between the septum and the wall of the shell. Although the sutures were internal, the chambers became filled with sediment in the course of preservation, and the details of the suture pattern have been beautifully preserved on the outer surface of the filling. The simplest suture lines were straight or slightly waved, as in *Nautilus* (Fig. 12-54, *K*); but one large group, the ammonoids, developed elaborate sutures that were zigzagged (Fig. 12-54, *L*), or more frequently minutely crinkled (Fig. 12-54, *M*). Such sutures indicate a corresponding complexity in the nature of the septum and the part of the mantle that secreted it.

Paleontologists, who work with only the preserved shells of fossil cephalopods, use a different scheme of classification from that of zoologists. Paleontologists separate those forms with complete shells, the subclass Tetrabranchia to most zoologists, into two subclasses—the Nautiloidea and the Ammonoidea. The Nautiloidea is characterized by straight or coiled shells and simple sutures. The Nautiloidea first appeared in the Cambrian period and is represented today by *Nautilus*. All members of the Ammonoidea were coiled and displayed complex septa and sutures. They appeared in the Silurian period after the nautiloids and disappeared at the end of the Cretaceous period.

We know nothing concerning the soft parts of fossil ammonoids and nautiloids and can only assume that they were somewhat similar to those of *Nautilus*.

The shell of the Dibranchia (the subclass Coleoidea of paleontologists) is internal or absent. These cephalopods are believed to have evolved from some early straight-shelled nautiloid, and during this evolutionary stage the shell became completely enclosed by the mantle. The basic structure of the dibranch shell is illustrated by the fossil belemnoids, the oldest known dibranchs. Without introducing any new nomenclature, the belemnoid shell differs from that of the nautiloids only in that the apical and lateral walls were greatly thickened and that the anterior dorsal wall projected over the viscera as a protective shell (Fig. 12-55).

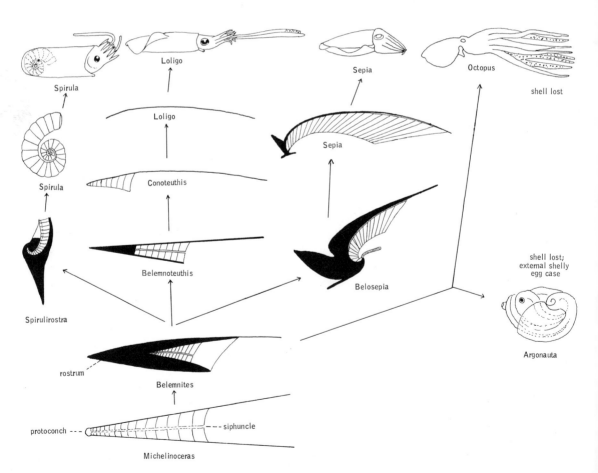

Figure 12-55.   Evolution of shells of the Dibranchia, or Coleoidea. (After Shrock and Twenhofel.)

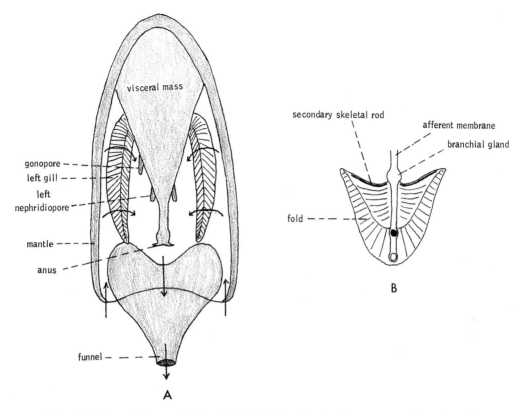

Figure 12-56.   *A.* The squid, *Sepia officinalis,* showing direction of water current through mantle cavity (ventral view). *B.* Gill filament of a squid. (Both after Yonge.)

From some primitive belemnoid form the dibranch shell evolved in four directions, all leading to modern forms and all involving a reduction in the weight of the shell. This evolutionary development is illustrated in Figure 12-55. In *Spirula,* a common world-wide deepwater squid, the thickened wall and shelf have disappeared, and the shell has become coiled. In the evolutionary line leading to *Loligo*—the long bodied squids and the genus to which the common squid of the North American Atlantic coast belongs—all of the shell, including the septa, has disappeared except the shelf and a strip of the dorsal wall. The shell is horny and called a pen.

A third evolutionary line, represented by the European squid, *Sepia,* has retained the septa, but the shelf and thickened parts of the wall have disappeared. Finally, in *Octopus* the shell has disappeared completely. Not only has the shell of squids undergone great reduction to facilitate swimming, but the body has become more rigid through the development of an internal cartilaginous skeleton. Cartilage plates are located in the mantle wall, in the "neck" region, and surrounding the brain. The cartilage plates that surround the brain form a protective encasement.

Water Circulation and Locomotion. All cephalopods swim by rapidly expelling water from the mantle cavity. The squids are most highly specialized for this type of movement and have attained the greatest speed of any aquatic invertebrate. In many cases, the squid body is long and tapered posteriorly, and a pair of posterior lateral fins act as stabilizers. The mantle contains both longitudinal and circular muscles fibers. During the inhalant phase of water circulation, the circular fibers relax and the longitudinal muscles contract. This action increases the volume of the mantle cavity, and water rushes in laterally and ventrally between the anterior margin of the mantle and the head (Fig. 12-56, *A*). When the mantle cavity is filled, the action of the mantle muscles is reversed.

The contraction of the circular muscles not only increases the water pressure within the cavity but also locks the edges of the mantle tightly around the head. Thus water is forced to leave through the ventral tubular funnel. The force of water leaving the funnel propels the animal in the opposite direction. The funnel is highly mobile and can be directed anteriorly or posteriorly, resulting in either forward or backward movement.

The rapidity of movement depends largely

on the force with which water is expelled from the funnel, but the movements are beautifully controlled. Squids can hover, perform subtle swimming movements, or dart so rapidly and with such force that they may leave the surface of the water and glide in the air for a short distance. There are reports that squids have leaped onto the decks of ships 12 feet above the surface of the water. Squids often rest motionless on the bottom. In normal swimming, the arms are outstretched anteriorly and held closely together, forming a point behind which the animal swims; the fins are extended and undulate gently. In very rapid movements, the fins are wrapped against the body.

Nautilus can also swim with surprising rapidity, although not with the speed of squids (Fig. 12-53, *B*). The locomotor mechanism is the same as that of squids, although the ejection of water through the funnel results from the retraction of the body and contraction of the muscles of the funnel rather than by the mantle. *Nautilus* often rests on the bottom in a horizontal position with the tentacles forming a stabilizing platform (Fig. 12-53, *A*). Whether swimming or resting, the gas-filled chambers keep the shell upright. How the *Nautilus* regulates the amount of gas required for the

different depths it occupies is an interesting problem that has not yet been completely solved, for *Nautilus* ranges from relatively shallow water to depths of over 2000 feet.

The octopods have reverted to more sedentary habits. The body is globular and bag-like, and there are no fins (Fig. 12-57). The mantle edges are fused dorsally and laterally to the body wall, resulting in a much more restricted aperture into the mantle cavity. Although octopods are capable of swimming in the same manner as squids, the movements are rather jerky; they more frequently crawl about over the rocks around which they live (Fig. 12-57, *A*). The arms, which are provided with adhesive suction discs, are used to pull the animal along or anchor to the substratum. Abbott (1954) tells of an octopus that escaped from an aquarium and crawled 100 feet toward the ocean before being overcome by the sun. There are also reports of octopods being able to keep up with a man walking at a brisk pace.

Octopods of the family Vitreledonellidae have secondarily returned to a swimming existence, but they have abandoned the conventional method of locomotion by water propulsion (Fig. 12-57, *C*). Instead, the arms have become webbed like an umbrella and are used

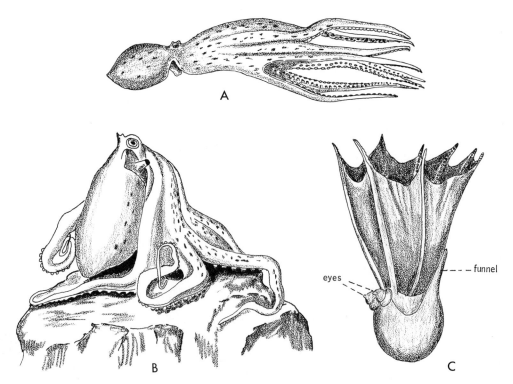

Figure 12-57.   *Octopus vulgaris. A.* Swimming. *B.* Resting. (After Merculiano from Parker and Haswell.) *C. Amphitretus,* a vitreledonellid octopod with webbed arms for swimming. (After Hoyle from Parker and Haswell.)

for swimming. The webbed arms are employed somewhat like the arms of a swimmer using the breast stroke.

Respiration. The circulation of water through the mantle not only produces the power for locomotion but, as in other mollusks, also provides oxygen for the gills. The Tetrabranchia (*Nautilus*) have four gills, but the Dibranchia have the usual two. The surface area of the gill filament has been increased by a type of folding similar to that of a fan, and all cilia have disappeared (Fig. 12-56, *B*). The loss of cilia is not surprising. Removal of sediment is not a problem for pelagic animals and the mantle contractions create the water current passing through the mantle cavity.

Still another modification found in dibranch gills is the conduction of blood through the filament in capillaries. Lastly, the circulation of water over the gills is the reverse of that in gastropods. Since water leaves the mantle cavity by way of the funnel, the exhalant current is ventral to the inhalant current. It is interesting that the anus and nephridiopore have also shifted to a ventral position with relation to the gills, thus again placing these openings in the path of the exhalant current. In the swimming Vitreledonellidae, the gills are vestigial and respiration takes place through the general body surface.

Many zoologists consider the two pairs of gills in *Nautilus* to be the more primitive cephalopod state and the dibranchiate state to have arisen through a loss of one of the original pairs. Yonge (1947) holds that the single pair of gills is primitive for cephalopods as well as other mollusks. As cephalopods increased in size, the duplication of gills appeared in the nautiloid line as a means of increasing the respiratory surface. The dibranchs retained the single pair of gills but respiration was improved as a result of more efficient water circulation, capillaries in the filaments, and the addition of a pair of branchial hearts, which caused an increase in blood pressure.

Nutrition. Cephalopods are all carnivorous. A radula is present, but more important is the pair of powerful beak-like jaws that enable the animal to bite and tear (Figs. 12-53, *C* and 12-58). Squids prey on fish and various invertebrates, depending upon the size of the species. *Loligo* darts backwards rapidly into a school of young mackerel, seizes a fish, and quickly bites a triangular chunk out of the neck, severing the nerve cord. Remarkably, the bite is always made at the same place. The octopods, being more sluggish and secretive, lie in wait near the entrance of their dens located in holes or rock crevices. Passing snails, crabs, and fish are

seized and dragged into the interior of the lair and eaten. Octopods also make nocturnal excursions in search of food. The feeding habits of *Nautilus* are not very well known, but it is reasonable to assume that they are similar to those of the dibranchs.

The capture of prey is effected by the tentacles or arms. *Nautilus* displays approximately 94 tentacles, arising from lobes that are arranged in both an inner and an outer circle around the head (Fig. 12-53). The tentacles are annulated but lack adhesive suckers or discs. Each tentacle can be withdrawn into a sheath. Located above the head and tentacles is a large leathery protective hood that represents a fold of one of the tentacular lobes. When the animal withdraws into the shell, the hood acts like an operculum and covers the aperture. A hood is not found in the other living cephalopods.

Squids possess only ten arms, arranged in five pairs around the head (Fig. 12-58). Eight are short and heavy and called arms; the fourth pair down from the dorsal side are twice the length of the arms and are called tentacles. The inner surface of each arm is flattened and covered with stalked, cup-shaped adhesive discs that function like suction cups. Often a horny reinforcement, or in some cases hooks, are located around the rim of the suction cup. Attached to the inner surface of the floor of the cup are muscle fibers, the contraction of which create a vacuum when the cup is applied. Suckers are present only on the flattened spatulate ends of the longer tentacles. The highly mobile tentacles are used for seizing the prey, which is then drawn toward the mouth; the arms aid in holding the prey.

Octopods have only eight tentacles, or arms. The arms are all of equal length and are similar to the arms of squids except that the suckers are sessile and lack horny rings and hooks. The numerical difference in tentacles in dibranch cephalopods provides the basis for dividing the subclass into two orders, the Decapoda (an unfortunate name since it is also used for an order of crustaceans), which contain the squids with ten tentacles, and the eight-armed Octopoda.

The beak, located in the buccal cavity, can bite and tear off large pieces of tissue, which are then pulled into the buccal cavity by the radula using a tongue-like action (Fig. 12-58). The radula is rudimentary or absent in some deep-sea octopods that have apparently adopted a bottom detritus feeding habit. In squids and octopods, two pairs of salivary glands empty into the buccal cavity. One pair is located in the buccal mass and is believed to secrete enzymes and mucus. The second pair, which may be

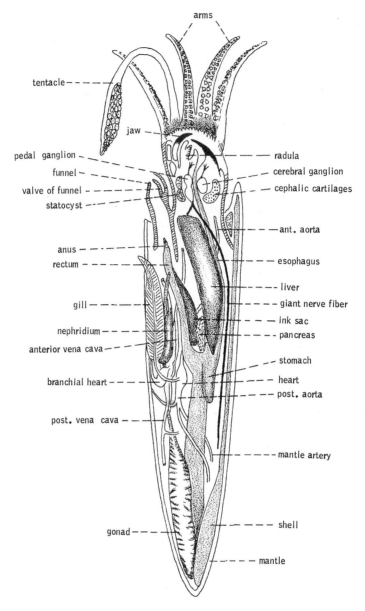

Figure 12-58.   The squid, *Loligo.* (After Schlecter.)

fused as in *Loligo,* is located more posteriorly in the esophagus. The duct from the second pair of salivary glands, which is actually a poison gland, opens behind the lower jaw. The poison enters the tissues of the prey through the wound inflicted by the jaws. The esophagus is muscular and conducts food by peristaltic action into the stomach or, as in *Nautilus* and *Octopus,* into the crop, which is an expansion of one end of the esophagus.

The stomach is very muscular, and attached to its anterior is a large cecum (Figs. 12-58 and 12-59). The cecum is straight in *Loligo* and spiraled in *Sepia, Octopus,* and *Nautilus.* The digestive gland in cephalopods is divided into

a small spongy diffuse portion, sometimes called the pancreas, and a large solid "liver" (paired in *Sepia*), which is probably homologous to the digestive gland of the other mollusks. In squids the two divisions of the digestive gland are morphologically separated from each other, and the pancreas empties into the liver duct. Digestion is entirely extracellular. Enzymes from both digestive gland divisions empty through a common duct into the cecum. Pancreatic enzymes are continually secreted and stored in the cecum when digestive activity is absent. Hepatic secretions enter the cecum only during feeding.

When food enters the stomach, both pancreatic and hepatic secretions are poured into

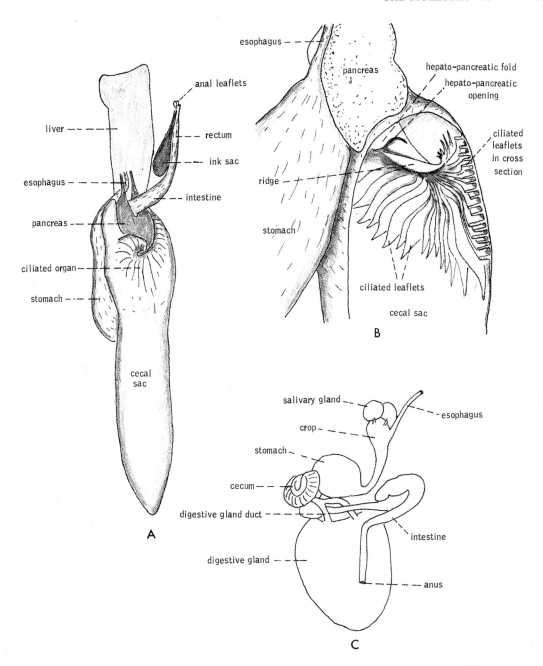

Figure 12-59. *A*. Digestive tract of the squid, *Loligo* (ventral view). *B*. Ciliated folds in cecum of *Loligo* (ventral view). (Both after Bidder.) *C*. Digestive tract of *Octopus vulgaris*. (After Masao.)

the stomach through a groove in the cecal wall. Digestion therefore begins in the stomach, where food is kneaded and mixed with the glandular secretions. Fluid and particulate matter then pass into the cecum, where digestion is completed. The anterior walls of the cecum contain an elaborate series of spiral ciliated folds that separate nondigestible particles from the cecal contents and conduct the particles by way of a ciliated groove back into the stomach

and thence into the intestine (Fig. 12-59, *B*). Absorption takes place in the cecal walls and not in the digestive gland as in the other mollusks. Residue in the stomach is also passed into the intestine. Some intestinal absorption takes place. The straight or coiled intestines carry waste to the anus, which opens into the mantle cavity. As has been pointed out by Bidder (1950), the digestive modifications of cephalopods, particularly squids, probably represent an adaptation for rapid digestion correlated with an active pelagic life and a carnivorous diet.

Ink Gland. In cephalopods other than *Nautilus,* a large ink sac is located in the region of the intestine (Figs. 12-58 and 12-59, *A*). The apparatus consists of an ink-producing gland, a reservoir, and a duct that opens into the rectum just behind the anus. The gland secretes a brown or black fluid containing a high concentration of melanin pigment, which is stored in the reservoir. When a squid or an octopod is alarmed, the ink is released through the anus, and the cloud of inky water forms an effective screen behind which they can escape. It is also believed that the alkaloid nature of the ink is objectionable to predators, particularly fish, in which it may anesthetize the chemoreceptive senses. Sepia ink is obtained commercially from species of squid living in the Mediterranean Sea and off the coast of China.

Excretion. The two nephridia characteristic of both squids and octopods follow the basic molluscan design; but they are rather compact and sac-like, and the reno-pericardial canal has become enclosed within the sac (Figs. 12-58 and 12-60). Through the middle of each kidney passes a large vein surrounded by glandular tissue that picks up waste from the blood and deposits it into the cavity of the sac. The nephridiopores open into the mantle cavity near the anus. Waste is excreted principally as ammonia. A peculiar feature of the cephalopod nephridia is that they are anteriorly connected, and a large median dorsal sac arises from the point of junction. The pancreas is imbedded in this sac and functions in waste removal.

The nephridia of *Nautilus* are somewhat aberrant. Four nephridia are present, and they have lost any connection with the pericardial cavity.

Circulation. The circulatory system of cephalopods is largely closed and therefore consists of the most extensive system of vessels of any mollusks. In dibranchs, blood returns from the head region in the large vena cava, which divides into two branches near the nephridia (Fig. 12-60). Each branch penetrates a nephridial sac and then passes through a muscular branchial heart before entering the gills. The right branch of the vena cava also receives blood from a vein draining the ink sac and from another vein draining the gonads. Finally an anterior pair and a posterior pair of mantle, or abdominal, veins return blood from the mantle and viscera.

The contraction of the branchial hearts, which receive unoxygenated blood from all parts of the body, boosts the pressure of the blood, sending it through the capillaries of the gills. The two auricles of the heart drain blood from the gills and then pass it into the median ventricle. The ventricle pumps blood out to the body through both an anterior and a posterior aorta and eventually through smaller vessels into tissue capillaries. The blood of cephalopods is like that of the other mollusks.

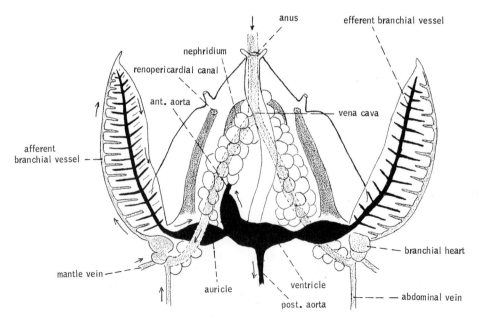

anus

efferent branchial vessel

nephridium

renopericardial canal

ant. aorta

vena cava

afferent branchial vessel

branchial heart

mantle vein

auricle   ventricle   abdominal vein

post. aorta

Figure 12-60.   Circulatory system of *Sepia.* Arrows indicate direction of blood flow. (After Borradaile and others.)

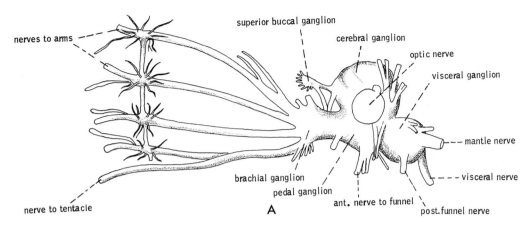

nerves to arms

superior buccal ganglion

cerebral ganglion

optic nerve

visceral ganglion

mantle nerve

visceral nerve

brachial ganglion

pedal ganglion

ant. nerve to funnel

post. funnel nerve

nerve to tentacle

A

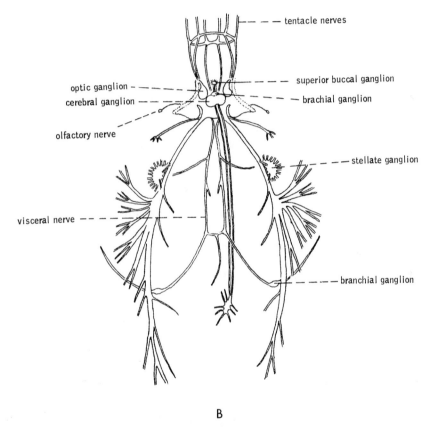

tentacle nerves

optic ganglion

cerebral ganglion

olfactory nerve

superior buccal ganglion

brachial ganglion

stellate ganglion

visceral nerve

branchial ganglion

B

Figure 12-61.   *A.* Brain of *Sepia* (lateral view). (After Hillig from Kaestner.) *B.* Nervous system of *Sepia*. (After Hillig from Borradaile and others.)

Nervous System. The high degree of development of the dibranch nervous system is attained only by some insects and arachnids among the other invertebrates. All of the typical molluscan ganglia are concentrated and more or less fused to form a brain that encircles the esophagus (Fig. 12-61, *A*). Moreover, the ganglia themselves have become so well-differentiated that it has been possible to detect experimentally certain areas, or centers, within particular ganglia that control particular

regions or functions of the body. For example, the brain centers for both forward swimming and the closing of the suckers have been located in the cerebral ganglia.

The large cerebral ganglia comprise that part of the brain lying above the esophagus. They give rise to a pair of buccal nerves that run anteriorly to a pair of superior buccal ganglia and then, by way of a commissure around the esophagus, to a pair of inferior buccal ganglia. Both pairs of buccal ganglia lie just behind the buccal mass. Also, a large optic nerve extends from each side of the cerebral ganglia. The pedal ganglia supply nerves to the funnel, and anterior divisions of the pedal ganglia, called brachial ganglia, send nerves to each of the tentacles. The innervations by the pedal and brachial ganglia are evidence that the tentacles and the funnel of cephalopods are homologous to the foot of other mollusks.

The visceral ganglia (perhaps representing both the pleural and visceral ganglia of other mollusks) give rise to three pairs of posteriorly directed nerves: (1) One pair of visceral nerves innervates the various internal organs (Fig. 12-61, *B*). One branch from each of these nerves innervates the gills and contains a branchial ganglion. (2) A pair of sympathetic nerves, which join together in a gastric ganglion between the stomach and the cecum, innervate the stomach region. (3) The third pair of nerves are large and supply the mantle. The mantle nerves contain giant motor neurons, which have been used extensively by neurophysiologists in studies on neuron function. These giant neurons are part of a two-chain system innervating the respiratory muscles of the mantle. The point of synapse in the chain is located in a large stellate ganglion, which is visible beneath the undersurface of the mantle just anterior to each gill.

The peripheral nervous system of *Nautilus* is similar to that of the dibranchs, but the brain lacks distinct ganglia and forms a heavy collar around the esophagus.

Sense Organs.   Like the nervous system, the sense organs of cephalopods are highly developed. Particularly well developed are the eyes, which in squids and octopods are able to form an image (Fig. 12-62). The most striking feature of the dibranch eye is its close similarity in structure to that of the vertebrate eye. A spherical housing containing cartilaginous plates fits into a sort of orbit or socket of cartilages associated with those surrounding the brain.

External muscle attachments enable limited movement of the eye. The lens is suspended within the interior cavity by a ciliary process, and in front of the lens is an iris diaphragm, which can control the amount of light entering the eye. Focusing does not involve a change in shape of the lens; however, as in some vertebrates, the lens is moved forward or backward. The retina contains rod-like photoreceptors that are directed toward the source of light. The eye is thus of the direct type, instead of indirect as in vertebrates. The rods are connected to retinal cells that send fibers back to an optic ganglion. These ganglia in turn are located at the outer ends of the optic nerves.

The eyes of *Nautilus* are much less complex. They are large simple open pits borne at the ends of short stalks, and they lack the internal structure or differentiation displayed by those of the dibranchs.

Statocysts are found in both tetrabranchs and dibranchs but are particularly well developed in the latter, in which they are large and imbedded in the cartilages located on each side of the brain. Osphradia are present only in *Nautilus*.

The tentacles are liberally supplied with tactile cells and perhaps chemoreceptor cells. This is particularly true of *Nautilus*, in which certain tentacles appear to primarily have a sensory function.

Chromatophores.   The unusual coloration

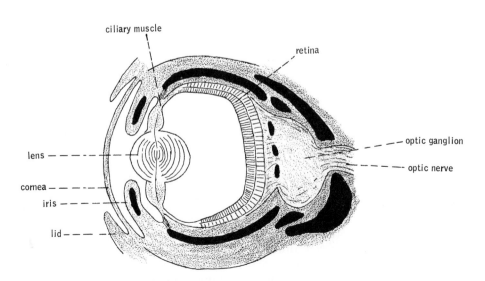

Figure 12-62.   Eye of *Sepia.*

of cephalopods, other than *Nautilus,* is caused by the presence of chromatophores in the integument. The expansion and contraction of these cells result from the action of tiny muscles that are attached to the periphery of the cell. When the muscles contract, the chromatophore is drawn out to form a large flat plate; when the muscles relax, the pigment is concentrated and less apparent. Particular species possess chromatophores of several colors—blue, purple, pink, brown, and black—and the chromatophores of a particular color appear in groups. The chromatophores are controlled by the nervous system, with vision being the principal initial stimulus. The degree and rapidity with which these animals can simulate background coloration is remarkable. A squid can rapidly change from a pale transparent color to a dark grey as it first swims over a light sand bottom and then over rock. An octopus when alarmed can literally blush as color changes flow over the body.

Reproduction. Except in a few species, cephalopods are dioecious, and the gonads are located at the posterior of the body (Figs. 12-53, *C* and 12-58). The testis is a saccular structure with an internal cavity, considered to be derived from the coelom. Sperm are formed in the wall of the sac, pass into the lumen, and then issue through a ciliated opening into the vas deferens. The highly coiled vas deferens conducts the sperm anteriorly to a seminal vesicle, which has ciliated grooved walls. Here in the seminal vesicle the sperm are rolled together and encased in a very elaborate spermatophore. The prostate gland joins the seminal vesicle at its distal end. From the seminal vesicle spermatophores pass into a large storage sac or reservoir called Needham's sac, which opens into the left side of the mantle cavity.

In females the ovary is also saccular and occupies a position similar to that of the testis. The oviduct is looped and terminates in a oviducal gland. In *Octopus* two oviducts are present.

Fertilization may take place within the mantle cavity or outside but in either case involves copulation. Because of the restricted opening into the mantle cavity, one of the arms of the male—the right or left fourth in squids and the right third in octopods—has become modified as an intromittent organ, a phenomenon called hectocotyly. The modified arm is called a hectocotylus. The degree of modification varies. In squids such as *Sepia* and *Loligo,* several rows of suckers are smaller and form a sort of groove extending the length of the hectocotylus. In octopods the modification is much greater. The tip of the arm carries a spoon-like depression in *Octopus;* in *Argonauta* and others, there is actually a cavity or chamber where the spermatophores are stored.

At copulation, which often includes courtship behavior, the hectocotylus plucks a mass of spermatophores from the Needham's sac. The male hectocotylus is then inserted into the mantle cavity of the female and deposits the spermatophores on the mantle cavity wall near the openings from the oviducts. In octopods with storage chambers at the end of the hectocotylus, the arm may break off and remain in the mantle cavity of the female, as in *Argonauta* and *Philonexis.* The detached hectocotylus was originally thought to have been a parasitic worm and was described as *Hectocotylus;* hence the derivation of the term.

In *Loligo* and other genera of the same family, the spermatophores may be received by the mantle cavity as just described; or the hectocotylus may be inserted into a horseshoe-shaped seminal receptacle, located in a fold beneath the mouth.

The spermatophore is shaped like a baseball bat and consists of an elongated sperm mass, a cement body, a coiled spring-like ejaculatory organ, and a cap (Fig. 12-63, *A*). When the spermatophore is pulled from the Needham's sac, the cap is loosened and the spiral ejaculatory organ dislodged. When the released cement body adheres to the seminal receptacle or mantle wall, the sperm mass disintegrates, liberating the sperm.

As the eggs are being discharged from the oviduct, each is enveloped by a membrane or capsule in the oviducal gland. Additional protective covering is produced by a nidimental gland, which is located in the mantle wall near the oviducal gland and opens independently into the mantle cavity. In *Loligo,* secretions from the nidimental gland surround the eggs in a gelatinous mass. After leaving the mantle cavity, the egg mass is held by the arms, and the eggs may be fertilized by sperm from the seminal receptacle under the mouth. The female then attaches the fertilized eggs to the substratum in a cluster of ten to fifty elongated masses, each mass containing as many as one hundred eggs. The gelatinous covering of each mass hardens on exposure to sea water, and the individual egg capsules swell to several times the original diameter, leaving a distinct space around the egg.

Although the eggs of *Sepia* and *Octopus* are fertilized in the mantle cavity, they are deposited in a manner similar to those of *Loligo.* The egg clusters of *Octopus* resemble a bunch of grapes and are attached within rocky recesses. Some squids, such as the oegopsids, deposit their

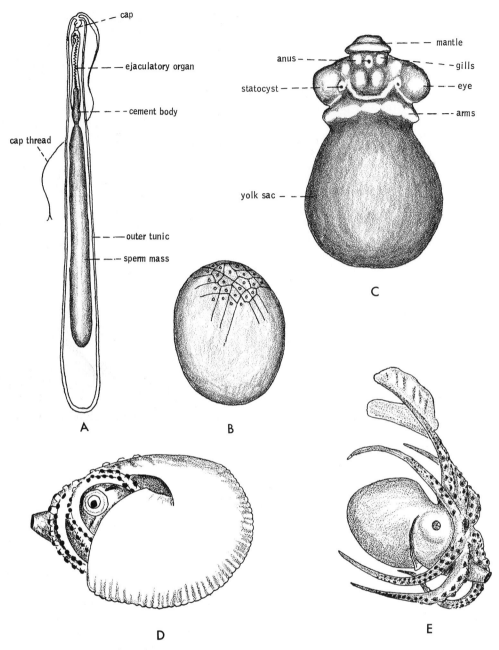

Figure 12-63.   *A.* Spermatophore of *Loligo. B.* Discoidal meroblastic cleavage in *Loligo.* (After Watase from Dawydoff.) *C.* Embryo of *Loligo.* (After Naef from Dawydoff.) *D. Argonauta argo* female in shelly egg case. (After Naef from Kaestner.) *E. Argonauta hians.* (After Verrill from Abbott.)

eggs singly, and the eggs are free-floating rather than attached. Octopods remain to care for the eggs after they are deposited (Fig. 12-64). Debris and sediment are continually removed from the deposited eggs by the tentacles and water is periodically ejected over the eggs from the funnel. Brooding behavior is not exhibited by squids.

Perhaps the most remarkable adaptation for egg deposition is found in a genus of pelagic octopods, *Argonauta*, commonly known as the paper nautilus (Fig. 12-63, *D* and *E*). The two dorsal arms of the female are greatly expanded at the tip to form a veil or membrane. The expanded portion of each arm secretes one half of a beautiful calcareous bivalved shell into which the eggs are deposited. The shell is carried about and serves both as a brood chamber and a retreat for the female. The posterior of the female usually remains in the shell;

Figure 12-64.   *Octopus*, caring for eggs. (Courtesy of Marineland, Florida.)

when disturbed, she withdraws completely into the retreat. The much smaller male does not secrete a shell and frequently is a cohabitant in the shell of the female.

The reproductive system of *Nautilus* is somewhat similar to that of dibranchs, although the ducts are paired. Little is known about copulation and fertilization. The male copulatory organ consists of four tentacles. The eggs are deposited and attached to the substratum singly within rather elaborate capsules.

Cephalopod eggs are much more heavily yolk-laden than other mollusk eggs. The eggs of *Sepia* and *Eledone* are very large and may reach 15 mm. in diameter. The eggs of *Loligo* and *Octopus* contain less yolk.

Embryology.   Embryological development is direct in all cephalopods. As in the telolecithal eggs of reptiles and birds, cleavage in cephalopods is meroblastic. Cleavage results in the formation of a germinal disc, or cap, of cells at the animal pole (Fig. 12-63, *B*). Here the embryo will form (Fig. 12-63, *C*). The margin of the disc grows down and around the yolk mass and forms a yolk sac; the yolk is gradually absorbed during development. The eyes arise as ectodermal invaginations. The arms form posteriorly and then migrate forward to locations surrounding the mouth. The funnel, which represents a part of the foot, ultimately is located within the mantle cavity owing to overgrowth and enclosure by the developing mantle. Nothing is known concerning development in *Nautilus*.

Distribution and Economic Importance. Cephalopods inhabit oceans throughout the world. Pelagic squids and octopods range from the surface to great depths. *Eledonella,* a deep-sea octopod, has been taken from a depth of 17,400 feet. Many of the deep-sea squid are bioluminescent, with luminescent spots arranged in various patterns along the body. *Heteroteuthis* even secretes a luminescent ink.

The more littoral cephalopod species include the pelagic squids, *Loligo* and *Sepia,* and the benthic *Octopus,* which lives in holes and crevices on rocky shores. *Nautilus* occurs around coral reefs in the South Pacific.

The principal enemies of cephalopods are fish and whales. The same species (such as mackerel), which when young served as food for the cephalopod, may in adult life prey on the cephalopod. Squids are important to the diet of sperm whales. These whales sometimes bear circular sucker scars on the skin from a battle with a giant squid.

Squids used for bait are caught commercially in the Grand Banks region but are not widely eaten as food in North America. However, squids are eaten in many parts of the world, including Europe.

Systematic Résumé of Class Cephalopoda

This résumé of the cephalopods employs the system of classification used by paleontologists. This system is not only a more natural system than that used by zoologists, but is also a more useful one in light of the much larger number of fossil cephalopods than of living forms. The corresponding terms used by zoologists appear in parentheses.

Subclass Nautiloidea (Subclass Tetrabranchia). Possess external shells, which may be coiled or straight; sutures not complex. Existing forms possess many slender suckerless tentacles. Two pairs of gills and two pairs of nephridia are present. All members are extinct except *Nautilus;* the class has been in existence from the Cambrian period to the present time. Genera include *Endoceras* and *Nautilus.*

Subclass Ammonoidea (Subclass Tetrabranchia). Fossil forms with coiled external shells having complex septa and sutures. Existed from the Silurian period to Cretaceous period. Includes *Ceratites, Scaphites,* and *Pachydiscus.*

Subclass Coleoidea (Subclass Dibranchia). Shells are internal or absent. A few tentacles bear suckers. One pair of gills and one pair of nephridia are present. Members have existed from the Mississippian period to the present.

Order Belemnoidea. Fossil forms with relatively complete internal shells. Wall of shell thickened and anterior dorsal wall extended forward as a shelf. Includes *Belemnites.*

Order Decapoda. The squids. Two long tentacles and eight shorter arms present; body more or less elongated and bears fins. Includes *Spirula, Loligo,* and the oegopsids—*Heteroteuthis* and *Architeuthis.*

Order Octopoda. The octopods. Possess eight arms; body globular with no fins. Includes *Eledone, Octopus, Philonexis,* the Vitreledonellidae, and *Argonauta.*

The Monoplacophora and the Origin of the Mollusca

In 1952, ten living specimens of *Neopilina,* a group of mollusks previously known only from Cambrian fossils, were dredged from a deep ocean trench off the Pacific coast of Costa Rica. Additional specimens have been collected since this initial discovery.

Neopilina belongs to a group of mollusks known as the Monoplacophora. Because they had previously been known only from fossil shells, they had been classified with either the Amphineura or the Gastropoda. The living specimens displayed some rather unexpected features.

Neopilina is a little more than one inch long and externally resembles a combination of gastropod and chiton. There is a single, large, bilateral shell, in which the apex is curved both

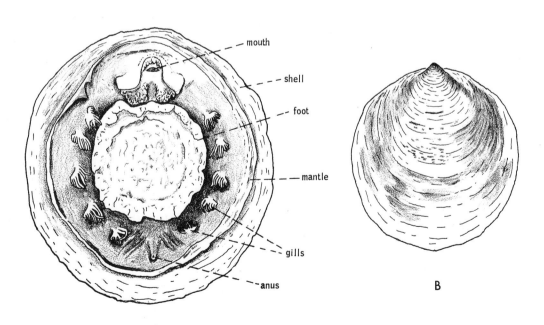

A   B

Figure 12-65.   The monoplacophoran, *Neopilina. A.* Ventral view. *B.* Dorsal view of shell.

anteriorly and ventrally (Fig. 12-65, *B*). The undersurface of *Neopilina* very much resembles that of a chiton (Fig. 12-65, *A*). The head is reduced in size, and a broad flat foot is present. A pallial groove separates the edge of the foot from the mantle on each side. As in chitons, the mouth is located in front of the foot, and the anus is located in the pallial groove at the posterior of the body. The pallial groove contains five pairs of gills, but filaments exist only on one side of the gill axis.

Internally, five pairs of retractor muscles are present. The digestive tract is very similar to that of primitive gastropods; a crystalline style has been reported present, but whether a true style actually is present or it is merely a mucus style, as in primitive gastropods and pelecypods, remains to be proven. A single ventricle and two pairs of auricles are present. The first pair of auricles receives blood from the first four pairs of gills. The pericardium is paired, and the heart lies between the two divisions. Six pairs of nephridia are arranged metamerically on each side of the body, and the nephridiopores of the last five open near the five gills. The nervous system is essentially the same as that in chitons. The sexes are separate, and two pairs of gonads are located in the middle of the body. Each gonad connects through a gonoduct to one of the two pairs of kidneys in the middle of the body.

The striking similarity between the embryogeny of the mollusks and the embryogeny of the polychaete annelids has long been recognized. Both exhibit spiral cleavage and virtually identical trochophore larvae. This similarity has been the principal evidence to support the view that annelids and mollusks arose from some common coelomate stock. The annelid line evolved in the direction of metamerism, while the molluscan line remained nonmetameric.

The most unusual feature of *Neopilina* is its apparent metameric plan of structure. *Neopilina* displays five pairs of retractor muscles, five pairs of gills, and six pairs of nephridia; these pairs of organs all more or less coincide and are serially arranged. A number of zoologists believe that the metamerism displayed by *Neopilina* is evidence that mollusks comprise a fundamentally metameric phylum and therefore must have evolved from the annelids. The molluscan trochophore is thus believed to be additional evidence of the annelid origin of mollusks.

There is one rather important objection to such a theory. If mollusks are actually primitively metameric, it is difficult to understand why one embryonic or one anatomical vestige of metamerism has not remained in any molluscan group other than the monoplacophorans. Even

the eight shell plates of the chiton arise from a single shell gland in the embryo. The basic question that must be answered first is whether the metamerism found in *Neopilina* is primitive or secondary. The lack of metamerism in all other mollusks seems to indicate that the metamerism displayed by *Neopilina* is secondary and not primary.

Although it may be necessary to revise our thinking in the future, at the present the older theory that assumes a common origin for mollusks and annelids still seems to have the greatest weight of evidence. In regard to the position of the Monoplacophora, elevation of the group to that of a sixth class of the Mollusca—a class characterized by an independent tendency toward metamerism—is completely justified.

BIBLIOGRAPHY

Abbott, R. T., 1954: American Sea Shells. D. Van Nostrand Co., Princeton, N. J. An excellent semitechnical guide to the marine mollusks of the Atlantic and Pacific coasts of North America. Contains beautiful colored photographs and useful bibliography.

Alder, J., and Hancock, A., 1845–1855: A monograph of the British nudibranchiate Mollusca. Ray Soc., London. A classic descriptive work on the nudibranchs with full-page colored plates.

Arey, L. B., and Crozier, W. J., 1919: The sensory responses of *Chiton*. J. Exp. Zool., *29*:157.

Atkins, D., 1936: On the ciliary mechanisms and interrelationships of lamellibranchs. Pts. I, II, and III. Quart. J. Micr. Sci., *314*:181–308; *315*:339–373; *315*:375–421. A detailed account of the ciliary food tracts of pelecypod gills.

Baker, F. C., 1939: Fieldbook of Illinois land snails. Nat. Hist. Surv. Div. Illinois, manual 2. A brief introduction to the common land snails of eastern United States with keys and figures.

Bidder, A. M., 1950: Digestive mechanisms of European squids. Quart. J. Micr. Sci., new series, *91(1)*:1–43.

Brunn, A. F., 1943: Biology of *Spirula spirula*. Dana Report, Copenhagen, *4(24)*:1–44.

Carriker, M. R., 1959: Comparative functional morphology of the drilling mechanism in *Urosalpinx* and *Eupleura*. Proc. 15th Int. Congr. Zool., London.

Clench, W. J., 1946: The poison cone shell. Occas. Pap. on Mollusks, Harvard Univ., *1(7)*:49–80.

Clench, W. J., 1959: Mollusca. *In* Ward and Whipple's Freshwater Biology (W. T. Edmondson, ed.). 2nd Edition, Wiley, New York, pp. 1117–1160. Key to the common freshwater mollusks of the United States.

Coe, W. R., 1936: Sexual phases in *Crepidula*. J. Exp. Zool., *72(3)*:455–477. A classic paper on protandry in *Crepidula*.

Crofts, D. R., 1955: Muscle morphogenesis in primitive mollusks and its relation to torsion. Proc. Zool. Soc. London, *125*:711–750.

Eigenbrodt, H., 1941: Untersuchungen über die Funktion der Radula einiger Schnecken. Z. Morph. Okol. Tiere, *37(4)*:735–791.

Fretter, V., 1937: The structure and function of the alimentary canal of some species of Polyplacophora. Trans. Roy. Soc. Edinburgh, pt. 1, *59(4)*:119–164.

Fretter, V., 1939: The structure and function of the alimentary canal of some tectibranch mollusks, with a note on excretion, Trans. Roy. Soc. Edinburgh, pt. 3, *59(22)*:599–645.

Fretter, V., 1946: The genital ducts of *Theodoxus, Lamellaria* and *Trivia,* and a discussion of their evolution in prosobranchs. J. Mar. Biol. Assoc. U. K., *26(3)*:312–351.

Garstang, W., 1928: Origin and evolution of larval forms. Report British Assoc., section D, p. 77.

Graham, A., 1938: The structure and function of the alimentary canal of aeolid mollusks, with a discussion of their nematocysts. Trans. Roy. Soc. Edinburgh, pt. 2, *59(9)*: 267–305.

Graham, A., 1939: The alimentary canal of style-bearing prosobranchs. Proc. Zool. Soc. London, series B, *109(1)*: 75–112.

Graham, A., 1949: The molluscan stomach. Trans. Roy. Soc. Edinburgh, pt. 3, *61(27)*:737–778. A comparative treatment of the molluscan stomach, it deals primarily with gastropods and pelecypods.

Graham, A., 1955: Molluscan diets. Proc. Malacol. Soc. London, *31*:144–159. A list of molluscan groups and their diets.

Kline, G., 1956: Notes on the stinging operation of *Conus*. Nautilus, *69(3)*:76–78.

Lebour, M. V., 1937: The eggs and larva of the British prosobranchs J. Mar. Biol. Assoc. United Kingdom. *22*:105–166.

Lemche, H., 1957: A new living deep-sea mollusk of the Cambro-Devonian class Monoplacophora. Nature, *179*: 413–416.

Lemche, H., 1959: Molluscan phylogeny in light of *Neopilina*. Proc. 15th Int. Congr. Zool., London.

MacGinitie, G. E., and MacGinitie, N., 1949: Natural History of Marine Animals. McGraw-Hill, New York, pp. 327–401.

Morton, J. E., 1954: The biology of *Limacina retroversa*. J. Mar. Biol. Assoc. United Kingdom, *33*:297–312.

Morton, J. E., 1956: The tidal rhythm and action of the digestive system of the lamellibranch *Lasaea rubra. J. Mar.* Biol. Assoc. United Kingdom, *35(3)*:563–586.

Morton, J. E., 1958: Molluscs. Hutchinson Univ. Library, London. A general account of the mollusks.

Nakazima, M., 1956: On the structure and function of the midgut gland of Mollusca, with a general consideration of the feeding habits and systematic relations. Japanese J. Zool., *2(4)*:469–566. A good comparative account of the digestive gland of mollusks.

Orton, J. H., 1913: The mode of feeding of *Crepidula*. J. Mar. Biol. Assoc. United Kingdom, *9*:444–478.

Pelseneer, P., 1906: Mollusca. Vol. 5 *in* A Treatise on Zoology (E. Ray Lankester, Ed.), London. An old but still useful general account of the Mollusca.

Pennak, R. W., 1953: Freshwater Invertebrates. Ronald Press, New York, pp. 667–726. A general account of the fresh-water gastropods and pelecypods with figures and keys to the North American genera.

Pilsbry, H. A., 1939–1946: Land Mollusca of North America. Vol. 1, pts. 1 and 2; vol. 2, pts. 1 and 2. Acad. Nat. Sci., Philadelphia, Monogr. 3. This is the most authoritative work on the North American land snails.

Raven, C. P., 1958: Morphogenesis: The Analysis of Molluscan Development. Pergamon Press, New York. A very complete account of molluscan embryology with extensive bibliography.

Saxena, B. B., 1955: Physiology of excretion in the common Indian apple snail, *Pila globosa*. J. Animal Morph. and Physiol., *2(2)*:87–95.

Shrock, R. R., and Twenhofel, W. H., 1953: Principles of Invertebrate Paleontology. McGraw-Hill Co., New York, pp. 350–502. A good general treatment of the fossil mollusks, particularly the cephalopods.

Yonge, C. M., 1932: The crystalline style of the Mollusca. Sci. Progr., *26*:643–653. A general account of the structure and function of the crystalline style of gastropods and pelecypods.

Yonge, C. M., 1937: Circulation of water in the mantle cavity of *Dentalium*. Proc. Malacol. Soc. London, *22(6)*:333–337.

Yonge, C. M., 1939: On the mantle cavity and its contained organs in the Loricata. Quart. J. Micr. Sci., *323*:367–390.

Yonge, C. M., 1941: The protobranchiate Mollusca: a functional interpretation of their structure and evolution. Phil. Trans. Roy. Soc. London, series B, *230*:79–147. An excellent account of the protobranchiate mollusks.

Yonge, C. M., 1947: The pallial organs in the aspidobranch Gastropoda and their evolution throughout the Mollusca. Phil. Trans. Roy. Soc. London, series B, *232*:443–518. A very good treatment of the evolution of the gills and mantle cavity in mollusks.

Yonge, C. M., 1957: Mantle fusion in the Lamellibranchia. Staz. Zool. Napoli, *29*:151–171.

There are several scientific journals devoted exclusively to mollusks. Two are British—Proceedings of the Malacological Society of London, and the Journal of Conchology. The Nautilus, published in Philadelphia, contains mostly short taxonomic and ecological papers.

Chapter 13

INTRODUCTION TO THE ARTHROPODS; THE TRILOBITES

The phylum Arthropoda surpasses all other groups of animals both in diversity of ecological distribution and in numbers of species and individuals. Arthropods are the only invertebrates to have actually adapted to living on land on a highly successful scale. They also are the only animals other than the vertebrates to have become modified for flight. As a result of this invasion of the terrestrial and aerial environments, arthropods have undergone an adaptive radiation that has enabled them to fill every conceivable ecological niche. More than 800,000 species have been described. This includes approximately 80 per cent of all known animal species.

Arthropods represent the culmination of evolutionary development in the protostomes. They arose either from a primitive stock of polychaetes or from an ancestor common to both; and the relationship between arthropods and annelids is displayed in several ways:

1. Arthropods like annelids, are metameric. Although metamerism has been reduced in many arthropod groups and has almost disappeared in such forms as mites and ticks, it remains quite evident in many and in the embryonic development of all arthropods.

2. Primitively, each arthropod segment bears a pair of appendages (Fig. 13-1, *A*). This same condition is displayed by the polychaetes in which each metamere bears a pair of parapodia. However, the homology between parapodia and arthropod appendages has been questioned by some authors.

3. The nervous systems in both groups are constructed on the same basic plan. In both, a dorsal anterior brain is followed by a ventral nerve cord containing ganglionic swellings in each segment (Fig. 13-1, *A*).

4. The excretory organs of some arthropods, for example the green glands of crustaceans and the coxal glands of arachnids, are perhaps homologous to the coelomoducts of polychaetes.

5. The embryonic development of primitive arthropods such as certain crustaceans displays traces of spiral cleavage, with the mesoderm in these forms arising from the *4d* blastomere.

Although the arthropods display these annelidan characteristics, they have undergone a great many profound and distinctive changes in the course of their evolution. The most important of these has been the development of a unique body covering, or external skeleton, which serves members of the phylum as an armor-like cuticle encasement (Fig. 13-2). This cuticular material is secreted by the single layer of epithelial cells known as the hypodermis. The cuticular skeleton is not uniform in construction but basically consists of two layers. The thin outer layer is known as the epicuticle and is composed of proteins and lipids but lacks chitin.

Beneath the epicuticle is a much thicker layer known as the procuticle, which contains chitin as the principal constituent (Richards, 1951). The procuticle is composed of an outer exocuticle and an inner endocuticle. Chemically, chitin is an acetate of the polysaccharide that contains glycosamine as its most important

321

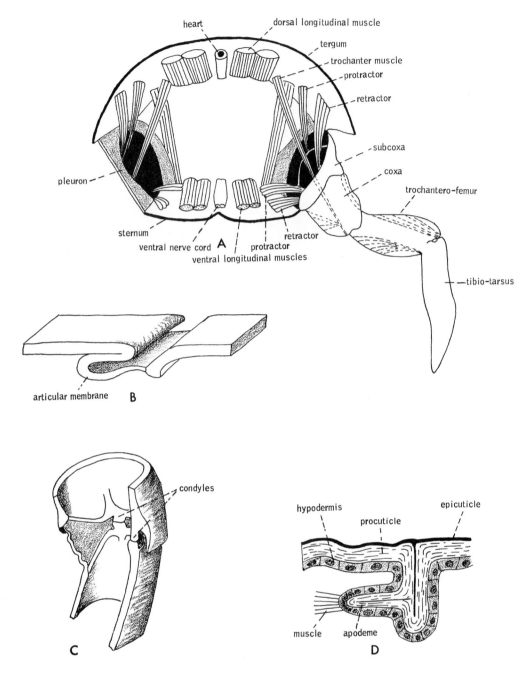

Figure 13-1. *A.* Arthropod body segment (transverse section). (After Weber from Kaestner.) *B.* Intersegmental articulation. Note articular membrane folded beneath segmental plate. (After Weber from Vandel.) *C.* Appendicular articulation, showing condyles. (After Weber from Vandel.) *D.* An apodeme. (After Janet from Vandel.)

constituent. In many arthropods the procuticle is also impregnated with mineral salts. This is particularly true for the Crustacea in which calcium carbonate and calcium phosphate deposition takes place in the procuticule. The cuticle is a relatively impermeable covering except where it is thin in certain areas and allows the passage of gases or the absorption of water.

The arthropod cuticle is not restricted entirely to the exterior of the body. The hypodermis develops from the embryonic, surface ectoderm, and all infoldings of this original layer thus become lined with cuticle. Therefore the derivatives of the stomodeum, which make up the foregut part of the digestive tract, are lined with cuticle. In the same way, the procto-

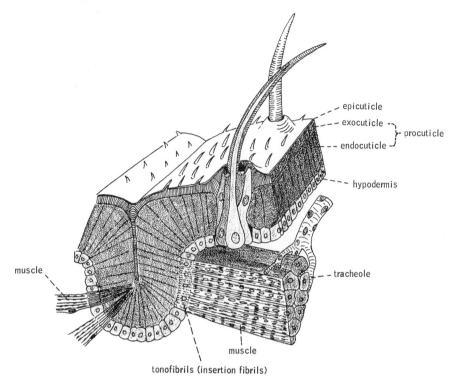

epicuticle

exocuticle

endocuticle

}procuticle

hypodermis

tracheole

muscle

muscle

tonofibrils (insertion fibrils)

Figure 13-2.   Three dimensional section of an arthropod integument (insect). (After Weber from Kaestner.)

deal derivatives, forming the hindgut, are lined with cuticle. Only the connecting midgut region, derived from entoderm, lacks cuticle. These three regions of the digestive tract are characteristic of all arthropods. Other ectodermal derivatives lined with a cuticle are: the tracheal (respiratory) tubes of insects, chilopods, diplopods, and some arachnids; the book lungs of scorpions and spiders; and parts of the reproductive systems of some groups.

The color of arthropods commonly results from the deposition of brown, yellow, orange, and red melanin pigments within the cuticle. However, iridescent greens, purples, and other colors result from fine striations of the epicuticle, which cause light refraction and give the aspect of color. Often body coloration does not directly originate in the cuticle but instead is caused by blood and tissue pigments that are visible through a thin transparent cuticle.

The presence of an external skeletal covering created two problems that had to be overcome in the evolution of arthropods—problems of movement and growth. If the animal were solidly encased in cuticle, all movement would be prohibited. This problem was eliminated by the division of the cuticle into separate plates. Primitively, these plates are confined to segments, and the plate of one segment is connected to the plate of the adjoining segment by means

of an articular membrane, a region in which the cuticle is very thin and flexible (Fig. 13-1, B). Basically the cuticle of each segment is divided into four primary plates—a dorsal tergum, two lateral pleura, and a ventral sternum (Fig. 13-1, A). This pattern has frequently disappeared because of either secondary fusion or subdivision.

The cuticular skeleton of the appendages, like that of the body, has been divided into tube-like segments, or sections, connected to one another by articular membranes, thus creating a joint at each junction. Such joints enable the segments of the appendages, as well as those of the body, to move. In most arthropods, the articular membrane between body segments is folded beneath the anterior segment (Fig. 13-1, B). In some arthropods, the additional development of articular condyles and sockets is suggestive of vertebrate skeletal structures (Fig. 13-1, C).

The second problem, that of growth, caused by the presence of an external skeleton, has been eliminated because of the development of the periodic shedding of the cuticle. The process both of ridding the body of the old cuticle and of secreting a new cuticle is called molting or ecdysis. While the details of molting vary within the different arthropod classes, the process is essentially the same in all. Prior to the actual shedding, the hypodermis secretes an enzyme that completely erodes the base of the old cuticle, thus separating the cuticle from the hypodermis. This is followed by the hypodermal secretion of a new epicuticle, which is impervious to the previously secreted enzymes.

After the formation of the new epicuticle, the hypodermis secretes the new procuticle. This inner layer is perhaps protected from the enzymes by the epicuticle above it. Once the new cuticle is formed, the animal sheds its old skeleton. This process is accomplished in most arthropods by a longitudinal rupturing of the cuticle along the dorsal or lateral sides of the body. The animal then pulls itself out of the old cuticle and leaves it behind.

The new cuticle is relatively soft and pliable and thus enables the animal to stretch and increase in size. Shortly after the animal molts, the cuticle hardens and no further increase in body size can take place until the next ecdysis. The growth stage assumed between molts is called an instar. The number of instars appearing in the life span of an individual varies from species to species, and in general the time spent in each instar increases with the age of the animal. One disadvantage of molting is the vulnerability of the animal while the new cuticle is still soft and unprotective. Frequently the animal goes into hiding until the new cuticle hardens.

As movement became restricted to flexion between plates of the cuticle, a profound change took place in the nature of the body musculature. In annelids the somatic musculature takes the form of two cylinders lying beneath the epidermis. The outer cylinder is composed of circular fibers, while the inner cylinder is composed of longitudinal fibers. In arthropods on the other hand, these muscular cylinders have disappeared, and distinct striated muscles have formed, which are attached to the inner surface of the skeletal system (Figs. 13-1, A and 13-2).

The muscles are not attached to the hypodermis but are attached to the procuticle by special fibers inserted on the inner surface. Flexion and extension between plates are effected by the contraction of these muscles, with muscles and cuticle acting together as a lever system. This cofunctioning of the muscular system and skeletal system to bring about locomotion is essentially the same as in vertebrates. The only difference is that the muscles in the arthropods are attached to the inner surface of an external skeleton, whereas in the vertebrates the muscles are attached to the outer side of an internal skeleton. Extension, particularly of the appendages, is accomplished, in part or entirely, by an increase in blood pressure. Thus, while annelids move by muscular undulations resulting from the antagonistic action of the muscular cylinders and by the paddle-like or anchoring action of the parapodia, arthropods employ as their chief means of locomotion jointed appendages, which act either as paddles in the aquatic species or as legs in the terrestrial groups.

Accompanying the development of muscle connection to the procuticle has been the development of what is sometimes called the endoskeleton—an infolding of the procuticle that produces inner projections, or apodemes, on which the muscles are inserted (Fig. 13-1, D). The nature of the endoskeletal system in arthropods varies considerably; in some cases sclerotization of internal tissue has taken place, forming free plates for muscle attachment within the body.

The well developed metameric coelom characteristic of the annelids has undergone drastic reduction in the arthropods and is represented by only two structures: the space or cavity of the gonads—the gonocoel and its associated ducts—; and in certain arthropods, the excretory organs, which are homologous to the annelidan coelomoducts. The other spaces of the arthropodan body do not constitute a true coelom but rather a hemocoel—that is, merely sinuses or spaces in the tissue filled with blood.

The arthropodan circulatory system has evolved from a closed system, such as that displayed by annelids, to an open one. What functioned as the dorsal vessel in the annelids has become in the arthropods a distinct heart. The development of a distinct heart is not surprising, because the dorsal vessel in annelids is contractile and is the chief center for blood propulsion.

The heart varies in position and length in different arthropod groups, but in all of them the heart consists essentially of one or more chambers with muscular walls arranged in a linear fashion and perforated by pairs of lateral openings called ostia (Fig. 14-23). The ostia enable the blood to flow into the heart from the large surrounding sinus known as the pericardium (Fig. 14-23). In this case, the term *pericardium* is misleading, because in arthropods the pericardium does not derive from the coelom as in the vertebrates, but instead is a part of the hemocoel. After entering the heart, blood is pumped out to the body tissues through vessels frequently called arteries and is eventually dumped into sinuses in which it bathes the tissues directly. The blood then returns by various routes to the pericardial sinus.

The blood of arthropods is essentially the same as the blood of annelids. Respiratory pigments such as hemoglobin and hemocyanin are sometimes present, dissolved in the plasma. Several forms of amebocytes are present in the

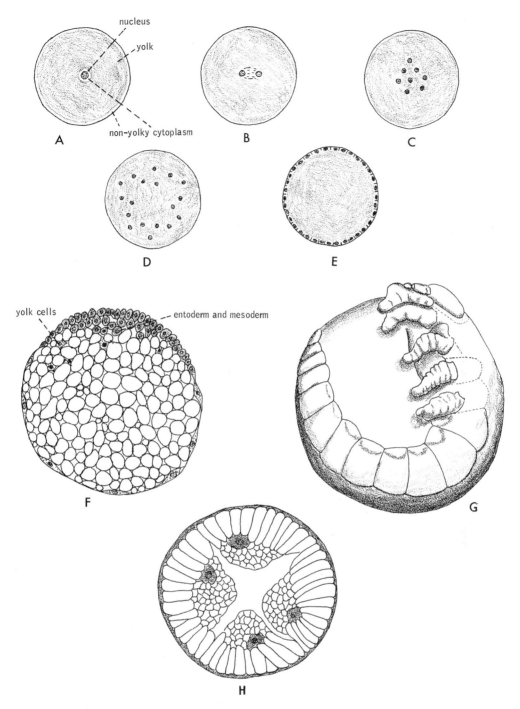

Figure 13-3.   *A* to *E*. Superficial cleavage. *A*. Centrolecithal egg. *B* and *C*. Nuclear division. *D*. Migration of nuclei toward periphery of egg. *E*. Blastula. Cell membranes have developed, separating adjacent nuclei. *F*. Gastrula of the spider, *Theridion maculatum,* showing development of germinal center. (After Dawydoff.) *G*. Embryo of the arachnid, *Thelyphonus.* (After Kaestner.) *H*. Initial complete cleavage in the spider, *Theridion maculatum.* (After Morin from Dawydoff.)

blood. They are treated in the discussions of the various arthropodan classes.

The nervous system in arthropods has reached a high degree of cephalization. The increase in brain size is correlated with well developed sense organs, such as eyes and antennae; this has resulted in rather complex behavioral patterns in some arthropod groups.

With few exceptions arthropods are dioecious. Furthermore, many employ modified appendages during copulation. Fertilization is always internal in terrestrial forms but may be external in aquatic species. The eggs of most arthropods are extremely rich in yolk and are centrolecithal. In the centrolecithal egg the nucleus is surrounded by a small island of cytoplasm in the middle of a large mass of yolk (Fig. 13-3, *A*). The presence of such a large amount of yolk and the change in its distribution have effected considerable modification in the development of arthropods when compared with development in the typical polychaetes. Although a few arthropods display traces of spiral cleavage, most have a modified type of cleavage that is associated with centrolecithal eggs and is called superficial cleavage (Fig. 13-3, *B* to *E*).

After fertilization, the centrally located nucleus undergoes mitotic divisions, but without the formation of cell membranes and without any cleavage of the yolk. The result, after several such divisions, is an uncleaved egg containing a large number of syncytial nuclei within the center. As division continues, the nuclei gradually migrate to the periphery, where cell membranes form but do not extend into the yolky interior. This stage of development represents a stereoblastula. Development continues with the formation of a primordial germinal disc located on one side of the embryo (Fig. 13-3, *F*). This germinal center proliferates entoderm and mesoderm and eventually forms the embryonic body, which appears to be wrapped around the egg (Fig. 13-3, *G*).

In many arthropods, there is a type of cleavage that is somewhat intermediate between total cleavage and superficial cleavage. After a few divisions of the nucleus, the yolk undergoes segmentation or breaks up into pyramids, each of which contains one of the nuclei (Fig. 13-3, *H*). Gradually the yolk pyramids disappear, and development shifts to the superficial type.

EVOLUTION OF THE ARTHROPODS

There is very little doubt that arthropods arose from the annelids or at least from some common ancestor. The characteristics just described show a very clear relationship between these two groups. However, the nature of the primitive ancestral arthropods and their evolution into the modern classes is by no means so clear. It is impossible to discuss here all of the different and widely divergent theories and points of view. The evolutionary sequence that follows is one modern concept based on recent work in comparative anatomy and embryology.

It is assumed that after their origin from the annelids, the major arthropod innovations described in the preceding section had developed. The primary consideration here is with the nature of the head, the body, and the appendages of this primitive ancestral form. At the present time, no direct paleontological evidence

of this structure has been discovered. Our knowledge must therefore be based largely on two primary sources of evidence—the comparative anatomy, and the embryology of living arthropod groups.

The body of the ancestral arthropod was composed of an unsegmented head, the acron, followed posteriorly by a trunk region, the soma. The acron is homologous to the prostomium of the polychaetes, and just as the prostomium bears a number of different sensory structures, the acron bears at least two pairs of eyes and one pair of antennules homologous to the prostomial palps of the polychaetes. Ventrally and posterior to the acron was located the mouth. It was bordered posteriorly by the first trunk segment. The same arrangement of parts is evident in the polychaetes.

The trunk region (soma) consisted of many segments arranged in a linear series. Each segment carried a pair of appendages except the last segment, called the telson. However, most important is that all the segments, and the appendages that they carried, were similar, displaying little differentiation or modification.

Two theories are prevalent as to the nature of the ancestral arthropod appendage. One theory states that each appendage was a biramous structure consisting of three regions (Fig. 15-1). The first, or proximal section is called the protopodite. This section connected the appendage to the body segment. The two distal branches articulated with the protopodite. The outer branch is called the exopodite; the inner branch is called the endopodite.

The proponents of this theory hold that all of the appendages of living arthropods have been derived from this basic biramous type; even if an appendage is now distinctly uniramous, this conformation is a secondary one, caused by the loss of either the exopodite or the endopodite. The principal evidence for this theory is the structure of the crustacean appendages, which are quite clearly of the biramous type. Unfortunately, when the terrestrial arthropods are considered, this theory runs into difficulties. The appendages of terrestrial groups are almost all uniramous, and no evidence of a biramous condition is displayed during embryonic development.

The second theory concerning the nature of the ancestral arthropod appendage states that this appendage was of a uniramous type and that the exopodite, when present in modern arthropods, represents nothing more than a secondary development or a side branch of an originally uniramous structure. This second theory is satisfactory for the terrestrial arthropods, but it does not explain the apparently primitive biramous appendage present in the crustaceans.

During the evolution of the arthropods from the primitive ancestral stock to the present classes, an early divergence into two major lines of evolution took place. One line gave rise to the classes collectively known as the Mandibulata, which includes the crustaceans, the insects, the centipedes, and the millipedes. The second line, known as the Chelicerata, includes the horseshoe crabs, the arachnids, and the sea spiders. In the evolution of both lines of arthropods two general trends are evident. First, there is a tendency toward modification of appendages and segments through fusion, reduction, and differentiation. Second, there is a tendency for the more anterior segments to fuse with the acron, thus giving rise to a composite head. The head of all living arthropods therefore consists of a primitive anterior and unsegmented acron plus the varying number of trunk segments that have fused with it.

In the Mandibulata the antennules of the acron (homologous to the prostomial palps of polychaetes) are represented in the crustaceans by the first pair of antennae or antennules, and are represented in the insects, the diplopods, and the chilopods by the antennae. Posteriorly, four trunk segments have fused with the acron. Originally, the appendages of these segments were located behind the mouth (that is, post-oral) and in embryological development, they always arise in this position. In many cases, however, a secondary shift causes those appendages to take up a pre-oral position—to lie in front of the mouth.

The appendages borne by the first of these four "cephalic" segments gave rise in the Crustacea to the second pair of antennae. Thus the second antennae are true trunk appendages in contrast to the antennules. In the insects this appendage is either vestigial or is completely lacking and is evident only in embryonic development. The second fused trunk segment carries a pair of appendages represented in all mandibulates by the first of the feeding appendages, known as the mandibles. The third and fourth pairs of appendages borne by the fused segments developed into the first and second maxillae of crustaceans, the maxillae and labium of insects, and the maxillae of the chilopods and diplopods (only one pair of maxillae are present in diplopods). Although the labium in insects is a single structure, it has developed from a fusion of originally paired appendages.

Evidence that the arthropod head is of a compound nature is best seen in the structure of the brain. Typically, the arthropod brain consists of three basic regions—an anterior protocerebrum, an intermediate deutocerebrum, and a posterior tritocerebrum (Fig. 13-4, B). The protocerebrum and deutocerebrum are homologous to the single ganglionic mass of the polychaete brain. Thus, these two regions have evolved directly from the primitive brain found within the acron. The division of the primitive brain into two distinct regions probably resulted from a secondary development associated with the sense organs, since the deutocerebrum innervates the antennules and the protocerebrum innervates the eyes found in most arthropods.

The tritocerebrum represents a new addition to the brain resulting from the fusion of the first trunk segment to the head. Evidence that the tritocerebrum represents the ganglion of the first trunk segment is apparent, because it innervates the second pair of antennae in crustaceans, which are the appendages for the first trunk segment. Furthermore, although the tritocerebrum is pre-oral, this location is undoubtedly secondary, for the commissure connecting the paired ganglionic masses of which it is composed is located behind the esophagus (Fig. 13-4, B).

The tendency for trunk segments to become associated with the head has advanced even further in the more highly developed crustaceans, in which the appendages of the fifth, sixth, and seventh segments have turned forward and are used in feeding. In such crustaceans, the appendages of these three segments are known as the first, second, and third maxillipeds.

Turning now to the other main branch of evolutionary development, which leads to the chelicerates (king crabs, scorpions, spiders, and mites), the problem of head development is found to be more difficult. Although, as in the mandibulates, the head of living chelicerates undoubtedly has resulted from a fusion of trunk segments with the acron, it is difficult to homologize these segments with the head segments of mandibulates. In the chelicerates, the antennules have disappeared as well as the deutocerebrum that innervated them (Fig. 13-4, C). The first trunk segment bears a pair of appendages known as the chelicerae. The chelicerae, like the second pair of antennae in the crustaceans, are innervated by the tritocerebrum. Thus the second pair of antennae in crustaceans, and the chelicerae of chelicerates must be homologous.

All chelicerates, except some sea spiders, are characterized by a pair of pedipalps and four pairs of legs located posterior to the chelicerae. The obvious conclusion would be to homologize these postcheliceral segments with the postantennal segments of mandibulates. Thus the pedipalps would be homologous to the

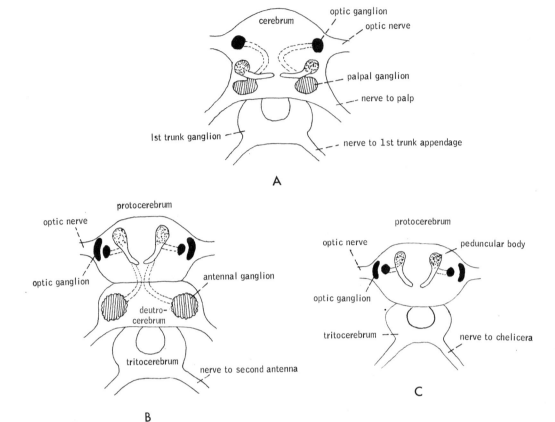

Figure 13-4.   Annelid and arthropod brains. *A.* A polychaete annelid. *B.* A mandibulate arthropod. *C.* A chelicerate arthropod. (All after Hanstrom from Vandel.)

mandibles, and the first two pairs of chelicerate walking legs would be homologous to the two pairs of mandibulate maxillae. Such a conclusion may well be an oversimplification; for this conclusion to be valid, it must be assumed that these postcheliceral segments are actually the second, third, and fourth trunk segments and that no intervening segments have been lost. This has not been proved.

Synopsis of the Arthropod Classes

Subphylum Trilobitomorpha. The fossil trilobites.
Subphylum Chelicerata.
    Class Merostomata. The living horseshoe crabs and fossil eurypterids.
    Class Arachnida. The largest of the chelicerate class; includes the scorpions, harvestmen, spiders, ticks, and mites.
    Class Pycnogonida. The sea spiders.
Subphylum Mandibulata
    Class Crustacea. The crustaceans.
    Class Insecta. The insects.
    Class Chilopoda. The centipedes.
    Class Diplopoda. The millipedes.
    Class Symphyla. The symphylans.
    Class Pauropoda. The pauropodans.

THE TRILOBITES

The subphylum Trilobitomorpha is the most primitive of all known arthropod groups and from an evolutionary standpoint represents the best starting point in discussing the arthropod classes. Trilobites are an extinct group of marine arthropods, which were once abundant and widely distributed in the Paleozoic seas. They reached their height of distribution and abundance during the Cambrian and Ordovician periods and disappeared at the end of the Paleozoic era. Over 3,900 species have been described from fossil specimens.

The trilobite body was in general somewhat oval and flattened and displayed a dorsal cuticle, or exoskeleton, that was much heavier and thicker than the ventral surface, which carried the appendages (Fig. 13-5). This difference is the reason in most cases only the dorsal skeleton has been preserved to form the fossil record. Most trilobite species ranged between 3 and 10 cm. in length, although some planktonic forms were only 0.5 mm. in length; some species attained a length of 2½ ft., about the same size as living horseshoe crabs.

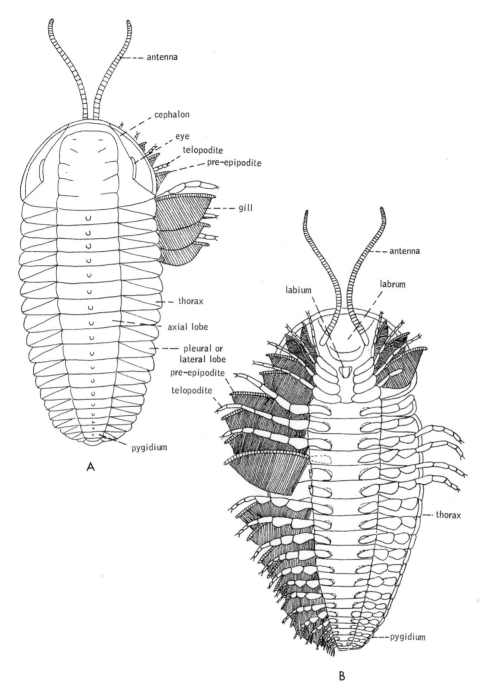

Figure 13-5.   The Ordovician trilobite, *Triarthrus eatoni*. *A*. Dorsal view. *B*. Ventral view. (Both after Walcottt and Raymond from Störmer.)

The trilobite body was divided into three more or less equal sections—a solid anterior cephalon; an intermediate thorax or trunk region, consisting of a varying number of separate segments; and a posterior pygidium. Each of these body divisions was in turn divided into three regions by a pair of furrows running from anterior to posterior and forming a median axial lobe flanked on each side by a lateral lobe. The

name Trilobita refers to this transverse trilobation of the dorsal body surface.

The anterior body section, the cephalon, was composed of four fused segments in addition to the acron and was covered by a shield-like carapace with the posterior lateral margins projecting backward. The original head segmentation was frequently indicated by short transverse grooves on the carapace. The cephalic shield

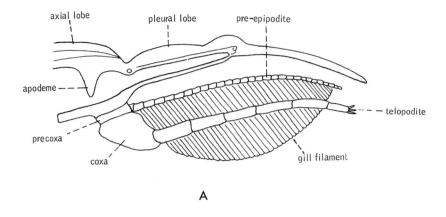

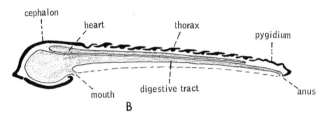

Figure 13-6.   *A.* Trilobite, showing a trunk appendage (transverse section through left half). (Modified after Walcott and Raymond from Störmer.) *B.* Trilobite (sagittal section). (After Moore, Lalicker, and Fischer.)

not only covered all the dorsal surface but was folded under at its margins so that the original ventral surface was quite narrow and restricted. The pleural skeleton was reduced to thin membranes to which the appendages were attached. This condition was true not only for the cephalon, but also for the other two divisions of the body. On each side of the middle of the carapace were a pair of compound eyes that varied considerably in size, depending upon the species.

The mouth (Fig. 13-6, *B*) was located in the middle of the underside of the cephalon just behind and beneath a lip-like prominence called the labrum (Fig. 13-5, *B*). On each side of the labrum was a long sensory antennule, homologous to the first pair of antennae of the crustaceans and the antennae of insects.

Behind the mouth were located four pairs of similar appendages identical to the appendages of the trunk and pygidium. Each appendage was biramous and consisted of an inner walking leg (telopodite) and an outer gill-bearing branch (pre-epipodite) (Fig. 13-6, *A*). The appendages articulated with the pleural membrane through a small precoxal segment that also bore on its outer side the pre-epipodite. The pre-epipodite was situated between the lateral

extension of the pleural lobe and the walking leg and consisted of numerous segments, each of which bore (or at least the terminal segment bore) a fringe of filaments extending posteriorly. The fringe of one appendage overlapped the fringe of the next. These filaments were probably gills, with gases diffusing between blood within the filament and the external water.

The undersurface of the precoxa was connected to a large coxal segment that in turn articulated with the walking leg (the telopodite). Each walking leg consisted of seven segments, the last of which was modified to form a hook.*

The trilobite trunk (thorax) consisted of a varying number of separately articulating segments; some species were able to roll up into a ball as do sow bugs. Like the cephalon, the thorax possessed segments with posterior lateral margins that were frequently prolonged and extended backward. The lateral margins of the trunk tergites were folded ventrally. Each segment bore ventrally a pair of appendages similar to the appendages of the cephalon.

---

* This description of trilobite appendages is based on the work of Störmer (1949). The principal alternative morphology is described in the section on the phylogenetic relationships of the group.

The pygidium was constructed on the same plan as the thorax except that the segments were fused and formed a solid shield. The appendages of the pygidium usually were successively smaller toward the posterior end.

The majority of trilobites were bottom dwellers and crawled over sand and mud using the walking legs. The flattened body and dorsal eyes were adaptations for this type of existence. Some trilobite groups had a shovel-shaped or plow-shaped cephalon adapted for burrowing (Fig. 13-7, A). Such bottom-dwelling forms were probably scavengers or consumed mud and silt and then digested the organic materials from it as do many annelids. In addition, the branchial filaments possibly could have sifted food materials from the surrounding water and then passed the food anteriorly to the mouth from one overlapping fringe to the next.

Some zoologists have considered that the coxal segments of the legs functioned as gnathobases—that is, functioned in food grinding. The two coxae of each segment bore tubercles or short spines on their inner faces and the movement of one coxa against the opposite coxa enabled food to be ground and passed anteriorly.

The principal objection to this theory is that the coxal segments or gnathobases of the trilobites were too widely separated to function efficiently in this manner. Furthermore, spines and tubercles were not confined to the coxae, but were also present on other segments of the walking legs where they could have had no masticating function.

Some groups of trilobites were apparently not confined to the bottom but took up a swimming existence (Fig. 13-7, B). In these forms the body was narrower, and the eyes were located on the sides of the head. Although nothing is known about their appendages, the walking legs may have been flattened and adapted for swimming. The smallest species of trilobites were planktonic. The dorsal surface displayed long radiating spines that have been considered flotation devices (Fig. 13-7, C).

Fossil material has yielded not only much information on the structure of adult trilobites, but has also made possible a remarkably complete understanding of the developmental stages. For some forms, such as species of *Sao* and *Olenus,* almost the entire larval series has been determined from fossil specimens.

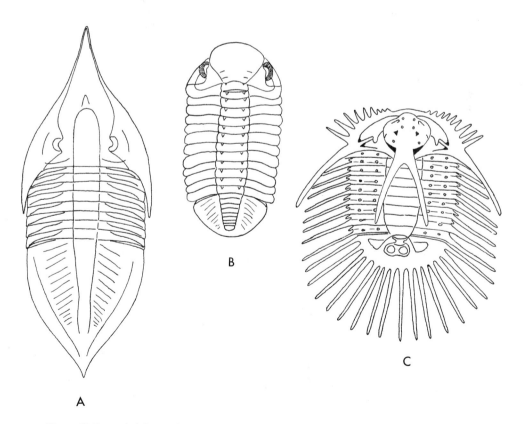

Figure 13-7. *A.* A burrowing trilobite, *Megalaspis acuticauda,* from the Ordovician period with a plow-shaped cephalon. (After Störmer.) *B.* A pelagic trilobite, *Phacops steenbergi,* from the Silurian period. (After Barrande from Störmer.) *C.* A planktonic trilobite, *Radiaspis radiata,* from the Devonian period. The long spines may have been flotation devices. (After Störmer.)

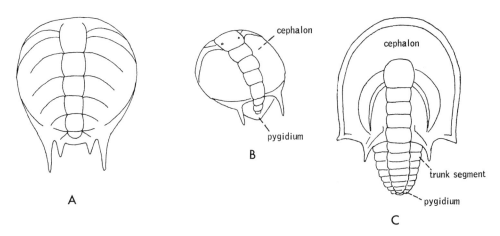

Figure 13-8.   Trilobite larvae. *A*. Protaspis of *Olenus,* with four segments. *B*. Late protaspis of *Olenus.* Pygidium just formed. *C*. Meraspis of *Paedeumias.* (All after Moore, Lalicker, and Fischer.)

During their post-embryological development, trilobites passed through three larval periods, each of which consisted of a number of instars. The trilobite emerged from the egg as a tiny protaspis larva. The protaspis was undoubtedly planktonic, measuring between 0.5 mm. and 1.0 mm. in length, and the body was covered by a single dorsal carapace consisting of the acron and four post-oral segments (Fig. 13-8, *A* and *B*). After passing through several instars, in which additional segments were added to the carapace, the protaspis passed into a meraspis larva. In this larval stage the pygidium was located behind the cephalon (Fig. 13-8, *C*).

The thoracic region appeared during succeeding molts as segments were gradually freed from the anterior border of the pygidium. This indicates, at least in the trilobites, that the pygidium was older than the thoracic region. This fact is particularly important in explaining the variation in the sizes of the adult pygidium. In most species, the pygidium approximately equalled the other two body sections in length. However, in early primitive forms the pygidium was quite small. Apparently the large adult pygidium of later species resulted from a retention of thoracic segments that were originally freed by the pygidium during larval development.

The final larval stage is known as a holaspis larva, which, though still very small, displayed the general adult structure. Additional molts merely involved minor changes and an increase in size.

The details of the relationship of the trilobites to other groups of arthropods is still undetermined. Some zoologists believe that the trilobites are related to the crustaceans, while others maintain that the trilobites represent a primitive group of chelicerates. Still others regard them as ancestral to both the mandibulates and the chelicerates.

The chief arguments in favor of a close relationship to the crustaceans is the presence of biramous appendages and antennules on the trilobites. The proponents of such a supposition do not recognize the existence of a precoxa but believe the precoxa and coxa were combined as a single segment, from which the two branches of the appendages stem. If this was true, the two branches could be considered an exopodite and endopodite, and the appendage would be homologous with those of the crustaceans.

There are three principal lines of evidence for a phylogenetic relationship between trilobites and chelicerates. First, if the branchial division of the appendage stems from a separate precoxal segment, as Störmer theorizes and as described above, then the trilobite appendage cannot be considered homologous to that of crustaceans. The most convincing evidence, however, is seen in the embryology and fossil history of a true chelicerate, the horseshoe crab. The origin of body segments in this group recapitulates to a remarkable degree the trilobite cephalon and pygidium. Finally, certain fossil members of both groups are so intermediate in structure that it is difficult to draw a sharp line between the two subphyla.

The last theory, which places the trilobites in an ancestral position to both mandibulates and chelicerates, is held by a number of zoologists and utilizes evidence from both of the arguments just presented.

From all of the evidence available at present the most convincing theory considers the trilobites to be either primitive chelicerates or at least the common ancestor for both chelicerates and mandibulates.

BIBLIOGRAPHY

Moore, R. C., Lalicker, C. G., and Fischer, A. G., 1952: Invertebrate Fossils. McGraw-Hill, New York, pp. 475–520. A good morphological account of the trilobites.

Richards, A. G., 1951: The Integument of Arthropods. University of Minnesota Press, Minneapolis. A detailed comparative treatment of all aspects of the arthropod integument.

Shrock, R. R., and Twenhofel, W. H., 1953: Principles of Invertebrate Paleontology. McGraw-Hill, New York, pp. 536–641. A general account of the trilobites; good bibliography.

Störmer, L., 1949: Sous-embranchement des Trilobitomorphes. *In* Traité de Zoologie (P. Grassé, ed.). Masson et Cié, Paris, Vol. 6, pp. 159–216. An authoritative treatment of the trilobites.

Vandel, A., 1949: Généralités sur les Arthropodes. *In* Traité de Zoologie (P. Grassé, ed.). Masson et Cié, Paris, Vol. 6. pp. 79–158. An excellent comparative treatment of the anatomy, embryology, and evolution of the arthropods. This is the best and most recent general account available.

Chapter 14

THE CHELICERATES

All classes in this chapter belong to the sub-phylum Chelicerata, one of the two great evolutionary lines within the Arthropoda. Although the chief characteristics are discussed in the introduction to the arthropods, it might be well to review them briefly before surveying the chelicerate classes.

Unlike the body of the mandibulates, that of the chelicerates is divided into a cephalothorax (or prosoma) and an abdomen (or opisthosoma). The two regions involve an incorporation of entirely different segments than the corresponding regions in the mandibulates. The antennules have disappeared, and the first pre-oral appendages (originally post-oral) are feeding structures called chelicerae. The first post-oral appendages are called pedipalps and are modified to perform various functions in the different classes.

CLASS MEROSTOMATA

The Merostomata are aquatic chelicerates characterized by five or six pairs of abdominal appendages modified as gills and by a spike-like telson at the end of the body. The group can be divided into two distinct subclasses—the Xiphosura (horseshoe crabs) and the extinct Eurypterida (giant water scorpions).

Subclass Xiphosura

Although the fossil record of the Xiphosura extends back to the Ordovician period, three

genera and five species compose the only living representatives today. One of these, *Xiphosura* (*Limulus*) *polyphemus,* is the horseshoe or king crab, common to the northwestern Atlantic coast and Gulf of Mexico. All the other members of this group are found along Asian coasts from Japan and Korea south through the East Indies and Philippines.

The living horseshoe crabs reach a length of 60 centimeters and are dark brown in color. The carapace is horseshoe-shaped, convex above and concave below, with the posterior lateral angles prolonged backward to about half the length of the abdomen (Fig. 14-1). The dorsal surface is relatively smooth except for the presence of a median and two longitudinal ridges. To the outside of each lateral ridge is located an eye, and between the lateral and median ridge is located a pair of longitudinal furrows. Two pairs of small median eyes are also present, one pair on each side of the median ridge at the anterior end.

The anterior dorsal surface is reflected ventrally, and in the front forms a large triangular surface that tapers back toward the mouth (Fig. 14-2, *A*). A frontal organ and a pair of degenerate eyes are located on the ridge formed by this triangle. Behind the apex of this ridge is a narrow labrum or upper lip. A pair of tri-segmented chelicerae are attached to each side of the labrum; the last two segments form a pair of pincers. The mouth is located behind the labrum and is followed by a short narrow sternum.

Five pairs of walking legs are located pos-

334

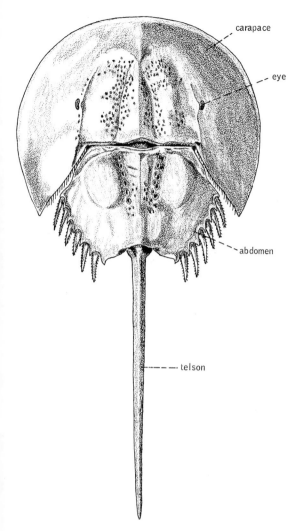

carapace

eye

abdomen

telson

Figure 14-1.   The king crab, *Xiphosura polyphemus* (dorsal view). (After Van der Hoeven from Fage.)

the sternum between the last pair of walking legs. These appendages are believed to represent the coxae of a pair of degenerate appendages associated with the seventh, or pregenital, segment. Each chilarium consists of a single article armed with hairs and spines, as are the gnathobases, and probably functions similarly.

The abdomen (opisthosoma) is unsegmented and fits into the concavity formed by the posterior border of the cephalothorax and its lateral extensions (Figs. 14-1 and 14-2, *A*). The median longitudinal ridge of the cephalothorax and its lateral furrows extend posteriorly over the abdomen. Along each furrow are six small pits marking the location of internal muscle attachments. Six short mobile spines border the posterior edge of the abdomen.

A long triangular spike-like tail (telson) articulates with the posterior of the abdomen. The telson of horseshoe crabs is not actually a true telson, since it does not bear the anal opening. Rather, the tail of the horseshoe crab represents a series of fused tergites (dorsal plates) of the more anterior abdominal segments. The tail of these animals is highly mobile and is used like a pole when the animal plows through sand. The telson is also used for righting the body when it is accidentally turned over. The telson is never used for defense, and horseshoe crabs can be picked up and carried by it.

The abdomen bears six pairs of appendages (Fig. 14-2, *A*). The first pair forms the genital operculum, a large membranous flap-like structure resulting from the median fusion of the paired appendages of the eighth, or genital, segment. Two genital pores are located on the underside of this flap.

Posterior to the genital operculum are located five pairs of appendages modified as gills. Like the genital operculum, they are flap-like and membranous, and each pair is fused along the midline. The undersurface of each flap is formed into many leaf-like folds called lamellae, which provide the actual surface for gaseous exchange (Fig. 14-2). Each gill contains approximately 150 lamellae. This arrangement of leaf-like lamellae has caused the appendages to be called book gills. The movement of the gills maintains a constant circulation of water over the lamellae, and in addition provides added propulsion by functioning as paddles for rapid movement.

Horseshoe crabs are scavengers and feed on mollusks, worms, and other organisms, including bottom-dwelling algae. Food material is picked up by the chelate appendages, passed to the gnathobases where it is macerated, and then moved anteriorly to the mouth.

The mouth, located just behind the chelic-

terior to the chelicerae on the underside of the cephalothorax (Fig. 14-2, *A*). Each walking leg consists of a coxa, a prefemur, a femur, a patella (fused with the tibia), a tibia, and two tarsal segments. The first four pairs of legs are all similar and have coxae heavily armed with spines located on the median side to form gnathobases for macerating and moving food anteriorly. The two tarsal segments form pincers. The coxa of the last pair of legs are not modified to form gnathobases but bear on the median side a short spatulate process known as a flabellum, which is used for cleaning the gills. Furthermore, the fifth or last pair of walking legs is not chelate and possesses four leaf-like processes attached to the end of the first tarsal segment. This last pair of appendages clears and sweeps away the mud and silt during burrowing.

The last pair of cephalothoracic appendages is known as chilaria and is located behind

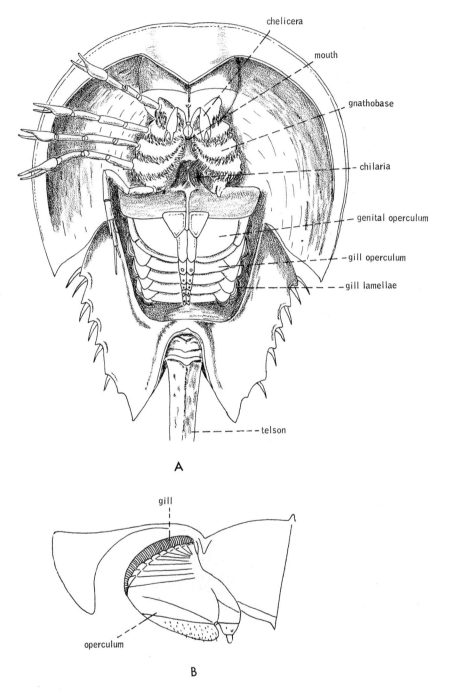

A

B

Figure 14-2. *A. Xiphosura polyphemus,* showing appendages on one side (ventral view). (After Versluys and Demoll from Kaestner.) *B.* Posterior surface of a gill operculum of *Xiphosura* in position beneath the body. (After Störmer from Fage.)

erae, opens into an esophagus that is sclerotized and forms longitudinal folds; it extends anteriorly through a dilated portion, the crop, and into a grinding chamber, the gizzard (Fig. 14-3, *A*). The longitudinal folds of cuticle in the gizzard possess denticles, and the whole structure is provided with strong muscles. After the food is ground in the gizzard, the large un-

digestible particles are regurgitated through the esophagus, while the usable food material passes posteriorly through a valve into the enlarged anterior part of the nonsclerotized midgut known as the stomach. The remainder of the midgut, called the intestine, extends posteriorly into the abdomen. Opening into each side of the stomach is one of two pairs of ducts from

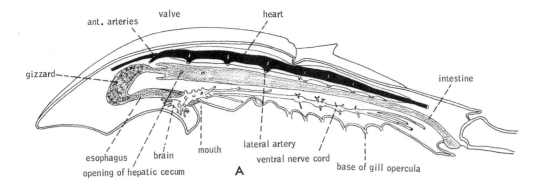

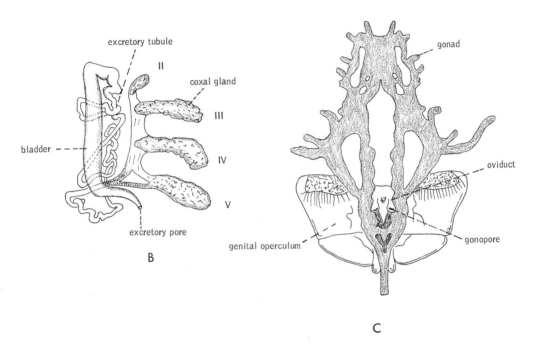

Figure 14-3. *A.* Sagittal section through *Xiphosura.* (After Patten and Redenbaugh from Kaestner.) *B.* Coxal glands and ducts of *Xiphosura.* (After Patten and Hazen from Fage.) *C.* Female reproductive system of *Xiphosura.* (After Owen from Fage.)

two large glandular hepatic ceca that ramify throughout the cephalothorax and abdomen. Enzyme production and digestion take place within the midgut region and the hepatic ceca. The hepatic ceca are also the principal area for absorption of digested food materials. Digestion is not entirely extracellular; dipeptides are digested intracellularly within the hepatic ceca.

Wastes are egested through a short sclerotized rectum and out of the anus, which is located on the ventral side of the abdomen just in front of the telson.

The circulatory system is well developed. A dorsal tubular heart, enclosed within the pericardial cavity, is located throughout most of the length of the intestine (Fig. 14-3, *A*). Blood enters the heart from the surrounding pericardial cavity through eight ostia, each guarded by valves on both sides. The blood then is pumped out through three large anterior arteries and four pairs of lateral arteries. The lateral arteries open from the heart at points opposite the first four pairs of ostia and lead into a pair of collateral arteries, one located on each side of the heart.

These principal arteries branch into a well developed arterial system supplying the body. The arteries eventually terminate in tissue sinuses, and the blood collects ventrally in two large longitudinal sinuses.

From the ventral sinuses the blood flows into the five book gills located on each side of the body. Within these gills, the blood is oxygenated. The exchange of gases takes place between the blood in the lamellae and the surrounding water. The movement of the gills not only causes the water to circulate over the lamellae, but also pumps blood in and out of these structures. When the gills move forward, the lamellae become filled with blood; when the gills move backward, blood is expelled. From the gills the blood returns to the pericardium. The blood contains hemocyanin as well as a single type of amebocyte that functions in the clotting mechanism.

Excretion takes place through four pairs of coxal glands, two pairs located on each side of the gizzard (Fig. 14-3, B). The waste removed from the surrounding blood by one of four glands is collected within a common sac-like chamber, then enters a coiled tubule and enlarged bladder before being passed to the outside through an excretory pore at the base of the last pair of walking legs.

The nervous system displays a large degree of fusion plus the very unique feature of being almost entirely enclosed within arterial vessels (Fig. 14-3, A). The brain forms a collar around the esophagus. The anterior part of the collar forms the protocerebrum, while the lateral portions represent a fusion of the tritocerebrum plus the ganglia for all of the remaining first seven segments. Thus all of the appendages anterior to the operculum are directly innervated by the brain. The collar circumscribes and unites behind the esophagus giving rise to both a ventral nerve cord with five ganglia and lateral nerves extending through the abdomen.

The lateral eyes of horseshoe crabs are peculiar in a number of respects. They are compound eyes made up of 10 to 15 clusters of retinal cells grouped around a rhabdome (Fig. 14-1). Usually, such a cluster represents an ommatidium. However, unlike a typical compound eye, the clusters are separated from each other with no pigment cells between them. Each cluster has a lens and cornea.

The median eyes are invaginated cups. The interior of the cup forms a lens that is continuous with an exterior cornea and is surrounded by retinal cells. On each side of the ventral frontal organ is located a third pair of eyes. These are degenerate in the adult but apparently function during the larval stages. The frontal organ is believed to have an olfactory function. All three pairs of eyes and the frontal organ are innervated by the protocerebrum.

Horseshoe crabs are dioecious, and the reproductive system has essentially the same structure in both the male and female (Fig. 14-3, C). The gonad is comprised of a symmetrical network of tissue, composed of tiny ovarian tubules in the female and sperm sacs and ductules in the male. The gonad is located subjacent to the intestine and extends from the posterior half of the cephalothorax through the abdomen. The sperm or eggs pass to the outside through short ducts that open onto the median region and the underside of the base of the genital operculum.

During mating and egg-laying, male and female horseshoe crabs congregate in the intertidal zone along the shores of sounds, bays, and estuaries. The male climbs onto the abdominal carapace of the female and maintains its hold with the modified hook-like first pair of walking legs. Meanwhile, the female scoops out a depression in the sand and deposits two to three hundred large eggs. These are fertilized by the male during their deposition. The mating pair separate, and the eggs are covered and left in the sand.

The eggs are centrolecithal, between 2 and 3 mm. in diameter, and covered by a thick envelope, or chorion. Cleavage is total. A solid gastrula is formed containing two mesodermal (germinal) centers, one anterior and the other posterior in relation to the future embryo. The anterior germinal center forms the first four segments of the cephalothorax; the posterior center forms all the remaining body segments. The first three segments formed by the posterior center (the fifth, sixth, and seventh segments) fuse with the four segments formed by the anterior center, creating the adult cephalothorax.

As it hatches, the trilobite larva, so named because of its superficial similarity to trilobites, emerges from the egg. This larva is approximately one centimeter long, and actively swims about and burrows in sand. The cephalothorax of the horseshoe crab is very similar to the cephalon of the trilobite. The telson is very small and does not project beyond the abdomen. Only two of the five pairs of book gills are present, although all anterior appendages are present. As successive molts take place, the remaining book gills appear, the telson increases in length, and the young crab assumes the adult form. Sexual maturity is not reached until the third year. In Japanese species, it has been calculated that attainment of sexual maturity requires 13 instars in the male and 14 in the female.

Subclass Eurypterida

The second group composing the class Merosto-mata are the extinct giant water scorpions, which belong to the subclass Eurypterida (or Gigantostraca). The eurypterids were aquatic and existed from the Cambrian to the Permian period. The eurypterids probably attained the largest size of any of the arthropods. One spe-cies of the genus *Pterygotus* was almost three meters long.

Eurypterids were quite similar to horseshoe crabs in their general body plan (Fig. 14-4). They had the same prosomal appendages and a telson, but the cephalothorax was smaller and lacked posterior lateral extensions. Lateral and median eyes were present. The chief differences between the two groups are that the abdomen of the eurypterids was composed of separate seg-ments and consisted both of a seven-segmented pre-abdomen (mesosoma) bearing appendages and a post-abdomen (metasoma) of five nar-rower segments lacking appendages. The telson was attached to the last abdominal segment.

The appendages of the cephalothorax varied in size within different genera. They con-sisted of one pair of chelicerae, usually small; four pairs of walking legs; and one pair of large elongated oar-like appendages. The fourth pair of walking legs was also often elongated and paddle-like. Most eurypterids, judging from the appendages, not only were able to crawl over the bottom but were active swimmers. Two modes of swimming have been suggested. Either the paddle-like legs were used as flippers or the animal swam on its back, using the abdominal appendages for propulsion and the last two elongated legs as balancers.

The abdominal appendages consisted of six pairs of gills, the first pair also forming the

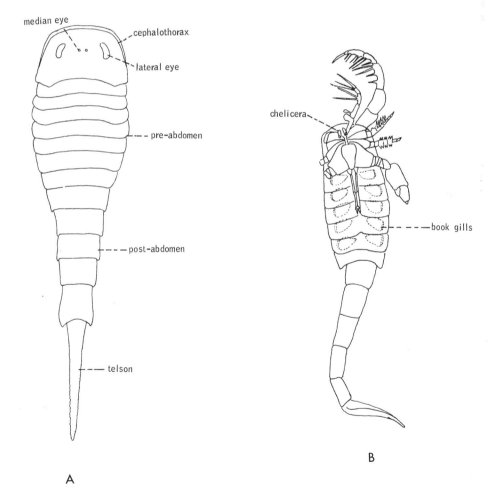

Figure 14-4.   Eurypterida. *A. Eurypterus remipes* (dorsal view). (After Clarke and Ruedermann from Fage.) *B. Mixopterus kiaeri,* showing appendages of one side (ventral view). (After Störmer from Fage.)

operculum. The exact nature of the gills, however, is still undetermined.

Fossil larval stages indicate a post-embryonic development in the eurypterids similar to that of the horseshoe crabs.

The location of fossils indicates that the eurypterids, after a marine origin, gradually invaded both brackish and fresh water and perhaps even assumed a terrestrial existence.

The merostomes display an apparently close relationship to the trilobites, and the trilobites may have been ancestral to the merostomes. Evidence for this affinity is illustrated in the presence, during the embryological development of the horseshoe crabs, of two germinal centers equivalent to the cephalon and the larval pygidium of the trilobites. The abdomen of the adult horseshoe crab thus corresponds to the trilobite pygidium, while the cephalothorax corresponds to the cephalon, to which have fused the three thoracic segments from the pygidium. A second source of evidence is found in the structure of many fossil forms that are transitional and intermediate between the two groups.

Of all merostomes, the horseshoe crabs are the only members to have survived to the present day. But they too are members of a dying race. However, the account of the eurypterids, does not end with their extinction in the Permian period, for it is believed that they were the ancestors of the largest and most abundant class of chelicerates, the Arachnida.

CLASS ARACHNIDA

The Arachnids comprise the largest and from a human standpoint the most important of the chelicerate classes; included are many common and familiar forms, such as spiders, scorpions, mites, and ticks. Arachnids also have the dubious honor of probably being the most objectionable group of arthropods as far as the layman is concerned, a bias largely unwarranted.

Except for the few groups that have adopted a secondary aquatic existence, arachnids are terrestrial chelicerates. Yet the original environment was apparently aquatic, since their most probable ancestors were the fossil giant water scorpions. As has already been noted, the eurypterids, originally marine, invaded fresh water; the fossil remains indicate some may have become amphibious or terrestrial. These terrestrial forms may have been the ancestral arachnid stock from which the modern groups arose.

The arachnids are an old group. Fossil representatives of all of the orders date back to the Carboniferous, and fossil scorpions have been found dating from the Silurian period. Thus the original evolution from water scorpions must have antedated this period, and arachnids may well have been the first terrestrial arthropods.

Like all evolutionary conquests of land, this migration from an aquatic to a terrestrial environment required certain fundamental morphological and physiological changes. Thus the book gills became modified to use air, resulting in the development of the arachnid book lungs and tracheae. In addition, the appendages became better adapted for terrestrial locomotion. Furthermore, once a terrestrial existence was established, a great many unique innovations evolved independently along different lines. The development of both silk in spiders, pseudoscorpions, and some mites and poison glands in scorpions, spiders, and pseudoscorpions are but two examples.

The General Structure and Physiology of Arachnids

Despite the diversity of forms, arachnids exhibit many features in common. This discussion emphasizes only the general morphological and physiological characteristics and the major evolutionary trends within the class. This discussion is followed by a brief treatment of the distinctive and specialized features and the natural history of each of the arachnid orders.

External Anatomy. The body is divided into a prosoma and an abdomen (Figs. 14-9 and 14-10). The unsegmented prosoma is usually covered dorsally by a solid carapace, while the ventral surface is provided with one or more sternal plates or is covered by the coxae of the appendages. Primitively, the abdomen is segmented and divided into a pre-abdomen and a post-abdomen. In most arachnids these two subdivisions are no longer conspicuous (Fig. 14-13), and a tendency for segmentation to disappear because of fusion has developed. In mites, primary segmentation has become lost, and the abdomen has fused with the prosoma to form a single body region (Fig. 14-36).

The appendages common to all arachnids are those arising from the prosoma and consist of a pair of chelicerae, a pair of pedipalps, and four pairs of legs (Fig. 14-13). The chelicerae and pedipalps are variously modified, and the number of articles composing the legs is not constant within the class.

Nutrition. The majority of arachnids are carnivorous, and digestion partly takes place outside the body. Prey, usually small arthropods are captured and killed by the pedipalps and chelicerae. While the prey is held by the chelicerae, enzymes secreted by the midgut are poured out over the torn tissues of the prey. Digestion proceeds rapidly and a partially digested broth is produced. This fluid is then taken into the prebuccal cavity, located in front of the mouth. The roof of this chamber is formed by the anterior wall of the prosoma and is known as the labrum. An anterior sternal piece frequently forms the floor, and the sides are usually formed by the coxae of the pedipalps.

The liquid food passes through the mouth and into the sclerotized pharynx and esophagus of the foregut (Figs. 14-23 and 14-37, *A*). The tubular pharynx is the chief pumping organ, driving the liquid food into the foregut. Its walls are composed of longitudinal cuticular strips connected by membranes. The diameter of the tube can be increased or decreased by the action of externally attached muscles, thus effecting a sucking action. In some arachnids the esophagus is enlarged, forming an additional pump.

The esophagus conveys the food to the midgut or mesenteron, which consists of a central tube with lateral diverticula (Fig. 14-23). The diverticula are located in both the prosoma and the abdomen, and become filled with the partially digested liquid pumped into the foregut. The midgut wall is composed of secretory cells and absorptive cells. The secretory cells produce the enzymes for external digestion and other secretions that complete digestion after the food reaches the mesenteron.

When digestion is completed, food products are taken up by absorptive cells. Since not all of the absorbed food is immediately needed for metabolism, much of it is stored in the interstitial cells surrounding the diverticula. The mesenteron extends to the posterior part of the abdomen, where it is connected to the anus by a short sclerotized intestine, forming the hindgut.

Excretion.   The principal excretory organs of arachnids are coxal glands and Malpighian tubules. Some groups possess both; some one or the other. Coxal glands are so named because they open onto the posterior of the coxae of the appendages. The coxal gland itself is located at the side of the prosoma, and is a thin-walled spherical sac immersed in blood (Fig. 14-5). Waste materials are absorbed from the blood by the cells of the gland, and passed into the lumen. A long convoluted tubule connects the gland to the excretory pore. Arachnids never have more than four pairs of coxal glands, and the excretory pore, or pores, are located on different coxae in different orders. This variation has arisen because the glands are derived from coelomic sacs, which in the embryo are located one pair per segment. Different pairs of coelomic sacs are retained as the coxal glands in the adults by the different orders.

Malpighian tubules, the second type of arachnid excretory organ, consist of one or two pairs of slender tubes that arise from the posterior of the mesenteron at its junction with the intestine (Fig. 14-23). The tubules are directed anteriorly, and ramify between the abdominal diverticula of the hindgut. The thin syncytial walls of the tubule absorb waste from the cells of the diverticula. The waste is then excreted into the lumen of the tubules as guanine crystals, and passed into the intestine.

In addition to Malpighian tubules and coxal glands, arachnids possess certain large cells, called nephrocytes, that are localized in clusters in certain parts of the prosoma and abdomen. These cells have been found to pick up dyes injected experimentally in the animal, but their exact function has not been determined.

Nervous System.   The nervous system of most arachnids is greatly concentrated, resulting from ganglionic fusion (Fig. 14-6, *A*). The brain,

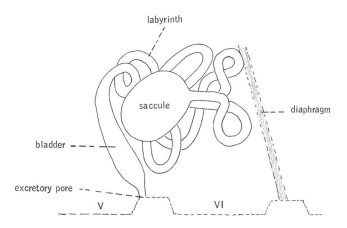

Figure 14-5.   Coxal gland of a scorpion. (After Millot and Vachon.)

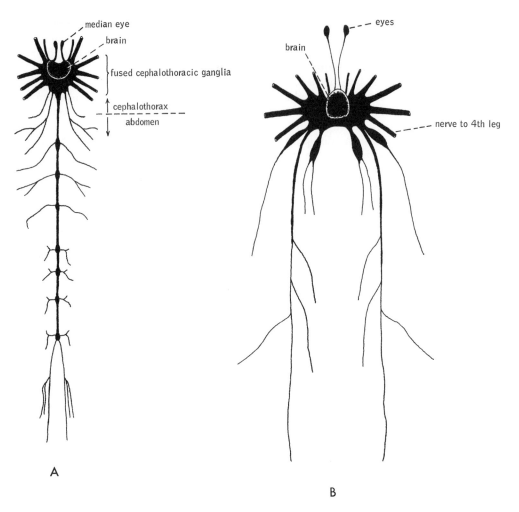

Figure 14-6.   *A.* Scorpion nervous system, in which abdominal ganglia are distinct. *B.* An opilionid nervous system, in which all ventral ganglia have migrated forward and fused. (Both after Millot.)

composed of the protocerebrum and tritocerebrum, is an anterior ganglionic mass lying superior to the esophagus. The protocerebrum contains the optic centers and optic nerves; the tritocerebrum contains the nerves supplying the chelicerae. The remainder of the central nervous system is subjacent to the esophagus. In many orders, most or all of the ganglia originally located in the thorax and abdomen have migrated anteriorly and fused with the subesophageal ganglion—the ganglion of the pedipalpal segment (Fig. 14-6, *B*). Some of the abdominal ganglia have disappeared in the course of migration and fusion, and in some groups a single free abdominal ganglion may lie in the prosoma. Thus the arachnid nervous system resembles a collar or ring encompassing the esophagus. The posterior ventral half of this collar gives rise on each side to nerves innervating the appendages, and a single posterior nerve bundle extends back into the abdomen.

Primitively, each fused ganglion provides two pairs of nerves for the innervation of its original segment. A ventral pair innervates the appendages, book lungs, and ventral muscles; and a smaller dorsal pair innervates the internal organs. However, this arrangement has frequently become obscured.

Three types of sense organs are common to most arachnids—tactile hairs, eyes, and slit sense organs. The tactile hairs can be either movable hairs or fine bristles of varying lengths (Fig. 14-8, *C*). The base is expanded to form a small ball that fits into a socket in the integument and that contains a process from a sensory nerve cell of the hypodermis. These tactile-hair sense organs are scattered over the body surface but are particularly prevalent on the appendages. For most arachnids, the tactile hairs are believed to be the most important of the sense organs. They are highly sensitive and one long delicate type of sensory hair, known as a trichobothrium is able to detect slight air movements and probably sound waves. However, these long sensitive hairs should not be considered to have a true auditory function.

The eyes of all arachnids are similar (Fig. 14-7). They are always composed of a combined cornea and lens, which is continuous with the cuticle but much thicker. Beneath the lens is a layer of hypodermal cells known as the vitreous body. The retinal layer, containing the photoreceptor cells, lies behind the vitreous body. Finally, the retina is backed by a postretinal membrane.

The photoreceptors are oriented either toward the light source (a direct eye) or toward the postretinal membrane (an indirect eye). In the indirect eyes, the postretinal membrane functions as a reflector, called the tapetum, that reflects the light toward the receptors. Some arachnids possess only direct or only indirect eyes; others, such as spiders, have both.

The receptors may be separated from each other by pigment, or they may be arranged in groups. The number of receptors is directly correlated to the ability of the eye to form an image, a phenomenon achieved by relatively few arachnids. This problem is more fully discussed in the section on spiders.

Unlike the compound eyes of insects and crustaceans and the eyes of vertebrates, the sensory cells of arachnid eyes both receive the stimuli and transmit the impulses. The optic nerves connect to optic ganglia within the brain.

The last type of sense organs is the slit sense organ. Some of these are probably chemoreceptors and consist of slit-like pits in the cuticle, covered by a very thin membrane. The undersurface of the membrane is in contact with a hair-like process that projects upward from a hypodermal sensory cell. Experimental data indicate that the slit sense organs have an olfactory function, and they may detect chemical substance on direct contact. Some other types of slit sense organs also function as both auditory organs and kinesthetic organs, reacting to changes in the tension of the exoskeleton.

Respiration. Arachnids possess either book lungs or tracheae, or both. Book lungs are undoubtedly a modification of book gills, resulting from the migration of the arachnids to a terrestrial environment. The two are very similar in structure, but in contrast to book gills the book lungs of arachnids are internal. Book lungs occur in pairs and are located on the ventral side of the abdomen. An arachnid may possess as many as four pairs, each pair occupying a separate abdominal segment.

Each book lung consists of a sclerotized pocket that represents an invagination of the ventral abdominal wall (Fig. 14-8, A). The wall on one side of the pocket is folded into leaf-like lamellae. The lamellae are held apart by bars that enable the air to circulate freely. Diffusion of gases takes place between blood circulating within the lamellae and the air in the interlamellar spaces (Fig. 14-8, B). The nonfolded side of the pocket forms an air chamber (atrium) that is continuous with the interlamellar spaces, and that opens to the outside through a slit-like opening (spiracle). Ventilation results from the contraction of a muscle attached to the dorsal side of the air chamber. This contraction dilates the chamber and causes an inward movement of air; relaxation reverses the process.

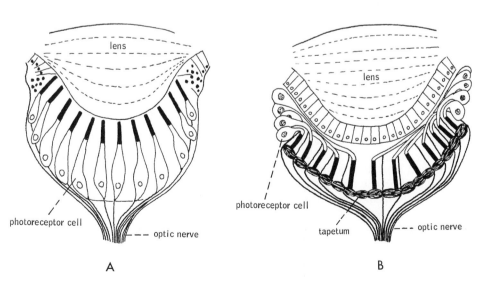

A   B

Figure 14-7.   *A.* Direct eye (lateral) of a scorpion. *B.* Indirect eye (lateral) of a spider. (Both after Verluys and Demoll from Millot.)

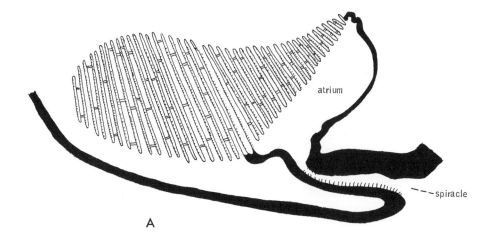

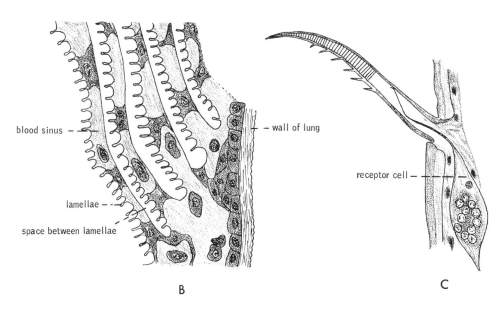

Figure 14-8.   *A.* Section through a book lung of the uropygid, *Thelyphonus caudatus.* (After Börner from Millot.) *B.* Section through the lamellae of the book lung of a spider. (After Millot.) *C.* Sensory hair of a mite. (After Gossel from Millot.)

The tracheal system of arachnids is similar to that of insects but has evolved independently. In fact, the tracheal system appears, in some cases, to be derived from the book lungs. This certainly seems to be true in spiders and is discussed in more detail in the section dealing with spiders.

In most arachnids the spiracles, or openings into the tracheal system, are paired and similar in position to the spiracles of the book lungs (Fig. 14-24). The spiracles may open into a chamber (atrium), as in the book lungs, and then into a large trunk trachea; or they may

open directly into the large trunk trachea. The main trunk gradually branches into smaller tubes that eventually terminate in blind fluid-filled tracheoles. The latter branch and ramify over various organs, supplying them directly with oxygen. The interior of the tubes except for the tracheoles are lined with a thin layer of cuticle, which may be sculptured in the form of rings or spirals. As would be expected, in those arachnids that respire exclusively by tracheae, the circulatory system plays little part in oxygen transport and is reduced in size.

Circulation.   The arachnid heart, as it is in

most arthropods, is a dorsal tube within a pericardial chamber. In arachnids the heart is almost always located in the anterior half of the abdomen. Primitively, the heart is segmented, corresponding to the metamerism of the abdomen, and is expanded between each segment because of the attachment of suspensory ligaments (Fig. 14-23). Located one on each side are a pair of slits, or ostia, which allow blood to enter the heart from the pericardial chamber. The greatest number of heart segments, totaling seven, appear in scorpions. However, reduction in all degrees of the number of heart segments is displayed by the class. The number of segments in some forms is reduced even to a single segment or, as in certain mites, to complete absence.

Histologically, the heart wall is composed of an outer epithelial layer, encompassing two muscle layers and an inner lining of endothelium. The muscles are responsible for heart contraction, while the pull exerted by the ligamentous suspension causes dilation. During diastole, blood flows through the ostia from the pericardial chamber to fill the heart. On contraction the valves guarding the ostia close to prevent backflow, and blood is forced out of the heart through the several vessels—a large anterior aorta that supplies the prosoma, a small posterior aorta leading to the posterior half of the abdomen, and from each heart segment a pair of small abdominal arteries. Small arteries eventually empty the blood into tissue spaces and then into a large ventral sinus that bathes the book lungs. One or more pairs of venous channels conduct blood from the ventral sinus or the book lungs back into the pericardial chamber. Arachnid blood is more or less colorless and contains amebocytes but no respiratory pigments.

Reproduction. Arachnids are always dioecious, and except in mites and ticks the genital orifice in both sexes is usually found on the ventral side of the second abdominal, or eighth body segment (Fig. 14-10). The gonads lie in the abdomen, and may either be single or paired. The ducts of the reproductive system are more easily discussed in connection with each of the orders.

Summary of Evolutionary Tendencies in the Arachnids

The most important evolutionary tendency among the arachnids has been the reduction of metamerism resulting from fusion, loss of segments, and the migration of structures away from the segments they originally occupied.

This tendency has produced profound modifications in both the external and internal structures. The most conspicuous of these modifications are: progressive loss of external abdominal segmentation and fusion of the abdomen with the prosoma to form a single body region; forward migration and fusion of prosomal and abdominal ganglia with the brain; reduction in the number of heart segments; and reduction of the number of book lungs or tracheal openings.

At first glance, the ten orders of arachnids described next appear to be a heterogeneous assemblage. However, the majority of differences between these groups results from different degrees or stages in the loss of metamerism. The two extremes in the loss of metamerism are exemplified by the scorpions, in which reduction of metamerism has progressed only slightly, and by the mites and ticks, in which all of the modifications discussed here have taken place. The other orders exhibit various stages of modification between these two extremes.

The class Arachnida includes these ten orders with living representatives.*

Order Scorpionida. The scorpions.
Order Pseudoscorpionida. The false scorpions.
Order Solpugida. The sun spiders, or wind scorpions.
Order Palpigradi. The palpigrades.
Order Uropygi. The whip scorpions.
Order Amblypygi. The amblypygids.
Order Araneae. The spiders.
Order Ricinulei. The ricinuleids.
Order Opiliones. Harvestmen, or daddy longlegs.
Order Acarina. The mites and ticks.

Order Scorpionida

The scorpions are the oldest known terrestrial arthropods and may have been the first members of this phylum to have conquered land. Their fossil record dates back to the Silurian period. While abundant today, they are largely restricted to tropical and subtropical areas. In North America scorpions are found as far north as Virginia in the East and British Columbia in the West, but they are not common at these extreme latitudes. They are much more abundant in the Gulf states and the Southwest.

Scorpions are secretive and nocturnal, hiding by day under wood and stones and in crevices in the ground. They are often found near

* The system of classification adopted here is based on that of Grassé (1949).

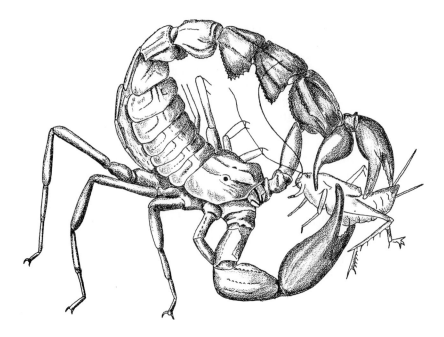

Figure 14-9.   The North African scorpion, *Androctonus australis,* capturing a grasshopper. (After Vachon from Kaestner.)

dwellings, and the custom in the tropics of shaking out shoes in the morning is a wise precaution. Scorpions are popularly believed to inhabit desert regions, but although many desert species exist, they are by no means restricted to arid situations. Many scorpion species require a humid environment and live in tropical rain forests and similar jungle habitats.

External Anatomy.   The scorpion body consists of a prosoma covered by a single carapace, and a rather long abdomen, ending in a stinging apparatus (Figs. 14-9 and 14-10). The prosoma is relatively short and four-sided, and the anterior border is narrower than the posterior border. In the middle of the dorsal carapace is a pair of large median eyes, each raised on a small tubercle. In addition, two to five pairs of small lateral eyes are present along the anterior lateral margin of the carapace. The coxae of the legs occupy most of the ventral surface, and the original sternites are represented by only a tiny median plate.

The chelicerae are small, tri-articulate, and chelate; and they project anteriorly from the front of the carapace (Fig. 14-9). The pedipalps are the largest of the appendages and are characteristic of scorpions. The pedipalps are composed of six articles, the last two of which are greatly enlarged and form a pair of pincers for capturing prey. Only the pseudoscorpions have similar pedipalps. The legs are made up of eight articles—an elongated coxa (particularly

in the second, third, and fourth pairs of legs), a trochanter, a prefemur, a femur, a tibia, a basitarsus, a tarsus, and a post-tarsus. The post-tarsus is a small, inconspicuous piece that bears two pairs of claws.

The scorpion abdomen is believed to be very primitive. It is composed of a seven-segmented pre-abdomen and a postabdomen of five narrow segments, so the two regions are clearly differentiated. The genital opercula are located on the ventral side of the first abdominal segment (which is the eighth body segment, the seventh body segment, or first abdominal segment, of most arachnids having been lost in scorpions). The opercula consist of two small plates, contiguous along the midline of the ventral side, and covering the genital opening. These plates actually are modified appendages.

Posterior to the genital plates and attached to the second abdominal segment is a pair of sensory appendages known as the pectens, which are peculiar to scorpions. Each pecten is made up of three rows of chitinous plates forming an elongated axis that projects to each side from the point of attachment near the ventral midline. Suspended from the body of the pecten is a series of tooth-like processes that give the whole appendage the appearance of a comb. During movement of the scorpion, the pectens are held out from the sides of the body in a horizontal position so that the teeth touch the ground.

The second through the fifth abdominal

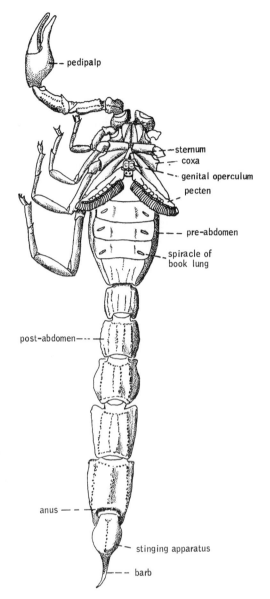

Figure 14-10. *Androctonus australis* (ventral view). (After Lankester from Millot and Vachon.)

10). The venom is produced by a pair of oval glands, each enveloped by a layer of smooth muscle fibers within the base of the apparatus. By a violent contraction of the muscular envelope, the liquid venom is ejected from the lumen of the glands into a sclerotized common duct that leads to the outside through the terminal stinging barb. The scorpion raises the postabdomen over the body so it is curved forward, and a stabbing motion is used in stinging.

The venom of most scorpions, while sufficiently toxic to kill many invertebrates, is not harmful to man. At most, the sting is equivalent to that of a hornet or a yellow jacket. The scorpions of the southeastern United States and Gulf Coast region would fall in this category, as well as many of our midwestern and western forms.

However, certain species exist that possess a highly toxic venom that can be fatal to man. The most notorious of these are *Androctonus* of North Africa and various species of *Centruroides* in Mexico, Arizona, and New Mexico. Vachon (1949) states that *Androctonus australis* of the Sahara Desert has venom equivalent in toxicity to cobra venom, and this venom can kill a dog in seven minutes. With human victims, death usually occurs in six to seven hours. Species of *Centruroides* have been responsible in Mexico for many deaths, mostly in children. Species of this genus in Arizona and New Mexico are said to be less dangerous.

Venom from these forms is neurotoxic and causes convulsions, paralysis of the respiratory muscles, or cardiac failure in fatal cases. Antitoxins are available for those species appearing in populated regions. If administered in adequate time, these antitoxins are completely effective.

Internal Anatomy and Physiology. Scorpions are entirely carnivorous and feed on invertebrates, particularly insects. The prey is caught and held by the large pincers of the pedipalps while being killed or paralyzed by the sting (Fig. 14-9). The prey is then transferred to the chelicerae, which slowly macerate it, and digestion begins. The pre-oral chamber is framed at the top by the chelicerae, on the sides by the coxae of the pedipalps, and at the bottom by the maxillary processes of the first pair of walking legs. The intestine is restricted to the last abdominal segment.

The scorpion heart is seven-segmented and extends the length of the pre-abdomen. According to Vachon, the heartbeat is quite rapid and varies from 60 to 150 per minute depending upon the species and the state of the animal. Nine pairs of ventro-lateral arteries supply the pre-abdomen, and nine pairs of venous channels

segments each bear on the ventral side a pair of transverse slits (spiracles), opening into the book lungs.

The segments of the postabdomen, sometimes called the tail, carry no appendages. The tergites, pleurites, and sternites of these segments are completely fused so that each segment resembles a complete ring. The last segment bears the anal opening on the posterior ventral side and also bears the stinging apparatus characteristic of scorpions.

Stinging Apparatus and Venom. The sting is attached to the posterior of the last segment and consists of a bulbous base and a sharp curved barb that injects the venom. (Fig. 14-

conduct blood from the book lungs to the peri-cardial cavity.

Respiration is accomplished solely by book lungs. Excretion takes place through the action of two pairs of Malpighian tubules and a single pair of coxal glands, which open on the coxae of the third pair of walking legs.

The scorpion nervous system unlike that of other arachnids retains a distinct nerve cord with seven unfused ganglia (Fig. 14-6, A). The first three ganglia innervate the last three pre-abdominal segments, but are located further forward in the pre-abdomen than the segments they innervate. The remaining four ganglia innervate segments of the postabdomen and the telson. Closely connected to the tritocerebrum is a sympathetic nerve center. From this nerve center issue a single anterior nerve to the muscles of the pharynx and two pairs of posterior nerves supplying the prosomal part of the midgut.

The sense organs of scorpions consist of the median and lateral eyes, sensory hairs and slits, and the pectens. All the eyes are of the direct type, but it is doubtful whether an image is ever formed, because these animals are largely nocturnal.

The pectens are undoubtedly sensory, for the ventral side of each tooth of the comb is liberally provided with sensory cells (Fig. 14-11, A). The distal ends of these cells are contained within little spigot-like projections. Various functions, such as equilibrium, tactility, chemoreception, and sex recognition, have been suggested for the pectens, but none have been proven.

Reproduction and Life History.   Scorpions exhibit little sexual dimorphism, and the few exceptions to this rule vary from one group to another. The most useful character for distinguishing the sexes in scorpions is the hook present on the opercular plates of the male.

The female reproductive system is located between the midgut diverticula in the pre-abdomen (Fig. 14-11, C). The ovarian tubules are ladder-like in formation, and a short oviduct leads from each set of tubules. Prior to emptying into a single genital atrium, each oviduct dilates to form a small seminal receptacle. The genital atrium opens to the outside between the genital opercula. In some forms the genital atrium projects posteriorly into a median pocket, which is perhaps used in receiving the spermatophore.

The male reproductive system occupies a corresponding position within the body to that of the female (Fig. 14-11, B). The testes in most scorpions are tubules that have the same general ladder-like structure as the ovarian tubules. A slender vas deferens carries the sperm from each set of tubules to a single genital atrium. Before emptying into the genital atrium, each vas deferens enlarges to form a seminal vesicle. The genital atrium extends posteriorly on each side to form two large diverticula, to which are attached several accessory glands, and into which the vas deferens opens. A diverticulum and an accessory gland together are known as a paraxial organ.

Before mating, scorpions carry on an extended courtship. Male and female face each other, extend each abdomen high into the air, and move about in circles. The male then seizes the female with his pedipalps, and together they walk backward and forward. This behavior may last hours or even days. Eventually the male deposits a spermatophore that is attached to the ground. He then maneuvers the female so that the chitinous hooks of the spermatophore become attached to the open genital operculum of the female.

Development in scorpions is particularly interesting because the entire order is either ovoviviparous or truly viviparous. The ovoviviparous species have very large telolecithal eggs exhibiting meroblastic cleavage; development takes place in the lumen of the ovarian tubules. The eggs of viviparous species lack yolk and display total and equal cleavage. This type of development is found in the tropical Asian species, *Hormurus australasiae*. Its eggs develop within the diverticula of the ovary. Each diverticulum in turn develops a tubular appendage distally that contains a cluster of absorbing cells at the end (Fig. 14-11, D). These cells rest against the maternal digestive ceca, from which nutritive material is absorbed. The nutritive material passes through the tubule to the embryo at the base. This arrangement is certainly a unique parallel to the mammalian umbilical cord.

Development takes several months or even a year or more with anywhere from six to ninety young produced, depending on the species. At birth the young are only a few millimeters long, and they immediately crawl upon the mother's back (Fig. 14-12). The young remain there through the first molt, which occurs in about one week. The young scorpions then gradually leave the mother and become independent. Adulthood is reached in about a year. Schultz (1927) reports that seven molts take place during this period in *Heterometrus longimanus,* a Philippine species.

Order Pseudoscorpionida

Pseudoscorpions are tiny arachnids rarely longer than eight millimeters. They live in leaf mold,

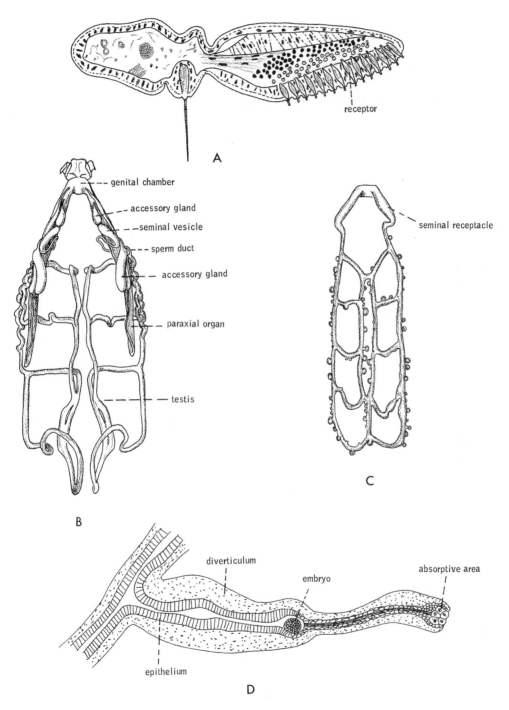

receptor

A

genital chamber

accessory gland

seminal vesicle

sperm duct

accessory gland

paraxial organ

testis

seminal receptacle

B

C

diverticulum

embryo

absorptive area

epithelium

D

Figure 14-11. *A.* Transverse section through the pecten of a scorpion. (After Schröder from Millot and Vachon.) *B.* Male reproductive system of the scorpion, *Buthus* (dorsal view). (After Millot and Vachon.) *C.* Female reproductive system of the scorpion, *Parabuthus* (dorsal view). (After Pavlovsky from Millot and Vachon.) *D.* Ovarian diverticulum of the tropical Asian scorpion, *Hormurus australasiae,* a viviparous species. (After Pflugfelder from Dawydoff.)

Figure 14-12.   Female scorpion carrying young (Courtesy of H. L. Stahnke.)

in soil, beneath bark and stones, in moss and similar types of vegetation, and in the nests of some mammals. A few species inhabit caves, and one genus, *Garypus,* lives on seaweed along the Mediterranean coast. A cosmopolitan species, *Chelifer cancroides,* is found in houses.

Because of their small size and the nature of their habitat these animals are rarely seen although they are actually quite common. A few handfuls of leaf mold sifted through a Berlese funnel usually will yield several individuals. Pseudoscorpions are found throughout the world and over a thousand species have been described.

Pseudoscorpions superficially resemble the true scorpions but differ in several important respects other than size. The body is composed of eighteen segments—six fused prosomal segments and twelve segments forming the abdomen (Fig. 14-13). The abdomen contains a pregenital segment that is lacking in scorpions. The prosoma is covered by a single rectangular carapace. One or two eyes are located at each anterior lateral corner, or the eyes may be absent. The ventral surface of the prosoma is entirely occupied by the coxae of the walking legs and pedipalps.

Pseudoscorpion appendages are much more

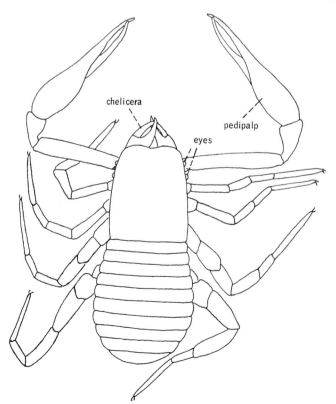

chelicera

pedipalp

eyes

Figure 14-13.   A pseudoscorpion (dorsal view). (After Hoff.)

highly modified than those of the scorpions. The chelicerae are made up of two articles forming a pair of pincers and bearing several accessory structures (Fig. 14-14). Within the movable finger of the chelicera are located several ducts leading from a pair of silk glands in the prosoma to a group of pores on the end of the upper side of the finger. Frequently the ducts do not open at the surface but open at the end of horn-like processes collectively known as the galea. The movable finger and the fixed finger are each provided with a comb-like structure along their inner borders. These structures are known as the serrula externa and serrula interna respectively. On the internal face of each chelicera at the base of the fixed finger is a cluster of short heavy stiff hairs called flagella. The function of these structures is discussed later.

Pseudoscorpion pedipalps are similar to those of the scorpions. However, these pedipalps are peculiar in that each has a poison gland located in one or both fingers or in the hand. A duct issues from the poison gland and opens at the end of a tooth at the tip of the finger.

Posterior to the pedipalps are four pairs of walking legs, each provided with an adhesive organ located between two terminal claws. Pseudoscorpions are slow-moving and hold their pedipalps to the front when they walk. If the pseudoscorpion is disturbed, it pulls the pedipalps back over the carapace, and becomes immobile.

The abdomen is relatively wide, forms a

broad juncture with the prosoma, and is rounded posteriorly. It bears no appendages, although both the genital operculum on the second segment and the two pairs of spiracles on the third and fourth segments are probably derived from abdominal appendages.

Pseudoscorpions feed on small arthropods, such as collembolans and mites. The prey is caught, and paralyzed or killed by the poison glands in the pedipalps. It is then passed to the chelicerae, which tear open the exoskeleton. This action enables the pseudoscorpion to insert the anterior tip of its head (labrum) into the tissues of the prey. Digestion then takes place in typical arachnid fashion. Hairs at the front of the prebuccal chamber strain out the solid particles. When a large mass of solid particles accumulates, the chelicerae are withdrawn, and the flagellar hairs thereon catch the mass of debris and eject it from the prebuccal chamber. This process is repeated whenever the front of the prebuccal chamber becomes clogged. Eventually all the internal tissues of the prey are dissolved, and the meal is terminated.

After feeding, the buccal pieces are cleaned by the comb-like internal and external serrulae on the fingers of the chelicerae (Fig. 14-14). The chelicerae are, in turn, cleaned by the pedipalps.

Respiration in pseudoscorpions is accomplished by means of a tracheal system that opens through two pairs of spiracles on the ventral side of the third and fourth abdominal segments. Coxal glands that open on the coxae of the third pair of walking legs provide for excretion. The sense organs consist of indirect eyes, tactile hairs, and lyriform organs (a type of slit sense organ).

There is little secondary differentiation between sexes. The ovary and testis are unpaired and the accessory structures are complex in both sexes. In the species that have been observed, sperm transmission is peculiar (Fig. 14-15, A to C). Either the male performs a long elaborate dance in front of a passive female, or both members dance as the scorpions do. Toward the end of the dance the male presses his abdomen against the ground and secretes a globule of material, which is attached to the ground. The globule is pulled out to form a stalk, and a spermatophore forms at the top. Next the male pulls the female over the stalk until her genital orfice is just in contact with the spermatophore, permitting the spermatophore to enter the orifice.

The eggs appear after sperm transmission (a month in *Chelifer cancroides*). Prior to egg-laying, the female uses small bits of dead leaves and debris to build a nest and lines it with silk emitted from the galeae of the chelicerae. First

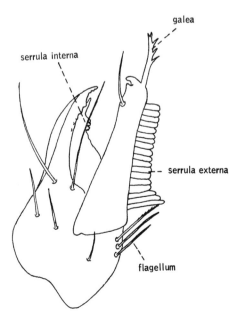

Figure 14-14. Chelicera of *Lamprochernes oblongus* (dorsal view). (After Hoff.)

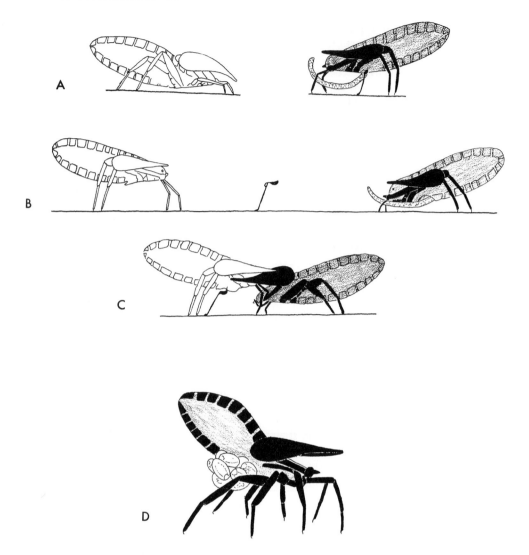

Figure 14-15.   *A* to *C.* Courtship and sperm transmission in *Chelifer cancroides* (male is black). *A.* Male, producing spermatophore. *B.* Spermatophore, attached to substratum. *C.* Male pressing female down onto spermatophore. *D.* Female of *Chelifer cancroides,* carrying embryos. (All after Vachon.)

the liquid silk is attached, and then the thread is drawn out as the chelicerae are moved to another position.

After the eggs are laid, they remain in a membranous sac that is attached to the genital opening on the ventral side of the body. Development takes place within the sac (Fig. 14-15, *D*). In a later stage of development, the embryo is supplied with a nutritive material secreted by the mother's ovaries. The young undergo one molt before hatching and emerge from the brooding sac during the second instar, or as protonymphs. Depending on the species, two to more than fifty young may be brooded. The protonymph undergoes three additional molts before adulthood, passing through instars known as the deutonymph and the tritonymph. Be-

tween each instar, molting takes place within a nest of silk that is constructed like the nest of the female at the time of egg production. According to Vachon (1948), maturity is reached the year after egg formation, and individuals may live two or three years.

Order Solpugida

The solpugids are an interesting group of tropical and semitropical arachnids sometimes called sun spiders because of the diurnal habits displayed by many species. In the United States one species has been found in Florida, and fifty-nine species have been found in the Southwest, some as far north as Colorado. Most solpugids prefer an arid environment and for this reason are common in the hot desert regions of the world. They hide under stones and in crevices, and some species burrow. The nonburrowing forms are capable of very rapid movement and in North Africa are called wind scorpions.

Solpugids are large arachnids, sometimes reaching seven centimeters in length. The prosoma is divided into both a large anterior carapace bearing a pair of closely placed eyes on the anterior median border, and a short posterior section (Figs. 14-16 and 14-17). The unique feature exhibited by these two prosomal divisions is that they can articulate with one another in the nonburrowing species. The abdomen is large, broadly joined to the prosoma, and visibly segmented (Fig. 14-16).

The most striking characteristic of the solpugids is the enormous size exhibited by the chelicerae, which project in front of the prosoma. These chelicerae are extremely heavy, and the length of each exceeds the length of the prosoma. Each chelicera is composed of two pieces forming a pair of pincers that articulate vertically. The pedipalps are leg-like but terminate in a specialized adhesive organ used in the capture of prey. The first pair of legs are somewhat reduced in size and are used as tactile organs; the remaining legs are used for running.

Solpugids possess voracious appetites and feed on all types of small animals, including vertebrates. The pedipalps seize the prey and pass it to the chelicerae, which kill the captured animal and tear apart the tissues. For respiration the animal uses a highly developed tracheal system that opens to the outside through three pairs of ventral slit-like spiracles. One pair of spiracles is located on the prosoma just posterior to the coxae of the second pair of legs; a second pair is located between the third and fourth abdominal segments; and a third pair is located between the fourth and fifth abdominal segments. Excretion is accomplished both by a pair of coxal glands located in the anterior of the prosoma and by a pair of Malpighian tubules.

Except for a peculiar flagellum attached to each male chelicera, solpugids possess little sexual dimorphism. Courtship consists of a brief period of stroking and palpation by the male, which throws the female into a sort of cataleptic state. After courtship, the male turns the female over and opens her genital orifice with his chelicerae. The male emits a globule of semen on the ground, picks it up with his chelicerae,

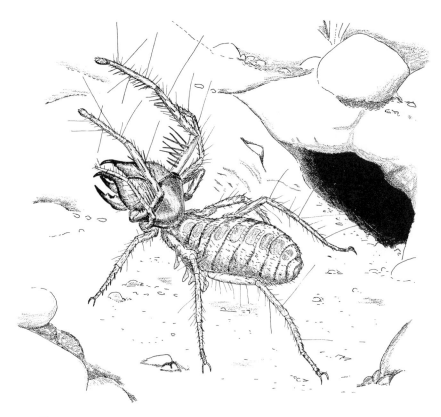

Figure 14-16.   North African solpugid, *Galeodes arabs*. (After Millot and Vachon.)

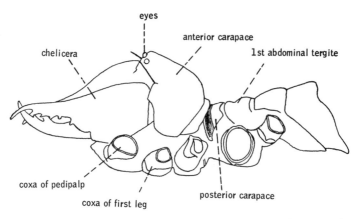

Figure 14-17.   Cephalothorax of the solpugid, *Galeodes graecus* (lateral view). (After Kaestner from Millot and Vachon.)

and deposits it into the genital orifice of the female. The entire act takes only a few minutes, and the male then leaps away.

The female constructs a burrow and nest in the ground where she lays between 50 and 200 eggs; she remains with the eggs through the hatching period. After hatching takes place, both the female and the young emerge from the burrow and remain together for some time, the mother capturing prey to feed the entire family.

Order Palpigradi

The palpigrades are a small order of little arachnids, not exceeding 2 mm. in length (Fig. 14-18). They live beneath stones and in soil or caves. Since their discovery in Sicily in 1885, twenty species have been described from tropical and the warmer temperate regions; three species occur in Texas and California. The biology of the group is still poorly known.

The integument is very thin and pale. As in the solpugids, the palpigrade carapace is divided into two principal plates between the third and fourth pairs of legs. In addition, a tiny third plate is located on each side of the prosoma in the same region. The chelicerae are well developed and extend in front of the prosoma. The pedipalps are undifferentiated and are used as a pair of walking legs. However, the first pair of legs has a sensory function and is held off the ground during locomotion. Eyes are lacking.

The abdomen is broadly joined to the prosoma and consists of eleven segments. The terminal segment bears not only the anal opening but also a long, narrow, and highly mobile flagellum possessing approximately fifteen articles.

The digestive tract is typical but feeding

habits are unknown. A pair of coxal glands is located within the prosoma, but no respiratory organs are present. Sexual behavior has not yet been observed. The eggs are large and laid only a few at a time.

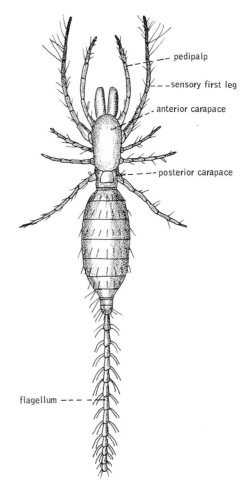

Figure 14-18.   *Koenenia,* a palpigrade. (After Kraepelin and Hansen from Millot.)

Order Uropygi

The uropygids, known as whip scorpions, are another small arachnid order, consisting of approximately one hundred species. They are found throughout tropical and semitropical parts of the world; one species, *Mastigoproctus giganteus,* lives in the southern United States from coast to coast.

The uropygids are all of nocturnal habit and hide during the day beneath leaves, rocks, logs, and other debris. A few species are desert dwellers, but the majority have a distinct preference for a humid environment.

The whip scorpions range in size from very small forms approximately 2 mm. long up to the large species, such as the American *Mastigoproctus giganteus,* which reaches 65 mm. in length (Fig. 14-19). The prosoma is covered by a dorsal carapace that is either single or divided in a manner similar to the solpugid and palpigrade carapace. The divided carapace, in general, is restricted to the smaller forms. The anterior part of the carapace often bears a pair of closely placed eyes. The ventral surface of the prosoma is largely covered by the coxae of the appendages.

Uropygid chelicerae are only moderate in size and are two-segmented. The distal piece of each chelicera is fashioned to form a hook or fang that folds against the large basal piece. The pedipalps are stout, heavy, and relatively short; the last two articles of the pedipalps are frequently modified to form a pincer used in seizing prey. The first pair of legs is very long, and the distal articles are often secondarily segmented. The first pair of legs is not used in locomotion but has a sensory-tactile function. The last three pairs of legs are unmodified. Except when excited, the whip scorpions move rather slowly using only the last three pairs of legs. The pedipalps and tactile first pair of legs are held in front of the animal as it moves forward, with the tactile legs frequently touching the ground.

The abdomen is composed of twelve visible segments, eight of which are relatively wide. The first segment, which joins the abdomen to the prosoma, and the last three segments are narrow. The last, or twelfth, segment bears the anus and a flagellum of varying length similar to the palpigrade flagellum. In large species that have an undivided carapace, the flagellum is very long and composed of many articles. In small species that have a divided carapace, the flagellum is short and composed of not more than four articles.

The posterior half of the abdomen contains a pair of large anal glands, which open one on each side of the anus. When irritated, the ani-

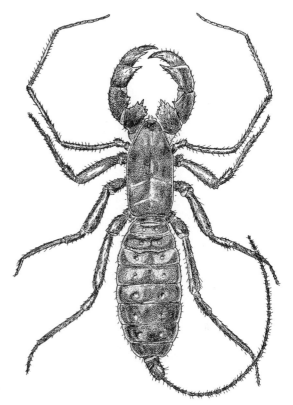

Figure 14-19.   American whip scorpion, *Mastigoproctus giganteus.* (After Millot.)

mal elevates the end of the abdomen and discharges a stream of fluid secreted from these glands. The secretion apparently contains formic or acetic acid and is used for defense. The repellent odor of this fluid has resulted in these animals sometimes being called vinegarroons.

During feeding, the prey is seized and torn apart by the pedipalps and then passed to the chelicerae, which complete maceration of the tissues. Two pairs of book lungs are located on the ventral side of the second and third abdominal segments. A pair of coxal glands situated in the prosoma opens just behind the modified first pair of legs. Malpighian tubules are also present.

Prior to mating, whip scorpions perform a curious courtship dance similar to that exhibited by scorpions (Fig. 14-20). During this dance, the female is held by her long modified sensory legs, which the male crosses in front of his chelicerae.

When the time for egg-laying is at hand, the female secludes herself in some sort of shelter or retreat and lays from seven to thirty-five large eggs. She remains in the shelter with the eggs attached to her body until they have hatched and undergone several molts. The female dies shortly after the young disperse. Some forms require up to three years to mature sexually.

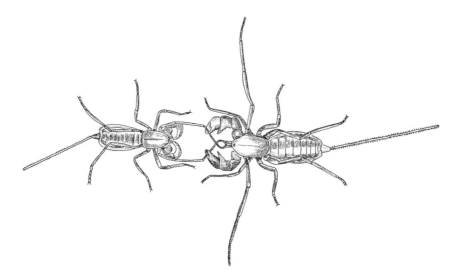

Figure 14-20.   Courtship in the uropygid, *Thelyphonus sepiaris*. Male holding antenniform legs of female. (After Gravely from Millot.)

Order Amblypygi

The amblypygids are a tropical and semitropical group of some sixty species, that were formerly grouped taxonomically with the uropygids. The order is represented in the United States by several forms in the South and Southwest. The amblypygids, like the uropygids, are a nocturnal and secretive group, hiding during the day beneath logs, stones, leaves, and similar objects. In addition, several species inhabit caves. In general, the members of this group prefer a humid environment.

Amblypygids range in length from 4 to 45 mm. and have a somewhat flattened body (Fig. 14-21). The prosoma is covered by an undivided carapace, which bears a pair of median eyes anteriorly and two groups of three eyes each laterally. The chelicerae are moderate in size and are similar to uropygid chelicerae. The pedipalps are heavy and have a pair of pincers at the tip. The first pair of legs is modified as sensory-tactile appendages; they are extremely long and whip-like and are composed of many articles. The last three pairs of legs are unmodified and are used for locomotion. The gait of the amblypygid is quite crab-like because of its flattened body and its ability to move laterally. The long tactile legs are always directed toward the direction of movement. The abdomen is composed of twelve visible segments. The first and last segments are narrow, and the flagellum characteristic of the uropygids is lacking.

The insect prey is captured and killed with the pedipalps and then passed to the chelicerae, where juices are sucked into the digestive system in typical arachnid fashion. Two pairs of book lungs are located on the ventral side of the second and third abdominal segments. The excretory organs consist of coxal glands and Malpighian tubules. The coxal glands open to the outside as in uropygids.

Nothing is as yet known about the courtship behavior in this group. Between six and sixty large eggs are laid. When egg laying is at hand, the reproductive glands secrete a parchment-like membrane that holds the eggs to the underside of the female abdomen. The mother carries the eggs in this manner until hatching and the first molt of the young have taken place.

Order Araneae

Except for perhaps the Acarina, which comprise the mites and ticks, the spiders constitute the largest order of arachnids. Approximately 30,000 species have been described, and this represents only a portion of the actual number. Also, spider populations are very large. Bristowe (1938) has calculated that an acre of undisturbed, grassy meadow in Great Britain contained 2,265,000 spiders.

Two adaptations by the spiders make them unusual—first, the production of silken threads and the great variety of uses to which this silk has been put in different spider families; and second, the modification of the pedipalps in the male to form a copulatory organ. Furthermore, in a number of families, acuity of vision has been perfected to a remarkable degree.

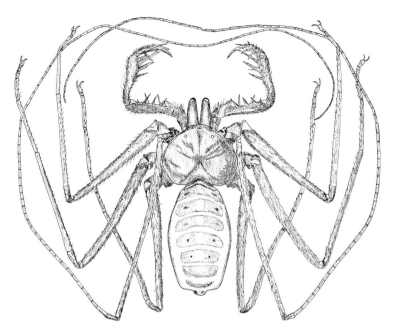

Figure 14-21.   The African amblypygid, *Charinus milloti.* (After Millot.)

Anatomy and Physiology. Spiders range in size from tiny species less than .5 mm. in length to large tropical tarantulas with a body length of 9 cm. The prosoma is covered dorsally by a single carapace, which usually bears eight eyes anteriorly (Fig. 14-22). A large sternum is present on the ventral surface, and a small median plate known as the labium is attached directly in front of the sternum (Fig. 14-24).

Each chelicera is of moderate size and, like uropygid and amblypygid chelicerae consists of a distal and a basal piece (Fig. 14-24). The distal piece resembles a fang which, when the animal is at rest, fits into a groove at the end of the large basal piece. Spiders are unique among arachnids in having chelicerae provided with poison glands that open at the tip of the fang (Fig. 14-23). The glands themselves are located within the basal segments of the chelicerae and usually extend backward into the head. A duct runs from the poison gland out through the fang. When the animal bites, the fangs are raised out of the groove in which they lie and are rammed into the prey. Simultaneously, a muscular envelope around the poison gland contracts, and fluid from the gland is discharged from the tip of the fang into the body of the prey.

The venom of most spiders is not toxic to man. A few species, however, have venomous bites. Among these are several species of black widows (*Latrodectus*), which are found in most of the warmer parts of the world, including the United States and southern Canada (Fig. 14-30, *A*). The venom is neurotoxic. Although the bite may be unobserved, the symptoms are severe and very painful, and include pain in abdomen and legs, high cerebrospinal fluid pressure, nausea, muscular spasms, and respiratory paralysis. Fatal cases, which are usually restricted to small children, result from respiratory paralysis.

Lycosa raptoria, a Brazilian wolf spider, has an entirely different type of venom. It is hemolytic rather than neurotoxic and produces a necrosis, or decomposition, of tissue that gradually spreads out from the bite, which is slow to heal. The bite of *Loxosceles reclusa,* which is indigenous to Missouri and Arkansas, also produces a necrotic spot.

The pedipalps of male spiders have become greatly modified. The female pedipalps are short and leg-like, but in the male they have become modified, forming copulatory organs. The last segment of the spider is greatly enlarged and knob-like and resembles a boxing glove. The structure of this segment is discussed later. The legs are variable in length and consist of six segments—a basal coxa, a small trochanter, a long femur, a short patella, a long tibia and metatarsus, and a distal tarsus. The tarsus terminates in two or three claws.

The globular or elongated abdomen is unsegmented except in a few groups of primitive spiders and is connected to the prosoma by a short and narrow portion called the pedicel (Fig. 14-22, *B*). Anteriorly, the ventral side of the body bears a transverse groove known as the epigastric furrow (Fig. 14-25, *A*). The reproductive

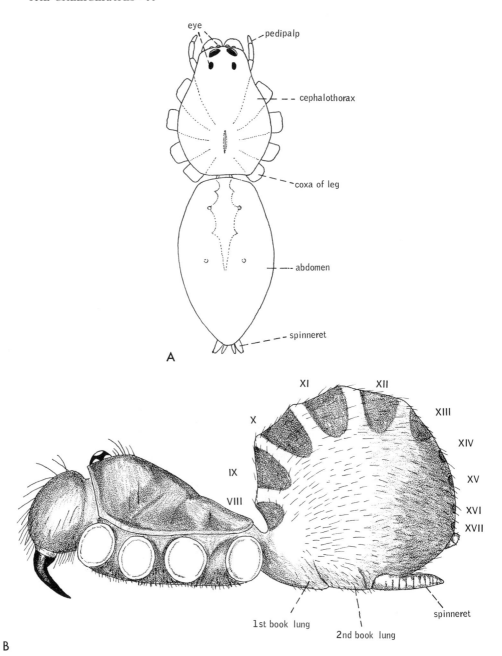

Figure 14-22.   *A.* A spider (dorsal view). *B.* The primitive Asian mygalomorph spider, *Liphistius malayanus,* with legs removed (side view). (Both after Millot.)

openings are located in the middle of this furrow, and the spiracles of the book lungs on each side of it.

The abdomen of spiders bears a group of modified appendages known as spinnerets (Fig. 14-24). These are spinning organs and are located on the ventral surface just anterior to the terminal anus. In primitive spiders, eight spinnerets are located more anteriorly on the abdomen; but most spiders have only six, in-cluding a vestigial or modified pair, and they are located at the posterior of the abdomen. Each spinneret is a short, conical, spigot-like structure encasing the openings from the silk glands (Fig. 14-23). The glands themselves are large and are located within the posterior half of the abdomen. The ducts from the silk glands extend posteriorly and terminate at the end of the spinnerets. Each spinneret contains many duct openings.

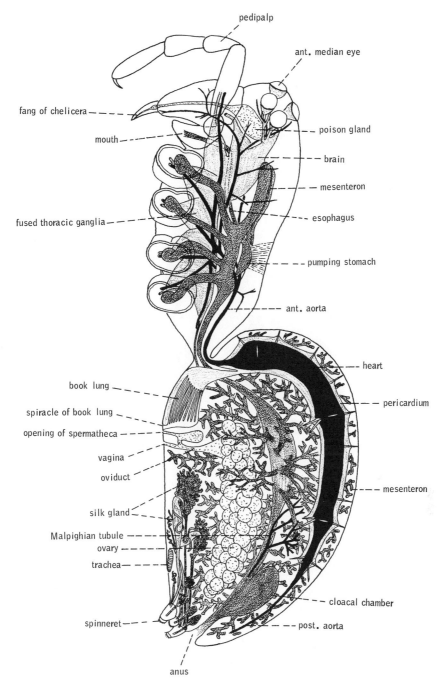

Figure 14-23. Internal anatomy of a two-lunged spider. (After Comstock.)

The silk of spiders is a scleroprotein that is emitted as a liquid. It is extremely strong and elastic and the webs of some species are used by natives of some tropical regions for catching fish, as well as for other purposes. Hardening of the silk results, not from exposure to air, but from the actual drawing-out process itself. A single thread is composed of several fibers, each drawn out from liquid silk supplied at a separate duct opening. Most spiders produce more than one type of silk from a corresponding number of different silk glands.

Silk plays an important role in the life of the spider and is put to a variety of uses. One function of silk, common to most spiders, aside from its use as a casing for the eggs, is its use as a dragline. Spiders continually lay out a line of dry silk behind them as they move about. At intervals it is fastened to the substratum with adhesive silk. The dragline acts as a safety line

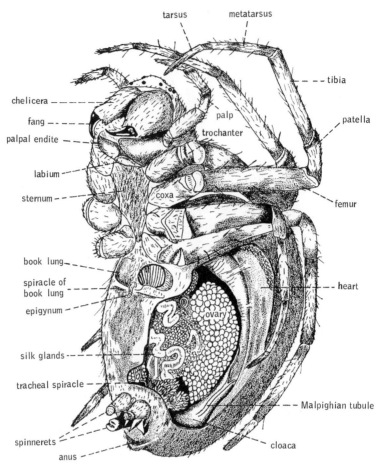

Figure 14-24.   The orb weaver, *Araneus diadematus* (ventral view). (After Pfurtscheller from Kaestner.)

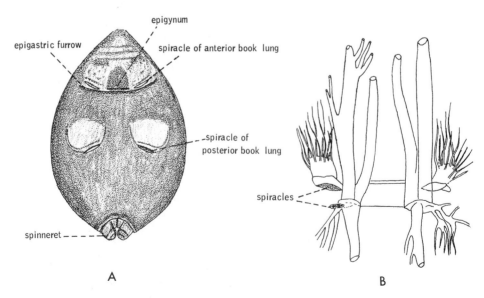

A   B

Figure 14-25.   *A*. Abdomen of a mygalomorph spider, showing the two pairs of book lungs (ventral view). (After Comstock.) *B*. Central part of tracheal system of the caponiid spider, *Nops coccineus,* in which both pairs of book lungs have been replaced by tracheae. (After Bertkau from Kaestner.)

similar to that used by mountain climbers. The common sight of a spider suspended in mid air, after being brushed off of some object, results from its continual retention of its dragline.

Spiders, like most other arachnids, are carnivores and feed largely on insects, although small vertebrates may be captured by larger species. The prey is either caught in a silken snare, as in the case of members of the web-building families, or is pounced upon by members of the more active hunting groups. The victim is bitten with the chelicerae, which also hold and macerate the tissues during digestion.

The pre-oral chamber is framed by the labium at the bottom, the coxal processes, or endites, on the sides, and the labrum at the top. Hairs on the labium and endites strain out coarse particles, and the liquid, which remains, enters the mouth at the back of the pre-oral cavity. Sucking force comes from the pharynx and a posterior enlargement of the esophagus known as the pumping stomach (Fig. 14-23). It is located at about the middle of the prosoma.

The mesenteron fills almost the entire abdomen, as well as the posterior half of the prosoma. The conformation and the degree of complexity of the diverticula vary within different families, but in some the diverticula are extremely extensive and even ramify into the head and legs (Fig. 14-23). The posterior part of the midgut becomes enlarged in the back of the abdomen to form a cloacal chamber. Waste is collected here and then discharged from the anus through a short sclerotized intestine.

Respiratory organs in spiders are of two forms, book lungs and tracheae. Spiders considered primitive, such as the mygalomorphs (tarantulas), have no tracheae but display two pairs of book lungs derived from the second and third abdominal segments (Figs. 14-22, *B* and 14-25, *A*). Almost all other spiders have only a single pair of book lungs, the posterior pair having evolved into tracheae. Coinciding with this transformation in most spiders, a posterior migration and fusion of the tracheal openings have taken place forming a single spiracle located just in front of the spinnerets (Fig. 14-23). The spiracle leads into a small chamber from which four primary tracheal tubes extend anteriorly. The complexity of these tubes is highly variable. In some groups, the tracheal tubes are simple and do not extend beyond the abdomen; in others they exceed the book lungs in providing the body with oxygen and extend even into the head and legs. In several small-sized groups, the anterior book lungs have also been transformed into tracheae, so that respiration is accomplished entirely by this means (Fig. 14-25, *B*).

The spider circulatory system is similar to that of scorpions, although the heart varies in length and in the number of ostia (Fig. 14-23). These variations are apparently related to the nature of the respiratory organs. On one extreme, the heart is five-segmented with a corresponding number of ostia. This is the more primitive structure and is only found in forms with four book lungs. As the book lungs become reduced in size and the tracheae become increased in complexity, there is a corresponding loss in the number of heart chambers, of ostia and of arteries, until in the exclusively tracheate spiders, most of which are small, the number of ostia is often reduced to two.

Another peculiarity of the spider circulatory system is that the anterior aorta is considerably larger than the posterior aorta; thus, the anterior part of the abdomen and the cephalothorax receives greater irrigation with oxygenated blood. The tracheae, when present, compensate for this since they almost always supply at least the posterior part of the abdomen.

Blood pressure in a resting spider is equal to that of man and may double in an active spider or one ready to molt. Blood pressure also causes the legs to extend in opposition to flexor muscles. A valve in the anterior aorta is believed to maintain the high pressure.

Coxal glands are not as well developed in spiders as in other arachnids. Groups considered primitive have two pairs of coxal glands opening onto the coxae of the first and third pair of walking legs. The coxal glands are highly developed in these forms. In all others, only the anterior pair of glands remain and they display various stages of regression.

Although coxal glands in many spiders have become reduced functionally as excretory organs, it is probable that the silk glands and perhaps even the poison glands evolved from them.

More important functionally as excretory organs are the two Malpighian tubules, which are connected to the cloacal chamber in the posterior part of the abdomen (Fig. 14-23). Each tubule extends anteriorly to branch over the abdominal diverticula. Guanine wastes are excreted not only by the cells of the Malpighian tubules but also by the cloacal wall. Certain cells located beneath the integument and over the surface of the intestinal diverticula also produce guanine crystals. These waste products eventually pass into the lumen of the diverticula where they dissolve and are passed posteriorly to be excreted from the cloacal pocket. The white color of some spiders may be caused by guanine stored in the body wall.

The nervous system of spiders is like that

of other arachnids. Several independent ganglia associated with the digestive system have been described. The first of these is a stomodeal ganglion located over the esophagus and just behind the brain. It gives rise to a single median nerve, supplying the muscles of the pharynx and the labrum. The second visceral center consists of a pair of ganglia, one located on each side of the pumping stomach. From these ganglia extend one pair of nerves forward toward the brain and another pair of nerves posteriorly to a third pair of ganglia located more posteriorly in the prosoma. The second and third centers innervate the pumping stomach and the prosomal and abdominal diverticula of the intestine.

The eyes of some spiders surpass those of all other arachnids in degree of development. Usually, there are eight eyes arranged in two rows of four each along the anterior dorsal margin of the carapace (Fig. 14-24). Frequently, the arrangement of the eyes is characteristic of certain families. In the wolf spiders and jumping

spiders, the eyes are situated over the surface of the anterior half of the carapace, resulting in perception over a wide field (Fig. 14-26, B and C). Spiders in a few families have the eyes reduced in number to six, four, or even two, or they completely lack eyes.

Of the two rows of four eyes usually found in spiders, the anterior median eyes are of the direct type, and all the remaining eyes are indirect. Since the indirect eyes are provided with a tapetum, which reflects light rays, the anterior median eyes appear dark and the others often appear pearly white. In some families, notably the wolf spiders, the tapetum has developed to such an extent that these spiders can easily be located at night and captured by using a flashlight to look for the reflection of the eyes.

In most spiders, the eyes are unable to form an image owing to an insufficient number of receptors. The number of receptors is much greater in cursorial (hunting) species than in the sedentary web-builders; in the hunting

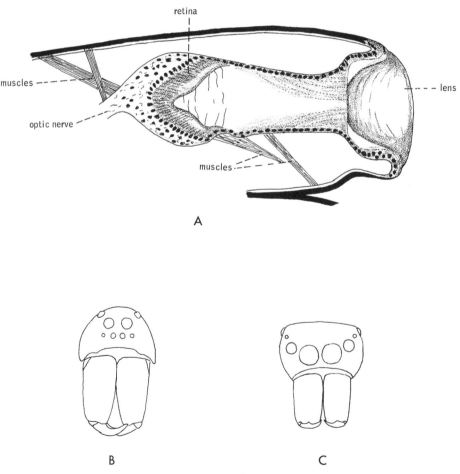

Figure 14-26. *A.* Anterior median eye of the jumping spider, *Salticus scenicus* (sagittal section). (After Scheuring from Kaestner.) *B.* Head and chelicerae of the wolf spider, *Lycosa aspersa,* showing eye pattern (anterior view). *C.* Head and chelicerae of the jumping spider, *Icius elegans,* showing eye pattern (anterior view). (*B* and *C* after Kaston.)

spiders, eyes are important for detecting movement and locating objects. However, the jumping spiders are the only cursorial species capable of perceiving a sharp image. In this family, the number of receptors is extremely large, particularly in the anterior median eyes in which the tapered ends of the retinal cells are greatly narrowed and compact. All spiders are very near-sighted owing to the lack of any sort of accommodating mechanism. This obstacle has been overcome in the jumping spiders in many instances by an increase in the depth of the anterior median eyes resulting in a somewhat tubular structure (Fig. 14-26, *A*). Some members of this family, such as species of the genus *Phidippus,* can perceive an object more than one foot away.

The sensory hairs are second only to the eyes in providing spiders with environmental information, and in the sedentary species they are undoubtedly the most important of the sense organs. Isolated or grouped slit sense organs are located over the entire surface of the body and may be important for sex recognition by the male when he comes in contact with the threads, excrement, or body of the female.

Spiders also display a sense of taste, for certain pungent insects are rejected as food after being captured and killed. The same holds true when prey experimentally "flavored" with quinine or other substances is offered (Millot, 1949). The sensory receptors for taste are located within a short band on each side of the central region of the pharynx.

Reproduction and Life History. Ovaries of the female consist of two elongated parallel sacs located in the ventral part of the abdomen (Figs. 14-23, 14-24, and 14-27). The germinal epithelium gives rise to the oocytes, which in the process of development and enlargement bulge outward from the ovarian lumen. During egg formation, this gives the ovary the appearance of a cluster of small grapes. In a gravid female, the ovaries may occupy two thirds or more of the abdomen. The epithelial cells not involved in egg formation secrete an adhesive material used to agglutinate the eggs in the cocoon. At maturity, the eggs rupture into the lumen of the ovary and pass into the curved oviduct leading from each ovary. Each oviduct extends forward, downward, and toward the midline and converge to form a median tube (Fig. 14-27). This tube extends ventrally and backward to join with a short chitinous vagina, which opens at the middle of the epigastric furrow.

Associated with the vagina and uterus are two or more seminal receptacles and glands (Fig. 14-27). In most spiders, these have separate openings to the outside and are connected internally to the vagina. These external openings are for the reception of the male copulatory organ during mating and are located just in front of the epigastric furrow on a special sclerotized plate called the epigynum. Fertilization occurs at the time of egg-laying, mating having taken place some time earlier. The semen is stored in the seminal receptacles, or spermathecae, until the time of egg-laying.

The male reproductive system is relatively simple. The testes consist of two large tubes lying ventrally along each side of the abdomen. When the sperm leave the testes, they pass anteriorly into two convoluted sperm ducts, which extend downward and open to the outside through a single genital pore in the middle of the epigastric furrow.

The copulatory organs of the male are not connected to the sperm duct opening but are located at the ends of the pedipalps. The tarsal segment of these appendages has become modified to form a truly remarkable structure for the transmission of sperm. Basically, each palp consists of a bulb-like reservoir from which extends an ejaculatory duct (Fig. 14-28, *B* and *C*). This leads to a penis-like projection called the embolus. At rest, the bulb and embolus fit into a concavity, the alveolus, on one side of the tarsal segment.

During mating (Fig. 14-29, *A*), the tarsal segment becomes engorged with blood, causing the bulb and embolus to be extended and project out of the alveolus (Fig. 14-28, *D*). The embolus is

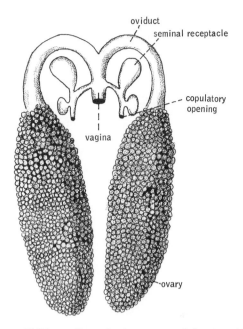

Figure 14-27.   Reproductive system of female spider. (After Millot.)

then inserted into one of the female reproductive openings leading to the seminal receptacles.

In groups of spiders believed to be primitive, the palpal organ has remained simple and consists only of the basic parts previously described (Fig. 14-28, *B*). In the majority of families, however, the palp has become much more complicated with the addition of a great many accessory parts, such as the conductor, bulbal apophyses and various other processes (Fig. 14-28, *D*). These structures, in combination with the sclerotized configurations of the female epigynum, may aid in the orientation of the palp and in the insertion of the embolus into the female openings.

The structure of the palp and the epigynum

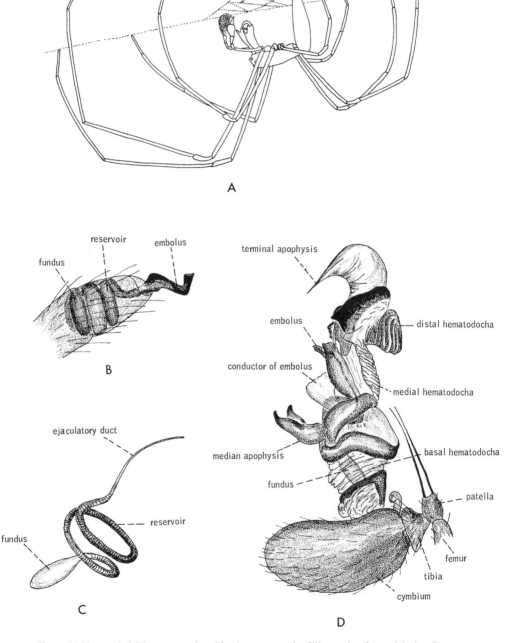

Figure 14-28. *A*. Male tetragnath spider in sperm web, filling palps from globule of semen. (After Gerhardt from Millot.) *B*. Simple palp of *Filistata hibernalis*. *C*. Receptaculum seminis, the semen-containing part of the male palp. *D*. Complex palp of the orb weaver, *Aranea frondosa*, in expanded state. (*B* to *D* after Comstock.)

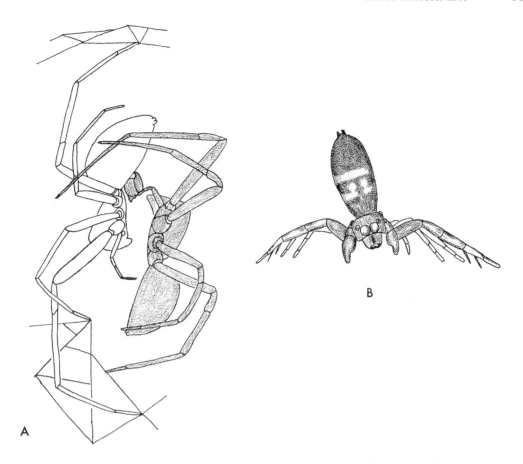

Figure 14-29. *A.* Mating position of *Chiracanthium* (male shaded). (After Gerhardt from Kaston.) *B.* Courting posture of the male jumping spider, *Gertschia noxiosa.* (After Kaston.)

remains relatively constant within a species, while differing from those of other species. As a result, these organs are the primary structural characteristics used by araneologists for classifying and identifying species.

The female and the male reproductive systems and the male palpal organ are not completely formed until the last molt has taken place. The male then fills, or charges, the pedipalps with sperm in the following manner. He first spins a tiny sperm web, or at least a strand of silk, onto which is ejaculated a globule of semen (Fig. 14-28, *A*). Next the palps are dipped into the globule until all of the semen is taken up into the reservoirs. With the palps filled, the male spider then seeks a female with which to mate.

To accomplish mating the male is faced with a rather formidable obstacle. The female is usually larger than the male and is a rather unromantic lady with a healthy appetite for all intruders of edible size. As a result behavioral patterns and even physical changes have developed in the male spiders to overcome or avoid the voracity of the female. In the sedentary web-builders, the male often plucks the strands of webbing, producing vibrations that are detected and recognized by the female. In some cases the male has become so small that he is below the prey-size threshold of the female and clambers over her body undisturbed (for example, in *Mastophora bisaccata*, the female averages 12.00 mm. and the male 1.85 mm. in length).

The cursorial, or hunting, forms display the most unique courtship behavior. The approach may be direct, the male pouncing on the female, palpating her body with his pedipalps and legs, and causing her to fall into a cataleptic state. In families with well developed eyesight, courtship takes the form of dancing and posturing by the male in front of the female (Fig. 14-29, *B*) This involves various movements and the waving of appendages, which are often brightly colored. For a more detailed account of this subject, the reader is referred to Gertsch's *American Spiders* (1949).

Some time after copulation, the female lays her eggs. Several to 3000 eggs are laid in one to several batches, depending on the species. Just before the deposition of the eggs, the female spins a small sheet and the eggs are fertilized with stored sperm as they lie on the silk sheet. A second sheet is then spun over the egg mass. The two sheets are sealed at the edges and usually are given an additional covering of silk so that they assume a spherical shape known as the cocoon (Fig. 14-30, *A*). The cocoon is either attached to webbing (in web-building families), hidden in the spider's retreat, or is attached to the spinnerets and dragged about after the mother (as in the wolf spiders and a few others). In many spiders the female dies after completing the cocoon; in others she may remain with the young for some time after hatching.

The spiderlings hatch inside the cocoon and remain there until they undergo the first molt. They usually emerge from the cocoon either in later summer and fall or in the follow-ing spring. The spiderlings of many species, as well as the adults of some small forms, display a phenomenon known as ballooning, which aids in the dispersal of the species. On leaving the cocoon, the little spider climbs to the top of nearby twigs or grass; releases a strand of silk; and as soon as air currents are sufficient to produce a tug on the strand, the spider releases its hold and is carried some distance by the air currents. Ballooning spiders have landed on ships several hundred miles off shore and have been collected from airplanes flying at 5,000 feet. The female wolf spider carries her young on her back after they hatch (Fig. 14-30, *B*). The spiderlings gradually disperse over a period of time.

Although some of the "tarantulas" (mygalomorph spiders) have been kept in captivity for as long as twenty-five years, most spiders live only one year. The number of molts required to

Figure 14-30.   *A.* Black widow, *Latrodectus mactans,* with egg case. *B.* Female wolf spider carrying young. (Both by Walker Van Riper, Colorado Museum of Natural History.)

reach sexual maturity varies, depending upon size of the species. Large species undergo up to fifteen molts before the final instar, while tiny species molt only a few times. Female myga-lomorph spiders molt at periodic intervals after reaching maturity.

Systematic Résumé of the Order Araneae

Suborder Mygalomorphae. This suborder includes the "tarantulas" and trap-door spiders (Fig. 14-31). There are numerous representatives in North America. They are rather large, possess two pairs of book lungs, two pairs of coxal glands, and the fang of the chelicera articulates in the same plane as the long axis of the body.

Suborder Araneomorphae. This is the largest suborder and includes most of the spiders. With few exceptions, only a single pair of book lungs is present, and in all cases the plane of articulation of the chelicerae is at right angles to the long axis of the body.

The araneomorphs can be roughly divided into two ecological groups, web-builders and cursorial forms. The web-builders comprise families that are more or less sedentary and snare their prey with silk webbing. Associated with their web-building activities has been the retention of three tarsal claws, the small median claw being used to hook the silk strands of the web, thus facilitating movement about the web. A description of a few of the larger and more common families of this group follows.

Family Pholcidae. Small and often long-legged, resembling phalangids or daddy longlegs. Members spin small webs of tangled threads in sheltered recesses. Several species commonly live in houses and with other web-building house-dwellers are responsible for cobwebs.

Family Theridiidae. A large family of tangled web-builders known as comb-footed spiders because of the presence of a series of serrated spines on the fourth tarsus. These spines comb out a band of silk used for trussing up the prey. To this family belongs the black widow, *Latrodectus*, and also one of the most common house spiders, *Achaearanea tepidariorum*.

Figure 14-31. Trap-door spider capturing a beetle. (By Walker Van Riper, Colorado Museum of Natural History.)

Family Argiopidae. The orb-weaving spiders. Members of this family spin circular webs. Many species are of considerable size and brightly colored, such as the black and yellow garden (or "writing") spider, *Argiope aurantia*.

Family Linyphiidae. The sheet-web spiders. Webs are horizontal silken sheets or bowls constructed in shrubs and similar vegetation.

Family Micryphantidae. Dwarf spiders. This family is closely allied to the linyphiids. They are all tiny species and are found in large numbers in fallen leaves and humus, where they build the same type of web as the linyphiids.

Family Agelenidae. Funnel-web spiders. Although web-builders, they are more closely related to certain hunting spider groups. The web forms a funnel, the narrowed end acting as a retreat for the spider. The web is constructed in dense vegetation or in crevices of logs or rocks, and it is easily visible, especially in grass covered with dew.

The cursorial, or hunting, families do not use silk to snare prey, and thus they never build a web. Prey is captured directly by pouncing upon it. As a result, the third or middle tarsal claw, used in climbing through webbing, has disappeared in a number of these families. As would be expected, the eyesight of the hunting forms is much more highly developed than in the sedentary web-builders. The following families have the most distinctive characteristics and are frequently encountered.

Family Lycosidae. Wolf spiders. These are rapid moving and rather hairy spiders with dull brown and black coloration. They are most active at night and are common members of the ground fauna.

Family Pisauridae. Fisher spiders. This family is somewhat similar to the wolf spiders in appearance but with longer legs. They are common around the edges of ponds, lakes, and streams.

Family Thomisidae. Crab spiders. This and the following family commonly hunt on vegetation. Crab spiders get their name from their crab-like movements and the position of their legs.

Family Salticidae. Jumping spiders. Species of this family are heavy-bodied and capable of jumping short distances. They are often brightly colored and possess the best eyesight of all spiders. Numerous species live in the temperate and tropical regions of the world.

Order Ricinulei

The ricinuleids are a small order of arachnids containing only one family with two genera and nine described species. They are found in Africa (*Ricinoides*) and in the American hemisphere (*Cryptocellus*) from Brazil to Texas. They have been collected from leaf mold and caves and apparently require a rather humid environment.

Ricinuleids are heavy-bodied animals that measure between 5 and 10 mm. in length (Fig. 14-32). The cuticle is very thick and often sculptured. The prosoma is covered by a single carapace above and by the coxae of the appendages below. Attached to the anterior margin of the carapace is a curious hood-like structure that can be raised and lowered. When lowered, the hood covers the mouth and chelicerae. The chelicerae are two-segmented and in the form of pincers. The pedipalps are shorter than the legs and also terminate in small pincers, but they are not enlarged as those in the scorpions and pseudoscorpions are. The legs are unmodified except in the male, and movement is slow and sluggish. The third pair of legs in the male have become modified to form copulatory organs.

The abdomen is narrowed in front, forming a pedicel attached to the prosoma, and behind, forming a short tubercle that bears the anus at the end. The twelve segments composing the abdomen are fused and highly sclerotized.

Nothing is known concerning the feeding habits of the ricinuleids, although the digestive tract is more or less like that of other arachnids. However, the diverticula of the midgut are oriented parallel to the central tract. The excretory organs consist of Malpighian tubules and a pair of coxal glands. The coxal glands open between

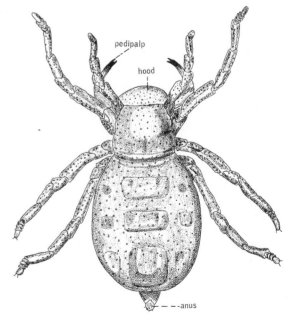

Figure 14-32.   *Ricinoides*, a ricinuleid. (After Millot.)

the coxae of the first and second walking legs. The circulatory system is degenerate, and the sense organs are limited to tactile hairs.

Respiration takes place through tracheae, but the paired openings are not abdominal, as they are in most other arachnids, but are located on each posterior lateral angle of the prosoma. Also, the atrial chamber gives rise, not to a few trunks that later branch, but to hundreds of minute sclerotized tubules that directly supply the various prosomal organs.

The third walking leg of the male has become modified to form a copulatory organ. Three segments of this leg are hollowed out on one side, and they carry a process that undoubtedly is used for transferring the spermatophore; no reservoir for containing liquid semen is present. Copulation has never been observed and little is known about egg-laying or early development. However, a six-legged "larva," similar to those in mites and ticks, has been described.

Order Opiliones

The order Opiliones, or Phalangida, contains the familiar long-legged arachnids known as daddy longlegs, or harvestmen (Fig. 14-33). These animals live in both temperate and tropical climates, and all prefer humid habitats. They are abundant on the forest floor, on tree trunks and fallen logs, in humus, and in caves. Many species are nocturnal, while others display diurnal activity.

The average body length is between 5 and 10 mm. exclusive of the legs, but some of the tropical giants reach 20 mm. and have a leg length of 160 mm. In contrast to these are certain tiny mite-like species that are never larger than one millimeter in length.

The prosoma of phalangids is broadly joined to the abdomen with no constriction between the two divisions (Fig. 14-34, A). As a result, the body is rather elliptical in shape. In the center of the simple prosomal carapace is a tubercle of varying shape and size, with an eye located on each side of it. In some groups such as the genus Caddo, the tubercle extends almost the entire width of the carapace, so that the eyes appear along the sides of the carapace rather than in the middle.

Along the anterior lateral margins of the carapace are located the openings to a pair of scent glands (Fig. 14-34, A). The secretions of these glands have been described as having an acrid odor similar to nitric acid, rancid nuts, or walnut husks.

The chelicerae are small, rather slender and tri-articulate, the last two segments forming a pair of pincers. The pedipalps are usually somewhat leg-like and similar to those in spiders, although in some groups the tarsus contains a long claw-like hook that folds back to form a pincer. Each coxa bears a process (the endite), which projects anteriorly (Fig. 14-34, B).

The legs in most phalangids are extremely long and slender and exceed the length of the body many times (Fig. 14-33). The tarsus is always multisegmented with many articles and as a result is very flexible. The normal gait of phalangids is rather slow and deliberate, but when disturbed, phalangids can run very rapidly. Each coxa of the first and second pairs of legs, like those of the pedipalps, bears an anterior process, or endite.

The abdomen is visibly segmented but, although composed of nine or ten somites, only about seven are conspicuous. The sternites of the first two abdominal segments are fused together to form a plate known as the operculum, which has migrated forward and lies between the last two pair of coxae (Fig. 14-34, B). The operculum bears the genital openings.

Harvestmen have a more varied diet than have other arachnids. Bishop (1949) has observed North American species feeding on small invertebrates, dead animal matter, and pieces of fruits and vegetables.

The prey or food is seized by the pedipalps and passed to the chelicerae, which hold and crush it. The coxal endites of the appendages are then used to pass food into the mouth. Suction is applied by the pharynx and unlike other arachnids the ingested food is not limited to liquid material but includes small particles. Thus, a greater part of digestion must take place in the midgut.

A pair of coxal glands, opening on each side between the third and fourth coxae, provides for excretion. Respiration takes place through tracheae, which are probably not homologous with the tracheae of other arachnids. The spiracles are located on each side of the second sternite. Sense organs consist of two direct eyes, tactile hairs, and lyriform organs, located on the prosoma and the appendages.

The female reproductive system includes an ovipositor, a structure that is absent in other arachnids except certain mites (Fig. 14-35). In phalangids, the ovipositor is a tubular organ lying in the midventral part of the abdomen. Its walls contain sclerotized rings connected by thin extensible membranes. The entire structure lies within a sheath, and at the time of egg-laying the ovipositor is projected some distance out of the genital orifice.

Mating is not preceded by any distinct

Figure 14-33. Two harvestmen (opilionids) on an aphis-infested rose shoot. (By E. W. Teale.)

courtship, although males fight other males for possession of a female. The male faces the female and projects a tubular penis, into the genital orifice of the female, and the sperm are then ejaculated. Bishop (1949) states that mating is frequent and at random between individuals.

Shortly after mating, the female seeks a damp location for depositing her eggs. The long ovipositor is extended, and when the proper location is found, such as in humus, moss, and rotten wood, the ovipositor penetrates the substratum to deposit the eggs (Fig. 14-35). The number of eggs layed at one time ranges in the hundreds, and several batches are layed during the life of a female. In temperate regions the life span is only one year. The individual may winter over in the egg or as an immature, depending only upon the time of hatching.

Order Acarina

The order Acarina, which contains the mites and ticks, is without question the most important of the arachnid orders from the standpoint of human economics. Numerous species are parasitic on man, his domesticated animals, and his crops, while others are destructive to food and other products. Mites certainly surpass all other arachnid orders in numbers of individuals. A small sample of leaf mold from a forest floor often contains hundreds of individuals. In fact,

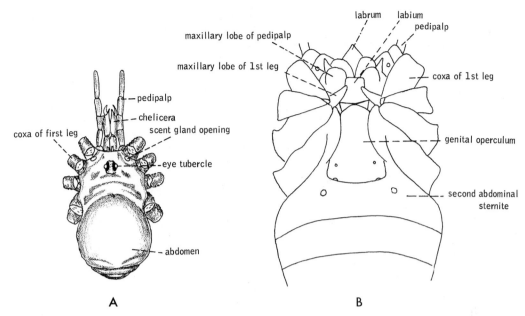

Figure 14-34.   *A.* The opilionid, *Leiobunum flavum,* with only bases of legs shown (dorsal view). The abdomen of this species is not as conspicuously segmented as many other opilionids are. (After Bishop.) *B.* Ventral surface of *Phalangium.* (After Hansen and Sörensen from Berland.)

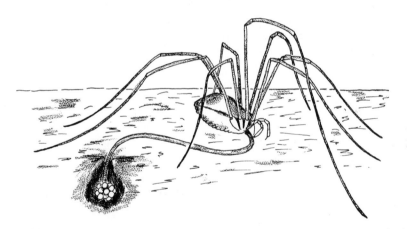

Figure 14-35.   Female of the opilionid, *Leiobunum rotundum,* depositing eggs in ground. (After Henkin from Kaestner.)

one American authority on this group has said that a few handfuls of leaf mold would contain enough specimens to occupy a taxonomic investigator for several years. This is an indication, not only of the numbers of mites that exist, but also the lack of knowledge pertaining to the taxonomy and biology of the order.

Because of the economic importance of mites, many zoologists are directing their attention entirely to this group of arachnids; as a result, a special field has developed known as acarology, the study of mites.

Much of acarology belongs in the realm of parasitology, but the mites should not be considered as an entirely parasitic group. Many

species are free-living, and others are parasitic only for a brief period during their life cycle. The emphasis of this discussion is on the free-living forms, although much of the discussion also applies to the parasitic species.

Unfortunately, acarologists have developed a special nomenclature, largely borrowed from entomology, that tends to isolate the order rather than reflect its relationship to other arachnids. To avoid confusion, much of this terminology is avoided here and the group is treated in the same manner as the previous orders. This treatment affords a much better comparison with the other arachnids.

The Acarina are so morphologically diverse

and display so few unifying features that acarologists consider the order to be polyphyletic. This makes a general discussion rather difficult, and it should be realized that exceptions exist for almost every statement.

The majority of adult mite species average one millimeter or less in length, although many are larger. The ticks are the largest members of the order (Fig. 14-38, *A*).

The most striking characteristic is the apparent lack of body divisions (Fig. 14-36, *A* and *B*). Abdominal segmentation has disappeared, and the abdomen has fused imperceptibly with the prosoma. Except in a few primitive forms, segmentation is secondary when present. Thus the positions of the appendages, the eyes, and the genital orifice are the only landmarks that differentiate the original body regions. Coinciding with this fusion, the entire body has become covered with a single sclerotized shield, or carapace, in many forms.

Another general feature of the group is the change that has taken place in the head region carrying the mouthparts, this region being called the capitulum (Fig. 14-37, *A*). The dorsal body wall projects forward to form a rostrum, or tectum. Ventrally the large pedipalpal coxae extend forward to form the floor and sides of the prebuccal chamber. The roof of the chamber is formed by a labrum. These processes, which house the prebuccal chamber, together form a buccal cone, which fits into a sort of socket at the anterior of the mite body and which is roofed over by the rostrum. The chelicerae are attached to the back wall of the socket above the buccal cone, while the pedipalps are attached to both sides of the cone. The attachment of the buccal cone into the anterior socket is such that extension and retraction of the cone is possible in a few species.

The chelicerae and pedipalps are variable in structure, depending on their function. They are usually composed of two or three segments and may terminate in pincers, or the distal piece may fold back on the base to form a crushing and grasping appendage (Fig. 14-37, *D*). In some species of mites the chelicerae have become needle-like for piercing (Fig. 14-37, *B*), and in ticks the fingers of the pincer are provided with large teeth for anchoring into the integument of the host (Fig. 14-37, *C*). The pedipalps may be relatively unmodified and leg-like, heavy and chelate like an additional pair of chelicerae, or in some parasitic forms they may be vestigial.

In many forms the four pairs of legs are

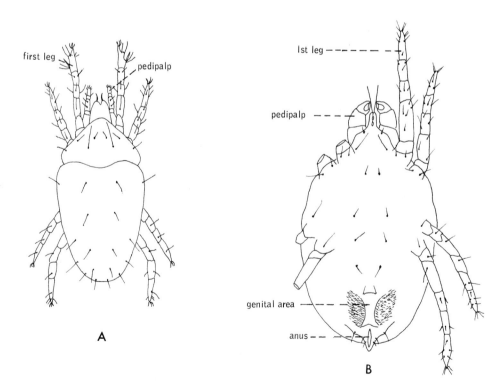

A

B

Figure 14-36.   *A.* A trombidiform mite, *Tydeus starri* (dorsal view). (After Baker and Wharton.) *B.* A trombidiform mite, *Schizotetranychus schizopus* (ventral view). (After Vitzthum from Baker and Wharton.)

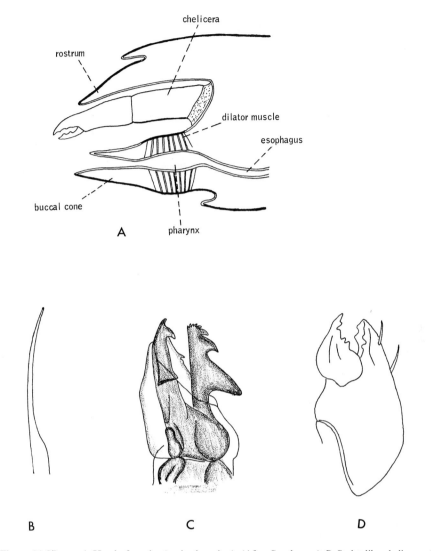

Figure 14-37. *A.* Head of a mite (sagittal section). (After Snodgrass.) *B.* Stylet-like chelicera of *Dermanyssus gallinae.* (After André.) *C.* Hooked chelicera of the tick, *Ixodes reduvius.* (After Neumann from André.) *D.* Chelate chelicera of *Belba verticillipes.* (After Nicolet from André.)

each six-segmented and are composed of a coxa, a trochanter, a femur, a genu, a tibia, and a tarsus, the last bearing a pair of claws. These appendages have become modified in some groups for purposes other than walking. In the swimming mites these appendages have long setae which help propel the mite through water (Fig. 14-38, *C*), while in some other genera the posterior legs have become adapted for jumping.

In mites and ticks, the ventral side of the body is covered by plates that vary in form and number, depending on the family (Fig. 14-36, *B*). The genital plate, located between the last two pairs of legs, bears the genital orifice. This location indicates a forward migration of abdominal segments, as in the opiliones.

The hairs and spines that clothe the mite body are called setae. As in other arachnids, many of these setae are sensory. They assume every conceivable shape and form, from simple hairs to pilose, club-shaped, and flattened types. The nature and position of the setae in mites is an extremely important diagnostic characteristic in the classification and identification of species. The symmetrical arrangement of the variously shaped setae and the ornate sculpturing of their cuticle make many mites some of the most beautiful and spectacular of all animals.

Mites compete with spiders in the variety of coloration. Most mites are varying shades of brown, but many display a wide range of hues, such as black, orange, green, or combinations of these colors. Many of the water mites are bright red.

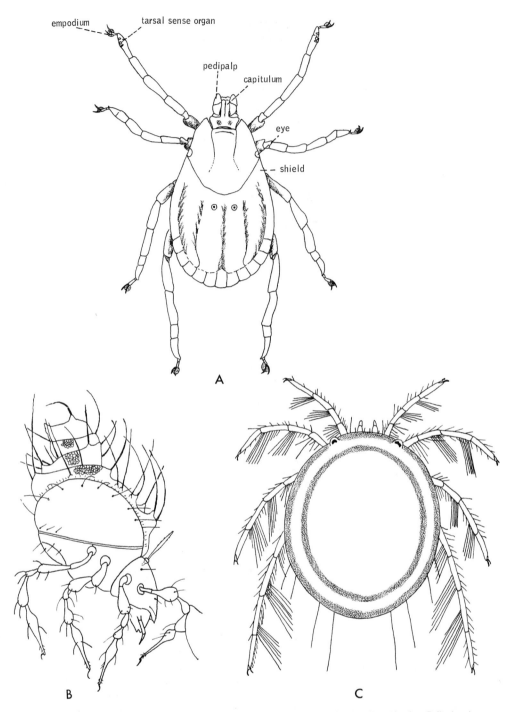

Figure 14-38.   *A*. Tick, *Dermacentor variabilis*. (After Snodgrass.) *B*. An oribatid mite, *Belba jacoti*, carrying five shed nymphal skins. (After Wilson from Baker and Wharton.) *C*. Water mite, *Mideopsis orbicularis*. (After Soar and Williamson from Pennak.)

Most free-living mites have a typical digestive tract. The prebuccal cavity, mouth, and the anterior of the pharynx lie in the buccal cone. With few exceptions, the pharynx is the chief pumping organ. In one large group of mites, the Trombidiformes, the hindgut has become degenerate and changed into an excretory organ.

Some predacious mites are known to have a typical arachnid digestive process. Others feed on living plant juices or dead plant and animal material. Sections of the midgut have revealed in a few species large food particles that have been ingested. This fact plus the differences in feeding habits makes it probable that there is considerable variation in the digestive physiology of the group.

Excretory organs of mites consist of one to four pairs of coxal glands, or a pair of Malpighian tubules, or both. In the trombidiform mites, these typical arachnid excretory organs are lacking and have been replaced by special excretory organs modified from the hindgut. The midgut of mites, like that of spiders, has taken on an excretory function.

The circulatory system is reduced and except in a few groups consists only of a network of sinuses. Circulation probably results from contraction of body muscles.

Although in some mites the respiratory organs have completely disappeared, most mites have tracheae. The spiracles vary in number from one to four pairs, located on the anterior half of the body.

The nervous system is like that of other arachnids. The sensory setae act the same as tactile hairs in other arachnids and are perhaps the most important of the sense organs. In certain mites, the first pair of legs are especially well supplied with setae. These legs have lost their locomotor function and have become entirely sensory in nature. Eyes are displayed by the Prostigmata, but most other mites are blind. When eyes are present, they usually number four, a pair on each side of the head. Some forms such as the water mites have a fifth median eye. Only rarely are the eyes well developed. Innervated pits and slits are common in mites and are perhaps homologous to the slit sense organs of other arachnids, although their exact function has not been determined.

The male reproductive system consists of a pair of lobate testes, located in the midregion of the body, and these are often quite extensive. A vas deferens, sometimes supplied with accessory glands, extends from each testis. These may join ventrally to form a chitinous penis that can project through the genital orifice.

In the female there is usually a single ovary of varying shape and size, which is connected to the genital orifice by an oviduct. A seminal receptacle and accessory glands are also present.

Mating behavior is still poorly known. Sperm are commonly produced in a spermatophore, which may be deposited and later picked up by the female or may be transferred to the female orifice by the male chelicerae or by the third pair of legs (as in water mites). In one group of mesostigmatid mites, the male backs his abdomen under the posterior of the female until the penis is able to penetrate the female orifice (André, 1949).

The number of eggs laid varies in different forms; they are deposited in soil and humus. A few species are ovoviviparous, and the oribatid mites possess an ovipositor.

After an incubation period of two to six weeks, a six-legged "larva" hatches from the egg. The newly hatched young differ from the adult in that they lack the fourth pair of legs and in certain other features. The fourth pair of legs is acquired after a molt, and the "larva" changes into a protonymph. Successive molts transform the protonymph into a deutonymph, tritonymph, and finally into an adult. During these stages, adult structures are gradually attained. Modifications of this typical life cycle are frequently encountered.

Mites are found everywhere, and they rank as one of the most ubiquitous groups in the Animal Kingdom. Even polar regions, deserts, and hot springs possess a mite fauna.

The terrestrial species are extremely abundant, particularly in fallen leaves, humus, soil, rotten wood, and detritus. The Oribatei (beetle mites) are a particularly striking group of free-living, terrestrial mites (Fig. 14-38, B). These little mites are usually globular in shape with the dorsal surface covered by a convex, highly sclerotized shield, so that they often resemble tiny beetles. The ornamentation of the cuticle and the symmetrical retention of shed skins on the dorsal surface give many of them a spectacular appearance. The oribatids feed on organic matter in the soil and thus contribute to soil development. They are also vectors for sheep tapeworms. Although the oribatids are detritus feeders, many of the other free-living terrestrial groups are predacious and feed on small arthropods including other mites.

One group of Acarina, the Hydracarina, (water mites) has returned to an aquatic existence and is found in both fresh and salt water (Fig. 14-38, C). The marine forms live largely in the littoral zones of the sea. They do not swim but crawl about over algae, bryozoans, hydroids and sponges. Many of these marine forms feed on algae, and others are either predacious or scavengers. Most water mites, however, are not marine but live in fresh water. They are often bright red in color, and many are active swimmers with long hairs on the legs. Most are predacious and feed on other small invertebrates. The larval stages may be parasitic on gills of fresh-water clams or aquatic insects.

CLASS PYCNOGONIDA

The pycnogonids are a small group of marine animals known as the sea spiders. The name sea spider is derived from the somewhat spider-like appearance of these animals, which crawl about slowly on long legs.

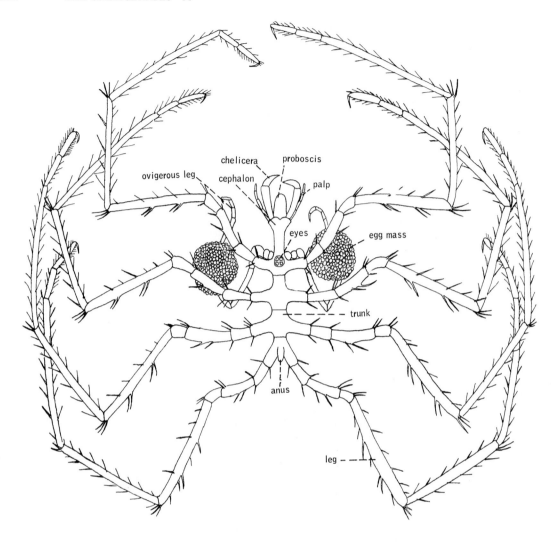

Figure 14-39.   *Nymphon rubrum,* a sea spider. (After Sars from Fage.)

Pycnogonids are mostly small animals with a body length ranging from one to 10 mm. but specimens of the deep sea *Colossendeis colossea* reach over 2 in. in body length and have a leg span of 2 feet.

The body is often long and narrow and is composed of a number of distinct segments (Fig. 14-39). The head, or cephalon, bears at the anterior end a cylindrical proboscis that is directed forward or in some species is curved ventrally. The posterior part of the cephalon is narrowed to form a short neck that bears on its dorsal surface four eyes mounted on a central tubercle. Posterior to the head is a trunk of four to six cylindrical segments. The first trunk segment is fused with the cephalon, but the remaining segments articulate with one another. The most striking feature of the trunk is the pair of large processes that project laterally from each segment. A leg articulates with the end of each

process, which often exceeds the length of the segment itself.

The appendages consist of a pair of chelicerae, a pair of palps, a pair of ovigerous legs, and four to six pairs of walking legs. The chelicerae are attached to both sides of the base of the proboscis. They are relatively short and one-to-four-segmented, the last segment forming a movable finger. In some genera such as *Pycnogonum,* the chelicerae are absent. The reduction in the chelicerae is concurrent with a correspondingly greater development of the proboscis. The leg-like palpi contain eight to ten segments or more and are well supplied with sensory hairs. The polyps are absent in some species. The ovigerous legs, which are peculiar to pycnogonids, are used by the male to carry the eggs and are less well developed or even absent in the female.

The walking legs are attached to the lateral

extensions of the trunk segments. There may be four, five, or six pairs of legs, depending on the number of trunk segments. Each leg is eight-segmented and terminates in a claw. The legs are very long in pycnogonids with slender bodies but are shorter in the more compact species. There are no abdominal appendages.

Some pycnogonids are exclusively bottom-dwellers, and they slowly crawl about over hydroids and bryozoans; others are able to

swim, using vertical flapping movements of the legs and have been picked up in plankton samples.

Pycnogonids are carnivorous and feed on hydroids, soft corals, anemones, bryozoans, and sponges. The chelicerae wrench off the polyps and pass them to the mouth at the tip of the proboscis. The mouth contains three lip-like teeth that not only regulate the size of the opening but also act as a rasp. From the mouth a tubular

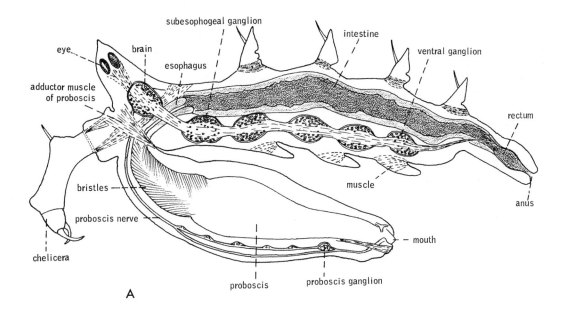

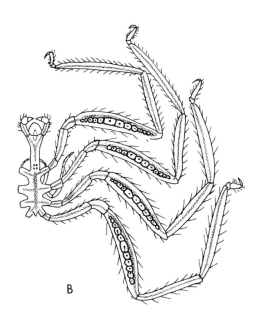

Figure 14-40. *A.* The pycnogonid, *Ascorhynchus castelli* (sagittal section). (After Dohrn from Fage.) *B.* Female of *Pallene brevirostris*, with eggs in femurs. (After Sars from Fage.)

pharynx extends through the proboscis (Fig. 14-40, *A*). The wall of the pharynx is composed of three articulating sclerotized plates, resulting in a triangular lumen. By means of exterior muscles attached to the pharyngeal plates, the size of the lumen can be increased or decreased, and a sucking force is produced. The pharynx not only acts as a pump, but also macerates the food by means of bristles projecting into the lumen from the plates. The pharynx leads into a short esophagus located in the neck; the esophagus opens through a valve into the intestine.

The intestine constitutes the midgut of the digestive tract and is very extensive. A long lateral cecum extends into each appendage and in the legs extends almost their entire length. Digestion is intracellular in the walls of the intestine and the ceca. After digestion, the cells involved are said to detach and circulate in the intestinal lumen. Wherever the detached digestive cells come to rest, the food materials are absorbed by adjacent cells. If such a process actually takes place, it is certainly a devious means of absorption.

Undigestible waste materials pass into a short rectum and then out the anus at the tip of the abdomen.

The circulatory system is composed of a heart and a hemocoel. The hemocoel is divided throughout the body into an upper and lower portion by a horizontal membrane. The heart is located in the dorsal division and pumps blood anteriorly. In the ventral portion of the hemocoel, blood flows posteriorly and out into the legs. Openings in the membrane permit blood to enter the dorsal hemocoel and thence through the ostia back into the heart.

There are no special organs for respiration and excretion.

The nervous system and sense organs are quite similar to those of arachnids (Fig. 14-40, *A*). The brain is located beneath the ocular tubercle and consists of a protocerebrum and tritocerebrum. A pair of ocular nerves from the protocerebrum and a pair of cheliceral nerves from the tritocerebrum provide for the innervation of the eyes and chelicerae. The lack of a deutocerebrum and the innervation of the chelicerae by the tritocerebrum indicate very clearly the relationship of the pycnogonids to the chelicerates.

The brain connects with a subesophageal ganglion, from which extend nerves for the palps and ovigerous legs. A pair of ventral nerve cords extends posteriorly from the subesophageal ganglion and bears a pair of fused ganglia for each trunk segment. A terminal nerve or pair of nerves from the last pair of ganglia innervates the abdomen.

The sense organs consist of sensory hairs and four eyes mounted on the dorsal tubercle. Both the eyes and the sensory hairs are constructed essentially like those of arachnids.

Pycnogonids are dioecious. Females can be distinguished from males by the poorly developed ovigerous legs or by their complete absence. Also, gravid females have very enlarged femurs. The gonad, either testis or ovary, is single, U-shaped, and located in the trunk above the intestine. The open end of the U is directed forward, and from each arm lateral branches extend far into the legs. In both males and females, the reproductive openings are located on the ventral side of the coxa of different pairs of legs. The specific legs and the number of legs possessing gonopores vary in different species and are not necessarily the same in both sexes. The eggs on reaching maturity migrate into the femurs of the legs containing gonopores (Fig. 14-40, *B*).

In most pycnogonids in which egg-laying has been observed, the male fertilizes the eggs as they are emitted by the female, and he then gathers them into his ovigerous legs (Fig. 14-39). Glands on the femurs of the male provide cement for forming the eggs into an adhesive spherical mass. The eggs are brooded by the male and the egg masses are held around the middle joints of the ovigerous legs. Bristles on the inner side of the segments aid in retaining the eggs. The male is not limited to one mating during a season and may carry several egg clusters.

The eggs are brooded by the male until they hatch. In most pycnogonids, a larva called a protonymphon hatches from the egg. The larva has only three pairs of appendages, representing the chelicerae, palps and ovigerous legs, and each appendage is only three-segmented. A short proboscis is present, but the trunk segments are still lacking. The larva either remains on the ovigerous legs of the male or more frequently becomes an ectoparasite or endoparasite on hydroids. In either case the larva eventually metamorphoses into a young pycnogonid.

Although largely unknown to the layman, sea spiders are actually common animals. Careful examination of bryozoans and hydroids scraped from a wharf piling or rocks will always yield a few specimens. They live in all oceans from the Arctic and Antarctic to the tropics, and there are many littoral forms, as well as species that live at great depths. The abundance and distribution of pycnogonids are very often related to the abundance and distribution of both the coelenterates and the bryozoans on which they feed.

There is no question but that pycnogonids are chelicerates. The structure of the brain, the nature of the sense organs, and the presence of chelicerae indicate this quite clearly. However, their exact relationship to arachnids and merostomes is by no means clear, for pycnogonids are aberrant in many respects. The presence of ovigerous legs, the segmented trunk, and the additional pairs of walking legs in many species have no counterpart in the other chelicerate classes. How to account for the ovigerous legs is the most intriguing problem. There are two possible solutions. Either the ovigerous legs are appendages of a segment that has been lost in other chelicerates, or they are homologous to the first pair of walking legs in arachnids and merostomes. The second alternative appears to be the most likely.

BIBLIOGRAPHY

Baker, E. W., and Wharton, G. W., 1952: An Introduction to Acarology. Macmillan, New York. An essential introductory work on the taxonomy of ticks and mites. Includes keys to the acarine families, figures, and extensive taxonomic references.

Bishop, S. C., 1949: The Phalangida of New York. Proc. Rochester Acad. Sci., *9(3)*:159–235. A taxonomic study of New York harvestmen. Keys, figures, and bibliography of taxonomic papers included.

Buck, J. B., and Keister, M. L., 1950: Arthropoda: *Argiope aurantia. In* Selected Invertebrate Types (F. A. Brown, ed.). Wiley, New York, pp. 382–394. Directions for a detailed study and dissection of the common garden spider.

Cloudsley-Thompson, J. L., 1958: Spiders, Scorpions, Centipedes, and Mites. Pergamon Press, New York, pp. 70–228. A discussion of the natural history and ecology of arachnids.

Fage, L., 1949: Classe des Merostomaces. *In* Traité de Zoologie (P. Grassé, ed.), Masson et Cié, Paris, Vol. 6, pp. 219–262. An excellent general treatment of the giant water scorpions and horseshoe crabs. Includes an extensive bibliography.

Fage, L., 1949: Classe des Pycnogonides. *In* Traité de Zoologie (P. Grassé, ed.), Masson et Cié, Paris, Vol. 6, pp. 906–941. A good general account of the pycnogonids with an extensive bibliography.

Gertsch, W. J., 1949: American Spiders. Van Nostrand, New York. An excellent semitechnical volume on the natural history of spiders by the curator of arachnids at the American Museum of Natural History.

Hedgpeth, J. W., 1948: The Pycnogonida of the Western North Atlantic and the Carribean. Proc. U. S. Nat. Mus., *97*:157–342.

Hoff, C. C., 1949: The pseudoscorpions of Illinois. Bull. Illinois Nat. Hist. Surv., vol. 24, art. 4. A good starting point for students interested in the taxonomy of pseudoscorpions. Keys, figures, and bibliography of taxonomic papers included.

Kaston, B. J., 1948: Spiders of Connecticut. State Geol. Nat. Hist. Surv. Bull., *70*:874. This work is essential for any American student interested in the taxonomy of spiders. Keys for most families and genera are provided; almost every species is illustrated. Includes extensive bibliography of taxonomic papers. The major part of the Connecticut spider fauna is found throughout eastern United States.

Lockhead, J. H., 1950: Arthropoda: *Xiphosura polyphemus. In* Selected Invertebrate Types (F. A. Brown, ed.). Wiley, New York, pp. 360–381. Directions for a detailed laboratory study and dissection of the Atlantic horseshoe crab.

Millot, J., Dawydoff, C., Vachon, M., Berland, L., André, M., and Waterlot, G., 1949: Classe des Arachnides. *In* Traité de Zoologie (P. Grassé, ed.), Masson et. Cié, Paris, Vol. 6, pp. 263–905. An authoritative treatment of the arachnids. Begins with introductory chapters on the comparative anatomy, physiology and embryology of the class, followed by separate chapters on the arachnid orders each written by a specialist on the group. Figures and bibliography are excellent.

Newell, I. M., 1959: Acari. *In* Ward and Whipple's Freshwater Biology (W. T. Edmondson, ed.). 2nd Edition, Wiley, New York, Pp. 1080–1116. Keys and figures to the common water mites of the United States.

Pennak, R. W., 1953: Freshwater Invertebrates of the United States. Ronald Press, New York, 470–487. A valuable introductory work on the taxonomy of fresh-water Hydracarina. Key, figures, and bibliography are inculded, as well as an introductory section on the biology of the group.

Snodgrass, R. E., 1948: The feeding organs of Arachnida, including mites and ticks. Smithsonian Misc. Collect., *110(10)*:1–93. A detailed review of the anatomy of the mouthparts of principal arachnid orders.

Chapter 15

THE CRUSTACEANS

With the crustaceans we turn to the first of the mandibulate classes of arthropods. In contrast to the chelicerate groups, the members of the mandibulate classes possess antennae, mandibles, and maxillae as head appendages, and their eyes are typically compound.

The 26,000 species of crustaceans include some of the most familiar arthropods, such as crabs, shrimp, lobsters, crayfish, and wood lice. In addition, there are myriads of tiny crustaceans that live in the seas, lakes, and ponds of the world and occupy a basic position in aquatic food chains.

The Crustacea is the only large class of arthropods that is primarily aquatic. Most crustaceans are marine, but there are many fresh-water species. In addition there are some semiterrestrial and terrestrial groups, but in general, the terrestrial crustaceans have never undergone any great adaptive evolution for life on land.

It is convenient to divide crustaceans into two groups, the entomostracans and the malacostracans. The entomostracans include the smaller species, such as fairy shrimp, water fleas, copepods, and barnacles. The malacostracans include the larger, more familiar crustaceans, such as crabs, shrimp, and lobsters. The Malacostraca is an actual subclass of crustaceans, but the Entomostraca, which is composed of a number of subclasses, has no real taxonomic significance.

External Anatomy. The head is more or less uniform throughout the class and bears five pairs of appendages (Fig. 15-29, *A*). Anteriorly, there is a first pair of antennae, or antennules, which are homologous to the antennae of the other mandibulate classes. They are innervated by the deutocerebrum and are probably not true segmental appendages. The antennules are followed by the second antennae, often referred to simply as the antennae. Innervated by the tritocerebrum, the antennae probably constitute the appendages of the most anterior body segment that has become incorporated in the head. As such, the antennae are homologous to the arachnid chelicerae. This segment lacks appendages in all other mandibulates, and thus the presence of two pairs of antennae constitutes a distinguishing feature of crustaceans.

Flanking and often covering the ventral mouth are the third pair of appendages, the mandibles (Fig. 15-29, *A*). These are usually short and heavy with opposing grinding and biting surfaces. Behind the mandibles are two pairs of accessory feeding appendages, the first and second maxillae. In front of and behind the mouth there are the variously developed upper and lower lips, or the labrum and the labium respectively. The labrum is developed from the body wall, and the labium is developed from the anterior end of the foregut.

The trunk is much less uniform than the head. Primitively, the trunk is composed of a series of many distinct and similar segments and a terminal telson bearing the anus. However, only the fairy shrimp and the Cephalocarida approximate this condition (Fig. 15-7). In most crustaceans, the trunk segments are characterized by varying degrees of regional specialization, of reduction or restriction in number, of fusion, and of other modifications (Fig. 15-29, A). Usually a thorax and an abdomen are present, but the number of segments they contain varies from group to group.

In most crustaceans, the thorax, or anterior trunk segments, is covered by a dorsal carapace (Fig. 15-29, A). The carapace arises as a posterior fold of the head that fuses with varying numbers of the tergites located behind it. Usually the lateral margins of the carapace overhang the sides of the body at least to some extent, and in extreme cases the carapace may completely enclose the entire body like the valves of a clam (Fig. 15-15).

Crustacean appendages are typically biramous (Fig. 15-1). There is a basal protopodite composed of two pieces—a coxopodite (coxa) and a basopodite (basis). To the basopodite is attached an inner branch (the endopodite) and an outer branch (the exopodite), each of which may be composed of one to many pieces. There are innumerable variations of this basic plan. Sometimes an appendage has lost one of the branches and has become secondarily uniramous. Often different parts of the appendage bear highly developed processes or extensions that have been given special names. Most frequently encountered are the terms *epipodite, exite,* and *endite,* referring to processes respectively borne by the coxopodite, exopodite, and endopodite.

Primitively, the appendages are numerous and similar and together perform a number of different functions. But, as in other arthropods, the evolutionary tendency in crustaceans has been toward a limitation in the number of appendages and a specialization of different appendages for particular functions. Thus, in a family of swimming crab, appendages are modified for swimming, crawling, prehension, sperm transmission, egg-brooding, and food handling.

Integument.   The crustacean cuticle, in contrast to that of most other arthropods, is usually calcified. Both the epicuticle and the procuticle contain depositions of calcium salts. The procuticle consists of three layers. The outer, thin, pigmented layer often has a vacuolated appearance and is calcified. Beneath the pigmented layer is a calcified layer that comprises most of the procuticle. It is not vacuolated, nor does it contain the pigment typical of the layer above. The innermost layer of the procuticle is thin and uncalcified.

Associated with the integument, but

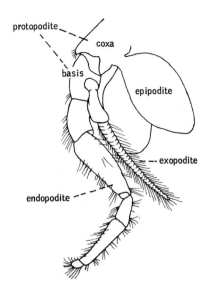

Figure 15-1.   Right 5th periopod, or leg, of the syncarid, *Anaspides tasmaniae,* showing basic structure of a crustacean appendage. (After Waterman and Chace.)

located beneath the hypodermis, are tegmental glands and chromatophores. The tegmental glands are composed of a cluster of secretory cells and a long duct that penetrates the exoskeleton and opens onto the surface of the epicuticle. The function of the tegmental glands is still uncertain. Chromatophores are characteristic of malacostracans only and are discussed later in the chapter.

Locomotion.   The ancestral crustaceans were probably swimming planktonic animals, and many modern forms have retained this primitive mode of existence. Propulsion in swimming is produced by the oar-like or propeller-like beating of certain appendages. The swimming appendages are usually supplied with fringed swimming setae that increase the water-resisting surface.

The majority of crustaceans have taken up a bottom existence. Although some swimming ability is often retained, certain appendages have usually become heavier and adapted to crawling and burrowing.

Nutrition.   A great range of diets and feeding mechanisms are used by crustaceans. At least some representatives of almost every order are filter feeders, eating plankton and detritus. Filter feeding is the arthropod counterpart of ciliary feeding. Fine setae on certain appendages function as a filter for the collection of food particles (Fig. 15-2). The necessary water current is produced by the beating of the filtering appendages or, more commonly, by special appendages modified for this purpose. The collected particles are removed from the filter setae by special

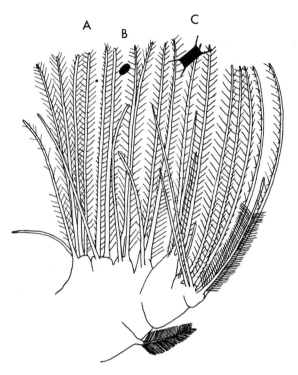

Figure 15-2. Filtering setae on the left maxilla of the copepod, *Calanus*. Three diatoms, representing species of different sizes, are drawn to scale to indicate the filtering ability of setae. Diatom *B* is approximately 25 microns long. The diatoms are: *A, Nannochloris oculata; B, Syracosphaera elongata;* and *C, Chaetoceros decipiens.* (After Dennell from Marshall and Orr.)

sediment to increase the concentration of particles for filtering.

Depending on the group of crustaceans concerned, virtually every pair of appendages, even the antennules, antennae, and mandibles, may be modified for filter feeding. Filter feeding probably first arose in connection with swimming and is therefore primitively associated with the trunk, the same limbs creating both the swimming and feeding currents. The tendency in most groups has been for the filtering apparatus to migrate forward, nearer to the mouth, and to use only the anterior trunk appendages or the head appendages.

Other crustaceans are scavengers, herbivores, or carnivores. Either the anterior trunk or the thoracic appendages are adapted for grasping or for picking up food, and the maxillae and mandibles function in holding, biting, and maceration. Raptorial feeding is most highly developed in the larger crustaceans, and frequently certain appendages are modified for seizing or stunning prey.

Many crustacean species utilize more than one method of feeding. For example, some scavengers supplement their diet with filter feeding or also feed upon living plants and animals; some filter feeders occasionally capture and consume small animals.

There are several groups of parasitic crustaceans. The ectoparasites usually have mandibles, maxillae, and sometimes neighboring appendages that are modified for piercing or lacerating the integument of the host. Tissue fluid or blood is then sucked from the wound. Endoparasites usually absorb food materials directly through the body surface, and in these forms appendages have frequently disappeared.

The mouth is ventral and in many filter feeders is directed posteriorly. The digestive tract is almost always straight (Fig. 15-10, *A*). The foregut may only be a simple tubular esophagus, but commonly it is enlarged and functions as a triturating stomach, the walls of which bear opposing chitinous ridges, denticles, and calcareous ossicles. The midgut varies greatly in size and in entomostracans may be expanded to form a stomach. One to several pairs of ceca are almost always present. One pair of ceca, especially in malacostracans, has usually become modified to form large digestive glands (the hepatopancreas).

The hepatopancreas is composed of ducts and blind secretory tubules and is relatively solid. Although glands that may produce an amylase are sometimes associated with the oral appendages or even with the esophagus, the secretions of the hepatopancreas are the primary source of digestive enzymes. The nature of the hepato-

combing or brushing setae and these particles are transported to the mouthparts by other appendages or sometimes in a ventral food groove.

There is usually little if any qualitative selection of food particles; instead the size of the filtering net determines the nature of the material that is trapped (Fig. 15-2). Usually each filtering seta is provided with lateral rows of smaller bristles (setules) and the overlapping of adjacent setae can provide a very fine mesh. In small crustaceans, the setules may be as close together as four microns, permitting the collection of very small diatoms and other phytoplankton. Some filtering species have been cultured solely on a diet of bacteria. Some idea of the amount of food trapped and ingested by filter-feeding crustaceans is indicated by the studies of Marshall and Orr (1955) on the marine copepod, *Calanus finmarchicus.* Using radioactive diatom cultures, these zoologists reported that this little crustacean, which is about five millimeters long, may filter out and ingest from 11,000 to 373,000 diatoms every 24 hours, depending upon the size of the diatoms. Detritus is primarily used by benthic crustaceans, and some forms actually stir up the bottom pancreatic fluid has been studied chiefly in malacostracans. This secretion contains protease, lipase, and several carbohydrate-splitting enzymes carried in a slightly acid medium. Even bile salts are present in the crayfish, *Astacus*. The presence of cellulase in some species is debated. It may be present in a few wood-inhabiting crustaceans, or cellulose digestion may be dependent upon symbiotic bacteria. Perhaps both situations occur.

The action of the digestive fluid takes place in the midgut and in the triturating stomach of the foregut when this chamber is present. Absorption is confined to the midgut walls and the tubules of the hepatopancreas, which also contains cells for glycogen, fat, and calcium storage.

An intestine, composed in part or entirely by the hindgut, comprises the posterior portion of the digestive tract.

Blood Circulation. The circulatory system is similar to that of chelicerates, although the heart, or arteries, or both are absent in some groups of entomostracans. The heart varies in form from a long tube to a spherical vesicle (Fig. 15-3). It is usually located in the dorsal part of the thorax, but when it is tubular, it may extend through the entire length of the trunk.

The number of ostia is greatest in the more primitive tubular heart; when the heart is a small vesicle, the ostia may be reduced to a single pair. The arteries are elastic but usually lack muscle fibers. Except in those groups that lack an arterial system, the heart always gives rise to a median anterior aorta. In addition, there may also be a median posterior abdominal artery, lateral arteries, and a ventral artery all leaving the heart.

In some small crustaceans, the arterial system is restricted to a tiny unbranched anterior artery; in other forms the principal arteries are large and branch extensively to supply various areas of the body. They may even branch into capillary networks, especially around the nerve cord and brain. Regardless of the development of the arterial system, the terminal vessels almost always empty into tissue spaces (lacunae) and thence into intercommunicating sinuses. The sinuses are bounded by membranes derived from adjacent connective tissue. Return blood flow to the pericardium and heart is generally through distinct sinus channels, which in many larger forms may assume the character of vessels.

Membranous partitions usually cut through the sinuses, resulting in more definite pathways and facilitating blood flow. For example, in appendages there is commonly a longitudinal sep-

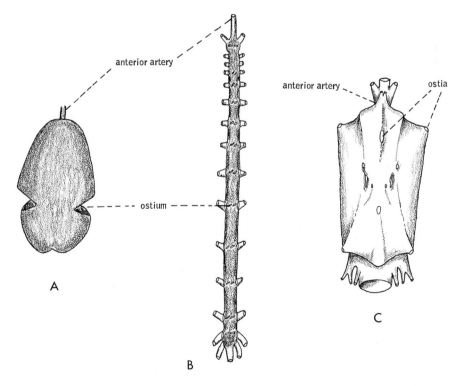

Figure 15-3. Crustacean hearts. All dorsal views. *A.* Copepod, *Calanus finmarchicus.* (After Lowe from Maynard.) *B.* Stomatopod, *Squilla mantis.* (After Alexandrowicz from Maynard.) *C.* Crayfish, *Astacus.* (After Baumann from Maynard.)

tum dividing the appendage sinus into two channels. One channel receives the arterial flow, and the other drains into the pericardium.

Accessory hearts, or blood pumps, that increase pressure are not uncommon and usually consist of a local arterial enlargement onto which muscles are inserted. Such an accessory heart, called the cor frontale, is found in most malacostracans and represents an enlargement of the anterior median artery in front of the triturating stomach. In small crustaceans, the beating of the appendages and the movement of internal organs, such as gut peristalsis, play an important role in augmenting blood flow. Blood flow is further regulated by valves that, aside from the afferent ostia, are most commonly present at the junction of heart and arteries; but arterial valves sometimes are also present, and crustaceans that lack hearts often have valves in the sinus channels.

The blood contains small hyaline and larger granular amebocytes, but the numerous variations and intergradations may indicate that these differences are all phases of a single type. The number of cells range from 1000 to over 50,000 per cubic centimeter of plasma, depending on the species, the age of the individual, the nutritional state, the proximity to ecdysis, and other physiological factors.

In addition to phagocytosis, the blood cells are also involved in clotting. Under certain irritating conditions such as amputation, certain amebocytes called explosive cells disintegrate and liberate a substance that converts plasma fibrinogen to fibrin. Islands of coagulated plasma then appear to which other islands connect and in which blood cells are trapped thus forming a clot. Other clotting mechanisms that do not involve explosive cells also may be present, but their presence has not as yet been definitely confirmed.

Respiration. Gills are the usual respiratory organs of crustaceans and are typically associated with the appendages. In their simplest and most primitive form, each gill is a plate-like process (lamella) on the coxa of most trunk appendages (Fig. 15-8, B). In malacostracans the gills are usually restricted to the thoracic appendages, and the surface area is often greatly increased by the development of filaments or lamellae arranged along a central axis (Fig. 15-48, A and D).

In many groups, particularly those that are very small, gills are absent, and gaseous exchange takes place over the general body surface. Integumentary respiration is probably of varying importance in all crustaceans.

The water current for respiration is generally provided by the beating of the append-ages. These appendages may be gill-bearing or certain appendages may be modified for producing a ventilating current. Within the circulatory medium, oxygen is transported either in simple solution or bound to hemoglobin or hemocyanin. Hemoglobin is found only in the entomostracans, and hemocyanin only in the malacostracans, but both pigments have a sporadic distribution. The respiratory pigments are dissolved in the plasma, but hemoglobin may also be found in muscle and nervous tissue and even in the eggs of some species.

Modifications for amphibious and terrestrial respiration are considered in later discussions of groups that contain terrestrial species.

Excretion and Osmoregulation. The excretory organs of crustaceans are similar in structure and origin to the coxal glands of chelicerates. Crustacean excretory organs are paired and composed of an end sac and an excretory tubule (Fig. 15-4, A). The end sac arises from an anterior coelomic compartment, and the duct may represent a persisting coelomoduct. In adult crustaceans, the excretory organs are located in either the antennal or second maxillary segments and are therefore called antennal or maxillary glands. The excretory pores of the antennal glands open on the underside of the bases of the second antennae, and those of the maxillary glands open onto or near the bases of the second maxillae. Both antennal and maxillary glands are commonly present in crustacean larvae, but usually only one pair persists in the adult. A few groups possess both types.

Although small amounts of urea and uric acid have been detected, the principal nitrogenous waste product is ammonia. This is true even in terrestrial forms, an indication of the rather limited terrestrial adaptation of these crustaceans. In addition to ammonia, there is considerable excretion of amines.

At the present time it is uncertain whether excretion through the end sac takes place by filtration or secretion. Whatever the mechanism, these organs in most crustaceans are not highly developed for waste elimination. If, for example, the antennal glands are removed or the excretory pores are plugged, the removal of ammonia is only partially hindered and in some cases only slightly so. Experimental evidence indicates that the gills are important accessory organs for the excretion of ammonia.

The antennal and maxillary glands also do not appear to play an important role in osmoregulation. Most crustaceans, even many fresh-water species, produce a urine that is isosmotic with the blood. In such forms, the only ionic regulations effected by the excretory glands appear to be the conservation of potas-

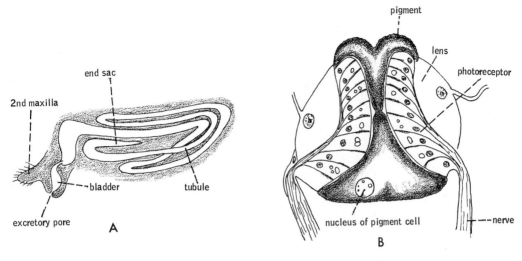

Figure 15-4.   *A.* Maxillary gland of a tadpole shrimp, *Apus.* (After Bernard from Parker and Haswell.) *B.* Section through the nauplius eye of the ostracod, *Eucypris crassa.* (After Nowikow from Kaestner.)

sium and calcium and the elimination of excess magnesium and sulfates. This is not true, however, of the fresh-water crayfish in which the antennal glands do elaborate a hypotonic urine. Another exception is the brine shrimp, *Artemia,* which is the only crustacean known to produce a urine hypertonic to its blood. For most crustaceans, the gills are apparently the chief organs for maintaining salt balance. In fresh-water and brackish-water forms that cannot excrete a hypotonic urine, the gills actively absorb salts.

Crustaceans, like most other arthropods, possess nephrocytes—cells capable of picking up and accumulating waste particles. Nephrocytes are most commonly located in the gill axes and in the bases of the legs.

Nervous System.   As in most other arthropods, the nervous system of crustaceans displays the usual tendency toward concentration and fusion of ganglia. In the most primitive condition, the ventral cord displays a ladder-like configuration (Fig. 15-12). Varying degrees of medial and longitudinal fusion have developed independently within most crustacean groups. In crayfish, for example, medial fusion has taken place resulting in a single cord with single, rather than obviously paired, ganglia. In most crabs, all ventral ganglia have fused with the subesophageal ganglia to form a single mass.

Usually three pairs of lateral nerves issue from each pair of ganglia. The posterior pair of nerves are commonly composed of motor fibers and innervate the flexor muscles of the body wall. The anterior and middle pairs of lateral nerves are large and mixed. The first pair supplies the appendages, and the second pair supplies the other parts of the segment.

Four pairs of major nerves arise from the brain—a pair to the antennules, a pair to the antennae, a pair to the compound eyes, and a pair of circumesophageal connectives to the ventral cord. In addition there may be a pair of dorsal nerves to the head integument and a nerve to the median nauplius eye.

As in annelids, giant fibers are found in the central nervous system of many crustaceans. The giant fibers are particularly well developed in forms such as shrimp and crayfish, which can dart rapidly backward by a sudden flexion of the tail. Decapods, in which these fibers have been most studied, usually possess a pair of dorso-median giant fibers arising from cell bodies in the brain and a pair of dorsal-lateral giant fibers.

The dorso-lateral giant fibers are composed of a series of neurons. The cell body of each component nerve cell is located in a ventral ganglion, from which an axon runs dorsally and anteriorly to the next ganglion. Here the axon terminates in contact with the axon arising from the ganglion of that segment. Impulses for the median giant fibers arise in the brain, but impulses for the lateral fibers can arise from any ganglion, and transmission between members of the series can occur in any direction. A single impulse along either the medial or lateral fibers is sufficient to evoke the complete escape reflex.

Lack of space does not permit discussion of the numerous studies on crustacean reflexes (see Wiersma, 1961). It is interesting, however, that some of the more complex reflexes such as feeding and copulation occur even when the brain is removed. The brain apparently exercises an inhibiting and regulating control over these functions rather than being the center of initiation and in this respect is rather like the annelid brain.

Sense Organs. The sense organs of crustaceans consist of eyes, statocysts, proprioceptors, general tactile receptors, and chemoreceptors. The eyes are of two types, median eyes and compound eyes. A median eye is a characteristic feature of the nauplius larva of crustaceans and is therefore often referred to as the nauplius eye (Fig. 15-6). It may degenerate or persist in the adult. The median eye is composed of three or sometimes four small pigment-cup ocelli of the inverse type (Fig. 15-4, B). The cups are located directly over the protocerebrum, where they form either a compact mass or are somewhat separated.

Only a few photoreceptor cells compose each ocellus, and in most ocelli no lens is present. A median nerve extends from the eye to the protocerebrum. Both the function and physiology of the median eye are obscure. The median eye is probably largely an organ of orientation, at least in planktonic larvae and in such groups as the copepods, which lack compound eyes. As such, the eye would enable the animal to determine the direction of the light source and thus enable the animal to locate the upper surface of the water or, in burrowing forms, to locate the surface of the substratum.

Two compound (lateral) eyes are found in the adults of most species. These compound eyes typically are well separated on each side of the head, but median fusion has taken place in some groups. The eyes may be located at the end of a usually movable stalk (peduncle) (Fig. 15-65, B), or they may be sessile (Fig. 15-42). The basic structural and functional units composing the compound eyes are divergent cones called ommatidia (Fig. 15-5, A).

Each ommatidium at its outer end is covered by a translucent cornea derived from the skeletal cuticle. The external surface of the cornea, called a facet, is usually square or hexagonal. The cornea is secreted by two underlying modified epidermal cells called corneagenous cells. Behind the corneal elements, the ommatidium contains a long cylindrical or tapered element called the crystalline cone, which functions as a second lens.

The crystalline cone is produced by usually four cells and often has a somewhat four-part structure. The basal end of the cone is formed by the receptor element (the retinula). The center of the retinula is occupied by a translucent cylinder (the rhabdome), around which are arranged elongated photoreceptor, or retinular, cells. There are typically seven similar retinular cells plus one dissimilar cell. The latter cell is shorter and has an eccentric position in reference to the rhabdome and rosette of other retinular cells.

The retinular cells contain black or brown pigment granules, which comprise the proximal retinal pigment. Distally the ommatidium is surrounded by a number of special pigment cells, forming the distal retinal pigment. Either the proximal or distal pigment or both can migrate centrally or distally, depending on the intensity of light (Fig. 15-5, B).

The axons of the retinular cells issue from the ommatidium as a bundle and extend to an optic ganglion located below the eye or in the distal end of the eye stalk. Here the axons connect to second-order neurons. In entomostracans there are two optic ganglia and in malacostracans there are four, although the basal ganglion in the malacostracans is actually an extension of the brain. Also, malacostracans possess two optic chiasmata.

In bright light, a compound eye produces an apposition image (Fig. 15-5, B). Light enters an ommatidium either at an angle or perpendicular to the facet. The proximal and distal retinal pigments are extended and act as a screen to prevent light from passing from one ommatidium to another and thus light rays are restricted to the axial region of the crystalline cone and rhabdome.

The crystalline cone is essentially a lens cylinder and is formed of concentric lamellae. The outer lamellae have lower refractive indices than do the central lamellae and probably function by refraction to eliminate oblique rays and to direct the more axial light rays to the rhabdome. There is no mechanism for accommodation, because the crystalline cone provides for a fixed focus. On emerging from the crystalline cone, light rays pass to the retinula. Current research indicates that the rhabdome, rather than the retinular cells, is the photoreceptive element and the center of the initial photochemical response. Assuming that this is true, the rhabdome would then in turn stimulate the retinular cells as a unit.

The retinula of each ommatidium receives and transmits an inverted spot of light, which overlaps to some extent the light spot received by adjacent ommatidia. The total image formed by the compound eye results from the number of ommatidia involved and the varying intensities of the light spots they receive. The image is thus analogous to the image produced on a television screen, on which the "picture" is essentially a grid composed of dots of light each with different intensities. The apposition image formed by a compound eye is often called a mosaic image, since the total image results from

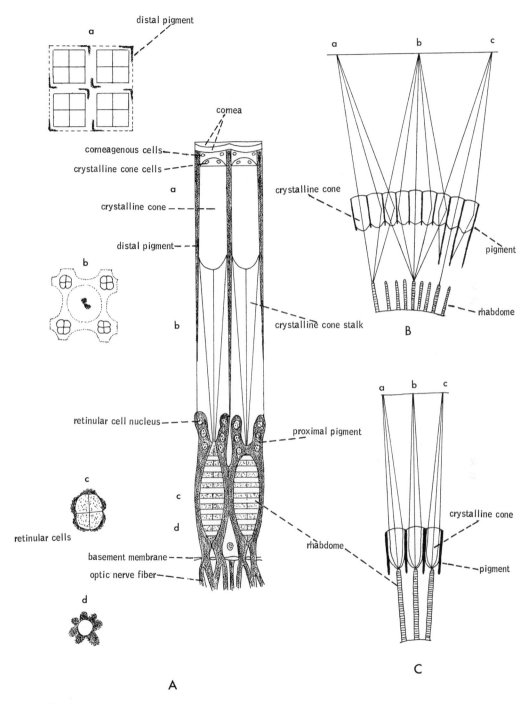

Figure 15-5.   *A.* Two ommatidia from compound eye of the crayfish, *Astacus* (longitudinal view). Cross sections shown for indicated levels. (After Bernhards from Waterman.) *B.* Compound eye especially adapted for superposition image formation. Light rays from points *a* and *b* are being received as a superposition image. Pigment is retracted and light rays, initially received by a number of ommatidia, are concentrated on a single ommatidium. Point of light *c* is being received as an apposition image. Pigment is extended, preventing light rays from crossing from one ommatidium to another. *C.* Compound eye especially adapted for apposition image formation. (*B* and *C* after Kühn from Prosser and others.)

small pieces put together like a mosaic. Unfortunately, the term *mosaic image* implies a special or different sort of image. Actually, the human eye receives and transmits light stimuli in an essentially similar manner, a single point of light stimulating a functional unit of approximately seven cones; the only difference is that the mosaic in the human eye is of a finer grain (composed of smaller and more numerous spots).

A supposed advantage of the compound eye is its facility to detect movement. A slight shift in a point of light results in a corresponding shift in the ommatidia being stimulated. The overlapping feature should be of value here, because several ommatidia would then be responding to the same point of light. Another advantage of the compound eyes found in many crustaceans is that the total corneal surface is greatly convex, resulting in a wide visual field. This is particularly true for stalked compound eyes, in which the cornea may cover an arc of 180 degrees or more (Fig. 15-65, *B*).

In weak light, the compound eyes function in a somewhat different manner and form a superposition image (Fig. 15-5, *B*). The pigment is retracted, so no screening effect is present. Thus light can pass from one ommatidium to another, and one retinula responds to light rays that originally entered several adjacent facets. The intensity of the stimulus resulting from the light is therefore greater and more likely to activate the retinula than light entering a single facet.

The compound eyes of most crustaceans are able to adapt, to at least some extent, to both bright and weak light and form either an appositional or superpositional image. But, in general, crustacean eyes tend to be specially modified for functioning under one of these two conditions. Thus lateral eyes can be classified as either apposition or superposition eyes, although there are many intergradations between the two types.

Crustaceans that are diurnal and live in well lighted habitats, such as terrestrial and littoral species, usually possess apposition eyes (Fig. 15-5, *C*). The screening pigment is well developed. The length of the crystalline cone is approximately equal to its focal length, and the lower end of the cone and the upper end of the rhabdome are contiguous, or nearly so. The retinular cells are quite long, extending from the crystalline cone to the basal membrane of the retina. All of these modifications tend to confine light entering a single ommatidium and to funnel the light down the axis of the ommatidium to the rhabdome.

Superposition eyes are found in nocturnal and deep-water crustaceans. This type of eye is especially modified for collecting and concentrating onto one ommatidium light originally striking a large patch of facets (Fig. 15-5, *B*). Screening pigment is usually present but may be reduced or absent in cave-dwelling and bathypelagic species and perhaps in all hyperiid amphipods. The length of the crystalline cone tends to be twice as long as its focal length, and there is considerable space between the end of the crystalline cone and the rhabdome. The retinular cells are much shorter than those in apposition eyes, and they are restricted to the base of the ommatidium. A special reflecting pigment is often present around the retinula and may be movable.

Of the several factors that affect the degree of visual acuity in compound eyes (i.e., how well various parts of the field can be resolved), the number of ommatidia composing the eye in relation to eye size is of obvious importance. The greater the number of ommatidia, the finer is the retinal grain and the less crude is the image. The number of ommatidia in crustacean lateral eyes varies enormously. A single eye in the wood louse, *Armadillidium*, is composed of not more than 25 ommatidia, while the eye of the lobster, *Homarus*, may possess as many as 14,000 ommatidia. Studies on crustaceans with well developed compound eyes indicate some ability to distinguish in regard to form and size, but the degree of visual acuity is certainly slight and the total image crude as compared to that formed by the human eye.

Color discrimination has been demonstrated in a number of crustaceans, and may be of general occurrence throughout the class. For example, the hermit crab, *Pagurus*, can discriminate between painted yellow and blue snail shells and shells colored different shades of grey. The chromatophores of the shrimp, *Crangon*, adapt to a background of yellow, orange, or red, but not to any shade of grey (the chromatophore changes are mediated through the eyes.) The mechanism of color vision is still unknown, and in some entomostracans such as *Daphnia* it has not been definitely proven that color responses are actually mediated through the compound eye.

Statocysts are restricted to a few groups of Malacostraca. Only a single pair are present and are located in the base of the antennules or in the base of the abdomen, uropods, or telson. Each statocyst arises as an ectodermal invagination and usually retains an opening to the exterior. The statolith may be secreted, but commonly it is composed of a mass of agglutinated sand grains. The physiology of crustacean statocysts is best known in the decapods (shrimp, crayfish, lobsters, and crabs) and is discussed with these groups.

Special proprioceptive structures called muscle receptor organs are found in malacostracans, especially the decapods. Each organ consists of a specially modified muscle cell, two of which are located in the dorsal musculature of each abdominal segment and the last two thoracic segments, at least in the lobster, *Homarus*. The muscle cell displays a complex dual sensory innervation, which is stimulated by the stretching of the dendritic processes within the muscle cell. The processes may be stretched by the alternate contraction and extension of the muscle receptor organ itself or by the action of adjacent muscle cells.

Proprioceptors also are present in the appendages. Although these sensory receptors at present have only been found in the decapods, at least similar receptors will probably be found in other crustaceans as well. One type of sensory receptor, called elastic receptors, are present in the joints of the walking legs and consists of a specially innervated strand of connective tissue that extends across the joint. On the basal side of the joint, the strand is connected to the tendon of the flexor muscle and on the distal side to the wall of the segment. The sensory neurons are stimulated by both the stretching and the movement of the connective tissue strand.

Another type of sensory receptor, called myochordotonal organs, is found in the basal end of the third segment of each walking leg in decapods; they are thought to be proprioceptive from their structure. The organ is a thin membrane containing the cell bodies of a cluster of bipolar sensory neurons. The dendritic processes are anchored in the ventral wall of the segment.

The remaining sensory structures are represented by isolated receptors located over the surface of the body. The most important of these are the sensory (tactile) hairs, which are essentially like those of other arthropods. Each hair consists of a hollow chitinous shaft, which often possesses lateral setules. The shaft is swollen at the base and articulates with the surface skeleton. A canal in the integument enables a process from a bipolar neuron to enter the base of the hair. The hair must be moved rather than touched for the receptor to be stimulated.

Although tactile hairs can appear anywhere on the body surface, they are especially prevalent on the appendages. Among other functions, the tactile hairs are probably important in orienting the animal with regard to the substratum. If the statocysts of the spiny lobster, *Panulirus*, are removed, the loss of postural

orientation is quickly regained once the legs establish contact with the substratum. The long delicate tactile hairs that are found on many crustaceans appear to function in the detection of water currents. Such hairs are present on the antennules of the crab, *Carcinus*, which can detect the movement of objects in water even when blinded. Tactile hairs are also present on the antennules or antennae of many raptorial tube-dwelling crustaceans that project these appendages from the entrance of the tube or burrow to detect passing prey.

Chemoreception is the function of a variety of sensory structures found on the appendages, especially the antennules, antennae, and feeding appendages. Of these, esthetascs are the most common and occur in the majority of crustaceans. Esthetascs are long delicate sensory hairs that are usually present in rows. The dendritic processes of a group of bipolar sensory neurons extend through the entire length of the hair. In terrestrial crustaceans, the esthetascs have the form of tiny plates instead of hairs.

Other supposed chemoreceptors are funnel canals and pores, which are found in decapods. Both are canals in the cuticle containing dendritic processes of sensory neurons.

Although chemoreception has been demonstrated in many crustaceans, evidence that the receptors described above are involved is only indirect. The wood louse, *Oniscus*, prefers to congregate on filter paper soaked in distilled water than on one soaked in a dilute sugar solution, but the ability to discriminate disappears with the loss of the ends of the antennae containing the esthetascs. The amphibious marine isopod, *Ligia*, can distinguish fresh water from salt water either with the antennae or with the tips of the legs, depending on the species. Response to food stimuli on contact with the mouthparts in blinded decapods has been repeatedly demonstrated.

Thermoreception has been experimentally demonstrated in a number of different crustaceans, but the mechanism of thermoreception is still unknown. Sensitivity to water pressure has been demonstrated in the amphipod, *Synchelidium*, and there is also evidence for it in some crab larvae and other planktonic crustaceans.

Reproduction and Development. The barnacles plus a few scattered members of other groups are the only hermaphroditic crustaceans. The gonads of crustaceans are typically elongated paired organs, lying in the dorsal portion of the thorax or abdomen, or in both (Fig. 15-10, *A*). The oviducts and sperm ducts are usually paired simple tubules that open either at the base of a pair of trunk appendages or on a sternite. However, the segment that bears the gonopores varies from one group to another.

Copulation is the general rule in crustaceans, the male usually having certain appendages modified for clasping the female. In many crustaceans, the sperm lack a flagellum and are nonmobile, and in some crustaceans the sperm are transmitted as spermatophores. A seminal receptacle is sometimes present in the female. The seminal receptacle may be located near the base of the oviduct, but frequently it is a separate pouch-like ectodermal invagination of the genital segment or a neighboring segment. In a few groups, the sperm ducts open at the end of a penis, or certain appendages may be modified for the transmission of sperm.

Most crustaceans brood their eggs for different lengths of time. The eggs may be attached to certain appendages, may be contained within a brood chamber located in various parts of the body, or may be retained within a sac formed when the eggs are expelled.

Although the eggs are typically centrolecithal and cleavage is superficial, holoblastic cleavage is not uncommon. Often only the initial cleavage divisions are complete, as in some arachnids, but there are a considerable number of species, both entomostracans and malacostracans, in which a hollow blastula is formed.

A free-swimming planktonic larva is characteristic of most marine crustaceans and also some fresh-water entomostracans and undoubtedly represents the primitive type of development. The earliest and basic type of crustacean larva is a nauplius larva (Fig. 15-6). Only three pairs of appendages are present— the antennules, antennae, and mandibles. The antennae and mandibles are biramous and bear swimming setae. No trunk segmentation is evident, and a single median, or nauplius, eye is borne on the front of the head.

In the course of successive molts, trunk segments and additional appendages are gradually acquired, development proceeding from anterior to posterior. When the first six pairs of appendages are functional and all of the trunk segments and the lateral eyes have appeared, the larva in higher malacostracans is called a zoea (Fig. 15-68, A). Since the corresponding stage of development in other crustaceans is not as clearly defined from the earlier stages, the term *zoea* is generally not applied. With the acquisition of a full complement of functional appendages, the young crustacean is called a postlarva.

The postlarva may be quite similar to the adult in general appearance or may still be strikingly different in some respects. For example, the postlarva of crabs has a crab-like thorax, but the abdomen is still large and extended (Fig. 15-68, B). After additional molts, all of the adult features are attained except for size and sexual maturity.

The basic developmental pattern of nauplius, zoea (or its equivalent), and postlarva is very frequently modified. In many groups there has been a tendency for some or all of the larval stages to be suppressed. In most decapods, for example, the nauplius stage is passed in the egg, and the zoea larva is the hatching stage. Both the nauplius and zoea may be suppressed, and the young hatch as postlarvae. All larval development is suppressed in some crustaceans, such as the crayfish.

When development is direct or when there is a graded series of larval stages without radical changes from one stage to the next, development is said to be anamorphic. When the young hatch as postlarvae, development is said to be epimorphic. However, in most crustaceans development tends to be metamorphic. Metamorphosis is especially striking in the sessile barnacles and in many parasites. In barnacles the larva, after a free-swimming existence, attaches and undergoes radical structural changes to assume the adult structure.

Since the postlarval stages of different groups are usually distinctive, these stages have often received special names, such as the megalops of crabs, and the acanthosoma of sergestid prawns. Moreover, the zoea, if particularly distinctive, may be given a special designation, such as the mysis of lobsters. The intermediate stages have also received different names. For example, the later nauplius instars are called metanauplii, and the prezoeal instar is called a protozoea.

Molting and Growth.   In many crusta-

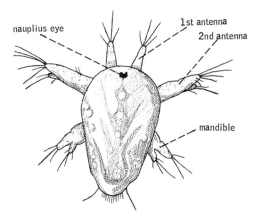

Figure 15-6.   First nauplius larva of *Cyclops fuscus,* a copepod. (After Green.)

nauplius eye

1st antenna

2nd antenna

mandible

ceans, such as barnacles and the lobster, *Homarus,* molting and growth continue through-out the life of the individual, although molts become spaced further and further apart. In other crustaceans, molting and growth cease with the attainment of sexual maturity, a certain size, or after a certain number of instars.

The process of molting has probably been investigated in more detail in crustaceans, especially decapods, than in any other arthropods. It was formerly thought that all physiological processes involved in molting ceased during most of the intermolt period, (i.e., the time between two periods of actual shedding, or ecdysis). It is now realized that molting is virtually a continuous process in the life of a crustacean and that as much as 90 per cent or more of the intermolt period may be involved with concluding and preparatory processes associated with the preceding and the future molt. This is especially true in species that molt all year round. In species that molt seasonally, such as species of the crayfish, *Cambarus,* and the fiddler crab, *Uca,* there is a rather definite intervening rest period during the intermolt. But even during the rest period, food reserves are accumulated for the next molt.

The preparatory phase, or pro-ecdysis, is marked by a continuing accumulation of food reserves and a rise in blood calcium, probably resulting from the activity of the hepatopancreas. Later there is a re-absorption of calcium from various parts of the old skeleton. The re-absorption takes place along lines where splitting later occurs or where the old skeleton must be stretched or broken to permit extraction of a large terminal part of an appendage, such as a claw. After the separation of the old cuticle from the epidermis and the secretion of the new epicuticle, the animal is prepared for the actual process of ecdysis and usually seeks some protected retreat or remains in its burrow. The body swells from the uptake of water through the gut and quickly emerges from the old skeleton.

During the concluding phase of ecdysis (postecdysis), the endocuticle is secreted and calcification and hardening of the skeleton take place. The animal remains in its retreat and does not feed during the first part of this phase. This is the longest part of the molt cycle and may occupy a considerable part of the intermolt period.

Systematic Résumé of Class Crustacea

The classification of the higher ranks of Crustacea is still unstable. The system followed in succeeding pages has been taken from Waterman and Chace (1960). A synopsis is given below. The number after each name refers to the approximate number of described species that the group contains.

Class Crustacea (26,000+)
 Subclass Cephalocarida (2)
 Subclass Branchiopoda (800)
  Order Anostraca (175)
  Order Notostraca (15)
  Order Diplostraca (605)
   Suborder Conchostraca (180)
   Suborder Cladocera (425)
 Subclass Ostracoda (2000)
  Order Myodocopa (300)
  Order Cladocopa (30)
  Order Podocopa (1600)
  Order Platycopa (30)
 Subclass Mystacocarida (3)
 Subclass Copepoda (4500)
  Order Calanoida (1200)
  Order Harpacticoida (1200)
  Order Cyclopoida (1000)
  Order Notodelphyoida (300)
  Order Monstrilloida (35)
  Order Caligoida (400)
  Order Lernaeopodoida (300)
 Subclass Branchiura (75)
 Subclass Cirripedia (800)
  Order Thoracica (550)
   Suborder Lepadomorpha (300)
   Suborder Verrucomorpha (50)
   Suborder Balanomorpha (200)
  Order Acrothoracica (12)
  Order Ascothoracica (25)
  Order Apoda (1)
  Order Rhizocephala (200)
 Subclass Malacostraca (18,000)
  Series Leptostraca (7)
   Superorder Phyllocarida (7)
    Order Nebaliacea (7)
  Series Eumalocostraca (18,000)
   Superorder Syncarida (32)
    Order Anaspidacea (32)
   Superorder Hoplocarida (180)
    Order Stomatopoda (180)
   Superorder Peracarida (9000)
    Order Thermosbaenacea (4)
    Order Spelaeogriphacea (1)
    Order Mysidacea (450)
     Suborder Lophogastrida (30)
     Suborder Mysida (420)
    Order Cumacea (650)
    Order Tanaidacea (250)
    Order Isopoda (4000)
     Suborder Gnathiidea (75)
     Suborder Anthuridea (100)
     Suborder Flabellifera (1400)
     Suborder Valvifera (600)

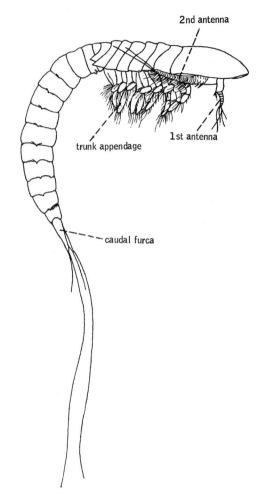

Figure 15-7.   The cephalocaridan, *Hutchinsoniella macracantha.* (After Giesbrecht from Waterman and Chace.)

Subclass Cephalocarida

The Cephalocarida is the most recently discovered and perhaps the most primitive of the existing groups of crustaceans. Only three species, belonging to two genera, comprise the subclass, which was first described in 1955 from specimens collected from the bottom sand and mud of Long Island Sound.

Cephalocarids are tiny shrimp-like crustaceans that measure a little less than three millimeters in length (Fig. 15-7). The horseshoe-shaped head is followed by an elongated trunk of nineteen segments, of which only the first nine bear appendages. Both pairs of antennae are short, and the eyes have disappeared, probably as a result of the burrowing existence of the animals. The trunk appendages are interesting in several respects. Not only are all the trunk appendages similar, but they are not markedly different from the second pair of maxillae. Also the basal section of each appendage bears a large flattened outer piece (pseudepipodite) that gives the limb a triramous rather than the usual biramous structure (Fig. 15-72).

The internal anatomy and the physiology and habits of cephalocarids are still largely unknown. Unlike most crustaceans, they are hermaphroditic; the genital openings are located on the ninth segment. A metanauplius is the earliest known larval stage.

Subclass Branchiopoda

Branchiopods are small crustaceans that are largely restricted to fresh water. Although several structurally diverse groups compose the subclass, all are characterized by having trunk appendages that are of a flattened leaf-like structure (Fig. 15-8, *B*). The exopodite and

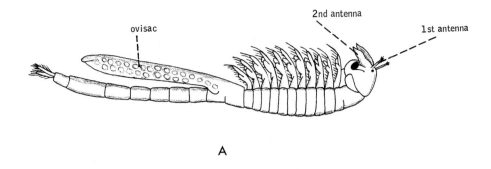

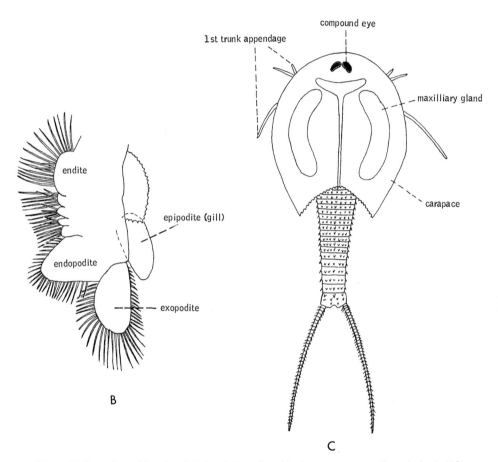

Figure 15-8. Branchiopoda. *A.* Fairy shrimp, *Branchinecta,* an anostracan (lateral view). (After Calman.) *B.* Trunk appendage of *Branchinecta paludosa,* showing foliaceous structure. (After Sars from Pennak.) *C.* Tadpole shrimp, *Apus,* a notostracan (dorsal view). (After Pennak.)

endopodite each consists of a single flattened lobe, bearing dense setae along the margin. The coxa is provided with a flattened epipodite that serves as a gill; hence the name Branchiopoda— "gill feet." In addition to respiration, the trunk appendages are usually adapted for filter feeding and commonly for locomotion. The first antennae are small, uniramous, and frequently unsegmented. The second maxillae are reduced and may even be absent. The telson bears a

pair of large terminal processes called cercopods.

The Branchiopoda is composed of four distinct groups. The order Anostraca, called the fairy shrimps, is characterized by an elongated trunk containing some twenty or more segments, of which the anterior eleven to nineteen segments bear appendages (Fig. 15-8, *A*). There is no carapace (hence the name Anostraca— "without carapace"), and the compound eyes are stalked.

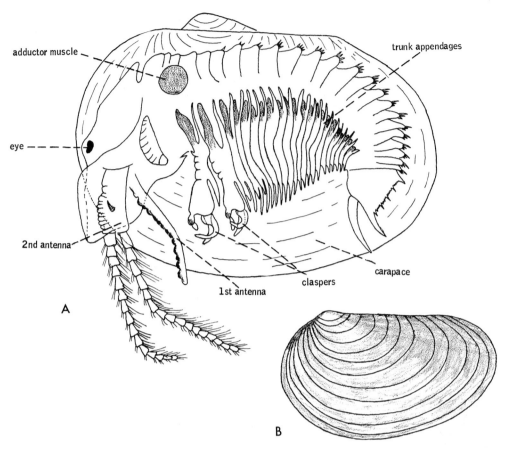

Figure 15-9.   *A.* Male of the conchostracan, *Cyzicus mexicanus,* with left valve removed. (After Mattox from Ward and Whipple.) *B.* Left shell valve of the conchostracan, *Cyzicus.* (After Sars from Calman.)

In the order Notostraca, or tadpole shrimp, the head and anterior half of the trunk are covered by a large shield-like carapace (Fig. 15-8, *C*). The anterior half of the trunk bears 35 to 70 pairs of appendages. Since there are only 25 to 44 "segments," some of which carry as many as ten or more pairs of appendages, the original external segmentation has probably been replaced by a secondary annulation. Only vestiges of the second antennae remain. The compound eyes are sessile and located close together at the front of the dorsal shield.

The order Diplostraca contains two suborders of laterally compressed branchiopods, in which the body is at least partially enclosed within a bivalve carapace. In the suborder Conchostraca, called the clam shrimps, the entire body is nearly or completely enclosed within the carapace, and externally the animal looks strikingly like a little clam (Fig. 15-9). Dorsally the carapace is folded rather than hinged, and the two valves are closed by a transverse adductor muscle. Ten to thirty-two trunk segments are present, each bearing a pair

of appendages. The second antennae are well developed, biramous, and setose, and the compound eyes are sessile.

The second suborder is the Cladocera, or water fleas, of which the genus *Daphnia* is a common representative (Fig. 15-10, *A*). The carapace of most cladocerans encloses the trunk but not the head and usually terminates posteriorly in an apical spine. The head projects ventrally and somewhat posteriorly as a short beak, so that the body has the appearance of a plump bird. External segmentation has been lost, and the number of trunk appendages is reduced to five or six pairs. The tip end of the trunk, commonly called the postabdomen, is turned ventrally and forward and bears special claws and spines for cleaning the carapace.

The majority of branchiopods are only a few millimeters in length, and some are as small as 0.25 mm. The largest are the fairy shrimps, which are usually more than 1 cm. long and may attain a length of 13 cm. Most branchiopods are pale and transparent, but rose or red colors sometimes are found, caused by the pres-

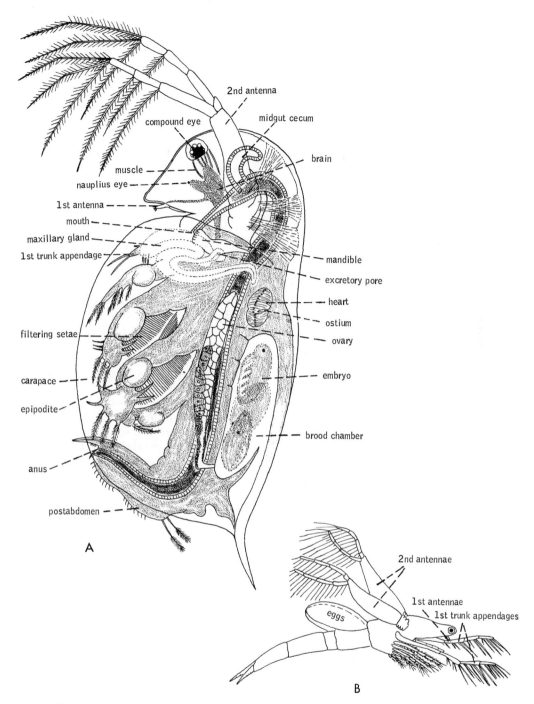

2nd antenna

midgut cecum

compound eye

brain

muscle

nauplius eye

1st antenna

mouth

maxillary gland

1st trunk appendage

mandible

excretory pore

heart

ostium

ovary

filtering setae

carapace

epipodite

embryo

brood chamber

anus

postabdomen

A

2nd antennae

1st antennae

1st trunk appendages

eggs

B

Figure 15-10.   *A.* Female of the cladoceran, *Daphnia pulex* (lateral view). (After Matthes from Kaestner.) *B.* Female of *Leptodora,* an aberrant pelagic cladoceran. (After Sebestyén from Pennak.)

ence of hemoglobin within the body; and some cladocerans and clam shrimp are brownish or blackish.

Branchiopods live almost exclusively in fresh water; only some cladocerans are marine. Moreover, only cladocerans inhabit streams, large ponds, and lakes. The other groups are all confined to temporary pools, springs, and small ponds. The only exception is the brine shrimp, *Artemia,* an anostracan that is found in salt lakes throughout the world. The noncladoceran branchiopods are also peculiar in that they are frequently absent from certain ponds but present in adjacent ones; or they may inexplicably disappear from a certain pond for a few years, then re-appear.

Locomotion. The water fleas swim by means of powerful second antennae (Fig. 15-10, *A*). Movement is largely vertical and usually jerky. The downstroke of the antennae propels the animal upward; then it slowly sinks, using the antennae in the manner of a parachute. A few species move in a smoother manner beating the antennae continuously, as in the aberrant cladoceran, *Leptodora,* which swims with long oar-like antennal strokes (Fig. 15-10, *B*). Although cladocerans ordinarily maintain the head upright, a few swim upside down. Also unusual are certain species that hang from the surface film by supposedly nonwettable antennal setae.

Other branchiopods use the trunk appendages in swimming, although the clam shrimp use the second antennae as well. Fairy shrimp usually swim upside down, but members of the other groups normally swim dorsal side up. Many clam shrimp and tadpole shrimp swim and crawl over the bottom, and some clam shrimp plow through the bottom sediment. Some cladocerans have also taken up a bottom existence. *Graptoleberis* is said to plow through mud, and some forms, such as species of *Camptocercus,* have become adapted for jumping. The post-abdomen is used as a spring or lever, tossing the animal forward several times its body length.

Internal Anatomy and Physiology. With few exceptions, branchiopods are filter feeders, and the margins of the trunk appendages are supplied with fine filtering setae. According to Cannon's (1933) study of the fairy shrimp, *Chirocephalus,* the space between limbs increases as the limbs move forward (Fig. 15-11, *B*). Water is sucked into this space from the midventral line, and the filtering setae collect particles from the incoming stream. On the backstroke, water is forced out of the interlimb space posterio-laterally and distally (Fig. 15-11, *A*).

By several complex mechanisms, the collected food particles are transferred to a midventral food groove extending forward to the mouth and bordered by curved setules. The forward movement of particles in the groove is accomplished by slight anterio-median spurts of water from the interlimb spaces whenever a limb changes from backstroke to forestroke. Glands in the walls of the food groove, as well as in the labrum, secrete an adhesive material (perhaps mucus), and the entangled particles are pushed into the mouth by the adjacent appendages, particularly the first maxillae.

The feeding mechanism of other branchiopods works on the same principle but with various modifications. In clam shrimp, only the anterior trunk appendages are used for filtering,

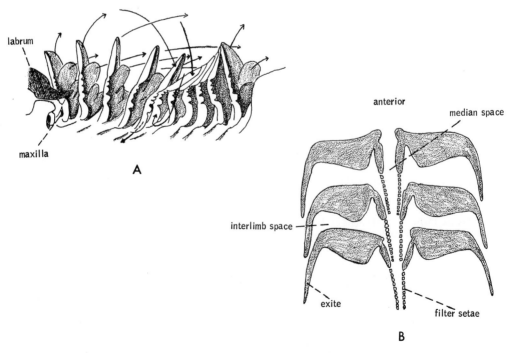

Figure 15-11.   *A.* Trunk appendages of the fairy shrimp, *Branchinella,* showing swimming and feeding currents (lateral view). Setae have been omitted. (After Cannon.) *B. Branchinella,* showing three pairs of trunk appendages (frontal section). (After Cannon from Green.)

and the posterior appendages are modified as jaws for grinding large particles. The cladocerans, which possess only four to six pairs of trunk appendages, have the second to fifth pairs or the third and fourth pairs (in Daphniidae) adapted for filtering, and the filter setae are usually arranged on the appendage to form a distinct comb (Fig. 15-10, *A*). The water current passes from anterior to posterior, and collected particles are transferred into the food groove by special setae (gnathobases) at the basal part of the appendages. In tadpole shrimp such gnathobases also move the food forward in the food groove.

Food particles for the branchiopods are either plankton (in the case of planktonic forms) or detritus (in the case of benthic forms). The efficiency of the filtering setae of *Daphnia* is indicated by the fact that some members of this genus can be grown using a diet of bacteria.

A few branchiopods are predacious. The planktonic cladocerans, *Leptodora, Bythotrephes,* and *Polyphemus,* have their anterior appendages modified for grasping. During feeding, these anterior appendages form a trapping basket, in which prey, particularly other small crustaceans, are captured. The prey is then chewed with the sickle-like blades of the mandibles.

The only parasitic branchiopods belong to the genus *Anchistropus.* They are reported to live on hydra and to tear off chunks of epidermal cells with three modified anterior pairs of trunk appendages.

The branchiopod foregut forms a short esophagus, and the midgut is often enlarged to form a stomach. In cladocerans, however, the midgut is more or less tubular and not easily distinguished from other parts of the digestive tract. There are often two small digestive ceca (Fig. 15-10, *A*). The intestine in some cladocerans is coiled one to several times.

The thin vesicular or lamellar epipodite on each of the trunk appendages of branchiopods is considered to function as a gill, but it is probable that the entire appendage and even the general integumentary surface are also important in respiratory exchange (Fig. 15-8, *B*).

Hemoglobin has been found in the blood, muscles, nervous tissue, and eggs of representative of all branchiopod orders, although its distribution is sporadic. Moreover, the presence of hemoglobin is frequently dependent upon the amount of oxygen in the water, so that both colored and colorless individuals of the same species exist. This is true for *Daphnia,* in which the animals are colorless in well-aerated water and pink in stagnant water. Fat cells, which are located along the sides of the digestive tract and at the bases of the limbs, constitute the chief site

for both the synthesis and destruction of hemoglobin. Hemoglobin is lost when the aquatic medium becomes well-aerated. Under this condition, the hemoglobin may either be transferred to the ovary and eggs, or the iron, after hemoglobin destruction, may be excreted through the maxillary glands.

The heart of cladocerans is a small globular sac with only two ostia, and it lies at the anterior of the trunk (Fig. 15-10, *A*). In all other branchiopods, the heart is tubular with many ostia and may extend into the abdomen, as in the fairy shrimp. The arterial system is restricted to a short unbranched anterior aorta, but on the basis of studies on the cladoceran, *Leptodora,* blood circulates through regular pathways despite the lack of an extensive arterial system. Movement of the appendages, particularly the antennae, aids in drawing blood into and expelling it from these structures. In addition to the heart and bulbous arteriosus at the base of the aorta, additional propulsion is also provided by the appendage organ, a pulsating membranous disc between the first and second segments of the first trunk appendage.

The heart of *Daphnia* beats at a rate of about 120 contractions per minute, but the rate is influenced by many factors. The innumerable physiological studies on this animal disclose, for example, that the heart beats faster in the late afternoon, faster when the population density is low, faster when the female is carrying eggs or young in the brood chamber, and faster at the first attainment of sexual maturity. Such an increased heart-beat rate merely reflects an increased metabolic rate, stimulated by various conditions and is certainly not limited to *Daphnia,* or even to crustaceans.

The excretory organs are maxillary glands, usually called shell glands when the duct can be seen coiled within the carapace wall (Fig. 15-8, *C*). Little is known regarding water balance mechanisms except in the brine shrimp, *Artemia,* which has been studied extensively. This crustacean can tolerate salinities ranging from 10 per cent sea water to the saturation point for sodium chloride. The internal osmotic pressure varies only slightly with external conditions. This pressure never falls below the equivalent of approximately 1 per cent NaCl nor exceeds 2.8 per cent, even when in a 30 per cent solution of NaCl. Ionic regulation is maintained by the absorption of salts through the gills when the animal is in a hypotonic medium. Also, *Artemia* is the only crustacean known to be capable of excreting a urine hyperosmotic to its blood. In brine, the osmotic pressure of the urine is four times that of the blood.

In most branchiopods, the ventral cord is

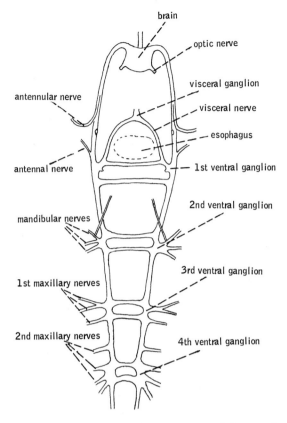

brain

optic nerve

visceral ganglion

antennular nerve

visceral nerve

esophagus

antennal nerve

1st ventral ganglion

2nd ventral ganglion

mandibular nerves

3rd ventral ganglion

1st maxillary nerves

2nd maxillary nerves

4th ventral ganglion

Figure 15-12.   Anterior of nervous system of *Apus cancriformis,* a tadpole shrimp. (After Lankester and Pelseneer from Parker and Haswell.)

a double ganglionic chain (Fig. 15-12). The ventral cord has become concentrated in a few cladocerans, such as *Leptodora.* The nauplius eye is persistent in almost all branchiopods (Fig. 15-10, *A*). The sessile cladoceran compound eyes are not only unusual in being fused into a single median eye, but also in that this single median eye can be rotated by special muscles (Fig. 15-10, *A*). The compound eye, at least in many cladocerans, is used to orient the body in swimming.

Reproduction and Development.   In tadpole shrimp, the gonads are ramified; in other branchiopods the gonads are tubular (Fig. 15-10, *A*). The united or separate male gonopores of cladocerans open near the anus or the postabdomen, which may be modified in the form of a copulatory organ; and the oviducts open into a dorsal brood chamber located beneath the carapace. In other branchiopod species, the gonopores open ventrally on varying segments located more toward the middle of the trunk.

During copulation, the male fairy shrimp clasps the dorsal side of the female abdomen with the large, modified clasping second anten-

nae, and the male inserts the paired eversible copulatory processes containing the openings of the vas deferens into the single median female gonopore. The female gonopore leads into a uterine chamber where the two oviducts also open. Similar copulatory behavior is displayed by the tadpole shrimp, but in clam shrimp the mating pair are oriented at right angles to each other, the male using modified, hooked, anterior trunk appendages for clasping (Fig. 15-9, *A*).

In all branchiopods, the eggs are brooded for varying lengths of time. In the tadpole shrimp, the brood chamber is formed by the overlapping cup-like exopodites on the eleventh pair of appendages. In the fairy shrimp, a special sac is formed on extrusion of the eggs from the glandular uterine chamber (Fig. 15-8, *A*). Both cladocerans and clam shrimp brood their eggs dorsally beneath the carapace (Fig. 15-10, *A*). The clam shrimp hold their eggs by special elongate exopodites situated on several pairs of posterior appendages.

The eggs are produced in clutches of two to several hundred, and a single female may lay several clutches. Except in *Leptodora,* in which the diploid eggs hatch as metanauplii, development in most cladocerans is direct, and the young are released from the brood chamber by the ventral flexion of the postabdomen of the female. In the other branchiopods, embryonated eggs are released by the female and fall to the bottom after only a brief brooding period; or they may remain attached to the female and reach the bottom when she dies. In any case, the eggs typically hatch as nauplius larvae.

Parthenogenesis is common in branchiopods, and in some species males are uncommon or unknown. In cladocerans, parthenogenetic eggs hatch into females for several generations until certain factors, such as change in water temperature or the decrease of the food supply as a result of population increase, induce the appearance of males, and fertilized eggs are produced. The fertilized eggs are large, and only a few are produced in a single clutch. The walls of the brood chamber are now transformed into a protective capsule (ephippium) that is cast off at the next molt, either separating from or remaining with the rest of the detached exoskeleton (Fig. 15-13, *A*). The ephippia float or sink to the bottom and can withstand drying and freezing. By means of such protected resting eggs, cladocerans may be dispersed by wind or animals for some distances and can overwinter or survive during summer droughts.

Thin-shelled summer eggs and thick-shelled resting (dormant) eggs are also produced by many species of the other branchiopod groups, but both types of eggs may be either partheno-

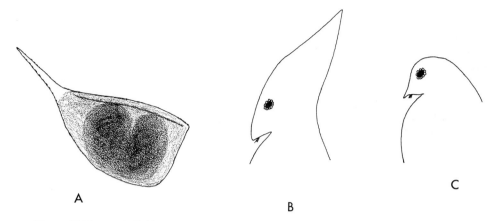

Figure 15-13.   *A.* Ephippium of *Daphnia pulex.* (From a photograph by Pennak.) *B* and *C.* Cyclomorphosis in *Daphnia. B.* Summer long-head form. *C.* Spring and fall round-head form. (*B* and *C* after Pennak.)

genetic or fertilized. Development in thin-shelled eggs is rapid, and hatching may take place while the eggs are attached to the female.

Population pulses, or cycles, are common in branchiopods. This is particularly true of many cladoceran species. Some cladocerans, such as species of *Diaphanosoma, Moina,* and *Chydorus,* exhibit a single population rise and fall during the warmer months in some lakes. Others are dicyclic and exhibit both spring and fall population peaks. The phenomenon is by no means always predictable. For example, some species of *Daphnia* may be monocyclic, dicyclic or even acyclic, depending on the lake or pond in which they live.

Many of these reproductive phenomena, such as two types of eggs, parthenogenesis, and population peaks, also are found in fresh-water rotifers. A further parallel is seen in cyclomorphosis. In some cladoceran species, such as the lake-inhabiting *Daphnia dubia* and *Daphnia retrocurva,* the head progressively changes from a round to helmet-like shape between spring and midsummer (Fig. 15-13, *B* and *C*). From midsummer to fall, the head changes back to a normal round shape. Cyclomorphosis is still poorly understood. It may, as in rotifers, result from internal factors; or it may, as has been postulated by Coker (1939), result from an interaction between external conditions (temperature) and internal factors (perhaps genetic).

Subclass Ostracoda

Ostracods, called mussel or seed shrimp, are small crustaceans that are widely distributed in the sea and in all types of fresh water. They superficially resemble clam shrimp in having a body completely enclosed in a bivalve carapace.

However, this group, rather than the Conchostraca, should really have the name clam shrimp, for the ostracod carapace has evolved along lines that are even more strikingly like those of pelecypods. In ostracods, the valves are rounded or elliptical and the outer wall of each valve is impregnated with calcium carbonate. Dorsally there is a distinct hinge line formed by a noncalcified strip of cuticle.

In some ostracods, such as the Cytheridae, the valves may be locked together by hinge teeth and ridges at the hinge line. The surface of the valves may be covered with setae and sculptured with pits, tubercles or irregular projections (Fig. 15-14, *B*). In the order Myodocopa there is a notch in the anterior margin of the valves permitting the protrusion of the antennae when the valves are closed (Fig. 15-14, *A*). The elastic hinge causes the valves to gape and acts antagonistically to a cluster of transverse adductor muscle fibers that are inserted near the center of each valve.

The head comprises almost half of the ostracod body for the trunk is very much reduced in size (Fig. 15-15). The head appendages, particularly the antennules and antennae, are well developed. All external trunk segmentation has disappeared, and the trunk appendages are usually reduced to two pairs. (This assumes that the first appendage after the first maxilla is the second maxilla. Some authorities consider this appendage to be the first leg, the second maxilla having been lost.) A few species have only one pair of trunk appendages (*Cytherella*), and in the small order Cladocopa there are no trunk appendages. The appendages may be more or less leg-like, or each pair may be modified for different functions. In the Conchoeciidae, the second maxilla has a leg-like structure and is similar to the first trunk appendage; the second

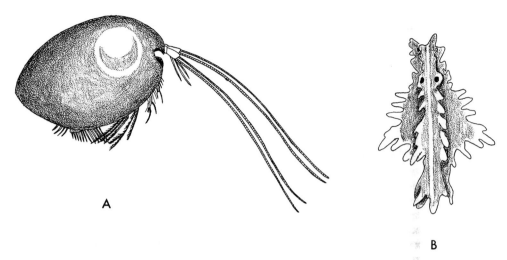

Figure 15-14. *A.* A myodocopid ostracod with antennal notches in valves (lateral view). *B.* The ostracod, *Cythereis,* with greatly sculptured valves (dorsal view). (Both after Müller from Schmitt.)

trunk appendage, however, is modified and directed dorsally. The trunk terminates in two long caudal rami that project ventrally and forward.

Most ostracods are minute, ranging from less than one millimeter to several millimeters in length. The giant of the group is the deep-sea *Gigantocypris mulleri,* which reaches a length of a little over one centimeter. Hues of gray, brown, or green are the most common colors, but some species may be colored red or yellow.

Locomotion. Although there are some planktonic ostracods, the majority live near the bottom, where they scurry over or plow through the upper layer of mud and detritus. The second antenna or both pairs of antennae are the locomotor appendages and are variously modified, depending on the habits of the animal. In swimming ostracods, the antennules and antennae are supplied with long setae, while in burrowing species the antennules are stout with short spines and are used for digging.

The fresh-water *Darwinula* uses the antennules for clearing away debris in front of the body, and *Candona* uses its antennules to balance upright on the bottom. Some species have antennules supplied with hooked setae that aid in climbing aquatic vegetation. Hopping is displayed by *Cypridopsis vidua;* the second antennae and the second pair of legs move simultaneously, kicking the animal forward on the backstroke. Perhaps the most remarkable ostracod is a terrestrial species, the South African *Mesocypris terrestris,* which can plow through forest humus. Terrestrial ostracods have also been reported from New Zealand.

Internal Anatomy and Physiology. Most ostracods are filter feeders, but a few are scavengers, predators, commensals, or parasites. Detritus particles, often stirred up by the antennae or mandibles are the principal source of food.

In the cypridinids, a water current is produced by the beating of the epipodites of the second maxillae and passes backward over the mouth region. Particles are caught on the anteriorly pointing filter setae of the first maxillae and first trunk appendages. The collected particles are then entangled in labral secretions and passed to the mouth. In other forms, the filtering setae are located on both the mandibles and the first maxillae. These filtering appendages in *Asterope* form a tube through which water must move.

The last pair of legs of cypridinids are long and worm-like and are used for clearing the interior of the valves of debris (Fig. 15-15).

Scavangers include species of *Cypridina* and *Cypridopsis,* which hold large food particles with the mandibles or antennae while they are torn by the maxillae. *Gigantocypris* is predacious and is reported to capture other crustaceans and even small fish with its antennae.

The terminal end of the foregut is developed into a triturating region in the order Podocopa. The midgut ceca vary greatly in number and degree of development. In the Cypridae, there is usually a single pair of ceca that in some species extend between the inner and outer valve walls. Such ceca are absent in the Myodocopa.

Gills are lacking and respiration is integumentary, the locomotor and feeding currents providing for ventilation. However, in *Asterope* and in some species of *Cypridina,* there are plate-like structures that may function as gills and are

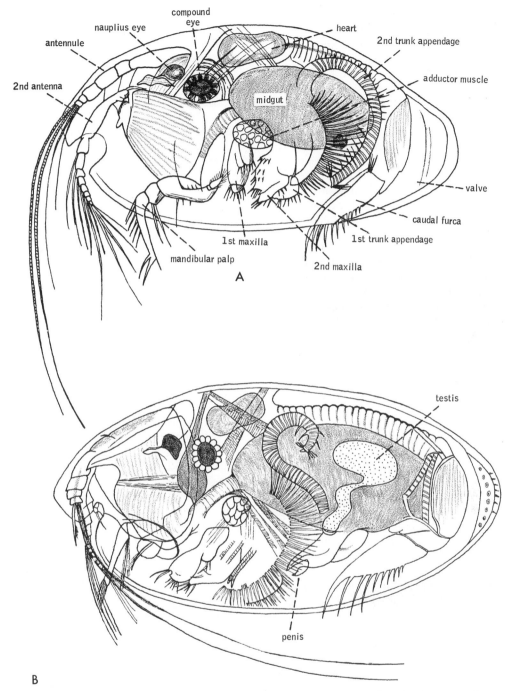

Figure 15-15.   *A.* Female marine myodocopid ostracod, *Cypridina*, with left valve removed (lateral view). *B.* A male *Cypridina* (lateral view). (Both after Claus from Calman.)

attached to the dorsal posterior surface of the trunk. Hemoglobin has been reported in a few species.

A heart and blood vessels are present only in the marine order Myodocopa. The heart in this group is a small vesicle with two ostia and gives rise to an anterior and to ventro-lateral arteries. Blood circulates between the valve walls.

Ostracods are among the few crustaceans that possess both antennal and maxillary glands in the adult. The maxillary glands are large and coiled and lie between the inner and outer walls of the valves. There is also a pair of glands of unknown function opening near the base of the antennules.

The ventral ganglia are considerably concentrated. In most ostracods, there are two or three groups of ganglia, but in the Cypridae the ganglia are all concentrated into a single mass. The nauplius eye is present in all ostracods, but compound eyes appear only in the Myodocopa and are sessile (Fig. 15-15, *A*).

Ostracods were the first crustaceans in which luminescence was observed. Three marine genera, *Cypridina, Pyrocypris,* and *Conchoecia,* contain the most common luminescent species. The bluish light is produced externally by secretions from a gland in the labrum. The gland contains, at least in *Cypridina,* two to four kinds of cells that empty to the outside by separate adjacent pores. Harvey (1960) suggests that luciferin and luciferase are probably secreted separately and mix when they reach the exterior. The light is produced only on stimulation by a reflex of muscle contraction, and a beam of light can initiate the reflex.

Reproduction and Development. The ovaries are paired tubes, that in the Cypridae and Cytheridae lie at least partly in the space between the valve walls. The oviducts are usually paired, and each terminates in a seminal receptacle. The female gonopores are located ventrally between the last pair of appendages at the caudal end of the trunk. In the Conchoeciidae, the oviducts are united, and they empty through a single gonopore on the left side.

The testis usually consists of four long and often coiled tubes that may lie within the shell valves. The paired sperm ducts each terminate in an ejaculatory duct, which opens through one of the two large sclerotized penes projecting ventrally in front of the caudal furca. In the marine family, Cypridinidae, the sperm ducts do not open through the penes but through a single median gonopore between the two penes. Corresponding to the unilateral female system, male conchoeciids have a single penis, located on the right side.

The sperm are motile and in many cyprids are of a remarkably large size. *Pontocypris monstrosa,* which is less than one millimeter in length, is reported to have sperm as long as seven millimeters.

During copulation, the female is clasped dorsally and posteriorly by the second antennae or the first pair of legs of the male, and the penes are inserted between the valves of the female into the gonopores.

The eggs are brooded in the dorsal part of the shell cavity in some ostracods, including the marine cypridinids and the fresh-water *Darwinula.* More commonly the eggs are shed freely in the water or are attached singly or in groups to vegetation and other objects on the bottom. The eggs hatch as nauplius larvae, but each nauplius is enclosed in a bivalve carapace like the adult.

Parthenogenesis takes place in the fresh-water genus, *Cypris.*

Systematic Résumé of Subclass Ostracoda

There are approximately 200 known species of living ostracods, and over 2000 fossil species have been described. The living ostracods are contained within four orders.

Order Myodocopa. Marine ostracods having a shell with antennal notches. The usually biramous second antennae have a very large basal segment. Two pairs of trunk appendages are present.

Family Cypridinidae. *Cypridina, Gigantocypris, Pyrocypris,* and *Asterope.*

Family Conchoeciidae. *Conchoecia.*

Order Cladocopa. Marine ostracods with no trunk appendages. Second antennae biramous. *Polycope.*

Order Podocopa. Second antennae uniramous. Two pairs of trunk appendages are present. This large order includes marine as well as fresh-water species.

Family Cypridae. *Cypris, Pontocypris, Candona, Cypridopsis, Mesocypris.*

Family Darwinulidae. *Darwinula.*

Family Cytheridae. *Cythere.*

Order Platycopa. Marine ostracods having biramous second antennae and a single pair of trunk appendages. *Cytherella* is the only genus.

Subclass Copepoda

The Copepoda is the largest subclass of entomostracans, over 4500 species having been described. Most copepods are marine, but there are many fresh-water species. Also there are many that are parasitic on various marine and fresh-water animals, particularly fish. Marine copepods exist in enormous numbers and are an important link in many marine food chains. A major part of the diet of many marine animals, such as whales and fish, is composed of copepods.

Copepods are very small crustaceans, most ranging from less than one millimeter to several millimeters in length. Parasitic forms are generally larger. For example, species of the genus *Penella,* which is parasitic on fish and whales, may be over one foot in length. Although most copepods are rather pale and transparent, some species may be colored a brilliant red, orange, purple, blue, or black.

The body of free-living copepods is usually short and cylindrical (Fig. 15-16). It is distinctly

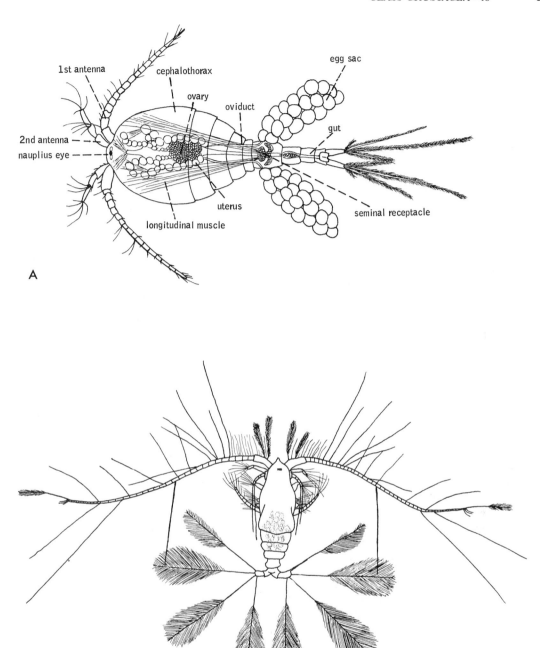

Figure 15-16.   *A.* A cyclopoid copepod, *Macrocyclops albidus* (dorsal view). (After Matthes from Kaestner.) *B. Calocalanus pavo,* a marine copepod with highly developed caudal rami. (After Giesbrecht from Kaestner.)

segmented and composed of a head, thorax, and abdomen. The head is either rounded anteriorly or may bear a rostrum. Compound eyes are absent, but the median naupliar eye is typical of all copepods. Posteriorly the head is fused with the first thoracic segment and sometimes the second segment, as well. The thoracic region is usually tapered and is composed of four or five unfused segments with appendages. Sometimes the last two thoracic segments are fused. The abdomen is narrow, cylindrical, and devoid of appendages. It is composed of four segments, but in females the first two are usually fused.

The telson bears two caudal rami, which in some planktonic marine species are spectacularly developed. For example, in *Calocalanus pavo,* each ramus is turned laterally and bears four long setae with bilaterally arranged setules, each seta resembling a feather (Fig. 15-16, *B*).

Of the ten somites composing the thorax and abdomen, articulation between the fourth and fifth or between the fifth and sixth is markedly greater than the articulation between the other somites. This point of greater articulation is commonly used to divide the copepod body into an anterior metasome, composed of the head and most of the thorax, and a posterior urosome, composed of the abdomen and the last one or two thoracic segments.

The uniramous antennules are long and conspicuous (Fig. 15-16). The second antennae are considerably smaller, and the exopodite has disappeared in many groups. The first pair of thoracic appendages have become modified to form maxillipeds for feeding. The remaining thoracic appendages, except the last one or two pair, are all more or less similar and rather symmetrically biramous (Fig. 15-17, *A*). Each ramus usually consists of three segments beset with setae. The last one or two pairs of setae are either variously modified or vestigial, depending upon the species and the sex.

Locomotion.   Of the three free-living orders of copepods, the calanoids are largely planktonic; the harpacticoids are largely benthic; and the cyclopoids contain both planktonic and benthic species. The thoracic limbs are the principal locomotor organs in copepods, and movement is usually jerky, particularly in swimming forms. The jerky sudden motions are produced by the extremely rapid oar-like beating of the legs, during which the antennules lie back

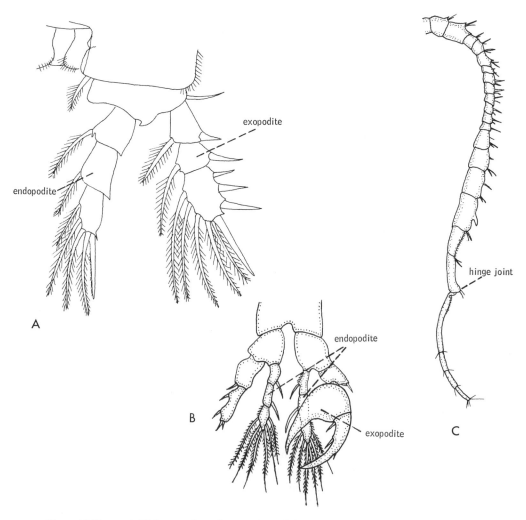

Figure 15-17.   *A.* Right second trunk appendage of *Cyclops,* showing markedly biramous structure. (After Pennak.) *B.* Last pair of thoracic appendages of a male *Centropages,* in which the exopodite is modified as a claw for clasping female abdomen. *C.* The clasping first antenna of a male *Centropages.* (*B* and *C* after Sars from Calman.)

against the body. When the beating of the legs ceases, the antennules are extended laterally to prevent sinking. After a short interval, the action of the thoracic limbs is repeated.

Many calanoids display a slow gliding movement, resulting from the feeding current produced by the appendages around the mouth. The gliding is punctuated by the jerky propulsions caused by the thoracic limbs. Some gliders, such as *Calanus* and *Diaptomus,* can also swim backwards.

The bottom-dwelling harpacticoids and some cyclopoids crawl over or burrow through the substratum, and many harpacticoids live between sand grains. The thoracic limbs are used in crawling, and this is accompanied in harpacticoids by lateral undulations of the body.

Most copepods keep the dorsal surface upward when they move; but some species of cyclopoids swim upside down, and *Cyclops leuckarti* keeps the long axis of its body oriented vertically.

Internal Anatomy and Physiology. Planktonic copepods are chiefly filter feeders in which the second maxillae are modified as filtering appendages. Diatoms constitute the principal part of the diet. The filter-feeding mechanism has been elucidated by Cannon (1928) for *Calanus* and *Diaptomus.* In these copepods, the second antennae, the mandibular palps, and the first pair of maxillae are clothed with setae and these appendages vibrate regularly between 600 and 2640 times a minute (Fig. 15-18, *B*). These vibrations create two swirls of water passing along both sides of the body producing the gliding movement described earlier (Fig. 15-18, *A*). That part of the swirl flowing toward the midline of the body spins anteriorly and is sucked forward into a median filter chamber by the maxillipeds (Fig. 15-18, *B*).

The feeding current is sucked out of the chamber anteriorly and laterally by the vibrations of the first maxillae; during the passage of the feeding current, it is filtered by the dense screen of setae on the second maxillae. The collected particles are cleaned off by the endites of the first maxillae and by special long setae on the base of the maxillipeds and are then passed to the mandibles and mouth.

The maxillae of *Diaptomus* and *Calanus* are passive filters, but in some copepods, such as species of *Acartia,* they act as a scoop net. Not all planktonic copepods are filter feeders; some capture larger organisms in addition to filtering for phytoplankton, and some are strictly predacious. Species of *Anomalocera* and *Pareuchaeta* even capture young fish. Members of the common fresh-water genus, *Cyclops,* are predatory, as are some of the other cyclopoid genera. The bottom-dwelling harpacticoids are not known to

be filter feeders and are probably predacious or graze directly on diatoms.

The digestive tract tends to be tubular throughout with little marked regionalization. Up to three ceca may be present and variously developed. Food reserves are stored as oils in some copepods and may give the body a brilliant red coloration, as in *Diaptomus.*

There are no gills in free-living copepods, and except in the calanoids and some parasitic species, there is neither heart nor blood vessels. In calanoids, the heart is saccular or tubular with three ostia, and it is located in the thorax (Fig. 15-3, *A*). There is a single unbranched anterior aorta leaving the heart. In those copepods that lack heart and vessels, circulation of blood is facilitated by the movement of the appendages and especially by the movement of the gut, which has special suspensory muscles originating from the body wall. Some parasitic lernaeopodoids are peculiar in possessing a system of closed vessels without a heart. It has been reported that blood hemoglobin is present in some free-living and parasitic copepods. The excretory organs are maxillary glands.

The nervous system is considerably concentrated, and the ventral nerve cord usually does not extend beyond the thorax. In some species, there are distinct ventral ganglia, but in others the ventral ganglia have coalesced into one mass. In the most extreme condition, the nervous system has become an esophageal collar.

Only the nauplius eye is present in copepods and typically consists of two lateral and one median ocelli (Fig. 15-16). In the pelagic *Sapphirina* and related genera, the lateral ocelli are highly developed containing lenses and other specialized structures, but the significance of this development is unknown. Lenses are also found in the ocelli of the calanoid Pontellidae, which live close to the surface.

Many luminescent copepods, such as *Metridia, Pleuromamma,* and *Oncaea,* have been reported. The luminescent secretion is produced by groups of gland cells in the integumentary epidermis. The number of light organs varies from 10 to 70 and are distributed at various points over the surface of the body. Sex attraction and escape have been suggested as possible functions of copepod luminescence.

Reproduction and Development. In copepods, the ovary is paired or single, and the two glandular oviducts are provided with lateral diverticula (Fig. 15-16, *A*). The oviducts open onto the ventral surface of the first abdominal segment, which also contains a pair of seminal receptacles with separate openings to the exterior. There is usually an internal connection between the seminal receptacles and the oviducts.

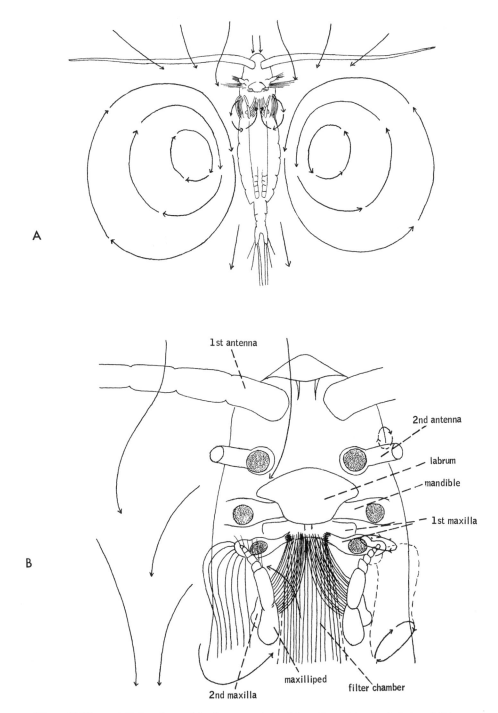

Figure 15-18.   *A.* Swimming and feeding currents in *Calanus finmarchicus*. *B.* Anterior of *Calanus finmarchicus*, showing filter currents and filter apparatus (ventral view). (Both after Cannon.)

The copepod testis is usually single in free-living forms. The sperm duct may be paired, but in the calanoids and some harpacticoids it is present only on one side of the body. Copepods are the only entomostracans that form spermatophores, and the lower end of the sperm duct is modified for this purpose. The male

opening is also located on the first abdominal segment.

During copulation, the male clasps the female with his antennules, which may be so modified that the distal half of the appendage folds over the basal half (Fig. 15-17, *C*). In some male calanoids, such as *Diaptomus,* only one antennule is specialized for copulation, and the right fifth thoracic appendage has become modified to form a large claw for clasping the female abdomen (Fig. 15-17, *B*). However, many, perhaps a majority, of the calanoids do not display any specialization of either of the male antennae for grasping the female. The spermatophores are transferred to the female by the thoracic appendages of the male and adhere to the receptacle openings by means of a special adhesive cement. The copulatory behavior of the calanoid, *Diaptomus,* involves pursuit by the male. After the female is caught and clasped by the antennule and right fifth thoracic appendage of the male, the opposite limb, which is provided with long bristles, is used to search for the female orifice.

Copepod eggs may be stored for some time before fertilization and egg-laying. When the eggs are emitted from the oviducts, they are surrounded by an ovisac produced by oviduct secretions. The two ovisacs formed remain attached to the female genital segment and act as brood chambers (Fig. 15-16, *A*). Each sac contains from a few to forty eggs, and clutches may be produced at frequent intervals. For example, in the fresh-water *Cyclops,* the eggs hatch in from twelve hours up to five days, and a new clutch is then immediately produced, all from a single mating. In some copepods, such as certain harpacticoids, the last pair of legs in the female have become modified forming plate-like shields to protect the ovisacs. The ovisacs are set free in a few species, and in most calanoids the eggs are shed singly into the water.

The eggs typically hatch as nauplius larvae. After four or five naupliar instars, the larva passes into the first copepodid stage. The copepodid larva displays the general adult features; but the abdomen is usually still unsegmented, and there may be only three pairs of thoracic limbs. The adult structure is attained typically after six naupliar and six copepodid instars. The entire course of development may take as little as one week or nearly as long as one year.

Some fresh-water calanoids and harpacticoids produce both thin-shelled eggs and thick-shelled dormant eggs, but this adaptation has not been as widely developed as in other entomostracans. Some copepods, such as species of *Cyclops,* secrete an organic cyst-like covering and become inactive under unfavorable conditions. Such cysts are particularly adapted to withstand desiccation and enable the copepod to estivate during a temporary drying of the pool or pond in which it lives.

Parasitic Copepods. The Copepoda contain most of the parasitic crustaceans. There are a few parasitic cyclopoids and harpacticoids, and the orders Notodelphyoida, Monstrilloida, Caligoida and Lernaeopodoida are exclusively parasitic. These four orders contain over one thousand species and display a great diversity of structural modifications and variations in life cycles.

Marine and fresh-water fish are the most common hosts of caligoid and lernaeopodoid copepods, which are called fish lice. Fish lice are ectoparasitic and attach to the gill filaments, the fins, or the general integument (Fig. 15-19). Other copepods are commensal or endoparasitic within polychaete worms, in the intestine of echinoderms (particularly crinoids), and in the digestive tract of tunicates and pelecypods. Some copepods are parasitic on other crustaceans.

All degrees of modification from the free-living copepod form are exhibited by these parasites. Species of notodelphyoids that are commensal within the pharynx of tunicates are only very slightly modified and move about freely within the host. The cyclopoid fish lice are also only slightly modified (Fig. 15-20, *A*). On the other hand, many ectoparasitic and endoparasitic copepods may be so highly modified and bizarre that they no longer have any resemblance to the free-living species (Fig. 15-20, *C, D,* and *E*). External segmentation is reduced or altogether absent; most of the appendages are reduced or have disappeared; and the body tends to become vermiform.

Certain appendages have usually become specialized as holdfast organs in the ectoparasites. In the Notodelphyoidea, which are commensal in the digestive tract of tunicates, the exopodite of the thoracic limbs bears a curved claw for attachment. More commonly, the second antennae and maxillae terminate in hooks used for holding onto the host (Fig. 15-20, *A*). In the common lernaeopodoid fish lice, a special attachment button and thread are produced by a frontal gland on the head. The button attaches to the gill filament of the host, and the thread provides for temporary attachment. Later the frontal gland produces another button (the bulla) into which the second maxillae are inserted for permanent attachment (Fig. 15-20, *B*).

The mouthparts of ectoparasites are adapted for piercing and sucking. Commonly the labrum and labium together form a tube containing the sickle-like or stylet-like mandibles. In the fish louse, *Lepeophtheirus pectoralis,* as well as in others, the antennae, maxillae, and maxillipeds are also used to lacerate the surface of the host.

Internal parasites have often lost their mouthparts, and food is absorbed directly from the host. For example, the body of the larva of

Figure 15-19. Parasitic copepods, *Penella exocoeti,* on a flying fish. The copepods are in turn carrying the barnacle, *Conchoderma virgatum* (striped body). (Modified after Schmitt.)

Monstrilla anglica, which is endoparasitic within the blood vessels of polychaetes, possesses two or four large absorptive processes (arms). Some endoparasites display a very intimate association with the tissues of the host. The sac-like *Xeno-coeloma brumpti* lives in the body wall of poly-chaetes, with one end of its body opening into the coelom and the other end opening to the exterior. The body is completely covered by epithelium from the host.

Generally, the female copepod is more highly modified for a parasitic existence than the male, and sometimes the male is entirely free-living and displays the typical copepod appearance.

In most parasitic copepods, the adults are adapted for parasitism, and the larval stages are usually typical and free-swimming. Contact with the host occurs at various times during the life cycle of the copepod, and modifications appear with each molt. The salmon gill maggot, *Salmincola salmonea,* which is parasitic on the gills of the European salmon, has a typical life cycle. When the salmon enters the coastal estuaries on its migration to fresh water, the copepod, in the form of a first copepodid larva, attaches to the gills. The larva attaches by a structure resem-bling a "button and thread" that is held by the second maxillae; the larva then undergoes a series of molts. The male matures first, and copulation takes place before the female is mature. The male then dies. The female under-goes a final molt and becomes permanently attached to the host by the second maxillae and bulla (Fig. 15-20, *B*). Egg sacs are then formed and may be as long as eleven millimeters. Several clutches are produced by a single female.

Larval parasitism is exhibited by the monstrilloids and some other copepods. In the Monstrilloida, the first nauplius larva and the adults are free-swimming, but the intervening stages are endoparasitic in polychaetes. Such larval parasites are often highly modified.

Systematic Résumé of Subclass Copepoda

Order Calanoida. Free-living, largely planktonic copepods with the metasome–uro-some articulation located between the fifth and sixth thoracic segments. Second antennae are biramous. *Calanus, Calocalanus, Diaptomus, Metridia, Pleuromamma, Centropages* and *Leuckartia.*

Order Harpacticoida. Metasome–urosome articulation located between the fourth and fifth thoracic segments. Antennules are very short, and second antennae are biramous. Abdomen is almost as wide as thorax, and the body is often linear in shape. Largely benthic in fresh and salt water; a few parasitic forms. *Harpacticus.*

Order Cyclopoida. Metasome–urosome articulation located between the fourth and fifth thoracic segments. Second antennae are uni-ramous. Includes planktonic and benthic cope-pods living in fresh and salt water; many are parasitic. *Cyclops, Sapphirina,* and *Oncaea.*

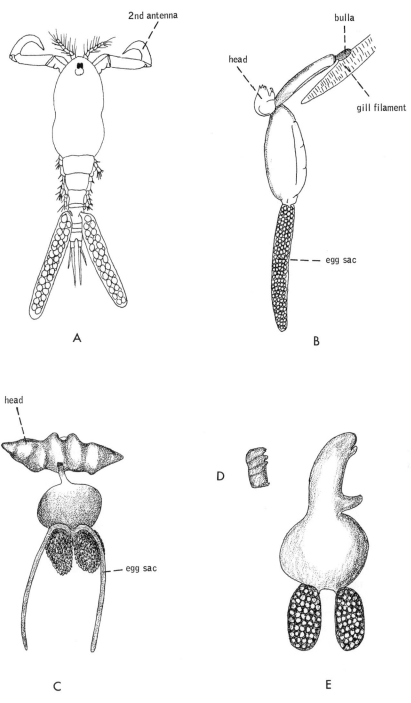

Figure 15-20.   Parasitic copepods. *A. Ergasilus versicolor,* one of the few cyclopoid parasites. It lives on gills of fresh-water fish. Only adult female is parasitic, hooking to fish with clasping antennae. (After Wilson from Pennak.) *B. Salmincola salmonea,* mature female attached to gill of European salmon. (After Friend.) *C. Lesteira.* Head is imbedded in skin of fish, remainder of body hangs free. (From Parker and Haswell.) *D* and *E.* Male (*D*) and female (*E*) of *Brachiella obesa* live on gills of red gurnard. (After Green.)

Order Notodelphyoida. Metasome–urosome articulation located between fourth and fifth thoracic segments in males and between the first and second abdominal segments in females. Commensals in tunicates but are not highly modified. *Doropygus.*

Order Monstrilloida. Second antennae and mouthparts of adults are absent. Includes marine copepods with larval stages parasitic in polychaetes. *Monstrilla.*

Order Caligoida. Metasome–urosome articulation located between the third and fourth thoracic segments, but this articulation may be absent in the more modified females. Second antennae are modified for attachment to host. Are largely ectoparasitic on fresh-water and marine fish. *Caligus* and *Lepeophtheirus.*

Order Lernaeopodoida. Segmentation is reduced or absent. Thoracic appendages are reduced or absent, especially in females. Second maxillae are modified for attachment to host. Are ectoparasites on fresh-water and marine fish. *Salmincola, Penella, Lernaea, Xenocoeloma, Brachiella,* and *Lesteira.*

Subclass Mystacocarida
and Subclass Branchiura

The Mystacocarida and the Branchiura are two small subclasses that are related to the copepods. The Mystacocarida was first described in 1943 by Pennak and Zinn from specimens collected in Long Island Sound. The only known genus, *Derocheilocaris,* has since been reported from the coasts of South America, southern Africa, and the western Mediterranean. These little crustaceans are only approximately 4.5 mm. long and are adapted for living between sand grains (Fig. 15-21, *A*).

The elongated cylindrical body is divided as is the copepod body, but the thoracic segment bearing the maxilliped is not fused with the head. The thorax proper is composed of four segments, each bearing a pair of appendages. Unlike the thoracic appendages of copepods, those of the mystacocarids are reduced to a single simple lamella. Both antennae are long and prominent, and the mouth appendages are more elongate than in copepods and provided with setae, probably for filter feeding. There is no distinct circulatory system and both antennal and maxillary glands persist as excretory organs. Only the nauplius eye is present. The sexes are separate, and a metanauplius larva is the youngest larval stage so far collected.

The subclass Branchiura contains seventy-five species of common ectoparasites on the skin or in the gill cavity of fresh-water and marine fish. The most striking differences between branchiurans and copepods are the greatly dorso-ventrally flattened body, the presence of a pair of sessile compound eyes, and the presence of a large shield-like carapace covering the head and thorax (Fig. 15-21, *B*).

The abdomen is small, bilobed, and unsegmented. Both pairs of antennae are very small, and the first pair is provided with a large claw for attachment to the host. Also important in attachment (except in *Dolops*) are two large suckers modified from the bases of the first maxillae, the rest of the appendage being vestigial. As in many copepods, the labrum and labium form a sucking mouth cone. In *Argulus,* there is also a large sheathed hollow spine located in front of the mouth cone (Fig. 15-21, *B*). The spine is used for puncturing the skin of the host and is supplied by a gland that is supposedly poisonous. The second maxillae are heavy, uniramous, and terminate in claws. There are no maxillipeds. The four thoracic appendages are large and biramous with swimming setae, for branchiurans can detach and swim from one host to another.

There are no gills, and gaseous exchange probably takes place through the carapace surface. A triangular thoracic heart with two ostia and an anterior artery comprise the circulatory system. In *Dolops ranarum,* the blood contains hemoglobin.

A single ovary and a single oviduct are present, the oviduct opening between the bases of the last pair of thoracic limbs; a separate pair of seminal receptacles is located on the abdomen. The testes are paired, and the confluent sperm duct and single seminal vesicle also open between the bases of the last pair of thoracic limbs. The eggs are deposited on the bottom. In some species of *Argulus,* a nauplius larva hatches from the egg, but usually the young have all of the adult appendages when they hatch.

Subclass Cirripedia

The Cirripedia includes the familiar marine animals known as barnacles. Cirripedes are the only sessile group of crustaceans, aside from the parasitic forms, and as a result they are one of the most aberrant groups of Crustacea. In fact, it was not until 1830, when the larval stages were first discovered, that the relationship between the barnacles and other crustaceans was fully recognized, and the barnacles were not classified as members of the Mollusca.

Barnacles are exclusively marine. Approximately two thirds of the some 800 described species are free-living, attaching to rocks, shells,

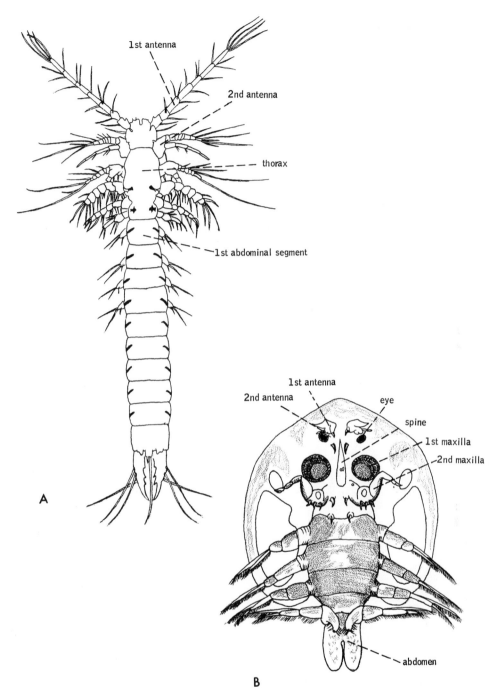

Figure 15-21.   *A. Derocheilocaris,* a mystacocaridan. (After Delamare and Chappuis.) *B. Argulus foliaceus,* a branchiuran fish parasite. (After Wagler from Kaestner.)

coral, floating timber, and other objects. Some barnacles are commensal on whales, turtles, fish, and other animals, and a large number of barnacles are parasitic. Many of the parasitic forms are so highly specialized that all traces of arthropod structure have disappeared.

External Structure.   Louis Agassiz described a barnacle as "nothing more than a little shrimp-like animal, standing on its head in a limestone house and kicking food into its mouth." A further analogy might be drawn if one can imagine an ostracod turned upside down and attached to the substratum by the anterior end.

The cypris larva of barnacles, which indeed looks very much like an ostracod, settles to the bottom and attaches to the substratum by means of cement glands located in the base of the antennules (Fig. 15-27, *B* to *D*). The larval carapace, which encloses the entire body as it does in ostracods, persists as the enveloping carapace, or mantle, of adult barnacles and becomes covered externally with calcareous plates. The carapace opening is therefore directed upward and enables the animal to project its long thoracic appendages for scooping plankton.

The free-living barnacles can be divided into stalked and nonstalked (sessile) types. In stalked barnacles, sometimes called goose barnacles, there is a long stalk (peduncle) that is attached to the substratum at one end and bears the major part of the body (capitulum) at the other (Fig. 15-22, *A*). The peduncle represents the pre-oral end of the animal and contains both the vestiges of the larval antennules and the cement glands that open at the peduncle base. Some goose barnacles, such as certain species of *Lepas,* attach to small floating objects, and form floating colonies (Fig. 15-22, *B*). The cement glands of such forms secrete a vesicular mass of material that increases the buoyancy of the colony.

The peduncle is provided with longitudinal and oblique muscles and is highly movable. Primitively, the outer surface is covered with calcareous plates or scales, which may be increased in size nearer the capitulum (Fig. 15-23). Usually, however, the calcareous plates of the peduncle have disappeared, and the surface is horny, or more frequently leathery or membranous, as in *Lepas.*

The capitulum contains all but the pre-oral part of the body and is surrounded by the carapace (mantle). The mantle surface is covered by five large plates (Fig. 15-23). The anterior surface of the mantle is covered by a keel-like carina, and the two lateral surfaces are covered anteriorly by a pair of terga and posteriorly by a pair of scuta. The unattached upper and opposing margins of the terga and scuta can be pulled together for protection or opened for the extension of the appendages. A large adductor muscle runs transversely between the two scuta (Fig. 15-22).

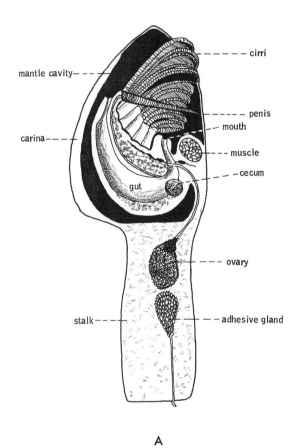

A

B

Figure 15-22.   *A. Lepas,* a stalked barnacle. (After Broch from Kaestner.) *B.* Japanese glass-ball fishing float fouled by *Lepas.* (By R. Shomura, Pacific Oceanic Fishery Investigations, U. S. Fish and Wildlife Service, Honolulu.)

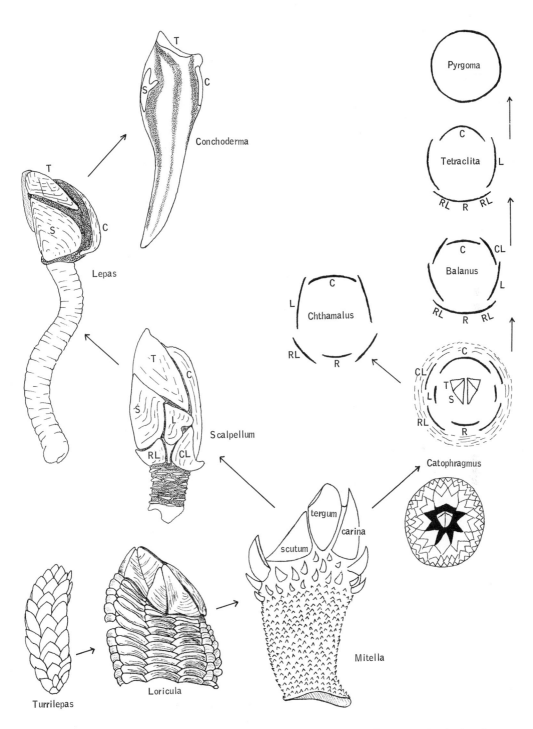

Figure 15-23.   A possible phylogeny of the barnacles, showing the tendency toward reduction of shell plates. Genera depicted represent stages rather than ancestral forms. The tergum and scutum are omitted from plans of the sessile barnacles except for *Catophragmus*. Structures shown include: carina (C), carino-lateral (CL), lateral (L), rostrum (R), rostro-lateral (RL), scutum (S), tergum (T). (Adapted from Green, Pilsbry, and others.)

Primitively, the base of the capitulum is surrounded by several rows of smaller lateral plates, one of which, a rostral plate, covers the posterior end of the capitulum (Fig. 15-23). In some species of *Mitella,* these lateral plates grade into those covering the peduncle. In the evolution of the stalked barnacles, there has been a tendency toward reduction of the mantle plates (Fig. 15-23). In *Scalpellum,* lateral plates are present but there are fewer than in *Mitella.* In *Lepas,* only the five principal plates mentioned earlier remain. In *Conchoderma,* which lives on whales, turtles, ship bottoms, and other floating or moving objects, the five plates are reduced to a vestigial state and are widely separated; or all but two of the plates have disappeared (Fig. 15-25, *C*). In the final extreme, the plates have completely disappeared as in *Heteralepas.*

The calcareous plates are secreted by the underlying mantle and are not shed at ecdysis. Growth of the plates takes place by the continual addition of material to the undersurface of the plates, thus increasing the thickness and diameter. The exposed mantle cuticle is shed.

There is no peduncle in sessile barnacles (Fig. 15-24). The attached undersurface of the barnacle is called the basis and is either membranous or calcareous. This is the pre-oral region of the animal and contains the cement glands. The lateral plates that are located on the operculum base of primitive stalked barnacles are retained in the sessile barnacles as mural plates, which form with the carina and rostrum a vertical wall ringing the animal (Fig. 15-24, *B*). The top of the animal is covered by the paired movable terga and scuta. Usually, however, the vertical wall extends upward considerably beyond the base of the terga and scuta, so that they appear to be at the bottom of a sort of vestibule. The plates composing the wall overlap each other and are always fused to some extent.

In the primitive genus, *Catophragmus,* the wall is composed of many rings of imbricated plates culminating distally in eight plates— three paired mural plates plus the carina and the rostrum (Fig. 15-23). In other sessile barnacles, only this distal ring of eight plates remains and composes the wall; these plates are usually reduced in number through loss or fusion (Fig. 15-23). *Octomeris* has eight plates; the common *Chthamalus* and *Balanus,* six; *Tetraclita,* four; and in *Pyrgoma,* fusion has taken place to such an extent that the wall is continuous with no evidence of the original separate plates.

Further reduction has taken place in the whale barnacles, where terga and scuta are reduced and the mantle integument along the upper margins of the wall has extended to form a slight hood (Fig. 15-25, *C*). The extreme development is attained in *Xenobalanus,* which is commensal on the fins of fish (Fig. 15-25, *A*). Here the terga and scuta are gone, and the wall is reduced to a vestige. The body is greatly lengthened, producing a superficial resemblance to a stalked barnacle, and the distal end is protected by a highly developed hood.

Most peculiar are the box-like species of the suborder Verrucomorpha, in which mural plates have disappeared, and the wall is formed from the tergum and scutum of one side and the carina and rostrum (Fig. 15-25, *B*). The remaining tergum and scutum form a movable lid.

The plates of sessile barnacles may be similar in structure to those of pedunculate types, as in the sessile barnacle, *Chthamalus,* but usually the inner surfaces of the plates have become infolded to form canals containing extensions of the hypodermis (Fig. 15-24, *A*). When the basis is calcareous, it always contains canals. In the whale barnacle, *Coronula,* which fits somewhat down into the host's skin, folding has taken place on both the inner and outer surfaces of the plates, and the outer canals or chambers contain extensions of the epidermis of the host. Growth in sessile barnacles takes place along the basal edge of the plates with a continual wearing away of the upper margins of the plates; or more commonly growth takes place along both the basal and the lateral margins, producing an increase in height and diameter.

Of the two types of free-living barnacles, the stalked barnacles are considered to be the most primitive. On the basis of fossil forms such as *Turrilepas,* the ancestral barnacle was probably an elongated animal without a distinct peduncle and capitulum (Fig. 15-23). The entire body was covered by imbricated plates. The distal ring of plates formed the carina, terga, scuta, and rostrum. With the differentiation of the elongated body into a basal peduncle and a distal operculum, a primitive stalked barnacle, such as the existing genus *Mitella,* probably evolved (Fig. 15-23).

The sessile barnacles probably arose from some stalked ancestral stock by a shortening and disappearance of the peduncle with retention of the lateral plates covering the operculum. As already noted, in both free-living barnacle groups, there has been a tendency toward reduction in the number of plates, culminating in completely naked forms.

Within the mantle the body is flexed backward at an angle of 90 degrees from the point of attachment of the head to the body, so that the long axis of the body is at right angles to the

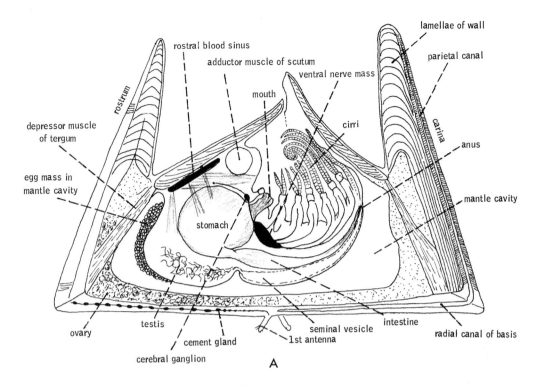

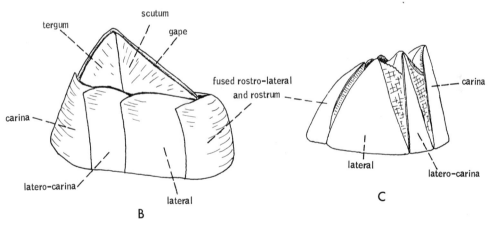

Figure 15-24.   *A. Balanus,* a sessile barnacle (vertical section). (After Gruvel from Calman.) *B. Balanus,* showing number and position of shell plates (diagrammatic lateral view). (After Broch from Kaestner.) *C. Balanus* (nondiagrammatic view). Tergum and scutum hidden by lateral plates. (After Pilsbry.)

vertical axis of the mantle (Figs. 15-22, *A* and 15-24, *A*). Thus, the appendages are directed upward toward the mantle aperture rather than toward the side. The major part of the body consists of a cephalic region and a thoracic region, for the posterior limbless part of the trunk is very much reduced, although a caudal furca is usually present. External segmentation is very indistinct.

The antennules are vestigial except for the

cement glands, and the second antennae are only present in the larva. The second pair of maxillae is united. There are typically six pairs of thoracic feeding appendages (cirri), from which the name Cirripedia is derived. The exopodite and endopodite of each limb are very long, segmented, and provided with long setae. In the naked boring Acrothoracica, the cirri are reduced to four pairs that are much less developed than in the more typical barnacles, and the first

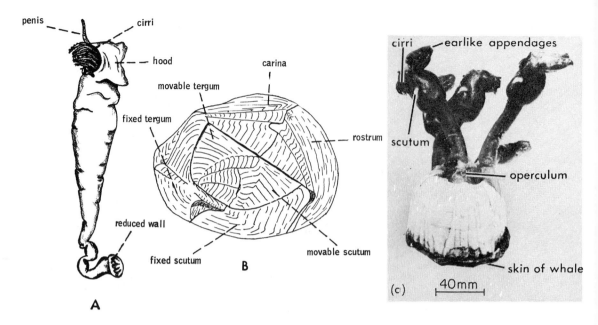

Figure 15-25. *A. Xenobalanus,* a sessile barnacle, which lives commensally on fish fins. Note loss of shell plates. (After Gruvel from Calman.) *B. Verruca* (apical view). (After Pilsbry.) *C.* The stalked barnacle, *Conchoderma,* attached to *Coronula,* a sessile whale barnacle. (By V. B. Scheffer, U. S. Fish and Wildlife Service.)

pair of cirri is closely associated with the mouthparts.

When not encrusted with other sessile organisms, barnacles are often colorful animals. White, yellow, pink, red, orange, and purple are common colors and striped patterns are encountered. Stalked barnacles, including the peduncle range from a few centimeters to 75 cm. in length. The majority of sessile species are approximately the size of small marbles, but some are considerably larger. *Balanus psittacus* from the west coast of South America reaches a height of 23 cm. and a diameter of 8 cm. The smallest barnacles, which are only a few millimeters in length, are species of the little order Acrothoracica, the members of which burrow into mollusk shells and coral.

Internal Anatomy and Physiology. During feeding, the paired scuta and terga open, and the cirri unroll and extend through the gape (Fig. 15-24, *B*). When outstretched, the set of six cirri on each side forms one side of a basket. The two sides sweep toward each other and downward, each half acting as a scoop net. The action is somewhat analogous to the opening and closing of your two fists simultaneously when the bases of the palms are placed together. The rate of beating (one cycle of opening and closing) averages approximately 140 times a minute.

On the closing stroke, food particles suspended in the water are trapped by the setae,

and the first pair of maxillae are used to scrape these particles off and transfer them to the mandibles and mouth. The size of plankton used for food varies. Some species of *Lepas* and *Tetraclita* capture copepods, isopods, and amphipods and could therefore be classified as predacious rather than filter feeders. When such large food particles are consumed, a cirrus that has captured some animal, bends down to the maxillae independently of the others.

Many barnacles feed on microplankton, and in at least some of these barnacles, such as *Balanus improvisus,* the setae are too widely separated to act as filters. The studies of Southward (1955) have disclosed that in these cases the last four pair of cirri perform the usually scooping motion but produce a water current rather than function as a filter. The water current is directed over the first two pairs of cirri, which remain within the mantle cavity close to the mouth. These anterior cirri have the setae closely placed, and the cirri filter phytoplankton from the water current.

In most barnacles, an esophagus leads into an enlarged, somewhat U-shaped midgut containing a pair of anterior ceca (Figs. 15-22, *A* and 15-24, *A*). Some boring barnacles possess a gastric mill at the inner end of the esophagus.

A heart and arteries are absent, but circulation of the blood is facilitated by a blood pump, consisting of a large sinus located between the esophagus and the adductor muscle

(Fig. 15-24, *A*). Muscle bands are inserted onto the lower side of the membrane enclosing the sinus, and they act as dilators. Blood circulates through the mantle walls and also into the peduncle.

Gills are lacking, and the mantle is probably the principal site of gas exchange. In sessile barnacles and also in *Lepas,* the surface area of the mantle around the upper margin has been increased by folding to produce finger-like projections.

The excretory organs are maxillary glands.

The cerebral ganglia lie in front of the rather vertical esophagus. The ganglia of the ventral cord are concentrated within a single mass in the sessile barnacles (Fig. 15-24, *A*). In pedunculate species, four ganglionic masses can be distinguished behind the subesophageal ganglion. Sensory hairs on the thoracic appendages are the most important sense organs. A nauplius eye is retained but it is buried deeply in the tissues overlying the stomach.

Reproduction and Development. Barnacles are the only large group of hermaphroditic crustaceans. However, cross fertilization is the rule, for a suitable substratum almost always contains a large number of adjacent individuals. The ovaries of sessile barnacles (Fig. 15-24, *A*) lie in the basis and in the walls of the mantle, and in stalked forms they are located in the peduncle (Fig. 15-22, *A*). The paired oviducts open at or near the bases of the first pair of cirri. The testes are located in the cephalic region but may extend into the thorax (Fig. 15-24, *A*). The two sperm ducts unite within a long penis, which is attached in front of the anus (Fig. 15-22, *A*). The penis can be protruded out of the body and into the mantle cavity of another individual for the deposition of sperm.

Tiny dwarf males that attach within the mantle cavity of normal individuals are characteristic of the pedunculate genera, *Scalpellum* and *Ibla,* and the boring Acrothoracica (Fig. 15-26). In addition to being very small, these males show all degrees of modification through degeneracy or loss of structures. In some species of *Scalpellum,* the males are but miniatures of the host individual, which is hermaphroditic, and these males are sometimes called complemental males (Fig. 15-26, *A*). When the males are greatly modified, the species is usually dioecious, and the larger host individuals are females.

The most extreme modification is found in the genus *Trypetesa,* which bores in snail shells. The dwarf males of this genus have lost the digestive tract and appendages except for the antennules (Fig. 15-26, *C*). The body consists of little more than a sac containing the testes, sperm ducts, and an enormous penis, all housed within the mantle. A single female of *Trypetesa* may contain as many as fourteen males within her mantle cavity.

The eggs are brooded within an ovisac in the mantle cavity. A nauplius larva represents the hatching stage for most barnacles and can be easily recognized by the triangular shield-shaped carapace (Fig. 15-27, *A*). The nauplius instars are succeeded by a cypris larva, which is so named because of its resemblance to an ostracod. The entire body is enclosed within a bivalve carapace and possesses a pair of sessile compound eyes and six pairs of thoracic appendages. The cypris larva is the settling stage and attaches to a suitable substratum by using the cement glands in the antennules (Fig. 15-27, *B*). Metamorphosis now takes place, in which the cirri elongate and the body undergoes flexion (Fig. 15-27, *C* and *D*).

According to the studies of Costlow and Bookhout (1953, 1956) on the sessile barnacle, *Balanus improvisus,* the shell of an attached one-day-old barnacle consists of the paired opercular plates (terga and scuta), two mural plates, and the basis. By the end of the fourth day, the two mural plates have divided, forming the six mural plates characteristic of the genus. Shell growth is more or less continuous and independent of body growth and ecdysis. In this species, the first twenty molts take place between two and three days apart on an average.

Ecology. Barnacles live throughout the world wherever a suitable substratum for attachment exists. They are among the most seriously important fouling organisms on ship bottoms, buoys, and pilings, and many species have been transported by shipping to locations all over the world.

Certain barnacles always live below the low-tide mark, and some are found at considerable depths. Others, however, live in the intertidal zone and can tolerate temporary exposure at low tide. A few barnacles are adapted for living in the spray zone at the high-tide mark on wave-lashed beaches. The number of individuals in a given area is often in thousands per square meter, and perhaps the most common causes of barnacle mortality are crowding and smothering by other barnacles or by other sessile organisms. Table 15-1 gives the location and aggregation of two species of barnacles on the English coast.

Commensal barnacles attach to a great variety of animals. Jellyfish, sharks, fish, whales, manatees, sea snakes, and crabs all may harbor commensal barnacles. Many are host specific. The little boring barnacle, *Trypetesa,*

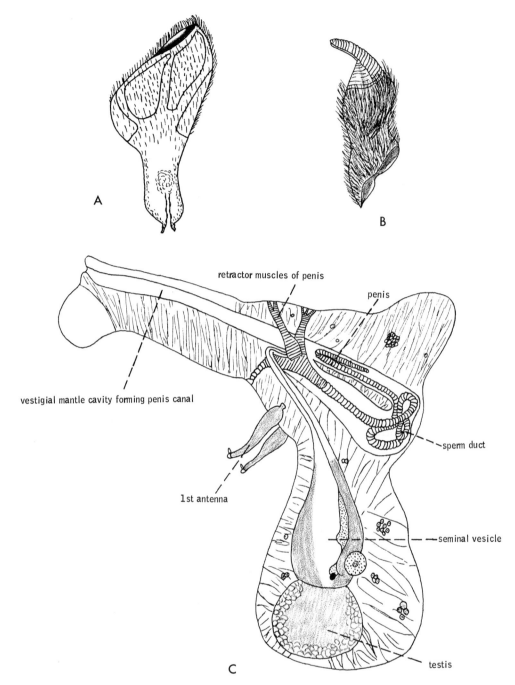

Figure 15-26.   Dwarf male barnacles. *A. Scalpellum* with shell plates still present. *B. Ibla.* (*A* and *B* after Gruvel from Calman.) *C. Trypetesa*, in which male is greatly modified. (After Bernak from Calman.)

lives in snail shells but only when the shell is occupied by a hermit crab.

PARASITIC BARNACLES. Considering the common occurrence of commensal barnacles, it is not surprising that parasitism has evolved within the class. There are a few parasitic Thoracica, and three other orders are exclusively parasitic. The most important of these is the order Rhizocephala, which is largely parasitic on decapod crustaceans. The body is saccular, and the mantle is devoid of calcareous plates. There is also a complete absence of appendages and segmentation.

The peduncle in parasitic barnacles develops absorptive root-like processes that invade the tissues of the host while the sac-like body

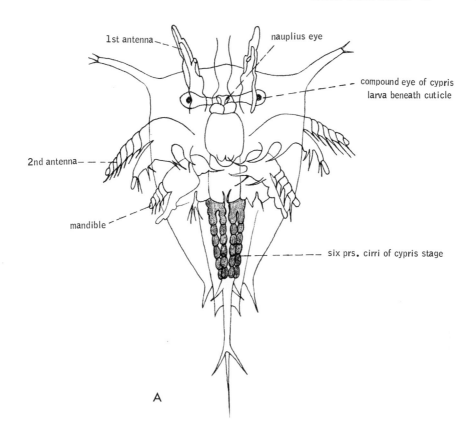

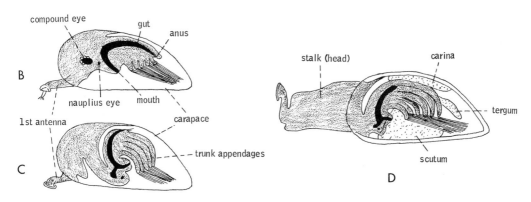

Figure 15-27. *A.* Nauplius larva of *Balanus* with structures of cypris larva visible beneath exoskeleton. (After Claus from Calman.) *B* to *D.* Metamorphosis of cypris larva of *Lepas. B.* Free-swimming cypris larva. *C.* Cypris shortly after attachment to substratum. Note rotation of body. *D.* Young barnacle near last stage of metamorphosis. (All after Korschelt from Kaestner.)

remains on the exterior. The ramifications of the peduncular root are often very extensive. In *Sacculina*, which is found on the underside of the abdomen of crabs, the absorptive processes may extend throughout the thorax and into the legs and claws of the host. In some species, asexual reproduction—a rare phenomenon among arthropods—may take place through budding

and separation of the processes. The larval stages of the Rhizocephala are typical, and the cypris, at least in *Sacculina*, apparently attacks the integument of the host when the host has just molted and the cuticle is soft (Fig. 15-28, *B* and *C*).

Members of the Order Ascothoracica are ectoparasites on sea lilies and serpent stars, or

Table 15-1. *Vertical distribution of two species of sessile barnacles on the Plymouth coast of England. (Moore, 1936.)*

Height above mean tide	NUMBERS OF INDIVIDUALS PER SQUARE METER					
	Balanus balanoides			*Chthamalus stellatus*		
	Adults	Young	Total	Adults	Young	Total
+3.4 m.	0	0	0	0	0	0
+2.7 m.	0	0	0	15,200	9,200	24,400
+1.8 m.	0	0	0	54,000	38,000	92,000
+1.8 m.	0	400	400	54,000	38,000	92,000
+0.8 m.	4,000	12,400	16,400	55,600	35,200	90,800
−0.2 m.	40,400	20,400	60,800	400	4,800	5,200
−2.1 m.	0	0	0	0	0	0

endoparasites in soft corals and in the coelom of sea stars and echinoids (Fig. 15-28, *A*). This order differs so greatly from other Cirripedia that it is sometimes considered a separate subclass. A naked saccular or bivalve mantle encloses the body, and there are six pairs of thoracic appendages, although these may be lost. There are no second antennae, but some species possess antennules, as well as a limbless abdomen. In the ectoparasites, the mouth appendages are modified for sucking; in the endoparasites, the mantle bears absorptive lobes or papillae.

Systematic Résumé of Subclass Cirripedia

Order Thoracica. Free-living and commensal barnacles with six pairs of well developed cirri. Mantle usually covered with calcareous plates.

Suborder Lepadomorpha. Pedunculate barnacles. *Lepas, Scalpellum, Mitella, Conchoderma,* and *Heteralepas.*

Suborder Verrucomorpha. Peduncle very much reduced; wall composed of carina and rostrum, and one tergum and one scutum; the other tergum and other scutum form the operculum. *Verruca.*

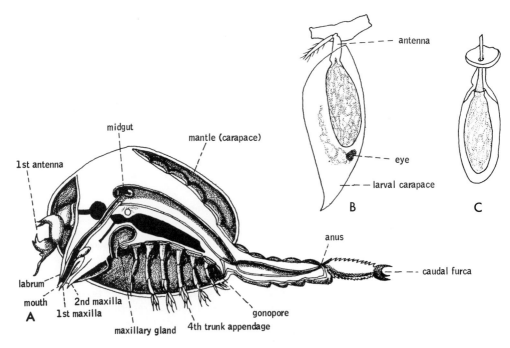

Figure 15-28. *A. Ascothorax ophioctenis,* a parasite in the bursae of brittle stars. (After Wagin from Kaestner.) *B* and *C.* Attachment to and penetration of crab integument by the parasitic barnacle, *Sacculina. B.* Cypris larva just attaching to integument. *C.* After the penetration of host's integument and shedding of larval carapace. (*B* and *C* after Delage from Kaestner.)

Suborder Balanomorpha. Sessile barnacles with a wall surmounted by the paired terga and scuta. *Balanus, Chthamalus, Catophragmus, Octomeris, Tetraclita, Pyrgoma, Coronula,* and *Xenobalanus.*

Order Acrothoracica. Naked boring barnacles with a chitinous attachment disc and only four pairs of cirri. They live in mollusk shells and coral. *Trypetesa.*

Order Rhizocephala. Naked barnacles parasitic on decapod Crustacea; a few parasitic on tunicates. Appendages and digestive tract are absent; peduncle forms foot-like absorptive processes. *Sacculina.*

Order Ascothoracica. Naked barnacles that parasitize echinoderms and soft corals. Bivalve or saccular mantle. Antennules and abdomen are sometimes present. *Synagoga, Laura, Dendrogaster,* and *Ascothorax.*

Subclass Malacostraca

The subclass Malacostraca contains almost three-quarters of all the known species of crustaceans, as well as all the larger forms, such as crabs, lobsters, shrimp, and wood lice.

The trunk of malacostracans is typically composed of fourteen segments, of which the first eight form the thorax and the last six the abdomen (Fig. 15-29, *A*). All of the segments bear appendages. The antennules are often biramous. The antennae are biramous; the exopodite is present in the form of a flattened scale. The mandible usually bears a palp, and the triturating surface of the mandible is divided into a grinding molar process and a cutting incisor. Each of the two maxillae bears a palp.

Primitively, the thoracic appendages, or legs, are similar, and the endopodite is the most highly developed of these appendages being used for crawling or prehension (Fig. 15-29, *B*). In most malacostracans, the first one, two, or three pairs of thoracic appendages have turned forward and become modified to form maxillipeds. Primitively, the thorax was probably covered by a carapace, but this has been lost in some orders. With a few exceptions, the gills are modified thoracic epipodites.

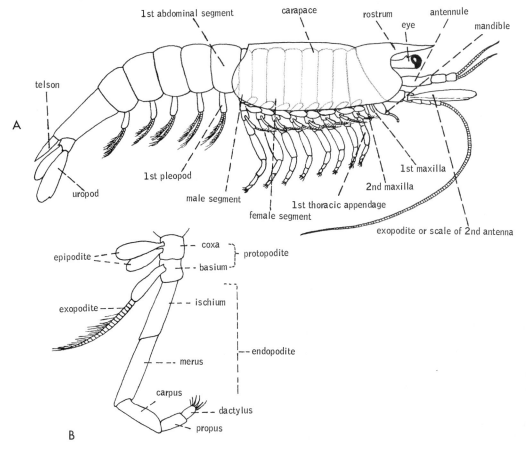

Figure 15-29.   A generalized malacostracan. *A.* Lateral view of body. *B.* A thoracic appendage. (Both after Calman.)

The first five pairs of abdominal appendages, called pleopods, are similar and biramous. The two rami of each abdominal appendage can usually be hooked together by special spines. The pleopods may be used for swimming, for carrying eggs in the female, and sometimes for respiration. In the males, the first two pairs of pleopods are often modified, forming copulatory organs. Each ramus of the sixth abdominal appendages (uropods) is composed of single large flattened piece, and, together with the usually flattened telson, forms a tail fan, which is frequently used in swimming.

The female gonopores are always located on the sixth thoracic segment, and the male gonopores are on the eighth. The nauplius larva is often passed within the egg.

Because of the size and diversity of the Malacostraca, each of the orders is considered separately.

Order Nebaliacea

This order is composed of seven species of small marine crustaceans that depart from the basic malacostracan plan in that they have seven abdominal segments instead of six. For this reason the Nebaliacea are placed in a separate series, the Leptostraca, instead of with the Eumalacostraca, which includes the remaining malacostracans.

The thorax and part of the abdomen of nebaliaceans is enclosed by a carapace, which anteriorly bears a little hinged rostral plate covering the head (Fig. 15-30, A). The thoracic appendages are similar and foliaceous, somewhat like the thoracic appendages of the branchiopods (Fig. 15-30, B). The exopodite is usually a flattened lobe; and the endopodite, and often the exopodite, is provided with long setae. Also as in the branchiopods, the foliaceous trunk limbs produce a water current from which food particles are filtered. The collected material is then transferred to a ventral groove and moved anteriorly to the mouthparts. According to Cannon (1922), all of these similarities to branchiopods represent a parallel evolution associated with a secondary adoption of filter feeding by the nebaliaceans.

The first four pairs of pleopods are used for swimming, and the last two pairs are reduced. The seventh abdominal segment lacks appendages. Unlike other malacostracans, the abdomen terminates in a caudal furca, and the telson is supplied with two rami.

The thoracic epipodites, which are flattened lamellae, form the gills. However, the inner surface of the carapace is also important to respiration. The compound eyes are stalked. The eggs are carried on the thoracic appendages of the female, and each egg hatches as a postlarva, called a manca stage, which still bears an incompletely developed carapace.

Although *Nebaliopsis* is bathypelagic, most species are littoral, living in shallow water. *Nebalia bipes,* which reaches about 12 mm. in length, lives in bottom mud and in seaweed along the Atlantic coast, as well as in many other parts of the world.

Superorder Syncarida; Order Anaspidacea

The Syncarida is represented by a single small order of primitive fresh-water crustaceans, the Anaspidacea.* Although no species have been described from North America, the order exists in most other parts of the world.

A carapace is lacking, and the first thoracic segment is fused with the head (Fig. 15-31). The thoracic appendages are biramous and similar, and the coxopodites of each appendage bear two simple lamellar gills. The pleopods have long fringed exopodites, but the endopodites are reduced or absent except for the first two pairs in the male, on which they function as copulatory organs. The uropods and telson are broad and form a well developed tail fan.

Syncarids include some of the smallest malacostracans. The European cave inhabitant, *Bathynella natans,* is only about 2 mm. long; and the brackish water inhabitant, *Thermobathynella amyxi,* from the Amazon is only 0.5 mm. At the other extreme, *Anaspides,* which inhabits Tasmanian pools and lakes, attains a length of 5.0 cm.

Syncarids swim and crawl over the bottom or on aquatic vegetation. The fringed pleopods serve as the principal swimming appendages for the syncarids, and for very rapid movement the tail fan is used in some species. The Tasmanian *Anaspides* is reported to sometimes leap out of the water.

Syncarids feed chiefly on detritus, particularly the cave-inhabiting bathynellids. In *Paranaspides,* which inhabits Tasmanian pools and lakes, the second maxillae have become modified for filtering, and a forward feeding current is produced by the beating of both the thoracic exopodites and the second maxillae. *Anaspides* feeds on algae, detritus, tadpoles, and worms scraped up or captured by the anterior thoracic

---

* The small, blind, cave-inhabiting Syncarida, which includes *Bathynella* and *Thermobathynella,* are often placed in a separate order called the Bathynellacea.

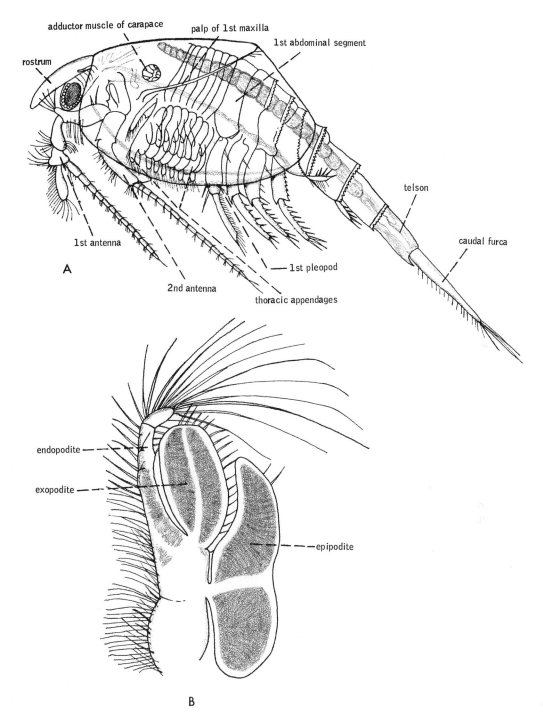

Figure 15-30.   *A.* Female *Nebalia bipes,* a leptostracan. *B.* First thoracic appendage of *Nebalia.*
(Both after Claus from Calman.)

appendages. The food is macerated by the mandibles, and the maxillary filter collects the small particles, which are then transferred to the mouth.

The heart is tubular, extending through both thorax and abdomen. The excretory organs are maxillary glands. A statocyst is located in the base of each second antenna, and the eyes are either stalked or sessile.

The anterior pleopods of the male function as copulatory organs, and a median pocket-like seminal receptacle is located on the sternum of the female between the last pair of thoracic appendages. The eggs are shed directly into the

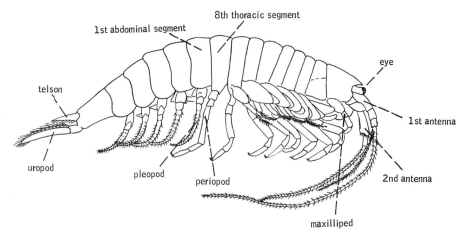

Figure 15-31.   *Anaspides tasmaniae,* a syncaridan. (After Calman from Waterman and Chace.)

water, and there are no free-swimming larval stages.

Superorder Hoplocarida and
Order Stomatopoda

The marine crustaceans called mantis shrimp comprise the Stomatopoda, which is the only order of hoplocaridans. The body is dorsoventrally flattened and elongate (Fig. 15-32, *A*). There is a rather shield-like carapace, which is fused with the first two thoracic segments only (Fig. 15-32, *B*). Anteriorly the carapace terminates short of the front of the head, so that the eyes and antennules are attached beneath a small free rostrum. The third and fourth thoracic segments are vestigial, but the last four are well developed and unfused. The abdomen is large, broad, and distinctly segmented. The surface of the carapace, the free thoracic and abdominal tergites, and the broad telson are usually ornamented with keel-like ridges and spines.

The eyes are large and stalked, and the antennules are larger than the antennae. The most conspicuous feature of the antennae is the large fringed scale that is almost as long as, or longer than, the endopodite. The most distinctive feature of the stomatopods is the structure of the thoracic appendages. The first five pairs are similar and subchelate. The second pair is enormously developed for raptorial feeding. The inner edge of the movable finger is provided with long spines or is shaped like the blade of a knife. The finger folds back into a deep groove in the heavy penult segment, which has a sharp and finely toothed margin. The last three thoracic appendages are slender and not chelate. Only the last three thoracic appendages contain exopodites, but epipodites are usually present

on the first five. The pleopods are well developed and bear the gills (Fig. 15-32, *C* and *D*). The uropods are very large.

Mantis shrimp range in size from small species approximately one and a half inches in length to giant forms over one foot long. Most mantis shrimp are tropical, but some species live in temperate waters. *Squilla empusa,* which is about six inches long, is a common species inhabiting the Atlantic coast and is frequently caught in shrimp trawls. Most species are brilliantly colored. Green, blue, and red with deep mottling are common, and some species are striped or display other patterns.

Most stomatopods live in burrows excavated in the bottom, or live in rock or coral crevices. One coral-inhabiting species, *Gonodactylus guerini,* has the entire surface of its telson ornamented with radiating spines. This armored telson is used to plug the entrance to the burrow when the mantis shrimp is inside. From the exterior, the telson accurately mimics a small sea urchin attached to the coral surface. Some stomatopods use burrows excavated by other animals.

Many mantis shrimp leave the burrow to feed and swim with a looping motion. The oarlike beating of the pleopods provides propulsion, and the large antennal scales serve as rudders. All mantis shrimp are raptorial and feed on small fish, crustaceans, and other invertebrates. Some species hunt prey; others lie in wait at the mouth of the burrow.

The victim is caught and dispatched by an extremely rapid extension and retraction of the movable finger of the large second pair of thoracic appendages. At the same time, the whole limb is lifted somewhat like an uppercut. The MacGinities (1949) report seeing a Pacific coast species, *Pseudosquilla bigelowi,* which has a sharp

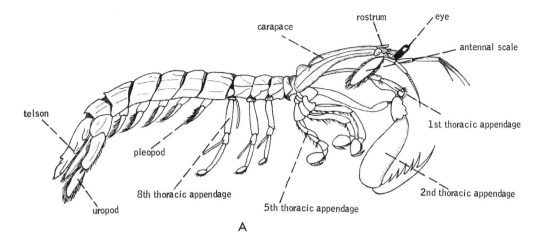

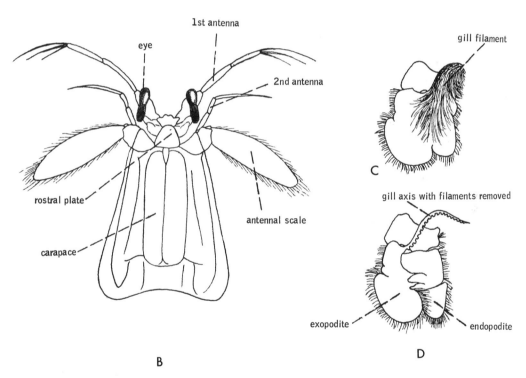

Figure 15-32.   Stomatopoda. *A. Squilla mantis* (lateral view). *B.* Head and carapace of *Squilla* (dorsal view). *C.* Second pleopod and gill of *Squilla*. *D.* Second pleopod with gill filaments removed. (All after Calman.)

blade-like finger, cut a shrimp neatly in two with one blow.

Mastication is accomplished primarily by the mandibles, and the second maxillae probably function as a screen covering the mouth. When food enters the mouth, it passes into a pre-oral extension of the cardiac stomach. Here

it is masticated by the upward projecting molar processes of the mandibles. The masticated food material is then passed into the post-oral division of the cardiac stomach, in which some additional trituration takes place by the action of two pairs of lateral ossicles acting against a ventral plate, which can be elevated and lowered.

The lumen of a second (pyloric) stomach is greatly occluded by large chitinous pads bearing screening bristles that filter the contents of the cardiac chamber. The digestive gland is very large and envelops the intestine throughout the length of the abdomen. A pair of ducts from the gland open into the back of the pyloric stomach, which comprises the midgut.

Mantis shrimp are the only malacostracans, aside from isopods, that have abdominal gills. These gills are filamentous, and the slender axis arises on the front sides of the exopodite near the basal suture. The heart is tubular and extends through most of the thorax and abdomen. It is strikingly segmental, displaying thirteen pairs of ostia. In addition to the single anterior artery, a pair of anterio-lateral arteries issue from the heart. Hemocyanin is present in the blood of at least some stomatopods. The excretory organs are maxillary glands.

The first eight ventral ganglia are fused, but the remainder are widely separated along the ventral cord. The stalked compound eyes are usually well developed, and the corneal surface forms a large swollen oval disc at the end of the peduncle. Considering the organization of the ommatidia and the proximity and position in which the eyes can be held, both binocular depth perception and monocular stereoscopic vision should be possible.

The testes are delicate convoluted tubules located in the abdomen and joined together within the telson. The sperm duct opens at the end of a long chitinous penis attached to the coxa of the last pair of legs. The ovaries extend from the middle of the thorax through the abdomen and also connect in the telson. The oviducts open on the middle of the sixth thoracic sternite, and in the same area there is a pouchlike seminal receptacle.

The eggs are agglutinated to form a globular mass by means of an adhesive secretion from special glands opening onto the sternites of the last three thoracic segments. According to Giesbrecht (1910), the eggs in *Squilla* are picked up by the maxillipeds as they are extruded and then kneaded for hours with the anterior thoracic appendages (Fig. 15-33).

The entire process of spawning may take four hours, during which time the female stands on the legs and the telson with her body arched upward. The agglutinated egg mass, which is about the size of a walnut, is carried by the smaller chelate appendages and is constantly turned and cleaned. The female does not feed while she is brooding. Some species keep their egg mass inside the burrow. For example, a Bahamian species of *Gonodactylus,* which lies curled up in a coral crevice, holds the egg mass over the back of the carapace and abdomen like a cap and does not pick it up unless disturbed (Fig. 15-33).

Figure 15-33.   Two species of stomatopods caring for eggs. *Squilla mantis* (*left*) carrying egg mass; *Gonodactylus oerstedi* (*right*) with egg mass in burrow. (Modified after Schmitt.)

Superorder Peracarida

The subsequent five orders comprise the superorder Peracarida.* At least the first thoracic segment is always fused with the head, and the last four thoracic segments are always unfused, even when a carapace is present. The nauplius eye never persists in the adult. The distinctive characteristic of the group is the presence of a ventral brood pouch, or marsupium. The marsupium is formed by large plate-like processes (oostegites) on the thoracic coxae. The oostegites project inward horizontally and overlap with one another to form the floor of the marsupium. The thoracic sternites form the roof.

Primitively, peracaridans are maxillary filter feeders, as in many mysids, cumaceans, and

*Two other orders, the Thermosbaenacea containing four species and the Spelaeogriphacea containing a single species, have been omitted.

tanaidaceans, but the tendency in most higher peracaridans has been toward a direct mode of feeding.

Order Mysidacea

Mysidaceans look much like little shrimp. The majority are between 1.5 and 3.0 cm. in length, but some, such as *Gnathophausia*, may attain a length of 35 cm. (Fig. 15-34, *A*). A few species live in fresh water, but most are marine.

The thorax is covered by a carapace, but as in all peracaridans, the carapace is not united with the last four thoracic segments. Anteriorly, the carapace often extends forward as a rostrum, below which project stalked compound eyes. The first thoracic appendages and sometimes the second pair as well (in the Mysidae) are modified as maxillipeds. The remaining six or seven thoracic appendages are more or less simi-

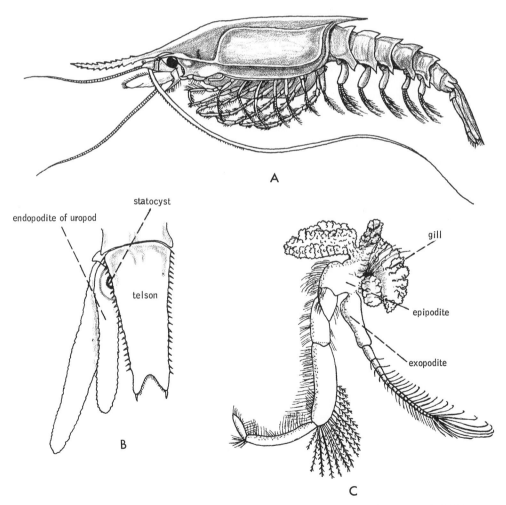

Figure 15-34.   Mysidacea. *A. Gnathophausia* (lateral view). *B.* Telson and one uropod of *Mysis*. *C.* Second thoracic appendage of *Gnathophausia*. (All after Sars from Calman.)

lar, although some may be subchelate. The thoracic exopodites are filamentous and sometimes bear swimming setae. The pleopods in some groups, such as the Mysidae, are reduced in the female; in males the fourth pleopod is usually modified and very long.

Some genera such as the deep-sea *Gnathophausia,* swim using the pleopods; others, such as *Mysis,* use the thoracic exopodites for swimming, particularly when the pleopods are reduced. Benthic forms crawl over the bottom or plow through the surface mud and silt.

The respiratory current is produced by the thoracic exopodites and the maxillipeds and flows from posterior to anterior. Thoracic gills are present in the lophogastrids and are branched and foliaceous (Fig. 15-34, *C*). In the Mysidae, the inner surface of the carapace acts as a gill.

Most mysidaceans are filter feeders. In *Gnathophausia,* the food current is produced by the beating of a large feathered exite on the second maxilla, and food particles are collected by filtering setae on the same appendage. Thus, in this genus, there is a swimming current produced by the pleopods, a respiratory current produced by the thoracic exopodites and maxillipeds, and a feeding current created by the maxillary exite; and all three currents are more or less separate and independent. This probably represents the primitive peracaridan condition.

In those genera such as *Hemimysis,* in which pleopods are reduced and the exopodites have secondarily assumed a natatory function, the current produced by the thoracic appendages provides to some extent for all three functions—that is, for swimming, respiration, and feeding. In swimming, the exopodite performs a slightly rotatory movement pulling water up along the axes of the leg to the midline of the body. From here the water is then moved forward by the beating of the maxillipeds and the exite of the maxillae, and food particles are filtered by setae on the maxillary endites. *Hemimysis* also feeds on large food masses, in addition to filter feeding. Many bathypelagic forms such as the lophogastrids, have completely lost the filtering mechanism and are scavengers.

A statocyst is present in the base of each uropod (Fig. 15-34, *B*). The chamber is closed or open to the exterior, and the statolith is a large single secreted body. The statocysts are innervated by the last pair of abdominal ganglia.

Development is direct within the brood chamber.

Marine mysids often live in large swarms and form an important part of the diet of such fish as shad and flounder. Many marine species are found in algae and tidal grass and can tolerate relatively foul conditions. The few freshwater species appear to be rather recent immigrants from the sea. Of the two North American species, *Neomysis mercedis* lives in estuaries, rivers, and lakes on the west coast, and *Mysis oculata* is confined to cold deep-water lakes of northern United States, Canada, and Europe. Lake trout feed extensively on this species.

Order Cumacea

Cumaceans are marine peracaridans of approximately the same size as mysids. Most cumaceans inhabit the bottom, where they live buried in sand and mud. The body shape is very distinctive (Fig. 15-35). The head and thorax are greatly enlarged, while the abdomen is very narrow and terminates in slender elongated uropods. A carapace is present and is fused with the first three or four thoracic segments. The carapace is peculiar in having two anteriolateral extensions. These extensions swing together in front of the animal to form a ventral false rostrum. When eyes are present, they are located on a common median prominence situated above the rostrum base.

The antennae are vestigial in the female; in the male they are extremely long and are borne folded back along the sides of the body, sometimes in a groove. The first three thoracic appendages are modified as maxillipeds, and the fourth pair is long and prehensile. Exopodites are present on some of the legs. Females lack pleopods, but they are usually present in males.

The thoracic exopodites are used in swimming and may be assisted by lateral movements of the abdomen. The more posterior legs are used for burrowing. The animal moves backward into the burrow as the sand is excavated and ends up in an inclined position with its head projecting above the surface (Fig. 15-35).

A series of filamentous gills are located on the epipodite of each first maxilliped. This epipodite also forms the floor of a branchial chamber that is walled and roofed in by the sides of the body and the carapace. As a modification for the partially buried existence, the inhalant respiratory current has become shifted anteriorly. The movement of the epipodite acts as a respiratory pump, and water is drawn in anteriorly over the mouthparts and passes upward through the branchial chamber. The water is then sent anteriorly again by the long concave plate-like exopodite of the first maxilliped, which fits against the pseudorostrum and

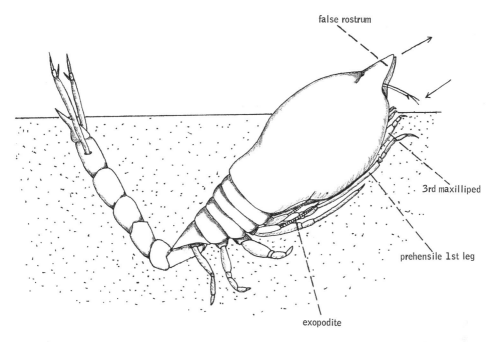

false rostrum

3rd maxilliped

prehensile 1st leg

exopodite

Figure 15-35. *Diastylis*, a cumacean, buried in sand. Arrows indicate direction of feeding–respiratory current. (Modified from several authors.)

forms an exhalant siphon. The exhalant current thus emerges anteriorly on both sides of the head as two parallel streams.

In *Diastylis* (Dennell, 1934), the inhalant respiratory current, while passing over the mouthparts, is filtered for food particles by setae on the second maxillae. The current flow is also reinforced by the beating of the endites of the first maxillipeds and the maxillary filters. Not all cumaceans are filter feeders. Some, such as *Cumopsis, Lamprops,* and *Iphinoe,* scrape organic matter from sand grains. While half buried in sand, the grains are swept up by the first pairs of legs, passed to the third maxillipeds, and then passed to the first and second. The latter two pairs of maxillipeds are modified to form a cup in which the sand grain is rotated and the food material is rasped from its surface. The cleaned grain is either thrown into the exhalant respiratory current or thrown over the eye onto the side of the carapace, where it rolls off. When the animal becomes too deeply buried or when too large a hole has been formed by the sweeping, it moves and reburies itself.

Swarming behavior is characteristic of many cumaceans. Large numbers, particularly males, leave their burrows and swim to the surface. It has been suggested that swarming may be an adaptation that facilitates mating. The eggs are carried in the marsupium, and

each hatches as a postlarva, called a manca stage, in which the last pair of legs is undeveloped.

More than 650 species of cumaceans have been described. Most are littoral but live in deeper water than is usually explored by most collectors. Species of *Diastylis, Leptocuma, Cyclaspis,* and other genera live along the North Atlantic coast.

Order Tanaidacea

The Tanaidacea displays similarities to both the Cumacea and to the Isopoda, with which they were formerly classified. These peracaridans are almost exclusively marine and generally very small, most of them being only one or two millimeters in length (Fig. 15-36). The majority are bottom inhabitants of the littoral zone, where they live buried in mud or construct tubes.

A carapace covers the anterior part of the body and includes the first and second thoracic segments. Many species lack eyes, but when eyes are present, they are located laterally on immovable processes. The first pair of thoracic appendages is maxillipeds and the second pair (gnathopods) is large and chelate, a distinctive feature of the tanaidaceans. The third pair of thoracic appendages is adapted for burrowing. The exopodites have disappeared in all thoracic appendages except the second and third, prob-

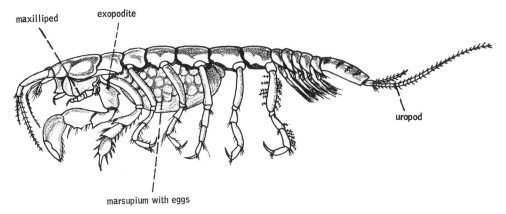

maxilliped   exopodite

uropod

marsupium with eggs

Figure 15-36.   A tanaidacean, *Apseudes,* with eggs in marsupium. (After Sars from Calman.)

ably as a result of the burrowing habit. Pleopods are sometimes reduced or absent in females. The last abdominal segment is fused with the telson.

The inner surface of the carapace functions as a gill. In *Apseudes talpa,* the respiratory current enters the posterior ventral margin of the carapace just in front of the bases of the third thoracic limbs. After passing through the limited branchial chamber, the respiratory current exits from the ventral margin of the carapace between the bases of the maxillipeds and the gnathopods. The current is produced by the beating of the epipodites of the maxillipeds and, to a lesser extent, by the exopodites of the second and third thoracic appendages.

The beating of the epipodites also produces a feeding current passing over the mouthparts. The second maxillae filter some food particles, but in *Apseudes* and other members of the same family, large particles are retained on the brushing setae of the maxillipeds. The diet is also supplemented by raptorial feeding. This tendency toward the loss of filter feeding in the Apseudidae is culminated in the Tanaidae, which are entirely raptorial. Associated with this change in feeding habits, the branchial chambers are less developed, the maxillae are greatly reduced, and the remaining thoracic exopodites have disappeared.

The eggs are brooded as in other peracaridans and the eggs hatch as postlarvae (manca stage) without the last pair of thoracic legs fully developed.

Order Isopoda

The order Isopoda is the largest order of crustaceans aside from the Decapoda. Most of the 4000 described species are marine; but a considerable number live in fresh water; and the pill bugs, or wood lice, are the only large group of truly terrestrial crustaceans. The order also includes several parasitic forms.

The most striking characteristic of the isopods is the dorso-ventrally flattened body (Figs. 15-37 and 15-38, *B*). The head is usually shield-shaped, and the terga of the thoracic and the abdominal segments tend to project laterally. A carapace is absent, although the first one or two thoracic segments are fused with the head. The abdominal segments may be distinct or fused to varying degrees. The last abdominal segment is almost always fused with the telson; and in the Asellota, which includes the greatest number of fresh-water species, all of the abdominal segments are fused with the telson to form a large abdominal plate (Fig. 15-37, *A*). The abdomen is usually the same width as the thorax, so that the two regions may not be clearly demarcated dorsally.

There are exceptions to most of these characteristics. Members of the mostly marine suborder, Anthuridea, have an elongated cylindrical body; and the fresh-water *Phreatoicus* is even laterally compressed (Fig. 15-38, *A*). The abdomen of the parasitic Gnathiidae is narrow and tail-like.

The antennules are short and uniramous, and in terrestrial isopods they are vestigial. The antennae, however, are well developed except in some parasitic forms, but the exopodite is typically absent (Fig. 15-37). The compound eyes are always sessile.

The first pair of thoracic appendages is modified to form maxillipeds; the other thoracic appendages are usually adapted for crawling. These appendages are uniramous, and the coxopodite is commonly expanded, forming a coxal plate, which may be fused with the sternum. Unlike those in most other crusta-

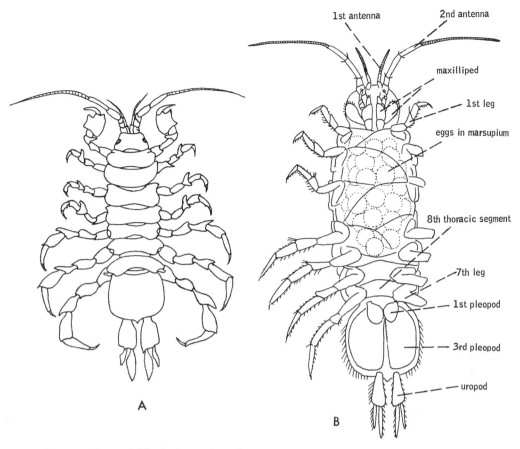

Figure 15-37. *A.* The fresh-water isopod, *Asellus* (dorsal view). (After Pennak.) *B. Asellus* (ventral view). Appendages complete only on one side. (After Van Name.)

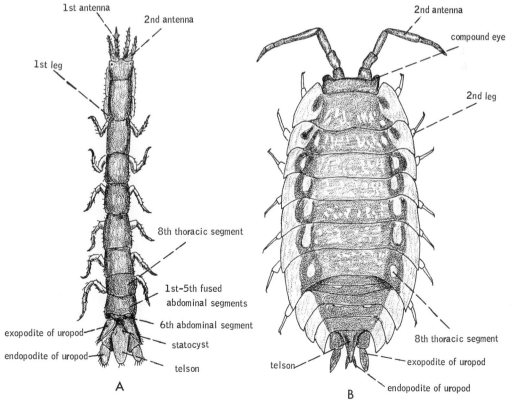

Figure 15-38. *A.* Marine isopod, *Cyathura carinata.* (After Gruner from Kaestner.) *B. Oniscus asellus,* a terrestrial isopod. (After Paulmier from Van Name.)

ceans, the isopod pleopods are modified for respiration. The uropods are usually fan-shaped or styliform.

Most isopods are 5 to 15 mm. long. The giant of the group is the deep sea *Bathynomus giganteus*, which reaches a length of 14 in. and a width of 5 in. The coloration in isopods is usually drab, gray to blackish being the most common.

Locomotion.   Almost all isopods crawl at least part of the time. The common amphibious marine isopod, *Lygia,* can run very rapidly over exposed wharf pilings and rocks. Manton (1951) states that each leg in *Lygia* may take sixteen steps per second, a frequency that is surpassed by few other arthropods. Some isopods such as *Cruregens* can run backward as rapidly as forward. Some terrestrial wood lice can climb vegetation, and *Lygia* commonly runs about upside down beneath stones or dock planking. *Astacilla,* which climbs over seaweed and hydroids, has posterior thoracic limbs that are adapted for clinging.

Many aquatic isopods burrow. Commonly the anterior legs are pressed down into the mud and then moved to the side like a breast stroke in swimming. Some burrowing species construct tunnels through the substratum, packing excavated material against the walls. *Limnoria* tunnels through wood and can cause extensive damage to docks and pilings (Fig. 15-39). Particularly remarkable is the tropical American isopod, *Cirolana salvadorensis,* which plows through dry beach sand.

Many aquatic isopods can swim, as well as crawl. In some forms, such as *Munnopsis,* certain of the legs are flattened and paddle-shaped, and they beat in an oar-like or rotary manner. However, most commonly the pleopods are used for swimming, and in the families Sphaeromidae and Serolidae, the first three pairs of pleopods are especially adapted for swimming; respiration is restricted to the more posterior pleopods. The tail fan is rarely employed in swimming, in contrast to the tail fan in many other malacostracans.

The ability to roll up in a ball has evolved in many terrestrial Oniscoidea, probably for protection or to reduce water loss from evaporation. *Oniscus* and *Armadillidium* assume a perfectly spherical shape when they roll up, from which characteristic the name *pill bug* is derived.

Internal Anatomy and Physiology.   Isopods have completely dispensed with filter feeding, and the majority are scavangers and omnivorous, although some tend toward a herbivorous diet. The wood lice feed on algae, moss, bark, and any decaying vegetable or animal matter. One species that is commensal in ant nests feeds on the feces of the host. A few wood lice are carnivorous.

The mouthparts tend to be compact, forming a ventrally projecting mound that is covered by the labrum in front and maxillipeds behind. The maxillipeds form a protective operculum, and often the maxilliped of one side is hooked to its opposite member by special coupling setae. During feeding, food is usually picked up by the anterior legs, which may be subchelate, and held while chewed upon by the mouthparts.

The triturating, or cardiac, stomach is well developed, particularly so in the terrestrial

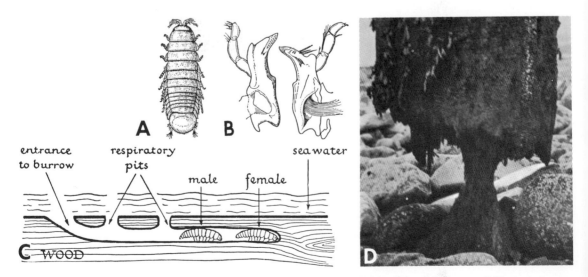

Figure 15-39.   *A.* The wood-boring isopod, *Limnoria lignorum. B.* Mandibles of *L. lignorum. C.* Diagrammatic section of burrow of *L. lignorum. D.* Jetty piling nearly eaten through at base by *L. lignorum.* (All modified from Yonge, 1949: The Seashore, Collins, London.)

wood lice. The midgut contains one to three pairs of ceca. The digestive secretions of the wood borer, *Limnoria,* are reported to contain cellulase, while in the wood louse, *Porcellio,* and probably many other isopods, cellulose digestion results from symbiotic bacteria. The wood louse, *Oniscus asellus,* and very likely other terrestrial isopods as well, has been reported by Beerstecher and others (1954) to be able to subsist on a very low protein diet. The protein may perhaps also be supplied by the bacterial flora of the gut.

There are several groups of parasitic isopods. The Gnathiidae in the larval stages and the adult Cymothoidae are ectoparasitic on the skin of fish and have mandibles adapted for piercing. Piercing mouthparts are also present in the parasites composing the suborder Epicaridea, all of which are blood-suckers, parasitic on many different crustacean groups. Many epicaridans are highly modified and show little resemblance to free-living forms. This is especially true of members of the family Entoniscidae, which live in the gill chambers of crabs. They bury themselves deep in the body wall of the host and become encased by the lymphocytes of the host. A hole is made through the lymphocytes to enable the parasite to feed.

Primitively, the pleopods possess the endopodite and exopodite, each modified as a large flat respiratory lamella, or gill. Both rami of all the pleopods function both in respiration and in swimming (Fig. 15-37, *B*). However, there is usually some modification of this arrangement. In some isopods, respiration and swimming are divided among the pleopods, the anterior ones being fringed and coupled for swimming and the posterior pleopods being respiratory.

The respiratory lamellae typically lie flat against the underside of the abdomen and are often protected by a covering (the operculum) derived in a variety of ways. In some forms, the first pair of pleopods is modified, forming an operculum that covers the more posterior pairs; the second or third exopodites may also form opercula. In the marine Valvifera, the uropods are greatly elongated and meet at the midline ventrally to form a gill covering resembling two doors. Sometimes the gill surface is increased by folding or by filamentous or villous projections, particularly in parasitic isopods.

In the amphibious and terrestrial Oniscoidea, the exopodite of each pleopod forms an operculum covering the respiratory endopodite. The undersurface of the abdomen is thus covered by two rows of overlapping opercula. Some gaseous exchange takes place through the opercular surface, as well as through the gill;

and in the truly terrestrial wood lice, the operculum contains a lung-like cavity (as in Oniscidae), or tube-like invaginations, or pseudotracheae (as in Porcellionidae and Armadillidiidae) (Fig. 15-40). Wood lice with pseudotracheae can tolerate much drier air than wood lice without them. If gill respiration is blocked in *Lygia* and *Oniscus,* oxygen consumption is only reduced by about 50 per cent, indicating that the general integumentary surface is equally important as a site of gaseous exchange.

The heart is either tubular or saccular and contains one to four pairs of ostia. The heart lies primarily in the abdomen, correlated with the abdominal position of the gills, but it may extend into the thorax to varying degrees. The arterial system is highly developed with anterior and lateral arteries issuing from the heart.

The excretory organs are maxillary glands but are reduced in some wood lice. Amphibious and terrestrial isopods display some modifications for controlling water loss, but the group as a whole is considerably less well adapted in this regard than are other terrestrial arthropods. Amphibious species such as *Lygia* are periodically emersed in sea water. Wood lice, however, while completely divorced from water, tend to be nocturnal and live beneath stones, wood, bark, and other places where the atmosphere is humid; they have never evolved a waxy cuticle, like that present in insects and spiders, for reducing integumentary evaporation.

Some families, such as the Armadillidiidae, can tolerate drier conditions than others. The replacement of water lost from integumentary

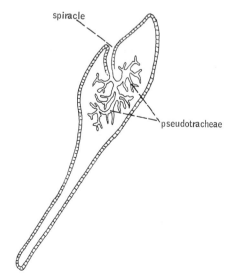

Figure 15-40. Section through exopodite, or operculum, of the terrestrial isopod, *Porcellio scaber,* showing pseudotracheae. (After Unwin from Kaestner.)

evaporation comes from moist food and drinking. In order to keep the respiratory pleopods moist, *Oniscus* and some other more specialized wood lice possess a remarkable series of external lateral channels in the cuticle, running the length of the body and extending onto the uropods. These longitudinal channels connect with cross channels that run ventrally down to the pleopods. When the uropods are pressed against a moist surface, water passes into the channels by capillary force and is conducted forward. In the absence of external water regurgitated fluid can be conducted backward from the mouth in the same manner. In contrast to most terrestrial animals, water loss through excretion has been reduced in wood lice by suppressing nitrogen metabolism, rather than by the synthesis of urea or uric acid; ammonia is still the principal nitrogenous waste product.

The nervous system displays all degrees of concentration, from the primitive ladder-like arrangement with paired ganglia and double cords, as in *Sphaeroma*, to the extreme forward migration and fusion of ganglia.

The compound eyes are always sessile and are located on each side of the head. Eyes are absent in some parasites and deep-sea species; in the fresh-water *Asellus*, the eyes contain only a few ommatidia. On the other hand, in *Bathynomus*, each eye is composed of approximately 3000 visual units. The few studies on visual responses in isopods are largely confined to the terrestrial Oniscoidea. Phototropism in *Oniscus* varies with humidity to a certain extent. When humidity is high, the animal is photonegative; when it is low, the animal is photopositive. A photopositive response is apparently an adaptation that helps prevent desiccation as a dark retreat dries out. The European beach-inhabiting *Tylos* is reported to be able to find its way back to the proper beach zone by the angle of the sun and by sky polarization, described later for some of the amphipods.

A pair of statocysts are located in the telson of some isopods, such as the burrowing *Cyathura*, and experiments on *Cyathura carinata* demonstrate a loss of ability for vertical burrowing if the statocysts are removed or destroyed (Fig. 15-38, *A*). There appear to be no special hygroreceptors in wood lice, and reactions to moisture changes perhaps are caused by general water loss from the body. The tendency of wood lice to congregate beneath a board or other objects is probably coincidental, resulting from simultaneous migrations to a favorable environment.

Reproduction and Development. The gonads are paired and separate. The male sperm ducts open onto the sternum of the genital segment by way of either separate or united papillae. The female gonopores are also paired sternal openings. In the Asellidae, each oviduct is enlarged basally, forming a seminal receptacle. Copulation has been studied in only a few species. In the American fresh-water asellid, *Lirceus*, the male seizes a pre-adult female that is about to, or has just, shed the posterior half of its pre-adult cuticle, and he presses his ventral surface against the side of her body. The endopodites of the first two pairs of pleopods, which are modified to form anteriorly directed copulatory organs, vibrate, apparently aiding in the transmission of sperm into one of the gonopores and seminal receptacles. The male then moves to the other side of the female's body, where the process is repeated. The eggs are fertilized in the oviduct.

In the Oniscoidea, the gonopores are reported to lead into blind sac-like seminal receptacles, which do not make connection with the oviducts until after copulation is completed and a molt takes place.

The parasitic Cymothoidae and Epicaridea are hermaphroditic.

The eggs are usually brooded in the marsupium, even in wood lice; but some sphaeromids possess special pouch-like invaginations of the thoracic sternites, and the oostegites may be absent(Fig. 15-37, *B*). In aquatic isopods, there is often a process from the basal portion of the maxilliped that projects backward into the marsupium. The vibrations of this process create a water current passing through the brood chamber that facilitates aeration of the developing young. As in cumaceans and tanaidaceans, the hatching stage is a postlarva, (manca stage) having the last pair of legs incompletely developed. The young usually do not remain with female after they leave the marsupium; but in *Arcturus*, the female carries the young about attached to her long antennae (Fig. 15-41).

Systematic Résumé of Order Isopoda

Suborder Gnathiidea. First and seventh thoracic segments reduced, so that only five large segments are visible dorsally. Seventh thoracic appendages are absent. Abdomen small and much narrower that thorax. Manca stage is ectoparasitic on marine fish. *Gnathia.*

Suborder Anthuridea. Body long and cylindrical; last abdominal segment not fused with telson. First pair of legs are heavy and subchelate; first pair of pleopods form an operculum covering other pairs. All are marine except a few fresh-water species. *Anthura, Cyathura,* and *Cruregens.*

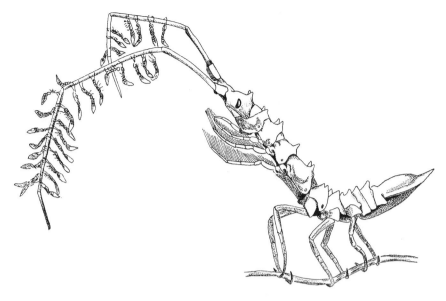

Figure 15-41.   Female of *Arcturus baffini,* a marine isopod, carrying young on antennae. (Modified after Schmitt.)

Suborder Flabellifera. Body is more or less flattened; some abdominal segments may be fused together; the last segment fused with the telson. The uropods are fan-shaped and form a tail fan together with the telson. Coxae are expanded to form coxal plates; they may be fused with the body. Members are largely marine; a few found in fresh water. Included are the wood borer, *Limnoria; Cirolana; Bathynomus; Serolis; Sphaeroma;* and the ectoparasites of fish, the Cymothoidae.

Suborder Valvifera. Abdominal segments are fused to some degree. Thoracic coxae are expanded to form coxal plates. Exopodite of uropods are either vestigial or absent; endopodite forms an operculum over gills. Members are marine. *Astacilla, Arcturus,* and *Idotea.*

Suborder Asellota. All abdominal segments fused with telson, forming a large plate. Coxae of thoracic appendages are never expanded to form plates. All pleopods are used as gills. Uropods are styliform. Includes marine and fresh-water species. *Asellus, Lirceus,* and *Munnopsis.*

Suborder Phreatoicidea. Abdominal segments are not coalesced. Body is laterally compressed. Thoracic coxae are small; uropods are styliform. Includes the fresh-water isopods of Australia and South Africa. *Phreatoicus.*

Suborder Epicaridea. Parasites on crustaceans. Suctorial mouthparts and piercing mandibles; both pairs of maxillae are either vestigial or absent. Females are often greatly modified; some without segmentation or appendages. *Bopyrus, Entoniscus, Portunion,* and *Liriopsis.*

Suborder Oniscoidea. Abdominal segments are usually distinct. Antennules are vestigial. Coxae are expanded to form coxal plates and are fused with body. Amphibious and terrestrial members. *Ligia, Oniscus, Porcellio, Armadillidium,* and *Tylos.*

Order Amphipoda

The amphipods comprise the second of the two major groups of peracaridans. Most are marine, including some semiterrestrial forms, but there are many fresh-water species. The structure of amphipods is similar to that of isopods in several respects (Fig. 15-42). The eyes are sessile and lateral. There is no carapace, and the first thoracic segment and sometimes the second (as in the Caprellidea) are fused with the head. Thoracic exopodites have disappeared. Also the abdomen is usually not distinctly demarcated from the thorax in both size and shape. In contrast to isopods, however, the amphipod body tends to be laterally compressed, giving the animal a rather shrimp-like appearance. Also, the gills are thoracic and not abdominal.

The antennules and antennae are usually well developed, although the antennae lack exopodites. The first pair of thoracic appendages is modified to form maxillipeds, and their coxae are fused together. The coxae of the other thoracic appendages are usually long flattened plates that increase the appearance of lateral body compression. The second and third

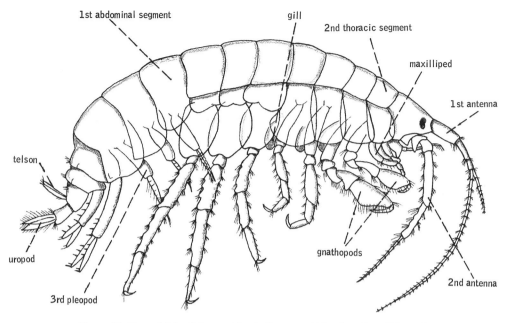

Figure 15-42.   Male of the amphipod, *Gammarus*. (After Sars from Calman.)

thoracic appendages are usually modified for prehension and are sometimes called gnathopods. Pleopods are present and are usually divided into two groups. The anterior three pairs are fringed and are used for swimming and for ventilation. The others are directed backward and are similar to the uropods.

Exceptions to all of these typical amphipod features can be found, and some groups have diverged widely from the general plan. In the caprellids, which are common marine amphipods found on seaweed, hydroids, and bryozoans, the abdomen is vestigial, and the thorax is long and slender (Fig. 15-43, *A*). The parasitic whale lice (Cyamidae) also have a vestigial abdomen, and the thorax is dorso-ventrally flattened as in the isopods (Fig 15-47). A dorso-ventrally flattened body also appears in some other amphipods, such as the Phliasidae and *Platyischnopus*. Other aberrant amphipods include the pelagic genera *Rhabdosoma* (Fig. 15-43, *B*), which has an elongated head with an extremely long needle-like rostrum, and *Mimonectes*, in which the body is enormously swollen and spherical, perhaps for mimicking jelly fish, on which *Mimonectes* is commensal or parasitic.

Amphipods are about the same size as isopods. The giant of the order is the marine *Alicella gigantea*, which may reach 14 cm. in length. The smallest forms are only a few millimeters long. Most amphipods are translucent or grayish in color, but some species are colored brown, red, green, or blue-green.

Locomotion and Tube Construction. All hyperiideans are pelagic; the majority of gammarideans are bottom-dwellers, but most members can swim, even if infrequently. Propulsion for swimming is provided by the anterior pleopods and in some gammarids by the thoracic appendages. The skeleton shrimp (the caprellids) swim by a curious looping motion, the anterior half of the body being rapidly flexed downward and then slowly raised.

Usually swimming takes place at intervals between crawling and burrowing; in leaving the substratum, initial thrust is commonly gained by a backward flip of the abdomen. Walking is effected by the legs; but in rapid movement over the bottom both legs and pleopods are used, and the animal often leans far over to one side. This type of movement is seen in many beach fleas (the Talitridae), semiterrestrial amphipods that live beneath drift near the high-tide mark; and some scull rapidly over the sand, gaining additional power with pushing strokes from the telson. Beach fleas can also jump, using a sudden backward extension of the abdomen and telson. *Talorchestia*, 2 cm. long, can leap forward a distance of one meter, a feat unequaled by any other animal of comparable size.

Many amphipods, especially the caprellids, are adapted for climbing. The tips of the legs are provided with grasping claws for clinging to hydroids, bryozoans, and algae (Fig. 15-44).

Many amphipods are accomplished bur-

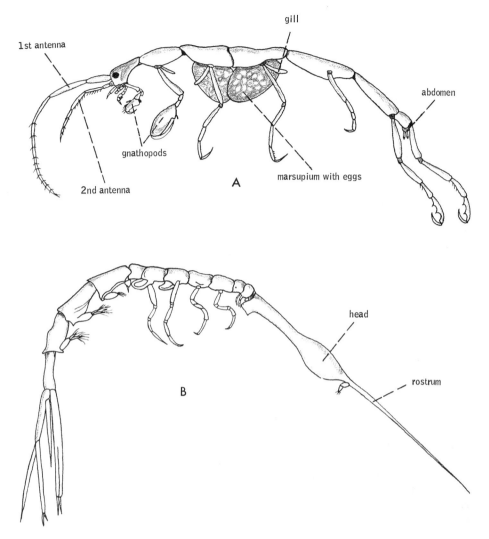

Figure 15-43.   *A. Phthisica,* a caprellid amphipod. (After Sars from Calman.) *B. Rhabdosoma,* an amphipod with elongated head and needle-like rostrum. (After Stebbing from Calman.)

rowers, and some construct tubes of mud or of secreted material. Enequist's (1949) studies on the soft-bottom amphipods of the Skagerak have contributed much to the knowledge of the burrowing habits of these forms. The methods of burrowing vary, but the anterior legs (gnathopods) are most commonly the appendages employed and are often specially adapted for the purpose.

The excavated material may be swept backwards (as done by the gammarids) and removed by the uropods and telson; or it may be moved forward. In *Neohela,* the hands of the gnathopods are placed together and function as a scoop. In the beach flea, *Talorchestia,* the body is braced with the second and third pairs of legs, while the gnathopods sweep the material back

to the uropods and telson, which flip it away. When burrowing, the beach flea looks very much like a dog digging. In some amphipods, the antenna may aid in digging; and in *Trypho- sites,* as well as others, the pleopods are used, the animal burrowing straight down from the swimming position. Usually the posterior respiratory current produced by the beating pleopods is important in sucking away the loosened material.

A great many burrowing species construct temporary or permanent burrows, tunnels, or tubes. The burrows may be horizontal, vertical, or U-shaped with two openings. Sometimes the walls are simply packed, but often they are reinforced with secreted material.

Tube construction is particularly common among amphipods, and a variety of materials,

Figure 15-44. *Caprella equilibra,* clinging to seaweed. (By D. P. Wilson.)

such as mud, clay, sand grains, and shell and plant fragments may be used. The material is usually bound together with a cementing secretion produced from glands opening at the bases of the fourth and fifth thoracic appendages. *Haploops* mixes the secretion with clay, and the resulting stiff mass is then drawn out between the end of the abdomen and gnathopods and applied to the walls. Cement glands are not always confined to the third and fourth thoracic appendages. They may appear on other appendages; and in the beach fleas, which line their burrows with sand, the glands are located all over the body.

Several tube dwellers, such as species of *Siphonectes* and *Cerapus,* build unattached tubes of shell fragments and sand grains and carry the tubes about with them (Fig. 15-45). *Siphonectes* drags itself about with its second antenna. *Cyrtophium* makes its tubes out of a section of a hollow plant stem, which it lines with secreted material; the animal can even swim with the tube.

A few amphipods have rather unusual retreats. Some species of *Siphonectes* live in old tooth-shells, and *Polycheria* constructs burrows in the tunic of ascidians. Like the isopod, *Limnoria,* the amphipod, *Chelura terebrans* bores in wood. Particularly remarkable are the species of the pelagic genus, *Phronima,* which fashion a home out of what are reported to be the swimming bells of siphonophorans or old pelagic tunicate tests, although definite proof of their nature is lacking. In *Polycheria sedentaria,* only the adult female occupies the case; the males and immatures are found free-swimming and closer to the surface.

Internal Anatomy and Physiology. Most amphipods are detritus feeders or scavengers. Mud or dead animal and plant remains are picked up with the gnathopods, or detritus is raked from the bottom with the antenna, particularly the second pair. Sometimes the mouthparts attack the food directly. The beach fleas feed on dead animal remains and seaweed washed up by the tide.

Figure 15-45. *Cerapus,* a tubicolous amphipod. The tube, which the animal can carry about, is composed of an inner secreted layer covered with fragments of foreign material. (Modified after Schmitt.)

Filter feeding is utilized by several amphipods. The calliopiids, *Aora, Corophium,* and others strain fine detritus through filter setae on the gnathopods, the feeding current being provided by the pleopods. *Corophium,* as well as species of *Maera* and *Eriopisa,* may dig up mud with the gnathopods and then filter it with the same appendages.

Other filter-feeding amphipods use the antennae or antennules as filters. Many gammarids, including the tube-dwelling *Haploops,* extend the antenna into the natural water current as a net. *Haploops* hangs upside down in the mouth of the tube, clinging to the rim with the legs (Fig. 15-46, *A*). The antennules are extended into the current as a trapping net and are periodically cleaned by the gnathopods. *Melphidippella,* which sits upside down on the bottom, uses not only the second pair of antennae as a filter but also uses the third and fourth pairs of thoracic appendages. All three limbs are held outstretched and catch falling detritus (Fig. 15-46, *B*). At intervals the limbs are scraped by the gnathopods.

A maxillary filter (second maxillae) is present in a few forms, such as *Haustorius arenarius.* In this species, the feeding current is produced by the maxillae and moves in the opposite direction (anteriorly) from the respiratory current.

Although some amphipods supplement their diet by catching small animals, strictly predacious feeding is not common. The most notable examples of predacious feeders include the caprellids, which feed on hydroid polyps, bryozoans, and other animals. Some species at-

tach to hydroids and to bryozoan stems with the last pair of thoracic appendages and project themselves motionless and outstretched, waiting to seize passing prey with the gnathopods. The hyperiid, *Parathemisto,* the most abundant pelagic amphipod genus in higher latitudes, seems to be highly predacious.

Parasitism is much less prevalent among amphipods than in isopods. The few parasitic forms include the cyamids, which are ectoparasites of whales, and a few ectoparasites of fish, such as *Lafystius* and *Trischizostoma.* The mouthparts are usually suctorial, and in the whale lice the legs are adapted for clinging to the host (Fig. 15-47).

The triturating stomach of the amphipods usually contains two armed lateral ridges and three setose ridges. The midgut is very capacious and usually gives rise to ceca.

The gills, which are thoracic in contrast to those of isopods, are usually simple lamellae or vesicles (Fig. 15-42). Occasionally, as in some gammarids and the whale lice, the surface area of the gills is increased by ridges, folds, or ramifications. The number of gills ranges from two to six pairs, but gills are never present on the first gnathopods. The talitrid beach fleas are unusual in having accessory gills on the first abdominal segments; in some gammarids and cyamids, the thoracic appendages bear accessory gills. Typically, the posteriorly flowing ventilating current is produced by the anterior pleopods. A ventilating current is particularly important in those amphipods that dwell in burrows or tubes; in a few tube-dwellers, the

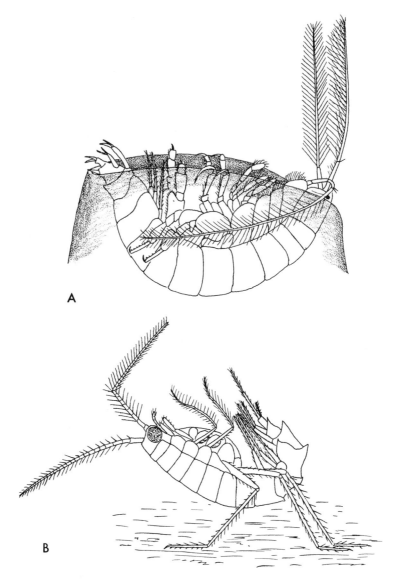

Figure 15-46.   *A. Haploops tubicola,* hanging on edge of tube in feeding position. Margin of tube is shaded but shown as transparent. *B. Melphidippella macra* in feeding stance. (Both after Enequist.)

antennae, rather than the pleopods, provide for ventilation.

Although they live out of water, the beach fleas have retained gills, although they are reduced in size and are poorly adapted for a terrestrial life. In order for beach fleas to respire, the air must be humid, and they are thus restricted to living in moist sand beneath drift or in other damp areas away from the sea. Some talitrids are common in forest litter on Pacific islands. Integumentary respiration is undoubtedly of considerable importance in these amphipods, for they can live for some time with the gills blocked.

The heart is tubular with one to three pairs of ostia and lies in the thorax. The arterial system is not as greatly developed as in the isopods. There is an anterior and posterior artery, but lateral arteries from the heart are present only in the Hyperiidea. The excretory organs are antennal glands.

In the least concentrated conformation (as in the Gammaridea), the ventral nerve cord contains eight pairs of thoracic and four pairs of abdominal ganglia, but fusion is frequently encountered in other groups. In the caprellids, for example, where the abdomen is vestigial, the abdominal ganglia are fused with the last pair of thoracic ganglia.

There are a few blind species, but sessile

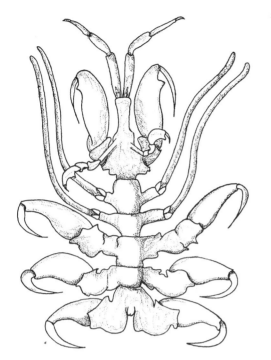

Figure 15-47. *Cyamus boopis,* an amphipod, ectoparasitic on whales. (After Green.)

compound eyes are typical in most amphipods. In the Hyperiidea, the eyes are enormous, covering most of the sides of the head. Many bathypelagic and other species in the Hyperiidea are peculiar in having each eye divided into an upper and lower portion, so that these animals have essentially double eyes. On the other hand, the eyes of the Oedicerotidae are fused together at the end of the rostrum. Except in the family Ampeliscidae and the genus *Phronima,* the eyes of amphipods are peculiar in lacking corneal facets.

Certain beach fleas, such as *Talitrus,* use the eyes to obtain astronomical clues for locating the high-tide zone, in which these amphipods normally live. If displaced either above or below the high-tide mark, the animals migrate accurately back to their normal zone. According to the studies of Pardi and others (1952, 1954, 1955), the angle of the sun is used as a compass in conjunction with a "knowledge" of the east-west orientation of the particular beach on which they live.

That the angle of the sun is a primary clue for orientation is proved by the fact that the direction of the movement of the animal can be controlled by reflecting the rays of the sun experimentally from different angles. An internal clock mechanism provides interpolation for the changing angle of the sun during the course of the day. This aspect of the mechanisms was proved by transporting *Talitrus* in the dark to a beach at different longitude. On liberation, the immigrants operated on the same time as that of the original location. In the absence of direct sunlight, these amphipods are reported to use sky polarization in the same manner.

Many amphipods are negatively phototropic and emerge to feed only at night. This is particularly true of the beach fleas and represents an adaptation for the prevention of desiccation.

Antennal statocysts are present in a few species.

The gonads are paired and tubular. The male gonopores open at the end of papillae on the sternum of the last thoracic segment, and the oviducts open on the fifth thoracic coxae. In species of *Gammarus* and some other genera, the males carry the female around on their back for days, separating briefly to permit the final preadult molt of the female. Actual sperm transfer is accomplished quickly. The male twists his abdomen around so that his uropods touch the female marsupium; when sperm are emitted, they are swept into the marsupium by the respiratory current of the female. The pair separate, and the eggs are immediately released into the brood chamber where fertilization takes place. One brood a year of 15 to 50 eggs is characteristic of most temperate fresh-water species. In marine forms, there may be 2 to 750 eggs in a clutch, and more than one brood per year is common. Development is direct in almost all amphipods.

Ecology. The preceding discussion has already indicated the diversity of habits and distribution of the marine amphipods. Fresh-water amphipods, of which about fifty species are known in the United States, are common animals in streams, ponds, and lakes and sometimes are found in great numbers. Pennak (1953) reports population densities for *Gammarus* of 10,000 per square meter in certain springs. Fresh-water species are not known to produce resting eggs, and perhaps they estivate in temporary ponds by burrowing into the bottom mud. A considerable number of species have been reported from cave pools and streams, and these are usually pale, blind, and provided with an abundance of sensory hairs.

Systematic Résumé of Order Amphipoda

Suborder Gammaridea. Head not fused with second thoracic segment. Maxilliped with a palp; thoracic legs with well developed coxal plates. Marine and fresh-water amphipods. *Gammarus; Maera; Eriopisa; Calliopius; Alicella;*

Melphidippidae; *Polycheria*. The semiterrestrial Talitridae (beach fleas) include *Talitrus, Orchestia, Talorchestia.* The Oedicerotidae; *Ampelisca; Haustorius; Corophium; Cyrtophium; Siphonectes; Chelura; Aora; Ampelisca; Haploops;* the parasites, *Lafystius* and *Trischizostoma*.

Suborder Hyperiidea. Head not fused with second thoracic segment. Maxillipeds have no palp; coxae often small or fused with body. Eyes usually very large, covering greater part of head. Entirely marine and pelagic. *Scina; Hyperia; Phronima; Rhabdosoma; Mimonectes.*

Suborder Caprellidea. Head fused with second thoracic segment. Abdominal segments fused, and reduced; has vestigial appendages. Includes the skeleton shrimp, Caprellidae; and the whale lice, Cyamidae.

Suborder Ingolfiellidea. Head not fused with second thoracic segment. Coxae are small. Abdominal segments are distinct, all but fourth and fifth pairs of abdominal appendages vestigial. *Ingolfiella.*

Superorder Eucarida

The Eucarida contains most of the larger malacostracans. The carapace is highly developed and fused with all of the thoracic segments. The eyes are stalked, and the basal section of the antenna is composed of only two segments. There is no thoracic brood chamber as in the peracaridans, and development is usually indirect, with a zoea larva. The Eucarida is composed of only two orders, the Euphausiacea and the Decapoda.

Order Euphausiacea

Euphausiaceans are pelagic shrimp-like crustaceans approximately one inch in length and are the most primitive eucaridans. They are all marine. The carapace does not tightly enclose the sides of the body, as is true of many decapods (Fig. 15-48, *A*). None of the thoracic appendages are specialized as maxillipeds, and each bears an exopodite (Fig. 15-48, *C*). The pleopods are well developed, have long setae, and are used for swimming. The telson bears a pair of movable spines.

Most euphausiaceans are filter feeders. The first six thoracic appendages compose the filtering apparatus. Each of the leg-like endopodites bears a long fringe of setae on one side, and together with the other limbs of that side they form one half of a funnel-shaped net or basket (Fig. 15-48, *A*). The feeding current passing through the net probably results from the forward swimming movement of the body. Many species, such as members of the genus *Euphausia*, trap microplankton; others consume zooplankton. *Meganyctiphanes*, which feeds on zooplankton possesses a maxillary filter in addition to the filtering net formed by the thoracic appendages. A few euphausiaceans, such as *Stylocheiron*, are predaceous, capturing arrowworms and other larger pelagic animals; the filtering apparatus is not developed, and the third pair of thoracic appendages are very long and chelate.

Large filamentous gills are present on all of the thoracic appendages, although poorly developed on the first (Fig. 15-48, *D*). The respiratory current is produced by the thoracic exopodites.

All but a single blind genus of euphausiaceans are luminescent. The light-producing material is not secreted, as in ostracods and other entomostracans, but is intracellular located within special light-producing organs called photophores. Each photophore is composed of a cluster of light-producing cells, a reflector, and a lens. A photophore is usually located on the upper end of the ocular peduncle, on the coxae of the seventh thoracic appendages, and one in the middle of each of the sternites of the first four abdominal segments (Fig. 15-48, *D*).

The sperm are transferred to the female as spermatophores, and the eggs may be liberated into the sea water when they are laid or they may be retained briefly within the filtering basket or attached to the undersurface of the sternum of the posterior thoracic segments. A nauplius larva represents the hatching stage. This is followed in succession by a calyptopis (protozoea), a furcilia (zoea), and a cyrtopia (postlarva) stage (Fig. 15-49).

The 90 some species composing the order Euphausiacea are strictly pelagic crustaceans. Such species as the antarctic *Euphausia superba*, which is about two inches in length and brilliant red, are surface forms; while others live at deeper levels or undergo vertical migrations. The bathypelagic genus, *Bentheuphausia*, lives at depths of 3000 to 5400 feet. Many members, including *Euphausia superba*, live in great swarms and constitute the chief food of many commercially important species of whales. Schmitt (1910) states that a moderate-sized blue whale may consume two to three tons of euphausiaceans at one feeding.

Order Decapoda

The order Decapoda contains the familiar shrimp, crayfish, lobsters, and crabs and includes the largest and some of the most highly

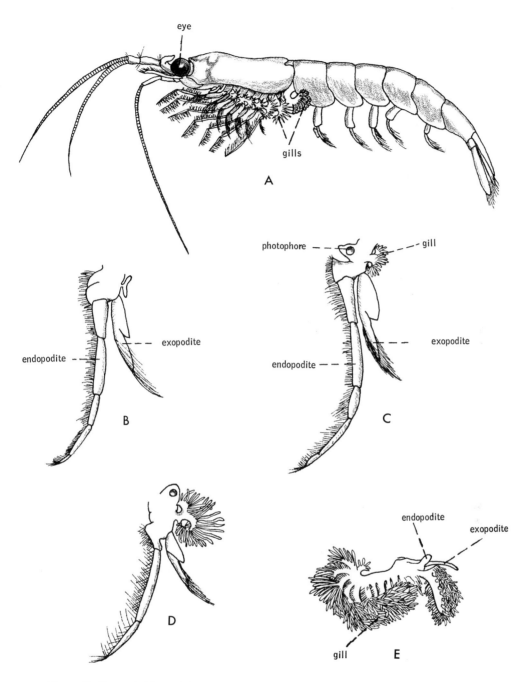

Figure 15-48.   *A. Meganyctiphanes,* a euphausiacean. *B* to *E.* Thoracic appendages of *Meganycti-phanes. B.* First. *C.* Second. *D.* Seventh. *E.* Eighth. (All after Calman.)

specialized crustaceans. It is also the largest order of crustaceans; the 8500 described decapods, represent almost one-third of the known species of crustaceans. Most of the decapods are marine, but the crayfish, some shrimp, a few anomurans, and a number of crabs have invaded fresh water. There are also some amphibious and terrestrial crabs.

Decapods are distinguished from the euphausiaceans, as well as from other malacostracans, in having the first three pairs of thoracic appendages modified as maxillipeds. The remaining five pairs of thoracic appendages are legs, from which the name Decapoda is derived (Fig. 15-50, *B*). The first pair of legs is often chelate and much heavier than the remaining pairs, and when so constructed, the limb is called a cheliped (Fig. 15-51). The head and

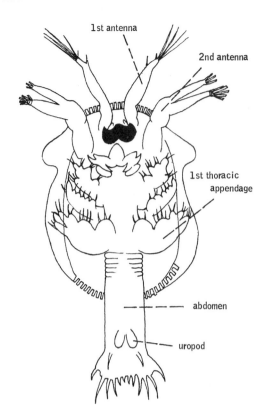

Figure 15-49.   Calyptopis (protozoea) larva of *Euphausia.*
(After Calman.)

heavier than those of natantians and never bear exopodites. The first pair of legs usually are powerful chelipeds. When pleopods are present, they are never especially adapted for swimming.

The abdomen of reptantians exhibits various degrees of reduction. In the section Macrura ("large tail"), which contains the lobsters and crayfish, the abdomen is well developed and bears the full complement of appendages, although they may be reduced. The carapace is always longer than broad and often bears a depressed rostrum.

The true crabs, which comprise the section Brachyura, have the abdomen greatly reduced and flexed beneath the cephalothorax, where it fits tightly within a shallow depression in the thoracic sternum (Fig. 15-51). The abdominal segments may all be distinct, but more commonly certain segments have fused together. The third, fourth, and fifth pairs of pleopods are absent in the male, and the first pair is usually lost in the female. The cephalothorax is as wide as, or wider than, its length, increasing the flattened appearance of the body. The rostrum is small or absent.

The section Anomura contains forms that are somewhat transitional between the Macrura and Brachyura. The last pair of legs is small and either covered by the sides of the carapace or directed dorsally. In the hermit crabs, the abdomen is not flexed beneath the cephalothorax but is modified to fit within the spiral chamber of gastropod shells (Fig. 15-52, *A*). The abdomen is asymmetrically developed, with a thin soft nonsegmented cuticle, and at least the appendages on the short side have been lost. Other anomurans look like true crabs in having the abdomen flexed beneath the thorax. However, the anomuran abdomen is not as greatly reduced or modified as the brachyuran abdomen, nor does it fit as tightly against the thoracic sternum.

Some of the anomuran crabs, such as the lithode crabs and the terrestrial coconut crab, *Birgus,* probably evolved from hermit crabs, because the abdomen exhibits certain asymmetrical features (Fig. 15-55, *B*). Other anomuran crabs, such as the porcelain crabs and the mole crabs, have a symmetrical abdomen and probably evolved directly from some ancestral macruran stock (Fig. 15-52, *B*). The Anomura is obviously a very artificial grouping, which is in need of radical revision.

All colors and combinations of colors are found in decapods. Many shrimp can adapt body coloration to the background. Also, the body surface and coloration of some decapods are especially adapted for certain habitats. The shrimp and crabs that live in *Sargassum* are colored olive yellow with mottling and spots, as

thoracic segments are fused together, and the sides of the overhanging carapace enclose the gills within well defined lateral branchial chambers (Figs. 15-61, *A* and 15-63, *A*). The respiratory current is produced by the beating of a paddle-shaped projection (the scaphognathite) of the second maxilla (Fig. 15-63, *D*).

The Decapoda is divided into two suborders—the Natantia, containing the shrimp; and the Reptantia, containing the lobsters, crayfish, and crabs. In the Natantia, the body is generally adapted for swimming (Natantia—"swimming"), and it tends to be laterally compressed with a well developed abdomen (Fig. 15-50). The cephalothorax bears a keel-shaped serrated rostrum and generally slender legs. The first two or three pairs of legs are chelate, and one of the chelate pairs may be longer and heavier than the others.

The legs of some primitive decapods bear exopodites (Fig. 15-50, *B*). The pleopods are large and fringed and are used for swimming.

The Reptantia are adapted for crawling (Reptantia—"crawling"), although some have become secondarily specialized for swimming. The body tends to be dorso-ventrally flattened to at least some degree. The legs are usually

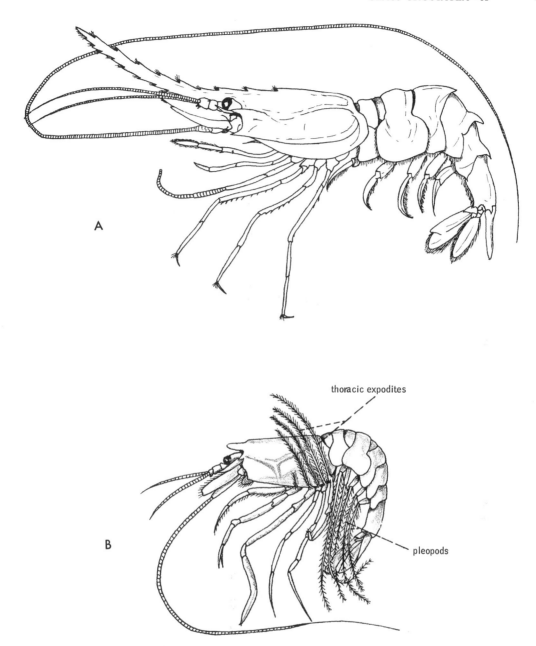

Figure 15-50.   Natantian decapods (shrimp). *A. Heterocarpus* (Caridea) *B. Psathyrocaris fragilis* (Caridea) with well developed thoracic exopodites. (Both after Alcock from Calman.)

is true of most other animals in this floating menagerie. The crab, *Parthenope investigatoris,* from the Indian Ocean has the body surface sculptured like a piece of old coral. Particularly remarkable are the brachyuran decorator crabs (Fig. 15-53). These are spider crabs that camouflage their hairy bodies and long slender legs by attaching pieces of seaweed, hydroids, bryozoans, and sponge to the carapace and legs.

The smallest decapods are species of the brachyuran crab, *Dissodactylus,* which are commensal on sand dollars. The cephalothorax of these species is only a few millimeters wide. *Macrocheira kaempferi,* a Japanese spider crab, is the largest living arthropod (Fig. 15-54). The cephalothorax may attain a length of fifteen inches and the chelipeds, a span of twelve feet.

Locomotion.   The pleopods are the principal swimming organs in shrimp, which include the relatively few truly swimming decapods. Most shrimp are bottom-dwellers and swim intermittently. The legs are used for swimming in some shrimp and in many crabs. Crabs of the pelagic family, Portunidae, which includes the

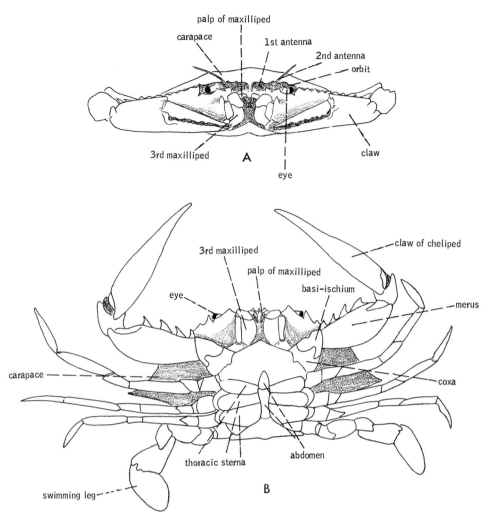

Figure 15-51. A brachyuran crab of the family Portunidae. The fifth pair of legs is adapted for swimming. *A.* Frontal view. *B.* Ventral view. (After Schmitt from Rathbun.)

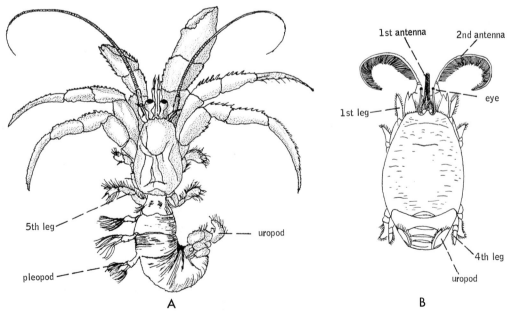

Figure 15-52. Anomuran crabs. *A.* The hermit crab, *Eupagurus bernhardus,* out of shell (dorsal view). (After Calman from Kaestner.) *B.* The mole crab, *Emerita talpoida* (dorsal view). (After Verrill, Smith, and Harger from Waterman and Chace.)

Figure 15-53. A decorator crab (spider crab), *Oregonia gracilis*, camouflaged with a covering of algae, hydroids, and bryozoans. (Modified after Schmitt.)

common edible blue crab, *Callinectes sapidus*, of the Atlantic coast, are the most powerful and agile swimmers of all crustaceans. The last pair of legs in members of this family each terminate in a broad flattened paddle (Fig. 15-51, *B*).

During swimming, the limb is extended laterally and somewhat above the level of the carapace and describes a figure eight in its movement. The action is essentially like that of a propeller, and the counterbeating fourth pair of legs act as stabilizers. Portunids can swim sideways, backward, and sometimes forward, with great rapidity; some species can even catch fish. Some of the other crabs are capable of swimming but usually not with the agility of the portunids. The amphibious woolly-handed crab, *Eriocheir*, can swim sideways, using a sort of dog-paddling motion by the walking legs (Fig. 15-55, *A*).

Sudden rapid escape movements in shrimp and macrurans are produced by the rapid flexing of the tail fan. This movement drives the animal backward, sometimes with such force that the animal jumps out of the water.

During walking and running, all five pairs of legs including the chelipeds may be used, as in the spiny lobster, *Panulirus*, and the crab, *Eriocheir;* or as few as two pairs may be used, as in many hermit crabs, which do not use the chelipeds for walking and have the last two pairs of legs modified and turned upward. Usually the anterior legs pull, and the posterior legs push. Forward, backward and lateral movements are variously developed in different decapods. Many crabs, both anomurans and brachyurans, have become highly specialized for walking and running sideways. In such a gait, the leading legs pull by flexing, and the trailing legs push by extending.

The ghost crabs, *Ocypode*, which live in burrows above the high-tide mark on sandy beaches and among dunes, are among the fastest running crabs, some species reaching speeds of better than 1.6 meters per second (Fig. 15-67). When running, the animal moves sideways; and at top speed, the body is raised well off the ground, and only two or three pairs of legs are used. In order to distribute the work load between the flexors and extensors on each side of the body when running rapidly, ghost crabs frequently turn the body 180 degrees without pausing and without changing direction. Such a turn reverses the leading and trailing sides of the body.

The decapods include some notable climbers. The woolly-handed crab, *Eriocheir*, and the coconut (or robber) crab, *Birgus*, which is a large terrestrial anomuran crab from the South Pacific, can both climb trees (Fig 15-55, *B*). *Birgus* has been reported to climb to the tops of palm and mangrove trees sixty feet high, using the sharp heavy ends of the legs like spikes. It descends backward.

Habitation. Many decapods burrow in sand and mud. The sand shrimp, *Crangon*, uses the beating pleopods for excavating and the mole crab, *Emerita*, which is a common burrowing anomuran living on open beaches, digs with its uropods (Fig. 15-52, *B*). In heavy surf, mole crabs are usually washed out with each wave, and while the wave is receding, they rapidly burrow backward in the soft sand until only the antennae are visible.

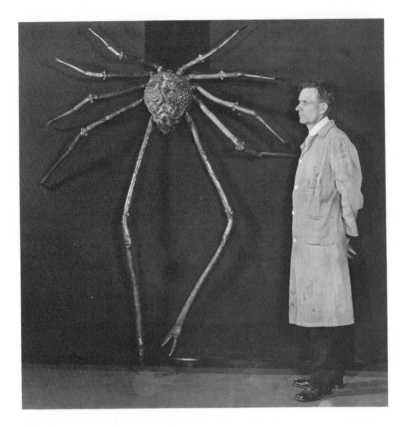

Figure 15-54. The Japanese spider crab, *Macrocheira kaempferi,* the largest living arthropod. (Courtesy of the American Museum of Natural History.)

Commonly legs are used for burrowing. Almost all of the terrestrial and amphibious crabs dig burrows. The depth of the burrow is usually determined by the level at which moist sand is encountered. Dune-inhabiting ghost crabs may burrow four feet down to reach moist sand. The fiddler crabs, *Uca,* are one of the most common amphibious crabs living along the North American coast (Fig. 15-56).

Some species inhabit protected sand beaches of bays and sounds; others can tolerate brackish water and burrow in the mud of marshes and estuaries. The burrows are located in the inter-tidal zone. At low tide, the crabs come out to feed, and enormous numbers may cover the surface of the beach.

The burrows of most species do not extend much deeper than one foot, and the excavated

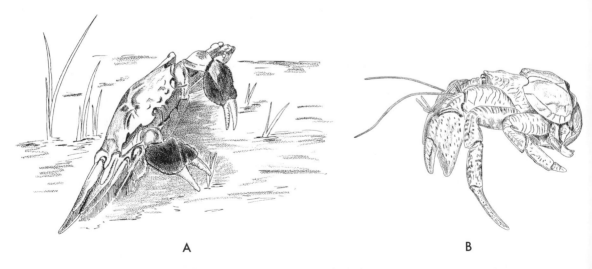

A   B

Figure 15-55. *A.* The woolly-handed crab, *Eriocheir sinensis,* in a rice paddy. This amphibious fresh-water brachyuran is native to southern Asia but has been introduced into the Rhine and Elbe rivers of Europe. *B.* The South Pacific robber (or coconut) crab, *Birgus latro.* (After Harm.)

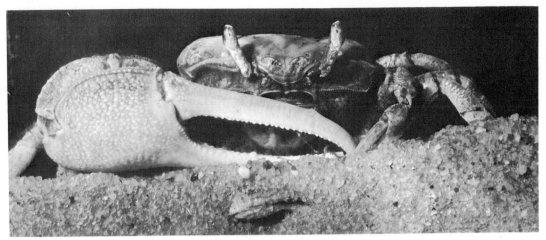

Figure 15-56.   Fiddler crabs, amphibious brachyurans. (Courtesy of American Museum of Natural History.)

sand is usually carried to the surface as small pellets or balls. The common Atlantic fiddler, *Uca pugilator,* carries the sand balls cradled in the second, third, and fourth legs of one side. On reaching the entrance to its burrow, the animal pushes the balls as much as one meter away. The west coast fiddler, *Uca crenulata,* carries its sand balls away from the entrance. As the incoming tide approaches the burrows, the crabs return and plug the entrance with sand or mud.

Many other decapods, including lobsters and crayfish, dig burrows or retreats. The macruran burrowing shrimp, *Callianassa* and *Upogebia,* spend their entire lives within tunnel-like burrows constructed in mud or sand near or below the low-tide mark. Digging is carried out using the first, second, and third legs, and the excavated material is carried to the surface with the third maxilliped in *Callianassa* and

with the large cheliped in *Upogebia.* Both construct two entrances to their burrows with enlarged chambers in which to turn around.

Not all retreats are excavated in mud and sand. The shrimp, *Alpheus pachychirus,* constructs tubes from the filamentous mats formed by certain algae (Fig. 15-58, *E*). Lying on its back, the shrimp pulls the mat around itself like a cloak and, using one of the slender pointed legs as a needle and the algal filaments as thread, stitches the edges of the mat together.

Natural retreats are used by many species. Rock and coral crevices are inhabited by many different species of shrimp, macrurans, and crabs. The anomurans are especially notable for using shells, skeletons, or even other animals for housing or covering. The hermit crabs are adapted for living in the shells of gastropods, and the soft naked crab abdomen is twisted to fit the spiral of the gastropod shell (Figs. 15-52,

Figure 15-57.   Hermit crabs. (Courtesy of the American Museum of Natural History.)

A and 15-57). The twist of the abdomen is adapted for right-handed spirals, although left-handed shells are sometimes used. The uropods are greatly modified, especially the left one, which is used for hooking to the columella of the shell. Usually one or both chelipeds are used to block the aperture of the shell when the crab is withdrawn.

Hermit crabs always use empty snail shells and never kill the original occupant. When the crab becomes too large for its shell, it seeks another, but normally does not leave the old shell until a suitable new shell has been found. Most species of hermit crabs inhabit the shells of many different gastropods.

Not all hermit crabs use gastropod shells for retreats. A Pacific coast species, *Pylopagurus minimus,* lives in *Dentalium* shells, and a species of *Pylocheles* from the Indian Ocean lives in sections of bamboo canes (Fig. 15-58, *A* and *B*). Another species of *Pylopagurus* lives within a mass of encrusting bryozoans. It is reported that this crab first inhabits a snail shell, which is supposedly dissolved after becoming covered with bryozoans. The hermit crab is also supposed to gradually dissolve the inner skeletal material of the bryozoan colony, and thus the crab is never forced to find a larger retreat.

The Dromiidae and the Dorippidae among the true crabs have developed certain habits that somewhat parallel those of hermit crabs. *Hypoconcha* and *Dorippe,* for example, cover themselves with one half of a pelecypod shell, and the carapace of these crabs has become modified to fit snugly into the concave inner surface of the shell. *Dromia* cuts out a cap of sponge with its chelipeds and fits the cap upon its back like an oversize beret (Fig. 15-58, *C* and *D*).

COMMENSALISM. Considering the tendency among so many crustaceans to build or seek protective retreats, it is not surprising that a great number have evolved commensal relationships with other animals. Some of these relationships have already been mentioned—the shrimp in glass sponges, the coral gall crabs and shrimp, and the crabs that inhabit the burrows or tubes of many polychaetes.

Most of the commensal crabs belong to the family Pinnotheridae, called pea crabs because of the small size of many of its species. In addition to inhabitants of polychaete tubes and burrows, there are species that live in the mantle cavity of pelecypods and snails, in the cloaca of sea cucumbers, in the tunnels of the burrowing shrimp, *Callianassa* and *Upogebia,* in the pharynx of tunicates, and in other animals. Often the body has become considerably modified for commensal existence. For example, the female of the oyster crab, *Pinnotheres ostreum,*

has a soft exoskeleton. The male of this species, which only visits the female, has normal chitinization.

Many of the smaller shrimp, particularly species of *Alpheus,* inhabit the water canals of sponges. A large sponge may become a veritable apartment house of shrimp.

Nutrition. The mouth of decapods is more or less ventral and flanked by the feeding appendages, which lie on top of one another (Figs. 15-59 and 15-61, *B*). The third maxillipeds are the outermost appendages and cover the other appendages. The mouthparts are framed above and anteriorly by a transverse plate (the epistome) and laterally by the sides of the carapace (Fig. 15-59). The arrangement of the mouthparts is particularly striking in crabs, in which the ends of the epistome have fused with the carapace and the third maxilliped is represented by two flattened rectangular plates (Fig. 15-51). These rectangular plates completely fill the usually square buccal frame, covering the inner mouth appendages like double doors.

Most of the decapods are predacious or predacious and scavengers. Any animal—fish, mollusks, other crustaceans—of a size that can be caught and handled are seized and killed by the chelate legs, particularly the chelipeds. The food is then passed to the third maxillipeds, which push it between the other mouthparts. While held by one of the mouth appendages, the food is cut and torn into pieces small enough to enter the mouth. Usually the mandibles serve as the chewing appendages; but sometimes they are used for holding and one of the other mouthparts is adapted for cutting.

Some predacious decapods have special modifications for capturing prey. The pistol, or snapping, shrimp, (Alpheidae) which are from one to two inches in length and live in natural or constructed burrows or retreats or live with other animals, have one of the chelipeds greatly enlarged. The base of the movable finger contains a large tuberculate process that fits into a socket on the immovable finger (Fig. 15-60). When the claw is opened, the movable finger is locked, or cocked, by a special mechanism. When released, the finger closes with great rapidity and force, producing a snapping or popping noise. The cheliped is used to stun prey.

Passing animals are detected by the antennae, which project from the burrow, and the shrimp then slowly creeps out upon the victim. Some pelagic peneid shrimp, such as species of *Sergestes,* have long antennae provided with hook-like setae. The antenna is used like a lash or a whip to catch prey.

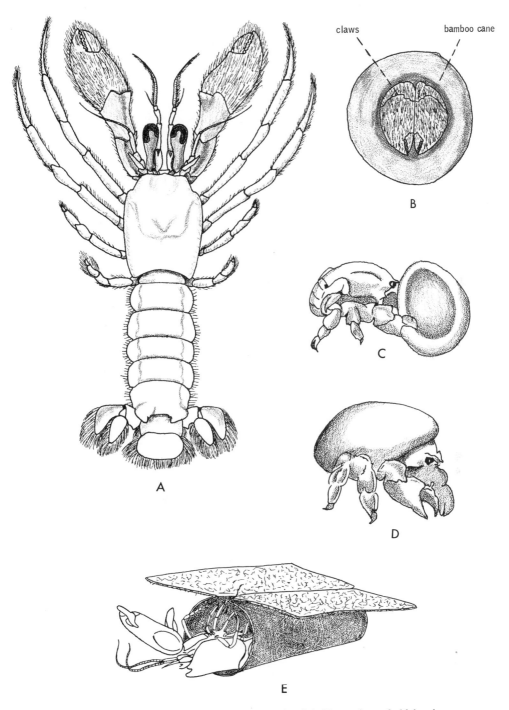

Figure 15-58.   *A. Pylocheles miersi,* an anomuran that inhabits sections of old bamboo canes (dorsal view). Note how little modified the abdomen of this anomuran is compared to those of typical hermit crabs (Fig. 15-52, *A*). *B. Pylocheles* in cane with claws blocking opening. (*A* and *B* after Alcock from Calman.) *C* and *D*. A dromiid crab putting sponge coat on its back. (After Dembowska from Schmitt.) *E.* The shrimp, *Alpheus pachychirus,* sewing together an algal mat. (After Cowles from Schmitt.)

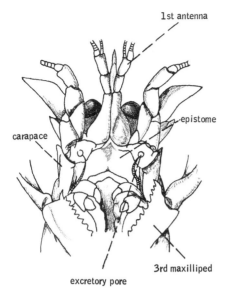

Figure 15-59.   Mouth region of *Nephrops*, a macruran. (After Calman.)

usually the source of food particles. The filtering appendages may be the anterior legs, the maxillipeds, or the antennules. Some species of the burrowing *Callianassa* and *Upogebia* create a current of water through the burrow with the pleopods and strain out plankton and detritus with fringed setae on the chelipeds and first legs. *Callianassa californiensis* digs up mud within its system of tunnels and strains it through the first two pairs of legs. The maxillipeds are used as combs for transferring the collected material to the other mouth appendages.

The maxillipeds are used as filtering appendages in many anomurans, in the commensal pea crabs, and in the fiddler crabs. In the pea crabs, *Polyonyx* and *Pinnixa,* which live in polychaete tubes, the endopodites of the maxillipeds are provided with filtering setae and are extended laterally or above the head like a net. The water current through the tube is provided by the host. A similar method of feeding is probably employed by many other members of this family, although some oyster crabs are known to feed on the mucus food strings collected by the host.

The fiddler crabs scoop up mud and detritus with the chelipeds or legs. The door-like third maxillipeds open, and the collected material is dumped into the buccal frame. Here the material is worked over and sifted, probably by brush and straining setae on the second and first maxillipeds. After organic material has been removed, the residue is spit out as round pellets, which may eventually surround the burrows, or cover the surface of the beach in forms that feed on detritus washed up by the receding tide.

Among the most interesting filter feeders are the mole crabs, *Emerita* (Fig. 15-52, *B*). The long densely fringed antennules project above

There is no sharp line between predatory forms and scavengers. Most predacious decapods feed on dead animal remains, in addition to catching living prey. Many species, especially anomurans, are omnivorous scavengers. This is true of the terrestrial coconut crab, *Birgus,* which feeds chiefly on carrion. While it will eat the meat of a ruptured coconut, it cannot husk and break them, nor is its tree-climbing ability used to obtain coconuts. Hermit crabs that are scavengers, as well as some other decapods with this type of feeding habit, use the third maxillipeds as scrapers to remove algae from rocks or to pick up and tear food.

Filter feeding takes place in many decapods, but detritus rather than plankton is

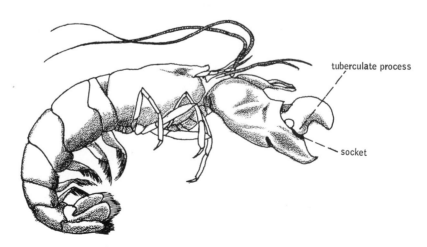

Figure 15-60.   A pistol (or snapping) shrimp, *Alpheus.* (After Schmitt.)

the sand surface after the crabs are buried. In species that inhabit open beaches, such as *Emerita talpoida,* the antennules filter plankton and detritus from the wave current; in species that live in quieter water, the projecting antennules are moved about.

In the typical decapod digestive tract a short esophagus leads into a large capacious cardiac stomach (Fig. 15-61, *B*). This stomach

is separated by a constriction from a much smaller and more ventral pyloric stomach, which lies in the posterior half of the thoracic region. A long intestine extends from the pyloric stomach through the abdomen and opens to the exterior on the ventral side of the telson. The esophagus, cardiac stomach, and the anterior half of the pyloric stomach are derived from the foregut and are lined with

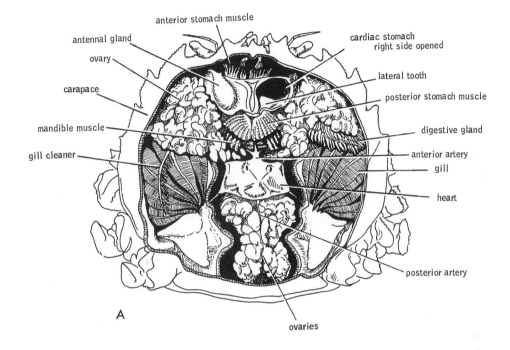

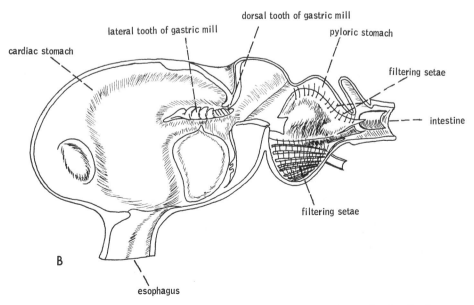

Figure 15-61.   *A.* The brachyuran crab, *Eriocheir sinensis* (dorsal dissection). (After Panning from Kaestner.) *B.* Stomach of the crayfish, *Astacus* (lateral view). (After Kaestner.)

chitin. The midgut may be extremely short, as in crayfish and crabs, when it is limited to the posterior half of the pyloric stomach. On the other hand, in the lobster, *Homarus,* and the snapping shrimp, *Alpheus,* all but the terminal portion of the intestine, lying in the last abdominal segment, is a part of the midgut.

One to several ceca arise from the midgut in most decapods. In the crayfish there is a very small single dorsal cecum pressed closely against the pyloric stomach. In lobsters there is also a dorsal midgut cecum, but it is located in the sixth abdominal segment near the junction with the hindgut. In most crabs there are two very long ceca that run anteriorly and laterally from their origin just behind the pyloric stomach.

The cardiac and pyloric stomachs contain a gastric mill in all decapods, but the degree of development varies. The mill is least developed in the Natantia, in which the mandibles and other mouthparts perform a relatively efficient job of chewing before the food reaches the cardiac stomach. The greatest development of the gastric mill is found in macrurans and crabs, in which food is poorly chewed but more quickly consumed. In crayfish, for example, food reaches the cardiac stomach in the form of long kneaded strands (Fig. 15-61, *B*).

According to Calman (1909) and Reddy (1935), the most primitive form of the gastric mill is found in the peneid shrimp, *Cerataspis monstrosa.* At the junction of the cardiac and pyloric stomachs, the roof of the cavity bears a heavy tooth. A pair of lateral ridges run the length of the cardiac stomach, and above and parallel to each lateral ridge is a row of denticles. The lateral ridges are not calcified, nor does the median dorsal tooth rest on a distinct calcified plate.

Limited trituration takes place from the action of the dorsal tooth moving against the lateral ridges and denticles. The lumen of the pyloric region is greatly reduced by a ventral fold, which is covered with setae and acts as a straining device to permit only the finest particles and fluid to enter the ducts of the digestive glands.

In most other decapods, including other natantians, the walls of the cardiac stomach and the anterior half of the pyloric stomach have been greatly strengthened with the development of a large number of sclerites, especially dorsally and laterally. Also there has developed a complex muscular system, which controls the movement of the stomach walls. Some of these muscles lie within the stomach wall; others run from the body wall to the stomach.

Among the natantians, the Caridea have lost the dorsal sclerite and tooth, while the Penaeidea have retained the general plan of *Cerataspis,* although the gastric mill is strengthened and more complex. The highly specialized gastric mill of the Reptantia probably evolved from that of the peneids. Crayfish, lobsters, and most crabs each have a very similar gastric mill (Fig. 15-61, *B*). It is composed of three large opposing teeth, one dorsal and two lateral. The dorsal tooth is probably homologous to the dorsal tooth of *Cerataspis,* and the two lateral teeth have probably developed from an original lateral row of denticles. The triturating action of the gastric armature plus the enzymatic action of the digestive secretion passed forward from the hepatopancreas reduces food in the cardiac stomach to a very fine consistency.

The lumen of the pyloric stomach is greatly reduced by the complex folded walls. Setae on the folds form a filtering system, with definite channels leading to the two ducts of the hepatopancreas and the intestine. The channels conducting material to the duct openings begin behind the esophagus as a single median ventral groove on the cardiac stomach floor. Prior to reaching the cardiac-pyloric junction the channel divides into a right and a left pathway.

Within the pyloric stomach each channel division passes through a gland filter provided with extremely fine setae. The gland filter appears externally as a small swelling on each side of the pyloric stomach. Only the smallest particles and fluid are permitted to enter the ducts, larger particles being directed to the intestine or hindgut. The walls of the pyloric stomach are also strengthened with plates, and a system of muscles controls the size of the channels and aids in squeezing material through the filters.

The hepatopancreas of decapods is usually a very large and compact paired mass that fills much of the cephalothoracic region. The pagurid hermit crabs are peculiar in having the digestive gland located in the abdomen. With few exceptions, each gland opens by a single duct into the sides of the midgut end of the pyloric stomach.

Respiration. Primitively, there are four gills on each side of every thoracic segment. One gill, called a pleurobranch, arises from the body wall above the point of attachment of the appendage. Two gills, called arthrobranchs, are attached to the articulating membrane between the appendage and the body wall; and one gill, called a podobranch, arises from the coxa of the appendage and represents a modification of part of the epipodite. The remainder of the epipodite extends between the gills as a supporting lamella, called a mastigobranch, an unfortunate term for it is not actually a gill.

If all of the gill series were present on

all segments, there would be a total of 32 gills on each side of the body, but no decapod has retained this maximum number. The peneid shrimp, *Benthesicymus,* with 24, has the greatest number, but reduction to far less than this is the general rule. A few examples serve to illustrate the great variation in branchial formulae. The snapping shrimp, *Alpheus,* with a total of six gills on each side, has one arthrobranch on the third segment (maxilliped), and one pleurobranch on each of the leg segments.

The lobster, *Homarus,* has a complement of 20 gills on each side of the body, distributed as follows: a podobranch on the second and third maxillipeds and the first four pairs of legs; two arthrobranchs on the third maxilliped and the first four pairs of legs; and a pleurobranch on the last four pairs of legs. The branchial formula of many crayfish is similar to *Homarus,* except that most of the pleurobranchs tend to be vestigial or absent. The swimming crab, *Callinectes,* has eight gills to a side—a podobranch on the second maxilliped; one arthrobranch on the second maxilliped and two on the third maxilliped and cheliped; and a pleurobranch on the second and third pairs of legs. Finally, the little pea crab, *Pinnotheres,* has only three gills to a side—one arthrobranch on the third maxilliped and two arthrobranchs on the chelipeds. In all decapods, the gills of the first maxillipeds are vestigial or absent.

Three types of gill structure are found in decapods, the particular type being characteristic of all gills of a species regardless of the gill position. The gill is composed of a central axis along which are arranged lateral extensions or branches. In the peneid shrimp, the axis bears biserially arranged main branches that are in turn sub-branched. This type of gill is said to be dendrobranchiate or dendritic (Fig. 15-62, *A* and *B*). The caridean shrimp and most anomurans and brachyurans have phyllobranchiate (lamellar) gills. In this type the gill axis bears flattened plate-like branches, which are usually arranged in two series along the axis (Fig. 15-62, *E* and *F*). The third type of gill is called trichobranchiate (filamentous) and is typical of most macrurans, a few genera of anomurans, and certain primitive dromiid crabs (Fig. 15-62, *C* and *D*). The branches are filamentous but not sub-branched, and there are several series along the axis.

In the axis of each gill runs an afferent and efferent branchial channel (Fig. 15-62, *A*). From the afferent channel blood flows into each filament or lamella and then back into the efferent channel. Studies on the filamentous gills of *Upogebia* have disclosed that a longitudinal partition in each filament divides it into two chan-

nels. One channel conducts blood to the tip of the filament. The other channel conducts it back and thence into the outflowing channel of another filament at the same level, until the blood eventually reaches the efferent axial channel. In the brachyurans, blood flows through the lamellae within a fine sinus network.

The blood of decapods contains hemocyanin for oxygen transport. The pigment is always dissolved in the blood plasma and never is found in the tissues, as is frequently the case with hemoglobin in many entomostracans.

The respiratory current is produced by the beating of the scaphognathite, or gill bailer, of the second maxilla (Fig. 15-63, *D*). Water is pulled forward and the exhalant current flows out anteriorly in front of the head. In the Natantia, the ventral margins of the carapace fit loosely against the sides of the body, and water can enter the branchial chamber at any point along the posterior and ventral edges of the carapace (Fig. 15-63, *A*).

The macruran carapace is applied somewhat more tightly, and the entrance of water is limited to the posterior carapace margins and around the bases of the legs (Fig. 15-63, *B*). The point of entrance of the respiratory stream is even more restricted in the brachyurans, in which the margins of the carapace fit very tightly against ventro-lateral body wall and the inhalant opening is located around the bases of the chelipeds (Fig. 15-63, *C*). The forward position of the inhalant openings in brachyurans results in water taking a U-shaped course through the gill chambers. On entering the inhalant opening, the water passes posteriorly into the hypobranchial part of the chamber, and then moves dorsally, passing between the gill lamellae. The exhalant current flows anteriorly in the upper part of the gill chamber and issues from paired openings in the upper lateral corners of the buccal frame.

Since the majority of reptantians are bottom-dwellers and include many burrowers, a variety of different mechanisms have evolved to prevent clogging of the gills with silt and debris. The bases of the chelipeds in crabs and the coxae of the legs of crayfish and lobsters bear setae that filter the incurrent stream. The gills are cleaned in crabs by the fringed epipodites of the three pairs of maxillipeds. These processes are elongated, especially that of the first maxilliped, and they sweep up and down the surface of the gills, removing detritus. As a further aid to the cleaning of the gills and branchial chamber, the gill bailer may periodically reverse its beat and thus reverse the direction of flow through the chamber.

In burrowing species, when the ventral parts of the body are covered by mud and sand,

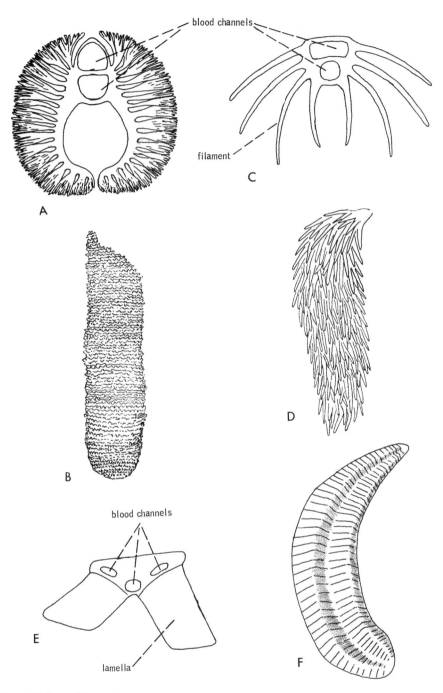

Figure 15-62.   Decapod gills. *A* and *B*. Dendrobranchiate gill of the shrimp, *Penaeus*. *A*. Transverse section. *B*. Entire gill. *C* and *D*. Trichobranchiate gill of the crayfish, *Astacus*. *C*. Transverse section. *D*. Entire gill. *E* and *F*. Phyllobranchiate gill of shrimp, *Palaemon*. This gill type is also characteristic of most anomurans and brachyurans. *E*. Transverse section. *F*. Entire gill. (All after Calman.)

a reversed current is used for respiratory purposes; when the body is free, a forward current is used. A further respiratory adaptation in many burrowing decapods is the development of inhalant siphons. For example, in some species of mole crabs and in certain shrimp, the antennules are held together, forming an inhalant passageway between them. The same thing is done with the antennal scales in the shrimp, *Metapenaeus,* and with the antennae in the burrowing crab, *Corystes cassivelaunus* (Fig. 15-64). The large box crabs of the genus *Calappa,* which

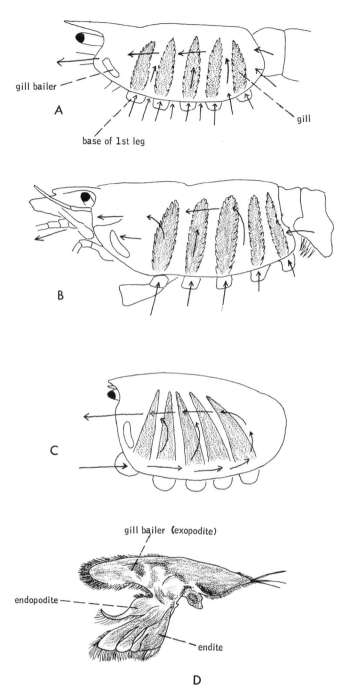

Figure 15-63.   *A* to *C*. Paths of water circulation through gill chamber of three decapods, showing progressive restriction of openings into chamber. *A*. Shrimp. Water enters along entire ventral and posterior margin of carapace. *B*. Crayfish. Water enters at bases of legs and at posterior carapace margin. *C*. Crab. Water enters only at base of cheliped. *D*. Second maxilla of the crayfish, *Astacus*, showing gill bailer (exopodite). (After Huxley from Kaestner.)

are sluggish bottom inhabitants, have greatly flattened chelipeds, which when folded fit tightly against the face but leave an inhalant channel between the inner side of the cheliped and the carapace.

A number of groups of crabs have evolved amphibious or terrestrial habits. Members of the brachyuran family, Ocypodidae, contain some of the most familiar amphibious crabs. This family includes *Dotilla* and the fiddler crabs, *Uca,* both of which are intertidal, and the ghost crabs, *Ocypode,* which are found at the high-tide

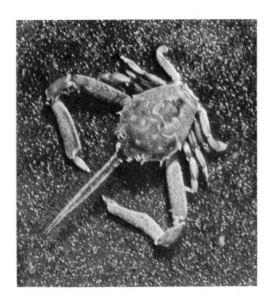

Figure 15-64.   The masked crab, *Corystes cassivelaunus.* Antennae form an inhalant tube when animal is buried. (By D. P. Wilson.)

mark or above. The Grapsidae also includes many amphibious brachyurans, such as *Sesarma,* which lives beneath drift at the high-tide mark, *Grapsus, Pachygrapsus,* and the woolly-handed crab, *Eriocheir,* which lives in the ditches and rice paddies of the Orient (Fig. 15-55, *A*).

There are two families of terrestrial crabs, as well as some terrestrial genera of grapsid crabs. All are tropical and migrate to the water only to breed. The anomuran family, Coenobitidae, contains the hermit crab, *Coenobita,* and the coconut crab, *Birgus,* which is perhaps the best adapted of all crustaceans for a terrestrial existence (Fig. 15-55, *B*). The brachyuran family, Gecarcinidae, is found in tropical America, West Africa, and the Indo-Pacific area and includes *Cardisoma,* which lives in fields and woods in the West Indies, and *Gecarcinus,* which inhabits forests along the coast of Africa and Central America. *Geograpsus* is the principal terrestrial genus among the Grapsidae.

Most amphibious species are periodically immersed in water, and the branchial chamber remains partially filled with water when the crab is on land. The water remaining within the chamber is aerated by the vibrations of the gill bailer. In *Ocypode* and *Uca,* air enters the branchial chambers through special posterior openings between the third and fourth legs, and the usual anterior inhalant openings in aquatic crabs are used for exhaling air in these genera. These same openings may also be used for replacing water lost from the gill chambers.

Some amphibious genera, such as *Sesarma*

and *Eriocheir,* aerate the water remaining in the branchial cavity externally. The scaphognathite drives the water out of the exhalant openings, and it flows back over the surface of the body in special sculptured channels, being aerated in the process. The water then re-enters the branchial chambers through the openings between the third and fourth legs or near the first legs.

The terrestrial crabs usually live in burrows and are commonly nocturnal. Water is not carried in the branchial chamber, but the gills are retained although they are usually modified. In the anomuran land crabs, the gills are reduced, and the walls of the branchial chambers contain highly vascular areas for respiratory exchange. The vascular surface is on the floor of the chamber in *Coenobita;* in *Birgus* highly vascularized epithelial folds, or appendages, hang from the roof of the branchial chamber. *Coenobita* is also provided with an accessory vascularized respiratory area on the anterodorsal surface of the abdomen.

The gecarcinid and grapsid land crabs have retained the gills for respiratory exchange. The lamellae are more rigid and held apart by various structures to permit the circulation of air between them. Usually there is also a supplementary respiratory surface formed by the development of a capillary network in the median wall of the branchial chamber. The movement of air through the respiratory chamber is usually maintained by the beating of the scaphognathite and ventilation is also facilitated by the raising and lowering of the carapace margins. The path of air entering and leaving the chamber is the same as in the amphibious crabs.

It should be noted that the conversion of the gill chamber into a lung in land crabs has taken place in a manner strikingly parallel to that in the gastropod mollusks.

The ghost crabs, *Ocypode,* are in many respects transitory between an amphibious and a truly terrestrial habit. As in other amphibious crabs, water is carried in the branchial chambers, but some species have vascularized areas in the branchial walls for supplementary respiratory exchange.

Circulation.   The heart is a coffin-shaped vesicle located in the thorax and is provided with three pairs of ostia, one ostium at each lateral angle of the heart and one dorsal pair (Fig. 15-3, *C*); or in crabs, there are one lateral pair and two dorsal pairs.

Five arteries leave the heart anteriorly—an anterior median (opthalmic) artery, a pair of lateral cephalic (antennary) arteries, and a pair of hepatic arteries. A median abdominal artery leaves the heart posteriorly, and a sternal artery

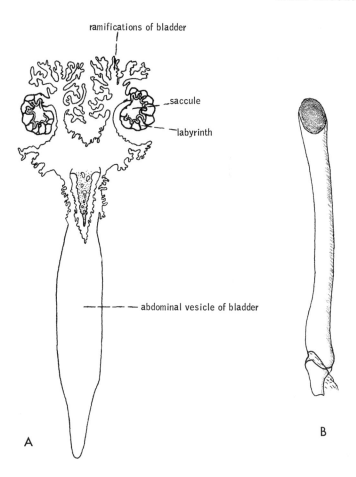

ramifications of bladder

saccule

labyrinth

abdominal vesicle of bladder

A

B

Figure 15-65. *A.* Excretory system of the hermit crab, *Eupagurus* (dorsal view). (After Marchal from Calman.) *B.* Eye of the crab, *Macrophthalmus,* with a long peduncle. (After Calman.)

arises either from the underside of the heart or from the base of the abdominal artery. The sternal artery descends to the sternum passing to one side of the gut and piercing the nerve cord. It then divides into an anterior and a posterior subneural artery. Each of these major arteries branches extensively, supplying various organs and structures.

Around the brain and the region of the ventral nerve cord, the smaller arteries branch into a capillary network before passing into the tissue sinuses. Blood eventually drains into a large median sternal sinus prior to passing through the gills and returning to the heart. Complete circulation has been estimated to take from 40 to 60 seconds in large decapods.

Excretion. Antennal (or green) glands are the excretory organs of decapods and reach their highest degree of development in this group. The end sac, which lies in front of and to both sides of the esophagus, is typically divided into a saccule and a labyrinth. The labyrinth walls are greatly folded and glandular,

converting the original vesicle into a spongy mass. The saccule may be a single vesicle, or its interior may also be partitioned. The labyrinth leads into a bladder by way of an excretory tubule.

The decapod bladder varies in complexity. It may either be a simple vesicle or may give rise to many diverticula. In brachyurans, the bladder is composed of three main divisions, one of which is quite large and is folded back over the stomach. In some caridean shrimp, similar diverticula from each side unite to form a single median lobe over the stomach. In the pagurid hermit crabs the ramifications of the bladder form an extremely complex network of tubules extending through much of the thorax; a paired or simple diverticulum runs the length of the abdomen (Fig. 15-65, *A*). From the bladder a short duct extends into the basal segment of the second antenna, where it opens to the outside on the summit of a little papilla (Fig. 15-59). In brachyurans the excretory pore is covered by a little movable operculum.

Strictly fresh-water decapods—that is, forms that complete the entire life cycle in fresh water —include the crayfish, the South American anomuran *Aegla*, a few shrimp (species of *Palaemonetes*), and some crabs. The crabs are represented by the family Potamonidae, which is found throughout the subtropical and tropical regions of the world (*Potamon edulis* is found in the rivers of Italy, Greece, and North Africa), and by a few grapsids. The little Jamaican grapsid, *Metopopaulias,* is found only in the water contained within bromeliads.

There are many decapods, especially crabs, that can tolerate either very brackish or fresh water, but must return to salt water to breed. In this category belongs the woolly-handed crab, *Eriocheir,* which is found in the rivers and rice paddies of Asia and has been introduced into the rivers of Europe, probably by ship ballast. Another is the brachyuran, *Rhithropanopeus,* of America, which is found in salt water as well as in fresh-water ditches. Many species of *Uca* live in very brackish estuaries and marshes. *Callinectes sapidus* is quite euryhaline and ranges far up into brackish estuaries and bays.

The crayfish are the only group among all of these brackish-water and fresh-water decapods in which the antennal gland is known to play a role in osmoregulation. The crayfish excretes a urine hyposmotic to its blood, as compared to the isosmotic urine produced by the fresh-water crabs, *Potamon* and *Eriocheir.* Ionic regulation in fresh-water and euryhaline crabs is apparently maintained by the gills, which actively absorb salt from the aqueous environment.

Nervous System and Sense Organs. Lobsters and crayfish possess the largest number of unfused ventral ganglia; only the first two thoracic ganglia are fused with the subesophageal, leaving five unfused thoracic and six abdominal ganglia. The ventral ganglia, in other groups, show varying degrees of additional fusion, culminating in the brachyurans, in which all of the abdominal ganglia have migrated anteriorly to fuse with the thoracic ganglia, forming a single ventral mass.

A well developed visceral nervous system is present in decapods. A single posterior cerebral nerve and a pair of nerves from the esophageal commissures provide the stomach walls with a nerve plexus. The heart is innervated by a local system, as well as by regulator fibers from the central system. The cell bodies of the local system are concentrated in a cardiac ganglion in the dorsal heart wall. The regulator nerves consist of a single pair of inhibitory fibers arising from the subesophageal ganglion, and two pairs of excitatory fibers arising a little more poste-

riorly along the ventral cord. All three fibers on each side unite as a single nerve before entering the heart wall and joining the cardiac ganglion.

Although there are some blind decapods, particularly among deep-sea forms and cave-dwelling crayfish, compound eyes are usually highly developed. The ocular peduncle is composed of two or rarely three segments and is much more mobile than in most other crustaceans. In some crabs, one of the peduncular segments is greatly lengthened, placing the eyes at the end of extremely long stalks (Fig. 15-65, *B*). The corneal surface is usually terminal, but this is not always the case. In some crabs, such as some species of *Ocypode*, the peduncle extends beyond the corneal surface, which is wrapped around the stalk.

The carapace is commonly modified in the region of the eyes. In shrimp and macrurans, the carapace is frequently notched above the eye. The snapping shrimp are peculiar in that the anterior margin of the carapace has grown down and completely enclosed the eyes; however, the covering is probably thin enough to permit light perception. In brachyurans, there are transverse orbits in which the eyes rest when not erected.

A pair of statocysts is present in nearly all decapods and is located in the basal segment of the antennules. The sac is always open to the exterior, although in crabs and some others the opening is reduced to a slit and is functionally closed. The statolith is composed of fine sand grains bound together by secretions from the statocyst wall (Fig. 15-66). Since the statocyst is an ectodermal invagination, its lining along with the statolith is shed at each molt. The statoliths are replaced when the head is buried in sand, or the animal actually inserts sand grains into the sac. Along the the floor of the sac are a number of rows of sensory hairs with which the statolith is directly connected or is in intermittent contact. The hairs arise from receptor cells in the sac wall, and the receptor cells are innervated by a branch of the antennular nerve.

The function of decapod statocysts has been elucidated in considerable detail by the studies of Schöne (1951) and Cohen (1955, 1961). Continual impulses from the receptor cells of one statocyst, independent of the statolith pull, tend to cause the animal to rotate or list to the opposite side. However, since the tendency initiated by one statocyst counteracts the other, rotation does not occur except when one statocyst is injured or removed.

When the animal is in a normal horizontal position, the floor of the statocyst is inclined about 30 degrees, which results in a medial

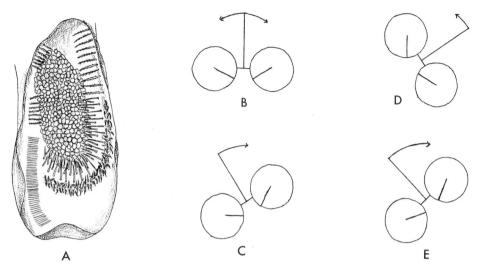

Figure 15-66.   *A.* Statocyst of the American lobster, *Homarus americanus* (with dorsal wall removed). Note the four crescent-shaped rows of sensory hairs; the inner three are in contact with the statolith. The row of long, delicate hairs (lower left) are thread hairs. The opening of the statocyst to the exterior is at upper left beyond the edge of the illustration. (After Cohen from Cohen, and Dijkgraaf.) *B* to *E.* Statocyst function. Circle represents statocyst chamber with floor inclined 30 degrees (bar). *B.* Counterbalancing pull exhibited by two statocysts when animal is in normal horizontal position. *C.* Animal rotated 30 degrees to right, placing floor of right statocyst in horizontal position and inclining left statocyst floor 60 degrees. Impulses initiated by left statocyst cause animal to rotate back to left (arrow). *D.* Animal rotated to left so floor of right statocyst is inclined 90 degrees, initiating impulses that cause animal to rotate back to the right. *E.* Animal rotated to right. The more inclined position of the left statocyst floor causes it to dominate the right statocyst, and the animal rotates back to the left. (*B* to *E* greatly modified from Schöne.)

gravitational pull on the statolith. This pull stimulates the receptor cells to initiate additional impulses causing the animal to rotate, but again one statocyst counterbalances the other (Fig. 15-66; *B*). If the animal is rotated or lists 30 degrees to the right side, this places the floor of the right statocyst in a horizontal position, and the statolith exerts no pull on the statolith hairs. However, the floor of the left statocyst is now inclined 60 degrees and the impulses initiated by its receptor cells cause the animal to rotate in the opposite direction—that is, back to a horizontal position (Fig. 15-66, *C*). Stimulation of the receptor cells by the statolith is maximum when the floor of the statocyst is vertical, or tilted 90 degrees (Fig. 15-66, *D*). When the floors of both statocysts are tilted, the one in which the receptor cells are most stimulated dominates the other (Fig. 15-66, *E*).

The statocysts of most shrimp, as well as many Reptantia, are simple sacs. More complex statocysts are found in crabs and in some macrurans and anomurans. The statocyst invagination in crabs is deep and irregular and may contain a labyrinth compartment, as well as a statocyst chamber. In forms with such complex statocysts, these organs not only indicate the gravitational position of the animal, but also its position in regard to movement. The rotation receptors give rise to special free sensory hairs, which are not associated with the statolith and are stimulated by the motion of the fluid within the statocyst chamber when the animal moves (Fig. 15-66, *A*). The mechanism is thus strikingly like that of the semicircular canals in vertebrates.

Quite a few decapods possess special structures for producing sound, but none are known to be able to hear in the sense of possessing special receptors for the detection of air- or water-borne pressure waves. A few species apparently can detect pressure waves through the general tactile receptors, and probably all can detect vibrations through the substratum.

Stridulation, in which one part of the body is rubbed against another, is the most common mechanism for sound production. The ghost crabs, *Ocypode,* produce a filing, creaking, or buzzing sound by rubbing a ridge of tubercles on the inner side of one hand against a process on the second segment of the same appendage (Fig. 15-67). The noise apparently serves to warn other individuals against entering its burrow. At least some species of *Uca* also stridulate when another crab enters its burrow. The noise produced by species of spiny lobsters, *Panulirus,* has been likened to the filing of a saw or the creaking of leather. The sound is created by the rubbing of a pad at the base of the antennae against a similar area on the rostrum.

The popping sound produced by snapping shrimp is very audible and easily detected on a rocky breakwater at low tides. The mechanism has already been described in connection with feeding, but apparently the claw is also "shot" to frighten away intruders.

Luminescence. Seventeen genera of shrimp contain species known to be luminescent. The luminescent organs are most commonly photophores and may arise anywhere on the body, even the roof of the branchial chamber (as in *Sergestes*). Among the best known luminescent species are those belonging to the genus *Sergestes,* one of which, *Sergestes challengeri,* possesses 150 light organs. Many species of this genus have a peculiar type of internal photophore formed from modified cells of the tubules of the digestive glands. Some luminescent shrimp secrete a luminous secretion into the water from glands on the mandibles.

Reproduction and Development. The paired testes lie primarily in the thorax but may extend posteriorly into the anterior portion of the abdomen. In the pagurid hermit crabs, the testes are entirely abdominal, and both are located on the left side. In most decapods, each testis is provided with numerous diverticula, and it is usually connected with the opposite member. The sperm are always transmitted in the form of spermatophores, and the more distal portion of the sperm duct is glandular and modified for spermatophore formation. The terminal end of the sperm duct is a muscular ejaculatory duct, which opens onto the coxa or the articulating membrane between the coxa and sternum. There is a single tubular penis in some

hermit crabs and a pair in all brachyurans. In brachyurans the penes fit in grooves on the first pair of pleopods.

The ovaries are similar in structure and location to the testis and in hermit crabs are also entirely abdominal (Fig. 15-61, *A*). The oviducts are usually unmodified and open onto the coxae. In brachyurans, however, the terminal end of each oviduct is modified as a glandular seminal receptacle and vagina for the reception of the male penis. A median seminal receptacle, opening separately to the outside, occurs in most other decapods and is in the form of a ventral pouch created by processes of the last one or two thoracic sternites.

Considerable sexual dimorphism is present in many species of decapods. It is particularly striking in fiddler crabs, for example, in which one claw of the male is very large, in contrast to the two small claws of the female. These crabs go through an elaborate courtship behavior, during which the male waves or signals with his large claw like a semaphore. Each species follows a distinct pattern of movement. In the more complicated rituals, courtship may also involve curtsies and a rapping on the ground with the large claw. At the end of the courtship ritual, the male attempts to seize and copulate with the female or, as in *Uca pugilator* and *U. annulipes,* the male entices the female into his burrow. Courtship is also known in some other species of crabs. For example, males of the blue crab, *Callinectes sapidus,* dance from side to side with outstretched claws in front of the female.

During copulation in crabs, the female lies beneath the male, ventral surfaces opposing each other. The first pair of pleopods, containing the penes, is inserted into the openings of the female. The sperm are emitted as spermatophores, which, at least in *Callinectes,*

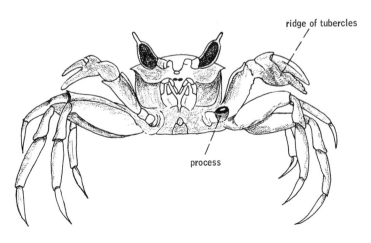

ridge of tubercles

process

Figure 15-67. A ghost crab, *Ocypode,* showing sound-producing mechanism. (After Schmitt.)

break up in transit. The sperm travel along the groove in the first pleopods, driven forward by the piston-like action of the second pleopods, which also fit into the same groove.

In natantians the copulating pair are usually oriented at right angles to each other with the genital regions appressed together. Mating may be preceded by caressing behavior on the part of the male. The male crayfish turns the female over and pins back her chelipeds with his own. The first two pairs of pleopods are then lowered to an angle of 45 degrees and held in this position by one of the last pair of legs (folded beneath the pleopods).

In crayfish possessing a seminal receptacle, the tips of the first pleopods are inserted into the chamber, and sperm flows along grooves in the pleopods, as in crabs. When the seminal receptacle is absent, the sperm are transmitted as spermatophores, which are attached to the body of the female, particularly between the last two pairs of legs. Copulation in lobsters is very similar to that in crayfish.

Courtship and copulatory behavior are particularly interesting in the anomurans. Male mole crabs possess an adhesive pad on each of the fourth legs, which are used for clinging to the female carapace. The sperm are emitted in a gelatinous ribbon shortly before egg-laying. Many hermit crabs seize the smaller females with a cheliped and drag them about. Mating takes place as soon as the female completes her pre-adult molt, and both animals remain within their shells.

In many decapods, including the blue crab, *Callinectes,* and the lobster, *Homarus,* mating only takes place just after the pre-adult molt of the female.

Egg-laying takes place shortly after copulation in forms with no seminal receptacles, but when sperm are deposited in seminal receptacles, which are commonly sealed and plugged by the semen, egg-laying may not take place until months later. This is true, for example, in *Callinectes,* in which the ovaries do not even begin development until after mating.

Peneid shrimp shed their eggs directly into the sea water or carry them only briefly. In all other decapods the eggs on extrusion are typically attached to the pleopods with a cementing material. The cement is commonly secreted by glands on the uropods and on the abdominal pleura; but cement glands may be located on pleopods themselves (as in *Callianassa* and *Upogebia*), on the ventral surface of the abdomen (hermit crabs), or in the oviducts (brachyurans).

Fertilization is internal in brachyurans, but in most decapods the eggs are probably fertilized at the moment of egg-laying. In crayfish the female lies on her back and curls the abdomen far forward, creating a chamber into which the eggs are driven by a water current produced with the beating pleopods. In crabs the usually tightly flexed abdomen is lifted to a considerable degree to permit brooding, and the newly laid eggs appear as a bright orange mass, sometimes called a sponge.

The hatching stage varies greatly. In some nonbrooding peneid and sergestid shrimp, the eggs hatch as nauplius, metanauplius, or protozoea larvae, but in almost all other marine decapods hatching takes place at the protozoeal or zoeal stage. The special names given the zoeal and postlarval stage of the different decapod groups are listed in Table 15-2. The decapod larvae have been beautifully illustrated and described by Gurney (1942) for the Ray Society of London.

The larval stages of crabs are particularly interesting. The zoea is easily recognized by the very long rostral spine and sometimes by a pair of lateral spines from the posterior margin of the carapace (Fig. 15-68, *A*). The postlarval stage, called a megalops, recapitulates the probable macruran ancestry of this group, for the abdomen is large, unflexed, and bears the full complement of appendages (Fig. 15-68, *B*).

Larval stages are absent in the strictly fresh-water decapods (see page 460). Brackish-water forms and river immigrants, such as *Eriocheir,* return to more saline water for breeding. Likewise development in terrestrial anomurans and brachyurans takes place in the sea. The female migrates to the shore and into the water, at which time the zoea hatch and are liberated.

Economic Significance. The decapods equal or surpass the pelecypod mollusks in importance as a source of human food, and the two groups together comprise the so-called shellfish industry. In the United States the commercial shrimpers are centered primarily along the southeastern Atlantic coast and the Gulf of Mexico. Species of *Penaeus* comprise most of the catch.

Shrimp are caught by trawling, in which a very long V-shaped net is towed behind the shrimp boat. Each arm of the V is connected by ropes to the boat, and at the apex the net forms a bag. On the south Atlantic coast, shrimp boats usually assume position a mile or so off shore in the evening and begin trawling very early in the morning. The nets are towed just off the bottom at slow speeds for half an hour to an hour, depending on the catch. In addition to shrimp, a wealth of other marine animals, called "trash" by shrimpers, is also collected. In

Table 15-2.   *Types of post-embryonic development and larvae in decapods*

GROUP	POST-EMBRYONIC DEVELOPMENT	LARVAE

Suborder Natantia
   Family Penaeidae
	Slightly metamorphic	Nauplius → protozoea → mysis → mastigopus
		                                        (zoea) (postlarva)

Family Sergestidae	Metamorphic	Nauplius → elaphocaris → acanthosoma → mastigopus (protozoea) (zoea) (postlarva)
Section Caridea	Metamorphic	Protozoaea → zoea → parva (postlarva)
Section Stenopodidea	Metamorphic	Protozoea → zoea → postlarva

Suborder Reptantia
   Section Macrura
      Superfamily Scyllaridea
	Metamorphic	Phyllosoma → puerulus, nisto, or pseudibaccus
		      (zoea) (postlarva)

Superfamily Nephropsidea	Slightly metamorphic	Mysis → postlarva (zoea)
Section Anomura	Metamorphic	Zoea → glaucothöe in pagurids, grimothea (postlarva)
Section Brachyura	Metamorphic	Zoea → megalopa (postlarva)

(Waterman and Chase, 1960.)

the Gulf of Mexico, trawling takes place further off shore and may continue for days or weeks before the trawler returns to port.

Three species of lobster are fished as food along the North American coasts. The east coast lobster, *Homarus americanus,* is found from Labrador to North Carolina but is not very prevalent in its southern range. This species has enormous chelipeds, which contain as much meat as the abdomen, or "tail". *Homarus* may attain a very large size; one specimen caught in 1934 weighed 42 pounds.

Off the Gulf and Pacific coasts, species of the spiny lobster, *Panulirus,* are used as food. The body is covered with spines, and in contrast to *Homarus* the chelipeds are very small. The lobster tails sold in markets are usually from spiny lobsters; many of the frozen lobster tails sold are shipped from Africa. Lobsters are secretive and nocturnal, hiding during the day. The animals are caught in traps, or pots, that the lobster enters as a retreat.

The portunid swimming crab, *Callinectes sapidus,* or blue crab, is the commercially important crab, occurring along the east and Gulf coasts of the United States. It can be caught in shallow water with a trap or line, but commercial fishermen catch them in large numbers by trawling. On the west coast and in Europe, species of *Cancer,* a nonswimming crab, are used as food and are caught by trapping.

Systematic Résumé of Order Decapoda

Suborder Natantia.   Body more or less compressed; the first abdominal segment no smaller than the more posterior segments. Rostrum well developed and compressed. The antennal scale is large. Any of the first three pairs of legs may be large and chelate; the others are relatively small and slender. The pleopods are well developed and adapted for swimming. Includes all shrimp.

Section Penaeidea.   Abdominal pleura of second segment do not overlap those of the first. The third legs usually chelate but not heavier than first. Dendrobranchiate gills. *Penaeus, Sergestes, Leucifer.*

Section Caridea.   Pleura of second abdominal segment overlap those of first. Third legs not chelate. Phyllobranchiate gills. To this section belongs the greatest number of natantians. Includes the sand shrimp, *Crangon;* the snapping shrimp, *Alpheus;* the marine, brackish, and fresh-water *Palaemonetes; Palaemon; Hippolyte; Benthesicymus.*

Section Stenopodidea.   Abdominal pleura of second segment not overlapping first. First three pairs of legs chelate and at least one member of the third pair is heavier than the first two pairs. Gills filamentous. *Stenopus.*

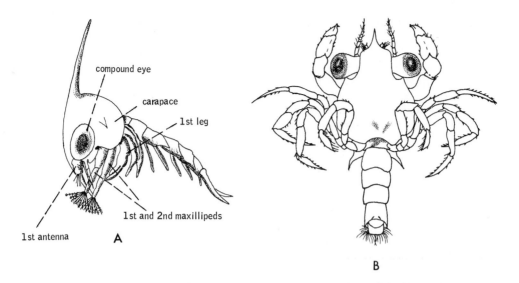

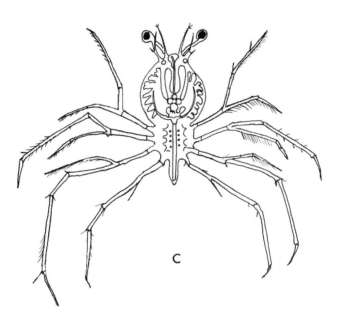

Figure 15-68.   Decapod larvae. *A*. Zoea larva of the crab, *Atelecyclus*. (After Lebour from Kaestner.) *B*. Megalops larva of the blue crab, *Callinectes*. (After Churchill from Waterman and Chace.) *C*. Phyllosoma (zoea) larva of the spiny lobster, *Palinurus*. (After Claus from Kaestner.)

Suborder Reptantia.   Body more or less dorso-ventrally flattened; the first abdominal segment smaller than the more posterior segments. Rostrum depressed if present, but usually reduced or absent. Second and third pairs of legs never heavier than first; first pair usually in the form of large chelipeds. Other legs usually adapted for crawling. Pleopods, when present, not especially adapted for swimming.

Section Macrura.   Abdomen extended and well developed; large uropods and telson.

Superfamily Eryonidea.   Rostrum small or absent. First segment of second antennae not fused with epistome. First four pairs of legs chelate. Broad depressed carapace. Marine, usually in deep water. *Polycheles.*

Superfamily Scyllaridea.   Rostrum small or absent. First segment of second antennae fused with epistome. First four pairs of legs not chelate. Marine. The spiny lobsters and

Spanish lobsters. *Panulirus, Jasus, Scyllarus, Ibacus.*

Superfamily Nephropsidea. Cylindrical carapace with a well developed rostrum. First three pairs of legs chelate; first pair typically in form of heavy chelipeds. Includes the lobsters, Homaridae—*Homarus, Nephrops;* the fresh-water crayfish—*Astacus, Cambarus.*

Superfamily Thalassinidea. Compressed carapace. First pair of legs in form of chelipeds but unsymmetrical; third pair not chelate (because of the different nature of the first and third legs, this group is frequently placed in the Anomura). Marine. The burrowing shrimp. *Thalassina, Callianassa, Upogebia.*

Section Anomura. Abdomen asymmetrical, soft and twisted, or flexed beneath thorax. Pleura and tail fan usually reduced or absent. Third legs never chelate. Fifth legs reduced and turned upward.

Superfamily Galatheidea. Crablike forms with a symmetrical abdomen flexed beneath thorax. Well developed tail fan. Rostrum often well developed; carapace not fused with epistome. First legs in form of chelipeds; fifth legs within gill chambers. *Galathea, Munida;* the porcelain crabs, *Petrolisthes, Pachycheles, Porcellana;* the South American fresh-water *Aegla.*

Superfamily Paguridea. Abdomen asymmetrical and usually soft. First legs in form of chelipeds. Rostrum small or absent. The hermit crabs, *Pagurus, Clibanarius, Eupagurus, Pylopagurus, Pylocheles.* This group also contains a number of crab-like forms that are probably secondarily derived from the hermit crabs. The abdomen is flexed beneath the thorax as in the Galatheidea and well chitinized, but like that in hermit crabs, the abdomen is not symmetrical, lacking some appendages on right side. Includes the lithodid (stone) crabs—*Lithodes, Paralithodes* (the commercial king crab of the North Pacific), *Lopholithodes;* the terrestrial crabs—*Coenobita* (typical hermit crab) and *Birgus.*

Superfamily Hippidea. Symmetrical abdomen flexed beneath thorax. Rostrum reduced or absent. Cephalothorax more or less cylindrical. First legs subchelate at the most. Marine in sand in surf zone. The sand, or mole, crabs—*Hippa, Emerita, Blepharipoda, Lepidopa, Albunea.*

Section Brachyura. Abdomen reduced and tightly flexed beneath thorax. Carapace fused with epistome. First legs in form of heavy chelipeds; third legs never chelate. The true crabs.

Subsection Gymnopleura. Primitive burrowing crabs with more or less trapezoidal or elongate carapace, subchelate first legs, and with some or all remaining legs flattened and expanded for burrowing. *Ranina.*

Subsection Dromiacea. Primitive brachyurans; marine. Last pair of legs are dorsal in position and modified for holding objects over the crab. Carapace usually not broader than long. Uropods greatly reduced but present. In female, first pair of pleopods are present and reproductive openings are on coxopodites. *Dromia, Hypoconcha.*

Subsection Oxystomata. Last pair of legs normal or modified as in Dromiacea. Mouth frame triangular rather than quadrate. Uropods absent, and first pair of pleopods absent in female. Female reproductive openings on sternum. Marine. *Dorippe;* the box crab, *Calappa; Lithadia.*

Subsection Brachygnatha. Mouth frame quadrate, and last pair of legs unmodified in size and position. No first pleopods in female.

Superfamily Brachyrhyncha. Carapace not narrowed anteriorly. Body shape round, transversely oval, or square. Pseudorostrum very small or absent. Orbits well developed. This superfamily contains the majority of crabs: Corystidae—*Corystes.* The cancer crabs, Cancridae—*Cancer, Pirimela.* The swimming crabs, Portunidae—*Portunus, Callinectes, Carcinus, Arenaeus, Ovalipes.* The fresh-water crabs, Potamonidae—*Potamon, Pseudothelphusa.* The mud crabs, Xanthidae—*Xantho, Menippe* (stone crab), *Pilumnus, Rhithropanopeus, Panopeus, Neopanopeus, Eurypanopeus.* The commensal pea crabs, Pinnotheridae—*Pinnotheres, Pinnixa, Polyonyx, Dissodactylus.* The amphibious crabs, Ocypodidae—*Ocypode* (ghost crabs), *Uca* (fiddler crabs), *Dotilla.* Marine, fresh-water, amphibious, terrestrial Grapsidae—*Geograpsus, Grapsus, Pachygrapsus, Planes, Sesarma, Eriocheir* (woolly-handed crab), *Aratus, Metaplax, Metopopaulias.* The landcrabs, Gecarcinidae—*Cardisoma, Epigrapsus, Gecarcoidea, Gecarcinus, Ucides.* The coral gall crabs, Hatalocarcinidae—*Hapalocarcinus, Cryptochirus, Troglocarcinus.*

Superfamily Oxyrhyncha. Carapace narrowed anteriorly into a pseudorostrum. Body shape roughly triangular. Incomplete orbits. Marine. The spider crabs—*Maja, Inachus, Macrocheira, Hyas, Libinia, Pelia, Parthenope.*

Vertical Migration in Crustaceans

In no other aquatic animals is the phenomenon of vertical migration of such wide occurrence nor has it been more extensively studied than in the Crustacea. Such movement is exhibited by some representatives of almost every order, and is particularly prevalent among cladocerans, calanoid copepods, and euphausiaceans. The adults, larval stages, or both may migrate. For example, the Antarctic *Euphausia superba* lives at the surface in the adolescent stages and the nauplii remain in deep water; the postnaupliar larval stages migrate.

Most commonly, vertical migratory movement follows a diurnal pattern, as in the copepod, *Calanus finmarchicus.* A few hours before sunset the animals begin to move upward from the depth of water occupied during the day to accumulate at the upper level by late evening. Around midnight the descent begins. This is interrupted briefly by a slight upward movement at dawn, after which descent continues to the day depth.

There are many variations on the typical pattern just described. Ascent and descent may occur earlier or later, or they may even be reversed, as in the copepod, *Acartia clausii,* and the euphausiacean, *Nyctiphanes couchii,* with upward movement occuring during the day and downward movement at night. Seasonal variation is also common.

In larger crustaceans, both the ascending and descending movement is probably kinetic— that is, through the locomotor activity of the animal. In smaller crustaceans the descent is, in part at least, a passive sinking, especially in such groups as copepods and cladocerans, in which the animal tends to be oriented vertically.

The distance traveled varies considerably, depending primarily upon the swimming ability of the animal. The larger crustaceans, such as shrimp and euphausiaceans, may travel a distance as great as 600 to 1000 meters. The smaller groups, such as copepods and cladocerans, have a migratory range of 30 to 150 meters. Although the upper position is commonly at the surface, it may be at lower levels. For example, bathypelagic species rarely rise to a level higher than 200 meters below the surface.

For the majority of crustaceans, light is the primary controlling factor in vertical migration. The animals are photopositive to certain light intensities, most commonly dim light, and tend to remain at that level where light conditions are optimum. Gravity is probably involved chiefly in orientation.

The value of diurnal vertical migration to the animal is still far from certain. It is commonly held that such movement brings the animal from the nonproductive twilight zone up into the rich photosynthetic stratum for feeding, at a time (night) when the animal would not be as exposed to predation or be injured by high light intensities.

Chromatophores, Hormones, Physiological Rhythms, and Autotomy

Chromatophores. A characteristic and striking feature of the integument of many malacostra-cans is the presence of chromatophores. The crustacean chromatophore is a cell with branched radiating noncontractile processes (Fig. 15-69, *A*). Pigment granules flow into the processes in the dispersed, or stellate, state and are confined to the center of the cell in the contracted, or punctate, state.

White, red, yellow, blue, brown, and black pigments may be present. The red, yellow, and blue pigments are carotene derivatives obtained from the diet. The blue pigment, or astaxanthin (carotenalbumin), is denatured in the presence of heat, forming the red compound so conspicuous in boiled crabs, lobsters, and shrimp. Curiously, a single chromatophore may possess one, two, three, or even four color pigments, any one of which can move independently of another. Crustacean chromatophores are thus usually classified as monochromatic, bi- or dichromatic, and polychromatic. In general polychromatic chromatophores are found only in shrimp.

Two types of color changes occur. One type, called morphological color change, involves the loss or formation of pigments within the chromatophores or change in the number of chromatophores when the animal is subjected to a constant background and constant light intensity for a long time. The other type, called physiological color change, is a rapid color adaptation to background and results from the dispersal and concentration of pigments within the chromatophores.

The most common type of physiological color change is a simple blanching (or lightening) and darkening. This response is typical of many crabs, such as the fiddler crab, *Uca.* Many crustaceans, however, especially shrimp, can adapt to a wide range of colors. The little shrimp, *Palaemonetes,* for example, possesses trichromatic chromatophores with red, yellow, and blue pigments and through the independent movement of these three primary colors can adapt to any background color, even black. Other species have similar abilities.

Hormones. The movement of chromatophore pigments is controlled by hormones elaborated by a neurosecretory system in the eye stalk (or below the eye, when the eyes are sessile) and by the central nervous system (Fig. 15-69, *B*). Located between the two basal optic ganglia is a glandular body called the sinus gland, which appears to be the center for hormone release. Through nerve fibers the sinus gland receives secretions from two other masses of secretory cells in the eye stalk and from other secretory parts of the nervous system. One of the secretory masses in the eye stalk is called the X-organ, and the other is called the medulla terminalis X-organ. The latter is probably the

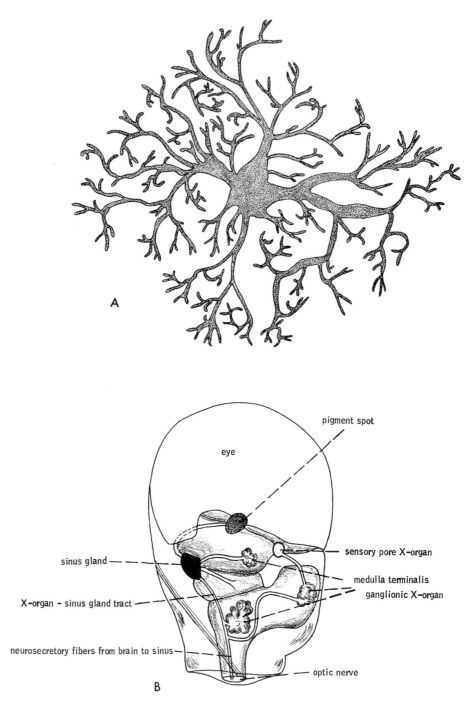

Figure 15-69.   *A*. Crustacean chromatophore in expanded state. (After Green.) *B*. Eye and eye-stalk of the shrimp, *Leander*, showing neurosecretory centers and tracts. (After Carlisle and Bart.)

most important source of eye-stalk hormones.

In shrimp (aside from *Crangon*), which have red, yellow, blue, and white pigments, removal of the eye stalks results in a darkening of the body through dispersion of the red and yellow pigments. If these eye-stalkless animals are then injected with sinus-gland extract, the white pigment disperses, and the body color rapidly

blanches. The opposite occurs in crabs which have black, red, yellow, and white pigments. Removal of the eye stalks causes blanching of the body color, resulting from a concentration of the black pigments and dispersal of the white. Injections of sinus-gland extract causes a body darkening.

The particular effect of sinus-gland extract

in the two groups is the same regardless of the origin of the extract. Thus sinus-gland extract from shrimp produces the same darkening in crabs as does crab extract, and vice versa. These results can be explained by the fact that decapod sinus glands release at least two chromatophorotropins. One, called Uca-Darkening Hormone (UDH), produces the darkening effect in crabs; the other, called Palaemonetes-Lightening Hormone (PLH), causes the blanching of shrimp.

The central nervous system also elaborates three or four chromatophorotropins. Some of these produce effects similar to the sinus-gland factors; others apparently antagonize the sinus-gland chromatophorotropins.

Eye-stalk hormones not only control the functioning of the chromatophores but other processes as well. In different crustaceans any one, or a combination of the three retinal pigments—distal, proximal, and reflecting pigments—may migrate distally or proximally in adapting the eye to bright or weak light.

Experimental evidence indicates that at least the movement of the distal retinal pigment and the reflecting pigment are under the control of sinus-gland hormones. Thus, if specimens of *Palaemonetes,* in which the eyes are dark-adapted, are injected with sinus-gland extract, the distal and retinal pigments move into the light-adapted position. Similar results for the distal pigment have been found for the crayfish, *Cambarus,* and certain other decapods. The cause of proximal pigment migration is still unknown. It does not seem to be under the control of the sinus gland, and there is some question as to whether it is under hormonal control at all.

The physiological processes involved in molting are regulated by complex hormonal interactions. The X-organ–sinus-gland complex produces three hormones: (1) A hormone that inhibits the various physiological processes involved in preparation for pro-ecdysis, such as the storage of food reserves and calcium. This hormone is thus important in regulating the length of the intermolt period. (2) A hormone that accelerates pro-ecdysis, once this stage is underway. This hormone is also secreted by the central nervous system. (3) A hormone that controls the amount of water taken up during ecdysis. Removal of the eye stalks of crabs just prior to this stage results in an abnormally increased water uptake.

These three hormones do not appear to affect the molting processes directly, but by way of a hormone or hormones secreted by the Y-organ. The Y-organ is a mass of secretory cells located in either the maxillae or in the base of the antennae, whichever does not carry the excretory glands. If the Y-organ is removed, molting will not proceed, even with eye-stalk extract injections.

Although sex in crustaceans is determined genetically, the development and function of the gonads and the development of secondary sexual characteristics is under hormonal control. If the Y-organ is removed prior to sexual maturity, gonadal development is seriously impaired; if the animal is adult, the gonads are unaffected. As yet, it is uncertain whether these results are caused by the loss of a specific hormone produced by the Y-organ or by a general metabolic malfunction from the absence of the Y-organ.

In female malacostracans, there exists a hormonal interrelationship between the ovary and the X-organ–sinus-gland complex that is strikingly similar to the pituitary-ovary relationship of vertebrates. The sinus gland produces a hormone that inhibits the development of eggs during the nonbreeding periods of the year. During the breeding season, the blood level of this hormone declines, egg development begins, and the ovary elaborates a hormone, initiating structural changes preparatory for egg-brooding, such as the development of ovigerous setae on the pleopods. These characteristics appear at the next molt.

The development of the testes and male sexual characteristics in malacostracans is controlled by hormones produced by a small mass of secretory tissue, the androgenic gland. This gland is located at the end of the vas deferens—except in isopods, in which it appears to be located in the testis itself. Removal of the androgenic gland is followed by a loss of male characteristics and conversion of the testes into ovarian tissue. If an androgenic gland is transplanted into a female, the ovaries become testes, although unfertile, and male characteristics appear.

Physiological Rhythms.   Pigment movement and other physiological processes often display a rhythmic activity in crustaceans. Such physiological rhythms, or physiological "clock mechanisms," have been studied extensively in the fiddler crabs, *Uca,* by F. A. Brown and fellow workers. Through chromatophore changes, the body color of *Uca* is dark during the day and pale at night. That such a periodicity is not mediated through the eyes can be demonstrated by the fact that the rhythm persists in *Uca,* even when the animal is kept in continual darkness. Superimposed on this diurnal rhythm is a tidal rhythm.

Fiddler crabs remain inactive within the burrows at high tide, and emerge with the receding tide. Within the burrows, the body color tends toward the nocturnal paleness and the motor activity and metabolic rate are at a minimum, regardless of the time of day. Thus, maximum dispersion of black pigment does not consistently occur at noon, but shifts across the daylight hours, following a 12.4 hour tidal cycle (Fig. 15-70). In addition to changes in body coloration, the spontaneous locomotor activity and metabolic rate also display distinct tidal rhythms.

Similar rhythms have been recorded for many other crustaceans. The blue crab, *Callinectes sapidus,* and the amphibious isopod, *Lygia exotica,* possess a color-change rhythm similar to that of *Uca,* although it is only diurnal in *Lygia.* Species of crayfish display a diurnal rhythm of loco-motor activity, but such a rhythm is never present in cave species. Diurnal rhythms have also been reported for the retinal-pigment movement in certain crayfish and shrimp, for luminescence in certain copepods, and for vertical migration in the copepod, *Acartia.*

Such physiological rhythms are typically adjusted to the solar and tidal conditions of the particular geographical location of the animal. For example, the *Uca* populations of two geographical areas with a four-hour difference in the high tide display a similar four-hour difference in their physiological rhythms. Moreover, the original geographical influence persists even when a population is moved to a new locality. This was demonstrated by Brown and others (1955) by flying a population of *Uca* from Woods Hole, Massachusetts to Berkeley, California. The physiological rhythms of the transplanted population compared exactly with a control population simultaneously observed at Woods Hole.

Physiological rhythms in Crustacea are not completely rigid, and some degree of phase shifting can be induced. For example, very low temperatures can inhibit the rhythms, which when restored may either stabilize in a new phase or shift back to the old. Similar shifts have been induced by manipulating light at critical periods during the daily cycle.

The causal mechanism is still far from understood. According to Brown (1961), the best hypothesis at the present time is that external environmental cycles, such as daily and lunar cycles, create corresponding metabolic cycles in the animal. These in turn act as pace-setters for basic continuous internal rhythms. The metabolic cycle would be environmentally induced; the internal rhythms, genetically induced.

Autotomy.   Many malacostracans are

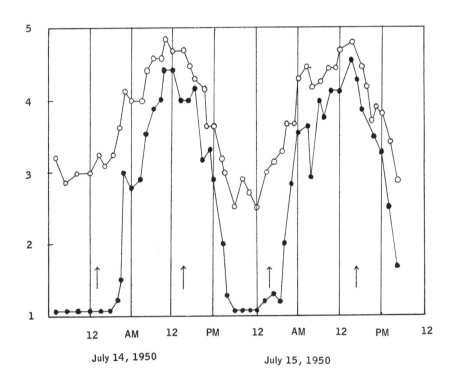

Figure 15-70.   Graph of changes in black and white pigment dispersion over a two-day period in chromatophores of the fiddler crab, *Uca pugnax.* Numbers on vertical axis indicate degrees of pigment dispersion, ranging from fully concentrated (1) to fully dispersed (5) pigment. Arrows indicate time of low tide. (After Brown, Fingerman, Sandeen, and Webb from Brown.)

capable of limb autotomy. It is especially well
developed in brachyurans and some anomurans
and is apparently absent in stomatopods and
most isopods.

Severance always takes place at a pre-
formed breakage plane, which runs across the
basi-ischium (Fig. 15-71). Internally there is a
corresponding double membranous fold that
divides the segment into basal and proximal
halves. The membrane is perforated by a nerve
and blood vessels. When the limb is cast off, the
plane of severance passes between the two membranes, leaving one membrane attached to the
basal stub. The membrane constricts around the
perforations, so that there is very little bleeding.

In some species, autotomy can only take
place if the limb is pulled either by the animal
itself or by an outside force; but in its most
highly developed state, as in most Reptantia,
autotomy is a unisegmental reflex. An autot-
omizer muscle, which also functions in locomotion under normal conditions, originates from
the thoracic wall and inserts on the basal half of
the basi-ischium. If a leg is caught or damaged
by a predator, a reflex is set up, and the autot-
omizer muscle is stimulated to undergo violent
contraction. The basi-ischium is pulled partially
beneath the coxa and fracturing takes place
along the breakage plane.

In brachyuran crabs, an autotomy reflex
exists in all five pairs of legs, but in the pagurid
hermit crabs the reflex is absent in the last two
pairs of legs; and in some macrurans, such as
the lobster, *Homarus,* only the chelipeds exhibit
the reflex. The other legs must be pulled off.

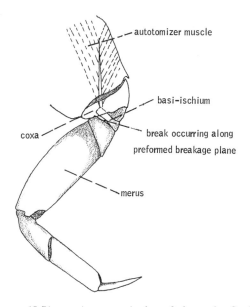

Figure 15-71.   Autotomy in leg of the crab, *Carcinus
maenas.* (After Wood and Wood from Bliss.)

Crustacean Phylogeny

Crustaceans are known to have existed since the
Cambrian period, but their origin and relationship to the other arthropod groups are very
obscure. Embryonic and larval development
provide no clue, and the comparative anatomy
of fossil and living forms is almost equally bar-
ren. Thus, theories relating to crustacean origins
are even more conjectural than usual. Those
authorities who consider the arthropods to have
had a polyphyletic origin (more recently Tiegs
and Manton, 1958) suggest that some ancestral
marine proto-onychophoran or protomandibu-
late gave rise to the terrestrial onychophoran–
myriopod–insect line on one hand and to the
crustaceans on the other. Other investigators
have maintained a trilobite origin for crustaceans. Such an affinity has been most recently
championed by Sanders (1957, 1959) on the
basis of his extensive studies on the cephalocarids.
He maintains that the triramous trunk appendages of cephalocarids are comparable to the
trunk appendages of trilobites (Fig. 15-72).
Moreover, he believes that this triramous structure is the primitive one for crustaceans, and
from it all of the appendage types of other
crustacean groups can be derived.

The nauplius larva has sometimes been
thought to recapitulate the ancestral protocrus-
tacean, but no crustacean, much less any
arthropod, is limited to three pairs of appendages. The crustacean nauplius is therefore of
little phylogenetic significance regarding the origin of the class; it probably represents nothing
more than an ontogenetic stage in segmentation, and as such would be equivalent to corresponding stages in the postlarval development
of annelids.

On the basis of the comparative anatomy
of living forms, it is generally agreed that the
ancestral crustacean was a small swimming animal possessing a head and a trunk of numerous
similar segments. The head bore two pairs of
antennae, a pair of mandibles, two pairs of
maxillae, a pair of compound eyes, and a
nauplius eye. The trunk appendages were numerous and similar, not only to each other but
probably also to the maxillae. Certainly among
living crustaceans, the cephalocarids most
closely resemble such a hypothetical ancestral
crustacean. The nature of the ancestral appendage—that is, whether it was triramous as in
cephalocarids, foliaceous as in branchiopods, or
biramous as in copepods—has evoked pages of
verbiage that has shed little light on the
problem.

During the evolution of the existing crustacean groups, the ancestral stock probably

protopodite
pseudepipodite
coxa
trochanter
prefemur
femur
patella
tibia
tarsus
pretarsus
telopodite
exopodite
endopodite

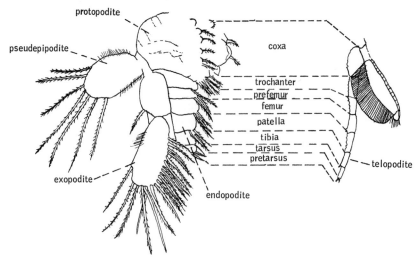

Figure 15-72. Sanders' comparison of a cephalocaridan appendage with that of a trilobite.

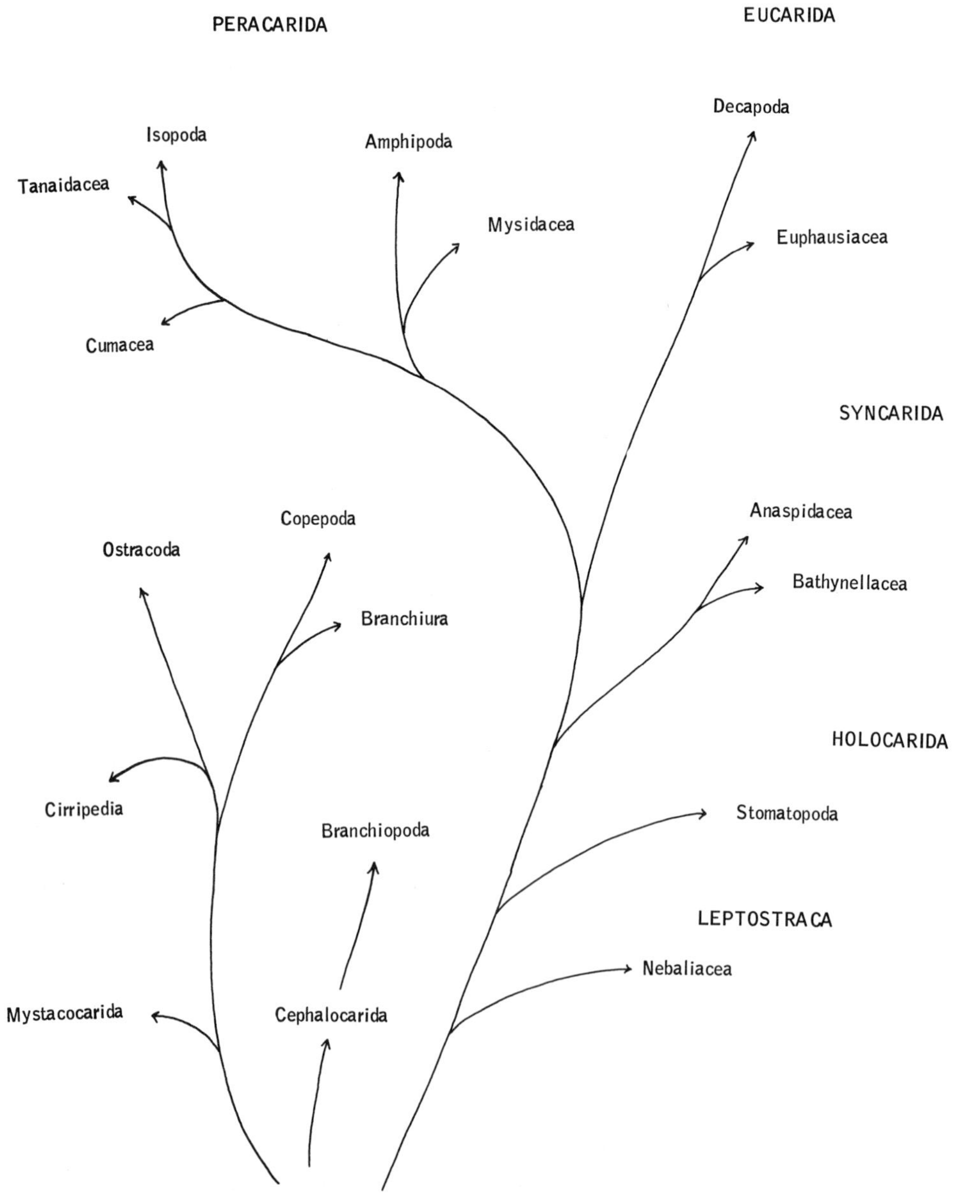

PERACARIDA
EUCARIDA
Decapoda
Isopoda
Amphipoda
Tanaidacea
Mysidacea
Euphausiacea
Cumacea
SYNCARIDA
Anaspidacea
Copepoda
Ostracoda
Bathynellacea
Branchiura
HOLOCARIDA
Cirripedia
Stomatopoda
Branchiopoda
LEPTOSTRACA
Nebaliacea
Mystacocarida
Cephalocarida

Figure 15-73. A suggested phylogeny of the Crustacea. (Modified from Waterman.)

divided early into two lines—one leading to the entomostracans, and the other to the malacostracans (Fig. 15-73). Among the entomostracans, the Cirripedia, the Ostracoda, and the Copepoda appear to be more closely related to each other than to the Branchiopoda, which group perhaps departed early from the entomostracan line. The malacostracan line culminates in two major groups, the peracaridans and eucaridans.

BIBLIOGRAPHY

Beerstecher, E., Jr., Cornyn, J., Volkmann, C., Cardo, L., and Harper, R., 1954: Invertebrate nutrition. I. A preliminary survey of the nutritional requirements of an isopod, *Oniscus asellus*. Texas Rep. Biol. Med., *12*:207–211.

Brown, F. A., Jr., 1961: Physiological Rhythms. *In* Waterman's Physiology of Crustacea. Vol. II, pp. 401–430.

Brown, F. A., Jr., Webb, H. M., and Bennett, M. F., 1955: Proof for an endogenous component in persistent solar and lunar rhythmicity in organisms. Proc. Nat. Acad. Sci. U. S., *41*:93–100.

Calman, W. T., 1909: Crustacea. *In* Ray Lankester's Treatise on Zoology. Vol. VII. A classic account of the Crustacea. Largely anatomical.

Cannon, H. G., 1927: On the feeding mechanism of *Nebalia bipes*. Trans. Roy. Soc. Edinburgh, *55*:355–369.

Cannon, H. G., 1933: On the feeding mechanism of the Branchiopoda. Phil. Trans. Roy. Soc. London, *222(B)*: 267–339.

Cannon, H. G., 1949: On the anatomy of the pedunculate barnacle *Lithotrya*. Phil. Trans. Roy. Soc. London, *233(B)*: 89–136.

Carlisle, D. B., and Knowles, F., 1959: Endocrine Control in Crustaceans. Cambridge Univ. Press. An excellent general account of crustacean hormonal mechanisms.

Cloudsley-Thompson, J. L., 1958: Spiders, Scorpions, Centipedes, and Mites. Pergamon Press, New York. A good discussion of the biology of wood lice is presented in the first chapter.

Cohen, M. J., 1955: The function of receptors in the statocyst of the lobster *Homarus americanus*. J. Physiol., *130*:9–34.

Cohen, M. J., and Dijkgraaf, S., 1961: Mechanoreception. *In* Waterman's Physiology of Crustacea. Vol. II, pp. 65–108.

Coker, R. E., 1939: The problem of cyclomorphosis in *Daphnia*. Quart. Rev. Biol., *14*:137–148.

Costlow, J. D., Jr., 1956: Shell development in *Balanus improvisus*. J. Morph., *99*:359–416.

Costlow, J. D., Jr., and Bookhout, C. G., 1953: Moulting and growth in *Balanus improvisus*. Biol. Bull., *105*:420–433.

Dahl, E., 1956: On the differentiation of the topography of the crustacean head. Acta Zool., *37*:123–192. This paper includes considerable discussion on the feeding mechanisms of crustaceans.

Darwin, C., 1851–1854: A Monograph on the Subclass Cirripedia. 2 vols. Ray Society, London. A classic and still valuable account of the barnacles.

Dennell, R., 1934: The feeding mechanism of the cumacean crustacean *Diastylis bradyi*. Trans. Roy. Soc. Edinburgh, *58*:125–142.

Edmondson, W. T. (ed.), 1959: Ward and Whipple's Freshwater Biology, 2nd Edit. Wiley, New York, pp. 558–901. Keys and figures to the common genera and species of North American fresh-water crustaceans.

Enequist, P., 1949: Studies on the soft-bottom amphipods of the Skagerak. Zool. Bidrag från Uppsala, *18*:297–492.

Friend, G. F., 1941: The life history and ecology of the salmon gill-maggot *Salmincola salmonea*. Trans. Roy. Soc. Edinburgh, *60*:503–541.

Giesbrecht, W., 1910: Stomatopoden. Fauna u. Flora Golfes Neapel, Monogr., *33*:1–239.

Green, J., 1961: A Biology of Crustacea. Quadrangle Books, Chicago.

Gurney, R., 1942: Larvae of Decapod Crustacea. Ray Society, London.

Harris, J. E., 1953: Physical factors involved in the vertical migration of plankton. Quart. J. Micr. Sci., *94*:537–550.

Harvey, E. N., 1961: Light Production. *In* Waterman's Physiology of Crustacea. Vol. II, pp. 171–190.

Hult, J., 1941: On the soft-bottom isopods of the Skagerrak. Zool. Bidrag från Uppsala, *17*:1–234.

Kaestner, A., 1959: Lehrbuch der Speziellen Zoologie., Teil I: Wirbellose. Gustav Fischer, Stuttgart, Pp. 659-979. An excellent general account of the Crustacea.

MacGinitie, G. E., and MacGinitie, N., 1949: Natural History of Marine Animals. McGraw-Hill, New York.

Manton, S. M., 1952: The evolution of arthropodan locomotory mechanisms. Part 2. J. Linnean Soc. London (Zool.), *42*:93–117. General introduction to the locomotory mechanisms of the Arthropoda.

Marshall, S. M., and Orr, A. P., 1955: On the biology of *Calanus finmarchicus*. VIII. Food uptake, assimilation and excretion in adult and stage V *Calanus*. J. Mar. Biol. Assn. U. K., *35*:495–529.

Pardi, L., 1954: Über die Orientierung von *Tylos latreillii*. Z. Tierpsychol, *2*:175–181.

Pardi, L., and Grassi, M., 1955: Experimental modification of direction finding in *Talitrus saltator*. Experimentia, *11*:202–203.

Pardi, L., and Papi, F., 1952: Die Sonne als Kompass bei *Talitrus saltator*. Naturwissenshaften, *39*:262–263.

Pennak, R. W., 1953: Fresh-water Invertebrates of the United States. Ronald Press, New York, pp. 321-469. A brief general account of the biology of the different groups of fresh-water crustaceans, with keys and figures for the identification of common genera and species.

Pennak, R. W., and Zinn, D. J., 1943: Mystacocarida, a new order of Crustacea from intertidal beaches in Massachusetts and Connecticut. Smithsonian Misc. Collect. *103*:1–11.

Pilsbry, H. A., 1907: The barnacles contained in the collections of the U. S. National Museum. Smithsonian Inst. Bull. *60*:1–114. An old but still valuable taxonomic treatment of the American stalked barnacles. The following paper covers the sessile barnacles.

Pilsbry, H. A., 1916: The sessile barnacles contained in the collections of the U. S. National Museum; including a monograph of the American species. Smithsonian Inst. Bull. *93*:1–357.

Reddy, A. R., 1935: The structure, mechanism, and development of the gastric armature in Stomatopoda with a discussion as to its evolution in Decapoda. Proc. Indian Acad. Sci., Biol. Ser., *1*:650–675.

Sanders, H. L., 1957: The Cephalocarida and crustacean phylogeny. Syst. Zool., *6*:112–128.

Sanders, H. L., 1959: The significance of the Cephalocarida in crustacean phylogeny. XV Internat. Congr. Zool., London (1958), Proc., pp. 337–340.

Schmitt, W. L., 1910: Crustaceans. *In* the Smithsonian Series. Series Publishers, New York, pp. 96–248. An old but still very interesting popular treatment of crustaceans.

Schöne, H., 1951: Die stätische Gleichgewichtsorientierung dekapoder Crustaceen. Verhandl. deutsch. zool. Gesellsch., *16*:157–162.

Southward, A. J., 1955: Feeding of barnacles. Nature, *175*:1124–1125.

Tiegs, O. W., and Manton, S. M., 1938: The evolution of the Arthropoda. Biol. Rev. Cambr. Phil. Soc., *33*:255–337.

Van Name, W. G., 1936: The American Land and fresh-water isopod crustaceans. Amer. Mus. Bull., *71*:1–535. A very complete taxonomic treatment of the American wood lice and fresh-water isopods.

Waterman, T. H. (ed.), 1960: The Physiology of Crustacea. Vol. I. Metabolism and Growth; 1961: Vol. II. Sense Organs, Integration, and Behavior. Academic Press, New York. An excellent survey of current knowledge of crustacean physiology. Each chapter is written by a specialist in the field. Extensive bibliographies.

Waterman, T. H., and Chase, F. A., Jr., 1960: General Crustacean Biology. *In* Waterman's Physiology of Crustacea. Vol. I, pp. 1–33.

Wiersma, C. A. G., 1961: Reflexes and the Central Nervous System. *In* Waterman's Physiology of Crustacea. Vol. II, pp. 241–279.

Chapter 16

THE MYRIAPODOUS ARTHROPODS

Four groups of mandibulates—the centipedes, the millipedes, the pauropods, and the symphylans—have a body composed of a head and an elongated trunk with many leg-bearing segments. This common feature was formerly considered sufficient reason for uniting all four groups within a single class, the Myriapoda. However, these arthropods differ greatly from one another in many respects, and modern zoologists are now generally agreed that most of them are probably not much more closely related to each other than to the other mandibulate groups. The Myriapoda has therefore been abandoned except as a convenient common collective name, and each of the four groups is now considered a separate class.

All of the myriapods are terrestrial and rather secretive animals, living beneath stones and wood and in soil and humus. They are widely distributed in both temperate and tropical regions.

The head bears a single pair of antennae and sometimes ocelli, but, except in certain centipedes, true compound eyes are never present. The mouthparts lie on the ventral side of the head and are directed forward. An epistome and labrum form the upper lip and the roof of a pre-oral cavity. The lower lip is formed by either a first or a second pair of maxillae, or both.

Respiration is typically by tracheae, and excretion takes place through Malpighian tubules. The heart is a dorsal tube extending through the length of the trunk, with a pair of ostia in each segment. There is usually little if any development of an arterial system. The nervous system is not concentrated, and the ventral nerve cord bears a ganglion in each segment.

Although the insects (Class Insecta) are beyond the scope of this book, this great arthropod class is believed by many zoologists to have evolved from the same ancestral stock that gave rise to the myriapodous classes.

Class Diplopoda

The Diplopoda are commonly known as millipedes or thousand-leggers. They are secretive and largely shun light, living beneath leaves, stones, bark, and logs. A few are commensal in ant nests. The more than 8000 described species live throughout the world, especially in the tropics; but the best known fauna are those of North America and Europe.

A distinguishing feature of the class is the presence of doubled trunk segments, or diplosegments, derived from the fusion of two originally separate somites. Each diplosegment bears two pairs of legs, from which the name of the class is derived (Figs. 16-1 and 16-2, *B*). The diplosegmented condition is also evident internally, for there are two pairs of ganglia and two pairs of heart ostia within each segment.

The diplopod head tends to be convex dorsally and flattened ventrally, with the epistome and labrum extending anteriorly in

475

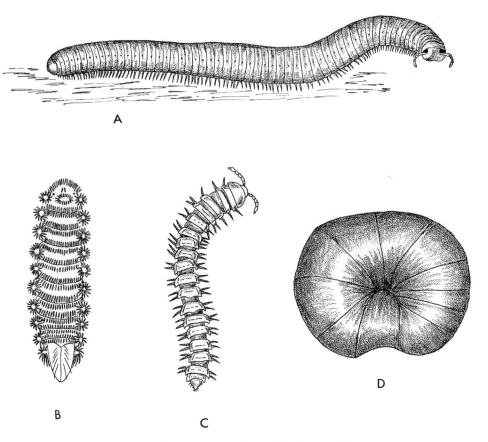

Figure 16-1.   Diplopoda. *A. Julus terrestris*, a juliform millipede. (After Koch from Borradaile and others.) *B. Polyxenus lagurus*, a pselaphognath. (After Brolemann.) *C.* A flat-backed millipede of the Strongylosomidae family. *D. Glomeris marginata*, a pill millipede. (*C* and *D* after Cloudsley-Thompson.)

front of the filiform, seven-segmented antennae (Fig. 16-3). The sides of the head are covered by the convex bases of the very large mandibles. Attached to the mandible base is a movable gnathal lobe, bearing teeth and a rasping surface. The gnathal lobes of each mandible oppose each other and lie within the pre-oral cavity beneath the labrum and epistome.

The floor of the pre-oral chamber is formed by a peculiar mouth appendage called the gnathochilarium (Figs. 16-2, *A* and 16-3). This is a broad, flattened plate attached to the posterior ventral surface of the head and bearing distally a few small lobes. Although its origin is still debatable, the studies of Silvestri (1950) indicate that the gnathochilarium is probably derived from the first maxillae and first maxillary sternite, and that the head of diplopods does not contain a second maxillary segment. The posterior floor of the pre-oral chamber bears a median and two lateral lobes, which are variously developed in different diplopod groups and represent the hypopharynx.

The trunk may be dorso-ventrally flattened, as in the order Polydesmoidea, the flat-backed millipedes (Fig. 16-1, *C*); or it may be essentially cylindrical, as in the familiar millipedes of the order Juliformia (Fig. 16-1, *A*). A typical segment (diplosegment) is covered by a convex dorsal tergum that, in the flat-backed forms and some others, extends laterally as a shelf, called a carina or paranotum (Fig. 16-2, *C*). Ventro-laterally, there are two small pleural plates, and ventrally, two small sternal plates. The sternal plates bear the legs. Primitively, the plates composing a segment are separate and distinct, but coalescence of varying degrees has usually taken place. In flat-backed and juliform millipedes, all of the plates are fused together, and in the latter group they form a nearly cylindrical ring.

Each leg of the two pairs of legs has six, or more usually seven, segments, and the legs in each pair are borne close together on the ventral sternites. The distal segment, or pretarsus, forms a claw.

The extreme anterior segments differ con-

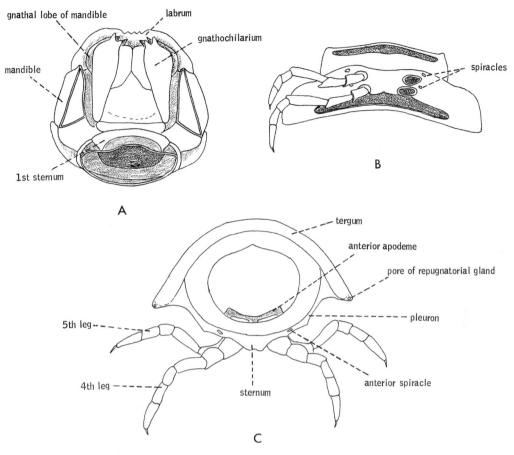

Figure 16-2.   *A.* Head of *Habrostrepus,* a juliform millipede (ventral view). *B.* A diplosegment of *Apheloria,* a flat-backed millipede (ventral view). A diplosegment of *Apheloria* (transverse section). (All after Snodgrass.)

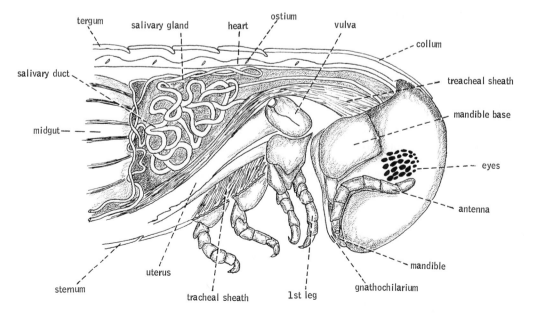

Figure 16-3.   Head and anterior trunk segments of the juliform millipede, *Spirobolus* (lateral view). (After Buck and Keister.)

siderably from the others and are probably not diplosegments. The first (the collum) is legless and forms a large collar behind the head (Fig. 16-3). The second, third, and fourth segments carry only a single pair of legs; and in the spirobolids and the colobognaths there are a greater number of segments with one pair of legs.

The last segment is legless and probably represents the telson. The lateral and ventral walls of the last segment often bear valve-like lobes covering the anus. In some millipedes, the preceding one (polydesmoids) to five segments are also legless.

The integument is hard, particularly the tergites, and, like the crustacean integument, is impregnated with calcium salts. The surface is often smooth, but in some groups the terga bear ridges, tubercles, spines, or isolated bristles.

The external anatomy just described applies to the subclass Chilognatha, which contains the vast majority of millipedes. The members of the small subclass Pselaphognatha are quite different. The integument is soft and covered with tufts and rows of scale-like hairs (Fig. 16-1, B). There is no gnathochilarium, but instead a pair of leg-like maxillae are present. The trunk is composed of eleven segments, of which the first four bear a single pair of legs each, and the last two are limbless.

Diplopods vary greatly in size. The pselaphognaths are minute, some species of Polyxenus being only 2 mm. long. There are also some minute chilognaths, such as the European Adenomeris and Chamaesoma, which are less than 4 mm. in length; but most members of this subclass are several centimeters or more in length. The largest millipedes are tropical species of the family Spirostreptidae and may be 28 cm. long. The number of segments is also extremely variable, ranging from eleven in the pselaphognaths and the oniscomorphs to over one hundred in the juliform groups. Moreover, in the juliform groups, the number varies within certain limits even within a particular species.

Most diplopods are blackish and different shades of brown; some species are colored red or orange, and mottled or spotted patterns are not uncommon.

Locomotion. In general, diplopods are not very agile animals. A few, such as the European Chordeuma, can move relatively rapidly, but most species crawl slowly about over the ground. According to the extensive studies of Manton (1954) on arthropod locomotion, the gait of diplopods, although slow, is adapted for exerting a powerful pushing force, enabling the animal to push its way through humus, leaves, and loose soil. The force is

exerted entirely by the legs, and it is with the evolution of such a gait that the diplosegmented structure is probably associated; the number of legs is increased, but the rigidity of the trunk is retained. The backward pushing stroke is activated in waves along the length of the body and is of longer duration than the forestroke. The number of legs involved in a single wave is proportional to the amount of force required for pushing. Thus, while the animal is running, as few as 12 legs or less may comprise a wave, but when pushing, a single wave may involve as many as 52 legs in some juliform millipedes.

The pushing gait has been most highly developed in the juliform species and is reflected in the smooth fused cylindrical segments, the rounded head, and the placement of the legs close to the midline of the body. The flat-backed millipedes are adapted for squeezing or wedging themselves into cracks and crevices, and according to Manton, the lateral carinae in these millipedes has probably evolved to provide a protected working space for the more laterally placed legs. Ability to climb is particularly striking in the colobognaths, which usually inhabit rocky situations. These millipedes can climb up smooth surfaces by gripping with opposite legs. Secretions from adhesive coxal sacs may perhaps be used to maintain a stationary vertical or inclined position.

Protective Devices. To compensate for the lack of speed in fleeing from predators, a number of different protective mechanisms have evolved in millipedes. Members of the order Oniscomorpha, called pill millipedes, can roll up into a ball (Fig. 16-1, D). The body is greatly convex dorsally and flattened ventrally and contains only 11 to 13 trunk segments. The second tergite is expanded laterally and covers the head when the animal is rolled up. Some tropical species, when rolled up, are larger than a golf ball. The long many-segmented millipedes, such as the colobognaths and the juliform groups, coil the trunk into protective spirals when at rest.

Repugnatorial glands are present in three orders of millipedes—the Colobognatha, the Polydesmoidea, and the Juliformia. There is one pair of glands per segment, present on all except the more anterior segments, or present on more or less alternate segments. The openings are located on the sides of the tergal plates, or (in the flat-backed millipedes) on the margins of the tergal lobes (Fig. 16-2, C). Each gland consists of a large secretory sac, which empties into a muscular duct and out through an external pore. The secretion contains hydrocyanic acid, iodine, and quinone, and has a brown or white color and iodoform odor. The secretion is probably toxic to other small animals; the secretion of some large tropical species is reportedly caustic to the human skin. The fluid is usually exuded slowly, but some tropical Juliformia can discharge it as a spray or jet for considerable distances. Cloudsley-Thompson (1958) states that a Haitian species, *Rhinocricus lethifer,* can emit a spray of fluid for a distance as great as 28 in. or more to either side of the body.

Nutrition.   Millipedes are primarily herbivorous, feeding on both living and decomposing vegetation. Occasionally dead snails, earthworms, and insects are also consumed. Lyford's (1943) studies on the diet of the British millipede, *Diploiulus londinensis,* showed that this species displays a distinct preference for leaves with a high calcium content. Food is usually moistened by secretions and chewed and scraped by the mandibles. However, the families of the order Colobognatha exhibit a progressive development of suctorial mouthparts with a corresponding degeneration of the mandibles. These changes culminate in the tropical Siphonophoridae, in which the labrum and gnathochilarium are modified to form a long piercing beak for feeding on plant juices. The beak contains the very much reduced mandibles. In the Polyzoniidae, which is represented in temperate regions (*Polyzonium*), the mouthparts are semisuctorial.

A single family of diplopods is reported to be predacious, feeding on earthworms and phalangids.

The digestive tract is coiled only in the pill millipedes. In others, it is a straight tube, most of which is formed by the long midgut. A short, narrow esophagus runs from the mouth, which is located in the back of the pre-oral cavity, through the anterior trunk segments. The wall of the esophagus is usually hexagonally folded, at least in the juliform millipedes, and bounded internally by a thin cuticle. Beneath the esophagus is a pair of salivary glands, from which a pair of ducts extends to reservoirs in the head (Fig. 16-3). From the reservoirs, the salivary ducts run downward and open onto the inner surface of the gnathochilarium.

The midgut is a simple tube extending through the greater part of the trunk. As in insects, the midgut lumen contains a separate cuticular tube, called the peritrophic membrane, which represents an extension of the cuticle of the posterior end of the foregut. Undigested food is always retained within the tube-like peritrophic membrane, which is believed to perhaps protect the midgut walls. A constriction demarcates the midgut from the hindgut (rectum). The rectum is quite muscular,

has folded walls, and opens posteriorly through the terminal anus. Virtually nothing is known concerning the physiology of digestion. The valves enclosing the anus are reported to function in molding the feces.

Respiration, Circulation, and Excretion. There are four spiracles per diplosegment, located just anterior and lateral to each of the four coxae. A pair of spiracles opens into the lateral hollow ends of the transverse apodeme (an internal chitinous projection) to which the leg muscles attach (Fig. 16-2, *B* and *C*). Bundles of slender nontapered and usually unbranched tracheae arise from the internal side of the apodeme. Snodgrass (1952) suggests that the respiratory function of the apodeme is secondary, since tracheae are usually absent from the three anterior segments, although apodemes are present. These segments are supplied by the tracheae of the fourth segment.

The heart ends blindly at the posterior end of the trunk, but anteriorly a short aorta continues into the head (Fig. 16-3). There are two pairs of lateral ostia for each segment except for the anterior segments, in which there is only a single pair. Two or sometimes four Malpighian tubules arise from each side of the midgut–hindgut junction and are often long and looped. For example, in the juliform *Spirobolus,* there are two tubules, each of which runs up to the esophagus, turns, and then extends back into the anal segment.

Nervous System and Sense Organs.   The brain is bilobed and gives rise to a pair of antennal nerves and clusters of nerves to the eyes, when eyes are present. The ventral nerve cord extends the length of the trunk and contains two ganglia in each segment, except in the anterior segments. From each ganglion issues a pair of lateral nerves.

Eyes may be totally lacking, as in the Limacomorpha and the flat-backed millipedes, or there may be two to eighty ocelli present. These are arranged above the antennae in one, or several, transverse rows or in two lateral clusters (Fig. 16-3). Each ocellus is a conical cup with a lens; the photoreceptors are directed toward the axis of the cone. When the ocelli are separately located, the lens is often convex; but when the ocelli form a compact cluster, as in *Julus,* there is usually a common corneal covering. Most millipedes are negatively phototropic, and even those without eyes have integumental photoreceptors. The antennae contain tactile hairs plus peg- and cone-like projections richly supplied with what are probably chemoreceptors. The animal continually taps the substratum with the antennae as it moves along.

A pair of sensory pits, called organs of

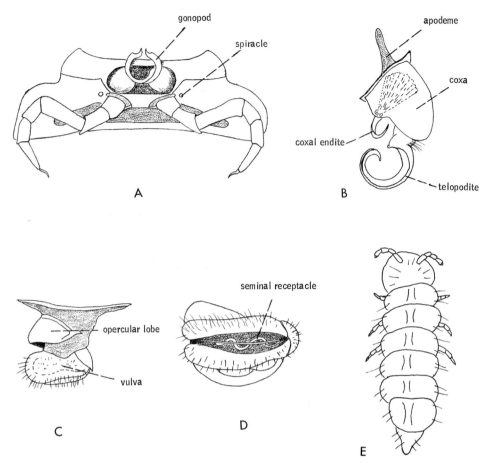

Figure 16-4. *A.* Seventh diplosegment of a male *Apheloria,* showing gonopods and legs (ventral view). *B.* Left gonopod of *Apheloria. C.* Right vulva of third segment of *Apheloria* (lateral view). *D.* Vulva (ventral view). (*A* to *D* after Snodgrass.) *E.* A newly hatched millipede. (After Cloudsley-Thompson.)

Tömösvary, is present in the glomeroids, the glomeridesmoids, and probably the choreumoids. The sensory cells lie beneath the cuticle at the bottom of a groove or circular depression located behind the base of each antenna. The function of these pits is unknown.

Reproduction and Development. A single long tubular ovary lies between the midgut and the ventral nerve cord. Anteriorly it passes into a narrow median oviduct and then into a uterus. In the region of the third, or genital, segment the uterus bifurcates, each horn opening into a vulva (Fig. 16-3). The vulvae are protractable pouches that open onto the ventral surface near the coxae (Fig. 16-4, *C* and *D*). When retracted, a vulva is covered externally by a sclerotized hood-like piece, and internally a small operculum covers the opening into the uterus. At the bottom of the vulva, a groove leads into a seminal receptacle.

The testes occupy positions corresponding to those of the ovary but are paired tubes with transverse connections. Anteriorly, near the re-

gion of the genital segment (the third), each testis passes into a sperm duct, which either opens through a pair of penes on or near the coxae of the second pair of legs, or opens through a single median penis, or into a median groove-like depression behind the coxal bases.

The actual copulatory organs of millipedes are usually highly modified trunk appendages (gonopods), and these are critical structures in identification of species. In the Oniscomorpha and Limacomorpha, the last pair of legs are modified as gonopods, but in other millipedes one or both pairs of legs of the seventh segment usually serve this function. In the flat-backed milliped, *Apheloria,* for example, where the first pair of legs on the seventh segment are gonopods, each gonopod consists of a coxal segment to which are attached a small hook-like process and a larger sickle-shaped piece (the telopodite) (Fig. 16-4, *B*). The telopodite contains a depression on its base from which a canal extends out to the tip. The two gonopods lie close together in a common ventral depression, and the sickle-shaped telopodites are so oriented that together they form a median ring-like opening (Fig. 16-4, *A*). When the male charges the gonopods with sperm, he bends the anterior part of the body ventrally and posteriorly, inserting the two coxal penes on the third segment through the ring formed by the telopodites. In this position sperm are deposited into the basal depression, (reservoir) of the telopodites. In the juliform millipede, *Arctobolus*, both pairs of legs of the seventh segment are gonopods, but only the second pair contains sperm reservoirs and canals. The telopodite resembles a short arm, and the hook-like process is absent. In the Colobognatha, the gonopods are the second legs of the seventh segment and the first legs of the eighth. Both pairs are leg-like and little modified.

During copulation, the body of the male is twisted about that of the female so that the gonopods are opposite the vulvae, and the body of the female is held by the legs of the male. The gonopods are protracted, and sperm are transferred through the tip of the telopodite into the vulva. In the European flat-backed millipede, *Polydesmus angustus*, the male runs up the back of the female; then crawls around to her ventral surface and seizes her gnathochilarium with his mandibles. According to Cloudsley-Thompson (1958), a fertilized female will run away as soon as the male touches her anal segment, and unfertilized females can be distinguished from fertilized ones by stroking the anal segment with a brush.

In the Limacomorpha and Oniscomorpha, the last one or two pairs of legs are modified for clasping the female, and the last pair also function as gonopods, each containing a sperm reservoir in the basal segment.

The diplopod eggs are fertilized at the moment of laying, and anywhere from ten to three hundred eggs are produced at one time, depending on the species. Some deposit their eggs freely in the soil; others, such as *Spirobolus*, regurgitate a material that is molded into a cup with the head and anterior legs. A single egg is laid in the cup, which is then sealed and polished. The capsule is deposited in humus and crevices, and it is eaten by the young millipede on hatching. The European pill millipede, *Glomeris*, has similar habits but forms the capsule with excrement.

Many millipedes construct a nest for the deposition of the eggs. Some flat-backed species and colobognaths construct the nest from excrement. The rectum of the female is everted and rapidly-drying excrement is deposited as she moves in a circular path. A thin-walled domed chamber is gradually built up and topped by a chimney. The vulvae are applied against the chimney opening, and the eggs fall into the chamber as they are laid. The opening is then sealed, and the chamber is covered with grass and other debris. The female may remain coiled about the nest for several weeks after the eggs are laid.

Some flat-backed and juliform millipedes construct the nest in soil, reinforcing the walls from the inside with excrement. The flat-backed *Strongylosoma pallipes* builds several such nests, each containing 40 to 50 eggs. The nest is closed from the outside. The nests of members of the order Nematomorpha are made with silk secreted by glands mounted on two papillae on the terminal segment.

Development is anamorphic. The eggs of most species hatch in several weeks, and the newly hatched young usually have only the first three pairs of legs and not more than seven segments (Fig. 16-4, *E*). With each molt, additional segments and legs are added to the trunk. Many millipedes, including the Polydesmoidea, the Juliformia, and the silk-spinning Nematomorpha, undergo ecdysis within specially constructed molting chambers similar to the egg nests. The shed exoskeleton is generally eaten, perhaps to aid in calcium replacement.

Systematic Résumé of Class Diplopoda

Subclass Pselaphognatha. Small millipedes with a soft integument bearing tufts and rows of scale-like bristles. A pair of leg-like maxillae instead of a gnathochilarium is present. Trunk composed of eleven segments, of which the first four bear a single pair of legs, and the last two pairs are limbless. No gonopods. Distributed throughout the world. *Polyxenus.*

Subclass Chilognatha. Gnathochilarium present. First trunk segment (collum) is limbless; the next three or four segments each possess a single pair of legs. Certain trunk limbs, usually those of seventh segment, modified as gonopods.

Order Oniscomorpha. Pill millipedes. Trunk of 11 to 13 ventrally flattened segments; body capable of being rolled up into a ball. Repugnatorial glands absent. Last two pairs of legs modified for clasping female, and last pair also used in transmitting sperm. Largely tropical; no members of this order have been reported from North America, but *Glomeris* is found in Europe.

Order Limacomorpha. Small, blind, tropical millipedes. Trunk of 19 to 20 segments with six-segmented legs. Repugnatorial glands absent. Last pair of legs modified for clasping and function as gonopods.

Order Colobognatha. Trunk of 30 to

70 segments; unfused sternites. Mouthparts often modified for sucking; reduced mandibles. Repugnatorial glands present. Largely tropical; a few North American and European species. *Siphonophora, Polyzonium.*

Order Ascospermophora (or Nematomorpha).   Trunk of 26 to 32 segments; unfused sternites. Repugnatorial glands absent. Each tergum bears lateral carinae and three pairs of bristles. Last tergal plate with a pair of papillae containing openings of silk glands. Are found in North America, Europe, and southern Asia. *Chordeuma, Chamaesoma.*

Order Proterospermophora (or Polydesmoidea).   The flat-backed millipedes. Trunk of 19 or more depressed segments with lateral carinae. Repugnatorial glands on more or less alternate segments. No eyes. Many species throughout the world. *Polydesmus, Strongylosoma, Apheloria.*

Order Opisthospermophora (or Juliformia).   Trunk of 40 or more cylindrical segments; continuous repugnatorial glands. Many species throughout the world. *Julus, Diploiulus, Spirobolus, Arctobolus, Rhinocricus, Habrostrepus.*

Class Pauropoda

The pauropods constitute a small class of soft-bodied, rather grub-like animals that inhabit leaf mold and soil (Fig. 16-5). All are minute, ranging from 0.5 to 2.0 mm. in length. Although once considered rare, pauropods have now been found to be frequently abundant in forest litter. There are approximately sixty described species, which are widespread in both temperate and tropical regions.

Pauropods appear to be more closely related to the diplopods that to any of the other myriapodous classes. The trunk contains twelve segments, of which nine each bear a pair of legs. The first segment (collum) and the eleventh and twelfth segments (pygidium) are legless. The dorsal side of the trunk is covered by only

six tergal plates, one doubled tergum for each two segments. All except the first tergal plate carry a pair of long laterally placed setae. Unlike the collum of diplopods, that of pauropods is very inconspicuous dorsally and expanded ventrally. The legs are six-jointed and terminate in a pad-like ventral lobe (empodium), a medial claw, and sometimes two lateral claws.

Each side of the head is covered by a peculiar sensory organ of unknown significance. A large convex cornea-like disc covers a fluid-filled chamber. The epidermal floor of the chamber contains sensory receptors from the protocerebrum. The antennae are two-branched. One division terminates in a single flagellum; the other, in two flagella and a peculiar club-shaped sensory structure. Each mandible is a single elongated piece carrying a comb of curved teeth. The lower lip is probably homologous to the gnathochilarium of diplopods, for it apparently represents the first maxillae, still distinct distally, fused to a triangular first maxillary sternite. The collum is possibly homologous to the second maxillary segment of other arthropods.

The diet and feeding habits are very poorly known. Different species have been reported to feed on fungus, humus, and the bodies of dead animals. There is neither heart nor trachea, their absence probably being associated with the small size of these animals.

As in diplopods, the third trunk segment is the genital segment. Paired ovaries lie below the gut, and the oviducts became confluent and open into a depression between the legs. A separate seminal receptacle also opens into the depression. The testes are located above the gut, and the sperm ducts empty through paired penes situated between the coxae of the legs. Little is known about the mechanism of copulation. The eggs are laid in humus, either singly or in clusters. Development is anamorphic, and as in diplopods, the young hatch with only three pairs of legs. Tiegs (1947) states that in *Pauropus sylvaticus* development to sexual maturity takes about 14 weeks.

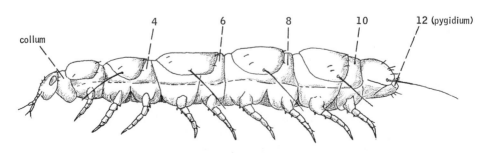

Figure 16-5.   The pauropod, *Pauropus silvaticus* (lateral view). (After Tiegs from Snodgrass.)

Class Symphyla

The Symphyla is a small class containing some 60 known species, which live in soil and leaf mold. They have evoked considerable interest as being the possible ancestors of the insects.

Symphylans are between 2.0 and 10 mm. long and superficially resemble centipedes (Fig. 16-6, *A*). The trunk contains 12 leg-bearing segments, which are covered by 15 to 22 tergal plates. The additional tergal plates have resulted from a subdivision of the original single plates of certain segments. The thirteenth, or pre-anal, segment carries a pair of spinnerets, which are believed to represent modified legs. The trunk terminates in a tiny oval segment that is provided with a pair of long sensory hairs.

A well developed epistome and labrum project in front of the laterally placed 30- to 60-segmented antennae (Fig. 16-6, *B*). Each mandible bears a toothed and independently movable gnathal lobe and lies beneath the epistome and labrum. The mandibles are covered ventrally by a pair of long first maxillae, each with two distal lobes. The second pair of maxillae are fused, forming a labium (lower lip), which has the form of an oval plate and bears six distal papillae (Fig. 16-6, *C*). It is thus strikingly similar to the labium of insects.

The legs are six-segmented, although the first pair may be somewhat reduced. Attached to the body wall beneath the base of each leg is a small appendage (the stylus) and an eversible vesicle, both of unknown function.

Most symphylans can run very rapidly. They feed on decayed vegetation, but *Scutigerella immaculata* may attack living plants and can be a serious pest on vegetable and flower crops, especially in greenhouses. The tracheal system is limited to the anterior part of the body. There

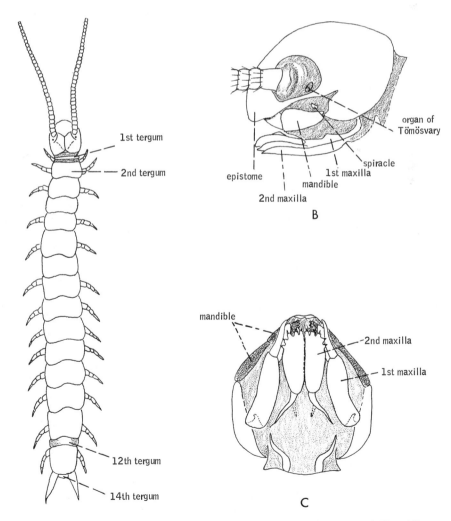

Figure 16-6.   Symphyla. *A. Scutigerella immaculata* (dorsal view). *B.* The head of *Hanseniella* (lateral view). *C.* The head of *Scutigerella immaculata* (ventral view). (All after Snodgrass.)

is a single pair of spiracles that open onto the sides of the head, and the tracheae only supply the first three trunk segments. There are no eyes, but the two organs of Tömösvary are well developed (Fig. 16-6, *B*). Each is an invaginated vesicle opening onto the surface of the head through the articular membrane and the base of the antennae.

Like those of the diplopods and pauropods, the genital openings are located on the ventral side of the third trunk segment. Copulatory behavior is unknown. The eggs are laid in clusters of 3 to 35 and are attached to the walls of crevices by a little stalk. The role, if any, of the spinning organs in reproduction is unknown. Development is anamorphic; the young on hatching have six or seven pairs of legs. *Scutigerella immaculata* lives for as long as four years and molts throughout its lifetime.

Symphylans are found in most parts of the world, although the northern limit in distribution appears to be determined by their inability to tolerate temperatures below −15° F.

Class Chilopoda

The members of the class Chilopoda, known as centipedes, are perhaps the most familiar of the myriapodous arthropods. They are distributed throughout the world in both temperate and tropical regions, where they live in soil and humus and beneath stones, bark, and logs. The approximately 3000 to 5000 described species are distributed within four principal orders. The order Geophilomorpha is composed of long worm-like centipedes that are adapted for living in soil (Fig. 16-7, *B*). The orders Scolopendromorpha (Fig. 16-7, *A*) and Lithobiomorpha (Fig. 16-7, *D*) both contain heavy-bodied centipedes that live beneath stones, bark and logs. The Scutigeromorpha are long-legged forms, some of which live in and around human habitations (Fig. 16-7, *C*). *Scutigera coleoptrata,* which is found in both Europe and North America, is not infrequently found trapped in bathtubs and wash basins.

The head of scutigeromorphs is convex, the epistome and labrum extended in front of the antennae as in the millipedes (Fig. 16-8, *A*). In other centipedes, the head tends to be more flattened, and the epistome and labrum are folded back into the pre-oral cavity, placing the antennae on the front margin of the head (Fig. 16-7, *A*). The antennae are filiform and are composed of varying numbers of segments. In the scutigeromorphs, the antennae are extremely long, slender, and annulate (Fig. 16-7, *C*). As in the millipedes, the mandibles consist of a basal portion and an unfused anterior gnathal lobe, except for the geophilomorphs, in which the mandible is a single piece (Fig. 16-8, *C*). The basal part of the mandible is elongated and lies beneath the ventro-lateral surface of the head. The gnathal lobes bear several large teeth and a thick fringe of setae. Beneath the mandibles are a pair of first maxillae, which form a functional lower lip (labium). The broad flattened basal lobes fit against one another and each bears a small palp-like distal lobe. A pair of second maxillae overlie the first pair. In the scutigeromorphs, the second maxillae are slender and leg-like, but in other centipedes they are short, heavy, and palp-like in form.

Covering all of the other mouth appendages are a large pair of poison claws, sometimes called maxillipeds, since they are actually the appendages of the first trunk segment but are involved in feeding (Fig. 16-8, *A, B,* and *D*). The coxae, which are fused together to form a single plate in the scolopendromorphs and geophilomorphs, cover the posterior ventral side of the head. Each claw is curved toward the midventral line and is composed of four pieces, the last one of which resembles a pointed fang. A poison gland is usually lodged within each claw and is drained by a duct that opens at the tip of the last segment.

Posterior to the first trunk segment, which carries the maxillipeds, are 15 or more leg-bearing segments. The tergal plates vary considerably in size and number. In the lithobiomorphs with fifteen pairs of legs and the scolopendromorphs with 21 to 23 pairs, there is a tergal plate for each of the leg-bearing sternites. But in the lithobiomorphs, the tergal plates are not of the same size; a short tergum generally alternates with a very long one (Fig. 16-7, *D*). The greatest number of segments, 31 to 181 or more, is found in the burrowing geophilomorphs; and, except in one family, the number is not fixed for a particular species. The worm-like nature of these centipedes is accentuated by the presence of a small intersternite and intertergite between each of the larger main sternal and tergal plates (Fig. 16-7, *B*). Each intertergite is actually a part of the preceding tergum.

Between the last leg-bearing segment and the terminal telson are two small limbless segments—the pregenital and genital segments.

The legs are seven-segmented with the last segment (the pre-tarsus) in the form of a claw. The coxae are attached laterally to each side of the sternal plates, in contrast to the medial position of the diplopod legs.

The largest centipede is the tropical American *Scolopendra gigantea,* which may reach one foot in length. Many other tropical forms,

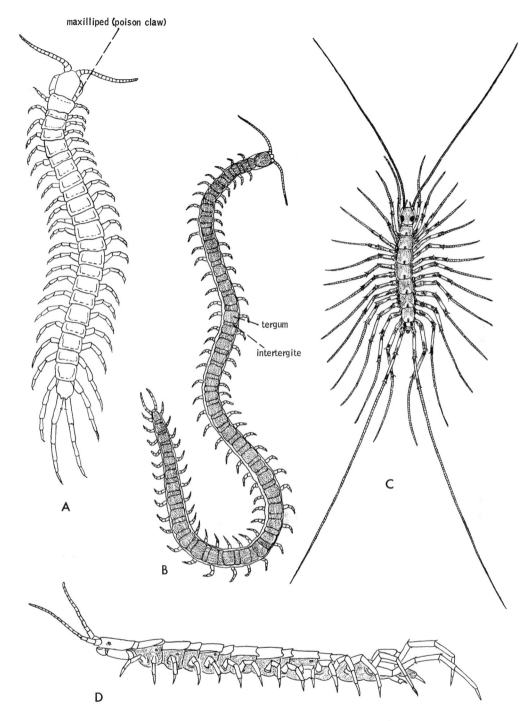

Figure 16-7. Chilopoda. *A. Otocryptops sexspinnosa,* a scolopendromorph centipede. *B.* A geophilomorph centipede. *C. Scutigera coleoptrata,* the common house centipede, a scutigeromorph. *D. Lithobius,* a lithobiomorph centipede. (All after Snodgrass.)

particularly scolopendrids, range from six to eight inches in length, but most North American and European species are only one or two inches long. Temperate zone centipedes are most commonly reddish brown, but many tropical forms, especially the scolopendromorphs, are colored red, green, yellow, blue, or combinations of colors, such as a yellow body and blue posterior legs or yellow with green crossbars.

Locomotion. Except for the geophilomorphs, centipedes are adapted for running

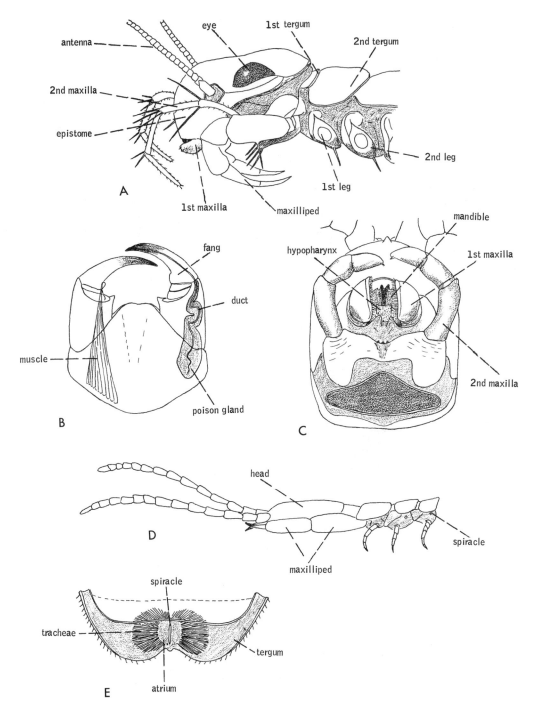

Figure 16-8.   *A.* The head of *Scutigera coleoptrata* (lateral view). *B.* Maxillipeds, or poison claws, of *Otocryptops* (ventral view). *C.* The head of *Otocryptops* (ventral view). *D.* The head and anterior trunk segments of a geophilid (lateral view). *E.* Posterior of *Scutigera* tergum showing pair of tracheal lungs. (All after Snodgrass.)

and many of their structural peculiarities are associated with the evolution of a rapid gait (Manton, 1952). In this respect, the scutigeromorphs are the most highly developed and they are active in the open, where their speed can be put to best advantage.

The legs of the running centipedes are long, especially so in the scutigeromorphs, and this enables the animal to take a greater stride. Moreover, there is a progressive increase in leg length from anterior to posterior. For example, in *Scutigera* the posterior legs are twice as long as the first pair (Fig. 16-7, *C*). This progressive increase in leg length toward the posterior enables the legs of the animal to cross over for rapid movement. A group of legs moving through the backward effective stroke passes to the inside of a wave of legs in the forward recovery stroke. To overcome the tendency to undulate, the trunk is strengthened by the alternately long and short tergal plates in the lithobiomorphs and by the reduced number but large and overlapping tergal plates in the scutigeromorphs. Finally, the annulated distal leg segments of the scutigeromorphs enable the animal to place a considerable section of the end of the leg against the substratum, very much like a foot, to decrease slippage.

In contrast to the other centipedes, the geophilomorphs are adapted for burrowing through loose soil or humus. They do not push with the legs as do the millipedes, but rather the pushing force is provided by extension and contraction of the trunk, as in earthworms. A British species of *Stigmogaster,* for example, can increase the body length by as much as 68 per cent. The powerfully developed longitudinal muscles of the body wall, the elastic pleural wall, the intercalary sternites and tergites, and the increase in number of segments without increasing the total length of the body, all facilitate great extension and contraction of the trunk in burrowing. The legs are short and anchor the body like the setae of an earthworm. In walking, regular locomotor waves may not take place, because a gait has evolved whereby the legs select effective footholds along the path on which the animal is traveling. To compensate for the shortened nature of the legs, each leg covers a much greater arc than in other centipedes.

Nutrition.   The class as a whole is believed to be predacious. Small arthropods form the major part of the diet, especially of the scutigeromorphs, but tropical scolopendromorphs have been observed feeding on toads and small snakes. According to Cloudsley-Thompson (1958), a large *Scolopendra* from Trinidad in the London zoo was fed for a year on small mice.

The prey is captured and killed or stunned with the poison claws, and some scolopendrids have been reported to rear up and capture insects in flight. Although the large tropical centipedes are often held in dread, the venom of even the largest forms is not sufficiently toxic to be lethal to man, even to small children. The effect of the bite of such forms is generally similar to a very severe yellow jacket or hornet sting. *Scolopendra gigantea* has been known to cause human death, but the condition of the victim may have been complicated by some concurrent disease. *Scolopendra heros* of the American Southwest is unusual in not only producing a painful bite but in making tiny incisions with its legs in walking. When the animal is irritated, a poison produced near the coxae is said to be dropped into these wounds causing an inflamed and irritated condition.

Food is chewed by the mandibles, and the tufts of setae on the mandibles and maxillae are perhaps used in cleaning the mouthparts. The digestive tract is essentially like that of the diplopods with a pair of salivary glands in the region of the esophagus.

Respiration, Circulation, and Excretion. Except in the scutigeromorphs, the spiracles of the tracheal system lie in the membranous pleural region above and just behind the coxae (Fig. 16-8, *D*). In the geophilomorphs, there is one pair of spiracles per segment except for the first and last leg-bearing segments and the postpedal segments. In the lithobiomorphs and scolopendromorphs, the number of spiracles and their pattern of distribution vary according to systematic groups within each order.

A few geophilomorph centipedes have been reported as inhabiting the intertidal zone along the coasts of Europe, Bermuda, Florida, and other parts of the world. These marine species live in algae, beneath stones and shells, in old barnacle shells, and in other protective places. Air retained within the tracheal system is probably sufficient to last during submergence at high tide, although in the Indian *Myxophilus indicus* and perhaps other species as well, additional air is trapped on the surface of the coxae and as a bubble lodged in the curled end of the trunk.

Associated with their more active habits and thus with a higher metabolic rate, the tracheal system of the scutigeromorphs is lung-like and probably evolved independently from that of the other centipedes. The spiracles are located mid-dorsally near the posterior margin of all but the last of the eight tergal plates covering the leg-bearing segment (Fig. 16-8, *E*). Each spiracle opens into an atrium from which extend two large fans of short tracheal tubes. The tracheae are bathed in the blood of the pericardial cavity.

There is usually a single pair of Malpighian tubules. Like diplopods, centipedes require a humid environment to maintain proper water balance, for the integument lacks the waxey cuticle of insects and arachnids and is not impregnated with calcium salts as in diplopods. Thus most centipedes are confined to the moist environment beneath stones and wood and in soil, and are only active on the surface of the ground at night.

Sense Organs.   All geophilomorphs and cryptopid scolopendromorphs, and a few cave-dwelling lithobiomorphs lack eyes. The Scolopendridae, however, have four small ocelli on each side of the head. The Lithobiomorpha and Scutigeromorpha have eyes that are similar to compound eyes; the optical units, of which there are one to thirty in lithobiomorphs and one to two hundred in scutigeromorphs, form a compact group on each side of the head and tend to be elongated with converging optic rods. In *Scutigera,* the combined corneal surface is greatly convex, as are the compound eyes of insects and crustaceans, and each unit is remarkably similar to an ommatidium (Fig. 16-8, *A*). The eye very likely functions in the manner of an appositional compound eye (Snodgrass, 1952).

A pair of organs of Tömösvary are present on the head at the base of the antennae in all lithobiomorphs and all scutigeromorphs. The other chilopod orders lack them entirely. In the scutigeromorphs, the last pair of legs is modified to form a pair of long, posteriorly directed, antennae-like appendages.

Reproduction and Development.   The ovary is a single tubular organ located above the gut, and the oviduct opens through a median aperture onto the ventral surface of the posterior, legless genital segment. The female aperture is flanked by a tiny pair of appendages, sometimes called gonopods. In the male, one to twenty-four testes are located above the midgut. The testes are connected to a single pair of sperm ducts, which open through a median gonopore on the ventral side of the genital segment. In all centipedes, the male aperture is located on a median penis, which may be variously developed. The genital segment carries small gonopods.

Nearly nothing is known concerning the copulatory behavior of centipedes, and the gonopods of the male seem unsuited for clasping the female. One species of *Lithobius* has been reported to deposit a spermatophore, which is then picked up by the female.

Both the scolopendromorphs and the geophilomorphs lay and then brood their eggs. The scolopendrids lay their eggs in cavities hollowed out in a piece of decayed wood and then wind themselves about the egg mass with the legs directed inward. The female guards the eggs in this manner through the hatching period and the dispersal of the young. The other orders of centipedes deposit the eggs in the soil and leave them. A mass of 15 to 35 eggs are layed in the geophilomorphs and the cryptopid scolopendromorphs. In the remaining two orders, the eggs are deposited singly in the soil after being carried about for a short time between the female gonopods.

In the orders Scolopendromorpha and Geophilomorpha, development is epimorphic, the young displaying the full complement of segments when they hatch. Development in the other two orders is at first anamorphic, like that of the diplopods. Young *Scutigera* on hatching have 4 pairs of legs and in the subsequent 6 molts pass through stages with 5, 7, 9, 11, and 13 pairs of legs. There are then 4 epimorphic stages with 15 pairs of legs before sexual maturity is reached. Development in *Lithobius* is similar, although newly hatched young have 7 pairs of legs; several years are required to reach sexual maturity.

Systematic Résumé of Class Chilopoda

Order Scolopendromorpha.   Twenty-one or 23 leg-bearing segments. Tergal plates are more or less similar in size and correspond in position to the ventral sternites. Antennae with approximately 17 to 30 segments. Spiracles with varying disposition. Many species distributed throughout the world, especially in the tropics. *Scolopendra, Theatops, Otocryptops.*

Order Lithobiomorpha.   Fifteen leg-bearing segments. Alternating large and small tergal plates. Disposition of spiracles varies. Antennae with approximately 19 to 70 segments. World wide in distribution but most genera and species are found in temperate and subtropical zones. *Lithobius, Bothropolys.*

Order Scutigeromorpha.   Fifteen leg-bearing segments, but covered by only eight tergal plates. Legs and antennae very long. Spiracles unpaired and located mid-dorsally on tergal plates. Distributed throughout the world, especially in the tropics. *Scutigera.*

Order Geophilomorpha.   Slender burrowing centipedes; with 31 to 180 or more leg-bearing segments. Intercalary sternites and tergites present. Legs short, and antennae with 14 segments. Eyes always absent. A pair of lateral spiracles on all leg-bearing segments except the first and last. Widely distributed in both temperate and tropical regions throughout the world. *Geophilus, Strigamia, Mecistocephalus.*

BIBLIOGRAPHY

Attems, G., 1926–1940: *In* Kukenthal and Krumbach's Handbuch der Zoologie. Vol. 4, Progoneata, Chilopoda, 1926; Vol. 52, Myriapoda, Geophilomorpha, 1929; Vol. 54, Chilopoda, Scolopendromorpha, 1930: Vols. 68–70, Diplopoda, Polydesmoidea, 1937–40. This and the works of Verhoeff (see below) contain the most extensive and detailed accounts of the myriapodous classes.

Brolemann, H. W., 1932: Chilopodes. Faune de France, Vol. 25.

Brolemann, H. W., 1935: Myriapodes. Diplopodes: Chilognathes 1. Faune de France, Vol. 29.

Cloudsley-Thompson, J. L., 1948: *Hydroschendyla submarina* in Yorkshire: with an historical review of the marine Myriapoda. Naturalist, pp. 149–152.

Buck, J. B., and Keister, M. L., 1950: *Spirobolus marginatus. In* F. A. Brown's Selected Invertebrate Types. Wiley, New York, pp. 462–475.

Cloudsley-Thompson, J. L., 1958: Spiders, Scorpions, Centipedes, and Mites. Pergamon Press, London. An excellent discussion of the natural history and ecology of the myriapodous arthropods is presented in chapters two, three, and four.

Manton, S. M., 1952: The evolution of arthropodan locomotory mechanisms. Part 3. The locomotion of the Chilopoda and Pauropoda. J. Linn. Soc. (Zool.), *42*: 118–167.

Manton, S. M., 1954: The evolution of arthropodan locomotory mechanisms. Part 4. The structure, habits, and evolution of the Diplopoda. J. Linn. Soc. (Zool.), *42*: 299–368.

Silvestri, F., 1950: Segmentazione del capo dei Colobognati. Proc. Eighth Internat. Congr. Entomol., Stockholm, pp. 371–576.

Snodgrass, R. E., 1952: A Textbook of Arthropod Anatomy. Cornell Univ. Press, Ithaca, N. Y. A good account of the external structure of the various myriapodous classes.

Tiegs, O. W., 1945: The postembryonic development of *Hanseniella agilis* (Symphyla). Quart. J. Micr. Sci., *85*: 191–328.

Tiegs, O. W, 1947: The development and affinities of the Pauropoda, based on a study of *Pauropus silvaticus.* Quart. J. Micr. Sci., *88*: 165–267, 275–336.

Verhoeff, K. W., 1926–1934: *In* Bronn's Klass. Ordn. Tierreichs. Chilopoda. Vol. 5, II (1); Diplopoda. Vol. 5, II (2); Symphyla and Pauropoda. Vol. 5, II (3).

Chapter 17

ANNELIDAN AND ARTHROPODAN ALLIES

This discussion treats five small phyla of coelomate protostomes that are believed to have stemmed from various points along the annelid–arthropod evolutionary line. Two of these groups, the sipunculids and the echiurids, are allied with the annelids; the other three phyla, the tardigrades, the onychophorans, and the pentastomids, probably stemmed from some point near the origin of the arthropods.

Phylum Sipunculida

The sipunculids, sometimes called peanut worms, are a group of some 250 species of marine worms that were formerly united with the priapulids and the echiurids as the phylum Gephyrea. The artificiality of this arrangement was soon recognized, and the three groups have since been separated. The priapulids, which have already been discussed, appear to be pseudocoelomates and have been treated in this text as a class of aschelminths; the sipunculids and echiurids are coelomates and related to the annelids.

Sipunculids are rather drab-colored worms that range in length from two millimeters to over two feet, although most are between six and twelve inches long. All are bottom-dwellers, living from the high-tide mark to depths as great as 15,000 feet, and they are rather sedentary in habit. Some live in sand or mud where,

like *Sipunculus*, they are active burrowers; some live in mucus-lined excavations. Others live in rock or coral crevices, in empty snail shells or annelid tubes, and in other sorts of protective retreats (Fig. 17-1, *B*). Although the burrow may be lined with mucus secretions, sipunculids do not build true tubes.

External Structure. The cylindrical body of sipunculids is divided into an anterior narrowed section, called the introvert, and a larger posterior trunk (Fig. 17-1, *A*). The introvert can be retracted into the anterior end of the trunk, but the introvert does represent the head and the anterior part of the body and is not simply a proboscis. The anterior end of the introvert contains the mouth surrounded by a scalloped fringe, lobes, tentacles, or by tentaculate lobes. All of these projections are ciliated and bear a deep ciliated groove on their inner side. Behind the anterior end, the surface of the introvert is typically covered with spines, tubercles, and other ornamentations.

The trunk is a simple cylinder, and its surface is not strikingly ornamented except in some forms, such as *Aspidosiphon*, that inhabit coral crevices. In these crevice-inhabiting sipunculids, the surface of the trunk is thickened at the anterior end to form a dorsal or a collar-like shield, which is presumably used to block the opening of the retreat when the introvert is invaginated.

Internal Structure and Physiology. The

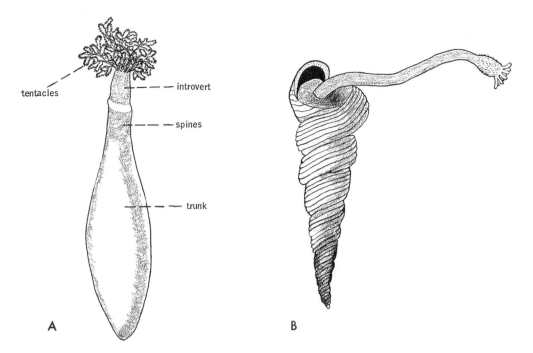

Figure 17-1. Sipunculida. *A. Dendrostomum pyroides,* a burrowing sipunculid (⅗ natural size). (After Fisher from Tétry.) *B. Phascolion* in a snail shell. Introvert is extended out of aperture. (After Cuénot from Tétry.)

body wall is constructed like that of the annelids. There is an external cuticle secreted by a simple layer of epidermis, a thin connective-tissue dermis, and a circular muscle layer and a longitudinal muscle layer, which is covered on the inner side by peritoneum.

A large coelom extends the length of the body; elevated coelomic fluid pressure brings about the protrusion of the introvert. The pressure is controlled by the contraction of the body wall. Retraction of the introvert is brought about by special retractor muscles that originate on the body wall of the trunk and run anteriorly. They are inserted on the end of the esophagus (Fig. 17-2, *A*).

The tentacles of the introvert are hollow but are not connected to the coelom. Rather, the tentacular lumen connects by a system of canals with one or two blind tubular sacs that are connected to the esophagus (Fig. 17-2, *A*). These sacs are contractile and receive fluid from, or supply fluid to, the tentacles when they are contracted or expanded.

Sipunculids are detritus feeders. The introvert and the tentacles are extended in feeding, but the exact mode of feeding is still uncertain and apparently varies in different species. In burrowing forms, such as *Sipunculus,* the worm ingests sand and silt through which it burrows. Nonburrowing species apparently utilize a ciliary mode of feeding. The expanded tentacles are placed against the substratum, and surface

detritus is trapped in mucus and driven into the mouth by the beating cilia. After the introvert collects material, it then invaginates for the purpose of ingestion. *Golfingia procera* from the North Sea is reported to prey upon the sea mouse, *Aphrodite.* The sipunculid penetrates the body wall of the annelid with its introvert and then sucks out the contents.

The digestive tract is U-shaped and coiled (Fig. 17-2, *A*). The mouth opens into an esophagus, which leads in turn into a long intestine. The intestine descends to the end of the trunk, turns, and ascends anteriorly. The entire intestinal loop is twisted in a single spiral coil. Anteriorly the intestine passes into a short rectum, which opens to the outside through the anus. The anus is located mid-dorsally at the anterior end of the trunk except for a single genus, *Onchnesoma,* in which it opens on the introvert.

The entire digestive tract is lined with a ciliated epithelium, and a well developed ventral ciliated groove runs either the entire length of the tract or through part of the intestinal region. Gland cells are prevalent in the epithelium of the descending arm of the intestine, and digestion and absorption are believed to take place in this region. The ascending intestine is probably involved in feces formation.

There are no blood-vascular system and respiratory organs, but the coelomic fluid functions in circulation and contains abundant corpuscles bearing hemerythrin. As in many

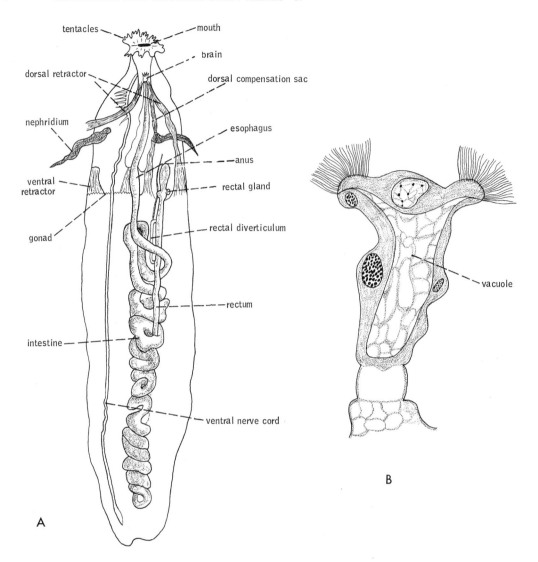

Figure 17-2. *A.* Dissection of *Sipunculus nudus.* (After Metalnikoff from Hyman.) *B.* Fixed urn from *Sipunculus nudus.* (After Selensky from Hyman.)

polychaete annelids, the hemerythrin functions in maintaining an oxygen reserve rather than in transport. The respiratory pigment is saturated with oxygen when the animal is immersed in aerated sea water, but when there is a decrease in surrounding oxygen, as for example at low tide, the hemerythrin gives up its oxygen to the coelomic fluid.

Sipunculids possess a single pair of large sac-like metanephridia, and the nephridiopores open anteriorly and ventrally at about the same level as the anus (Fig. 17-2, *A*). Associated with excretion in sipunculids are peculiar cells clusters called fixed and free urns. Fixed urns are clusters of peritoneal cells, each cluster elevated like a vase and capped by a ciliated cell (Fig. 17-2, *B*). The location on the peritoneum varies

in different species. Free urns are fixed urns that have become detached from the peritoneum and move about in the coelomic fluid. The free urns moving in the coelomic fluid gather particulate waste material, forming a trailing aggregate that is eventually dumped in various places within the coelom or removed by the nephridia. Coelomic amebocytes also function in accumulating waste material, which is then removed by the nephridia.

The nervous system is essentially like that of the annelids. The brain lies over the anterior end of the esophagus, and a pair of circum-esophageal connectives joins ventrally with the single ventral nerve cord, which runs the length of the body (Fig. 17-2, *A*). The nerve cord is in no way metameric. There are no ganglionic swellings along the cord, and in some species the lateral nerves arise as opposite pairs, while in others the lateral nerves alternate or emerge irregularly.

Sensory cells are particularly abundant on the end of the introvert that is used to probe the surrounding environment. In *Golfingia, Phascolosoma,* and a few other genera, the dorsal end of the introvert bears a pair of ciliated pits, called nuchal organs, which may be chemoreceptors. Also, a pair of pigment-cup ocelli is imbedded in the brain of many species.

Reproduction. Sipunculids are dioecious, and the sex cells arise from the coelomic epithelium covering the origin of the retractor muscles on the body wall. The immature gametes are shed into the coelom, where maturation is completed; ripe eggs or sperm leave the body by way of the nephridia. Fertilization takes place in the sea water, and the emission of sperm by the males induces neighboring females to shed their eggs.

The fertilized eggs undergo spiral cleavage and develop into trochophore larvae. In *Golfingia,* the trochophore is typical, but in *Sipunculus* it is elongated. After a free-swimming existence ranging from one day (in *Golfingia*) to a month (in *Sipunculus*), metamorphosis takes place, and the young worms sink to the bottom. There is no trace of metamerism during the course of embryonic development.

Although sipunculids are not metameric animals, they are clearly related to the annelids. The construction of the body wall, the nature of the nervous system, and the embryology are clearly annelidan in character. Sipunculids probably diverged from the line leading to the annelids at some point before the development of metamerism.

Phylum Echiurida

Echiurids are marine worms that are somewhat similar to sipunculids in size and general habit. Many species, such as *Echiurus, Urechis,* and *Ikeda,* live in burrows in sand and mud; others live in rock and coral crevices (Fig. 17-3, *D*). *Thalassema mellita,* which lives off the southeastern coast of the United States, inhabits the test of dead sand dollars. When the worm is very small, it enters the test and later becomes too large to leave. The majority of echiurids live in shallow water, but there are also deep-sea forms. During the last decade, Russian expeditions to the North Pacific have dredged up a number of new genera from depths as great as 27,000 feet. Sixty species of echiurids were known in 1928, but that number has been considerably increased by recent discoveries.

External Structure. The body of echiurids is composed of a sausage-shaped cylindrical trunk and an anterior proboscis (Fig. 17-3, *A*). The proboscis is a large flattened projection of the head and cannot be retracted into the trunk. The proboscis is actually a cephalic lobe and, since it contains the brain, is probably homologous with the prostomium of annelids. The edges are rolled ventrally so that the underside forms a gutter, and in some species the inrolled margins are fused near the junction with the trunk (Fig. 17-3).

The distal end of the proboscis is often flared and may even be bifurcated, as in *Bonellia* (Fig. 17-3, *C*). The length of the proboscis varies considerably. In the Japanese echiurid, *Ikeda,* a specimen with a trunk forty centimeters long may have a proboscis one and a half meters in length. However, in the common *Echiurus,* which lives on both sides of the North Atlantic, the proboscis is much shorter than the trunk. The proboscis is used in obtaining food and is very extensible in some echiurids. For example, an eight-centimeter specimen of *Bonellia* can extend the proboscis to a length of one meter.

The trunk is a relatively uniform cylinder. The surface may be smooth or ornamented with papillae that are irregularly distributed or arranged in rings around the body. On the underside, just back of the anterior end, is a pair of large, closely placed setae (Fig. 17-3, *A*). The setae are chitinous and are curved or hooked. As in annelids, each seta arises from a setal sac and is provided with a special musculature to enable movement. In addition to anterior setae, *Urechis* and *Echiurus* possess one or two circlets of setae around the posterior end of the trunk.

Echiurids are largely a drab gray or brown color; but some are green, such as *Bonellia,* and others are red or rose. A few are transparent.

Internal Structure and Physiology. The body wall is like that of the sipunculids and the annelids. The proboscis is especially glandular and the undersurface is ciliated. There is no indication of metamerism in the adult, and the coelom is continuous throughout the trunk and noncompartmented.

Most echiurids, such as *Echiurus,* are detritus feeders. The proboscis is projected from the burrow or retreat, and the ventral face is stretched out over the substratum (Fig. 17-3, *D*). Detritus adheres to the mucus on the proboscis surface, from which it is then driven into a median ciliated groove. Here the particles are conducted back into the mouth.

Urechis, which lives along the California coast in U-shaped burrows, has a mode of

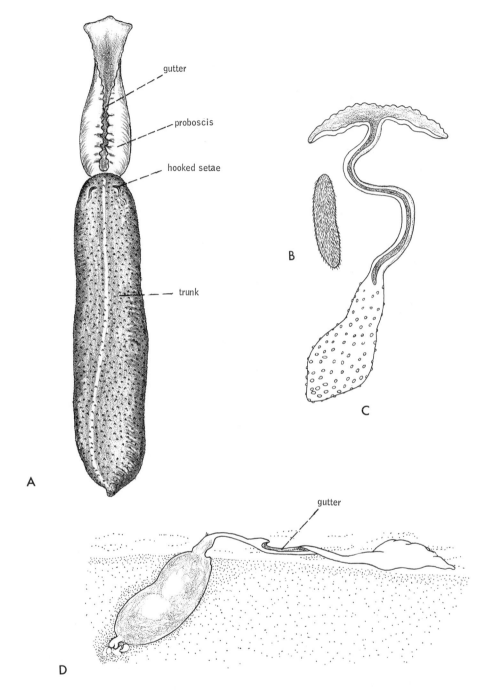

Figure 17-3.   Echiurida. *A. Echiurus sp.* from life (ventral view). *B* and *C.* Pygmy male (*B*) and female (*C*) of *Bonellia viridis*, showing the extreme sexual dimorphism in this species. (After Mac-Ginitie and MacGinitie.) *D. Tatjanellia grandis* in feeding position with trunk buried and proboscis extended out over surface of bottom. (After Zenkevitch from Dawydoff.)

feeding that is somewhat similar to the polychaete, *Chaetopterus.* The proboscis is very short, and a circlet of mucus glands girdles the anterior end of the trunk just behind the setae. During feeding, the glandular girdle is brought in contact with the burrow wall, and the glands begin secreting mucus. As the mucus is spun out, the worm backs up and eventually a funnel-shaped mucus collar surrounds the anterior end of the body. After the formation of the mucus collar, water is pumped through the burrow by peristaltic action of the trunk. Because the mucus "net" extends from the wall of the tube to the body of the worm, all sea water must pass through it, and even the finest particles are strained out. When loaded with food material, the net is detached from the body. The worm then moves backward, seizes the accumulated food mass using its short proboscis, and swallows the mass.

The digestive tract is extremely long and greatly coiled (Fig. 17-4). The mouth is located at the base of the proboscis and opens into a short muscular pharynx. A long, coiled esophagus connects the pharynx with a bulbous gizzard, and in some species there is an intervening stomach. A long, greatly coiled intestine comprises the remainder of the digestive tract. The lining of the tract is not completely ciliated, but there is a ciliated groove, as in the sipunculids.

A peculiar feature of the intestinal region is a small tube, called the siphon, that runs parallel to the intestine just outside the ciliated groove but enclosed within the intestinal peritoneum. Each end of the siphon opens into the ciliated intestinal groove. The end of the intestine joins a short rectum that opens through the anus at the posterior of the body.

There is little information about the digestive processes of echiurids, and the function of the siphon is unknown.

A closed blood-vascular system is present, except in *Urechis,* and is constructed on the same plan as that of the annelids. A ventral vessel runs beneath the digestive tract and, at different levels between the pharynx and the anterior part of the intestine, depending on the species, gives rise to a pair of dilated contractile vessels that encircle the intestine and join the dorsal vessel (Fig. 17-4). These peri-intestinal vessels are involved in the propulsion of blood. The dorsal vessel originates at the junction of the peri-intestinal vessels and runs forward over the anterior portion of the digestive tract. The blood is colorless and contains some amebocytes.

The coelomic fluid undoubtedly aids in circulation because, among the many cells that it contains, there are some with hemoglobin. These hemoglobin-bearing cells probably function in respiration in the same manner as do those of the sipunculids.

The excretory organs are metanephridia, which are large sacs similar to those of the sipunculids (Fig. 17-4). However, whereas there is only a single pair of nephridia in the sipunculids, echiurids possess one (in *Bonellia*), two (in *Echiurus*), or up to hundreds of pairs (in *Ikeda*). Moreover, in some genera, such as *Thalassema,* there are many more nephridia in the male than in the female. When there are only one or two pairs of nephridia, they are

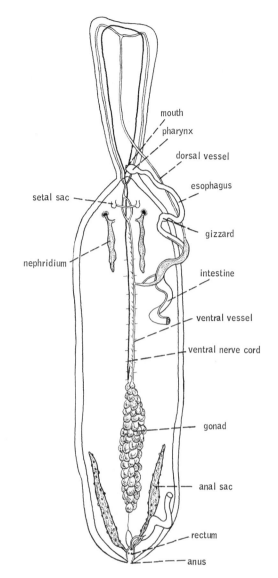

Figure 17-4.   Internal structure of an echiurid. (After Delage and Hérourard from Dawydoff.)

located anteriorly, and the nephridiopores open just behind the anterior setae.

In addition to the nephridia, echiurids possess a peculiar pair of accessory organs called anal sacs. These are simple or sometimes branched, contractile diverticula that arise from each side of the rectum. Distributed over the surface of the diverticula and often arranged in tufts are numerous ciliated funnels similar to nephrostomes. The funnels open into the coelom and lead into the lumen of the diverticula. The anal sacs are believed to function in excretion in the same manner as the nephridia, but the waste in this case leaves the body by way of the anus.

Coelomic urns like those of the sipunculids are known to be present in at least one species of echiurid and probably will be found in others.

The nervous system is like that of the sipunculids and the annelids. The peri-esophageal commissures run forward into the proboscis and make their dorsal connection at the anterior of the proboscis margin (Fig. 17-4). The cerebral ganglia are reduced, but the dorsal loop of the peri-esophageal connectives is their homolog. The single ventral nerve cord lies just beneath the ventral vessel and displays no ganglionic swellings. Lateral nerves arise along the length of the nerve cord, but these are not always regularly arranged.

There are no special sense organs. Isolated sensory receptors are located in the integument and are especially abundant on the proboscis.

Reproduction. The sexes are separate, and the gametes arise from the peritoneum of the ventral mesentery in the posterior of the trunk. As in annelids and sipunculids, the gametes are freed into the coelom, where maturation is completed, and the mature eggs or sperm are released through the nephridia. The anal sacs never function as gonoducts. Fertilization is external in the sea water except in *Bonellia,* in which the eggs are fertilized in the nephridial sacs, acting as uteri.

Species of *Bonellia* are peculiar in displaying an extreme sexual dimorphism. The males of such species are minute. In *Bonellia viridis,* the females may be one meter long, while the males are only one to three millimeters in length (Fig. 17-3, *B*). In addition to the reduction in size, the male is structurally modified in many ways. There is no proboscis nor circulatory system, and the digestive tract is reduced. The entire body surface is ciliated, and there is a system of genital ducts. These pygmy males enter the body of the female and live in the uteri or coelom.

Spiral cleavage and free-swimming trochophore larva characterize the embryology of echiurids. During the course of development, the mesodermal bands in some echiurids, such as *Echiurus,* are segmented and develop ten pairs of rudimentary coelomic pouches, which coincide with a similar transitory metamerism of the nerve cord.

The circulatory system, the setae, the presence of multiple nephridia in some species, and the transitory metamerism that appears during the course of embryological development, in addition to the annelidan character of the body wall and nervous system, all indicate a close phylogenetic relationship between the echiurids and the annelids, closer it would seem than between the sipunculids and the annelids.

It appears probable that the echiurids represent a group of worms that stemmed from the early ancestral polychaetes or at least from the line leading to the polychaetes. Some degree of metamerism had certainly been attained in the ancestral group from which the echiurids arose.

Phylum Tardigrada

The tardigrades are a group of very tiny but highly specialized animals called water bears. All are less than one millimeter in length, and the majority are less than half a millimeter. Although not uncommon, tardigrades are seldom encountered because of the rather restricted habitats in which they live.

There are a few marine tardigrades that live among sand grains in shallow water. Also there are some fresh-water species that live in the bottom detritus or on aquatic algae and mosses. The majority of tardigrades, however, live in the water films surrounding the leaves of terrestrial mosses and lichens. This very restricted habitat is shared primarily with some bdelloid rotifers, and the two groups present many parallel adaptations. About 340 species of tardigrades have been described, but the North American fauna has received little attention and is very poorly known. Only about 40 species have been reported from this continent.

External Structure. The bodies of tardigrades are short, plump, and cylindrical; and ventrally there are four pairs of stubby legs (Fig. 17-5). The anterior and posterior ends are more or less bluntly rounded, and the head and trunk are not demarcated. The legs are short cylindrical extensions of the ventro-lateral body wall, and each leg terminates in four single or two double claws. The body is covered by either a smooth or ornamented cuticle, which in some tardigrades, such as *Echiniscus,* is divided into symmetrically arranged plates (Fig. 17-5, *A*). A limited number of spines or bristles is frequently present.

The cuticle does not contain chitin, but its composition is otherwise unknown. The cuticle is secreted by an underlying epidermis that is composed of a constant number of cells, depending on the species. This constancy in cell number, like that in rotifers, is probably associated with the very small size of these animals. Periodically the old cuticle is shed, and the epidermis secretes a new one. Approximately six days prior to ecdysis, the cuticular pieces

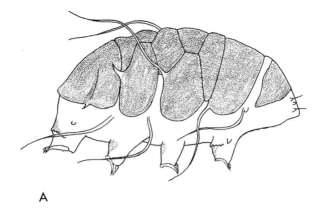

A

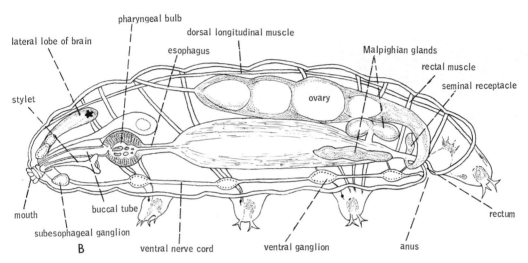

B

Figure 17-5.   Tardigrada. *A. Echiniscus,* showing cuticular plates (lateral view). (After Pennak.)
B. Internal structure of *Macrobiotus hufelandi* (lateral view). (After Cuénot.)

forming the buccal apparatus are cast out and re-formed. Also new claws are formed and lie beneath the old. During molting, the body contracts, pulling away from the old cuticle, which is then slipped off and left behind as a relatively intact casing.

Internal Structure and Physiology.   The musculature is not arranged in circular and longitudinal layers but in separate muscle bands, each composed of a single smooth muscle cell, extending from one subcuticular point of attachment to another (Fig. 17-5, *B*). Tardigrades move about slowly, crawling on their legs and using the hooks at the ends of the legs for grasping the substratum.

The coelom is confined to the gonadal cavity, but a fluid-filled hemocoel extends between the muscle bands and the other internal organs. There is neither a special respiratory system nor a circulatory system.

The majority of tardigrades feed on the contents of plant cells, which are pierced with a special feeding apparatus resembling that of herbivorous nematodes and rotifers (Figs. 17-5, *B* and 17-6). The anterior mouth opens into the buccal tube, which is followed by the bulbous muscular pharynx. These two divisions comprise the foregut and are lined by cuticle. One stylet lies on each side of the buccal tube. The anterior pointed ends of the two stylets project into the anterior end of the buccal tube, and their posterior ends are supported by two transverse pieces, that extend from the wall of the buccal tube to the stylet base. The buccal tube is also flanked by a pair of large glands, each of which opens into the buccal tube near the projecting stylet points. These glands secrete the stylets prior to each molt.

During feeding, the mouth is placed against the plant cells, and the stylets are projected to puncture the cell wall. The contents of the cell are then sucked out by the pharyngeal bulb. Some tardigrades have been observed to attack rotifers, nematodes, and other tardi-

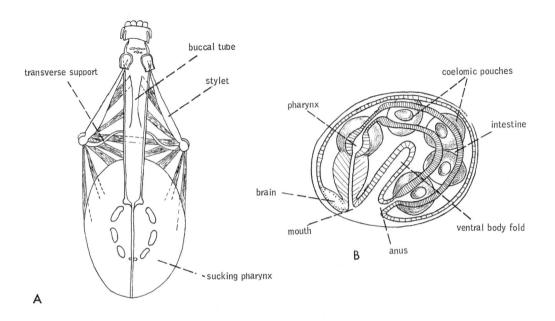

Figure 17-6.   *A.* Pharynx and buccal apparatus of a tardigrade (dorsal view). (After Pennak.)
B. Embryo of *Hypsibius.* (After Marcus from Cuénot.)

grades, but it is not known if such species are strictly carnivorous.

The pharyngeal bulb passes into the tubular esophagus, which opens in turn into a large midgut, or intestine (Fig. 17-5, *B*). Here digestion and absorption take place. The end of the intestine leads into a short hindgut (rectum), which opens to the outside through the terminal anus. In some tardigrades, such as *Echiniscus,* egestion is associated with molting, and the feces are left behind in the old cuticle. In these forms, the expulsion of the feces aids in the contraction of the body and separation from the old cuticle.

At the junction of the intestine and rectum are three large glands, sometimes called Malpighian tubules, that are thought to be excretory in function (Fig. 17-5, *B*). The buccal glands and intestinal lining have been suggested as playing some role in excretion, and there are indications that wastes accumulated in the epidermis are left behind in the old cuticle at molting.

The nervous system is distinctly metameric (Fig. 17-5, *B*). The brain is composed of three median lobes and two large recurved lateral lobes. A pair of commissures surround the buccal tube and connect ventrally to a subpharyngeal ganglion. From the subpharyngeal ganglion a double ventral nerve cord extends posteriorly, connecting a chain of four ganglia, the first of which is also connected dorsally to

the lateral lobes of the brain by a pair of connectives. From each ganglion issue several pairs of lateral nerves, one of which terminates in pedal ganglia in each pair of legs. Some of the bristles and spines are sensory, particularly those in the head region. Most tardigrades also possess a pair of simple eye spots, each containing a single red or black pigmented cell.

Reproduction.   Tardigrades are all dioecious and have a single saccular gonad, testis or ovary, located above the intestine. In the male, two sperm ducts leave the testis posteriorly, encircle the rectum, and open through a single median gonopore just in front of the anus. In the female, there is only a single oviduct, which passes to one side or the other of the rectum and either opens through the female gonopore above the anus or opens into the ventral side of the rectum (Fig. 17-5, *B*). In the latter case a small adjacent seminal receptacle also opens into the rectum.

Females are often more numerous than males, and in some genera, such as *Echiniscus,* males are unknown. In many tardigrades, particularly terrestrial species, fertilization takes place within the ovary. In such cases, sperm are either deposited in the cloaca, where they are temporarily stored in the seminal receptacle, or the sperm are deposited in the hemocoel by impregnation through the cuticle. In many aquatic species, sperm are deposited beneath the old cuticle of the female just prior to molting. When the female molts, the eggs are also deposited in the old cuticle, where they are fertilized.

One to 30 eggs are laid at a time, depending on the species. In aquatic tardigrades, they either may be deposited in the old cuticle, or attached singly or in groups to various objects. Like rotifers and gastrotrichs, some aquatic tardigrades are reported to produce thin-shelled eggs when environmental conditions are favorable and thick-shelled eggs when environmental conditions are adverse. The eggs of terrestrial species typically possess a very thick sculptured shell that can resist the frequent periods of desiccation to which mosses are subjected.

Development is always direct. Cleavage is holoblastic but does not follow any of the patterns that have been previously discussed. After the gut has formed, five pairs of coelomic pouches appear (Fig. 17-5, *B*). The coelomic pouches are arranged metamerically, but most peculiarly they arise as outpocketings of the gut. Such a mode of mesoderm formation (enterocoelous) is characteristic of the deuterostomes but not the protostomes. The last pair of coelomic sacs fuse together to form the gonad; the other coelomic pouches disintegrate, and their cells form the body musculature. Development is completed within 14 days or less, and the little tardigrades hatch by breaking the shell with their stylets. Further growth is attained by the increase in the size of cells rather than by the addition of cells.

Anabiosis.   Tardigrades, like moss-inhabiting rotifers, exhibit remarkable ability to withstand extreme desiccation and exposure to low temperatures. Thus during periods of dry weather when the moss becomes desiccated, the tardigrade inhabitants lose water, become contracted and shriveled, and pass into an anabiotic state. In this state, metabolism proceeds at a very low rate, and the animal can withstand abnormal environmental conditions. For example, specimens have recovered after immersion in liquid helium ($-272°$C.), brine, ether, absolute alcohol, and other substances.

When water is again present, the animal swells and becomes active within a few hours. There are records of tardigrades emerging from a state of anabiosis lasting seven years. Under natural conditions, the life of moss-inhabiting tardigrades is undoubtedly frequently interrupted by anabiosis, which may well lengthen the life span of these animals by years.

Despite similarities to the aschelminths, particularly rotifers, tardigrades are clearly coelomate animals. Moreover, the metameric character of the nervous system and the transitory appearance of metamerically arranged coelomic pouches (despite their enterocoelous origin) place this group somewhere along the annelid-arthropod line. Some zoologists believe that tardigrades are derived from the mites, the tardigrade cuticle being homologous to the arachnid epicuticle. However, the resemblance between tardigrades and mites is certainly very superficial. Moreover, many of the tardigrade structural peculiarities are undoubtedly specializations for living in their restricted habitats. Although tardigrades are not particularly intermediate in structure between annelids and arthropods, they may have stemmed from the main protostome line at some point between the annelids and the arthropods. At least this is as good a guess as any on the basis of present knowledge.

Phylum Onychophora

The onychophorans are sometimes described as the "missing link" between annelids and arthropods. The validity of such a statement is certainly questionable, but this little group of animals does present many interesting similarities to both annelids and arthropods.

There are only about 65 existing species of onychophorans, but the phylum is an ancient one and does not appear to have changed greatly since the Cambrian period, from which the only certain fossil specimen was discovered. The geographical distribution of existing forms is relatively restricted. All onychophorans live in tropical regions (the East Indies, the Himalayas, the Congo, the West Indies, and northern South America) or south temperate regions (Australia, New Zealand, South Africa, and the Andes). No species are found north of the Tropic of Cancer.

Most onychophorans are confined to humid habitats, such as in tropical rain forests, beneath logs, stones, and leaves, or along stream banks. During winter snows and low temperatures, or during dry periods, they become inactive and remain in protective retreats.

External Structure.   Onychophorans look very much like slugs with legs; in fact, they were thought to be mollusks when first discovered by Guilding in 1825 (Fig. 17-7, *A*). The body is more or less cylindrical and ranges from 1.4 cm. to 15 cm. in length. The anterior carries a pair of large annulated antennae and a ventral mouth, which is flanked on each side by short, conical oral papillae. The legs vary in number from 14 to 43 pairs, depending on the species and the sex. Each leg is a large conical protuberance bearing a pair of terminal claws (Fig. 17-7, *B*). At the

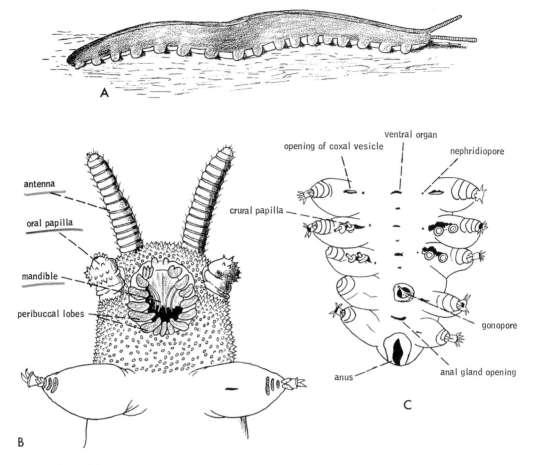

Figure 17-7.   Onychophora. *A. Peripatopsis capensis* (lateral view). (After Sedgwick from Borradaile and others.) *B.* Anterior of *Peripatopsis capensis* (ventral view). (After Cuénot.) *C.* Posterior of a male *Peripatus corradoi* (ventral view). (After Bouvier from Cuénot.)

distal end of the leg on the ventral side are 3 to 6 transverse pads, on which the leg rests when walking. The entire surface of the body is covered by large and small tubercles, that are arranged in rings or bands encircling the legs and trunk. The larger tubercles each terminate in a sensory bristle, and the tubercles are covered by minute scales. Onychophorans are colored blue, green, orange, or black, and the papillae and scales give the body surface a velvety and iridescent appearance.

Internal Structure and Physiology. The body surface is covered by a chitinous cuticle, but unlike the exoskeleton of arthropods, the cuticle of onychophorans is thin, flexible, and very permeable, and it is not divided into articulating plates. Beneath the cuticle is a single layer of epidermis, which overlies a thin connective-tissue dermis and three layers of muscle fibers—circular, diagonal, and longitudinal. The body wall is thus constructed on the typical annelidan plan. However, the coelom is reduced to the gonadal cavities and

to small sacs associated with the nephridia, and the body cavity is a hemocoel. Moreover, the hemocoel is markedly similar to that of the arthropods in that it is partitioned into a dorsal pericardial sinus, a median peri-intestinal sinus, a midventral perineural sinus, and two ventrolateral sinuses.

Onychophorans move by extension and contraction of the body very much like earthworms, except that the body is raised off the ground by the legs. Waves of contraction, affecting both sides of the body simultaneously and only a few segments at a time, progress from the anterior to the posterior. When a segment is extended the legs are lifted from the ground and moved forward. Needless to say, locomotion is not very rapid.

Most species are omnivorous and feed on decomposing vegetation and on small invertebrates, such as snails, insects, and worms. A number of species display a particular preference for termites. When onychophorans capture prey, they use a special pair of glands that secrete an adhesive material. The glands open at the ends of the oral papillae, and the secretion is discharged as two streams for a distance as great as 50 cm., and it hardens very rapidly (Fig. 17-7, *B*).

The mouth is located at the base of the prebuccal depression, which is surrounded by cutaneous lobes (Fig. 17-7, *B*). Within the depression are a pair of lateral mandibles and a median tooth that projects from the dorsal wall. All three pieces are movable and provided with a special musculature. As in arthropods, the mandibles are comprised of a pair of modified appendages and are homologous with the legs. A pair of salivary glands, representing modified nephridia, opens into a median dorsal groove that extends backward behind the dorsal tooth.

The prebuccal depression opens into a chitin-lined foregut, composed of a pharynx and an esophagus (Fig. 17-8, *A*). A large straight intestine is immediately posterior to the esophagus and is the site of digestion and absorption. The hindgut (rectum) is tubular and loops forward over the intestine before passing posteriorly to the anus. The anus opens on the ventral side at the end of the body.

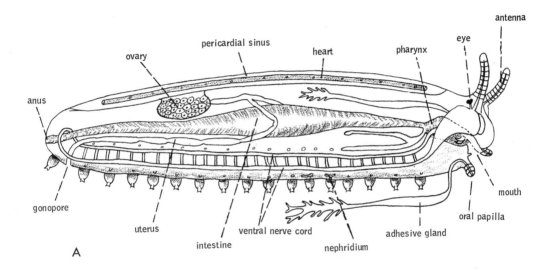

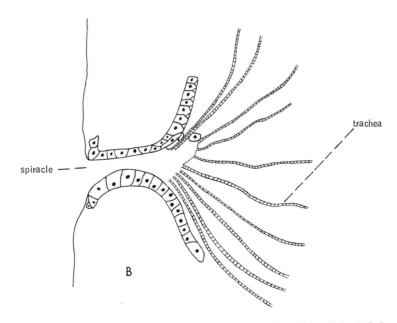

Figure 17-8.   *A.* Internal structure of an onychophoran (lateral view). (After Cuénot.) *B.* Section through spiracle and associated tracheae of *Peripatopsis capensis*. (After Balfour from Borradaile and others.)

The circulatory system is like that of the arthropods (Fig. 17-8, *A*). A tubular heart, open at each end and provided with a pair of lateral ostia in each segment, lies within the pericardial sinus and propels blood forward into the general hemocoel. The partitions between sinuses are perforated by openings that facilitate blood circulation. The blood is colorless and contains phagocytic amebocytes.

Each segment contains a single pair of nephridia located in the ventro-lateral sinuses (Fig. 17-8, *A*). The nephridium is tubular and opens into a small vesicle that represents a reduced coelomic sac. Before opening to the outside, the tubule becomes enlarged to form a contractile bladder. The nephridiopore is located on the inner base of each leg, except for the fourth and fifth segments in which it is mounted on a more distal tubercle (Fig. 17-7, *C*). The nature of the excretory waste is not known. The anterior nephridia are modified as salivary glands, and the posterior nephridia are modified as gonoducts in the female.

The respiratory organs are tracheae and probably represent at least the third independent evolution of a tracheal system (at least two others in arthropods). The spiracles are minute openings and are present in large numbers all over the surface of the body between bands of tubercles. The spiracle opens into a very short canal, at the end of which arises a tuft of minute tracheae (Fig. 17-8, *B*). Each trachea is a simple straight tube and extends directly to the tissue that it is supplying. In addition to tracheae, the legs of some onychophorans, such as *Peripatus,* possess a thin-walled vesicle opening to the exterior near the nephridiopore (Fig. 17-7, *C*). The vesicle may be evaginated to function as a gill when the atmosphere is humid.

The nervous system is composed of a large bilobed brain lying over the pharynx and a pair of ventral nerve cords connected together by commissures (Fig. 17-8, *A*). The brain supplies nerves to the tentacles, the eyes, and the mandibles. In each segment, the ventral nerve cords contain a ganglionic swelling and give rise to a number of paired nerves supplying the legs and body wall.

There is a small eye at the base of each antenna. The eyes are of the direct type with a large chitinous lens and a relatively well developed retinal layer. Onychophorans avoid light and are largely nocturnal. The large tubercles are equipped with a terminal sensory receptor and are especially abundant on the oral papillae and the legs.

Reproduction. The sexes are always separate; the males are a little smaller than the females and often have fewer legs. Both sexes are usually supplied with special glands called crural glands, which are thought to have some sort of sexual function. The glands are housed in some, or all, of the legs and open near the nephridiopore at the end of a prominent papilla (Fig. 17-7, *C*).

The ovaries are a pair of fused, elongated organs, located in the posterior part of the body (Fig. 17-8, *A*). Each ovary is connected to a nephridium that has become modified to form an elaborate genital tract containing a seminal receptacle and a uterus. The ends of each uterus join together and open to the exterior through a common genital pore, situated ventrally near the posterior of the body.

The male system contains two elongated nonfused testes and relatively complex paired genital tracts. Prior to reaching the exterior, the two tracts join to form a single tube in which the sperm are formed into spermatophores. The spermatophores are as long as one millimeter and are enclosed in a chitinous envelope. The male gonopore is ventral and posterior, like that of the female (Fig. 17-7, *C*).

Mating probably occurs only once in the lifetime of the female, for the process has never been observed, although the seminal receptacles of adult females are always filled with sperm. In the South African *Peripatopsis,* there are no seminal receptacles. The male in these species injects the spermatophore into the skin of the female, and the sperm reach the ovaries by way of the hemocoel.

Onychophorans are oviparous, ovoviviparous, or viviparous, and in most species reproduction appears to be continuous. Oviparous forms are limited to the Australian genera, *Ooperipatus* and *Symperipatus.* The females of these genera are provided with an ovipositor, and the large yolky eggs are laid in moist situations and enclosed in a chitinous shell. Like that of most arthropods, cleavage is superficial.

All other onychophorans are ovoviviparous or viviparous, and the eggs develop within the uterus. The eggs of viviparous onychophorans are small and have little yolk, and cleavage is either superficial or has become holoblastic. Uterine secretions provide for the nutrition of the embryo, and the nutritive material is obtained by the embryo through a special embryonic membrane or through a "placental" connection to the uterine wall.

Geographical Distribution. The geographical distribution of onychophorans is peculiar in a number of respects. The phylum consists of two families. Each has a wide discontinuous distribution around the world, but neither is found in the same area with species of the other family. The family Peripatidae is more or less equatorial in distribution, while the Peripatopsidae is limited to south temperate regions. Species within the same genus may be widely separated. For example, the genus *Opisthopatus* is found in Chile and South Africa, and *Mesoperipatus* of the Congo has its nearest allies in the Caribbean Islands.

Considering the geological antiquity of the onychophorans and the improbability of their being spread by other animals, the distribution of the phylum has been used as evidence to support the belief that the land masses of the equatorial regions and the southern hemisphere were connected by land bridges at various times during past geological ages.

The structure of the body wall, the ne-

phridia, the thin flexible cuticle, and the non-jointed appendages are certainly annelidan in character. But in other respects onychophorans are more like arthropods. The coelom is reduced, and the cuticle is chitinous. A pair of appendages is modified for feeding, and there is an open circulatory system with a dorsal tubular heart containing ostia. Thus onychophorans appear to be more closely allied to arthropods than to annelids, and perhaps the phylum arose as an offshoot from near the base of the arthropod line.

Phylum Pentastomida

Pentastomids comprise a little phylum of some sixty species of worm-like animals that are re-

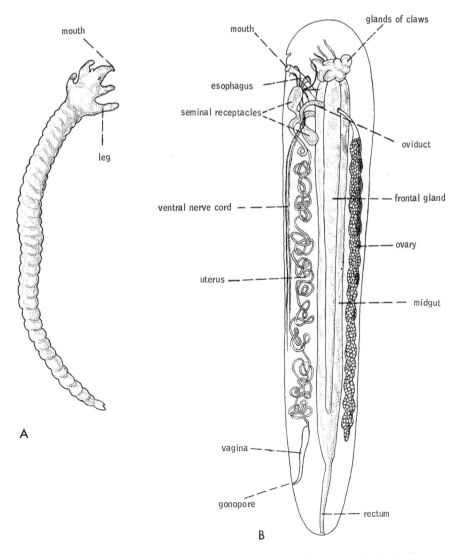

Figure 17-9.   Pentastomida. *A. Cephalobaena tetrapoda* from the lung of a snake. (After Heymons from Cuénot.) *B*. Internal structure of a female *Waddycephalus teretiusculus,* parasitic in certain Australian snakes. (After Spencer from Cuénot.)

lated to the arthropods. All members of the phylum are parasitic and live within the lungs or nasal passageways of carnivorous vertebrates. The principal hosts are tropical reptiles, such as snakes and crocodiles, but some species parasitize mammals and birds. No pentastomids are known from North America, but they have been reported from Europe (in mammals) and Australia, and one species is found in Arctic birds.

The body varies between 2 and 13 cm. in length and bears anteriorly five short protuberances, from which the name pentastomid is derived (Fig. 17-9, *A*). Four of these projections are leg-like, bearing claws and are located two to each side of the body. The fifth projection is an anterior median, snout-like process bearing the mouth. Not infrequently the legs are reduced to nothing more than the claws, which are used for clinging to the tissues of the host.

The body is covered by a thick chitinous cuticle that is molted periodically during larval development. The body-wall muscles are striated but arranged in layers as in the annelids. The digestive tract is a relatively simple straight tube with the anterior end modified to pump in the blood of the host, on which these parasites subsist (Fig. 17-9, *B*). The nervous system is like that of the annelids and the arthropods, with three pairs of metamerically arranged ganglia located along the ventral nerve cord. There are no respiratory, circulatory, or excretory organs.

The sexes are separate with a well developed genital system (Fig. 17-9, *B*). Fertilization is internal, and the embryonated eggs are passed into the digestive system of the host and then to the outside in the feces of the host. In most pentastomids, the life cycle requires an intermediate host, which may be fish (pentastomids in crocodiles), or herbivorous or omnivorous mammals, such as rodents, rabbits (intermediate host for *Linguatula* in dogs), or small ungulates. Larval development takes place within the intermediate host and involves a number of molts. When the intermediate host is eaten, the parasite is transferred to the stomach of the primary host and reaches the lungs and nasal passageways through the esophagus. Pentastomid larvae have been reported from man but are killed by calcareous encapsulation.

There is little question that pentastomids are related to arthropods. As in the case of the tardigrades, some zoologists argue that the pentastomids had an acarine origin, but the evidence again appears to be rather superficial and is probably prejudiced by the parasitic nature of the pentastomids. We can only speculate that this group, like the tardigrades and onychophorans, diverged from some point near the base of the arthropod line.

BIBLIOGRAPHY

Cuénot, L., 1949: Les Onychophores, Les Tardigrades, and Les Pentastomides. *In* P. Grassé's Traité Zoologie, Vol. VI. Masson et Cié, Paris, pp. 3–75. A general account of these three phyla; excellent figures.

Dawydoff, C., 1959: Classe des Echiuriens. *In* P. Grassé's Traité de Zoologie, Vol. V, Part 1. Masson et Cié, Paris, pp. 855–907. A good general account of the echiurids with figures and extensive bibliography.

Heymons, R., 1935: Pentastomida. In Bronn's Klassen und Ordnungen des Tierreichs, Bd. 5, Abt. IV. A complete monograph on the pentastomids.

Hyman, L. H., 1959: The Invertebrates. Vol. V. The Smaller Coelomate Groups. McGraw-Hill, New York, pp. 610–696. An excellent general treatment of the sipunculids with an extensive bibliography.

Marcus, E., 1929: Tardigrada. In Bronn's Klassen und Ordnungen des Tierreichs, Bd. V, Abt. IV. At the present time this is the most authoritative work on tardigrades.

Marcus, E., 1959: Tardigrada. *In* Ward and Whipple's Freshwater Biology (W. T. Edmondson, ed.) 2nd Edition, Wiley, New York, pp. 508–521. Figures and key to all of the nonmarine genera of the world and 76 species found in fresh water.

Pennak, R. W., 1953: Freshwater Invertebrates of the United States. Ronald Press, New York, pp. 240–255. A general discussion of fresh-water tardigrades, with key and figures to the common genera in the United States.

Tétry, A., 1959: Classe des Sipunculiens. *In* P. Grassé's Traité de Zoologie, Vol. 5, Part 1. Masson et Cié, Paris, pp. 785–854. A general account of the sipunculids.

Chapter 18

THE LOPHOPHORATE COELOMATES

Three related phyla of protostomatous coelomates remain to be considered—the Phoronida; the Ectoprocta, or moss animals; and the Brachiopoda, or lamp shells. Members of these three phyla all possess a food-catching organ called a lophophore and have been grouped together by Hyman (1959) as the lophophorate coelomates. Discussion of the lophophorates has been deferred until this point not because they hold a terminal position among the protostomes, but because of their apparent affinity with the deuterostomes, the other major evolutionary line of the Animal Kingdom that is discussed in the remaining chapters.

The food-catching organ, or lophophore, that is characteristic of these phyla, is a circular or horseshoe-shaped fold of the body wall that encircles the mouth and bears numerous ciliated tentacles (Fig. 18-1, *A*). The tentacles are hollow outgrowths of the body wall. Each contains an extension of the coelom. The ciliary tracts on the tentacles drive a current of water through the lophophore, and plankton is collected in the process.

In many deuterostomes, such as echinoderms and hemichordates, the body is divided, at least in the larval stage, into three regions—a protosome, a mesosome, and a metasome; and each region contains a coelomic compartment—a protocoel, a mesocoel, and a metacoel. Although there is no well developed protocoel in lophophorates perhaps as a result of the reduced head, the existing coelom is clearly

divided by a transverse septum into a mesocoel and metacoel. The mesocoel is contained within the anterior end of the body and the lophophore, and the metacoel occupies the trunk region of the body.

In addition to possessing a lophophore and a divided coelom, nearly all members of these phyla are sessile, have a reduced head, secrete a protective covering, and except for some of the brachiopods, possess a U-shaped digestive tract (Fig. 18-3). But all of these characteristics are correlated with a sessile existence and ciliary feeding and probably should not be given undue evolutionary importance.

From a phylogenetic standpoint, the embryology of lophophorates is particularly interesting, for both protostome and deuterostome features are displayed. In phoronids and brachiopods, the mouth is derived from the blastopore, and the larvae of phoronids and ectoprocts are modified trochophores. Thus these phyla are clearly protostomes. But only in some phoronids is there any evidence of spiral cleavage; in ectoprocts and especially brachiopods, cleavage is markedly radial. Moreover, in some brachiopods the mesoderm and coelom arise by enterocoelic pouching as is typical of deuterostomes.

The three lophophorate phyla are believed by Hyman (1959) to have stemmed from some common ancestral form that diverged from the coelomate line leading to the annelids. Hyman further suggests that the ancestor of the lophophorates may also have given rise to the

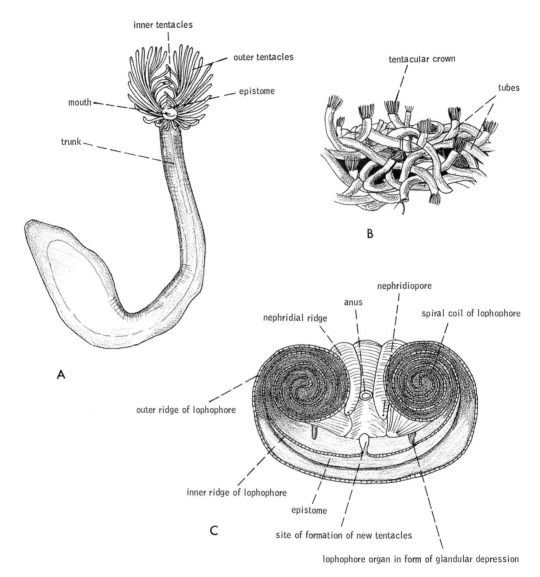

Figure 18-1.   *A. Phoronis architecta.* (After Wilson from Hyman.) *B.* Part of a *Phoronis hippocrepia* colony. (After Shipley from Hyman.) *C.* Anterior of *Phoronis australis.* Only base of rolled lophophore is shown. (After Benham from Hyman.)

deuterostome line. Thus the lophophorates perhaps represent the point at which the two major evolutionary lines of the Animal Kingdom diverged. Additional evidence supporting this relationship is discussed in the chapter on the echinoderms.

Phylum Phoronida

The phoronids are a small group consisting of two genera and approximately 15 species of worm-like animals. All members are marine and live within a chitinous tube that is either buried in sand or attached to rocks, shells, and other objects in shallow water (Fig. 18-1, *B*). A few species bore into mollusk shells. Although the body is free within the tube, only the anterior of the animal ever emerges from the opening of the tube.

The cylindrical body, which in most species is less than 8 inches long, is somewhat enlarged posteriorly and bears no appendages nor regional differentiation except at the anterior end (Fig. 18-1, *A*). Here the lophophore is the most conspicuous feature. The lophophore consists of two parallel ridges curved in the shape of a crescent or horseshoe (Fig. 18-1, *C*). The bend of the crescent is located ventrally with one ridge passing above, and the other ridge passing below the mouth. The horns of the ridges are directed dorsally and may be rolled up as a spiral.

Each lophophoral ridge bears a large number of hollow tentacles that are slender, ciliated extensions of the body wall (Fig. 18-1, *A*). A long narrow crescentic fold, called the epistome, overhangs the mouth. The anus opens above the mouth but outside of the upper lophophoral ridge and is flanked on each side by a nephridiopore. The lophophore is separated from the trunk by a groove in *Phoronis* and a collar-like fold in *Phoronopsis.*

The body wall is composed of an outer epithelium, under which lies a thin layer of circular muscle fibers and a thick longitudinal muscle layer. Gland cells are abundant at the anterior end of the body, particularly on the lophophore.

The coelom is divided into the posterior metacoel, which occupies the trunk region, and the anterior mesocoel, which extends into the lophophore and each of the tentacles. The two divisions are separated by a peritoneal septum. The coelomic fluid contains red corpuscles and coelomocytes.

Like all lophophorates, phoronids are ciliary feeders. The tentacular cilia beat downward, creating a water current directed toward a groove between the two lophophoral ridges. The current then follows the grooves inward on each side toward the mouth and exits dorsally over the anus and nephridiopores. Plankton and suspended detritus that are caught in the lophophoral current are entangled in mucus on contact with the tentacles and the basal groove. Cilia on the basal groove convey the food particles toward the mouth, the lateral angles of which are continuous with the lophophoral groove.

The digestive tract is U-shaped (Fig. 18-2, *A*). The mouth opens into a buccal region and then into a long tubular esophagus. The esophagus passes gradually into the enlarged stomach in the posterior end of the animal. The stomach joins a long tubular intestine, and at this point of junction, the digestive tract makes a 180-degree turn so that the intestine extends forward and dorsally to the anterior half of the alimentary tract. A terminal rectum opens to the outside through the dorsal anus located in the midline above the lophophore. Digestion probably takes place in the stomach and is believed to be intracellular.

A definite blood-vascular system is present in phoronids. There are two main vessels—a dorsal vessel that lies between the two limbs of the gut and carries blood anteriorly, and a ventral vessel that lies to the left of the esophagus and delivers blood to the posterior of the animal

(Fig. 18-2, *B*). Anteriorly the dorsal vessel supplies each tentacle with a small vessel. The lophophore is drained by the ventral vessel. Posteriorly, the dorsal and ventral vessels are connected by a network of sinuses within the stomach wall. Along its course, the ventral vessel gives off a large number of small blind contractile vessels called capillary ceca. The blood possesses red corpuscles that contain hemoglobin. The blood is driven through the system by waves of contraction that sweep over the dorsal and ventral vessels.

Excretion is accomplished by a pair of ciliated U-shaped metanephridia located at the anterior of the trunk coelom (Fig. 18-2, *B*). Each nephridium is retroperitoneal, but one arm of the U opens into the coelom as a nephrostome. The opposite arm ascends the body wall to open dorsally through one of the nephridiopores located on each side of the anus.

The nervous system consists of a nerve ring located in the epidermis at the outer base of the lophophore. The nerve ring gives rise to nerves supplying the tentacles, to motor fibers innervating the longitudinal muscle layer of the body wall, and to a single giant motor fiber that courses through the epidermis on the left side of the body as the lateral nerve. A small fiber is situated on the right side in a few species. The nerve ring is also continuous with a nervous layer located in the base of the epidermis over the entire body wall. The epidermal nerve plexus supplies motor fibers to the body wall musculature and also supplies the epidermis with numerous sensory cells. The sensory cells comprise the principal part of the sensory system of phoronids.

At least one species, *Phoronis ovalis*, that is found in aggregations is known to reproduce asexually, both by budding and by transverse fission. The majority of phoronids are hermaphroditic. The sex cells arise from the peritoneum covering the blind capillary ceca of the ventral vessel, and the gonads are merely masses of cells surrounding these vessels, the ovaries located on one side and the testes on the other. The gametes are shed into the coelom of the trunk and escape to the outside by way of the nephridia. The eggs of most species are fertilized externally and are either planktonic or are brooded in the concavity formed by the two arms of the lophophore. In brooding species, the eggs are held in place by the inner tentacles and probably by secretions from the lophophoral organs, a glandular area located on each side of the lophophoral concavity.

The early embryology of some species shows traces of spiral cleavage. The gastrula develops into an elongated ciliated larva called an

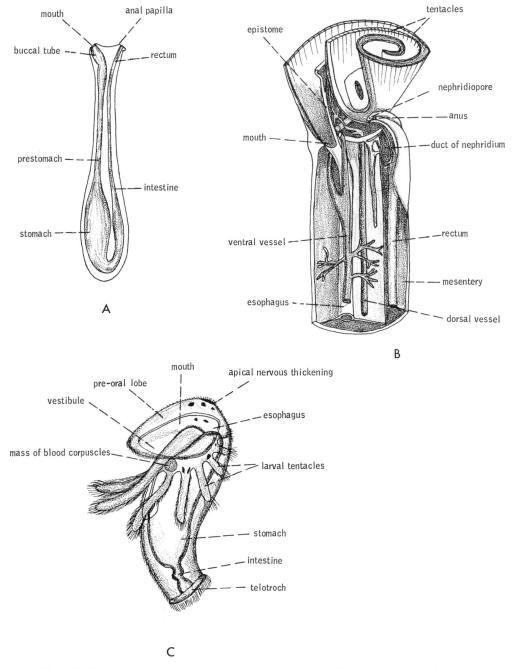

Figure 18-2.   *A.* Digestive tract of a phoronid. (After Hyman.) *B.* Internal structure of anterior of *Phoronis australis.* (After Benham from Parker and Haswell.) *C.* Actinotroch larva of *Phoronis.* (After Wilson from Hyman.)

actinotroch, which is a modified trochophore (Fig. 18-2, *C*). A large pre-oral hood covers the mouth, and behind the mouth is a slanting collar bearing ciliated tentacles. A heavily ciliated telotroch, which is probably the principal locomotor organ, rings the posterior of the trunk. There is a complete and more or less straight digestive tube, and like the trochophore of mollusk and annelids, the larval excretory organs are protonephridia. After several weeks of a free-swimming and feeding planktonic existence, the actinotroch undergoes a rapid metamorphosis and sinks to the bottom, where it secretes a tube and takes up an adult existence.

Phylum Ectoprocta

The phylum Ectoprocta is the largest and the

most common of the lophophorate phyla, and contains some 4000 living species. The group thus constitutes one of the major animal phyla, despite the fact that it has largely been left to the interest of a few specialists. The phylum was formerly united with the Entoprocta as the phylum Bryozoa, or moss animals, names that are still commonly applied to ectoprocts. However, the two groups are at the most only remotely related. The tentacular crown of entoprocts is not a lophophore, since the tentacles enclose the anus. Moreover, the entoproct body cavity appears to be a pseudocoel and not a true coelom.

With a very few exceptions, ectoprocts are all colonial and sessile animals, and the individuals (zooids) composing the colonies are usually less than one half millimeter in length. Zooids of most species are encased in a nonliving envelopment that contains an opening for the protrusion of the lophophore. The interior of the body is occupied largely by the rather spacious coelom and the U-shaped digestive tract. There are no respiratory, circulatory, or excretory organs, probably owing to the small size of these animals.

The phylum is divided into two classes—the Gymnolaemata and the Phylactolaemata. The class Gymnolaemata is almost exclusively marine and includes the majority of the ectoproct species. The class Phylactolaemata, on the other hand, is restricted to fresh water and although widely distributed, contains only about 50 species.

The Structure of the Zooid. The ectoproct individual (zooid) is box-like, oval, vase-like, or tubular in shape (Figs. 18-3 and 18-4). The nonliving outer covering is called the zooecium and varies in composition. Some fresh-water forms, such as the common *Pectinatella,* have a gelatinous zooecium, but in most ectoprocts the zooecium is at least partly composed of chitin.

In the majority of gymnolaemates, the external chitinous layer overlies a thick layer of calcium carbonate, so that the zooecium forms a rigid external skeleton. An opening (the orifice) in the zooecium enables the lophophore to protrude, and in a considerable number of marine ectoprocts the orifice is provided with a lid (operculum) which closes when the animal withdraws into the zooecium (Fig. 18-7, *A*). At the orifice, the zooecium is turned inward for some distance to form a chamber called the vestibule. At the bottom of the vestibule is a restricted opening through which the lophophore is protracted or retracted. This opening is provided with a sphincter, or diaphragm.

The zooecium is secreted by the epidermis of the living animal (Figs. 18-3 and 18-7, *A*).

The epidermis is attached to the secreted casing so that the animal is not free within the zooecium. As would be expected, there are no muscle layers composing the body wall underlying the rigid zooecium of gymnolaemates, and the epidermis overlies a thin delicate peritoneum. However, in the fresh-water phylactolaemates, in which the zooecial wall is gelatinous or composed only of a chitinous cuticle and is thus less rigid, the body wall contains a layer of circular and a layer of longitudinal muscle fibers.

Within the body wall, there is a large coelom surrounding the digestive tract. From the underside of the diaphragm a sheath of body wall extends downward to attach to the base of the lophophore. This sheath, called the tentacular sheath, is the only part of the body wall not attached to the zooecium (Fig. 18-3). The tentacular sheath encloses the tentacles of the lophophore when the animal is retracted. When the animal is feeding, the lophophore protrudes through the diaphragm, vestibule, and orifice, and the tentacular sheath surrounds the extended neck-like anterior of the trunk.

The lophophore of the fresh-water phylactolaemates, with the exception of the circular lophophore of *Fredericella,* is essentially like that of phoronids—that is, the lophophore is horseshoe-shaped and composed of two ridges bearing a total of 16 to 106 tentacles (Fig. 18-4). As in phoronids, one ridge passes above and one passes below the mouth at the bend of the horseshoe. A dorsal hollow lip (epistome) overhangs the mouth. In gymnolaemates, the lophophore is circular and consists of a simple ridge bearing 8 to 34 tentacles (Fig. 18-3); there is no epistome. When retracted, the tentacles are bunched together within the sheath; when protruded from the zooecium, the tentacles fan out forming a funnel with the mouth at the base.

The outer surface of each tentacle is unciliated, but on both the lateral surface and on the inner median surface is a longitudinal tract of cilia. Within the epidermal layer are longitudinal muscle fibers, and through the center of each tentacle runs an extension of the coelom.

The mouth at the center of the lophophore opens into a U-shaped digestive tract, the details of which are considered in the discussion on nutrition (Figs. 18-3 and 18-4). The anus opens through the dorsal side of the tentacular sheath. The coelom is divided by a septum into an anterior portion occupying the lophophore with extensions into the tentacles, and a larger posterior trunk coelom. The trunk coelom is crossed by muscle fibers and cords of tissue, one of the most conspicuous of which is a cord called the funiculus, which extends between the posterior end of the stomach and the

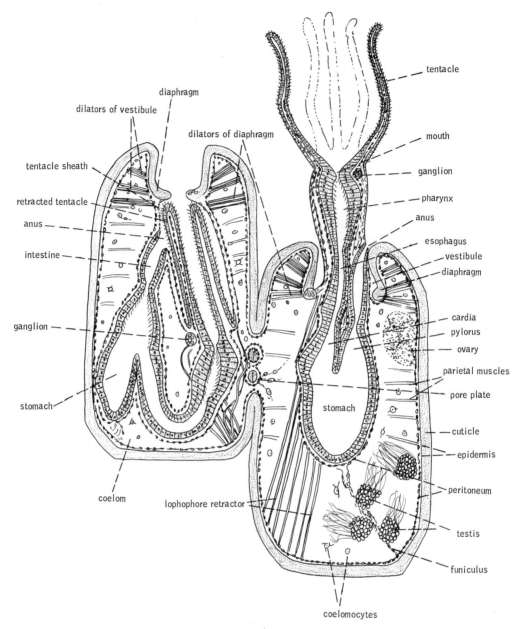

Figure 18-3.   Structure of two zooids of a gymnolaemate ectoproct. (After Marcus from Hyman.)

back body wall. The most conspicuous of the internal muscles are two sets of lophophore retractors, which extend on each side from the base of the lophophore or the septum to the back body wall.

Colony Organization. With this brief background of the structure of a zooid, the organization of ectoproct colonies can now be examined. Gymnolaemates are very common and abundant marine animals. Although some species have been recorded from depths as great as 18,000 feet, most species are littoral and attach to rocks, pilings, shells, algae, and other

animals. A few species form stoloniferous colonies (Fig. 18-5, *A*). The erect or creeping stolons are composed of modified zooids that give the stolon a jointed appearance. Those zooids that are unmodified are attached by the posterior end of the zooecium and are completely separate from one another. However, the vast majority of marine ectoprocts are not stoloniferous, and the colony is formed by the direct attachment and fusion of adjacent zooids. Moreover, the orientation of the body to the substratum is different. The dorsal surface is attached to the substratum, the lateral surfaces

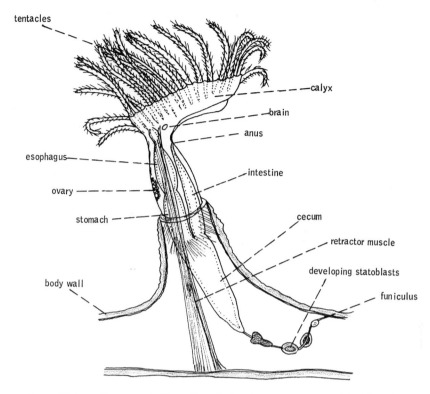

tentacles

calyx

brain

anus

esophagus

intestine

ovary

stomach

cecum

retractor muscle

developing statoblasts

body wall

funiculus

Figure 18-4.   Structure of *Plumatella,* a phylactolaemate ectoproct. (After Pennak.)

are attached to adjacent zooids, and the ventral surface becomes the exposed surface, now called the frontal surface (Fig. 18-7, *A*). Correlated with this change in position, the orifice has migrated toward the exposed ventral, or frontal, surface.

The growth pattern of nonstoloniferous ectoproct colonies varies greatly. Many noncalcified species, such as the common Atlantic *Bugula,* form erect branching colonies that look like seaweed. In *Bugula,* for example, such a plant-like growth form is attained commonly through a biserial attachment of zooids (Fig. 18-5, *C*). Species with calcareous zooecia, which includes most gymnolaemates, possess more solid and rigid colonies. *Membranipora, Microporella,* and *Schizoporella* are very common calcareous genera (Fig. 18-6) that form encrusting colonies. Such colonies are composed of a single sheet of zooids attached to rocks and shells. Other calcified species form erect, branched or lobate colonies reminiscent of coral.

The zooids of a colony communicate by pores through the transverse end walls or the lateral walls, depending on the growth pattern of the colony (Figs. 18-3 and 18-7, *A*). In the case of lateral communication, there is typically a pore plate with a number of small pores. In all gymnolaemates, the pores are plugged with epidermal cells, and only a slow diffusion

through the pores is permitted; in phylactolaemates, on the other hand, the pores are open or transverse septa may be incomplete, so direct flow of coelomic fluid between members of the colony is possible.

The colonies of most gymnolaemates are polymorphic. The zooid is a typical feeding individual, called an autozooid, and makes up the bulk of the colony. Reduced or modified zooids that serve other functions are known as heterozooids. The most common type of heterozooid and one that is found in most gymnolaemates is that which is modified to form stolons, attachment discs, root-like structures, and other such vegetative parts of the colony. These individuals are so reduced that they consist of little more than the body wall and a few interior strands of tissue passing through their interior.

Another common type of heterozooid, called an avicularium, is found in many cheilostomes. Avicularia are usually smaller than autozooids, and the internal structure is greatly reduced (Figs. 18-5, *C* and 18-7, *C*). However, the operculum is sometimes highly developed and modified, forming a movable jaw. Avicularia may be sessile or stalked; when stalked, they are capable of rapid bending or "pecking" movements. Such stalked avicularia are found in *Bugula* and resemble little bird heads attached to the colony (Fig. 18-7, *C*).

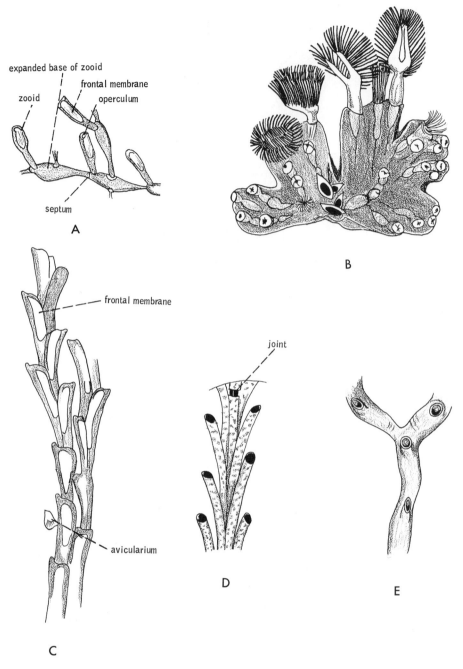

Figure 18-5.   Ectoproct colonies. *A*. Simple stoloniferous colony of the cheilostome, *Aetea*. *B.* *Lophopus crystallinus,* a phylactolaemate; zooids of the colony are located in a gelatinous mass. (After Kraepelin from Pennak.) *C*. Biserial arrangement of zooids in the upright colony of *Bugula*, a cheilostome. (After Hyman.) *D*. Section of the erect colony of the cyclostome, *Crisia*. (After Rogick and Croasdale.) *E*. Uniserial arrangement of zooids in a colony of the cyclostome, *Stomatopora*. (After Hincks from Hyman.)

Avicularia capture or fend off small organisms, particularly larvae of other sessile animals.

Another type of heterozooid, called a vibraculum, is found in some species of operculate ectoprocts. The operculum is modified to form a long bristle sometimes called a seta, that can be moved about and is apparently used to sweep away detritus and other settling larvae (Fig. 18-7, *B*). Modification of zooids for reproductive purposes is discussed later.

Although the zooids are microscopic, the colonies themselves are one to several centi-

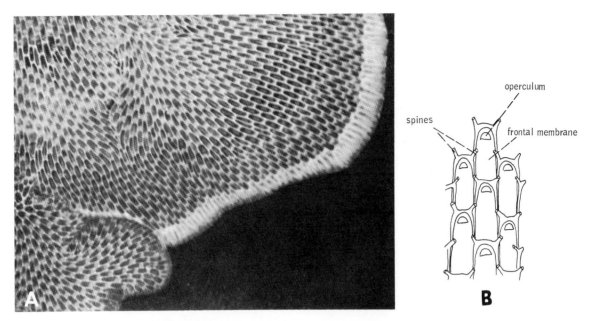

Figure 18-6.   The encrusting gymnolaemate, *Membranipora membranacea. A.* Part of a colony growing over an algal frond. (By D. P. Wilson.) *B.* Frontal view of a number of zooecia. (After Hincks from Hyman.)

meters in diameter or height and may attain a much greater size. Some erect species reach a height of over one foot, and some encrusting colonies may attain a diameter of several feet. White or pale tints are typical of most colonies, but darker colors may be found. The taxonomy of marine ectoprocts is based almost exclusively on the structure of the zooecia and the colonial organization.

The colonies of fresh-water phylactolaemates are of two types, the lophopodid and the plumatellid. In the lophopodid type, of which *Lophopus, Cristatella,* and *Pectinatella* are examples, the zooids project from one side of the soft colony sac resembling the fingers of a glove (Fig. 18-5, *B*). *Pectinatella* colonies secrete a gelatinous base, sometimes several feet in diameter, to which surface the zooids adhere. The plumatellid type of colony, of which *Plumatella, Fredericella,* and *Stolella* are examples, has a more or less plant-like growth form, in which there are either erect or creeping branches composed of a succession of zooids. The colonies of fresh-water ectoprocts are attached to vegetation, submerged wood, rocks, and other objects. *Cristatella,* in which the colony is a flattened gelatinous ribbon, is not fixed and creeps over the substratum at a rate of not more than one inch a day.

Internal Anatomy and Physiology.   During feeding, the lophophore is pushed outward through the diaphragm and vestibule, causing the tentacular sheath to evert. The tentacles then expand, forming a funnel. Protraction of

the lophophore is effected in all cases by the elevation of the coelomic fluid pressure, although the mechanism accomplishing this varies. In some nonrigid marine species with gelatinous or thin chitinous zooecia, the coelomic fluid pressure increases because of the contraction of parietal muscles, which are oblique strands of muscle fibers extending through the coelom from one wall to another; in fresh-water ectoprocts, increase of the coelomic fluid pressure is accomplished by the contraction of body wall muscles (absent in marine ectoprocts) and by contraction of the invaginated fold muscles and duplicature bands.

In many calcareous species and even some forms with rigid chitinous zooecia, such as *Bugula,* the exposed frontal surface of the zooecium contains a window covered by a thin chitinous membrane (the frontal membrane) (Fig. 18-7, *A, C, and D*). The parietal muscles are inserted on the inner side of the membrane. On contraction, the flexible frontal membrane is bowed inward, increasing the coelomic pressure. In some gymnolaemates in which even the frontal wall is completely calcified, there is a sac located beneath the frontal wall that opens onto the frontal surface just below the orifice (Fig. 18-7, *E*). Parietal muscles are attached to the wall of the sac that on contraction cause the sac to dilate. Water rushes in to fill the sac and simultaneously exerts pressure on the interior of the zooid causing the protraction of the lophophore.

The expanded lophophore can be moved

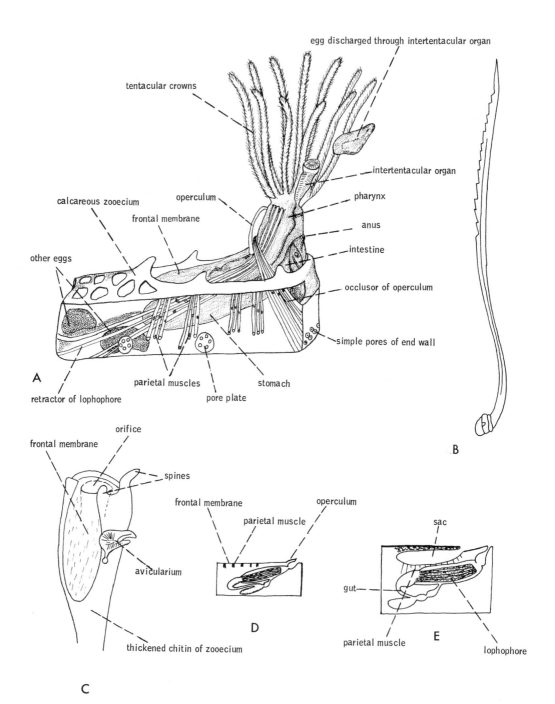

Figure 18-7.   *A.* A zooid of the encrusting cheilostome, *Electra* (lateral view). (After Marcus from Hyman.) *B.* A vibracular bristle. (After Härmer from Hyman.) *C.* Zooecium of *Bugula* with avicularium. (After Hyman.) *D* and *E.* Mechanisms of lophophore expulsion. *D.* A zooid in which elevation of coelomic fluid pressure is produced by bowing-in of the frontal membrane (lateral view). *E.* A zooid in which elevation of coelomic fluid pressure is produced by the filling of a sac with sea water. (*D* and *E* after Härmer and Silén from Hyman.)

or directed to any angle and the tentacles can be moved independently. Retraction of the lophophore into the zooecium is effected by the contraction of the lophophoral retractor muscles.

When the lophophore is protracted, the lateral ciliated tracts on the tentacles create a current that sweeps downward into the funnel and passes outward between the bases of the tentacles. Small plankton, chiefly diatoms, are collected from the water current by the tentacular cilia and driven into the open mouth. The ciliary beat of the tentacles can be slowed or reversed, causing rejection of the food particles.

The mouth at the center of the lophophore opens into a ciliated pharynx followed by an esophagus (Fig. 18-3). The esophagus leads into the stomach, which is an enlarged chamber occupying the bend of the U-shaped digestive tract. When the lophophore is retracted, the posterior of the stomach projects backward as a cecum. The stomach extends anteriorly into a tubular intestine, or rectum, that extends anteriorly to open through the anus located in the dorsal side of the tentacular sheath. The pharynx and the posterior of the stomach are lined with ciliated epithelium, while the stomach and intestinal lining contain abundant gland cells. The wall of the entire digestive tract is provided with muscle fibers.

From the mouth, food particles pass through the pharynx and collect in the esophagus. Periodically, waves of contraction pass down the esophagus, forcing the collected food particles into the stomach. In marine ectoprocts, food particles are entangled in mucus cords within the stomach and then rotated very rapidly by the anterior cilia. According to Ries (1936), protein and starches appear to be digested extracellularly and fats intracellularly. Nondigested particles are passed into the intestine, in which they are molded into fecal pellets and egested when the lophophore is protracted. In phylactolaemates, the food particles are shuttled back and forth within the stomach, and digestion is apparently entirely extracellular. The intestine may play some role in absorption. In all ectoprocts, the epithelial lining of the digestive tract is the primary site for storage of food reserves.

There are no blood-vascular, respiratory, or excretory systems in ectoprocts. General diffusion of gases through the exposed body surface and the transport of food, gases, and waste by the coelomic fluid are sufficiently effective in animals of such minute size. The coelomic fluid contains coelomocytes, which engulf and store waste materials. Wastes are also picked up by cells in the tentacles and stomach and passed to the outside.

In marine ectoprocts, the nervous system is composed of a ganglionic mass on the dorsal side of the pharynx, from which a nerve isssues on each side to encircle the pharynx as a nerve ring (Fig. 18-3). The ganglion and ring give rise to nerves extending to each of the tentacles, to the tentacular sheath, to the diaphragm, and to the digestive tract. A subepithelial nerve plexus is located in the body wall and in the tentacular sheath. The nervous system of fresh-water ectoprocts is similar, except that the somewhat larger dorsal ganglion gives rise to two large hollow ganglionated nerves, called lophophoral tracts, that extend into the lophophoral arms and into an epistomial ring, if an epistome is present. These tracts in turn innervate the tentacles. There are no specialized sense organs in ectoprocts.

Reproduction. All fresh-water ectoprocts and most marine species are hermaphroditic. The one or two ovaries and the one to many testes are masses of developing gametes covered by peritoneum; the masses bulge into the coelom. The ovaries are located in the distal end of the animal and the testes in the basal end (Fig. 18-3). In dioecious species, the entire colony may be composed of zooids of the same sex, or both male and female individuals may be present. There are no genital ducts, and the eggs and sperm rupture into the coelom.

Some marine species shed their eggs directly into the sea water. The vast majority of ectoprocts brood their eggs. A variety of different brooding mechanisms are employed. The eggs, which are always few in number, may be brooded in the coelom or, in some genera such as *Tendra,* may be retained on the frontal membrane, where they are held in place by overarching spines. In *Bugula* and many other gymnolaemates, the eggs are brooded in a special external chamber called an ovicell (Fig. 18-8). The body wall at the distal end of the zooid grows outward forming a large hood (the ovicell). A second smaller evagination bulges into the space formed by the ovicell. A single egg is brooded in the space between the two evaginations. The second evagination, which is directly connected to the coelom, apparently functions in providing the egg with food materials.

Coelomic incubation is the most common brooding method. The eggs somehow get into special invaginations of the body wall, called embryo sacs, that bulge into the coelom. Such embryo sacs are characteristic of many marine ectoprocts and all known fresh-water species. Usually the embryo increases in size within the embryo sac at the expense of other internal organs, which gradually degenerate. Zooids that become highly modified during the course of

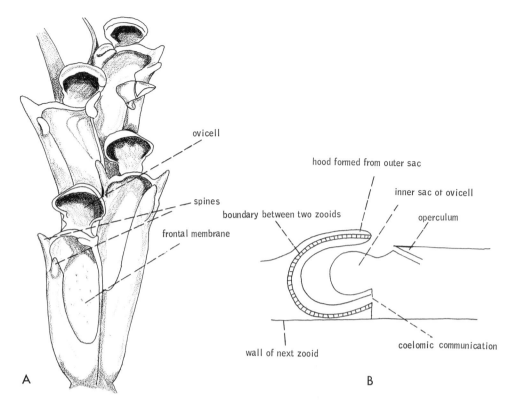

ovicell

spines

boundary between two zooids

frontal membrane

hood formed from outer sac

inner sac of ovicell

operculum

wall of next zooid

coelomic communication

A

B

Figure 18-8.   *A.* Part of a *Bugula* colony with ovicells. (After Rogick and Croasdale from Hyman.) *B.* An ovicell (sagittal section). (After Silén from Hyman.)

egg production and brooding are considered reproductive individuals and contribute to the polymorphic nature of the colony.

When the eggs are shed into the sea water or are brooded externally, they escape from the coelom by way of a special opening in the region of the lophophore. In *Bugula,* the eggs are fertilized in the coelom by sperm produced in the same zooid, but whether self-fertilization takes place in all species is not known. Self-fertilization obviously cannot take place in dioecious ectoprocts, but the mechanism of sperm entrance into the coelom is an enigma in species exhibiting coelomic brooding.

Cleavage in marine species is radial but leads to a modified trochophore larva. The larva escapes from the brood chamber, or in the case of nonbrooding species, hatches from the egg membranes. The larvae vary considerably in form, (Figure 18-9), but all possess a locomotor ciliated girdle, an apical nervous organ, an anterior tuft of long cilia, and a posterior adhesive sac. The larvae of some species of ctenostomes and cheilostomes are greatly compressed, and each lateral surface is covered by a chitinous valve. Only the larvae of nonbrooding ectoprocts possess a functional digestive tract and feed during larval existence. Feeding larvae may

have a larval life of several months, but the larvae of brooding species, which are nonfeeding, have a very brief larval existence prior to settling.

During settling the adhesive sac everts and fastens by means of secretions to the substratum. The larval structures of the attached larva undergo retraction and histolysis, followed by development of the larva into an adult. The first zooid is called an ancestrula and by budding gives rise to several other zooids. These zooids, in turn, bud off new individuals, and thus by subsequent asexual reproduction a new colony arises and gradually increases in size. Budding involves the cutting off of a part of the parent zooid by the formation of a body wall partition and may be preceded by the evagination of the parent body wall in this region. The new chamber evaginates either before or after its formation and develops a new zooid from the ectoderm and peritoneum of the body wall. The exact pattern of budding determines the growth pattern of the colony.

Development in fresh-water phylactolaemates takes place within an embryo sac that bulges into the coelom. Development leads to the formation of a cystid sac, which then proceeds to bud off one to several zooids. This

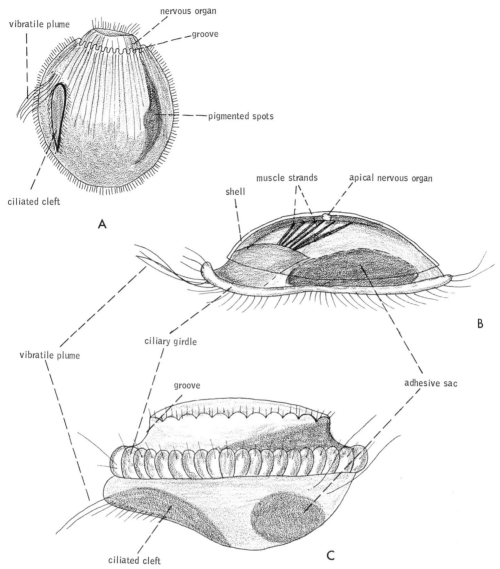

Figure 18-9.   Ectoproct larvae. *A. Bugula.* (After Cavel from Hyman.) *B. Flustrellidra hispida.* C. *Alcyonidium mytili.* (*B* and *C* after Barrois from Hyman.)

young ciliated colony or "larva" is released from the parent colony. It swims about for a short time prior to settling. After attachment, retraction and degeneration of the once ciliated outer cystid wall ensues. Meanwhile, the young colony that had been developing inside the confines of the cystid wall continues to bud successive zooids until an adult colony is formed. The parent zooid dies after producing a number of daughter individuals. Thus in branching colonies, only the tips of branches contain living zooids; and in the flattened gelatinous colonies, living zooids are restricted to the periphery.

In addition to sexual reproduction and to budding, fresh-water ectoprocts also reproduce asexually by means of special resistant bodies called statoblasts (Fig. 18-10). One to several

statoblasts develop on the funiculus and bulge into the coelom as masses of peritoneal cells that contain stored food material, and epidermal cells that have migrated to the site of statoblast formation. After organizing cellularly, each mass secretes both an upper and a lower chitinous valve that form a protective covering for the internal cells. Since the rims of the valves often project peripherally to a considerable extent, the statoblasts are usually somewhat disc-shaped. Statoblasts are continuously formed during the summer and fall.

The structure and shape of statoblasts are important in the taxonomy of the fresh-water ectoprocts. Some types of statoblasts adhere to the parent colony or fall to the bottom; others contain air spaces and float. These floating

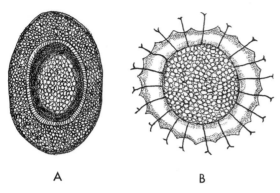

Figure 18-10.   Statoblasts of fresh-water ectoprocts. *A.* A floating statoblast of *Hyalinella punctata.* (After Rogick from Pennak.) *B.* Statoblast with hooks from *Cristatella mucedo.* (After Allman from Rogick.)

statoblasts are sometimes armed with hooks around the margins.

Statoblasts remain dormant for a variable length of time. During this period they may be spread considerable distances by animals, floating vegetation, or other agents and are able to withstand desiccation and freezing. When environmental conditions become favorable, as in the spring, germination takes place, the two valves separate, and a zooid develops from the internal mass of cells. The number of statoblasts produced by a fresh-water ectoproct is enormous. Brown (1933) reported drifts of statoblast valves one to four feet wide along the shores of Douglas Lake in Michigan and estimated that *Plumatella repens* colonies in one square meter of littoral lake vegetation produce 800,000 statoblasts.

Ecology and Systematics. Gymnolaemates are found in all seas and are one of the most common sessile animals of littoral waters. They attach to any firm substratum, and a few species, such as *Membranipora tuberculata,* commonly live on the leaves of floating *Sargassum.* A few genera, such as *Paludicella,* occur in fresh water. From an economic standpoint, marine ectoprocts are one of the most important groups of fouling organisms. Over 130 marine ectoproct species, of which different species of *Bugula* are among the most abundant, have been taken from ship bottoms.

Fresh-water ectoprocts are widely distributed in lakes and streams that do not contain excessive mud or silt and that are sufficiently rich in plankton. Many species, such as *Fredericella sultana* and *Plumatella repens,* are cosmopolitan. Although phylactolaemates were formerly a problem in water reservoirs and purification plants, these animals are of less economic significance today.

Marine ectoprocts appeared in the Ordovician period and reached their peak in the Mesozoic era. Fifteen thousand fossil species have been described, but this number is considered too large by some specialists. Of the two classes of living ectoprocts, the phylactolaemates are considered the more primitive. The anterior location of the orifice, the horseshoe-shaped lophophore, the presence of a protostome, and the nonpolymorphic colonies are all considered primitive features.

Systematic Résumé of Phylum Ectoprocta

Class Gymnolaemata.   Primarily marine ectoprocts with polymorphic colonies. Zooids possess a circular lophophore; an epistome and body wall musculature are lacking.

Order Ctenostomata.   Stoloniferous or compact colonies in which the zooecium is membranous or chitinous. The fresh-water *Paludicella.*

Order Cheilostomata.   Colonies composed of box-like zooids that are adjacent but have separate walls. Zooecia are usually calcified. Orifice is provided with an operculum. Avicularia, vibracula, or both may be present or absent. Eggs are commonly brooded in ovicells. *Bugula, Membranipora, Schizoporella, Microporella.*

Order Cyclostomata (Stenolaemata or Stenostomata).   Zooids are tubular, with calcified walls that are fused with adjacent zooids. Brooding is internal in modified zooids (called gonozooids) or takes place in special common brood chambers, of which there may be one or more for a single colony.

Class Phylactolaemata.   Fresh-water ectoprocts in which the zooids possess a horseshoe-shaped lophophore (except in *Fredericella*), an epistome, a body wall musculature, and noncalcified zooecia. Colonies are nonpolymorphic. *Fredericella, Plumatella, Pectinatella, Lophopus, Cristatella.*

Phylum Brachiopoda

The last of the three lophophorate phyla is the phylum Brachiopoda, commonly known as lamp shells. These animals resemble bivalve mollusks in possessing a mantle and a calcareous shell of two valves that approximates that of mollusks in size. In fact the phylum was not separated from the mollusks until the middle of the 19th century. However, the resemblance to mollusks is superficial, for in brachiopods the two valves enclose the body dorsally and ventrally instead of laterally, and the ventral valve is typically larger than the dorsal (Fig. 18-11, *A* and *B*). Moreover, the ventral valve is usually attached to the substratum directly or by means of a cord-like stalk (Fig. 18-11, *C*). The mantle lobes secrete the shell and enclose the lophophore.

All brachiopods are marine, and very few species are found at depths beyond the edge of the continental shelf. Most species live attached to rocks or other firm substrata, but some forms, such as *Lingula*, live in vertical burrows in sand and mud bottoms (Fig. 18-11, *D*).

The approximately 260 species of living brachiopods are but a fraction of the some 30,000 described fossil species that flourished in Paleozoic and Mesozoic seas. The phylum made its appearance in the Cambrian period and reached its peak of evolutionary development during the Ordovician period. After the Mesozoic era, the group rapidly declined to its present number and is apparently on the road to extinction. The genus *Lingula* (but none of the

present living species) dates back to the Ordovician period.

External Anatomy. Each of the two valves is bilaterally symmetrical and is usually convex. The smaller dorsal shell fits over the larger ventral shell, the apex of which in some groups is drawn out posteriorly and upward as a spout, like a Roman lamp—hence the origin of the name *lamp shell* (Fig. 18-11, *B*). In the burrowing lingulids, the valves are flattened and more equal in size. The valves may be ornamented with concentric growth lines and a fluted, ridged, or even a spiny surface. The color of the shell in most living brachiopods is dull yellowish or gray, but some species have orange or red shells.

The two valves articulate with one another along the posterior line of contact, called the hinge line (Fig. 18-11, *A*), and the nature of the articulation is the basis for the division of the

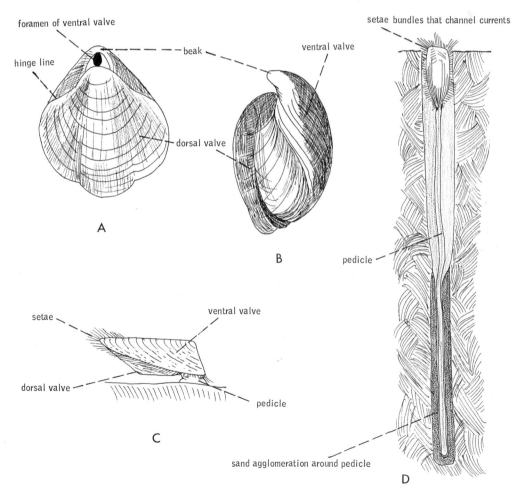

Figure 18-11.   *A.* The articulate brachiopod, *Hemithyris* (dorsal view). *B. Hemithyris* (lateral view). (Both after Blochmann from Hyman.) *C. Discinisca* attached to substratum (lateral view). (After Morse from Hyman.) *D.* The inarticulate, *Lingula,* in feeding position within burrow. (After Francois from Hyman.)

phylum into two classes, the Inarticulata and the Articulata. In inarticulate brachiopods, such as *Lingula* and *Glottidia,* the two valves are only held together by muscles and can be opened very widely.

In articulate brachiopods, on the other hand, the valves bear interlocking processes that greatly restrict the degree of gape. Along the hinge line, the ventral valve bears a pair of hinge teeth that fit into opposing sockets on the underside of the hinge line of the dorsal valve (Fig. 18-12, *A*). This articulating mechanism locks the valves securely together and allows only a slight anterior gape of approximately 10 degrees. Two or three pairs of muscles that extend be-

tween the valves and through the coelom control the movements of the valves in the articulates, and as many as five pairs of such muscles may be present in the inarticulates (Fig. 18-13).

The dorsal valve also provides support for the lophophore. The inner surface of the valve may be grooved and ridged for the reception of the lophophore, or the dorsal valve may bear complicated processes that are actually inserted into the lophophore to form an internal skeleton (Fig. 18-12, *A*).

The shell is secreted by the underlying dorsal and ventral mantle lobes. The outer surface of the shell is covered by a chitinous

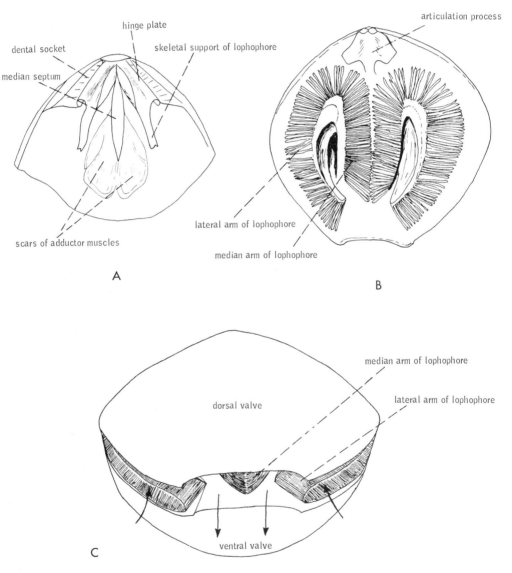

Figure 18-12.   *A.* Internal surface of dorsal valve of an articulate brachiopod. (After Davidson from Hyman.) *B.* Lophophore and dorsal valve of *Magellania.* (After Fischer and Oehlert from Hyman.) *C. Neothyris lenticularis* with valves held in feeding position (anterior view). Arrows indicate direction of water currents moving over lophophore. (After Richards from Hyman.)

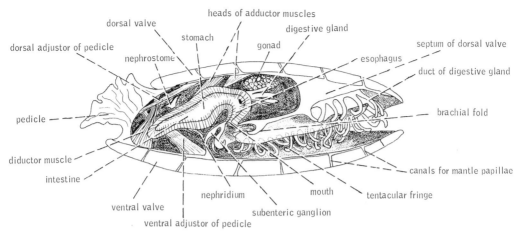

Figure 18-13.   Section through an articulate brachiopod. (After Shipley from Hyman.)

periostracum, beneath which are mineral layers, mainly of calcium phosphate in the inarticulate shells and calcium carbonate in the articulate shells. As in the mollusks, the periostracum and outer layers of mineral deposition are secreted by the mantle edge, and the inner layer of shell is secreted by the entire outer mantle surface. In addition to secreting the shell, the mantle edge bears in most species long chitinous setae or bristles that are believed to have a protective and perhaps a sensory function (Fig. 18-11, C).

The body proper of brachiopods occupies only the posterior part of the chamber formed by the two valves (Fig. 18-13). Anteriorly, the space between the mantle lobes (the mantle cavity) is filled by the lophophore. As in other lophophorates, the brachiopod lophophore is basically a crown of tentacles surrounding the mouth, but as a means of increasing the surface area the margin of the lophophore is formed into anterior lobes or arms, which may be coiled. In most articulate families, there are two lateral uncoiled arms and a single median coiled arm (Fig. 18-12, B). In the lingulids, or inarticulates in general, the lateral arms are coiled, and there is no median arm. The arms may bear one or two rows of tentacles. The tentacle-bearing ridge is flanked by a brachial groove at its base. The brachial groove conducts food particles and is continuous with the medial margins of the mouth.

Most brachiopods are attached to the substratum by a cylindrical extension of the ventral body wall called the pedicle. The pedicle of the inarticulate lingulids (*Lingula* and *Glottidia*) is long, provided with muscles, and emerges at the posterior of the animal between the two valves (Fig. 18-11, D). The lingulids live in vertical burrows excavated in sand and mud. The anterior ends of the valves are directed toward the burrow opening, and the pedicle extends downward toward the bottom of the burrow and is encased in sand. When the animal is feeding, the gaping valves are partially extended from the slit-like burrow opening; when disturbed, the pedicle contracts and pulls the animal downward into the burrow.

The pedicle of most other brachiopods is very short, lacks muscles, and is composed primarily of connective tissue (Figs. 18-11, C and 18-13). Moreover, the pedicle emerges either from a notch at the hinge line of the ventral valve or through a hole at the upturned apex (Fig. 18-11, A). This means, of course, that the pedicle emerges from the dorsal side of the ventral valve, which extends posteriorly considerably beyond the dorsal valve. These brachiopods are attached to the substratum upside down with the valves held in a horizontal position (Fig. 18-11, C). Movement is considerably more limited than in lingulids, but two pairs of muscles within the valves that are inserted on the side of the pedicle base permit erection or flexion of the animal on the pedicle (and even rotation to a limited degree). The end of the pedicle adheres to the substratum by means of root-like extensions or short papillae.

The pedicle has been lost completely in a few brachiopods of both classes, such as *Crania* (Inarticulata) and *Lacazella* (Articulata). Such species are attached directly to the substratum by the surface of the ventral valve and are thus oriented in a normal manner with the dorsal side up.

Internal Anatomy and Physiology.   The outer epithelium of the body wall is attached dorsally and ventrally to the inner surface of the valves. Beneath the epithelium is a layer of connective tissue, and where the body is free of the shell, there is a layer of longitudinal muscle fibers. Internally the body wall is lined with peritoneum. Since the mantle lobes are extensions of the anterior body wall, each is composed of a double wall with coelom in between. The epidermis of the exposed inner surface of each mantle lobe is ciliated.

The coelom is similar to that of other lophophorates. The anterior mesocoel surrounds the esophagus and extends into the lophophore arms and tentacles; the metacoel surrounds the other internal organs and extends into the pedicle, when present, and also into the mantle. Through the fusion of the two mantle walls, the mantle coelom has become divided into distinct channels. The coelomic fluid contains coelomocytes of several sorts, one of which contains hemerythrin.

When the animal is feeding, the valves gape anteriorly to permit the flow of water over the lophophore (Fig. 18-12, C). The tentacles extend to the margin of the valves and are held somewhat close to the dorsal valve. Lateral tracts of tentacular cilia beat at right angles to the long axis of the tentacles and create two water currents that enter the anterior gape one on each side of the midline. The currents converge posteriorly and turn to flow outward anteriorly as a single median current.

The tentacular inner surface that faces the brachial groove at the base of the lophophore bears mucus glands and tracts of frontal cilia that beat proximally toward the groove. Plankton, primarily diatoms in brachiopods other than lingulids, is trapped in mucus and carried by the frontal cilia down to the brachial groove. Cilia in the groove then transport food particles to the mouth. Rejected particles are carried away in the median outward flowing current.

The mouth leads into an esophagus that extends dorsally and a short distance forward prior to turning posteriorly and joining a dilated stomach (Fig. 18-13). The stomach is surrounded by a digestive gland that opens through the stomach wall by means of one to three ducts on each side. In articulates, a blind intestine extends posteriorly from the stomach, but in inarticulates the intestine opens to the outside through a rectum and anus. The anus is a posterior median opening between the valves in *Crania;* in *Lingula* and others, it opens into the mantle cavity on the right side. According to Chuang (1959), digestion in *Lingula* is chiefly intracellular within the digestive gland.

Brachiopods possess an open circulatory system. There is a contractile vesicle (heart) located over the stomach in the dorsal mesentery, and from the heart extend an anterior and a posterior channel. The anterior channel supplies sinuses in the wall of the digestive tract and sends channels into the arms of the lophophore and the tentacles. The posterior channel supplies the mantle, the gonads and the nephridia. The blood is colorless, and the relatively few formed elements are all coelomocytes.

Although contraction of the heart has been observed, the exact role of the blood-vascular system in the physiology of brachiopods is not definitely known. The circulation of food materials is perhaps its primary function. There are no specialized respiratory organs, but the lophophore and mantle lobes are probably the principal sites of gaseous exchange. Oxygen transport appears to be carried out by the coelomic fluid, for there is a definite circulation of coelomic fluid through the mantle channels.

One or two pairs of metanephridia are present in brachiopods. The nephrostomes open into the metacoel on each side of the posterior end of the stomach, and the tubules then extend anteriorly to open into the mantle cavity through a nephridiopore situated posteriorly and to each side of the mouth (Fig. 18-13). The lining of the nephridia is glandular and ciliated. Coelomocytes are active in the ingestion of particulate waste, and such waste-laden cells, as well as free waste particles, are picked up by the nephrostome from the coelomic fluid and then passed to the outside.

An esophageal nerve ring with a small ganglion on its dorsal side and a larger ganglion on the ventral side forms the nerve center of brachiopods (Fig. 18-13). From the ganglia and their connectives, nerves extend anteriorly and posteriorly to innervate the lophophore, the mantle lobes, and the valve muscles. In inarticulates, the nervous system is closely associated with the epidermis, and in all brachiopods there is probably a subepidermal nerve plexus.

The only known specialized sense organs are a pair of statocysts near the anterior adductor muscles in a Japanese species of *Lingula.*

Reproduction. With a few exceptions, brachiopods are dioecious and the gonads, usually four in number, are masses of developing gametes in the peritoneum of the metacoel (Fig. 18-13). In most inarticulates, including *Lingula,* the gonads are located in the peritoneum of the mesenteries associated with the viscera. In all other brachiopods, the gonads are located in the coelomic canals of the mantle. When ripe, the gametes pass into the coelom and are discharged to the exterior by way of the nephridia.

Except for a few brooding species, the eggs are shed into the sea water and fertilized at the

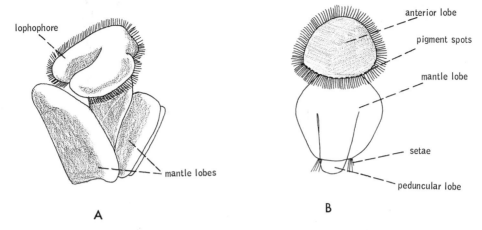

Figure 18-14.   *A.* Larva of the inarticulate, *Lingula.* (After Yatsu from Hyman.) *B.* Larva of the articulate, *Terebratella inconspicua.* (After Percival from Hyman.)

time of spawning. The embryology of brachiopods has evoked considerable interest because of the similarities to development in deuterostomes. Cleavage is radial and nearly equal and leads to a coeloblastula that undergoes gastrulation by invagination, except in *Lacazella,* in which entoderm develops by delamination or ingression. In contrast to the typical method of mesoderm formation in protostomes, the mesoderm in brachiopods appears to be enterocoelic—that is, arises from the archenteron. Masses of mesodermal cells may be proliferated laterally from the archenteron, as in *Lingula,* and later form an internal coelomic cavity; or the mesoderm may arise as pouches to form the archenteron. In *Terebratulina,* the anterior end of the archenteron separates as a primordial coelomic sac, which subsequently divides. This method of coelom formation occurs in many of the echinoderms.

The embryo eventually develops into a free-swimming and feeding larva. The larva of inarticulates resembles a minute brachiopod (Fig. 18-14, *A*). The pair of mantle lobes and the larval valves enclose the body and the ciliated lophophore, which acts as the larval locomotor organ. The pedicle is coiled in the back of the mantle cavity. As additional shell is laid down, the larva becomes heavier and sinks to the bottom. There is no metamorphosis in *Lingula;* the pedicle attaches to the substratum, and the young brachiopod takes up an adult existence. Articulate larvae differ in having a

ciliated anterior lobe representing the body and lophophore, a posterior lobe that forms the pedicle, and a mantle lobe that is directed backward (Fig. 18-14, *B*). In *Terebratulina,* the larva settles after a short free-swimming existence of approximately 24 to 30 hours, and then it undergoes metamorphosis. The mantle lobe reverses position and begins the secretion of the valves, and the adult structures develop from their larval precursors.

BIBLIOGRAPHY

Chuang, S. H., 1959: Structure and function of the alimentary canal in *Lingula unguis.* Proc. Zool. Soc. London, *132*:293–311.

Hyman, L. H., 1959: The Invertebrates. Vol. V. Smaller Coelomate Groups. McGraw-Hill, New York, pp. 228–609. An excellent general treatment of the lophophorate phyla and the only one in English at the present time. An extensive bibliography.

MacGinitie, G. E., and MacGinitie, N., 1949: Natural History of Marine Animals. McGraw-Hill, New York.

Pennak, R. W., 1953: Freshwater Invertebrates of the United States. Ronald Press, New York, pp. 256–277. A general discussion of the fresh-water ectoprocts and key to the species of the United States.

Rogick, M. D., 1959: Bryozoa. *In* Ward and Whipple's Freshwater Biology, (W. T. Edmondson, ed.). 2nd Edition, Wiley, New York, pp. 495–507.

Shipley, A. E., 1927: Brachiopods (Recent). In S. F. Harmer and A. E. Shipley's The Cambridge Natural History, Vol. 3. Macmillan, London. Pp. 463–488.

Chapter 19

THE ECHINODERMS

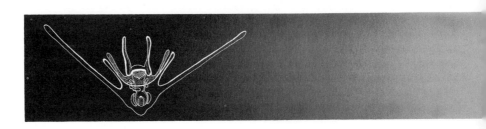

Members of the phylum Echinodermata are among the most familiar marine invertebrates and such forms as the sea stars have become virtually a symbol of sea life. The phylum contains some 5300 known species and constitutes the only major group of deuterostome invertebrates.

The echinoderms are exclusively marine and are largely bottom-dwellers. All are relatively large animals, the smallest being at least one half inch in diameter. The most striking characteristic of the group is their pentamerous radial symmetry—that is, the body can be divided into five parts arranged around a central axis. This radial symmetry, however, has been secondarily derived from a bilateral ancestral form, and the echinoderms are in no way related to the other three radiate phyla—the sponges, the coelenterates, and the ctenophores—which possess a primary radial symmetry. Furthermore, echinoderms are true coelomate animals and have a much higher level of structure than do the other radiate groups.

Characteristic of all echinoderms is the presence of an internal skeleton. The skeleton is composed of calcareous ossicles that may articulate with one another, as in sea stars and brittle stars, or may be fused together to form a rigid skeletal test, as in sea urchins and sand dollars. Typically the skeleton bears projecting spines or tubercles that give the body surface a warty or spiny appearance, hence the name echinoderm—spiny skin.

The most distinctive feature of echinoderms is the presence of a peculiar system of coelomic canals and surface appendages comprising the water-vascular system. Such a system is found in no other group of animals.

Echinoderms possess a spacious coelom in which is suspended a well-developed digestive tract. There is no excretory system. Respiratory structures vary in nature from one group to another and appear to have arisen independently within the different classes. All members of the phylum are dioecious. The reproductive tracts are very simple, for copulation does not take place, and fertilization is external in sea water.

The eggs are typically homolecithal, and the early embryology is relatively uniform throughout the phylum and displays the basic features of deuterostome development. In contrast to that of protostomes, cleavage in echinoderms is radial instead of spiral, and the axes of the spindles (the cleavage planes) are situated at right angles or parallel to the polar axis of the egg (Fig. 9-1).

The first two cleavage planes are vertical, dividing the egg into four equal blastomeres. The third cleavage plane is horizontal and nearly equatorial, thus dividing the egg into eight blastomeres of approximately equal size. With the third cleavage plane the radial pattern of cleavage becomes evident, for each blastomere is located directly above or below another blastomere.

The fourth cleavage plane is again vertical

and develops along two planes dividing the embryo into sixteen cells. Subsequent cleavage planes alternate between horizontal and vertical positions, conforming to the general law of radial cleavage, in which each cleavage plane always is situated at right angles to the preceding plane. Gradually, however, cleavage becomes increasingly irregular.

Determination of cell lineage is not possible in deuterostome cleavage, for unlike cleavage in protostome eggs, the fate of deuterostome blastomeres is usually not fixed at an early stage—that is, cleavage is indeterminate.

As cleavage continues, the blastomeres decrease in size, a segmentation cavity appears in the middle of the mass of cells, and eventually a blastula displaying a large blastocoel is formed. Gastrulation takes place primarily by invagination forming a narrow, tubular archenteron, (primitive gut). The archenteron grows forward and eventually connects with the anterior stomodeum, which will form the mouth. The blastopore remains as the larval anus. Thus, the origin of the mouth in relation to the blastopore is the reverse of that in protostomes.

In deuterostomes, the anus is either derived from the blastopore or is secondarily formed near the site of the closed blastopore. The mouth forms as a secondary opening (deuterostome—second mouth) at the opposite end from the blastopore. Prior to the formation of the mouth, the advancing distal end of the archenteron proliferates some mesenchyme into the blastocoel and then, primitively at least, gives rise to two lateral pockets or pouches that eventually separate from the archenteron (Fig. 19-22, A). The cavities of the pouches represent the future coelomic cavity, and the cells composing the pouch wall become the mesoderm. The remaining archenteron becomes the entoderm of the gut. Thus the mesoderm of deuterostomes is enterocoelous in origin—that is, the mesoderm arises by pouching (evaginations) of the archenteron and does not appear until after gastrulation. Furthermore, the coelom appears more or less simultaneously with the formation of mesoderm. The number of such pouches formed varies in different groups of deuterostomes.

Primitively, in echinoderms the two original pouches, one on each side, each give rise by evagination or subdivision to coelomic vesicles arranged one behind the other and called respectively the axocoel, the hydrocoel, and the somatocoel. The two somatocoels meet above and below the gut to form the gut mesenteries. The axocoels open dorsally through a pore called the hydropore. This primitive and somewhat hypothetical plan of the coelomic vesicles is considerably modified in the development of existing echinoderms. This plan does, however, provide a basis for understanding the origin and arrangement of the coelomic vesicles in the different classes that are discussed later.

The gastrula rapidly develops into a free-swimming larva (Figs. 19-10 and 19-11, A). The most striking feature of the echinoderm larva is its bilateral symmetry, which is in marked contrast to the radial symmetry of the adult. Wound over the surface of the larva are a varying number of ciliated locomotor bands. There is a complete functional digestive tract with a large ciliated stomodeum, an esophagus, a stomach, an intestine, and an anus. Food is obtained from the current of water produced by the stomodeal cilia. Later larval development in most echinoderms involves the formation of short or long slender projections (arms) from the body wall, and the nature and position of these arms, or the lack of them distinguishes the larvae of the different echinoderm classes. The arms disappear in later development and are not equivalent to the arms of certain adult echinoderms, such as sea stars and brittle stars.

After a free-swimming planktonic existence, the bilateral larva undergoes a remarkable metamorphosis in which the radial symmetry of the adult is developed.

The Evolution of Echinoderm Symmetry. The Echinoderms are believed by many zoologists to have arisen from some ancestral coelomate stock that perhaps diverged from the protostome line at the level of the lophophorate groups, although echinoderms have certainly not stemmed directly from any of the existing lophophorate phyla. Considering the symmetry of the echinoderm larva, the ancestral form was undoubtedly a bilateral ciliated animal. According to Semon (1888) and Bury (1895) and supported by Hyman (1955), this ancestral echinoderm, called a pentactula ancestor, must have possessed three pairs of coelomic compartments —the protocoel, the mesocoel, and the metacoel —which correspond to the larval axocoel, hydrocoel, and somatocoel (Fig. 19-45, B).

Around the mouth was a circlet of perhaps ten hollow tentacles representing evaginations of the body wall and containing extensions of the mesocoel. Such an arrangement of hollow tentacles gave rise to the lophophore of the lophophorate phyla and perhaps to the water-vascular system of echinoderms. Like the lophophore, the water-vascular system was probably originally a food-catching organ.

The coelomic channel in each tentacle connected to a ring canal surrounding the mouth, and the ring canal joined a stone canal. The stone canal connected to a hydroporic canal, which opened to the outside through a hydropore. The hydroporic canal was derived from the protocoel (axocoel), and the remainder of the system was derived from the paired mesocoels (hydrocoels). Since the mesocoel was originally paired, five of the ten tentacles were probably associated with one side and five with the other, and in addition there were probably two hydroporic canals and hydropores.

Some individuals of such an ancestral form may have become attached to the bottom and assumed a sessile mode of life. As in many other animal groups, such a sessile existence resulted in a shift to a more adaptive radial symmetry (Fig. 19-45, C). Attachment apparently took place at the anterior end of the animal. Based on the metamorphosis of living echinoderms, the change in symmetry involved a clockwise 90-degree rotation of the animal so that the left side became the upper (oral) side, and the right side became the lower (aboral) side. Simultaneously, the mouth moved around to the original left side, now the upper side. The right protocoel (axocoel) and mesocoel (hydrocoel) degenerated, leaving five tentacles surrounding the mouth and a single hydropore.

During the course of these changes, the echinoderm skeleton probably evolved as protection for the sessile animal. Stages in the development of a radial symmetry are illustrated by some fossil echinoderms that possessed the basic echinoderm plan of structure but were still only imperfectly radially symmetrical. Eventually a relatively perfect radial symmetry evolved. At this point, we have an echinoderm that was both sessile and radial. This stage in the evolution of echinoderm symmetry is illustrated by some extinct groups, as well as by certain of the living crinoids, or sea lilies.

After attaining a radial symmetry, some of these sessile echinoderms became detached and reassumed a free-moving existence. The radial symmetry was retained, but the oral surface, which was directed upward in sessile forms, was placed against the substratum, and the aboral surface became the functional upper side of the animal. Sea stars, brittle stars, and sea urchins all illustrate such a free-moving, radial existence.

A final stage in the evolution of echinoderm symmetry has been a shift back toward a bilateral symmetry correlated with the secondary assumption of a free-moving existence. All degrees between radial symmetry and a distinct bilateral symmetry are illustrated by sand dollars, cake urchins, heart urchins, and sea cucumbers. The latter stages in the evolution of echinoderm symmetry just described have undoubtedly developed independently within a number of evolutionary lines, and different living groups cannot be considered ancestral to one another solely on the basis of symmetry.

Although the crinoids (sea lilies) are the most primitive class of living echinoderms from the standpoint of symmetry and body form, the more familiar asteroids (sea stars) are treated first in the discussion of the echinoderm classes and serve to introduce the basic features of echinoderm structure.

Class Asteroidea

The class Asteroidea contains those echinoderms that are commonly known as starfish or sea stars. All are free-moving, radially symmetrical animals that crawl about over rocks and shells or live on sandy or muddy bottoms. The asteroid body is composed of a central disc from which extend projections of the body called rays or arms (Figs. 19-1 and 19-2). Unlike other echinoderms that possess arms, asteroid arms are not sharply set off from the central disc—that is, the width of the arm usually increases toward the base and grades into the disc.

The sea stars are typically pentamerous with most species possessing five arms. However, a greater number of arms are characteristic of many asteroids. For example, the sun stars (*Crossaster*) possess 7 to 14 arms, and the twenty-rayed star (*Pycnopodia*) of Puget Sound has 15 to 24 arms (Fig. 19-2, B). Most asteroids range between 4 and 8 inches in diameter, but there are some sea stars that are less than ½ inch in diameter, while the twenty-rayed star may measure one yard across. The length of the arms varies considerably. In most species the arm length ranges from one to three times the diameter of the central disc. From this average there are forms that have extremely long slender arms and others that have very short arms. In the cushion star, *Pteraster* (Fig. 19-1, A), each arm has the shape of an isosceles triangle, and in *Culcita* (Fig. 19-1, B) the arms are so short that the body is pentagonal.

Sea stars are commonly a drab yellow, but many species are more brightly colored. Red, orange, blue, purple, green, and darker shades are not infrequent. Also, combinations of colors exist. For example, in a common North Atlantic *Astropecten,* the upper surface of the disc and rays is bluish-purple, margined with a pale band (Fig. 19-2, A).

External Structure.   The mouth is located in the center of the underside of the disc, and the entire undersurface of the disc and arms is called the oral surface (Fig. 19-5). The opposite, or upper, side of the body is the aboral surface.

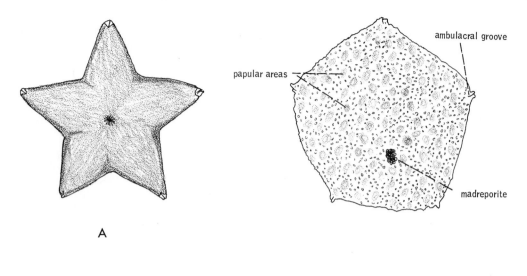

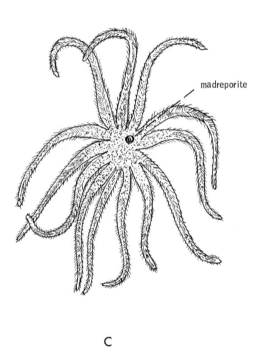

Figure 19-1.   *A.* The cushion star, *Pteraster tesselatus*, an inhabitant of Puget Sound. *B. Culcita,* an asteroid with very short arms. *C. Freyella*, with many long, slender arms. (All after Hyman.)

From the mouth extends radially a wide furrow into each arm (Fig. 19-6). Each furrow (ambulacral groove) contains two or four rows of small tubular projections, called tube feet or podia. These tube feet are the locomotor organs and form part of the water-vascular system.

The margins of the ambulacral grooves are guarded by a row of movable spines that are capable of closing over the groove. The tip of each arm bears a small tentacle and a red pig-ment spot. The aboral surface bears both the inconspicuous anus, when present, in the center of the disc and a large button-like structure (the madreporite) toward one side of the disc between two of the arms (Fig. 19-1). The general body surface is typically rough and beset with spines, tubercles, or ridges (Fig. 19-3, *B*). Also scattered over the surface are small finger-like projections of the coelom called papulae.

Body Wall.   The outer surface of the body

Figure 19-2.   *A. Astropecten irregularis,* a burrowing sea star (aboral view). *B.* The sun star, *Crossaster papposus* (aboral view). (Both by D. P. Wilson.)

is covered by an epidermis composed of flagellated columnar epithelium (Fig. 19-3, *A*). The epithelial cells are attenuated, at least at the base, and covered on the outer surface by a thin cuticle. The epidermis also contains slender neurosensory cells and mucus gland cells that provide the body surface with a protective mucus coating. Detritus that falls on the body is trapped in the mucus and then swept away by the epidermal flagella.

The direction of the cleansing currents varies in different asteroids. In some species, particles are swept to the tips of the arms; in others they are carried to the anal region in the center of the aboral surface of the disc. In sea stars, such as *Asterias,* in which the surface is highly irregular owing to large spines and tubercles, the cleansing currents sweep upward to the distal ends of the surface projections. Beneath the epidermis is a layer of nerve cells forming a subepidermal plexus (Fig. 19-3, *A*). Beneath the nervous layer is a thick layer of connective tissue (the dermis) that houses the skeletal system.

The asteroid skeleton is composed of separate ossicles in the shape of rods, crosses, or plates. The ossicles are so arranged that they form a lattice network and are bound together by connective tissue (Fig. 19-4, *A* and *B*). The amount of space between ossicles varies, depending on the form of the ossicles, and the space is particularly reduced when the ossicles are in the form of plates. Spines and tubercles are also part of the skeleton and each either consists of separate pieces resting on the deeper dermal ossicles or represents extensions of the dermal ossicles that project to the outer surface (Fig. 19-8).

Beneath the dermis is a muscle layer composed of outer circular and inner longitudinal fibers of the smooth type. The longitudinal muscles are best developed on the aboral side and are involved in the bending of the arms. The inner surface of the muscle layer borders the coelom and is covered with peritoneum.

In two orders of sea stars, the body surface bears small specialized jaw-like appendages (pedicellariae) that are used for protection and are used to capture small animals. The pedicellariae are of two types—stalked and sessile. The stalked pedicellariae are characteristic of the order Forcipulata, which includes *Asterias, Pycnopodia,* and *Pisaster.* These pedicellariae each consist of a short fleshy stalk surmounted by a jaw-like apparatus. This apparatus is composed of three small ossicles that are arranged to form forceps or scissors. In the forceps type, two opposing ossicles rest upon and articulate with a basal ossicle (Fig. 19-4, *E*). In the scissors type, the two opposing ossicles have curved bases that overlap and lie on each side of the basal ossicle (Fig. 19-4, *F*).

By means of special adductor and abductor muscles, the jaws can be opened and shut. All of the ossicles of the pedicellariae are covered by epithelial and dermal tissue. The distribution of stalked pedicellariae is variable. They may be scattered over the body surface, situated on the

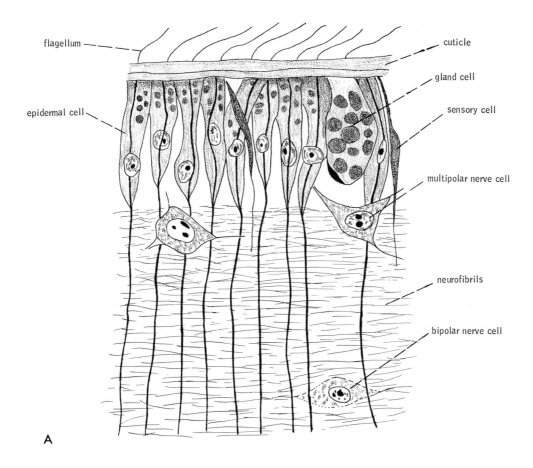

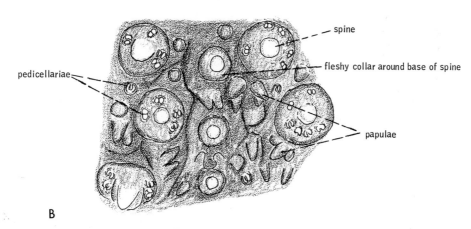

Figure 19-3.   *A.* Section through the integument of *Asterias glacialis.* (After Smith from Cuénot.)
B. Small area of aboral surface of *Asterias* (greatly magnified).

spines, or commonly, as in *Asterias,* they may form a wreath around the base of the spines (Fig. 19-3, *B*).

Sessile pedicellariae are quite different from the stalked type and are limited to the order Phanerozonia, which includes *Astropecten.* Sessile pedicellariae are composed of two or more short movable spines located on the same

or adjacent ossicles. The spines oppose each other and articulate against one another to act as pincers (Fig. 19-4, *C*). In one type of sessile pedicellariae, called alveolar pedicellariae, the spines are very short, broad, and shaped like the valves of a clam (Fig. 19-4, *D*). The two valves are imbedded in the body surface.

The papulae and podia, which are also ap-

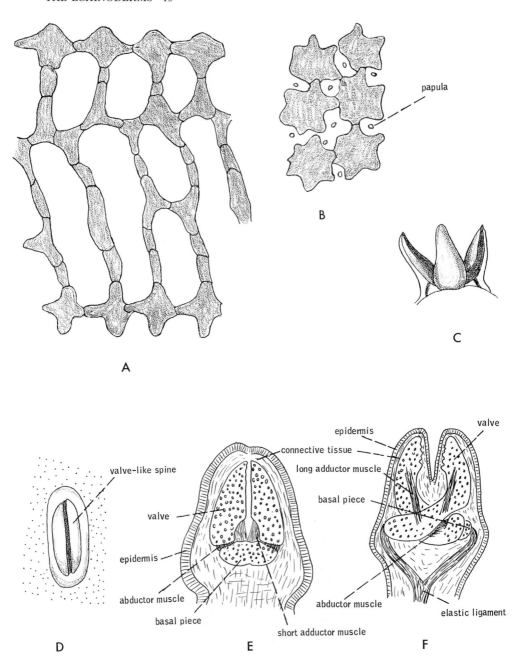

Figure 19-4.   *A.* Lattice-like arrangement of skeletal ossicles in the arm of an asteriid. (After Fisher from Hyman.) *B.* Small section of endoskeletal system of a phanerozonic sea star. (After Hyman.) *C.* Sessile pedicellaria with three valves, from *Luidia. D.* A sessile pedicellaria with two clam-like valves, from *Hippasteria* (frontal view). (*C* and *D* after Cuénot.) *E* and *F.* Distal ends of two-stalked pedicellariae from *Asterias. E.* Forceps type. *F.* Scissors type. (*E* and *F* after Hyman.)

pendages of the body wall, are discussed in connection with respiration and the water-vascular system.

Water-Vascular System.   The water-vascular system is a system of canals and appendages of the body wall that are peculiar to echinoderms. Since the entire system is derived from the coelom, the canals are lined with a flagellated epithelium and filled with fluid. The water-vascular system is well developed in asteroids and functions as a means of locomotion, although originally the system was probably a food-catching device. The internal canals of the water-vascular system connect to the out-

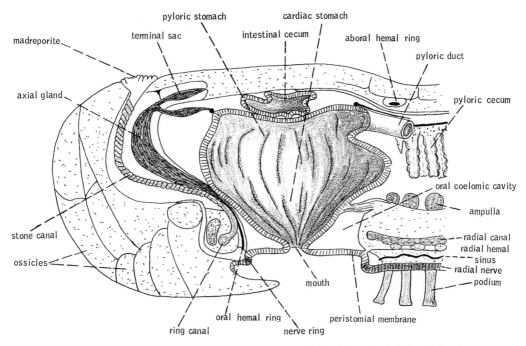

Figure 19-5.   Disc and base of one arm of an asteroid (vertical section). (After Cuénot.)

side through the button-shaped madreporite located on the aboral surface (Figs. 19-1 and 19-5).

The surface of the madreporite is creased with many fine furrows covered by the flagellated epithelium of the body surface. The bottom of each furrow contains pores that open into pore canals passing downward through the madreporite. A madreporite may be perforated by as many as 250 pores and canals and is thus constructed essentially like a sieve. The pore canals join collecting canals that open into a small space (the ampulla) beneath the madreporite.

The ampulla leads into a vertical stone canal that descends to the oral side of the disc (Fig. 19-5). The stone canal is so named because of the ring-like calcareous deposits located in its walls. On reaching the oral side of the disc, the stone canal joins a circular canal (the water ring) that is located just to the inner side of the ossicles that ring the mouth (Fig. 19-5). Not infrequently the walls of the water ring are folded to divide the lumen into a number of more or less separate channels. The significance of these divisions is not thoroughly understood, but they may represent a mechanism that facilitates the production of water currents.

The inner side of the water ring gives rise to four, or more usually five, pairs of greatly folded pouches called Tiedemann's bodies. Each pair of these pouches has an interradial position. Their function is unknown. Also attached interradially to the inner side of the water ring in

many asteroids, although not in *Asterias,* are a number of elongated sacs that are suspended in the coelom. These sacs are known as polian vesicles and range in number from one to five. Like the Tiedemann's bodies, their function is unknown.

From the water ring a long flagellated radial canal extends into each arm (Figs. 19-5 and 19-6). The radial canal runs on the oral side of the ossicles that form the center of the ambulacral groove, and it ends in a small external tentacle at the tip of the arm. Lateral canals arise from each side of the radial canal along its entire length. These lateral canals pass between the ambulacral ossicles on each side of the groove and enter the coelom (Fig. 19-6).

Each lateral canal is provided with a valve and terminates in a bulb and tube foot (Fig. 19-6). The bulb (ampulla) is a small muscular sac that bulges into the aboral side of the coelom. The wall of the ampulla contains circular and longitudinal fibers and connective tissue, and its inner and outer surface is clothed with peritoneum. The ampulla opens directly into a canal that passes downward between the ambulacral ossicles and leads into a tube foot (podium).

The podium is a short tubular external projection of the body wall located in the ambulacral groove. In most asteroids, the tip of the podium is flattened forming a sucker. However in some asteroids such as *Astropecten,* the tip of the podium is pointed. Like the body wall, the

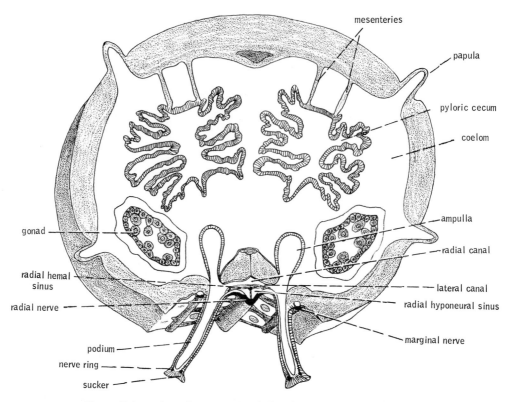

Figure 19-6.   Arm of a sea star (vertical section). (Modified from Cuénot.)

podium is covered on the outside with a flagellated epithelium and internally with peritoneum. Between these two layers lie connective tissue and longitudinal muscle fibers. Circular fibers are absent in the podium.

The podia are arranged in two or four rows along the length of the ambulacral groove, and the ampullae occupy a corresponding position on the coelomic side of the ambulacral ossicles. The difference in the number of rows results from the length of the lateral canals. For example, in asteroids, such as *Asterias,* that possess four rows of podia, the lateral canals along each side are alternately long and short, giving the appearance of four rows of podia instead of two. Species in which there are but two rows of podia have lateral canals that are of equal length, thus placing the podia at equal distances from the radial canal.

The entire water-vascular system is filled with fluid and operates during locomotion as a hydraulic system. On contraction of the ampulla, the valve in the lateral canal closes and water is forced into the podium, which elongates. When the podium comes in contact with the substratum, the center of the terminal sucker is withdrawn, producing a vacuum and adhesion. The tip of the podium also produces a copious adhesive secretion that aids in adherence.

After the adhesion of the sucker to the substratum, the longitudinal muscles of the podium contract, shortening the podium and forcing fluid back into the ampulla. Other parts of the water-vascular system—the madreporite, the stone canal, the water ring and the radial canal —perhaps function in maintaining the proper water pressure necessary for the operation of the ampullae and podia. However, this is still somewhat conjectural, and it is doubtful if there is much exchange of fluid through the madreporite.

During movement, each podium performs a sort of stepping motion. The podium swings forward, grips the substratum, and then moves backward. In a particular section of an arm, most of the tube feet are performing the same step, and the animal moves forward. The action of the podia is highly coordinated. During progression, one or two arms act as leading arms, and the podia in all of the arms move in the same direction but not in unison. The combined action of the podial suckers exerts a powerful force for adhering and enables sea stars to climb vertically over rocks or up the side of an aquarium.

Genera such as *Astropecten*, which live on soft bottoms, can dig and bury themselves by using the podia to flip away sand to either side of the arm. If a sea star is accidentally turned over, it can right itself. The most common method employed is by folding. The distal end of one or two arms twists, bringing the tube feet in contact with the substratum. Once the substratum has been gripped, these arms move back beneath the animal so that the rest of the body is folded over. Righting may also take place by arching the body and rising on the tips of the arms. The sea star then rolls over onto its oral surface. In general, sea stars move rather slowly and tend to remain within a more or less restricted area.

Movement in asteroids that lack podial suckers is not essentially different from that in other forms, although the powers of adhesion are less. Suckerless podia appear to be an adaptation for life on a soft bottom.

Nutrition. Asteroids are carnivorous and feed on snails, bivalves, crustaceans, polychaetes, other echinoderms, and even fish. They also consume the bodies of dead animals encountered on the bottom. However, decided preferences are displayed by different species. Some feed primarily on crustaceans and can pull hermit crabs out of their shells, although smaller crustaceans, such as amphipods and copepods, are also consumed. Some, such as the asteriids, feed primarily on mollusks, particularly bivalves. Hamann (1885) reported that the stomach contents of a specimen of *Astropecten auranciacus* contained 5 scaphopods, a number of snails, and 16 bivalves, 10 of which were scallops. A number of asteroids feed primarily on other echinoderms. The stomach of a specimen of *Luidia sarsi* was found to contain 26 brittle stars and 5 heart urchins. Some asteroids feed on sponges and the polyps of hydroids and corals.

A few sea stars are flagellary feeders. Plankton and detritus (*Porania, Henricia*), or mud (*Ctenodiscus*), that come in contact with the body surface are trapped in mucus and then swept toward the oral surface by the epidermal flagella. On reaching the ambulacral grooves, the food-laden mucus strands are carried by flagellary currents to the mouth. Some investigators suspect that such flagellary feeding in many sea stars may be an auxiliary method of obtaining food.

The digestive system is short, straight, and radial, and it extends between the oral and aboral sides of the disc (Figs. 19-5 and 19-7). The mouth is located in the middle of a tough circular peristomial membrane that is muscular and provided with a sphincter. The mouth leads into a short esophagus, which in some genera, such as *Echinaster,* gives rise to 10 esophageal pouches of uncertain significance. The esophagus opens into a large stomach that fills most of the interior of the disc and is divided by a horizontal constriction into a large oral chamber (the cardiac stomach) and a smaller flattened aboral chamber (the pyloric stomach).

The walls of the cardiac stomach are pouched and connected to the body wall by mesenteries. The most important of these attachments are 10 pairs of triangular mesenteries called gastric ligaments, that contain a

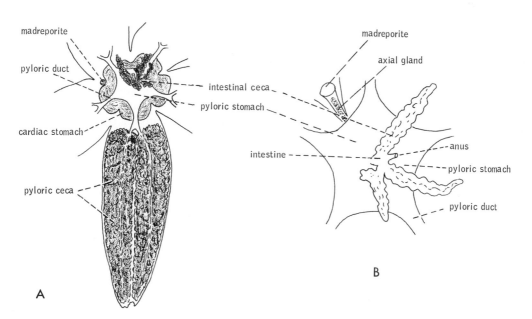

Figure 19-7.   *A.* Digestive system of *Asterias* (aboral view). Digestive ceca of only one arm are shown. (Modified from Hyman.) *B.* Pyloric stomach and intestinal ceca of *Asterias* (enlarged view). (After Hyman.)

considerable amount of connective tissue. There are two such ligaments connecting the stomach to the ambulacral ossicles of each arm.

The smaller aboral pyloric stomach is often star-shaped due to the entrance of the ducts from the pyloric ceca (Fig. 19-7). There are two pyloric ceca in each arm, each of which is composed of an elongated mass of glandular cells suspended in the coelom of the arm by a dorsal mesentery (Figs. 19-6 and 19-7, A). A longitudinal duct extends the length of each cecum and gives rise to many lateral ducts, into which the secretory lobules open. The secretory lobules are composed of secretory, absorptive, and storage cells. The longitudinal duct may open separately into the pyloric stomach, or may join with the longitudinal duct of the other cecum in the same arm, before emptying into the pyloric stomach (Fig. 19-7, A).

A short tubular intestine extends from the aboral side of the pyloric stomach to open through the anus in the middle of the aboral surface of the disc. The intestine typically bears a number of small out-pocketings called rectal ceca (Fig. 19-7, B). The rectal ceca may consist of a two-or three-branched mass on one side of the intestine, as in *Asterias,* or there may be a larger number of ceca arranged radially around the intestine. In some species of asteroids, the anus is lacking, and in several families both intestine and anus are absent. The entire digestive tract is lined with a flagellated epithelium, and in the ducts of the pyloric ceca the flagella are so arranged as to create fluid currents, both incoming and outgoing. Gland cells are particularly abundant in the cardiac stomach lining. Beneath the lining epithelium is a layer of connective tissue and muscle fibers.

In those sea stars that have short, or more or less inflexible, arms and in forms in which the podia lack suckers, the prey is swallowed whole and digested within the stomach. Shells and other indigestible material are then cast out of the mouth. Asteroids that have relatively long flexible arms, such as *Asterias,* display a different method of feeding. Through the contraction of the body-wall muscles, the coelomic fluid exerts pressure on the cardiac stomach, causing it to be everted through the mouth. The everted stomach, which is anchored by the gastric ligaments, engulfs the prey, and digestion proceeds outside of the body. The soft parts of the victim are reduced to a thick broth, which is then passed into the body. When digestion is completed, the stomach muscles contract, retracting the stomach into the interior of the disc, leaving the shell of the prey on the outside.

A considerable number of sea stars, particularly the asteriids, feed almost exclusively on bivalves and are notorious predators of oyster beds. During feeding, such a sea star extends itself over a clam, holding the gape of the clam upward against the mouth of the sea star and applying the arms against the sides of the clam valves. Considerable debate has centered around the mechanism by which a sea star opens the valves to enable its stomach to evert into the interior of the clam. Some zoologists have claimed that the sea star could exert a sufficient force to overcome the pull of the clam adductor muscles. Others have postulated the production of a narcotizing secretion to aid in opening the valves of the victim.

Recent studies by Burnett (1955; 1960), Feder (1955), and Lavoie (1956) have demonstrated rather conclusively that no narcotic agent is used. Instead, the sea star uses minute openings between the imperfectly sealed edges of the valves, or the pull exerted by the sea star is sufficiently great to produce a very slight gape in the clam. The gape is produced quite rapidly and not by causing the clam to fatigue over a long period. The everted cardiac stomach of some sea stars can squeeze through a space as slight as 0.1 mm. Furthermore, the echinoderm periodically relaxes its pull on the valves once the stomach has entered, allowing the valves to close. No damage to the stomach results. The gape increases as digestion ensues and the clam's adductor muscles are attacked. However, according to Feder (1955), an increased gape is not necessary for continued digestion, at least not in the Pacific *Pisaster ochraceus.* This species can consume mussels that are bound with wire.

In flagellary feeders such as *Porania* and *Henricia,* the pyloric stomach gives rise to five pairs of pouches, called Tiedemann's pouches, that extend back beneath the pyloric ceca. According to Anderson (1960), these pouches are flagellary pumping organs for drawing food particles from the stomach into the pyloric ceca.

Digestion appears to be primarily extracellular, and enzymes—protease, amylase, and lipase—are produced by the pyloric ceca. Some particles are swept along the flagellated ducts into the pyloric ceca, where some intracellular digestion is believed to take place. The pyloric ceca are probably also the primary sites of absorption. Products of digestion may be stored in the cells of the pyloric ceca or may be passed through the ceca into the coelom for distribution.

Circulation, Respiration and Excretion. The large fluid-filled coelom surrounding the internal organs within the disc and the arms provides the principal means for internal circulation. The coelomic peritoneum is composed of flagellated cuboidal cells, and the beating of the flagella causes a continual circulation of the coelomic fluid. In general, the circulatory current flows outward along the aboral wall and toward the disc along the lateral walls. The salt concentration of the coelomic fluid is identical to that of sea water; asteroids, as well as all other echinoderms, lack the ability to regulate internal osmotic pressure. The coelomic fluid contains free amebocytes (coelomocytes) that are phagocytic and have conspicuous pseudopodia. The coelomocytes are produced by the coelomic peritoneum. In addition to the major part of the coelom, there are some minor divisions or extensions associated with the water-vascular system and with the hemal system.

A blood-vascular (hemal) system is found in asteroids but is very much reduced and probably plays little role in circulation. The system consists of small fluid-filled sinus channels that lack a distinct lining. The channels are surrounded by special separate extensions of the coelom called perihemal spaces or sinuses. The principal hemal channels consist of an oral hemal ring located just beyond the periphery of the peristome (Fig. 19-5). From this ring a radial hemal sinus extends into each arm and lies beneath the oral surface along the midline of the ambulacral groove (Figs. 19-5 and 19-6). From the oral hemal ring a channel ascends through a dark elongated mass of spongy tissue (the axial gland). This gland extends along the length of the stone canal, and its lumen consists of hemal channels (Fig. 19-5).

In addition to the ascending channel from the oral hemal ring, the axial gland also receives small channels from the pyloric ceca and the walls of the cardiac stomach. After passing through the axial gland, the channel from the oral ring connects with an aboral hemal ring lying beneath the aboral surface of the disc. Branches to the gonads issue from the aboral hemal ring. The function of the hemal system and axial gland is unknown. Coelomocytes are present, and the system may represent a pathway for the distribution of food material carried by these cells.

The excretory products of asteroids consist of ammonia, urea, and creatine, and removal is probably accomplished by general diffusion through thin areas of the body surface, such as the tube feet and the papulae. Studies involving the injection of dyes into the coelom indicate that the coelomocytes function in the collection and removal of waste matter. These cells engulf waste and when laden migrate to the papulae where they collect at the distal end. The tip of the papula then constricts and pinches off,

discharging the coelomocytes to the outside. Some wastes may be excreted by the cells of the pyloric ceca and are removed with the egested waste.

The papulae and tube feet provide the principal respiratory surfaces for asteroids. The flagellated peritoneum that forms the internal lining of the papulae produces an internal current of coelomic fluid; the outer flagellated epidermal investment produces a current of sea water flowing over the papulae (Fig. 19-8). The tube feet play an equally important role as respiratory surfaces and are perhaps the primary respiratory structures in those asteroids with greatly reduced numbers of papulae. Meyer (1935) found that if the ambulacral grooves of *Asterias rubens* are covered, oxygen consumption decreases by as much as 60 per cent.

The Nervous System. The asteroid nervous system, like that of some other echinoderms, is nonganglionated, and the greater part of the system is intimately associated with the epidermis. The nervous center is a somewhat pentagonal circumoral nerve ring that lies just beneath the peristomial epidermis (Fig. 19-5). The circumoral ring supplies fibers to the esophagus and to the inner parts of the peristome. From each angle of the ring a large radial nerve extends into each of the arms (Figs. 19-5 and 19-6). The radial nerves are continuous with both the epidermis and the subepidermal nerve net, and these nerves form a V-shaped mass along the midline of the oral surface of the ambulacral groove. The radial nerve supplies fibers to the podia and ampullae.

At the margins of the ambulacral groove, the subepidermal nervous layer is thickened to form a pair of marginal nerve cords that

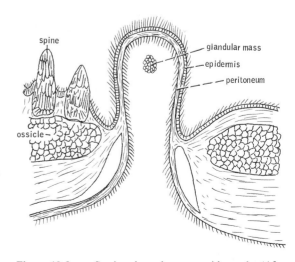

Figure 19-8.   Section through an asteroid papula. (After Cuénot.)

extend the length of the arm (Fig. 19-6). The marginal nerves give rise to lateral nerves that innervate the muscles of the ambulacral ossicles and then join a coelomic plexus that lies beneath the entire peritoneum to innervate the muscle layers of the body wall. A circumoral and radial system of hyponeural fibers lies just beneath the ectoneural system and is separated from the latter by a thin layer of connective tissue.

There are many experimental studies on the role of the nervous system in the movement of sea stars. The integrity of both the radial nerves and the circumoral nerve ring is essential in the coordination of the podia. Although the podia do not all "step" in unison, they are coordinated to the extent of their involvement in stepping—that is, to step or not to step—and they are coordinated in that they step in the proper direction, depending upon which arm is leading.

If the radial nerve of a particular arm is severed, the podia, although capable of movement, are not coordinated with podia of other arms. Moreover, if the circumoral nerve ring is cut between two radial nerves, all movement is inhibited, for coordination of the podia in all of the arms is lost. It is believed that a nerve center exists at the junction of each radial nerve with the circumoral nerve ring and that this center in a leading arm exerts a temporary dominance over the nerve centers of the other arms. In the majority of sea stars including *Asterias,* any arm can act as a dominant arm, and such dominance is determined by reaction to external stimuli. In a few species, one arm is permanently dominant.

With the exception of the eye spots at the tips of the arms, there are no specialized sense organs in the asteroids. The sensory cells contained within the epidermis are the primary sensory receptors and probably function for the reception of light, contact, and chemical stimuli. Each sensory cell consists of a distal hair-like process that runs to the cuticle and a proximal process that joins the subepidermal network. These epidermal sensory cells are present in enormous numbers and are particularly prevalent on the suckers of the tube feet, on the tentacles, and along the margins of the ambulacral groove. In the latter area, totals of 70,000 per square millimeter have been reported.

The eye spot at the end of each arm lies beneath the tentacle on the oral side of the arm tip and is composed of a mass of 80 to 200 pigment-cup ocelli that form an optic cushion. Each ocellus consists of a cup of epidermal cells containing red pigment granules that are said to be photolabile—that is, they change chemically in the presence of light. The photoreceptors are elongated sensory cells that bulge into the lumen of the cup. The thickened cuticle, which acts as a lens, overlies the cup.

Some asteroids are positively phototropic; others are negatively phototropic. The importance of the optic cushions in reactions to light stimuli apparently varies in different species. In some species, the tip of the arm turns upward to expose the ocelli to light. Diebschlag (1938) reported that the photopositive *Asterias rubens* and *Astropecten irregularis* could be lead around by shining a light on the optic cushions of a particular ray. However, all asteroids react to light, even when the optic cushions are covered, apparently because of photoreceptor cells in the general body epidermis.

Of all the reactions to external stimuli, that of contact of the podia with the substratum appears to be dominant and probably accounts for the righting reaction.

Regeneration and Reproduction.   Asteroids exhibit considerable powers of regeneration. Any part of the arm can be regenerated, and destroyed sections of the central disc are replaced. Studies on *Asterias vulgaris* have shown that if there is at least one-fifth of the central disc attached to an arm, an entire starfish will be regenerated. If the remaining section of the disc contains the madreporite, even less of the disc is required. Regeneration is typically slow and may require as long as one year for complete re-formation to take place.

A number of asteroids reproduce normally by asexual reproduction. Commonly this involves a division of the central disc along certain definite lines so that the animal breaks into two parts. Each half then regenerates the missing portion of the disc and arms. *Linckia,* a common Pacific sea star, is remarkable in being able to cast off its arms near the base of the disc. Unlike those of other asteroids, the severed arm regenerates a new disc and rays. Such regenerating specimens with small regenerating arms at the base of the original arm are popularly called comets (Fig. 19-9).

With a few exceptions, asteroids are dioecious, and there are ten gonads, two in each arm. Each gonad is unattached within the coelomic cavity except for a point near the junction of the arm and the disc (Fig. 19-6). The gonads are tuft-like or resemble a cluster of grapes, and they vary greatly in size depending on proximity to the time of spawning. When filled with eggs or sperms, the gonads almost completely fill each of the arms. At other times, the gonads are quite small and occupy only a small area at the base of the

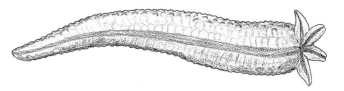

Figure 19-9. Comet of *Linckia*. Regeneration of body at base of detached arm. (After Richters from Hyman.)

arm. There is a gonopore for each gonad, usually located between the bases of the arms. In a number of astropectinids, as well as in some other groups, each arm contains many gonads, which are arranged in rows along the length of the arm. In such species, the gonopores open on the oral surface.

There are a few hermaphroditic asteroid species, such as the common European sea star, *Asterina gibbosa*. This species is protandric; small or young individuals are males, but as they become older and increase in size, they develop into females.

In the majority of asteroids, the eggs and sperm are shed freely into the sea water where fertilization takes place. The presence of eggs or sperm in the sea water acts as a stimulant for the shedding of the sex cells of an individual of the opposite sex. There is usually only one breeding season per year, which occurs in the spring in sea stars of temperate waters; during spawning, a single female may shed as many as 2,500,000 eggs.

In most asteroids, the liberated eggs and individuals in the later developmental stages are planktonic. However, a number of arctic and antarctic sea stars brood their eggs. The eggs of such brooding species are usually large and have considerable yolk material. A relatively small number are produced in these brooding species and unlike the majority of asteroids, development is direct with no larval stage. A variety of brooding methods may be exhibited. In some species, the female rises up on the tips of her arms and broods her eggs in the space between the substratum and the oral side of the disc. In other species, the eggs are brooded in depressions on the aboral surface of the disc or in brooding baskets formed by spines between the bases of the arms. The pterasterids have the entire aboral surface modified to serve as a chamber for the brooding of their eggs. *Leptasterias groenlandica,* a circumpolar arctic species, broods its eggs in the cardiac stomach. While not a brooding species, *Asterina gibbosa* is unusual in that it attaches its eggs to stones and other objects.

Embryology. Except in brooding species, development in the asteroids is indirect and involves the formation of a free-swimming larval stage. The eggs are small, homolecithal, and contain relatively little yolk material. The early stages of development conform to the pattern described in the introduction of this chapter. In most species, the coelom arises from the tip of the advancing archenteron as two lateral pouches. The two pouches separate from the archenteron, elongate, and develop lying along the right and left sides of the archenteron. The two pouches then connect anteriorly so that the coelom has the form of a U. The posterior ends of each arm of the U become constricted and pinch off, thus forming two separate coelomic vesicles, the right and the left somatocoel (Fig. 19-10). The remaining anterior coelomic vesicles represent the hydrocoel and axocoel, but they never separate. The left hydrocoel connects with the dorsal surface to form the hydropore.

In the European *Asterina gibbosa,* the formation of the coelom takes place somewhat differently. The anterior part of the archenteron is cut off to form the coelom, and the remaining posterior portion of the archenteron then forms the gut.

The asteroid embryo becomes free-swimming at some point between the blastula and gastrula stages. Feeding commences as soon as the digestive tract is completely formed. Diatoms that are collected from the water current produced by the stomodeal cilia are the principal food. At first the entire larval surface is covered with cilia but as development proceeds, the surface ciliation becomes confined to a definite locomotor band (Fig. 19-10). This locomotor band consists of two lateral longitudinal bands that extend anteriorly and then ventrally to connect in front of the mouth as a pre-oral loop.

Posteriorly, the two lateral bands turn forward on the ventral surface and connect in front of the anus, forming a pre-anal loop. The pre-oral loop later separates or in some cases arises separately from the rest of the locomotor band to form an anterior ciliated ring around the body. After the formation of the locomotor bands, projections, called arms, arise from the body surface. The locomotor bands extend along the arms, which in some species may be quite long. This larval stage is then known as a bipinnaria larva; several weeks may elapse in the attainment of this stage.

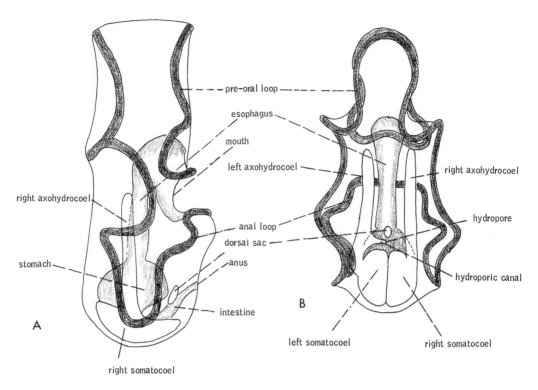

Figure 19-10.   Early (14 days) bipinnaria larva of *Astropecten auranciacus. A.* Lateral view. *B.* Dorsal view. (Both after Hörstadius from Hyman.)

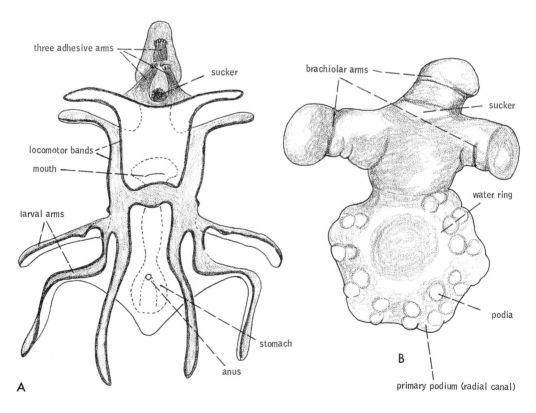

Figure 19-11.   *A.* Brachiolaria larva of *Asterias* (ventral view). (After Agassiz from Cuénot.) *B.* Metamorphosis in *Leptasterias hexactis.* (After Osterud from Hyman.)

The bipinnaria larva becomes a brachiolaria larva with the appearance of three additional arms at the anterior end (Fig. 19-11, *A*). These arms are short, ventral in position, and covered with adhesive cells at the tip. Between the bases of the three arms, there is a glandular adhesive area that forms a sucker. The three arms and the sucker represent an attachment device, and the brachiolaria then settles to the bottom. The tips of the arms provide a temporary attachment to some object until the sucker itself is attached.

Metamorphosis then takes place. The anterior end of the larva degenerates and forms only an attachment stalk, and the adult body develops from the rounded posterior end of the larva (Fig. 19-11, *B*). The left side becomes the oral surface, and the right side becomes the aboral surface. The adult arms appear as extensions of the body.

Internally, the mouth, the esophagus, part of the intestine, and the anus degenerate. All these parts are formed anew and in a position coinciding with the adult radial symmetry. The somatocoel forms the major part of the coelom. The axohydrocoel forms the water-vascular system, and from the hydrocoel develop five pairs of projections, two in each of the developing arms (Fig. 19-11, *B*). These projections represent the cavity and coelomic lining of the first pair of podia in each arm. As soon as additional podia are formed, they begin to grip the substratum and soon free the body from the substratum. At about this time, the skeletal system appears. The detached baby starfish is less than one millimeter in diameter with very short stubby arms.

Class Echinoidea

The echinoids are free-moving echinoderms commonly known as sea urchins, heart urchins, and sand dollars. The name Echinoidea, which means "like a hedge hog", is derived from the fact that the bodies of these animals are covered with spines. The echinoid body does not display arms like that of asteroids. Rather, the shape is circular or oval and the body is spherical or greatly flattened along the oral— aboral axis. The class is particularly interesting from the standpoint of symmetry, for while the sea urchins are radially symmetrical, other members of the class display various stages in the attainment of a secondary bilateral symmetry. A third distinctive feature of echinoid structure is the fusion of the skeletal ossicles into a solid case (the test).

External Structure. REGULAR ECHINOIDS. The radial, or regular, members of the class are known as sea urchins. In these forms, the body is more or less spherical in shape and armed with relatively long movable spines (Fig. 19-12). Sea urchins are colored brown, black, purple, green, white, and red; a few are multicolored, such as the West Indian urchin, *Diadema antillarum,* which when young has banded purple and white spines. Most sea urchins are two to four inches in diameter, but some Indo-Pacific species may attain a diameter of nearly one foot.

Figure 19-12.   Regular urchins, *Echinus esculentus,* showing spines and extended tube feet (viewed from side and above). (From Yonge, 1949: The Seashore, Collins, London.)

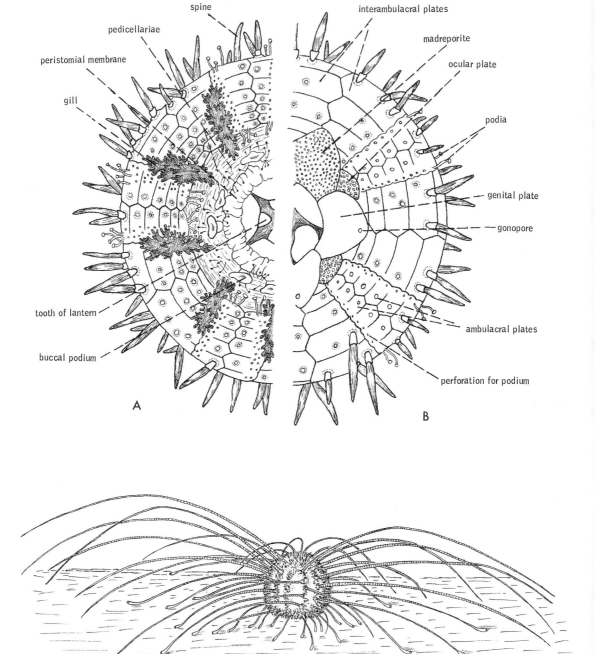

Figure 19-13.   *A* and *B.* The regular urchin, *Arbacia punctulata. A.* Oral view. *B.* Aboral view. (After Petrunkevitch from Reid.) *C. Plesiodiadema indicum,* a deep-water, regular urchin from the Indo-Pacific. Note long, curved spines with flattened ends. (After Mortensen from Cuénot.)

The sea urchin body can be divided into an aboral and an oral hemisphere with the parts arranged radially around the polar axis. The oral pole bears the mouth and is directed against the substratum. The mouth is surrounded by a peristomial membrane that is thickened along the inner edge to form a lip (Fig. 19-13, *A*). The peristome of sea urchins contains small imbedded supporting ossicles, and the surface bears a number of different structures arranged in a radial manner. There are five pairs of short heavy modified podia, called buccal podia, and five pairs of bushy projections, called gills.

In addition to the buccal podia and the gills, the peristomial membrane usually bears small spines and pedicellariae. The aboral pole contains the anal region, known as the periproct (Fig. 19-13, *B*). The periproct is a small circular membrane containing the anus, usually in the center, and a varying number of imbedded plates. In the Arbaciidae, there are four large periproct plates (Fig. 19-13, *B*), but in other families of sea urchins the plates are smaller and more numerous (Fig. 19-14). The globose body surface can be divided into ten radial sections extending between the oral and aboral poles (Fig. 19-13, *A*). Five sections contain tube feet and are called ambulacral areas. Between the ambulacral areas are sections devoid of podia, known as interambulacral areas. The body surface is thus composed of five ambulacral areas alternating with five interambulacral areas, all ten areas converging at the two poles.

The movable spines, which are so characteristic of sea urchins, are arranged symmetrically in rows along both the ambulacral and interambulacral areas. The spines are longest around the equator and shortest at the poles. Most sea urchins possess both long (primary) and short (secondary) types of spines, the two more or less equally distributed over the body surface. However, *Arbacia punctulata*, the common Atlantic sea urchin, possesses only the long type.

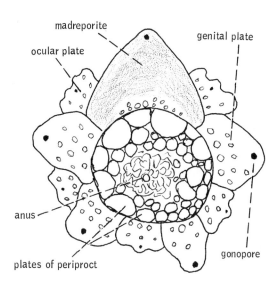

Figure 19-14. Periproct and surround plates of the regular urchin, *Strongylocentrotus*. (After Lovén from Hyman.)

Each spine contains a concave socket at the base that fits over a corresponding tubercle on the test (Fig. 19-15, *A* and *B*). Two sheaths of muscle fibers that extend between the spine base and the test encircle the ball-and-socket joint. Contractions of the outer muscular sheath serve to incline the spines in one direction or another. The inner sheath of muscle fibers (the cog muscle) by uniform contraction of its fibers

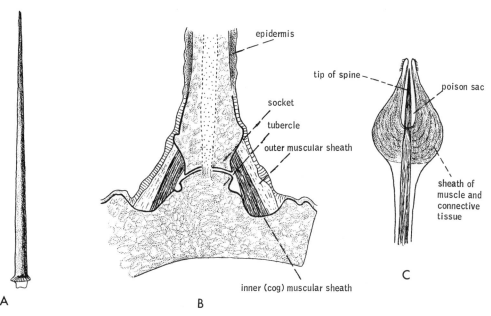

Figure 19-15. Spines of regular urchins. *A.* Primary spine of an urchin such as *Arbacia*. (After Hyman.) *B.* Section through the base of a *Cidaris* spine, showing muscular sheaths. (After Cuénot.) *C.* Poison spine of *Asthenosoma varium,* an Indo-Pacific species. (After Sarasins from Hyman.)

causes a rigid erection of the spines. The spines are usually circular and taper to a point, but they are flattened or triangular in some species. Moreover, in some species, the tips are expanded and flattened, and in a few the spines are curved (Fig. 19-13, *C*).

The Indo-Pacific sea urchin, *Asthenosoma,* bears special poison spines on the aboral surface (Fig. 19-15, *C*). The tip of each spine is surrounded by a large blue sac containing poison secreted by the epithelial lining. The poison is highly toxic and painful to man.

Pedicellariae, which are characteristic of all echinoids, are located over the general body surface as well as on the peristome. The echinoid pedicellariae are somewhat similar to the stalked pedicellariae of the asteroids in that each consists of a long stalk surmounted by jaws. However, in echinoid pedicellariae, the stalk contains a supporting skeletal rod, and there are usually three opposing jaws (Fig. 19-16, *A*). The bases

of the jaw ossicles articulate against one another and not against a basal ossicle as in the asteroids.

Of the various types of echinoid pedicellariae, the most interesting are those containing poison glands (Fig. 19-16, *B*). The outer side of each jaw is surrounded by one or two large poison sacs that open by one or two ducts just below the terminal tooth of the jaw. The poison has a rapid paralyzing effect on small animals and drives larger enemies away. The spines frequently incline away from the poison pedicellariae so that these pedicellariae are more easily exposed. Poison pedicellariae are absent in some sea urchins, such as *Arbacia,* but are present in many forms, including the Atlantic *Lytechinus.*

Other types of pedicellariae are used for defense, for capturing small prey, or for cleaning the body surface wherein they bite and break up small particles of debris that are then removed by the surface flagella.

In most sea urchins, the ambulacral areas

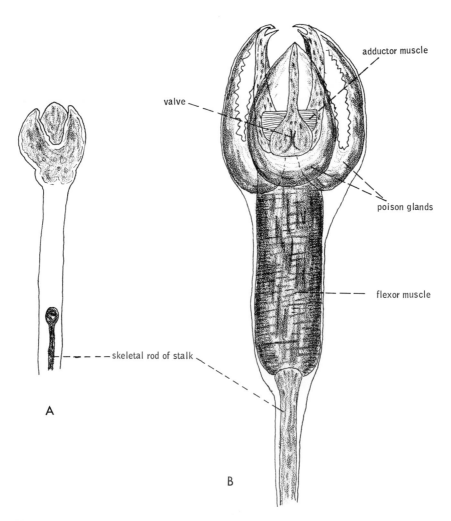

Figure 19-16.   Pedicellaria of a regular urchin. (After Hyman.) *B.* Poisonous pedicellaria of *Strongylocentrotus.* (After Mortensen from Hyman.)

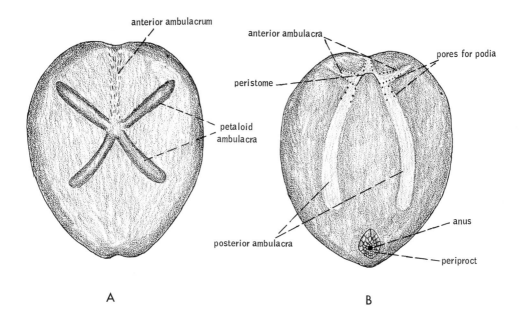

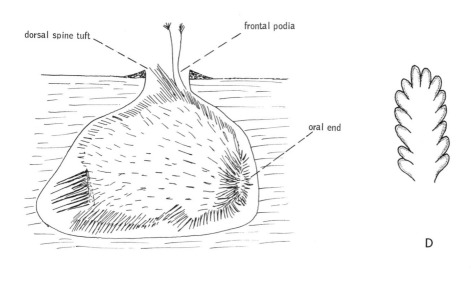

Figure 19-17.   Irregular echinoids, spatangoids (heart urchins). *A. Meoma ventricosa* from the West Indies (aboral view). *B. Meoma* (oral view). (Both after Hyman.) *C. Echinocardium flavescens* in its sand burrow (lateral view). (After Gandolfi-Hornyold from Hyman.) *D.* Branchial podium from the petaloid of *Spatangus*. (After Hoffman from Hyman.)

bear hard spherical or ovoid bodies (spheridia) that are thought to be organs of equilibrium. The spheridia may be limited in number and located only on the oral side, or there may be many throughout the length of the ambulacrum. In *Arbacia*, there is only one spheridium per ambulacrum, and each is located near the peristome.

IRREGULAR ECHINOIDS.   The bilateral, or irregular, echinoids include the heart urchins, cake urchins, and sand dollars. All are adapted for burrowing in sand and have much smaller and far more numerous spines than the sea urchins. The heart urchins (spatangoids) are more or less oval in shape, the long axis representing the antero-posterior axis of the body (Fig. 19-17).

The oral surface is flattened, and the aboral surface is convex. The entire center of the oral surface, containing the mouth and peristome, has migrated anteriorly. The center of the aboral surface usually remains in the center of the upper or dorsal surface, but the periproct and anus have migrated to the posterior end in what now becomes the posterior interambulacrum.

Podia are degenerate or absent around the circumference of the body, so that functional podia are confined to the oral and aboral surfaces. The conspicuous aboral ambulacral areas are each shaped like petals radiating from the aboral center and are known as petaloids. The podia of the petaloids are modified for respiration. The oral ambulacral areas (phyllodes) also have a flower-like arrangement and contain specialized podia for obtaining food particles. The small spines form a dense covering over the body surface but have the same basic structure as in the sea urchins.

Certain specialized spines (clavules) are extremely minute, ciliated at the base, and flattened at the distal end. The clavules appear together in tracts located over certain parts of the surface, such as around each of the petaloids. It is believed that the clavules produce a water current and are used to remove sand grains that are lodged on the body surface. Pedicellariae are present, but not the poisonous type. The spheridia are located in the phyllodes.

The cake urchins or sand dollars (clypeastroids) differ from the heart urchins in a number of respects. A few species, such as the sea biscuits, are shaped somewhat like heart urchins, but in typical sand dollars the body is greatly flattened, displaying a circular circumference (Fig. 19-18). The aboral center and the oral center, which contains the mouth, are both centrally located. The periproct, however, is ventral and like that of the heart urchins, is located in the posterior interambulacrum.

The body of some common sand dollars, called keyhole sand dollars (*Mellita*), contains large elongated notches or openings known as lunules (Fig. 19-18, *A* and *C*). Lunules vary in number from two to many and are symmetrically arranged. In most cases, the lunules arise from indentations that form along the circumference of the animal and then become enclosed in the process of growth. In the scutellid sand dollars, the posterior circumference is deeply scalloped or notched (Fig. 19-18, *B*).

The aboral surface bears conspicuous petaloids. There are no phyllodes, but the oral surface contains distinct radiating grooves. Spheridia and spination are similar to that of the

heart urchins, but there are no clavules. Poison pedicellariae are present.

Body Wall.   The body wall of echinoids is composed of the same layers as that in asteroids. A flagellated epidermis covers the outer surface, including the spines. Beneath the epidermis lies a nervous layer and then a connective tissue dermis that contains the skeleton. The skeleton is composed of ossicles formed into flattened plates that are fused together to produce a solid immovable test.

In all echinoids, the plates are arranged in rows running from the oral pole to the aboral pole. Each ambulacral area is composed of two rows of ambulacral plates, and each interambulacral area is composed of two rows of interambulacral plates. There are thus twenty rows of plates—ten ambulacral and ten interambulacral (Fig. 19-13, *B*). The ambulacral plates are pierced by holes enabling the canals to connect with the ampullae and podia.

Echinoids are the only group of living echinoderms in which the canals for the podia penetrate the ossicles; in all others, the canals are located between the ossicles. Each of the plates, both ambulacral and interambulacral, bears rounded tubercles on which the spines articulate. In the regular urchins, there is usually one large tubercle on each plate, thus accounting for the regular arrangement of the large spines. In the irregular urchins, each plate bears a large number of small tubercles to which the many small spines are attached.

Around the periproct of regular urchins and at the aboral center in irregular urchins are a special series of plates. These consist of five large genital plates, one of which is porous and serves as the madreporite, and five smaller ocular plates (Figs. 19-13, *B* and 19-14). The genital plates are oriented to line up with the interambulacral areas and alternate with the ocular plates, which coincide with the ambulacral areas.

The muscle layer is absent in echinoids, since the ossicles are immovable, and the inner surface of the test is covered by the peritoneum, composed of columnar epithelium.

Locomotion.   Sea urchins are adapted for an existence on rocks and other types of hard bottoms, and spines and podia are used in movement. The spines are used to push the animal, and the tube feet function in the same manner as those of the sea stars. Sea urchins can move in any direction, and any one of the ambulacral areas can act as the leading section. If overturned, these animals right themselves by attaching the aboral podia of one of the ambulacral areas. Attachment of the podia progresses

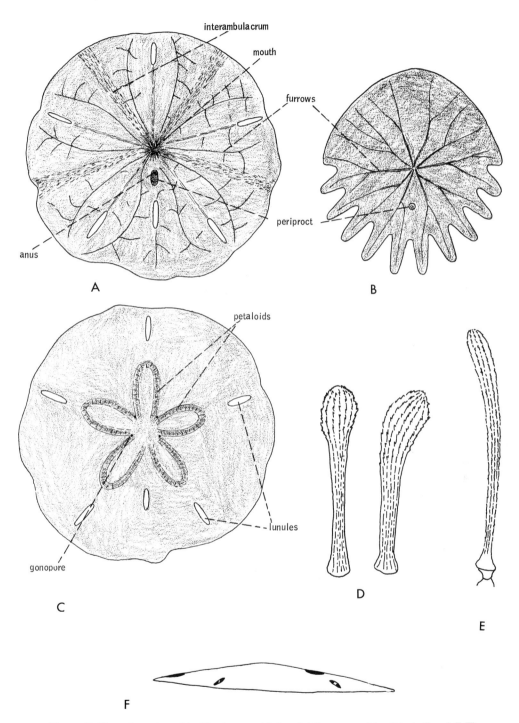

Figure 19-18.   Irregular echinoids, clypeastroids (sand dollars, or sea biscuits). *A, C,* and *F.* The West Indian sand dollar, *Mellita sexiesperforata. A.* Oral view. *B.* The African scutellid sand dollar, *Rotula orbiculus* (oral view). *C.* Aboral view. *D.* Aboral spines of *Mellita. E.* Oral spines of *Mellita. F.* Side view. (All after Hyman.)

in an oral direction, gradually turning the animal over onto the oral side. In forms with long spines, such as *Arbacia*, righting also involves specialized movements of the spines.

Some sea urchins tend to seek rocky depressions, and some species are actually capable of increasing the depth of such depressions or of even excavating burrows in rock and other firm material. Burrowing is performed by using the chewing apparatus and also by using the spines located around the circumference. These spines move in a rotating manner, grinding and wearing away the wall of the burrow.

Burrowing behavior appears to be an adaptation to counteract excessive wave action, and these species are largely found in habitats that are exposed to rough water. One of the most notable burrowing sea urchins is *Paracentrotus lividus*, which lives along the coast of Europe. This sea urchin literally riddles rock walls with burrows. When the burrows are shallow, the animal leaves to feed, but it remains permanently within deeper burrows, which often have entrances too small to permit exit. *Strongylocentrotus purpuratus* is a burrowing sea urchin that is found along the Pacific coast of North America. This species normally excavates cup-shaped depressions in stone; it has been reported to have attempted drilling into steel pilings.

The irregular echinoids are adapted for a life of burrowing in sand. They burrow with their anterior end forward. They cannot move backward but must turn in order to move in a new direction. Movement results entirely from the action of the spines, the podia being modified for other functions. Heart urchins burrow into the sand by inclining the anterior end downward and tossing sand to either side with specially modified curved spines located on the sides of the body. Normally these animals are not very active and tend to remain buried in one spot just beneath the surface of the sand. Contact with the surface is maintained by an opening in the sand over the aboral side of the animal. Some heart urchins, such as *Echinocardium flavescens*, form a chamber in the sand by plastering the walls of the burrow with mucus (Fig. 19-17, *C*). The long aboral spines project through the surface opening in the sand.

Sand dollars are somewhat more active than heart urchins and burrow just beneath the sand surface. Some species cover themselves completely with sand; in others the posterior end projects obliquely above the sand surface. The method of burrowing differs in different species, but in all cases the spines are used in moving sand grains.

In some species, the spines along the ante-

rior circumference throw sand upward into a pile in front of the animal. The spines on the oral surface then push the animal forward into the pile. The entire operation takes between 15 and 20 minutes. These same sand dollars are also able to right themselves if placed on their aboral surface. In righting, the anterior end burrows into the sand, gradually elevating the posterior end, and eventually the body is flipped over.

Other genera, such as *Mellita*, a genus of keyhole sand dollars, burrow by rotating the anterior edge back and forth, slicing its way through the sand, and they can completely bury themselves in one to four minutes. Ikeda (1941) studied the Japanese keyhole sand dollar, *Astriclypeus*, and found that the anterior lunule is essential in burrowing. The spines that border this lunule drive sand through it to the aboral side of the animal. If the lunule is plugged with paraffin, burrowing is considerably prolonged.

Water-Vascular System. The water-vascular system of echinoids is essentially like that of the sea stars (Fig. 19-20). One of the genital plates around the periproct contains pores and pore canals and functions as the madreporite (Fig. 19-14). A stone canal descends orally to the water ring, which lies above the peristome in heart urchins or just above the chewing apparatus in regular urchins and sand dollars. The radial canals extend from the water ring and run along the under side of the ambulacral areas of the test.

Each radial canal terminates in a small protrusion called a terminal tentacle, which penetrates the most apical ambulacral plate. The radial canal gives off alternately on both sides lateral canals to the bases of the ampullae.

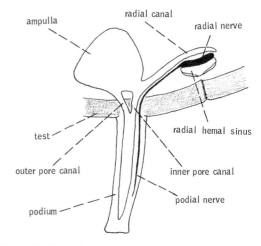

Figure 19-19. Radial canal and podium of an echinoid (transverse section). (After Chadwick from Reid.)

The canals connecting the ampullae and podia, unlike those in other echinoderms, penetrate the ambulacral ossicles rather than pass between them. Moreover, these canals are also peculiar in being doubled—that is, from each ampulla two canals pierce the ambulacral plate and become confluent on the outer surface to enter a single podium (Fig. 19-19).

Nutrition. Sea urchins feed on all types of organic material, plant or animal, living or dead, although different species display preferences for different types of food. Sea urchins living at great depths are probably detritus feeders, consuming minute organic particles in the bottom ooze.

All sea urchins have a highly developed chewing apparatus called Aristotle's lantern, which projects slightly through the mouth. The apparatus is composed of five large calcareous plates called pyramids, each of which are shaped somewhat like a barbed arrowhead with the point projected toward the mouth (Fig. 19-21). The pyramids are arranged radially with each side connected to that of the adjacent pyramid by means of transverse muscle fibers. Passing down the midline along the inner side of each pyramid is a long calcareous band. The upper end of the band is curled and enclosed within the dental sac that secretes it. The oral end of the band projects beyond the tip of the pyramid as an extremely hard pointed tooth. Since there is one such tooth band for each pyramid, there are five teeth projecting from the oral end of the lantern.

In addition to the teeth and pyramids, the Aristotle's lantern is composed of a number of smaller rod-like pieces located at the aboral end. By means of special muscles, the lantern can be partially protracted and retracted through the mouth. Other muscles control the teeth, which can be opened and closed. The lantern is an efficient chewing structure; but feeding is not rapid, and the consumption of a bunch of seaweed may take weeks.

The interior of Aristotle's lantern contains both a buccal cavity and a pharynx that ascends through the apparatus and passes into an esophagus (Fig. 19-21, *B*). The esophagus descends along the outer side of the lantern and joins an intestine (Fig. 19-20). At the junction of the esophagus and intestine, a blind pouch or cecum is usually present. The intestine is very long and can be divided into a proximal small intestine and a distal large intestine. The small intestine makes a complete turn around the inner side of the test wall to which it is suspended. It then passes into the larger aboral intestine, which makes a complete turn in the opposite direction. The large intestine then ascends to join the rectum, which empties through the anus within the periproct.

In most echinoids a narrow tube, called a siphon, parallels the intestine for about one half of its length. The ends of the siphon open into the lumen of the intestine.

Irregular urchins all feed on minute organic particles in the sand in which they burrow. In the heart urchins, food is obtained by means of modified podia that occupy the phyllodes on the oral surface. The distal end of each of these podia is covered by a mass of club-shaped projections, and the tips of the projections contain adhesive glands and numerous sensory cells, probably chemoreceptors. During feeding, the highly extensible podia project upward and out of the opening maintained in the sand above the animal (Fig. 19-17, *C*). These podia grope about the sand surface, picking up food particles that on retraction of the podia are brought back to special spines surrounding the anterior end of the animal. These spines then pass the food particles to the mouth.

The chewing lantern is absent in heart urchins, but, otherwise the alimentary tract is essentially like that of the sea urchins. Since the anus has shifted away from the center of the aboral surface, the rectum passes posteriorly from the intestine.

The sand dollars possess a modified lantern. It consists primarily of large pyramids and cannot be protracted from the mouth. These echinoids therefore feed on minute organic particles like the heart urchins.

According to Goodbody (1960), sand and debris through which the sand dollar burrows are passed backward over the aboral surface by special club-shaped spines. Fine particles, constituting the food materials, drop down between the spines and are carried by cilia to the margins of the body or the lunules and thence to the oral surface. Here special ciliated food tracts conduct the food particles to the ciliated ambulacral grooves, which deliver them in turn to the mouth. The alimentary canal differs from that of other echinoids only in that the rather large intestine makes but a single turn around the circumference of the test. The rectum descends to the posterior ventral anus.

In all echinoids, the digestive tract is lined with a flagellated columnar epithelium. The esophagus and especially the cecum contain gland cells, but none have been reported from the intestine. The little information that is available on digestion in these animals is conflicting. The intestine is probably the site of both digestion and absorption, although the cecum appears to be involved in the production of some enzymes. The siphon supposedly functions in the removal of excess water from the food. The products of digestion pass through the intestine wall into the coelom for distribution. Glycogen is one of the principal food reserves and apparently can be stored in any of the body tissues but may be particularly prevalent in the intestinal wall.

Circulation, Respiration, and Excretion. There is a large principal coelom, as well as a number of minor subcompartments, and as in asteroids, the coelomic fluid is the principal circulatory medium. Coelomocytes are abundant and as many as 7,000 per cubic centimeter have been reported in some echinoids. There are two major types of coelomocytes. One type consists of phagocytic cells with well developed pseudopodia. The other type is not phagocytic, contains conspicuous inclusions, and has short blunt pseudopodia. The dermal mesenchyme is apparently the principal site for the formation of coelomocytes. In addition to the transportation of food and waste materials, coelomocytes also function as a clotting mechanism. Clotting is apparently initiated by damaged tissue and causes the formation of a meshwork of coelomocytes at the place of injury.

A hemal system is present and has the same basic plan of structure as in the asteroids.

A hemal ring encircles the esophagus above Aristotle's lantern (Fig. 19-21, *B*), and from this ring extend radial sinuses, which lie beneath the radial canals of the water–vascular system (Fig. 19-19). The hemal system also includes a channel on each side of the intestine. These channels, known as the ventral and dorsal marginal sinuses, supply the intestine with a network of smaller vessels. Nothing is known concerning the nature of circulation within the hemal system or its importance in the physiology of these animals.

In regular echinoids, the five pairs of peristomial gills are probably the chief centers of gaseous exchange (Figs. 19-13, *A* and 19-21, *B*). Each gill is a highly branched outpocketing of the body wall and is therefore lined within and without by a ciliated epithelium. The internal cavities of the gills are filled with fluid and are continuous with a separate division of the coelom, called the peripharyngeal coelom, that surrounds the lantern (Fig. 19-21, *B*). Special ossicles and their associated muscles, composing the aboral part of the lantern, act as a pumping mechanism, changing the coelomic pressure within the peripharyngeal coelom and thereby forcing fluid into and out of the gills. Pumping is not continuous but depends on the

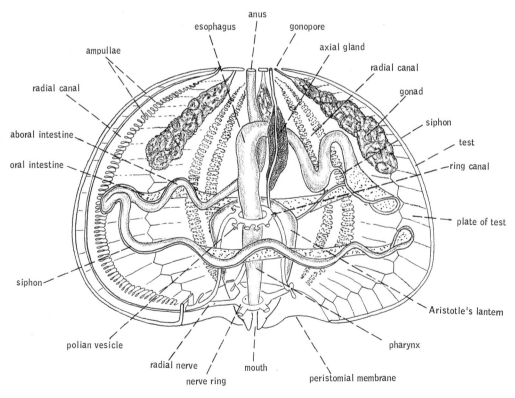

Figure 19-20.   Internal structure of the regular urchin, *Arbacia* (side view). (Modified after Petrunkevitch from Reid.)

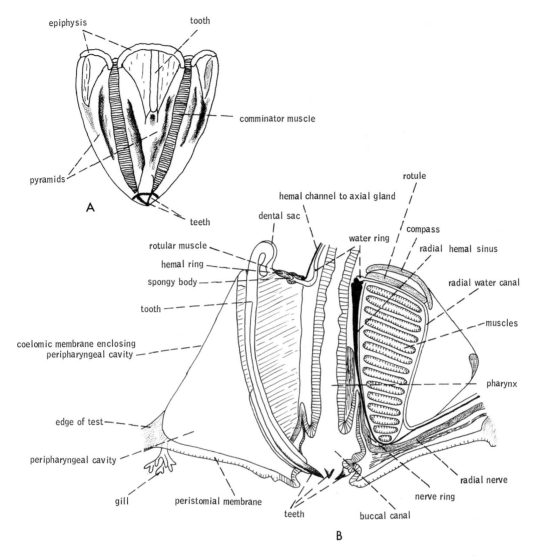

Figure 19-21. *A.* Aristotle's lantern of *Tripneustes esculentus,* a regular urchin (lateral view). (After Hyman.) *B.* Vertical section through Aristotle's lantern and peristomial region of the regular urchin, *Paracentrotus lividus.* (After Cuénot from Hyman.)

need for oxygen, and the apparatus is under the control of the nerve ring. The nerve ring is stimulated to emit impulses to the lantern by an increase in acidity resulting from an accumulation of carbon dioxide.

There are no peristomial gills in heart urchins and sand dollars. In these animals, the modified podia of the petaloids, which are thin-walled and lobulate, are believed to act as respiratory structures (Fig. 19-17, *D*).

As in asteroids, ammonia and urea are the principal excretory products and are probably removed by general surface diffusion. The coelomocytes are apparently active in the removal of particulate waste and are believed to carry these accumulations to the gills and podia for removal. The axial gland, which is similar to

that of the asteroids, is probably also a site of waste deposition. Its irregular internal lumen represents a part of the coelom, and its walls contain many inclusions, as well as coelomocytes.

Nervous System. The nervous system is basically like that of the asteroids (Figs. 19-20 and 19-21, *B*). In forms with a lantern, the circumoral ring encircles the pharynx inside the lantern. In heart urchins, the nerve ring is located above the peristome. The radial nerves pass between the pyramids of the lantern and run along the underside of the test, lying just beneath the radial canals of the water-vascular system. Each radial nerve gives rise to a nerve that supplies each of the podia. Each of these podial nerves terminates in a nervous network in the region of the sucker (Fig. 19-19). Other

nerves arising from the radial nerve also penetrate the test and supply both the pedicellariae
and the spines with a nervous network that is
continuous with the subepidermal plexus.

The numerous sensory cells in the epithelium, particularly on the spines, pedicellariae,
and podia, compose the major part of the echinoid sensory system. The spheridia are perhaps
the only specialized sense organs. These structures are believed to function in the maintenance of equilibrium. It has been found, for example, that if the spheridia of a sand dollar are
removed, the righting reaction is greatly delayed.
Even though maintenance of the equilibrium
may indeed be the function of these structures,
their physiology is still unknown. Although
ocelli are absent in almost all species, echinoids
are in general negatively phototropic and tend
to seek the shade of crevices in rocks and shells.
Some species cover themselves with shell fragments and other objects probably as a means of
avoiding light.

Reproduction.   All echinoids are dioecious,
and the majority display no sexual dimorphism.
In regular echinoids, there are five gonads suspended along the interambulacra on the inner
side of the test (Fig. 19-20). In most irregular
echinoids, the gonad of the posterior interambulacrum has disappeared. Each gonad is covered
on the outside with coelomic peritoneum and
lined internally with a germinal epithelium. Between these two layers are found muscle cells
and connective tissue. A short gonoduct extends
aborally from each gonad and opens through a
gonopore located on one of the five genital
plates (Fig. 19-13, B).

Sperm and eggs are shed into the sea water
by the contraction of the muscle layers of the
gonads, and fertilization takes place in the sea
water. As in asteroids, spawning in temperate
species takes place in the spring and early summer. Brooding is displayed by some cold-water
sea urchins and heart urchins, and there is one
brooding species of sand dollar. Brooding sea
urchins retain their eggs on the peristome or
around the periproct and use the spines in
holding the eggs in position. The heart urchins
and the single brooding species of sand dollar
brood their eggs in deep concavities on the
petaloids.

Embryology.   Cleavage is equal, up to the
eight-cell stage, after which the blastomeres at
the vegetal pole proliferate a number of small
micromeres. A typical blastula ensues, displaying
a wall of equal-size cells, with the exception of
the small micromeres and somewhat larger

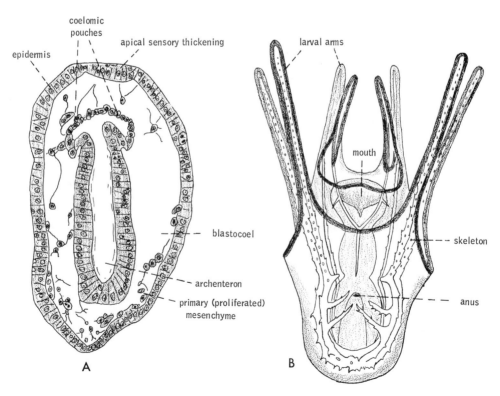

Figure 19-22.   *A.* Gastrula of the sea urchin, *Echinus esculentus.* (After McBride from Hyman.)
B. Echinopluteus larva of the sand dollar, *Fibularia craniola.* (After Mortensen from Cuénot.)

macromeres at the vegetal pole. The blastula becomes flagellated and free-swimming within 12 hours after fertilization.

Gastrulation is typical but is preceded by an interior proliferation of cells by the micromeres, which forms the mesenchyme. Additional mesenchymal cells are proliferated from the tip of the archenteron. The coelom is formed by the separation of the free end of the archenteron. This separated portion then divides into right and left pouches, or lateral divisions may ap-

pear prior to the separation from the main portion of the archenteron (Fig. 19-22, *A*). The gastrula becomes somewhat cone-shaped and gradually develops into a larval stage (the echinopluteus) that displays five or six pairs of elongated arms bearing ciliated bands (Fig. 19-22, *B*).

The echinopluteus differs from the asteroid bipinnaria in the general shape of the larval body and in the number and position of the arms. The echinopluteus is a planktonic and a feeding larva; its complete development may

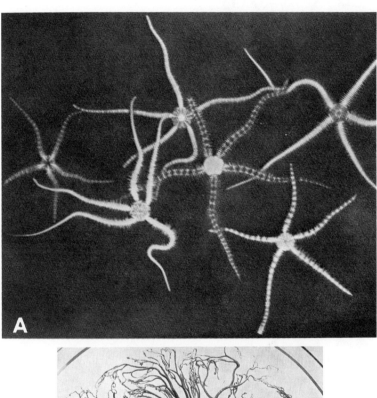

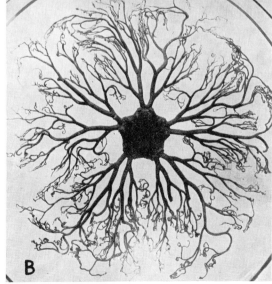

Figure 19-23.   *A.* The brittle star, *Ophiothrix fragilis.* (By D. P. Wilson.) *B.* The basket star, *Gorgonocephalus.* (Courtesy of the American Museum of Natural History.)

take as long as several months. During later larval life, the adult skeleton begins to form, and the echinopluteus gradually sinks to the bottom. However, there is no attachment as in asteroids, and metamorphosis is extremely rapid, taking place in about an hour. Young urchins are no larger than one millimeter. Inter-nal development is basically like that of asteroids, although differing in detail.

Class Ophiuroidea

The class Ophiuroidea contains those echino-derms known as basket stars and serpent stars,

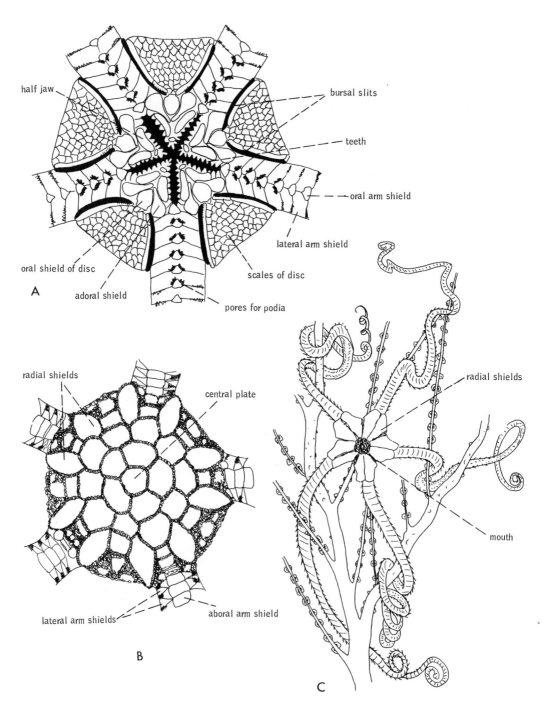

Figure 19-24.   *A.* The disc of *Ophiomusium* (oral view). *B.* The disc of *Ophiolepis* (aboral view). *C.* The brittle star, *Asteronyx excavata,* climbing on a upright coral. (All after Hyman.)

or brittle stars (Fig. 19-23, *A* and *B*). Ophiuroids superficially resemble asteroids in that they both possess arms. However, in other respects the two classes are quite different. The extremely long arms of ophiuroids are more sharply set off from the central disc. There is no ambulacral groove, and the podia are greatly reduced and play little role in locomotion. Moreover, the

arms have a relatively solid construction as compared to those of the asteroids.

External Structure. Ophiuroids are relatively small echinoderms. The disc in most species ranges from one quarter to one inch in diameter, although the arms may be quite long. The basket stars are the largest members of the class, and the disc in some species of this group

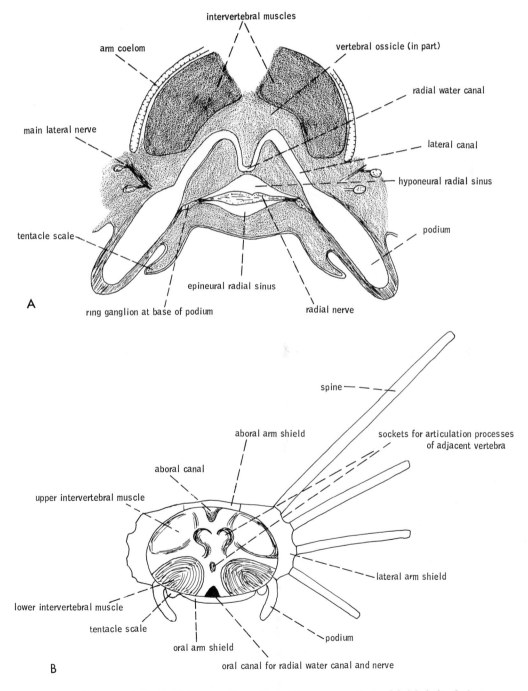

Figure 19-25. *A.* Oral half of an arm of an ophiuroid (transverse section). (Modified after Cuénot from Hyman.) *B.* End of an arm joint of the brittle star, *Ophiocoma.* (After Hyman.)

may attain a diameter of almost four inches. A great variety of colors are found in the ophiuroids, but in most cases the coloration is not particularly conspicuous because of their small size and the mottled and banded patterns.

The central disc is flattened displaying a rounded, pentagonal, or somewhat star-shaped circumference (Fig. 19-24). The aboral surface varies from smooth to granular with small tubercles or spines, and sometimes small calcareous plates, called shields, are conspicuous. The largest of the plates are a pair of radial shields located opposite the base of each arm (Fig. 19-24, B and C).

There are typically only five arms; however, in basket stars the arms branch either at the base or more distally, and the subdivisions repeatedly branch to produce a great mass of coils that resemble tentacles (Fig. 19-23, B). The arms characteristically appear jointed, because of the presence of four longitudinal rows of shields (Fig. 19-24, A and B; and 19-25, B). There are two rows of lateral shields, one row of aboral shields, and one row of oral shields. A single set—that is, two lateral, one aboral and one oral shield—completely surround the arm and correspond in position to an internal skeletal ossicle, which is described later. Not infrequently, the oral and aboral shields are reduced by the large size of the lateral shields, which may even meet on the oral and aboral surfaces (Fig. 19-24, A).

Each lateral shield usually bears 2 to 15 large spines arranged in a vertical row (Fig. 19-25, B). These spines vary considerably in size and shape, depending upon the species. For example, in *Ophiothrix* and others, the most oral spine in each row is hook-shaped; in *Ophiopholis* the spines toward the end of each arm are shaped like little umbrellas; and in *Ophiopteron* some of the spines are interconnected by webbing. Some serpent stars have what are probably poisonous spines, for the end of such a spine is provided with a thick glandular covering.

There is no ambulacral groove on the oral surface of the arms. The podia are very small tentacle-like appendages that extend between the oral and the lateral shields, and there is typically one pair of podia per joint (Fig. 19-25, A and B). Neither papulae nor pedicellariae are present in ophiuroids.

The center of the oral surface of the disc is occupied by a complex series of large plates that frame the mouth area and also form a chewing apparatus (Fig. 19-24, A). The plates are organized into five triangular jaws that are oriented longitudinally with the apex directed toward the center of the disc. Each jaw is composed of several plates, of which the most conspicuous are a pair of half jaws and a large basal oral shield. The jaws bear many small tooth-like plates along their margin. At the apex, the teeth also extend aborally in a vertical row (Fig. 19-26).

In most ophiuroids, one oral shield is modified, forming a madreporite. Thus, the madreporite is located on the oral surface in contrast to its aboral position in echinoids and asteroids. The arms extend inward to the jaws on the oral surface of the disc, leaving five large somewhat

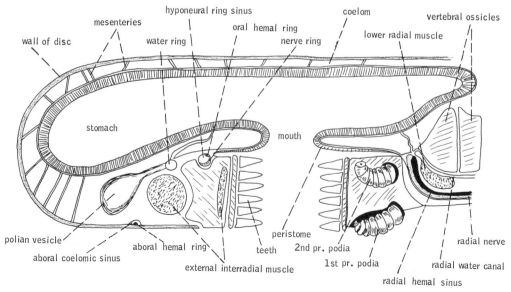

Figure 19-26.   The disc and base of an arm of a brittle star (vertical section). (After Ludwig from Hyman.)

triangular interradial areas, having essentially the same surface structure as the aboral side of the disc.

Body Wall and Skeleton. With the exception of the basket stars, the epidermis of the ophiuroids is a reduced syncytium, continuous with the underlying dermis. Moreover, aside from certain specialized areas, there are no surface flagella. The dermis contains the more superficial skeletal shields, as well as the large deeper ossicles of the arms. These ossicles are highly specialized, and it is believed that each represents two fused ambulacral ossicles. Each ossicle is a large disc-shaped skeletal piece (a vertebra) that almost fills the entire interior of the arm (Figs. 19-25, *B* and 19-26).

The vertebral ossicles are arranged linearly from one end of the arm to the other and each ossicle is covered by four superficial arm shields. The two end surfaces of a vertebral ossicle are structurally adapted for articulation with adjacent vertebrae. In serpent stars, this articulation allows great lateral mobility of the arm, but no vertical movement. However, in basket stars, which have a somewhat different vertebral articulation, the arms can bend and coil in any direction.

In basket stars, there is a muscle layer beneath the dermis, but in serpent stars the muscle layer is absent, and the coelomic peritoneum covers the inner surface of the dermis. There are, however, well developed intervertebral muscles for the movement of the arms (Fig. 19-25, *B*).

A considerable number of ophiuroids, such as the cosmopolitan *Amphipholis squamata*, are luminescent. A yellow or yellowish-green light emanates from the sides of the arms, particularly in the region of the spines. Large gland-like cells in these areas are believed to be the source of the luminescence, although actual secretion has not been observed.

Locomotion. The ophiuroids are the most highly mobile of all echinoderms. During movement the disc is held above the substratum with one or two arms extended forward and one or two arms trailing behind. The remaining two lateral arms perform a rapid rowing movement against the substratum that propels the animal forward in leaps or jerks. Serpent stars show no arm preference and can move in any direction.

Righting is accomplished by extending two adjacent arms away from each other so that they form a straight line tangent to the disc. Using the extended arms as a pivot, the disc is raised and pushed over by the other arms. In clambering over rocks or in seaweed and hydroid colonies, the ends of the supple arms often coil about objects (Fig. 19-24, *C*). A few ophiuroids reportedly are able to swim, using the same method of progression as in crawling. A few forms also burrow; *Amphiura* covers itself completely in sand except for the ends of the arms. The podia are used in digging.

Water-Vascular System. The oral shield that forms the madreporite in ophiuroids usually bears but a single pore and canal. In addition to the oral position of the madreporite, the stone canal ascends to the water ring, which is located in a groove on the aboral surface of the jaws (Fig. 19-26). The water ring bears four polian vesicles and also gives rise to the radial canals, which penetrate through the lower side of the vertebral ossicles of the arms (Fig. 19-26). In each ossicle, the radial canal gives rise to a pair of lateral canals, which may extend directly to the pair of ventro-lateral podia or may first loop upward and then downward to the podia (Fig. 19-25, *A*). Ampullae are absent, but a valve is present between the podium and the lateral canals. As in asteroids, the radial canal terminates in a small external tentacle at the tip of the arm. The entire water-vascular system is lined with a flagellated peritoneum.

Nutrition. Ophiuroids feed on bottom detritus and small dead or living animals. Large food particles are raked into the mouth by the arms, while smaller particles are passed to the mouth by means of the podia or perhaps in some cases by special flagella on the oral surface of the arms. The digestive tract is extremely simple (Fig. 19-26). The jaws frame a shallow prebuccal cavity, which is roofed aborally by the peristomial membrane containing the mouth.

The short esophagus connects the mouth with a large sac-like stomach. The stomach fills most of the interior of the disc, and in most ophiuroids the margins are infolded to form ten pouches. There is no intestine or anus, and with the exception of a single species, no part of the digestive tract extends into the arms. Although the stomach must obviously be the site of digestion and absorption, virtually nothing is known about the details of the digestive process.

Circulation, Respiration, and Excretion. The coelom in ophiuroids is much reduced when compared to that of other echinoderms. The vertebral ossicles restrict the coelom to the aboral part of the arms (Fig. 19-25, *A*); the stomach, bursae (see page 556), and gonads leave only small coelomic spaces in the disc (Fig. 19-26). The coelomocytes are active ameboid cells.

The hemal system is essentially like that of asteroids, but the axial gland is located below the oral hemal sinus, because the stone canal leads to the madreporite on the oral surface. The oral hemal ring lies above the jaw apparatus, and the radial hemal channels run along the oral side of the vertebral ossicles and lie just above the nerve cord (Fig. 19-26). An aboral hemal ring is also present and is connected to the oral end (originally aboral) of the axial gland (Fig. 19-26).

Respiration in ophiuroids takes place by means of ten internal sacs (bursae) that represent invaginations of the oral surface of the disc. Internally each bursa is lodged between two stomach pouches. The bursae are connected to the outside by way of a slit that runs along the margins of the arms on the oral surface of the disc (Fig. 19-24, *A*). The bursae are lined with flagellated epithelium, especially the slits. The beating flagella create a current of water that enters the peripheral end of the slit, passes through the bursa, and flows out the oral end of the slit. Many species also pump water into and out of the bursae by raising and lowering the oral or aboral disc wall.

Little scientific investigation has been done on excretion in ophiuroids, but there is little reason to assume that the excretory products are any different from those in echinoids and asteroids. The thin-walled respiratory bursae may well be the principal center for waste removal.

Nervous System.   As in the asteroids, the nervous system is doubled and is composed of the outer sensory and motor ectoneural system and the inner motor hyponeural system. The two systems parallel each other and are separated only by a thin layer of connective tissue. The circumoral nerve ring lies above the jaw apparatus between the water ring on the outside and the hemal ring on the inside (Fig. 19-26). The circumoral nerve ring supplies nerves to the esophagus, to the first podia (buccal podia) in each arm, and to the muscles of the jaw apparatus. The radial nerve runs along the outside of the vertebral ossicles of the arms just beneath the radial hemal channel (Figs. 19-25, *A* and 19-26).

At the level of each vertebral ossicle, the radial nerve contains a ganglionic swelling, a structure not present in the other echinoderms. From the hyponeural portion of each ganglion arises a pair of lateral motor nerves that innervate the intervertebral muscles. Between successive ganglia, a podial nerve and a pair of sensory lateral nerves issue from the ectoneural part of the radial nerve (Fig. 19-25, *A*). The lateral nerves innervate the lateral body wall and the spines; the podial nerve forms a ganglionic ring around the base of the podium, from which a nerve descends to the distal end of the appendage.

Experimental studies have demonstrated that the nerve ring plays the same coordinating role in arm movement as does the nerve ring in the asteroids.

There are no specialized sense organs in ophiuroids, the general epithelial sensory cells comprising the sensory system. Ophiuroids are negatively phototropic, as are echinoids and many asteroids. They are also able to detect food without contact, an ability that is poorly developed in other echinoderm classes. The chemoreceptors are probably located on the podia.

Regeneration and Reproduction.   Ophiuroids readily cast off one or more arms if disturbed. A break can occur at any point beyond the disc; the lost portion is then regenerated. In most ophiuroids, the disc does not have the regenerative powers of the arms, and in at least some species the entire disc and at least one arm must be present for the remaining arms to regenerate.

Asexual reproduction takes place in a few ophiuroids, notably the six-armed serpent star, *Ophiactis*. The disc divides into two pieces, each piece with three arms. Fission can take place along any plane; the missing half is then regenerated.

The majority of ophiuroids are dioecious. They usually exhibit no sexual dimorphism; however, the females of three species are known to carry dwarf males about, the two sexes being attached mouth to mouth. The gonads are small sacs attached to the coelomic side of the bursae near the bursal slit. There may be one, two, or numerous gonads per bursa with various positions of attachment. Hermaphroditic species are not uncommon. Many are protandric; the gonad first produces sperm and then eggs. In other ophiuroids, the bursae bear separate ovaries and testes.

When the gonads are ripe, they discharge into the bursae, probably by rupture, and the sex cells are carried out of the body in the respiratory water current. Fertilization and development take place in the sea water in most species, but like other echinoderms, brooding is common in arctic and antarctic ophiuroids. The bursae are used as brood chambers, and development takes place within the mother until the juvenile stage is reached. In most species, only a few young are brooded in each bursa, but as many as 200 embryos reportedly have been contained within each bursa in an antarctic form. In some brooding serpent stars, such as *Amphipholis squamata*, development is viviparous, for the embryo is attached to the bursal wall and receives nourishment from the mother. In a few species, such as the antarctic *Ophionotus hexactis*, a single egg is formed and passes into an

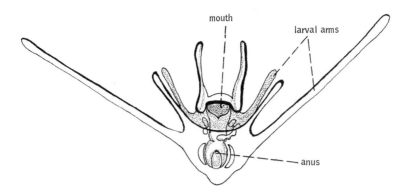

Figure 19-27.   Ophiopluteus larva of *Ophiomaza* (oral view). (After Mortensen from Cuénot.)

ovarian lumen, in which both fertilization and development take place; the young serpent star ruptures into the bursa.

Embryology.   In nonbrooding oviparous ophiuroids, early development is identical to that in the asteroids. A free-swimming stage is attained at the blastula stage that is completely flagellated. The coelom arises either by the separation of the free end of the archenteron, which subsequently divides into right and left pouches, or by pouching, which takes place just prior to separation from the archenteron. The larva, called an ophiopluteus, is very similar to the echinopluteus of the echinoids (Fig. 19-27). Metamorphosis takes place while the larva is still free-swimming, and there is no attachment stage. The tiny serpent star sinks to the bottom and takes up an adult existence.

Class Holothuroidea

The holothuroids are a class of some 500 echinoderms known as sea cucumbers. Like echinoids, the body of the holothuroids is not drawn out into arms, and the mouth and anus are located at opposite poles. Also, there are ambulacral and interambulacral areas arranged meridionally around the polar axis. However, holothuroids are distinguished from other echinoderms in having the polar axis greatly lengthened, which results in the body having an elongated cucumber shape (Fig. 19-28). This shape forces the animal to lie with the side of the body, rather than the oral pole, against the substratum. The class is further distinguished from other echinoderms by the reduction of the skeleton to microscopic ossicles and by the modification of the buccal podia into a circle of tentacles around the mouth.

External Anatomy.   Most sea cucumbers are colored black, brown, or olive green; but there are some rose, orange, or violet species,

and striped patterns are not infrequent. There is considerable range in size. The smallest species are less than one inch in length (oral to aboral end), while *Stichopus* from the Philippines may attain a length of over one yard and a diameter of eight inches. Most of the common North American and European species, such as *Cucumaria, Holothuria, Thyone,* and *Leptosynapta,* range from several inches to one foot in length.

The body shape varies from almost spherical, as in *Sphaerothuria,* to long and worm-like, as in *Synapta* and *Euapta* (Fig. 19-29, *A* and *B*). Not infrequently the mouth and anus are displaced from the ends of the long axis of the body. Although there are a few genera, such as *Psolus* and *Theelia,* that are provided with a protective armor of calcareous plates, the body surface in the majority of sea cucumbers is leathery as the result of reduction of the skeletal ossicles to microscopic size.

Holothuroids lie with one side of the body against the substratum, and this ventral surface is comprised of three ambulacral areas (the trivium), commonly called the sole (Fig. 19-28, *A*). The dorsal surface consists of two ambulacral areas (the bivium) and three interambulacral areas (Fig. 19-28, *B*). As might be expected, there has been a tendency for the dorsal and ventral surfaces to become differentiated, thus producing a secondary bilateral symmetry. However, the bilateral symmetry of holothuroids has evolved in an entirely different manner from that of the irregular echinoids.

The degree of differentiation between the dorsal and ventral surfaces varies considerably and is most easily seen in the nature of the podia. In the common genera, *Thyone* and *Cucumaria,* podia are present on both surfaces of the body, but suckers are best developed on the podia of the sole (Fig. 19-28). In other species, such as *Holothuria,* the dorsal and lateral podia are reduced to warts, tubercles or papillae. In still others, such as *Psolus,* dorsal and lateral podia have completely disappeared. The functional podia are thus restricted to the creeping sole.

There is a general tendency for the podia of sea cucumbers, whether reduced or not, to lose their radial distribution and to become more or less randomly scattered over the body surface. The primitive radial configuration is seen in *Cucumaria*, on which the podia are more or less restricted to the five ambulacral areas; in *Thyone*, on the other hand, podia are scattered over the entire body surface. Members of the order Apoda (*Synapta, Leptosynapta, Euapta*), which are elongated and worm-like, completely lack podia on any part of the body.

The mouth is always surrounded by 10 to 30 tentacles, which represent modified buccal podia and are thus part of the water-vascular system. The tentacles are highly retractile, and both mouth and tentacles can be completely re-

tracted by pulling the adjacent body wall over them. The form of the tentacles varies considerably. They may be long and irregularly branched, as in *Cucumaria*, *Thyone*, and *Psolus*, or the branches may be horizontal and restricted to the end of a basal stalk, like a mop (Fig. 19-28, *A*). In *Synapta* and *Leptosynapta*, the tentacles consist of a long central axis with regular side branches, and in the Molpadonia they are short and finger-like (Fig. 19-29, *A*).

Body Wall. The epidermis is composed of nonflagellated columnar epithelium that is covered externally by a thin cuticle. The basal ends of the epidermal cells merge with the dermis, which consists of a thick layer of connective tissue surrounding the microscopic calcareous ossicles. The ossicles are displayed in a great variety of shapes (Fig. 19-29, *C* to *F*). These different shapes are important in the taxonomy of holothuroids. Beneath the dermis is a layer of

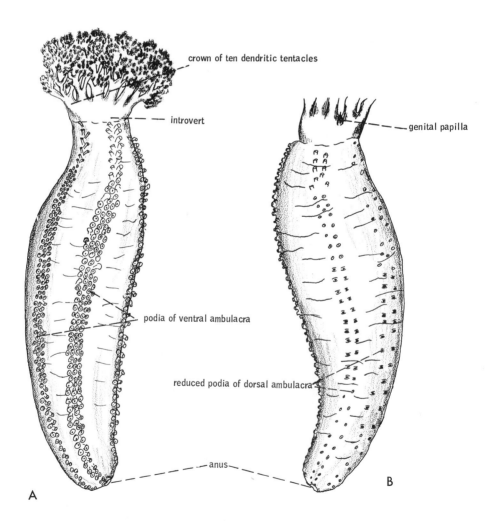

crown of ten dendritic tentacles

introvert

genital papilla

podia of ventral ambulacra

reduced podia of dorsal ambulacra

anus

A

B

Figure 19-28.   The North Atlantic sea cucumber, *Cucumaria frondosa*. *A*. Ventral view. *B*. Dorsal view. (Both after Hyman.)

circular muscle that overlies five single or doubled bands of longitudinal fibers located in the ambulacral areas.

Locomotion.   Sea cucumbers are relatively sluggish animals and live on the bottom surface or burrow in sand and mud. Forms with podia creep along on the sole with the podia functioning as those in asteroids; but many species, including *Cucumaria,* move very little and remain in one spot for long periods. Righting is accom-

plished by twisting the oral end around until the podia contact the substratum.

Burrowing species include the Apoda, which lack podia, as well as some pedate holothuroids, such as the common *Thyone*. Burrowing is accomplished by alternate contraction of longitudinal and circular muscle layers of the body wall in the manner employed by earthworms. The tentacles aid by pushing away the sand. Members of the Apoda burrow completely

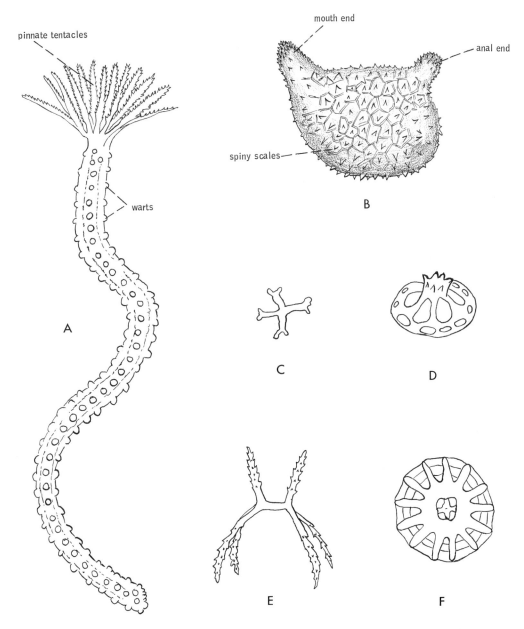

Figure 19-29.   *A. Euapta lappa,* a member of the order Apoda from the Bahamas. (After Hyman.) *B. Sphaerothuria,* a short-bodied holothuroid with scaly armor. (After Ludwig from Hyman.) *C* and *D*. Ossicles from *Holothuria.* (After Hyman.) *E* and *F*. Ossicles from an Elasipoda. (After Théel from Hyman.)

beneath the surface at a rate of two or three centimeters per hour (for example, *Leptosynapta*). *Thyone* keeps both anterior and posterior ends above the surface, but in other forms the anterior end is directed downward, and only the posterior end projects above the sand. Burrowing species move very little once they have attained the proper position.

The Elasipoda are a curious group of deep-

sea holothuroids that are thought to be pelagic. The papillae (modified podia) are highly developed and webbed together in various ways to form fins or sails. One genus, *Pelagothuria,* that has been collected at the surface, has a circlet of long, webbed papillae just behind the tentacles. Nocturnal swimming reportedly is displayed by young specimens of the normally burrowing *Leptosynapta.*

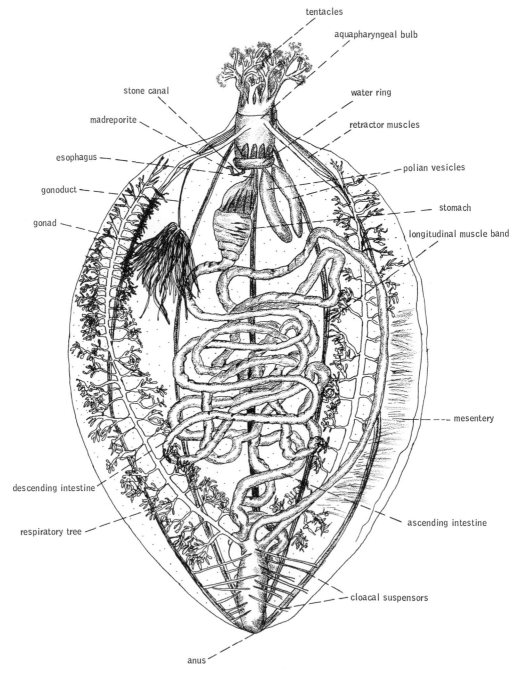

Figure 19-30.   Internal structure of *Thyone briaereus,* a common sea cucumber that inhabits North Atlantic coastal waters. (After Coe from Hyman.)

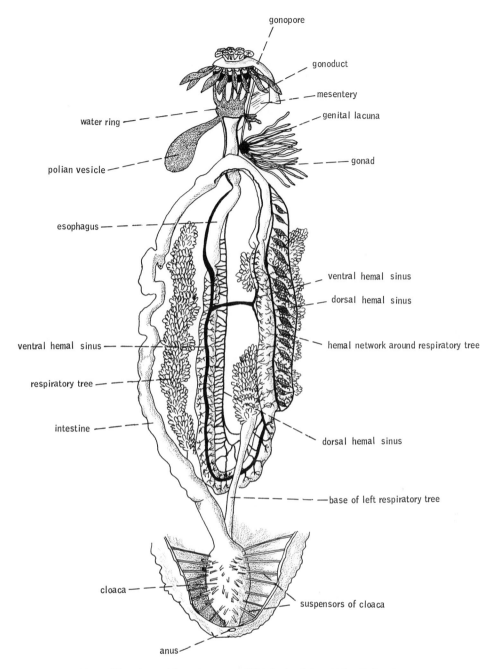

Figure 19-31.   Digestive and hemal systems of *Holothuria tubulosa*. (After Cuénot.)

Nutrition. Sea cucumbers with dendritic tentacles, such as *Holothuria, Cucumaria,* and *Thyone* (all of which live on the bottom surface or at least have the anterior end projecting above the sand), are plankton feeders. The highly-branched tentacles are stretched out to their greatest extent; then they either sweep over the bottom or are held in the sea water. In either case, protozoans, algae, diatoms, and other small organisms are trapped in mucus on the surface of each tentacle.

One at a time the tentacles are stuffed into the pharynx, and the adhering food particles are wiped off as the tentacles are pulled out of the mouth. Other sea cucumbers are deposit feeders, living on the bottom material in which they burrow. Sand and mud are swallowed in the process of burrowing or are swept into the mouth by the tentacles. *Stichopus* from Bermuda is estimated by Crozier (1918) to fill and empty itself of sand three times a day.

The mouth is located in the middle of a

buccal membrane at the base of the tentacular crown. The mouth opens into a pharynx, which is surrounded anteriorly by a calcareous ring (Figs. 19-30 to 19-32). The calcareous ring, which is perhaps homologous to the Aristotle's lantern of echinoids, is usually composed of five radial and five interradial rectangular plates, arranged somewhat like the staves in a barrel. The calcareous ring provides support for the pharynx and the water ring, and it serves as the site for the anterior insertion of the longitudinal muscles of the body wall and the retractor muscles of the tentacles and mouth region.

In some holothuroids, such as *Thyone,* the pharynx leads into a slender esophagus, which in turn opens into a short muscular stomach (Fig. 19-30). Frequently the esophagus is absent, as in *Cucumaria,* and if the stomach is poorly developed, which is true of *Cucumaria* and *Holothuria,* the pharynx appears to open directly into the intestine (Fig. 19-31). The long intestine is looped three times through the length of the body and is supported by mesenteries. In many holothuroids, the intestine terminates in a cloaca prior to opening to the outside through the anus.

The digestive tract is lined with columnar epithelium that is sometimes ciliated. Gland cells are often prevalent in the pharynx and the stomach but may be absent in the intestine. Beneath the lining epithelium, there is well developed connective tissue and circular and longitudinal muscle fibers.

Coelomocytes play an active and unusual role in digestion. These cells traverse the intestinal wall carrying digestive enzymes into the intestinal lumen. The products of digestion are then picked up by coelomocytes and transported out of the intestine for general distribution. Protein- and carbohydrate-splitting enzymes are present, but fat digestion is negligible.

Circulation, Respiration, and Excretion. The coelom is large and lined with a thin flagellated epithelium, and the usual divisions are present. The peritoneal flagella produce a current of coelomic fluid that contributes to the general circulation of materials within the body. Coelomocytes are abundant and consist of a number of different types, most of which are also found in other parts of the body. Of particular interest are coelomocytes called hemocytes. These are flattened discoidal ameboid cells, that

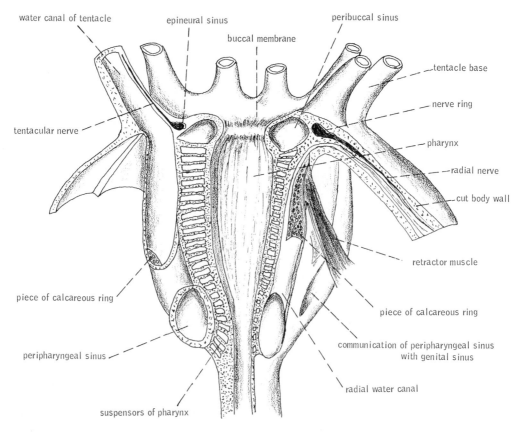

Figure 19-32. Anterior of *Cucumaria.* (After Hérouard from Hyman.)

contain hemoglobin; when they are present in large numbers, hemocytes give a red color to the coelomic fluid and hemal fluid. Other types of coelomocytes include phagocytic amebocytes, amebocytes containing colorless spherules, and amebocytes with yellow or brown spherules. A given species usually contains a number of different forms of coelomocytes.

Holothuroids possess the most highly developed hemal system of any of the echinoderm classes. The general organization of the system is essentially like that of other echinoderms. A hemal ring and radial hemal sinuses parallel the water ring and the radial canals of the water-vascular system (Figs. 19-31 to 19-33). The most conspicuous features of the system, at least in larger species, are a dorsal and a ventral sinus that accompany the intestine (Fig. 19-31). These main intestinal sinuses supply the intestinal wall with a large number of smaller channels. Between the arms of the first great loop of the intestine, formed by what may be called the descending and the ascending intestine, the dorsal sinus gives rise to a complex interconnecting network of channels containing many lacunae.

As in other echinoderms, the hemal channels do not have distinct linings, although muscle fibers and connective tissue are present. In the intestine, the sinuses are merely spaces in the connective-tissue layer. The hemal fluid is essentially the same as that in the coelom and contains the same coelomocytes; in fact, the coelomocytes are formed in the walls of the hemal channels. The primary role of the hemal system is apparently the distribution of food materials that are brought into the system by the amebocytes. The dorsal sinus is contractile, and fluid is pumped through the intestine into the ventral sinus and anteriorly into the hemal ring.

Except for the deep-water elasipods and burrowing apods, which obtain oxygen through the general body surface, respiration in holothuroids is accomplished by means of a remarkable system of tubules called respiratory trees. The respiratory trees are two in number and are located in the coelom on the right and left sides of the digestive tract (Figs. 19-30 and 19-31). Each tree consists of a main trunk with many branches, each of which ends in a tiny vesicle. The trunks of the two trees emerge from the upper end of the cloaca either separately or by way of a common trunk.

Water circulates through the tubules by means of the pumping action of the cloaca and the respiratory trees. The cloaca dilates, filling with sea water. The anal sphincter then closes, the cloaca contracts, and water is forced into the respiratory trees. Water leaves the system

because of the contraction of the tubules and the reverse action of the cloaca. Pumping is slow; Holothuria requires six to ten cloacal dilations and contractions to fill the trees, each contraction taking one minute or more. All the water is expelled in one action.

Evidence for the respiratory function of the trees was shown by Winterstein (1909), who found a reduction in oxygen consumption of 50 to 60 per cent when the anus was covered and water was prevented from entering the system. The branches of the left tree are intermingled in the hemal network between the ascending and descending intestine, and experimental evidence indicates that oxygen passes from the terminal vesicles of the left tree into the coelomic fluid and then into the hemal network (Fig. 19-31).

The type of nitrogenous waste excreted by the holothuroids is still undecided. Ammoniacal compounds appear to be the most common waste products, but small amounts of urea and uric acid have been reported by some investigators. As is true of other physiological processes in the holothuroids, coelomocytes play an important role in waste removal. Particulate waste, as well as nitrogenous material in crystalline form, is carried by coelomocytes from various parts of the body to the gonadal tubules, the respiratory tree, and the intestine. Waste then leaves the body by way of the lumens of these organs.

The Apoda, which lack respiratory trees, possess peculiar coelomic organs (ciliated funnels or ciliated urns) that probably have an excretory function. The urns are attached to the bases of the mesenteries or to the coelomic wall near the attachments of the mesenteries. They are relatively numerous and are sometimes clustered together. Each ciliated urn is covered externally with peritoneum and is lined internally with ciliated columnar epithelium. Coelomocytes laden with waste enter the funnels and then pass into the body wall.

Water-Vascular System. Although the water-vascular system of holothuroids is basically like that of other echinoderms, the madreporite in most species is peculiar in having lost connection with the body surface and in being unattached in the coelom (Fig. 19-30). Pores and pore canals are still present in the madreporite but coelomic fluid rather than sea water enters and leaves the system. The madreporite hangs just beneath the base of the pharynx and is connected to the water ring by a short stone canal.

The water ring encircles the base of the pharynx and gives rise to the elongated or rounded polian vesicles, which hang into the

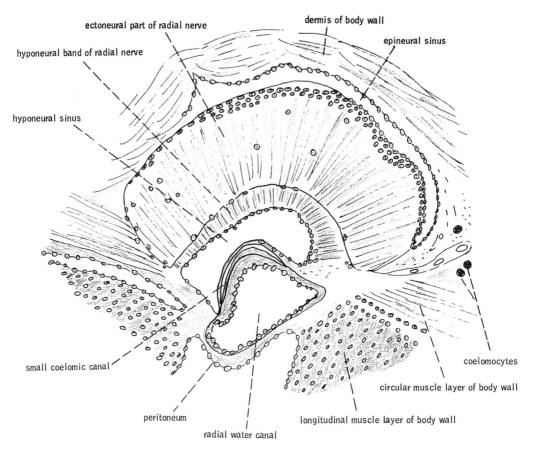

Figure 19-33.   An ambulacrum of *Caudina* (transverse section). (After Danielsson and Koren from Hyman.)

coelom (Figs. 19-30 and 19-31). The number of polian vesicles varies considerably. There may be one (*Cucumaria*), three, four (*Thyone*), or as many as ten or even fifty in certain Apoda. The vesicles are believed to function as expansion chambers in maintaining pressure within the water-vascular system.

From the water ring, five radial canals pass upward to the inner side of the calcareous ring and then outward through a notch at the end of each radial plate (Fig. 19-32). Just before leaving the calcareous ring, each radial canal gives off smaller canals to the tentacles. On leaving the ring, the radial canals then pass posteriorly within the body wall along the length of the ambulacra. Here lateral canals supply the podia. Ampullae are present for both podia and tentacles, although when the podia are reduced, there is a corresponding reduction in the ampullae.

Nervous System.   The circumoral nerve ring lies in the buccal membrane near the base of the tentacles (Fig. 19-32). The ring supplies nerves to the tentacles and also to the pharynx.

The five radial nerves on leaving the ring pass through the notch in the radial plates of the calcareous ring and run the length of the ambulacra in the coelomic side of the dermis. Like the radial nerves of the ophiuroids, the radial and tentacular nerves of sea cucumbers are ganglionated. Each radial nerve consists of both an ectoneural and hyponeural portion, but the hyponeural portion dwindles away before it reaches the nerve ring (Fig. 19-33). The outer sensory ectoneural band receives nerves from the podia and body wall; the inner motor hyponeural band gives rise to nerves innervating the body-wall muscles. There is a subepidermal nerve plexus and a well developed nerve plexus in the dermis.

Unlike most other echinoderms, the circumoral nerve ring does not play a dominating role in nervous integration. Pearse (1908) found that in *Thyone* most of the normal reactions—such as, movement, righting, and reactions to light—take place normally in an animal deprived of the anterior part of the body, which contains the nerve ring. Motor control of respiratory pumping is centered in the cloaca and is thus also independent of the nerve ring.

Sensory cells in the epidermis, which are most numerous at the two ends of the animal, comprise the sensory system in most of the holothuroids. In the burrowing Apoda, such as *Synapta* and *Leptosynapta,* the warts or tubercles of the body surface bear a cluster of sensory cells surrounded by gland cells. Fibers from the bundle of nerve cells descend as a nerve into a ganglion in the dermal plexus. The exact function of these sensory tubercles is unknown.

The Apoda also possess statocysts. There is one statocyst adjacent to each radial nerve, located near the point at which the nerve leaves the calcareous ring. Each statocyst is a hollow epidermal sphere containing one to many specialized vacuolated cells acting as statoliths (lithocytes) and containing an inorganic material. Although all holothuroids react to light, only a few species possess specialized photoreceptor organs. Photoreceptor organs are found in a few synaptids and consist of a simple cluster of photoreceptor cells with pigment located at the base of the tentacles.

The response of most holothuroids to adverse stimuli is contraction of the entire body or of parts of the body, such as the tentacles. All sea cucumbers are negatively phototropic, and most species are nocturnal, being relatively inactive during the day. The burrowing species, which possess statocysts, exhibit positive geotropism and tend to always maintain the oral end in a downward position.

Evisceration and Regeneration. The expulsion of sticky tubules from the anal region is commonly associated with sea cucumbers, but this defensive phenomenon is actually limited to some species of the genera *Holothuria* and *Actinopyga.* Such sea cucumbers possess from a few to a large mass of white, pink, or red blind tubules (tubules of Cuvier) attached to the base of one (frequently the left) or both of the respiratory trees, or to the common trunk of the two trees (Fig. 19-34). When these sea cucumbers are irritated or attacked by some predator, the anus is directed toward the intruder, the body wall contracts, and by rupture of the cloaca the tubules are shot out of the anus.

During the process of expulsion, each tubule is greatly elongated, probably by water forced into its lumen, and the tubules break free from their attachment to the respiratory tree. In *Holothuria,* the detached tubules are sticky and entangle the intruder in a mesh of adhesive threads. Small crabs and lobsters may be rendered completely helpless and left to die slowly, while the sea cucumber crawls away. After discharge of the tubules of Cuvier, they are regenerated.

Often confused with the discharge of the tubules of Cuvier is a more common phenomenon (called evisceration) that occurs in many holothuroids. Evisceration in the case of some genera, such as *Holothuria, Stichopus,* and *Actinopyga,* involves the rupture of the cloaca and the expulsion of one or both respiratory trees, the digestive tract, and the gonads. In *Thyone* and other sea cucumbers, the anterior end ruptures, and the tentacles, pharynx and associated organs, and at least part of the intestine are expelled.

Whether evisceration is of adaptive value or whether it occurs under normal conditions is debatable. The phenomenon has been largely observed in laboratory specimens that were subjected to crowded conditions, to foul water, to the injection of chemicals into the coelom, or to other abnormal conditions. Eviscerated specimens or individuals in the process of regeneration have been reported from natural habitats during warmer parts of the year, and it is possible that evisceration may be brought about normally by elevation of the water temperatures and reduction of the oxygen content of the sea water. Evisceration thus would reduce the metabolic requirements of the animal during such an unfavorable environmental period. Evisceration is followed by regeneration of the

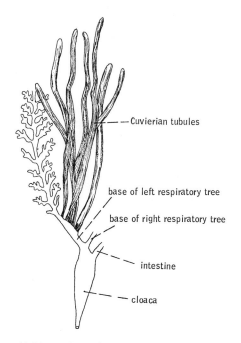

— Cuvierian tubules

base of left respiratory tree

base of right respiratory tree

intestine

cloaca

Figure 19-34.   Base of a respiratory tree of *Holothuria impatiens,* showing Cuvierian tubules. (After Russo from Hyman.)

lost part; the remaining stubs of the eviscerated organs or the associated mesenteries are the sites of the initial regenerative growth.

In the case of more radical loss of body parts, holothuroids differ considerably in their regenerative powers. In many forms, particularly species of *Cucumaria, Thyone,* and *Holothuria,* the cloacal region is the center of regeneration. In transversely bisected animals, each half regenerates, but if the animal is cut into numerous small sections, only the terminal piece, containing the cloaca, regenerates. In the burrowing synaptids, on the other hand, only the section of the body containing the anterior end is capable of regeneration, and all posterior pieces eventually die.

Reproduction.   Holothuroids differ from all other living echinoderms in possessing a single gonad. Most cucumbers are dioecious, and the gonad is located anteriorly in the coelom beneath the mid-dorsal interambulacrum (Figs. 19-30 and 19-31). Typically the gonad is composed of a large cluster of simple or branched tubules joining together at the end of

the gonoduct and attached to the left side of the dorsal mesentery suspending the anterior region of the gut. The gonoduct plus the tubules thus resemble a mop. Not infrequently the tubules are divided into two clusters, one on each side of the dorsal mesentery; in the synaptids, the gonad is composed of only two branched tubules. The tubule walls are lined with germinal epithelium, contain muscle fibers, and are covered externally with peritoneum. The gonoduct has a ciliated lumen and runs anteriorly in the mesentery to the gonopore, which is located mid-dorsally between the bases of two tentacles or just behind the tentacular collar (Fig. 19-28, *B*).

Hermaphroditic sea cucumbers also possess a single gonad; the gonad either produces sperm and eggs simultaneously or is protandric. The protandric gonad pertains in the American sub-antarctic *Cucumaria laevigata.* In this species, the first basal section of each developing tubule is female and produces eggs; as the tubules lengthen, the testicular portion is formed, and coelomocytes destroy the female

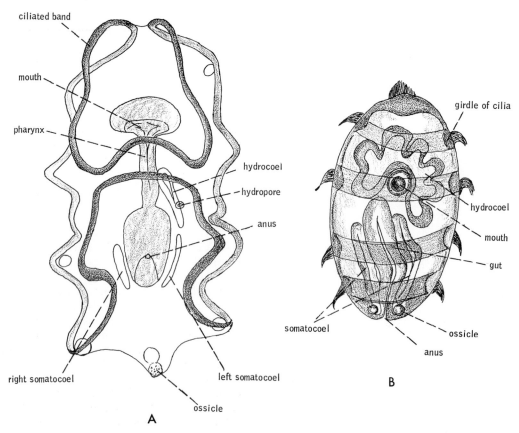

Figure 19-35.   *A.* An auricularia larva (oral view). (After Mortensen from Hyman.) *B.* The doliolaria larva of *Leptosynapta inhaerens,* a common North Atlantic holothuroid (oral view). (After Runnström from Cuénot.)

section. After sperm production, the tubules are phagocytized and resorbed, and a new cycle is initiated.

Some thirty brooding species are known, over half of which are cold-water forms, largely antarctic. During spawning, the eggs are caught by the tentacles and transferred to the sole or to the dorsal body surface for incubation. Frequently these two areas contain special brooding pockets for retaining the eggs; in a few species, such pockets have become so invaginated that they are actually internal. Even more remarkable is coelomic incubation, which takes place in the Californian *Thyone rubra*, in *Leptosynapta* from the North Sea, and in a few species from other parts of the world. The eggs pass from the gonads into the coelom and are fertilized in an undiscovered manner. Development takes place within the coelom, and the young leave the body of the mother by way of a rupture in the anal region.

Embryology. Except in brooding species, development takes place externally in the sea water, and the embryo is planktonic. Development through gastrulation is like that of the asteroids. The external surface of the gastrula shortly becomes clothed with flagella and takes up a free-swimming existence. The anterior half of the archenteron separates to develop as the coelom, leaving a shorter posterior portion to become the gut. The coelomic pouch then divides transversely to form a posterior somatocoel (which subsequently divides into a right and a left somatocoel) and to form an anterior coelomic pouch (representing the left hydrocoel and axocoel). The hydrocoel and axocoel remain connected, and in contrast to development in asteroids, echinoids, and ophiuroids, their right counterparts never form.

By the third day of development a larval stage called an auricularia has been reached (Fig. 19-35, *A*). The auricularia is very similar to the bipinnaria of the asteroids and possesses a flagellated locomotor band that comforms to the same development as the locomotor band of the bipinnaria. The auricularia of most species is one millimeter or less in length, but giant 15 millimeter larvae of unknown adults have been collected in plankton off Japan, Bermuda, and the Canary Islands.

Further development leads to a barrel-shaped larva, called a doliolaria, in which the original flagellated band has become broken up into three to five flagellated girdles (Fig. 19-35, *B*). Gradual metamorphosis, forming a young sea cucumber, takes place during the latter part of planktonic existence. The tentacles, which are equivalent to buccal podia, appear prior to the appearance of the functional podia. At this stage, the metamorphosing animal is sometimes called a pentactula larva. Eventually the young sea cucumber settles to the bottom and assumes the adult mode of existence.

Class Crinoidea

The crinoids are the most ancient and in some respects the most primitive of the living classes of echinoderms. Attached stalked crinoids, called sea lilies, flourished during the Paleozoic era, and some 80 species still exist today. The majority of living crinoids, however, belong to a more modern branch of the class, the suborder Comatulida. The comatulids, or feather stars, are nonsessile, free-swimming crinoids. There are approximately 550 species centered primarily in Indo-Pacific waters.

External Structure. The body of existing crinoids is composed of a basal attachment stalk and a pentamerous body proper, called the crown (Fig. 19-36). A well developed stalk is present in sea lilies but has largely disappeared in the free-swimming feather stars (Fig. 19-36, *B*). In the sessile sea lilies, the stalk may reach two feet in length but is usually much less. The basal end bears a flattened disc or in some cases root-like extensions by which the animal is fixed to the substratum.

The internal skeletal ossicles give the stalk a characteristic jointed appearance. The stalk of many crinoids bears small, slender, jointed appendages (cirri) that are displayed in whorls around the stalk (Fig. 19-37, *A*). Although the stalk is vestigial in comatulids, the most distal cirri of the stalk remain and spring as one or more circles from around the base of the crown (Fig. 19-36, *B*). The cirri of comatulids are used for grasping the substratum when the animal comes to rest. They are long and slender in forms that rest on soft bottoms and stout and curved in species that grasp rocks, seaweed, and other objects.

The pentamerous body (the crown) is equivalent to the body of other echinoderms and, like those of the asteroids and the ophiuroids, is drawn out into arms. The crown is attached to the stalk by its aboral side; thus in contrast to other living echinoderms, the oral surface is directed upward. The skeletal ossicles are best developed in the aboral body wall, usually called the calyx, which is thus somewhat cup-like. The oral wall (tegmen) forms a more or less membranous covering for the calyx cup, although it may contain imbedded calcareous plates (Figs. 19-36, *A* and 19-37, *B*). The mouth is located in the center of the oral surface; five ambulacral grooves extend peripherally from the mouth to the arms. The tegmen is thus divided into five ambulacral and five interambulacral areas. The anus opens onto the oral surface and is usually located in one of the interambulacral areas at the top of a prominence called the anal cone (Fig. 19-37, *B*).

The arms issue from the periphery of the crown and have a jointed appearance like the stalk. Although there are some primitive species that possess five arms, in most crinoids each arm forks immediately upon leaving the crown, forming a total of ten arms (Fig. 19-36, *A*).

However, some comatulids possess 80 to 200 arms resulting from the repeated forking of the original arm. The arms are usually only a few inches in length but may reach almost one foot in some species.

On each side of the arm is a row of jointed appendages called pinnules, from which the name feather star is derived (Figs. 19-36, *A* and 19-37, *C*). The ambulacral grooves on the oral surface extend along the length of both the arms and the pinnules. The margins of the grooves are scalloped to produce raised projections (lappets) that each bear on their inner side three podia united at the base (Figs. 19-37, *C*

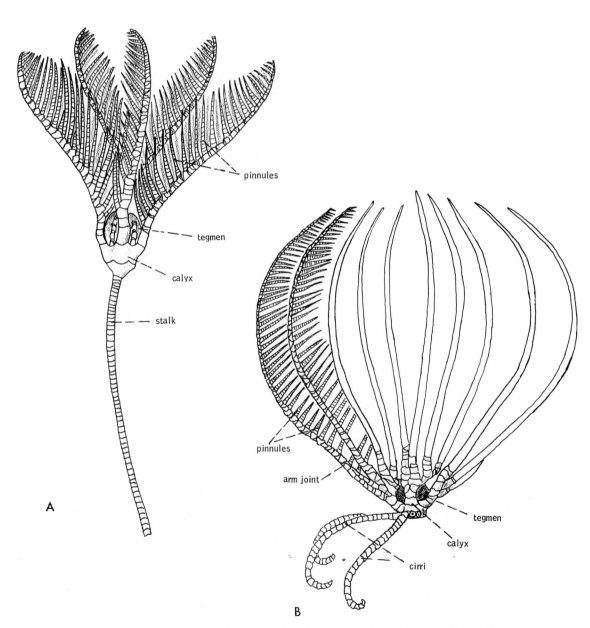

Figure 19-36.   *A. Ptilocrinus pinnatus,* a stalked crinoid (or sea lily) with five arms. *B.* A Philippine thirty-armed comatulid (or feather star), *Neometra acanthaster.* (Both after Clark from Hyman.)

and 19-38, *A*). Both podia and lappets also extend onto the pinnules. In the mouth region the podia, called oral podia, appear singly. Also paralleling the ambulacral grooves, but located to the outer side of the lappets, are small spherical surface bodies called saccules (Fig. 19-38, *A*).

Cold-water crinoids and those of the eastern Pacific are usually straw-colored, but littoral species from tropical waters, especially comatulids, display all possible colors in both solid and variegated patterns.

Body Wall. In the region of the ambulacral grooves, the epidermis is composed of flagellated columnar epithelium, but elsewhere the epidermis is for the most part a thin non-flagellated syncytium that is poorly demarcated from the underlying dermis and may be lacking

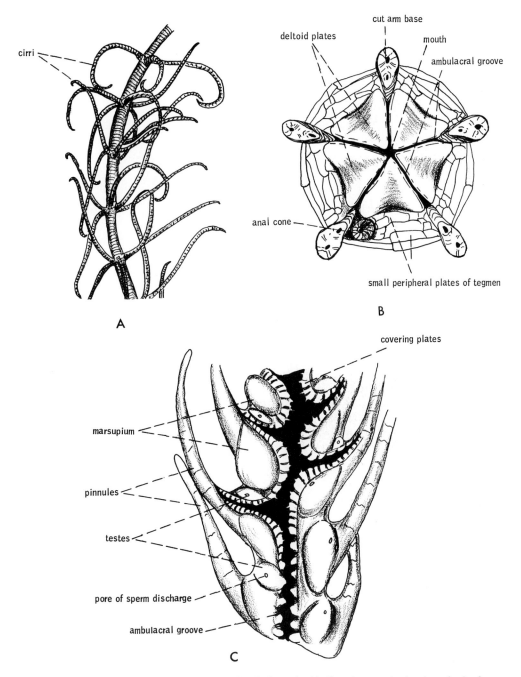

Figure 19-37.   *A*. Part of stalk of the West Indian crinoid, *Cenocrinus asteria,* showing whorls of cirri. *B*. Tegmen of *Hyocrinus,* a stalked crinoid (oral view). (*A* and *B* after Carpenter from Hyman.) *C*. An arm section from *Notocrinus virile,* a comatulid (oral view). (After Hyman.)

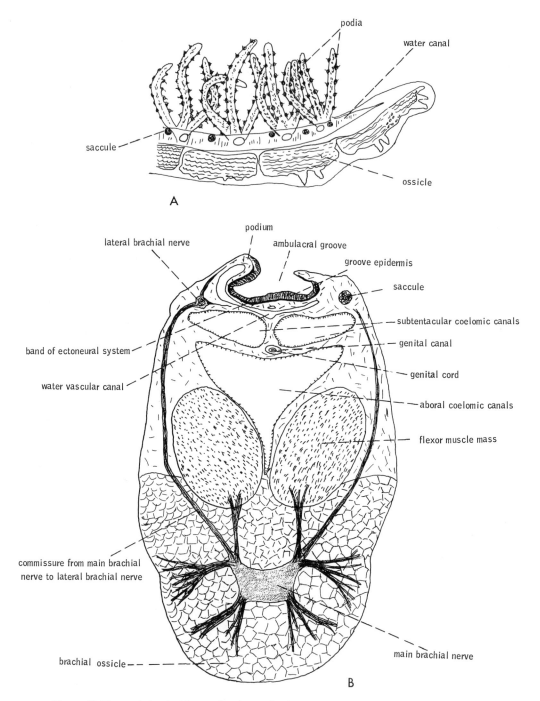

Figure 19-38.   *A.* A crinoid arm, showing podia (longitudinal section). (After Chadwick from Hyman.) *B.* A crinoid arm (transverse section). (After Hamann from Hyman.)

altogether (Fig. 19-38, *B*). Most of the dermis is occupied by the skeletal ossicles. The stalk, cirri, arms, and pinnules are of a solid construction, being composed almost entirely of a series of thick disc-shaped ossicles; this accounts for the jointed appearance of these appendages (Figs. 19-36, *B* and 19-38, *A*).

The oral and peripheral surfaces of the

ossicles articulate to permit at least some movement, similar to the ossicles composing the ophiuroid arms. The ossicles of the stalk are more securely interlocked than those of the arms, but even here some bending is possible. In more or less the center of the appendicular ossicles, there is a small canal through which runs a nerve and also, in the case of the stalk and cirri, an extension of the coelom. Also the arm and the pinnule ossicles each bear a deep groove on the oral surface in which is situated the ciliated ambulacral groove (Figs. 19-37, C and 19-38, B).

The ossicles are bound together by distinct connective tissue bands called ligaments. The ligaments must possess some contractile powers, for the stalk and cirri contain no muscle fibers, although these structures are capable of bending movements. Muscles are present in the arms and pinnules and act antagonistically to the ligaments. The position and elasticity of the ligaments is such that they cause the arms to extend. The pair of large muscles that extend between the ossicles and are located toward the oral side bring about flexion of the arms toward the oral side of the crown (Fig. 19-38, B).

Body-wall muscles are absent except for the muscles associated with the ossicles of the arms and pinnules, and the inner side of the dermis is lined with coelomic epithelium.

Locomotion. The sessile sea lilies are limited to bending movements of the stalk and flexion and extension of the arms. The stalkless comatulids, however, are free-moving and are capable of both swimming and crawling. The oral surface is always directed upward, and these animals always right themselves if turned over. Swimming is performed by raising and lowering one set of arms alternately with certain others. In the ten-armed species, every other arm sweeps downward while the alternate set moves upward. In species with more than ten arms, the arms still move in sets of five but sequentially. For example, in a forty-armed comatulid, there are eight sets of arms acting in sequence. Crawling movements are accomplished by the lifting of the body from the substratum and moving about on the tips of the arms. The arms are often used to grasp and pull the animal over irregular and vertical surfaces. Feather stars swim and crawl only for short distances and sit perched on the bottom for long periods by means of the grasping cirri.

Nutrition. Crinoids are flagellary feeders. During feeding, the arms and pinnules are held outstretched and the podia are erect. Any planktonic organism or detritus that comes in contact with the podia is tossed into the ambulacral grooves by a sudden whip-like action of the podia. Gland cells in the epithelium of the podia and the ambulacral groove secrete mucus that aids in entangling food particles. The flagella of the ambulacral grooves beat in an oral direction, carrying food down the arms, across the disc, and into the mouth.

Clark (1921) has pointed out that there is some correlation between the number and length of the arms and the food supply of the habitat. Crinoids living at great depths or in cold water, where detritus or plankton is rich, usually have a small number of arms (ten or less); the reverse is true of littoral warm-water species.

Crinoids are believed to display the primitive method of feeding used by the echinoderms and also to exemplify the original function of the water-vascular system—that is, the water-vascular system originally evolved as a means of capturing food and secondarily assumed a locomotor function in those groups that have become free-moving and inverted.

The mouth leads into the short esophagus, which then opens into an intestine (Fig. 19-39). The intestine descends aborally and laterally; when it reaches the calyx, it makes a complete turn around the inner side of the calyx wall. The terminal portion then passes upward into the short rectum, which opens through the anus at the tip of the anal cone. In most crinoids, the intestine bears a number of outpocketings along its inner side. The entire digestive tract, except the terminal portion of the rectum, is lined with cilia, and gland cells are abundant in both the esophagus and the rectum.

The details of digestion are still unknown. Wastes are egested as large compact mucus-cemented balls that fall from the anal cone into the surface of the disc and then drop off the body. Water is reportedly pumped into and out of the rectum through the anus, but whether this water circulation is of respiratory significance or is an aid to feces removal is uncertain.

Circulation, Respiration, and Excretion. The coelom is peculiar in being reduced to a network of communicating spaces as a result of invasion by connective tissue. In the oral side of the arms, the coelom extends as five parallel canals, and in the stalk five coelomic canals pass through the central perforation in the ossicles and give off one canal into each cirrus (Fig. 19-38). Several types of coelomocytes are present and move throughout the tissues of the body, as well as through the fluid of the coelomic, hemal, and water-vascular systems.

The hemal system is a network of spaces and sinuses within the connective tissue strands invading the coelom. There is a definite plexus that surrounds the esophagus, and from this plexus branches extend downward (aborally) through the center of the crown into a spongy mass of cells. This spongy mass is closely associated with the axial gland, which in crinoids is an elongated tubular mesh of glandular tissue occupying the polar axis of the crown. Branches of the hemal system also supply the intestine. There are no hemal spaces in the stalk, but one hemal sinus extends through the arms, along with the coelomic canals, and is involved in the transport of sex cells (Fig. 19-38, *B*).

Respiration takes place through any thin part of the body surface exposed to sea water. The podia are undoubtedly the primary center of gaseous exchange, and the great surface area presented by the branching arms makes unnecessary any special respiratory surfaces as are found in some other echinoderms.

Nothing is known of crinoid excretory products; but Cuénot (1948) believes that wastes are gathered by coelomocytes that then deposit them in the internal connective tissue, since older specimens contain conspicuous crystals and granules in these tissues.

Water-Vascular System. There is no madreporite in crinoids. The water ring encircles the mouth and gives off at each interradius approximately 30 short stone canals that open into the coelom. At each radius of the ring canal, a radial canal extends into each arm just beneath the ambulacral groove and forks into all of the branches and into the pinnules (Fig. 19-38, *B*). From the radial canals extend lateral canals supplying the podia. There are no ampullae, and one lateral canal supplies the cluster of three podia except for the single buccal podia. Hydraulic pressure for the system is probably maintained by coelomic fluid passing into and out of the stone canals, although the lining epithelium of the water-vascular system is not flagellated. Peculiar to crinoids are 500 to 1500 minute ciliated canals

(called ciliated funnels) that perforate the wall of the tegmen and open into the underlying coelomic spaces. These openings perhaps compensate for the absence of a madreporite, permitting maintenance of proper fluid pressure within the body and therefore indirectly within the water-vascular system.

Nervous System. In contrast to the nervous system of other echinoderm classes, the chief system in crinoids is an aboral (or entoneural) system located as a cup-shaped mass in the apex of the calyx. From the aboral system, a nervous sheath surrounding the five coelomic canals passes downward through the stalk ossicles and gives off nerves to the cirri along its course. Also arising from the aboral center are five brachial nerves, which after passing through an outer concentric pentagonal nerve ring, proceed through a canal in the arm ossicles and supply each pinnule with a pair of nerves (Fig. 19-38, *B*). The brachial nerve also gives off along its course a pair of nerves that innervate the muscles of the ossicles and adjacent epidermis, a pair of nerves innervating the aboral side of the arm, and a pair of commissures that connect to the lateral brachial nerves.

The lateral brachial nerves belong to the hyponeural system and lie along the sides of the arm (Fig. 19-38, *B*). These nerves innervate the pinnules, the podia, and the water-vascular canals of the arm. Orally, the five primary pairs of nerves from all of the arms connect to a pentagonal nerve ring that lies just peripheral

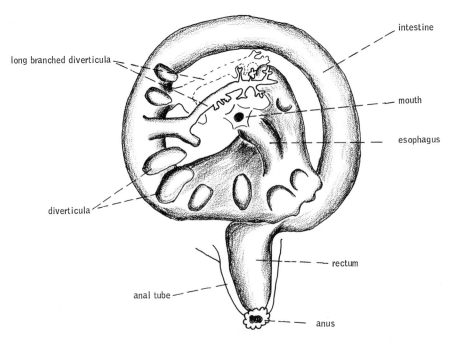

Figure 19-39.   Digestive tract of the comatulid, *Antedon*. (After Chadwick from Hyman.)

to the water ring. This ring also supplies some nerves to internal structures in the crown.

Finally, there is an oral (ectoneural) nerve system that is homologous to the principal system of other echinoderms. The crinoid ectoneural system consists of a subepidermal band of nervous tissue that runs just beneath the epidermis of the ambulacral groove in the arms (Fig. 19-38, B). After crossing the tegmen, the nerve bands descend in the region of the mouth as a nervous sheath encircling the esophagus and the intestine.

The importance of the aboral nervous system in the physiology of crinoids was demonstrated by the experiments of Marshall (1884), Langeloh (1937), and Moore (1924) on the comatulids. Destruction of both the hyponeural and ectoneural centers resulted in little modification of swimming, attaching, and righting behavior; but when the aboral center was destroyed, including the outer pentagonal ring, the animal was totally immobilized. Other experiments indicate that the brachial nerve is the primary center of nervous conduction in the arm.

There are no specialized sense organs, but the ambulacral and podial epidermis are richly supplied with sensory cells. The podia bear numerous papillae each of which contains a gland cell and a few sensory cells with bristles. The few available studies indicate that crinoids are negatively phototropic. In the comatulids, the cirri are strongly thigmotropic and appear to control the righting reflex. If an animal is inverted in such a way that the cirri maintain contact with the substratum, righting does not take place. As soon as the cirri are released, the animal turns over.

Regeneration and Reproduction. Crinoids possess considerable powers of regeneration and in this respect are quite similar to the asteroids and the ophiuroids. Part or all of an arm can be cast off if seized or if subjected to unfavorable environmental conditions. The lost arm is then regenerated. In like manner, pinnules and cirri are easily regenerated.

In *Antedon*, an animal can replace the loss of one fifth of the disc and the corresponding arm and can sustain the simultaneous loss of four of the five pairs of arms without death. The aboral nerve center is essential in regeneration, and provided this tissue remains intact, all of the visceral mass can be regenerated. The coelomocytes play an active role in regeneration. They migrate to the site of the wound in large numbers, carrying food materials and phagocytizing tissue debris.

Crinoids are all dioecious but not sexually dimorphic. Moreover, there are no distinct gonads. The gametes develop from germinal epithelium within an expanded extension of the coelom (the genital canal) located within the pinnules, as in *Antedon,* or within the arms (Fig. 19-38, B). Not all of the pinnules are involved in the formation of sex cells but only those along the middle of the arm length.

When the eggs or sperm are mature, spawning takes place by rupture of the pinnule walls. In *Antedon* and others, the eggs are cemented onto the outer surface of the pinnules by means of the secretion of epidermal gland cells. Hatching takes place at the larval stage. In other crinoids, the eggs are shed into the sea water. Brooding by cold-water species (all antarctic) is displayed by the crinoids as in the other echinoderms. The brood chambers are sac-like invaginations of the pinnule walls adjacent to the genital canals, and the eggs probably enter the brood chamber by rupture (Fig. 19-37, C).

Embryology. Development through the early gastrula stage is essentially like that in the asteroids and the holothuroids. After the formation of the archenteron, the blastopore closes, and the archenteron separates from the gastrula wall, forming an elongated vesicle. The archenteron then divides transversely in the middle to form both an anterior enterohydrocoel and a posterior somatocoel. The somatocoel elongates laterally and later divides into a right and left somatocoel.

After the elongation of the somatocoel, but prior to its division, the hydroenterocoel becomes crescent-shaped and curls dorso-ventrally around the middle of the somatocoel. The dorsal horn of the crescent gives rise to a process that separates as the left axocoel; the ventral horn puts forth a similar process that separates as the left hydrocoel. As in holothuroids, the right hydrocoel and the right axocoel never form. The remaining portion of the crescent, following the separation of the dorsal and ventral coelomic pouches, becomes the gut.

During the formation of the coelomic sacs, the embryo elongates and development proceeds toward a free-swimming larval stage. The crinoid larva (the doliolaria) is essentially like the doliolaria of holothuroids, being somewhat barrel-shaped with an anterior apical tuft and a number of transverse ciliated bands (Fig. 19-40, A). In crinoids, the doliolaria is attained directly without the formation of the intervening bipinnaria-like larva of sea cucumbers. At least in *Antedon*, in which the eggs at spawning adhere to the pinnule surface, hatching takes place at the formation of the doliolaria, which is free-swimming for only a few days at the most.

After a short free-swimming existence, the doliolaria settles to the bottom and attaches, employing a glandular midventral depression (the adhesive pit) located near the apical tuft. Then there ensues an extended metamorphosis resulting in the formation of a minute stalked sessile crinoid. In the comatulid, *Antedon,* actually the only crinoid for which development is well known, metamorphosis also results in a stalked sessile stage (the pentacrinoid larva) that resembles a minute sea lily (Fig. 19-40, *B*). The pentacrinoid of *Antedon* is a little over three millimeters long when the arms appear, and it requires about six weeks from the time of attachment of the doliolaria to attain this stage. After several months as a pentacrinoid, during which time the cirri are formed, the crown breaks free from the stalk, and the young animal assumes the adult free-swimming existence.

Fossil Echinoderms and Echinoderm Phylogeny

The echinoderms rank with mollusks, brachiopods, and arthropods in having one of the richest and oldest fossil records of any group in the Animal Kingdom. Echinoderms first appeared in the lower Cambrian period and were extremely abundant during the later periods of the Paleozoic era, when a number of fossil classes reached the peak of their evolutionary development.

Considering both fossil and living species, it is convenient to divide the phylum into two subphyla—the Pelmatozoa and the Eleutherozoa. The Pelmatozoa includes those echinoderms in which the oral surface is oriented upward therefore usually resulting in a sessile existence. The Eleutherozoa are free-moving echinoderms in which the oral surface is directed downward, or anteriorly in the case of holothuroids.

The crinoids are the only living representatives of the Pelmatozoa, but the subphylum includes a considerable number of extinct classes and the majority of the fossil echinoderms. Fossil pelmatozoans are particularly interesting in that they display many primitive features of the phylum. Almost all extinct pelmatozoans were sessile and were attached either directly to the substratum or indirectly by a stalk.

Like living crinoids, all fossil forms were probably ciliary feeders in which the podia and the ambulacral grooves were food-catching and food-conducting structures. Fossil evidence suggests that at first there were only three ambulacral grooves, and the typical pentamerous organization evolved through the branching of two of

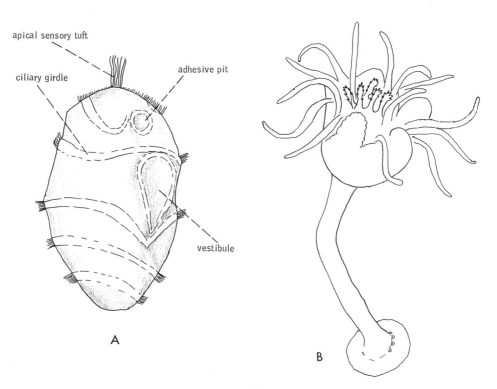

Figure 19-40.   *A.* Doliolaria larva of the comatulid, *Antedon mediterranea,* with five ciliary girdles (lateral view). (After Bury from Hyman.) *B.* Pentacrinoid larva of *Antedon.* (After Thomson from Hyman.)

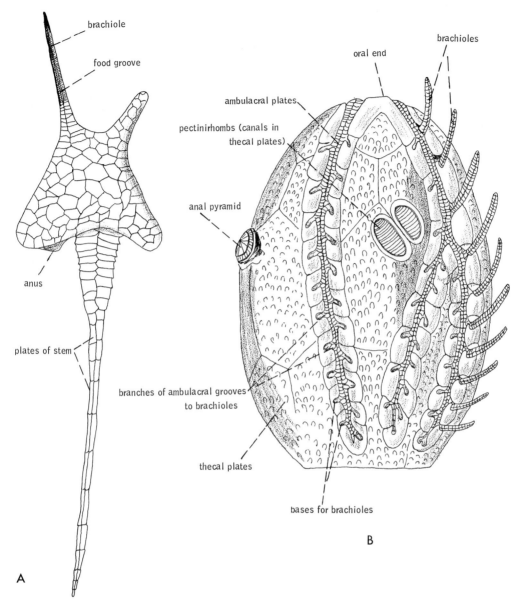

Figure 19-41.   Extinct Pelmatozoans. *A.* Class Heterostelea: *Dendrocystites* (lateral view). (After Bather from Hyman.) *B.* Class Cystidea: *Callocystites* (lateral view). (After Hyman.)

the original grooves. Unfortunately, such an origin is not supported by the embryology of any living echinoderms. Also, the ambulacral grooves at first were very short, were restricted to the oral surface around the mouth, and gradually extended outward.

In most pelmatozoans, the peripheral end of the groove is extended upon a slender arm (the brachiole) (Fig. 19-41, *B*). The term *brachiole* is used to distinguish the body extensions from the heavier arms of crinoids and eleutherozoans. Brachioles varied in number from a few to hundreds and undoubtedly evolved as a means of increasing the surface area for food collection.

Since fossil pelmatozoans were sessile and since the oral surface was always directed upwards, the original function of the podia could not have been locomotor.

The skeletal system of the extinct pelmatozoans was essentially like that of the crinoids with the exception that the ossicles (plates) of the crown were not limited to the aboral surface (calyx), but extended orally to the mouth, thus enclosing the internal organs within a test (or theca). The anus was usually located eccentrically in one of the interradii, as in the crinoids.

One of the most interesting and peculiar classes of extinct pelmatozoans was the Hetero-

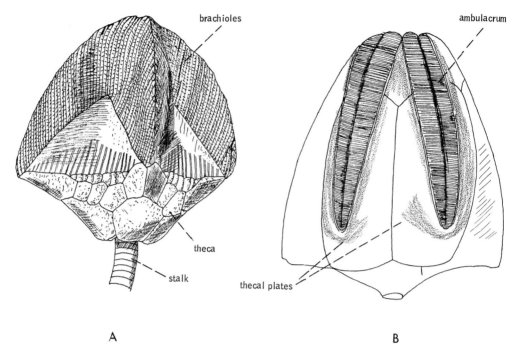

Figure 19-42.   Class Blastoidea. *A. Blastoidocrinus,* showing brachioles (lateral view). (After Jaekel from Hyman.) *B. Pentremites* (lateral view, brachioles not shown). (After Hyman.)

stelea, which is known to have lived from the middle Cambrian period to the early Devonian (Fig. 19-41, *A*). These animals were bilaterally symmetrical with no indication of radial symmetry. Although stalked and sessile, the body was apparently bent over so that the crown was oriented horizontally to the substratum—that is, one side of the oral-aboral axis faced toward the substratum and the other side faced away from the substratum. From the nature of the ossicles, the thecal wall must have been flexible, and only one or two brachioles were present.

The class Cystidea was a more typical group of extinct pelmatozoans that ranged from the middle Ordovician period to the Permian. The theca of cystids was more or less oval, with the oral end directed upward and the aboral end usually attached directly to the substratum (Fig. 19-41, *B*). A characteristic feature of the cystids was a peculiar system of canals of uncertain function that permeated the thecal plates. The three (primitive), or more commonly five, ambulacra were radially arranged and extended outward and downward over the sides of the theca, in some species to the aboral pole. Small brachioles were mounted on the plates along each side of the ambulacral grooves. Branches from the groove extended up each brachiole.

The class Blastoidea is another group of extinct pelmatozoans that flourished in the paleozoic seas (Fig. 19-42). The blastoids first appeared in the Ordovician period, reached their peak in the Mississippian period, and became extinct during the Permian period. *Pentremites* is a very common blastoid fossil found in Mississippian limestone (Fig. 19-42, *B*).

Like cystids, blastoids possessed an oval theca that was attached aborally by a short stalk or was attached directly to the substratum. Five ambulacra extended from the mouth at the oral pole down the sides of the theca. Characteristically, however, the ambulacral areas were elevated as broad ridges that alternated with the depressed interambulacral areas. The margins of the ambulacra were bordered by a single row of slender closely-placed brachioles, onto which extended branches from the ambulacral groove. In oral view, the brachioles gave the appearance of a thick fringe along the border of a five-pointed star.

Peculiar to blastoids was a system of folds, or folds and pores, called hydrospires, located at each side of the ambulacra. The hydrospires are thought to represent a respiratory mechanism by which water circulated inwardly through the thecal plates, allowing greater surface area for the exchange of gases between the coelom and the sea water. The hydrospires were thus somewhat like reversed asteroid papulae, the folds projecting into the coelom instead of externally from the coelom.

The Edrioasteroidea is a class of extinct pelmatozoans that first appeared in the lower Cambrian period and ranged into the Pennsyl-

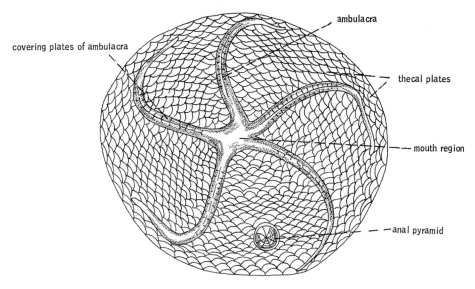

Figure 19-43.   Class Edrioasteroidea: *Cooperidiscus.* (After Clark from Hyman.)

vanian. Although there are only a relatively small number of fossil species, the group is of phylogenetic interest in perhaps being on the evolutionary line leading from the pelmatozoans to the eleutherozoans. The theca was oval and spherical and composed of imbricated plates (Fig. 19-43). There was no stalk, and the crown was either attached directly by the aboral surface or perhaps was free in some species. There were no brachioles present, and the five ambulacra, which extended over the theca, were usually curved. These animals thus looked very much like a brittle star wrapped around a ball. Of particular interest was the presence of pores in the ambulacral plates through which the podia extended. In this respect the edrioasteroids anticipated the echinoids.

The crinoids possess the richest fossil record of all the echinoderm classes and are the only pelmatozoans that still exist today. Crinoids first appeared in the Ordovician period, and they left a fossil record in every succeeding period. The class reached its climax in the Mississippian period, although there was a second somewhat lesser evolutionary development during the Permian period. During these periods, certain shallow seas supported enormous faunas. During the Permian period, such a sea covered the island of Timor, and the rocks composing this island today are one of the richest sources of fossil specimens. Paleozoic crinoids were all stalked, and the earlier species lacked pinnules. Modern crinoids, which contain the stalkless comatulids and which belong to a different subclass from the paleozoic species, did not appear until the Triassic period.

As would be expected from the nature of

the skeleton, the holothuroids have the poorest fossil record and the echinoids have the best fossil record of the living classes of eleutherozoan echinoderms; but compared to pelmatozoans the fossil record of eleutherozoans is sparse. Although fossil asteroids and echinoids first appeared in the Ordovician period and ophiuroids in the Mississippian, Paleozoic species are relatively rare; these classes are much better represented in Mesozoic and Cenozoic rocks. The earlier echinoids, including a number of extinct orders, were all regular forms, and the first fossil heart urchins and sand dollars appeared in the Triassic period. Rich deposits of fossil echinoids are known, but the fossil distribution of this class is too localized for them to be of any value as index fossils.

A single class of extinct eleutherozoans, the Ophiocistioidea, lived from the Ordovician period to the Devonian. Only ten fossil species are known. The body was encased in a test that was flattened orally and was dome-shaped aborally (Fig. 19-44). The anus was located eccentrically on the aboral surface and the mouth, which was surrounded by a peristome, was located in the center of the oral surface. A chewing apparatus was also present. Five radially arranged ambulacra extended peripherally from the peristome but were limited to the oral surface. Most remarkable were the three pairs of giant podia that occupied the ambulacra (Fig. 19-44, *B*). Each podium was covered by small overlapping scales and was thus preserved with the test.

Having a background of the structure of living and fossil echinoderms, we are now in a position to turn again to the problem of echino-

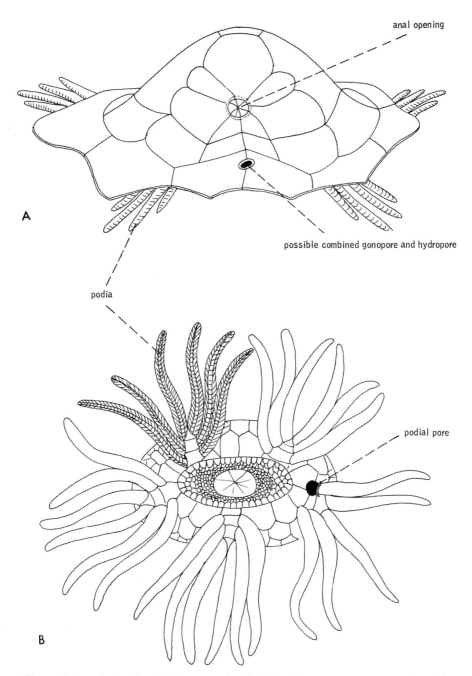

Figure 19-44.   The extinct eleutherozoans, class Ophiocistioidea. *A. Volchovia* (aboral view). (After Regnell from Hyman.) *B. Sollasina* (oral view). Podial scales only shown on podia of one ambulacrum; one podium removed to show podial pore. (Modified after Sollas from Hyman.)

derm origins. The classic interpretation has been that of Bather (1900). Bather's theory holds that the phylum evolved from a free-swimming soft-bodied bilateral animal (called a dipleurula ancestor) that possessed three pairs of coelomic sacs (Fig. 19-45, *A*). With the assumption of a sessile existence, bilateral symmetry was lost and the water-vascular system evolved from the two anterior left coelomic sacs. Thus the water-vascular system, according to this theory, repre-

sents a completely new development in the evolution of the phylum.

Another theory, originally proposed by Semon (1888) and Bury (1895), has been supported by Hyman (1955). According to these zoologists, the common ancestor of echinoderms, which they call a pentactula, was a bilateral animal with five pairs of hollow tentacles around the mouth, used for capturing food (Fig. 19-45, *B* and *C*). The tentacles, each containing

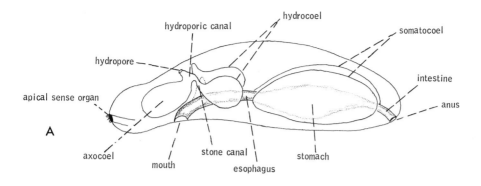

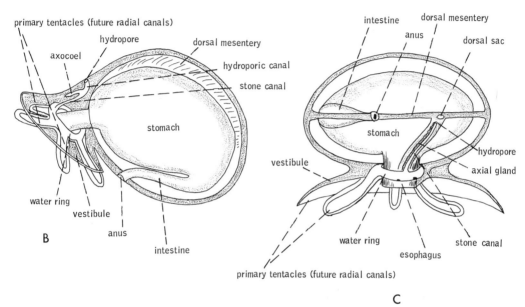

Figure 19-45. Hypothetical ancestors of echinoderms. *A.* Dipleurula ancestor. (After Bather from Hyman.) *B.* Bilateral pentactula ancestor. *C.* Pentactula ancestor after torsion. (*B* and *C* after Bury from Hyman.)

an extension of the coelom, a nerve, and a blood channel, were thus very much like a lophophore. The coelom into which the tentacular coelom opened had separated from the main coelom forming the water ring, and it had a special opening to the outside, the hydropore and the stone canal. According to this Pentactula Theory, each tentacle became a radial canal of the water-vascular system. With the assumption of a sessile existence and ciliary feeding, the podia arose as side branches of the original tentacles. The arms (brachioles) developed with the addition of protective plates in the tentacle walls, and the ambulacral groove evolved as a means for conducting captured food particles to the mouth. A reduction from ten to five tentacles or radial canals must obviously have occurred at some point during this evolution, perhaps during the shift from bilateral to radial symmetry.

This theory is attractive in supporting a connection between the lophophorates and echinoderms. But although embryological evidence is not conflicting, the pentactula concept conflicts to some extent with the fossil record. For example, in the vast majority of fossil pelmatozoans, the ambulacral grooves run over the test, and only branches of the grooves are mounted on brachioles. Moreover, the presence of three ambulacral grooves appears to be more primitive than the presence of five grooves. At least all evidence indicates that the water-vascular system first arose in conjunction with feeding rather than locomotion.

Despite the rich fossil record of echinoderms, paleontology has contributed little toward an understanding of the phylogenetic relationships between the living classes. Only the skeleton of fossil species is preserved; the internal organs and the nature of the embryological development are unknown.

The crinoids cannot be allied with any extinct pelmatozoan class, for the crinoids alone among pelmatozoans possess true arms instead of brachioles. Similarly, the eleutherozoans cannot be derived directly from any group of pelmatozoan. In fact Hyman (1955) considers the group, Eleutherozoa, to be an artificial concept, the connections between the different classes being very remote. In her opinion, the echinoids and ophiuroids are the most closely related of the five classes and have in common a similar larva and the lack of an open ambulacral groove.

The asteroids apparently diverged very early from the ophiuroid–echinoid line, for the sea stars alone of the free-moving echinoderms have retained the primitive open ambulacral groove and alone undergo attachment during metamorphosis. The holothuroids are primitive in possessing a single gonad and retaining the anus and madreporite in one of the interradii. However, the microscopic ossicles and the closed ambulacral groove are specialized features. A doliolaria is displayed by both the holothuroids and the crinoids, but the early auricularia of the holothuroids is very similar to the bipinnaria of the asteroids. Thus, according to Hyman, the asteroids and the holothuroids appear to be somewhat more closely related to crinoids than are the other two classes.

Ecological Relationships and Distribution

Echinoderms are unique in being virtually the only major phylum in the Animal Kingdom in which there are no parasitic species. Moreover, there are only a very few echinoderms that are commensal on other animals. All commensal echinoderms are ophiuroids. Species of *Ophiomaza,* an Indo-Pacific brittle star, live on the oral surface of feather stars, clutching the calyx with the arms. There are also several tiny Indo-Pacific brittle stars that live on the undersurface of sand dollars.

Although there are no parasitic echinoderms and only a few commensal species, echinoderms are favorite hosts for an enormous number of commensals and parasites from other animal groups. Parasitic myzostomes, snails, clams, and copepods and commensal scale worms, shrimp, and crabs are but some animals for which echinoderms supply food and shelter.

One of the most interesting relationships is that between the slender tropical pearlfish and sea cucumbers. These little fish, which are about five inches long, make their home in the trunk of one of the respiratory trees of certain sea cucumbers. The fish leaves the host at night while it searches for food; after such excursions, the fish forces its way into the anus and cloaca and back to the shelter of the respiratory tree.

Among the worst enemies of echinoderms are the parasitic snails belonging to the suborder Pyramidellacea. These snails either penetrate the body wall with the proboscis or live inside the body of the host. Birds take a heavy toll of littoral sea urchins, breaking the test and feasting on the soft internal organs.

From the human standpoint, echinoderms are a very minor food source. The ripe gonads of sea urchins are eaten raw or cooked in many parts of the world, and the body wall of sea cucumbers (called trepang) is a culinary delicacy in the orient. Large species of sea cucumbers are collected and boiled, which causes their bodies to contract and thicken and also brings about evisceration of the internal organs. The body wall is then dried and sold, mostly to Chinese, as trepang or bêche-de-mer. Trepang, when cooked in certain dishes, imparts a distinct flavor to the food.

Aside from limited use as food, echinoderms are of very little economic importance. Natives of the Pacific Islands use the body juices of certain sea cucumbers to poison fish in tidal pools. The poison is perhaps associated with the Cuvierian tubules, but this is not certain. Asteroids are of considerable importance as predators of oysters and are sometimes removed from commercial oyster beds by dragging a large mop-like apparatus over the bottom. The sea stars grasp, or become entangled in, the mop threads with their pedicellariae and are brought to the surface and destroyed.

Echinoderms are found in all oceans from littoral waters to great depths. Many tend to live in distinct aggregations and in enormous numbers. Sea urchins may be found in such densities in certain favorable spots that the entire bottom is covered. Similarly sand dollars can be collected by the bushels on some sand flats. Clark (1915) reported that the deck of the ship *Albatross* was covered by tons of comatulid crinoids dredged during a 1906 expedition; Verrill (1882) states that a single dredge haul at 240 meters off Martha's Vineyard in Massachusetts yielded 10,000 comatulids.

There are deep-water representatives from every class of echinoderms, and such species have been taken from depths of 12,000 to 18,000 feet. In general, crinoids tend to inhabit deep water. Feather stars live in shallow water and range down to depths of approximately 4,500 feet. Stalked crinoids, however, rarely are found at less than 700 feet and have been collected from depths of 15,000 feet. In contrast to crinoids, the majority of echinoids are littoral animals, although here too there are many deep-water forms.

The center of the greatest species density of

crinoids, holothuroids, echinoids, and ophiuroids is the Indo-Pacific, particularly the area encompassed by the Phillippines, Borneo, and New Guinea. From this center a relatively rich fauna spreads out in all directions as far as the Red Sea and southern Japan. For example, there are 91 species of crinoids known from southern Japan in contrast to some 85 species reported from the entire Atlantic basin. In addition to the Indo-Pacific, there is a relatively rich echinoid fauna in the West Indies and the Panamanic region (Southern California to Peru).

The northwest Pacific, particularly from Puget Sound to the Aleutians, possesses the greatest concentration of asteroid species. Seventy species alone are endemic to the Vancouver Island area.

BIBLIOGRAPHY

Anderson, J. M., 1960: Histological studies on the digestive system of a starfish, *Henricia,* with notes on Tiedemann's pouches in starfishes. Biol. Bull., *119(3)*:371–398.

Bather, F. A., 1900: The echinoderms. *In* A Treatise on Zoology (R. Lankester, ed.), vol. III.

Burnett, A. L., 1955: A demonstration of the efficacy of muscular force in the opening of clams by the starfish, *Asterias forbesi.* Biol. Bull., *109(3)*:355.

Burnett, A. L., 1960: The mechanism employed by the starfish *Asterias forbesi* to gain access to the interior of the bivalve *Venus mercenaria.* Ecology, *41*:583–584.

Bury, H., 1895: The metamorphosis of echinoderms. Quart. Jour. Micr. Sci., vol. 38.

Clark, A. H., 1915, 1921, 1931, 1941, 1947, 1950: A monograph of the existing crinoids, vol. 1, pts. 1, 2, 3, 4a, 4b, 4c. Bull. U. S. Nat. Mus. 82. A monumental work on living crinoids.

Crozier, W. J., 1918: The amount of bottom material ingested by holothurians. Jour. Exp. Zool., vol. 26.

Cuénot, L., 1948: Anatomie, Éthologie et Systématique des Échinodermes. *In* P. Grassé's Traité de Zoologie, Vol. 11, Échinodermes, Stomocordes, Procordes. Masson et Cié, Paris, pp. 1–363. A general account of the echinoderms.

Diebschlag, E., 1938: Ganzheitliches Verhalten und Lernen bei Echinodermen. Ztschr. Vergl. Physiol., vol. 25.

Feder, H. M., 1955: On the methods used by the starfish *Pisaster ochraceus* in opening three types of bivalved mollusks, Ecology. *36*:764–767.

Goodbody, I., 1960: The feeding mechanism in the sand dollar *Mellita sexiesperforata.* Biol. Bull., *119(1)*:80–86.

Hamann, A., 1885: Beiträge zur Histologie der Echinodermen. Heft 2, Die Asteriden.

Hyman, L. H., 1955: The Invertebrates. Vol. IV. Echinodermata. McGraw-Hill, New York. An excellent general treatment of the echinoderms with an extensive bibliography. The chapter *Retrospect* in the fifth volume (1959) of this series summarizes the literature on echinoderms from 1955 to 1959.

Ikeda, H., 1941: Function of the lunules of *Astriclypeus.* Annot. Zool. Japon. Vol. 20.

Langeloh, H., 1937: Über die Bewegungen von *Antedon.* Zool. Jahrb. Abt. Allg. Zool., vol. 57.

Lavoie, M., 1956: How sea stars open bivalves. Biol Bull., *111 (1)*:114–122.

Marshall, A., 1884: Nervous system of *Antedon.* Quart. Jour. Micr. Sci., vol. 24.

Meyer, H., 1935: Die Atmung von *Asterias rubens.* Zool. Jahrb. Abt. Allg. Zool., vol. 55.

Moore, A. R., 1924: The nervous mechanism of coordination in *Antedon.* Jour. Gen. Physiol., vol. 6.

Nicols, D., 1959: Changes in the chalk heart-urchin, *Micraster,* interpreted in relation to living forms. Phil. Trans. Roy. Soc. London (B), *242*:347–437.

Nicols, D., 1960: The histology and activities of the tube-feet of *Antedon bifida.* Quart. Jour. Micr. Sci., *101(2)*:105–117.

Pearse, A. S., 1908: Behavior of *Thyone.* Biol. Bull., vol. 15.

Semon, R., 1888: Die Entwicklung der *Synapta.* Jena. Ztschr. Wiss., 20.

Winterstein, H., 1909: Über die Atmung der Holothurien. Arch. Physiol., Vol. 7.

Verrill, A. E., 1880, 1882, 1885: Remarkable marine fauna occupying the outer banks. Amer. Jour. Sci., ser. 3, vols. 20, 23, 29.

Chapter 20

THE LESSER DEUTEROSTOMES

In addition to the echinoderms, there are five other groups of invertebrate deuterostomes—the Hemichordata, the Pogonophora, the Chaetognatha, the Urochordata, and the Cephalochordata. The last two groups are subphyla of the phylum Chordata. Although all are deuterostomes, they do not represent a close phylogenetic unit but stem from different points along the deuterostome line. The term *lesser* used in the chapter title refers only to the relatively small numbers of species comprising each group. Many are widely distributed and common invertebrate animals, and all are highly specialized.

PHYLUM HEMICHORDATA

The hemichordates are a small group of worm-like marine animals that until recently had been considered a subphylum of the chordates. As a consequence of this position, the common Atlantic hemichordate, *Saccoglossus kowalevskii,* alias *Balanoglossus,* has acquired some fame in comparative anatomy classrooms. Alliance with the chordates was based on the presence of gill slits and what was thought to be a notochord in hemichordates. It is now generally agreed that the hemichordate "notochord" is neither analogous nor homologous with the chordate notochord and that other than the common possession of pharyngeal clefts the two groups are dissimilar. The hemichordates have thus been removed from the Chordata in all modern treatments and have been given the rank of a separate phylum.

The hemichordates are composed of two classes—the Enteropneusta (acorn worms) and the Pterobranchia. The acorn worms are the most common and best known hemichordates. The pterobranchs consist of three genera of small tube-dwelling animals and for the most part are not found in European and North American waters. The salient features of the Pterobranchia are described after discussion of the Enteropneusta.

Class Enteropneusta

The Enteropneusta (acorn worms) are all inhabitants of shallow water. Some live under stones and shells, but many common species, including *Saccoglossus,* burrow in mud and sand. Exposed tidal flats are frequently dotted with the coiled rope-like castings of these animals.

Acorn worms are relatively large animals, the majority ranging from 9 to 45 cm. in length. The cylindrical and rather flaccid body is composed of an anterior proboscis, a collar, and a long trunk (Fig. 20-1, *A*). These regions correspond to the typical deuterostome body divisions —protosome, mesosome, and metasome.

The proboscis is usually short and conical, from which the name acorn worm is derived, and is connected to the collar by a narrow stalk. The collar is a short cylinder that anteriorly overlaps the proboscis stalk and ventrally contains the mouth. The trunk comprises the major part of the body. Behind the collar, the trunk bears a longitudinal row of gill pores at each side of

582

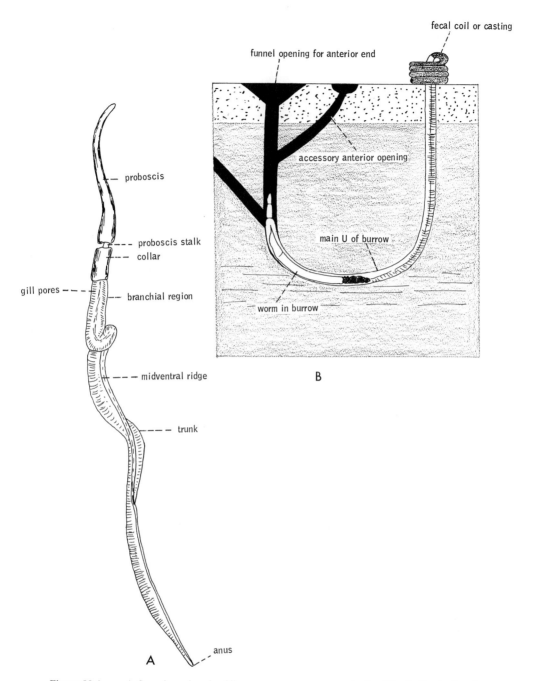

fecal coil or casting

funnel opening for anterior end

accessory anterior opening

main U of burrow

worm in burrow

proboscis

proboscis stalk

collar

gill pores

branchial region

midventral ridge

trunk

anus

A

B

Figure 20-1. *A. Saccoglossus kowalewskii,* an acorn worm common to the Atlantic Coast of southeastern United States. (After Hyman.) *B.* Burrow system of the Mediterranean *Balanoglossus clavigerus.* (After Stiasny from Hyman.)

a mid-dorsal ridge. More laterally, the anterior half of the trunk contains the gonads, and in some hemichordates, such as *Balanoglossus,* the lateral body wall in this region is drawn out on each side, forming wing-like plates (Fig. 20-3, *B*). The remaining postbranchial region of the trunk may be undifferentiated, or the darkened wall of the intestine may be visible through the body wall, forming the hepatic region. The

hepatic region may also be marked externally by sacculations of the body wall. When an hepatic region is present, the trunk is terminated by a caudal region.

The body is covered by ciliated columnar epithelium that is well provided with gland cells, especially in the collar and trunk regions. A well developed nervous layer is present in the lower part of the epidermis.

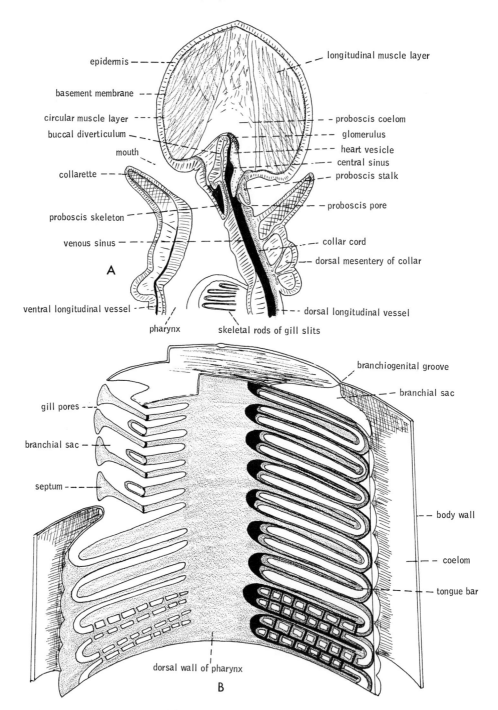

Figure 20-2.   *A.* Anterior of *Glossobalanus minutus* (sagittal section). (After Spengel from Hyman.)
B. Stereodiagram of gill region of an enteropneust. (After Delage and Hérouard from Hyman.)

Hemichordates display the usual tricoelo-mate structure of deuterostomes. A single coelomic cavity occupies the proboscis, a pair of cavities is present in the collar, and a pair of cavities is present in the trunk. However, enteropneusts are peculiar in that the coelomic epithelium has formed connective tissue and muscle fibers that fill much of the original coelomic cavity, and a distinct peritoneal lining has disappeared. Moreover, this coelomic mus-culature replaces in large part the typical body-wall musculature.

The protocoel is restricted to the posterior end of the proboscis and opens to the exterior through a mid-dorsal pore (Fig. 20-2, *A*). The anterior part of the old coelom is filled with a mass of circular and longitudinal muscle fibers and connective tissue. The paired coelomic cavities of the collar also open to the exterior through a pair of canals and pores located on each side of the mid-dorsal line. Muscles are poorly developed in the collar. The trunk coelom is also paired, the dorsal and ventral mesenteries of the gut separating the two cavities on each side. There is no opening to the exterior. Radial fibers traverse the trunk coelom, and longitudinal fibers are well developed ventrally.

Acorn worms have limited locomotor powers and are rather sluggish animals. Many burrowing species construct mucus-lined excavations in mud and sand. The burrows of *Balanoglossus, Saccoglossus,* and others are U-shaped with two openings to the surface, and one or both ends of the worm at times protrude from the openings (Fig. 20-1, *A*). Burrowing is accomplished by the proboscis, and sand is removed by the surface cilia. The proboscis cilia drive the sand grains to the collar, where a girdle of sand forms and gradually passes posteriorly over the trunk as additional material accumulates anteriorly. Other acorn worms live in masses of seaweed, under rocks and stones, or buried in sand and mud (not in burrows), and they move about relatively little.

Burrowing enteropneusts consume sand and mud from which organic matter is digested. The quantity of substrate ingested is indicated by the great piles of castings that accumulate at the posterior opening of the burrow. Nonburrowing species are ciliary feeders. Detritus that comes in contact with the proboscis surface is trapped in mucus and carried posteriorly to the collar by strong ciliary currents. Cilia at the anterior end of the collar then either reject the particles or drive them ventrally into the mouth.

The digestive tract is a straight tube that is histologically differentiated into a number of regions. The large mouth, located between the ventral anterior margin of the collar and the dorsal proboscis stalk, leads into a buccal tube within the collar, (Fig. 20-2, *A*). Dorsally a long narrow diverticulum extends from the buccal tube and projects forward into the proboscis. It is this proboscis diverticulum that was for so long thought to be a "notochord" and accounted for the placement of the acorn worms among the chordates.

Histologically, the wall of the diverticulum is identical to the wall of the buccal tube into which it opens, and Hyman (1959) and current investigators of the hemichordates agree that the buccal diverticulum is apparently nothing more than a pre-oral extension of the gut and is certainly not a notochord. The buccal tube passes posteriorly into the pharynx, which occu-

pies the branchial region of the trunk and is laterally perforated by the gill slits. The gill slits are usually limited to the dorsal half of the pharynx, and the digestive portion of the tract occupies the ventral half of the pharynx.

Behind the pharynx, the gut continues as an esophagus, and in two families, containing the genera *Saccoglossus, Spengelia,* and *Glandiceps,* it opens externally to the dorsal surface through a number of canals and pores. The intestine comprises the remainder of the gut. Anteriorly the intestinal epithelium of the hepatic region is colored green or brown because of inclusions, and in some species, such as *Balanoglossus,* it is sacculated. Behind the hepatic region, the intestine exhibits no further histological differentiation. In *Saccoglossus,* the intestine opens directly to the exterior through the terminal anus, but commonly the anus is preceded by a rectum.

Muscles in the gut wall are weakly developed, and food particles are probably moved posteriorly by the backward beating cilia. Knowledge of the digestive process is still very incomplete. Enzymatic secretions are produced by the hepatic region and probably also in other regions. In *Glossobalanus minutus,* the mucus covering the proboscis surface, where food is initially trapped, has been found by Barrington (1940) to contain amylase.

Enteropneusts possess an open blood-vascular system composed of two main contractile vessels and a system of sinus channels. The blood, which is colorless and is largely lacking in cellular elements, is carried anteriorly in a dorsal vessel located in the mesentery suspending the digestive tract (Fig. 20-2, *A*). At the level of the collar, the dorsal vessel passes into a venous sinus and then into a central sinus located at the base of the proboscis.

The central sinus is situated beneath a closed fluid-filled sac (the heart vesicle) that contains muscle fibers in its ventral wall (Fig. 20-2, *A*). The pulsations of this wall aid in driving blood through the central sinus chamber. From the central sinus, all of the blood is delivered anteriorly into a special system called the glomerulus. The heart vesicle, buccal diverticulum, and central sinus together bulge into the coelom at the base of the proboscis. The peritoneal covering of the faces of these bulging structures is greatly evaginated into the proboscis coelom. These evaginations contain blood sinuses and collectively make up the glomerulus, and all blood from the central sinus is driven anteriorly through the glomerular sinus system. Although the glomerulus is thought to have an excretory function, there is as yet no experimental proof.

From the glomerulus, blood is delivered by

a system of channels to the ventral longitudinal vessel, which runs posteriorly beneath the digestive tract. Along the length of its course, the ventral vessel supplies both the body wall and the gut wall with a rich network of sinuses that eventually drain back into the dorsal vessel.

The pharyngeal gill slits in the anterior trunk region are assumed to be the respiratory organs of enteropneusts. The number of slits can range from a few to one hundred or more pairs, since new slits are continually being formed during the life of the worm. Each slit opens through the side of the pharyngeal wall as a U-shaped cleft with the arms of the U directed upward (Fig. 20-2, B). The pharyngeal wall between clefts (the septum) and that part of the wall projecting downward between the arms of the U (the tongue bar) are supported by skeletal pieces that have arisen as thickenings of the basement membrane of the pharyngeal epithelium.

The U-shaped pharyngeal clefts perforate the pharyngeal wall and then open into the branchial sacs. There is one sac per gill slit, and each sac opens to the exterior by a dorso-lateral gill pore, which along with the other pores on that side is often located in a longitudinal groove.

The septa and tongue bars are ciliated on both the pharyngeal and the lateral faces and internally contain a plexus of blood sinuses from the ventral longitudinal vessels. The beating cilia produce a stream of water passing into the mouth and out through the gill slits. This water current plays an important role in pulling mucus strands containing food particles into the mouth.

The gill slits of the hemichordates and the chordates probably evolved originally as a feeding mechanism, in which small particles were strained out of the water current passing through the pharyngeal clefts. This is still the method of feeding in the tunicates and the cephalochordates. A respiratory function has been only secondarily assumed by the gill slits, and in hemichordates it is believed that respiratory exchange takes place between the water current and the hemal sinuses in the septa and tongue bars. However, these structures are not true gills in the strict sense of the term, since they bear no outgrowths.

The nervous system is relatively primitive (Fig. 20-3, A). In different regions of the body, the nerve plexus at the base of the surface epithelium has become thickened to form nerve cords, in which the nerve fibers are arranged longitudinally. For the most part, these nerve cords retain their epidermal location and their connection with the rest of the epidermal nerve plexus.

The principal nerve cords are the mid-

ventral and the mid-dorsal proboscis cords connected at the proboscis base by an anterior nerve ring. Similarly, there is a midventral and mid-dorsal trunk cord connected at the anterior end of the trunk by a circumenteric nerve ring. The ventral trunk cord terminates at the collar, but the dorsal cord continues into the collar as the collar cord.

The collar cord actually becomes internal —that is, it is separated from the epidermis above and is continuous with the general epidermal nerve plexus only at the two ends. In some acorn worms, the collar cord is hollow and may even open to the outside through an anterior and a posterior neuropore. The collar cord possesses giant nerve cells and, as Hyman (1959) notes, is apparently a conduction path. Digging and peristaltic waves are initiated in the proboscis, and the collar cord conducts these impulses posteriorly. The giant nerve cells are involved in rapid transmission, as is true of giant cells in other animals. Cutting the collar cord therefore greatly slows down conduction. There seems to be little coordination and integration of response. In the trunk, conduction can take place through the general epidermal plexus, as well as through the ventral and dorsal cord.

Neurosensory cells scattered throughout the surface epithelium comprise the sensory system of hemichordates. Some enteropneusts possess a U-shaped ciliated depression (the pre-oral ciliary organ) on the ventral side of the proboscis base. The nervous layer is thickened beneath this depression, and the ciliary organ is perhaps a chemoreceptor.

Enteropneusts are all dioecious. The sac-like gonads are located in the coelom along each side of the trunk, beginning in the branchial region and extending to or through the hepatic region. In some species, the gonads are located behind the gill slits. There are a number of genera, such as *Balanoglossus, Stereobalanus,* and *Ptychodera,* in which the sides of the body containing the gonads bulge to the outside as genital wings or ridges. Usually one such wing is present on each side and below the gill pores, but in *Stereobalanus* there is both a dorsal and a ventral wing with the gill located in between (Fig. 20-3, B). Each gonad opens to the exterior through a pore that is often located in the same groove as the gill pores.

Masses of eggs imbedded in mucus are shed from the burrow and are fertilized externally by sperm emitted from nearby males that are apparently stimulated by the presence of the released eggs. The egg masses very shortly disintegrate as a result of tidal action.

Early development is strikingly like that of the echinoderms. Equal holoblastic cleavage leads

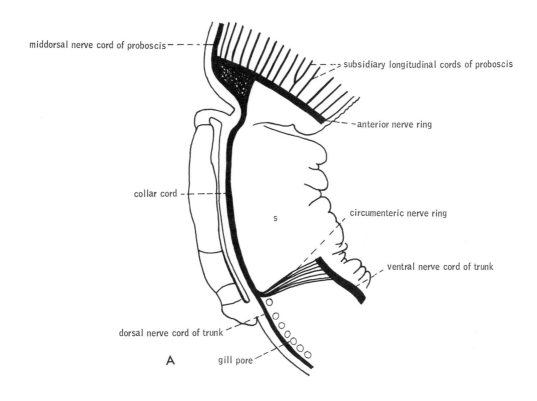

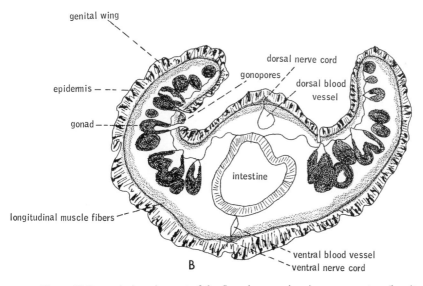

Figure 20-3.   *A.* Anterior part of the *Saccoglossus cambrensis* nervous system (longitudinal view). Nerve networks not shown. (After Knight-Jones from Hyman.) *B.* Trunk of *Ptychodera bahamensis,* showing genital wings (transverse section). (After Van der Horst from Hyman.)

to a coeloblastula, which then undergoes invagination to form a narrow archenteron. The blastopore, which marks the future posterior end of the embryo, closes, and the embryo lengthens along the antero-posterior axis and becomes ciliated. At this stage, hatching takes place, and the embryo assumes a planktonic existence.

The anterior tip of the archenteron sepa-

rates to form a coelomic vesicle (the protocoel), which will form the proboscis coelom. Later the protocoel gives rise to two posterior extensions that form the collar and the trunk coelom. In some species, the two posterior coelomic divisions arise as evaginations of the archenteron independent of the formation of the protocoel.

Development from this point may be either

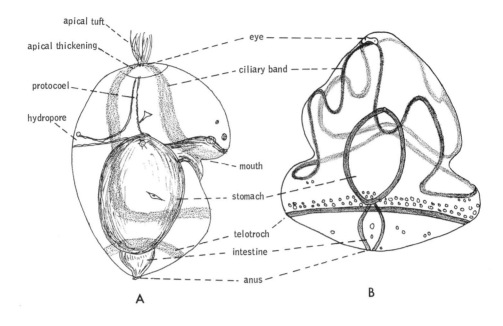

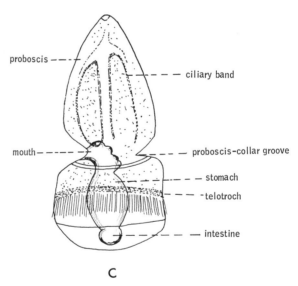

Figure 20-4.   Development of *Balanoglossus clavigerus*. *A*. Early tornaria larva (lateral view). *B*. Fully developed tornaria (lateral view). (*A* and *B* after Stiasny from Hyman.) *C*. Postlarval development. (After Morgan from Hyman.)

direct or indirect. In indirect development, the embryo develops into a free-swimming tornaria larva. The ciliation becomes restricted to a distinct band, which at first is very similar to the ciliated band in the bipinnaria larva of sea stars (Fig. 20-4, *A*). Gradually the band becomes more winding, and there develops a separate posterior girdle of cilia, that forms the principal locomotor organ of the larva (Fig. 20-4, *B*). An apical nervous plate flanked on each side by an eye is located at the anterior end. After a plank-

tonic existence of several days to several weeks, the larva becomes girdled by a constriction initiating the division between proboscis and collar (Fig. 20-4, *C*). The larva elongates, sinks to the bottom, and assumes an adult existence.

Development is direct in a number of enteropneusts, including the Atlantic acorn worm, *Saccoglossus kowalevskii*. A ciliated gastrula may hatch from the egg, or hatching may take place at a later stage; but in any case a tornaria larva never forms, and development proceeds directly, terminating in the young worm. In *Saccoglossus,* the eggs hatch as young worms.

Class Pterobranchia

The Pterobranchia consists of a small number of species belonging to three genera, and these are rarely encountered. All are bottom-dwellers in relatively deep water, and except for *Rhabdopleura,* which has been dredged up close to the European coast, most species are found in the Southern Hemisphere. With the exception of *Atubaria,* pterobranchs live in secreted tubes that are located in aggregations or colonies attached to the bottom (Fig. 20-5).

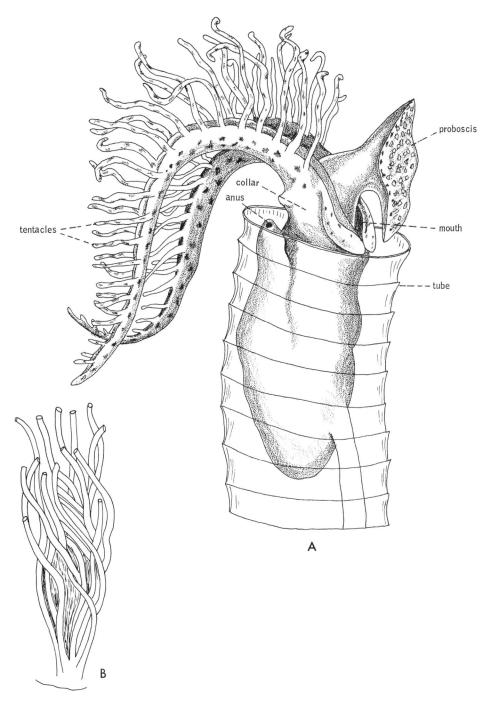

Figure 20-5.   *A.* The pterobranch hemichordate, *Rhabdopleura,* in its tube (lateral view). (After Delage and Hérouard from Dawydoff.) *B.* Tubes of a colony of *Cephalodiscus densus.* (After Andersson from Hyman.)

The proboscis is shield-shaped, but the most striking features of these worms are the food-catching arms and tentacles carried on the dorsal side of the collar. In *Rhabdopleura*, there are two recurved arms, and in *Cephalodiscus* there are five to nine pairs of arms (Fig. 20-5, *A*). The arms bear numerous small tentacles that are heavily ciliated. The tentacles capture minute organisms, which are then driven by the cilia to the mouth. Both the arms and the tentacles are hollow, each containing an extension of the mesocoel, and in this respect they are thus somewhat similar to a lophophore. There are no gill clefts in the genus *Rhabdopleura;* and as is true of many sessile tube-dwelling animals, the gut is U-shaped, the anus opening anteriorly on the dorsal side of the collar. The sexes are separate, and a ciliated larva, unlike a tornaria, is known for *Cephalodiscus.*

Hemichordate Phylogeny

The evidence of a phylogenetic relationship between hemichordates and both the echinoderms and the chordates is very convincing. Although the adults are quite different, the early embryogeny of the hemichordates is remarkably like that of the echinoderms. The formation of the gastrula and the coelom is very similar to these stages in echinoderms, and the early tornaria larva is virtually identical to the bipinnaria of the asteroids. Of the two major classes of hemichordates, the pterobranchs are considered the more primitive, and the lophophore-like arms and tentacles are thought to represent a primitive feature of the phylum that has been lost in the enteropneusts.

It is believed by Hyman (1959) and others that the pterobranchs are perhaps similar to the common ancestor of both the echinoderms and the hemichordates; and it may have been from such arms and tentacles that the echinoderm water-vascular system, which is believed to have been originally a food-catching device, arose. Certainly a close relationship between the hemichordates and the echinoderms is difficult to deny, and Hyman places the hemichordates close to the base of the echinoderm line.

An affinity with the chordates is also indicated, although not as close a one as that with the echinoderms. Only in the hemichordates and the chordates are pharyngeal clefts found. Also, the dorsal collar nerve cord of hemichordates, which is sometimes hollow, is somewhat similar to the dorsal hollow nerve cord of chordates, and perhaps the two structures are homologous. However, the lack of a notochord and segmentation and the differences in the general body structure exclude hemichordates from the phylum Chordata. As suggested by Hyman, the same line from which the hemichordates stemmed probably culminated in the chordates.

PHYLUM POGONOPHORA

Closely related to the hemichordates is another small phylum of vermiform deuterostomes, the phylum Pogonophora. By the middle of the 19th century, almost all phyla of animals had been at least observed by zoologists. The Pogonophora, however, were completely unknown prior to the 20th century. The first specimen was dredged from Indonesian waters in 1900. Since that time 22 species have been described, most of which have been taken from the northwest Pacific.

Pogonophorans are almost exclusively deep-sea animals, a fact which accounts for their delayed discovery. They are sessile, living in secreted chitinous tubes that are probably fixed upright in the bottom ooze. The long, worm-like body ranges from 10 to 35 cm. in length and is composed of the typical deuterostome divisions. The protosome and mesosome, which are not always demarcated externally, form a short anterior section, and a long cylindrical trunk comprises most of the body (Fig. 20-6).

The distinguishing feature of the phylum is the presence of long tentacles carried by the underside of the protosome. Depending on the species, the tentacles range in number from a single spiral tentacle to over 200 (Fig. 20-6). The tentacles are especially peculiar in bearing minute pinnules that are extensions of single epithelial cells. Tracts of cilia run the length of each tentacle.

Internally, there is a coelomic compartment in each of the body divisions. The protocoel extends into the tentacles, and the coelom of the mesosome and trunk is paired. A well developed, closed blood-vascular system is present, and each tentacle is supplied with two vessels.

The most remarkable feature of pogonophorans is the complete absence of a digestive tract. In fact, zoologists who examined the first specimen thought that part of the body was missing. In the absence of a digestive tract, the mode of nutrition in these animals is puzzling to say the least. It has been suggested that the tentacles are extended from the mouth of the tube like a piston from a cylinder and are used to gather organic detritus suspended in the surrounding water. Food particles so obtained might then be digested externally and absorbed directly by the tentacular epithelium.

Pogonophorans are dioecious, and two

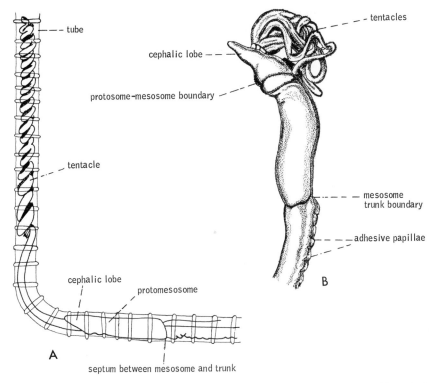

tube

cephalic lobe

protosome-mesosome boundary

tentacles

mesosome trunk boundary

adhesive papillae

tentacle

cephalic lobe

protomesosome

B

A

septum between mesosome and trunk

Figure 20-6.   Phylum Pogonophora. *A.* Anterior of *Siboglinum,* a pogonophoran with a single tentacle, in its tube. (After Caullery from Hyman.) *B.* Anterior of *Birsteinia vitjas* (lateral view). (After Ivanov from Hyman.)

cylindrical gonads are located one on each side in the trunk coelom. The eggs of at least some species are brooded in the tube, and embryos collected with tubes have yielded some information concerning development. Significantly, the coelom forms in the typical deuterostome manner, very similar to its development in the hemichordates. A mouth, as well as a vestigial digestive tract, forms in the course of development but later disappears. The eggs apparently hatch into some sort of larval stage.

PHYLUM CHORDATA

The chordates are the largest phylum of deuterostomes, but most chordates are vertebrates and fall outside the scope of this book. Two subphyla, the Urochordata and Cephalochordata, lack a backbone but possess the three distinguishing chordate characteristics—at some time in the life cycle, there can be found a notochord, a dorsal hollow nerve cord, and pharyngeal clefts. Since cephalochordates (*Amphioxus*) initiate every course in comparative vertebrate anatomy, this group is not treated here. The urochordates, however, deserve some attention, for members of this group are less familiar, although they are very common marine animals.

Subphylum Urochordata

Adult urochordates, commonly known as tunicates, little resemble other chordates. Most are somewhat barrel-shaped animals attached by one end to the substratum. Only the larval stage, which looks like a microscopic tadpole, possesses distinct chordate characteristics. The tunicates consist of three classes—the Ascidiacea, the Thaliacea, and the Larvacea. The ascidians contain the majority of species and the most common and typical tunicates. The other two classes are specialized for planktonic existence.

Class Ascidiacea

External Structure.   Ascidians, often called sea squirts, are sessile tunicates and are common marine invertebrates throughout the world. The majority are found in littoral waters; they attach to rocks, shells, pilings, and ship bottoms or are sometimes fixed in mud and sand. Some species have been dredged from considerable depths.

The bodies of solitary species range from spherical to cylindrical in shape (Figs. 20-7, *A* and 20-8, *A*). One end is attached to the substratum, and the opposite end contains two openings that may be extended as two separate siphons. All

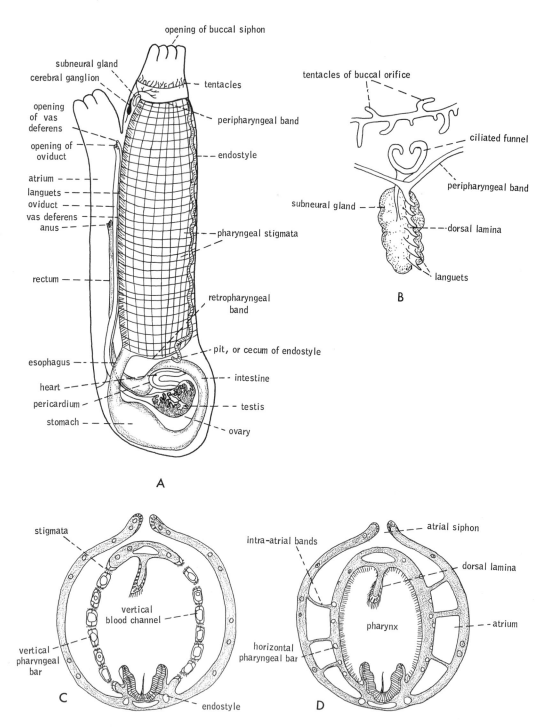

Figure 20-7.   *A.* The solitary ascidian, *Ciona* (lateral view). *B.* Subneural gland and adjacent pharyngeal area of *Ciona.* (*A* and *B* after Bullough.) *C* and *D.* The thoracic region of an ascidian (transverse sections). *C.* At the stigmata level. *D.* At level of a horizontal pharyngeal bar between stigmata. (*C* and *D* after Seeliger from Brien.)

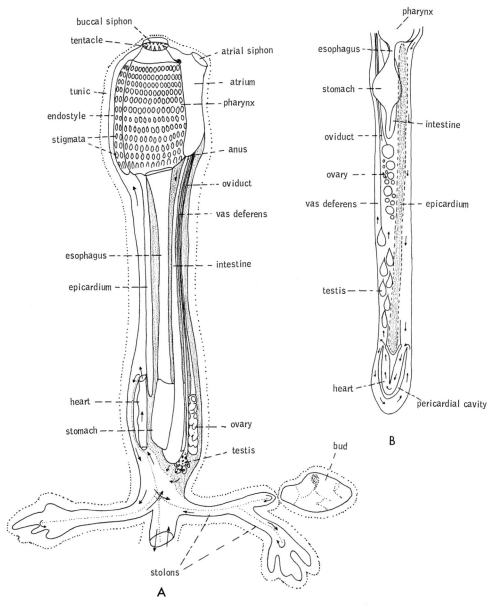

Figure 20-8.   *A. Clavelina,* an ascidian with a long abdominal region. (After Brien.) *B.* Abdominal and postabdominal region of *Sydnium.* (After Berril from Brien.) Arrows indicate paths of circulating blood.

shades of coloring are found in ascidians, although gray and green colors are common, and the body ranges in size from that of a pea to that of a large potato, which some species closely resemble. *Halocynthia pyriformis,* which is found on the Atlantic coast north of Cape Cod, is called the sea peach because of its similarity to the fruit in size, shape, and coloration. Often, ascidians are covered by other smaller sessile organisms that impart a general shapelessness to the body.

The two openings at the free end of the body are the buccal siphon and the cloacal (atrial) siphon. These provide for the passage of a current of water through the animal. On the basis of the position of various organs within the body of the free-swimming larva, it is known that the buccal siphon in the metamorphosed adult marks the anterior end of the body. The atrial siphon indicates the dorsal side, and the visceral organs at the attached end of the body represent the morphological posterior end of the animal.

Body Wall, Atrium, and Pharynx. The body of ascidians is covered by a single layer of epithelial cells, but this epidermal covering does not form the external surface. Instead the entire body is invested with a special mantle (the tunic) that is characteristic of most members of the subphylum and from which the name *tunicate* is derived (Fig. 20-8, *A*). The tunic is usually quite thick but varies from a soft delicate consistency to one that is tough and similar to cartilage. The tunic of *Amaroucium stellatum*, called sea pork, has both the appearance and texture of salted pork. The tunic may be colored and commonly looks and feels like marble or glass. Not infrequently the tunic is translucent, and the colors of the internal organs account for the coloration of the animal.

Curiously, the principal component of the tunic is a type of cellulose, called tunicine. Except for the tubes of sessile hemichordates, cellulose is produced by no other metazoan animal. In addition to cellulose, the tunic also contains proteins and inorganic compounds, and in some species calcium salts are precipitated in the form of distinct spicules. Another unusual feature of the tunic is the presence of ameboid cells that have migrated from the body mesenchyme. Moreover, in some species such as *Ciona*, the tunic is supplied with blood vessels. It is by means of the tunic that ascidians adhere to the substratum, and the tunic is often roughened or papillose in this region. Often root-like extensions called stolons ramify from the base of the body, and these too are covered by the tunic (Fig. 20-8, *A*).

Within the tunic, the body of ascidians can be conveniently divided into three regions —an anterior or distal pharyngeal region containing the pharynx, an abdominal region containing the digestive tract and other internal organs, and a postabdomen (Fig. 20-8, *A*). The postabdomen is the most basal part of the body and is commonly indistinct from the abdominal region (Fig. 20-7, *A*). In some species, however, the postabdomen is as long as the thoracic and abdominal regions combined and contains the heart and reproductive organs (Fig. 20-8, *B*).

The anterior buccal siphon opens internally into a large pharyngeal chamber. The walls of the pharynx are perforated with small slits, permitting water to pass from the pharyngeal cavity into the surrounding atrium and then out by way of the atrial siphon.

Within the buccal siphon is a circlet of projecting tentacles that prevent large objects from coming in with the water current (Fig. 20-7, *A* and *B*). Exterior to the tentacles, the wall of the siphon is lined with an infolded layer of the epidermis and the tunic. Below the tentacles, the pharyngeal wall begins, and its lining is derived from entoderm.

The pharynx may be cylindrical or some-what laterally compressed. On the ventral side— the side opposite the atrial siphon—a deep groove (the endostyle) extends the length of the pharyngeal wall (Fig. 20-7, *C* and *D*). The lateral walls of the groove are ciliated and project inward toward each other, so that the endostyle is shaped somewhat like a keyhole. The bottom of the groove is lined with both mucus-secreting cells and a median row of cells with long flagella. Posteriorly, the endostyle terminates in a little pit at the base of the pharynx, but its lateral walls continue across the pharynx floor to the esophagus as two parallel adjacent ciliated ridges called the retropharyngeal band (Fig. 20-7, *A*). On reaching the anterior end, the lateral ridges of the endostyle separate and encircle the top of the pharynx, forming the right and left peripharyngeal ridges (Fig. 20-7, *A* and *B*).

Above and adjacent to each peripharyngeal ridge is another ridge that may or may not be ciliated. The two ridges thus form a groove between them. On reaching the dorsal side, each peripharyngeal ridge passes downward a short distance and then to each side of a large projecting ridge (the dorsal lamina) that runs posteriorly to the esophagus along the dorsal side of the pharynx (Fig. 20-7, *C*). The margin of the lamina usually bears finger-like processes (languets) that curve to the right and thus form a gutter along that side of the ridge (Fig. 20-7, *A* and *B*).

Between the dorsal lamina and the endostyle, the side walls of the pharynx are perforated by vertical slits called stigmata (Figs. 20-7, *A* and *C*; and 20-8, *A*). The stigmata are arranged in horizontal rows with horizontal bars separating successive rows and vertical bars separating adjacent stigmata within the same row. The overall structure is therefore very much like a grid. There are typically very many stigmata, and in many groups the number has been greatly increased by subdividing the rows of stigmata so that there are primary, secondary, and tertiary rows. This tendency to increase the surface area for respiration and for straining food from the passing water current attains its greatest development in the molgulids. In this family, not only has multiplication of stigmata developed, but also the orderly grid-like pattern has been replaced by an arrangement in which groups of stigmata are displayed in spirals (Fig. 20-9, *A*).

The pharynx is completely surrounded by the atrium except along the midventral line where the pharynx is attached to the body wall. In addition, the atrium is crossed by cord-like strands of tissue that apparently function to limit the expansion of the cavity during the flow of water through the body (Fig. 20-7, *D*).

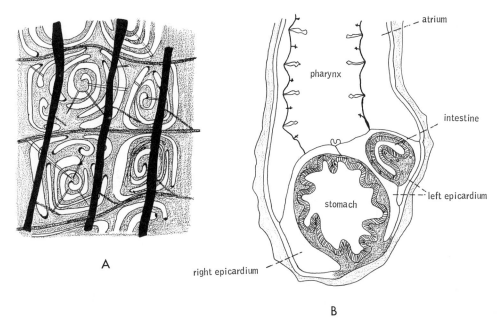

A

B

Figure 20-9. *A.* Spiral stigmata of *Corella parallelogramma.* (After de Selys Longchamps from Brien.) *B.* Abdominal region of *Ciona intestinalis,* showing epicardia (longitudinal section). (After Damas from Brien.)

Dorsally the atrium opens to the exterior through the atrial siphon. The atrial region just in front of the siphon is sometimes called the cloaca, because the anus and the gonoducts empty here. All of the atrium, both the pharyngeal and outer sides, is lined with an epithelium derived from ectoderm and is continuous through the atrial siphon with the external epidermis. The inner lining of the pharynx is thus derived from entoderm and the outer covering from ectoderm; between these two layers lies mesenchymal tissue. The body wall in the atrial region consists of an inner and an outer layer of ectodermal epithelium with mesenchyme inbetween.

The body-wall mesenchyme contains striated muscle bands extending longitudinally toward the siphons. Circular bands are also present and are particularly well developed in the siphon walls, where they act as sphincters. The body-wall muscles can cause a limited degree of general body contraction, depending upon the thickness and rigidity of the tunic. When an animal is exposed at low tide or taken out of the water, contractions of the body and siphons cause the water in the pharynx and atrium to be forced from the siphons as jets —hence the name *sea squirt.*

Nutrition. Ascidians, like all tunicates, are ciliary feeders and remove plankton from the current of water that passes through the pharynx. The water current is produced by the beating of long cilia located on the margins of the stigmata, and an enormous quantity of water is strained for food. A specimen of *Phallu-*

sia only a few centimeters long can pass 173 liters of water through the body in 24 hours.

The endostyle is the principal center for the elaboration of mucus. The beating of the long flagella at the bottom of the gutter forces out the mucus and drives it onto the horizontal bars between the rows of stigmata (Fig. 20-7, *D*). The bars are ciliated and carry the mucus in the form of cords across the pharynx toward the dorsal lamina. Mucus is also carried in the same direction by the peripharyngeal groove at the anterior of the pharynx. During the course of transport across the pharynx, plankton suspended in the stream of water passing through the stigmata becomes trapped on the mucus cords. The mucus cords converge on the dorsal lamina and pass into the basal gutter formed by the bending of the lamina and languets to one side. The ciliated languets apparently also function in rolling the mucus in cords. The food-laden mucus strands are now carried downward toward the base of the pharynx.

The base of the pharynx on the dorsal side contains the esophageal opening, toward which the dorsal lamina and the retropharyngeal band (from the endostyle) are directed. The post-pharyngeal part of the digestive tract is located in the abdomen and is arranged in a U-shaped loop (Figs. 20-7, *A* and 20-8, *A* and *B*). The esophagus forms the descending arm, the stomach occupies the turn of the loop, and the intestine forms the ascending arm, which opens into the cloacal region of the atrium beneath the atrial siphon. This basic plan may be variously modified; not infrequently the loop is twisted or the intestine is coiled to various degrees, and the loop may be greatly abbreviated or quite long.

The esophagus is a narrow tube of varying length. Its walls lack muscles, but the internal lining is ciliated for the movement of food particles. The stomach is an enlargement of the digestive loop at the turn of the U, and there is usually a relatively well developed sphincter at each end. Internally, the stomach is lined with secretory and absorptive cells, and in many species, such as *Clavelina* and *Styela,* there is a ciliated gutter extending the length of the dorsal surface. In two families, the Molgulidae and Cynthiadae, the stomach wall contains glandular outgrowths, collectively called the "liver," that open by a variable number of pores into the stomach lumen. The ascending arm of the digestive tract is formed by the intestine, a slender tube lined with absorptive and mucus-secreting cells. The terminal end of the intestine is modified as a rectum and opens through the anus into the cloacal region of the atrium.

Digestion is probably extracellular within the stomach, which contains abundant secretory cells. On the basis of its histology, the intestine appears to be involved in absorption and to be a site for glycogen storage.

Epicardium, Circulation, and Excretion. Associated with the digestive loop of many tunicates, including *Clavelina* and *Ciona,* is a very peculiar structure of unknown function and significance called the epicardium. The epicardium is usually a simple tube that parallels the digestive loop (Fig. 20-8, *A* and *B*). The epicardium arises as a double evagination of the base of the pharynx on each side of the retropharyngeal band and is thus entodermal. Distal to their origin from the pharynx, the two evaginations fuse and extend downward to one side of the digestive loop. In *Ciona,* the distal unpaired portion has disappeared, but the basal right and left tubes are present and are located one on each side of the digestive loop. Moreover, these tubes are greatly enlarged, and they surround the stomach, intestine, and other organs in the same manner as a coelom (Fig. 20-9, *B*).

The tunicate blood-vascular system is remarkable in many respects. The entire system is open, even the heart. The heart is a short tube lying in a pericardial cavity at the base of the digestive loop. The heart is peculiar in that it is a fold of the pericardial wall, it is supplied with muscle fibers, and it bulges into the pericardial cavity (Figs. 20-7, *A* and 20-8, *A* and *B*). Thus the heart is really only a specialized part of the pericardium and has no true wall or lining. The heart is somewhat curved or U-shaped, and one

end is directed dorsally and the other ventrally. Each end opens into a large vessel or channel, but all of the circulatory pathways lack true walls and are merely sinus channels in the mesenchyme.

From the ventral end of the heart, blood passes beneath (outside) the endostyle by way of a large subendostylar vessel that runs along the ventral side of the pharynx. Along its course, the subendostylar vessel gives off transverse channels to the bars between the rows of stigmata. These channels also connect with vertical channels. Thus blood circulating through the pharyngeal grid is provided with a great surface area for respiratory exchange with the water current passing through the pharynx.

Dorsally, the network of pharyngeal channels drains into a longitudinal vessel (median dorsal sinus) that runs beneath the dorsal lamina of the pharynx. On reaching the abdomen, the median dorsal sinus breaks up into many smaller channels supplying the digestive loop and other visceral organs. These channels eventually drain into a dorsal abdominal sinus, which leads to the dorsal end of the heart. In those ascidians, such as *Ciona,* in which the tunic is provided with blood vessels, a vessel to the test usually arises from each of the two main channels leading into the heart, and both of these vessels penetrate the test at the posterior ventral side of the animal.

One of the most interesting features of the tunicate circulatory system is the periodical reversal of blood flow direction. For a time, the heart pumps blood out of its dorsal end into the dorsal abdominal sinus, and blood enters the heart from the subendostylar sinus. After a short period of rest, the direction of contraction is reversed, and blood is pumped in the opposite direction. The heart beat appears to be neurogenic but not under direct control of the dorsal ganglion (the brain). According to Skramlik (1930), there is an excitation center at each end of the heart. Each center is responsible for initiating contractile waves over the heart from that point, and each alternates in dominance over the other.

The blood of tunicates is no less interesting than other parts of the vascular system. The plasma, which is slightly hypertonic to sea water, contains numerous amebocytes (or lymphocytes). A number of different types have been described. Some actively migrate between the blood and the tissues; some are phagocytic.

In certain ascidians, such as the Ascidiidae and the Perophoridae, the blood contains a type of green cell called a vanadocyte. These cells are unique in containing vanadium that is bound up with hydrosulfuric acid and perhaps protein. Considering the low concentration of vanadium in sea water, the ability of these ascidians to take up and concentrate vanadium to high levels is remarkable. In two families, the Cionidae and the Diazonidae, the vanadium chromogens are found in the blood plasma rather than in the cells. Vanadium chromogens in ascidians do not function in oxygen transport, but the exact function is unknown. This vanadium compound is kept in a reduced state by the presence of a high concentration of sulfuric acid within the same cell.

Some amebocytes are filled with crystals or with yellow, pink, red, white, black, or blue pigment. These cells constitute the excretory system of ascidians. After accumulating waste in the course of circulation, the laden cells in most tunicates tend to become fixed in certain regions of the body, especially the digestive loop and gonads, where they form a diffuse covering on the outer walls of the organs. Within this network of fixed cells, vesicles develop that contain accumulations of uric acid. The deposition of excretory cells begins in the larval stage, accelerates during metamorphosis, and during the life of the animal steadily increases in thickness and density.

In all tunicates is another network of vesicles and tubules (pyloric glands) on the outer wall of the intestine. By way of one or many collecting canals, this network drains into the anterior end of the stomach. Although they are found in the same region as the excretory vesicles, the pyloric glands, according to Azema (1937), are distinct from the excretory vesicles. The products of the pyloric glands have been reported by Azema to be calcareous and probably are of excretory nature.

Nervous System. The nervous system is relatively simple and consists of a cylindrical to spherical cerebral ganglion, or "brain," located in the mesenchyme of the body wall between the two siphons (Fig. 20-7, *A*). When the ganglion is cylindrical or ovoid, as is usually the case, one end is directed toward one siphon and the other end toward the opposite siphon. From each end of the ganglion there arises a variable number of mixed nerves, and in some species there are also lateral nerves. The nerves arising from the anterior end of the ganglion supply the buccal siphon; those issuing from the posterior end innervate the greater part of the body—the atrial siphon, the gills, and the visceral organs.

Beneath the cerebral ganglion lies a glandular body called the neural or subneural gland (Fig. 20-7, *A* and *B*). The lumen of the gland extends anteriorly as a duct opening into the pharynx by way of a large ciliated funnel. Posteriorly the gland continues as a cord of tissue that represents the larval nerve cord and is therefore homologous to the neural tube of other chordates.

Experiments involving the removal of the cerebral ganglion indicate that the cerebral ganglion is not an especially important center for the control of vital reflexes in the physiology of ascidians. *Ciona* is at first quite flaccid following decerebration, but after a 24-hour period of recovery, all of the body functions are carried out normally. Body contractions, however, are somewhat slower.

There are no special sense organs in ascidians, but sensory cells are very abundant on the internal and external surfaces of the siphons, on the buccal tentacles, and in the atrium. Tactile cells and probably chemoreceptors are included among these sensory cells and very likely play a role in controlling the current of water passing through the pharynx. Pigmented cups containing cylindrical cells with distal tufts of cilia reportedly have been found in a number of species, but whether these structures warrant the name *eyes* is not certain.

Reproduction. With few exceptions, tunicates are hermaphroditic. There are usually a single testis and a single ovary that lie in close association with the digestive loop (Figs. 20-7, *A* and 20-8, *A* and *B*). The ovary is typically located above the stomach and is a saccular body with two band-like ventro-lateral thickenings. These bands are the germinal areas of the ovaries, and the developing eggs deflect the ovarian wall outward to form follicles. When mature, the eggs are carried in an oviduct that runs parallel to the intestine and opens into the cloaca in front of the anus.

The testis lies below the ovary and is composed of a cluster of small sacs that open into a sperm duct. The sperm duct parallels the course of the oviduct and opens into the cloaca.

In a few families, which include *Molgula* and *Styela*, the gonads are doubled, and an ovary and a testis are located in the right body wall of the branchial region; a left set is located within the digestive loop. The gonoducts are also doubled and empty separately into the cloaca.

Colonial Organization. Most of the larger ascidians, such as *Styela, Ascidia,* and species of *Clavelina* and *Molgula,* are solitary forms and are often called simple ascidians. There are, however, many colonial or compound species. Colonial organization has arisen independently a number of times within the class, and a number of different types of colonies occur. In general the individuals composing a colony are very small, although the colony itself may reach a considerable size.

In the simplest colonies, the individuals themselves are discrete, but are united by stolons. For example, in *Perophora* the colony is like a vine with a long, trailing, branching stolon to which are attached the globular individuals (Fig. 20-10, *A*). In others of these compound forms, such as some species of *Clavelina* and *Molgula,* the stolons are short, and the individuals are joined, forming tuft-like groups.

A more intimate association is seen in certain ascidians, such as *Clavelina phlegrea*, in which not only the stolons but also the basal parts of the bodies are joined to other individuals forming a common tunic.

In the most specialized colonial families, all of the individuals composing the colony are completely imbedded in a common tunic. Usually there is a very regular arrangement of individuals within the test. *Botryllus* forms flat encrusting colonies, in which the members are organized in a star-shaped pattern (Fig. 20-10, *B*). The buccal siphons of each member open separately to the exterior, but the atria open into a common cloacal chamber, which has one central aperture in the middle of the colony. The individuals of *Botryllus* are only a few millimeters in diameter, but since a single tunic may contain a number of star-shaped clusters, the entire colony may be 12 to 15 cm. in diameter.

Similar configurations are found in other compound ascidians. In *Cyathocormus*, the colony is shaped like a goblet with a stalk-like attachment to the substratum and a large common cloaca (Fig. 20-11, *A*). The individuals are oriented horizontally with the buccal siphons located on the external surface and the atrial siphons opening into the common cloaca. In *Coelocormus*, the wall of the cup is doubled by folding so that each wall of the cup contains two layers of individuals (Fig. 20-11, *B*). The buccal siphons of one layer open to the exterior and those of the other open to the interior. Between the two walls, the atria open into an internal cloacal canal that exits through a single aperture at the bottom of the cup.

Asexual Reproduction. Regeneration and asexual reproduction are highly developed in colonial ascidians but absent in the families

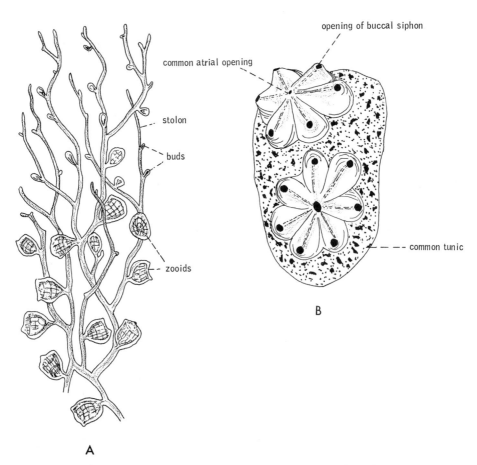

Figure 20-10. *A.* Colony of *Perophora viridis.* (After Miner.) *B. Botryllus schlosseri,* a compound ascidian. (After Milne-Edwards from Yonge.)

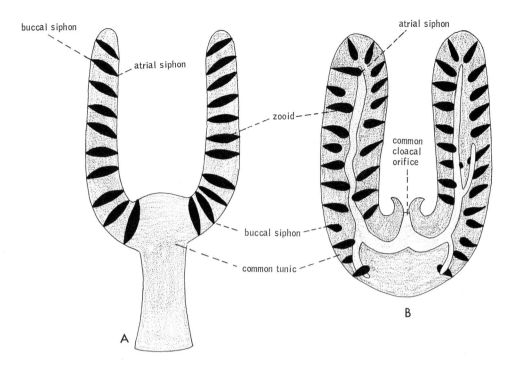

Figure 20-11.   *A* and *B*. Diagrammatic sections through ascidian colonies. *A. Cyathocormus. B. Coelocormus.* (After Okada from Brien.)

Cionidae and Ascidiidae. Asexual reproduction takes place by means of budding, but is complex and exceedingly variable. In fact, Brien (1948) maintains that ascidians display the greatest variation in asexual budding of any group of metazoans.

A tunicate bud is called a blastozooid and originates in different parts of the body in different groups of ascidians. With the variation of the site of bud formation, there is a corresponding variation in the germinal tissues included within the bud. The most primitive type of budding appears in *Clavelina* and other forms in which the bud arises from the stolon (Fig. 20-8, *A*). The bud first appears as a swelling of the stolon filled with reserve food material and may not develop until the stolon breaks away from the parent or the parent degenerates. In *Clavelina* and other members of this family, epidermis and mesenchyme comprise the germinal tissues of such stoloniferous buds.

In the colonial Polyclinidae, which have a long postabdomen bearing an extension of the epicardia and a cord of tissue from the gonads, the postabdomen breaks up within the tunic like a string of sausages (Fig. 20-12, *A*). Each section becomes a bud with the epidermis, genital cord, and epicardial tissue acting as germinal tissues. The blastozooids reorganize in the base of the old tunic to form a new colony.

Budding in *Diazona* and other members of

the same family takes place in the abdominal region. The thorax degenerates, and the abdomen divides into buds, starting with the anterior and proceeding posteriorly. Germinal tissues in this case are epidermis, epicardium, and parts of the digestive loop.

In a number of families, budding is precocious and begins at the larval stage. For example, in the Didemnidae a few hours after the settling of the larva, two buds form in the abdominal region (Fig. 20-12, *B* and *C*). The two buds fuse, one forming the thoracic half and one the abdominal half of the new individual. In the Botryllidae, which forms the star-shaped colonies described earlier, a single bud develops on the larva. After fixation, the larva dies, and the bud develops as the initial member of the colony. The star-shaped pattern of the adult colony results from geometrical secondary budding.

Embryology.   It is in the embryogeny and the larval stage of tunicates that the chordate affinities of the class become strikingly apparent. Solitary species generally have small eggs with little yolk. The eggs are shed from the atrial siphon, and development takes place in the sea water. The eggs of such oviparous species are frequently surrounded by special membranes that act as flotation devices. The eggs of colonial species are typically richer in yolk material and are usually brooded in the atrium, which sometimes contains special incubating pockets. Hatch-

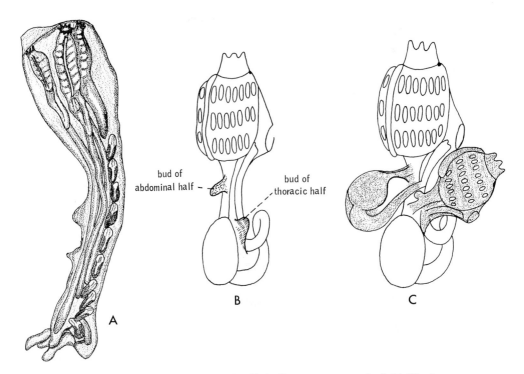

Figure 20-12.   *A.* Budding in the colonial *Circinalium concrescens,* a polyclinid. The long post-abdomen becomes sectioned into buds within the common tunic of the colony. (After Brien.) *B* and *C.* Budding in the Didemnidae. *B.* Two buds develop in abdominal region of parent body. *C.* Buds fuse, one forming the abdominal half of the new individual and one forming thoracic half. (After Salfi from Brien.)

ing may take place at the larval stage, and the larva then leaves the parent; or the entire course of development may take place within the atrial cavity. In general, development in brooding species with considerable yolk material is more rapid and condensed than in nonbrooding forms.

Cleavage is complete, slightly unequal, and leads to a flattened coeloblastula. Gastrulation is accomplished by epiboly and invagination, and the large archenteron completely obliterates the old blastocoel. The blastopore marks the posterior end of the embryo and gradually closes while the embryo elongates along the antero-posterior axis. Along the mid-dorsal line, the archenteron gives rise to a supporting rod—the notochord. Laterally, the archenteron prolifer-ates mesodermal cells that form a cord of cells along each side of the body. In this respect, development departs from that shown in *Am-phioxus* and other deuterostomes, because there is no pouching of the archenteron. The meso-derm forms the body mesenchyme, and a coe-lomic cavity never appears nor is there any seg-mentation. The ectoderm along the mid-dorsal line differentiates as a neural plate, sinks inward, and rolls up as an internal neural tube.

Continued development leads to an elon-gated microscopic larva, called an appendicularia or more commonly a "tadpole" larva (Fig. 20-13, *A*). A distinct tail represents the posterior half of the larva and contains the notochord and the neural tube. Dorsally, the anterior half of the larva contains a pigmented cup, a statocyst, and the dilated end of the neural tube, which be-comes the cerebral ganglion. The mouth, which later becomes the buccal siphon, is located an-teriorly and may not be open during the larval stage. The mouth leads into the pharynx, which in turn is followed by a twisted digestive loop with a dorsally directed intestine. The pharynx contains a ventral endostyle, but at first the pharynx possesses only two stigmata. The stig-mata empty into a small pocket, the future atrium. At the extreme anterior of the larva are three ectodermal projections—the fixation papil-lae. The entire larva is covered by a tunic secreted by the surface ectoderm, and in the tail region the tunic is extended dorsally and ventrally to form a fin. The tail is the larval locomotor organ, and movement is brought about by special muscle bands.

After a short free-swimming, but non-feed-ing, planktonic existence, the larva settles to the bottom and attaches at the anterior end, using the fixation papillae (Fig. 20-13, *B*). Metamor-phosis now ensues. The larval tail with the noto-chord and neural tube are resorbed and disap-pear. As a result of the rapid growth of the chin

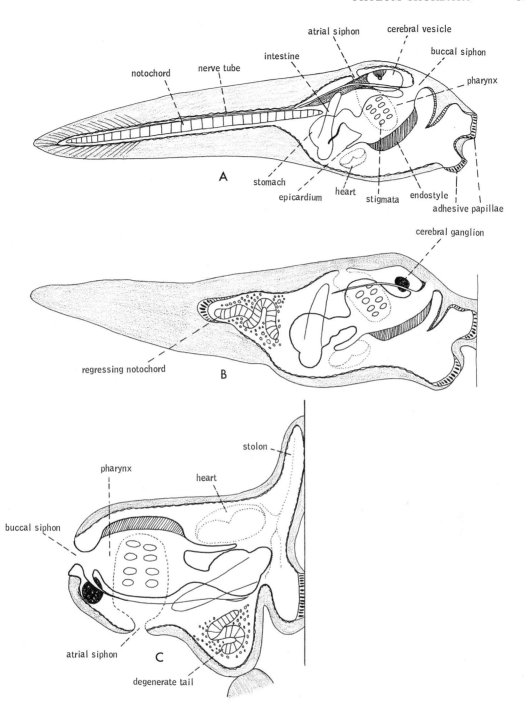

Figure 20-13.   Metamorphosis in *Clavelina. A.* Free-swimming "tadpole larva." *B.* Attachment of larva and beginning of metamorphosis. *C.* A young individual in end stages of metamorphosis. Note new positions of siphons. (Modified after Seeliger from Brien.)

region—the area between the adhesive papillae and the mouth—the entire body is turned 180 degrees. The mouth, or buccal siphon, is carried backward to open at the end opposite that of attachment, and all other internal organs are rotated in the same manner. The number of stigmata rapidly increases; the atrium greatly expands and makes contact with the end of the intestine, or anus. The siphons become functional, and the metamorphosed larva has become a young ascidian (Fig. 20-13, *C*).

Class Thaliacea

The other two classes of tunicates, the Thaliacea

and the Larvacea, are both specialized for a free-swimming planktonic existence. Thaliaceans differ from ascidians in having the buccal and atrial siphons at opposite ends of the body. The water current is thus utilized not only for respiration and feeding but also as a means of locomotion. The class contains only six genera, and most species live in tropical and semitropical waters.

The tropical *Pyrosoma* are brilliantly luminescent colonial thaliaceans, having the form of a cylinder that is closed at one end (Fig. 20-14, *A*). The length ranges from a few centimeters to over two meters. The individuals are oriented in the wall of the colony, so that the buccal siphons open to the outside and the atrial siphons empty into the central cavity, which acts as a common cloacal chamber. *Pyrosoma* is thus organized in a manner very similar to some colonial ascidians.

Salpa and *Doliolum* are solitary thaliaceans that live in the North Atlantic. The body in both is somewhat barrel-shaped, particularly in

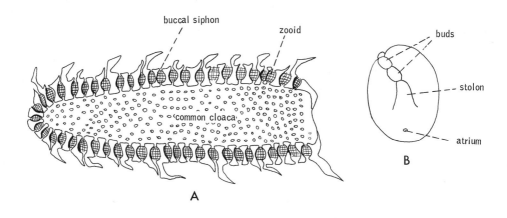

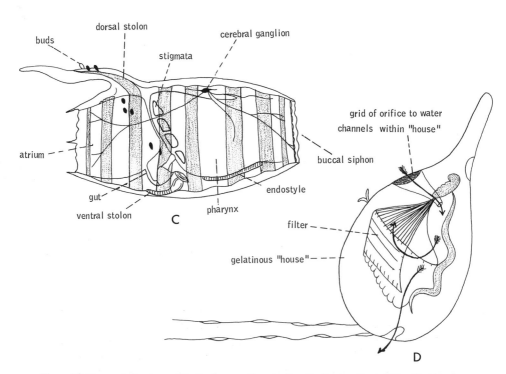

Figure 20-14.   *A*. A colony of the thaliacean, *Pyrosoma* (longitudinal section). (After Grobben from Brien.) *B*. Oozooid of *Pyrosoma* with stolon and buds. (After Borradaile and others.) *C*. Oozooid of the solitary thaliacean, *Doliolum*. (Modified after Uljanin and Barrois from Borradaile and others.) *D*. *Oikopleura albicans,* a larvacean. (After Borradaile.)

Doliolum (Fig. 20-14, *C*). Circular muscle bands, complete in *Doliolum* and incomplete in *Salpa*, produce contractions of the body wall that drive water through the atrial cavity. *Salpa* is especially peculiar in having only two gill clefts, which are so enormous that there are virtually no side walls of the pharynx remaining.

The life cycles of all thaliaceans involve asexual budding. Since the sexually reproducing stages are derived as buds (blastozooids) from the individual formed from the egg (oozooid), thaliaceans are often considered to exhibit metagenesis, but there seems no more justification for considering these animals metagenetic than there is for the hydroid coelenterates.

There is no larva in *Pyrosoma*. Each member of the colony produces a single yolky egg that undergoes meroblastic cleavage in the parent atrium. The later embryo (oozooid) produces four buds along the length of a stolon, which is coiled about the oozooid (Fig. 20-14, *B*). Rupture of the parental atrium liberates the oozooid and buds, which sink to the bottom. The oozooid degenerates, and the four primordial buds, already organized in a ring, form a new colony by secondary budding. The new colony then assumes a pelagic existence.

Like *Pyrosoma*, the solitary salpids produce a single egg that develops in the parent, attached to the atrial wall, from which it obtains nutrition. There is no larval stage, and when development is completed, the oozooid breaks free of the parent and is free-swimming. A trailing stolon develops a chain of buds that eventually separate to form sexually reproducing adults.

The life cycle of the doliolids is the most complex of all thaliaceans. In *Doliolum*, three eggs are produced by the parent and are shed into the sea water, where each develops into a tail-bearing larva. The larva metamorphoses into an adult oozooid, which is provided with a stolon on which buds are formed (Fig. 20-14, *C*). These buds, called prebuds, then give rise to several generations of highly specialized buds, all of which are attached to the parent oozooid. Eventually buds form which develop into the sexually reproducing adults. These detach and swim away. The adult oozooid and sexual blastozooid differ in only minor details of structure.

Class Larvacea

The last class, the Larvacea, or Appendicularia, is the most specialized of all tunicates. These are tiny transparent animals that reach only a few millimeters in length and are found in marine plankton throughout the world. The Larvacea are so named because the adults are neotenic and have retained some of the larval characteristics (Fig. 20-14, *D*). A tail is present, and the body looks somewhat like a typical ascidian tadpole larva bent at right angles or in the shape of a U.

The mouth is located at the anterior of the body, and the intestine opens directly to the outside on the ventral side. There are only two pharyngeal clefts, one on each side, and each opens directly to the exterior.

A remarkable feature of the Larvacea is the "house" in which the body is enclosed or to which it is attached. There is no cellulose tunic in larvaceans, but the surface epithelium secretes a delicate gelatinous material that completely encloses the body in three genera—*Oikopleura*, *Appendicularia*, and *Kowalewskaia*. In *Fritillaria*, the animal lies outside of the "house" but is attached beneath it. In *Oikopleura*, the gelatinous enclosure is somewhat egg-shaped with a projecting peak and is much larger than the body of the animal (Fig. 20-14, *D*).

The interior of the "house," in which the animal is suspended, contains a number of interconnecting cavities and both an incurrent and an excurrent orifice. The beating of the tail of the animal creates a water current that passes through the "house." The orifice through which water enters is covered by a grid or screen of fine fibers that keep out all but the finest plankton. During its passage through the "house," the water is strained a second time through a finer net. This second straining delivers plankton to the anterior of the body, where it enters the mouth with water and is strained a final time in passing through the pharynx. The "house" is continually shed and replaced, and according to Fol (1872), a single "house" is kept no longer than three hours in *Oikopleura*, probably as a result of a clogging of the filters.

Only sexual reproduction occurs in the Larvacea. Development leads to a free-swimming tadpole larva that undergoes metamorphosis without settling.

Urochordate Phylogeny

The tunicates undoubtedly departed early from the chordate line of evolution. Most of their adult peculiarities are associated with a sessile mode of existence, but they differ in two basic respects from other chordates. There is no evidence of segmentation, and there is no coelom in the adult nor does it appear in the course of embryological development. The coelom has undoubtedly been lost, since it is characteristic of other deuterostomes, and the coelom was certainly present in the ancestral chordate stock. Regarding metamerism, the complete lack of any segmentation, even in embryological development, seems to indicate that the ancestral chordate was not a metameric animal and that metamerism evolved in the line leading to the cephalochordates and vertebrates *after* the departure of the tunicates.

PHYLUM CHAETOGNATHA

The chaetognaths, known as arrowworms, are common animals found in marine plankton. The entire phylum of some 50 species is marine, and except for the benthic genus *Spadella*, all arrowworms are adapted for a planktonic existence. The adults possess none of the features common to the other deuterostome phyla, and they are like aschelminths in many respects. Only the embryogeny of arrowworms indicates a deuterostome position for these animals.

External Structure. The body of arrowworms is shaped like a torpedo or feathered dart and is commonly about 3 cm. long, although a length of 10 cm. is attained in some forms (Fig. 20-15). The body is divided into a head, a trunk, and a post-anal tail region, and a distinct nar-

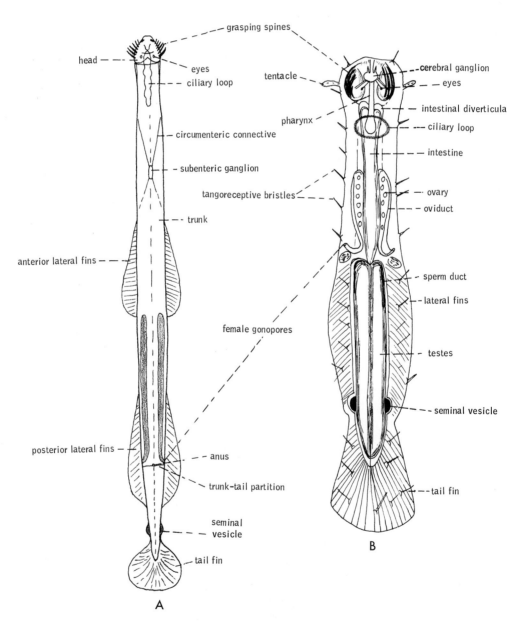

Figure 20-15.   Phylum Chaetognatha. *A. Sagitta elegans* (ventral view). (After Ritter-Zahony from Hyman.) *B. Spadella* (dorsal view). (After Hertwig from Hyman.)

rowed neck separates the head and trunk. On the underside of the rounded head is a large chamber (the vestibule) that leads into the mouth (Fig. 20-16).

Hanging down from each side of the head and flanking the vestibule are four to fourteen large curved spines that are used in seizing prey. Several rows of much shorter spines (anterior and posterior teeth) that are curved around the front of the head also assist in capturing prey. All the teeth and spines are composed of chitin, a compound that is relatively uncommon in deuterostomes. A pair of eyes is located posteriorly on the dorsal surface. In the neck region is a peculiar fold of the body wall (the hood) that can be pulled forward to enclose the entire head. The hood is thought to perhaps protect the spines when they are not in use and reduce water resistance during swimming.

The remainder of the body is composed of the elongated trunk and the tail. A characteristic feature of the chaetognaths is the horizontal fins that border these regions of the body. In some arrowworms such as *Sagitta*, there are two pairs of lateral fins, but in most species a single pair of lateral fins projects from the sides of the body along the posterior half of the trunk and overlaps the tail region (Figs. 20-15, *A* and *B*). Posteriorly, a large spatula-like caudal fin encompasses the end of the tail. Both the caudal and the lateral fins contain ray-like supports.

Internal Structure and Physiology. The construction of the body wall is particularly reminiscent of aschelminths. A thin but distinct cuticle covers the surface epithelium, which is single-layered except along the sides of the body on which large vacuolated cells form a thick stratified layer. A basement membrane lies beneath the epithelium and is thickened to form the supporting rays between the two epithelial layers of the fins; this membrane also forms special supporting plates in the head. The muscles of the body wall are all longitudinal and are arranged in two dorso-lateral and two ventro-lateral bands. In the head are special muscles for operating the hood, the teeth, the grasping spines, and other structures.

The coelom resembles a pseudocoel, because there is no peritoneum. However, the coelom is compartmented. The head contains a single coelomic space that extends into the hood and is separated by a septum from the paired trunk coelomic spaces. One or two coelomic compartments occupy the tail, but these spaces are believed to represent a secondary separation from the trunk coelom.

Chaetognaths alternately swim and float. The fins play no role in propulsion and are only flotation devices. When the body begins to sink, the longitudinal trunk muscles contract rapidly, and the animal darts swiftly forward. This forward motion is then followed by an interval of gliding and floating. The benthic *Spadella* adheres to bottom objects by means of special adhesive papillae, but it can swim short distances.

Arrowworms are all carnivorous and feed on other planktonic animals, particularly copepods. *Sagitta* has reportedly consumed young fish and other arrowworms as large as itself. In capturing prey, chaetognaths dart forward, the hood is withdrawn, and the grasping spines are spread. The teeth are used in holding, while the spines close down over the victim. The entire operation is accomplished with incredible speed.

The digestive tract is simple (Figs. 20-15, *B* and 20-16). The mouth leads into the bulbous pharynx that penetrates the head-trunk septum to join a straight intestine. The intestine extends

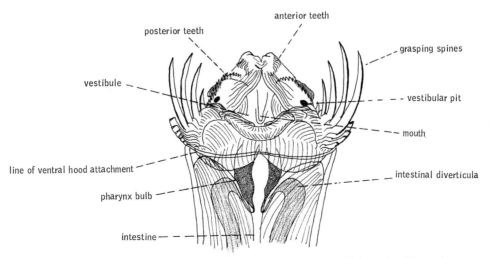

Figure 20-16.   Head of *Sagitta elegans* (ventral view). (After Ritter-Zahony from Hyman.)

through the length of the trunk and at its anterior gives rise to a pair of lateral diverticula. Muscles are best developed in the pharyngeal wall, but a thin circular layer is present in the intestine. Although the intestine is suspended by a dorsal and a ventral mesentery, these mesenteries appear to be extensions of the basement membrane of the body wall and are not cellular.

After capture, the prey is pushed into the mouth, in which it is lubricated by pharyngeal secretions and then passed to the posterior of the intestine. Here the food is rotated and moved back and forth until it is broken down. The intestine is lined with secretory and absorptive cells, and digestion is probably entirely extracellular. Grey (1930) in studies on *Sagitta* reported that the entire digestive process takes place in 40 minutes.

There are no specialized respiratory or excretory organs, and the coelomic fluid acts as a circulatory medium.

The nervous center of chaetognaths is a nerve collar surrounding the pharynx. The ring contains dorsally a large cerebral ganglion, and a number of lateral ganglia (Fig. 20-15, *B*). The ganglia give rise to a large number of nerves that innervate different head structures. The sides of the cerebral ganglion give rise to a pair of large circumenteric connectives that extend posteriorly and end in a single midventral subenteric ganglion in the anterior part of the trunk (Fig. 20-15, *A*). The subenteric ganglion in turn gives rise to a large number of paired nerves that supply the muscles and sensory receptors of the trunk and tail.

Sense organs include the eyes, the sensory bristles, and possibly a head organ (the ciliary loop) (Fig. 20-15, *A* and *B*). Each of the two eyes, at least in *Sagitta*, is composed of five fused pigment-cup ocelli, in which the photoreceptors are directed toward the cup. The sensory bristles are arranged in longitudinal rows along the length of the trunk and are probably tactile in function. The ciliary loop is usually a U-shaped tract of cilia that extends from the head back over the neck or the anterior end of the trunk. The loop is thought to function in the detection of changes in the water current or perhaps in chemoreception.

Chaetognaths are hermaphroditic, and a pair of elongated ovaries is located in the trunk coelom in front of the trunk–tail septum. A pair of elongated testes is located in the tail coelom behind the septum (Fig. 20-15, *A* and *B*). From each testis a sperm duct passes posteriorly and laterally to terminate in a seminal vesicle imbedded in the lateral body wall. Along its course, each sperm duct opens into the tail coelom through a funnel. Sperm leave the testis

as spermatogonia, and spermatogenesis is completed in the coelom. When mature, the sperm pass into the ciliated funnel of the sperm duct and from there into a seminal vesicle in which the sperm are formed into a single spermatophore. The seminal vesicle ruptures enabling the spermatophore to escape.

An oviduct runs along the lateral side of each ovary; they end posteriorly in separate receptacles. Each seminal receptacle opens to the exterior through a short vagina and a gonopore. The two gonopores are located one on each side of the body just in front of the trunk–tail septum.

The eggs do not begin to mature until after spermatogenesis has commenced in the tail coelom. In *Sagitta* at least, self-fertilization takes place. When a spermatophore escapes from the seminal vesicle, it adheres to the body surface, especially the fins, of the same animal. Sperm then leave the spermatophore and migrate to the female gonoduct and seminal receptacle. At the time of fertilization, the sperm migrate up the oviduct. The oviduct does not open directly into the ovary, but in the vicinity of a mature egg, two cells from the oviduct wall grow inward and make contact with the egg. These attaching cells then form a lumen, or canal, through which the sperm pass into the egg. In *Spadella*, fertilization is reciprocal, and self-fertilization does not take place.

In *Sagitta*, the eggs are planktonic and are surrounded by a coat of jelly. In other arrowworms, the eggs may be attached to the body surface of the parent and carried about for some time.

Cleavage is radial, complete, and equal and leads to coeloblastula. Gastrulation is accomplished by invagination, and as in the lower chordates, the invaginating mesentoderm fits closely against the outer ectoderm and obliterates the blastocoel. The anterior end wall of the archenteron invaginates, folding backward on each side and cutting off two pairs of lateral coelomic sacs (Fig. 20-17, *A* and *B*). The coelom is thus enterocoelic in origin. Further development is direct, and although the young are called larvae when they hatch, they are similar to the adult, and no metamorphosis takes place.

There are approximately 50 species of described arrowworms. Most of them are found in tropical waters, but the phylum is represented in the plankton of all oceans; at times enormous numbers appear. A considerable number of species are cosmopolitan. Although all chaetognaths except *Spadella* are planktonic, there is a distinct vertical stratification of species. Many species live only in the upper lighted zone—that is, above approximately 600 feet; of these, some are

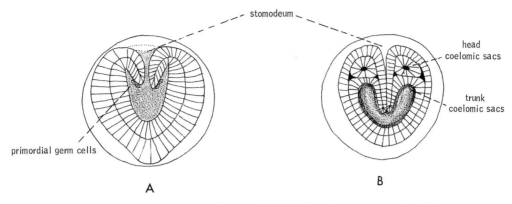

Figure 20-17.   Coelom formation in *Sagitta*. *A*. Initial folding of archenteron walls. *B*. Separation of head coelomic sacs. (Both after Burfield from Hyman.)

restricted to coastal waters; others always appear well off shore in open water where there is little fluctuation in salinity. Another group of species occupies a depth range of between 600 and 3000 feet; a few forms live below 3000 feet. Like many planktonic crustaceans, some arrowworms undergo a diurnal or seasonal migration between the surface and lower depths.

Despite the similarities of adult chaetognaths to aschelminths, the embryogeny of the phylum is clearly deuterostome in nature. There are, however, some peculiarities. For example, the coelom is enterocoelic in origin but does not arise by a direct outpocketing of the archenteron, and only two pairs of coelomic pockets are formed instead of three. Moreover, there is no larval stage comparable to that of the echinoderms and the hemichordates. Thus, the chaetognaths cannot be allied with any specific deuterostome phylum. In view of these facts, Hyman (1959) postulates that the phylum departed very early from the base of the deuterostome line and is only remotely related to the other deuterostome groups.

BIBLIOGRAPHY

Azema, M., 1937: Recherches sur le sang et l'excrétion chez les Ascidies. Ann. l'Institut Océanographique de Paris, *17*: 1-150.

Barrington, E., 1940: Observations on feeding and digestion in *Glossobalanus*. Quart J. Mic. Sci., *82*

Brien, P., 1948: Embranchement des Tuniciers. *In* P. Grassé's Traité de Zoologie, Vol. XI. Échinodermes, Stomocordes, Procordes. Masson et Cié., Paris, pp. 553–930. An excellent treatment of the tunicates with an extensive bibliography.

Bullough, W. S., 1958: Practical Invertebrate Anatomy. MacMillan, New York, pp. 446–464. Descriptions of representative tunicates, including the Thaliacea and the Larvacea.

Dawydoff, C., 1948: Embranchement des Stomocordes. *In* P. Grassé's Traité de Zoologie, Vol. XI. Échinodermes, Stomocordes, Procordes. Masson et Cié, Paris, pp. 367–551. A general account of the hemichordates.

Fol, H., 1872: Études sur les Appendiculaires du Détroit de Messine. Mem. Soc. Phys. Hist. Nat. Geneve, *21* (*2*).

Grey, B., 1930: Chaetognatha from the Society Islands. Proc. Roy. Soc. Queensland, *42*.

Hyman, L. H., 1959: The Invertebrates: Vol. V. Smaller Coelomate Groups. McGraw-Hill, New York, pp. 1-71. A complete account of the chaetognaths.

Skramlik, E., 1930: Observations sur le battement du coeur des Ascidies. Bull. l'Institut Océanographique de Monaco, fasc. 548.

INDEX

Page numbers in **bold face** type indicate illustrations.